AA Lifestyle Guides in association with Millennium & Copthorne

D0526939

WIN one of 20
Fabulous 'Weekends Away' for two in 5 Free Prize Draws

see overleaf for terms & conditions

Enjoy a break with a difference with Millennium & Copthorne Hotels. Choose from any one of the 17 exclusive 4-star hotels around the UK, offering the highest standard of accommodation, food and leisure facilities.
The recipe for a perfect weekend away.

MILLENNIUM
HOTELS AND RESORTS

For more information on Millennium & Copthorne Hotels, call 0845 30 20001, quoting "AA Lifestyle Guides".

HOW TO ENTER

Just complete (in capitals please) and send off this card or alternatively, send your name and address on a stamped postcard to the address overleaf (no purchase required). Entries are limited to one per household and to residents of the UK and Republic of Ireland over the age of 18. This card will require a stamp if posted in the Republic of Ireland. **Closing date 6 September 2002.**

MR/MRS/MISS/MS/OTHER, PLEASE STATE: _____

NAME: _____

ADDRESS: _____

_____

_____

POSTCODE: _____

TEL. NOS: _____ E-MAIL: _____

Are you an AA Member?   Yes/No

Have you bought this or any other AA Lifestyle Guide before?   Yes/No

If yes, please indicate the year of the last edition you bought:

AA Hotel Guide	____	AA Caravan & Camping (Europe)	____
AA Bed and Breakfast Guide	____	AA Britain Guide	____
AA Restaurant Guide	____	AA Days Out Guide	____
AA Pub Guide	____	Other, please state _____	
AA Caravan & Camping (Britain & Ireland)	____		

If you do not wish to receive further information or special offers from AA Publishing please tick the box ☐

We may use information we hold about you to write to, or telephone, you about other products and services offered by us and our carefully selected partners. Information may be disclosed to other companies in the Centrica plc group (including those using the British Gas, Scottish Gas, Goldfish and AA brands) but we can assure you that we will not disclose it to third parties. Tick the box if you do NOT wish to hear about other products and services.'

BBF02

Terms and Conditions

1. Four winners will be drawn from each of the five prize draws to take place on 04 January, 08 March, 03 May, 05 July and 06 September 2002.

2. Closing date for receipt of entries is midday on the relevant draw date. Final close date for receipt of entries is 06 September 2002.

3. Entries received after any draw date other than the final one will go forward into the next available draw. Each entry will only be entered in one draw. Only one entry per household accepted.

4. Winners will be notified by post within 14 days of the relevant draw date.

5. Prizes must be booked within 3 months of the relevant draw date. Prizes are not transferable and there is no cash alternative.

6. This prize cannot be used in conjunction with any other discount, promotion or special offer.

7. Each prize consists of two nights' accommodation and full traditional breakfast for two adults sharing a standard twin/double room in a UK Millennium or Copthorne Hotel. Supplements may be charged for feature or family rooms. All accommodation is subject to availability.

8. Millennium & Copthorne Hotels provide all hotel accommodation, services and facilities and the AA is not party to your agreement with Millennium & Copthorne Hotels in this regard.

9. No purchase required

10. The prize draw is open to anyone resident in the UK or the Republic of Ireland over the age of 18, other than employees of the Automobile Association or Millennium & Copthorne Hotels, their subsidiary companies or their families or agents.

11. For a list of winners, please send a stamped, self addressed envelope to AA Lifestyle Guide Winners 2002, AA Publishing, Fanum House (4), Basingstoke, Hants, RG21 4EA.

12. If this card is posted in the Republic of Ireland, it must have an appropriate stamp.

13. Once a prize weekend has been booked, cancellation will invalidate the prize.

BUSINESS REPLY SERVICE
Licence No BZ 343

PLEASE NOTE: Requires a stamp if posted in
Republic of Ireland

AA Lifestyle Guide 2002 Prize Draw
AA PUBLISHING
FANUM HOUSE (4)
BASING VIEW
BASINGSTOKE
HANTS RG21 4EA

Welcome to
BED & BREAKFAST IN FRANCE

AA

from the **AA** and **Gîtes de France**

The AA carries out inspection and classification for its best-selling Bed & Breakfast and Hotel guides to Britain and Ireland. By joining forces with Gîtes de France we aim to bring you the same reliable, high quality information for France.

You will find an easy-to use layout, clear gradings, a useful description of the B&B and its facilities and lots of colour photographs. We hope this guide will be invaluable every time you plan a visit to France.

Gîtes de France aims to promote country holidays and breaks by developing quality accommodation. The Gîtes de France logo guarantees that all the accommodation in this guide complies with a national charter and meets specific standards of comfort.

The Gîtes de France grading goes from 1 up to 4 and for this guide we have selected over 3,000 of those with a grade of 3 or 4 to ensure the highest quality and a wide choice. You can rest assured that your host's first priority is to make sure you enjoy your stay.

1st edition March 2002
Published by the Automobile Association.

Directory information supplied by and
reproduced with the permission of the
Fédération Nationale des Gîtes de France.

Maps reproduced with the permission of
iNFOGRAPH, Le Chesnay, France.
© iNFOGRAPH – France – 33 1 39 55 70 40 –
Autorisation nᵒ A011031

The contents of this publication are believed
correct at the time of printing. Nevertheless, the
publishers cannot be responsible for any errors
or omissions or for any changes to the details
given in this guide or for the consequences of
reliance on the information provided by the
same. Assessment of Gîtes de France
establishments is based on the experience of the
inspector on the occasion(s) of their visit(s) and
therefore information given in this guide
necessarily contains an element of subjective
opinion which may not reflect or dictate a
reader's own opinion on another occasion. We
have tried to ensure accuracy in this guide,
however things do change and we would be
grateful if readers would advise us of any
inaccuracies they may encounter.

A CIP catalogue record for this book is
available from the British Library
ISBN 0 7495 3251 3

Published by AA Publishing, a trading name
of Automobile Association Developments
Limited, whose registered office is:
Millstream
Maidenhead Road
Windsor
Berkshire SL4 5GD
Registered number 1878835

Cover concept by Imageri,
Whitchurch, England

Layout design by Ego Creative,
Basingstoke, England

Main cover photograph shows Les Bruyères,
Villefargeau, Yonne © Alain Courtois; this
and selected illustrative images in pages 1-20
courtesy of Gîtes de France

Typeset by Anton Graphics, Andover, England
Printed and bound by Graficas estella, S.A.,
Navarra, Spain

Advertisement production:
advertisingsales@theAA.com
Editorial team: lifestyleguides@theAA.com

~ CONTENTS ~

How to use
~ THE GUIDE ~

Where in France?

If you know of a particular town or village where you plan to stay, you can look for the name in the location index at the back of the guide. Chambres d'hôtes (B&Bs) are located under the nearest town or village although many of them are rural and will be outside the town. If there is no chambre d'hôtes listing under the town or village you have chosen, look at the relevant page in the atlas section to find the nearest town with a chambre d'hôtes. Towns or villages where there are chambres d'hôtes listed in this guide are marked with a red dot on the atlas page.

To find the general area of France that you want to visit you can use the **key map** on pages 6-7 to identify the French region (e.g. Brittany), shown in capitals. If you are happy to browse through the whole region then turn to the **index of regions** on page 20 for the page numbers. The region name also appears at the top of each page of the gazetteer. Regions are in alphabetical order through the guide.

All AA maps and guides can be purchased in bookshops or on the AA website www.theAA.com

To find a smaller area to look through, you can use the **key map** to identify the *département* (county division) within each region (e.g. Finistère within Brittany). Each *département* has a number as well as the name (e.g. Finistère 29). The *département* numbers appear on the key map, atlas page and with the *département* name at the top of each page in the guide. *Département* names are also indexed with the locations at the back of guide.

The atlas section of this guide is arranged in numerical order of *départements* (one *département* per page), beginning with Ain 01, Aisne 02 and so on. The atlas is intended solely to help you find your way around the guide and should not be used as a road map. We recommend the AA Big Road Atlas France or AA Road Atlas France for general navigation. For more detailed information we recommend the AA's regional maps of France.

Which Chambre d'hôtes?

For general information about staying in a chambre d'hôtes and details of the Gîtes de France grading system, turn to page 9. You may wish to contact a number of chambres d'hôtes in your chosen area to ask for further information or brochures before you make a booking.

Sample Entry

The sample entry here shows how the information appears in the guide and what the symbols and abbreviations mean.

SARCY

▓▓▓▓ ▶ ⦿⦿ & Le Manoir Michel & Michelle OLIVIER ⑧
33 rue du Maréchal Foch, 51170 Sarcy
☎ 01 23 45 67 89 🖷 01 23 45 67 89
e-mail: lemanoir@wanadoo.fr

Reims and the Marne Valley 15 mins. This quiet, comfortable ⑨
house, in the beautiful countryside of the Parc Régional de la
Montagne de Reims, is decorated in a warm, rustic style. The two
family rooms have private bathrooms. Breakfast, featuring home-
made jams, bread and fruit juice, is served next to a log fire, or on
the covered terrace overlooking the garden and orchard. There is
ample parking and a lockable garage. Open all year round.
PRICES: s €26-€38; d €34-€53; t €59; extra person €13 **ON SITE:** Hiking
Tennis **NEARBY:** Horse riding (10km) Railway station (7km) Shops (3km)
REIMS (8km) **NOTES:** Pets admitted CC English spoken ⑫
⑩ ⑪ ⑬

Directions and Signs

Directions cannot be provided in sufficient detail to be useful in this guide and we recommend that you request specific details from your host, indicating where you will be travelling from. Every Gîtes de France chambre d'hôtes displays the Gîtes de France sign with the chambres d'hôtes panel. Places selected for this guide will also have a window sticker identifying them as recommended in this AA guide.

1 Town or village name. This is the nearest town or village to the chambre d'hôtes and corresponds with the location shown on the atlas at the back of the book.

2 Gîtes de France grading (see page 9 for details).

3 A ▶ symbol may appear here if the chambre d'hôtes is on a farm.

4 Table d'hôtes evening meals (see page 10) are available where this symbol appears.

5 Places with this symbol have been assessed by a French disability organisation (l'APF). For precise details of accessibility please contact the host direct.

6 Name of the chambre d'hôtes. Many houses do not have a name so these appear as 'Chambre d'hôtes'.

7 Contact details for the establishment. The names of the hosts, the address, telephone and fax numbers, e-mail and web addresses appear where applicable.

8 A photograph may appear where this has been provided by the establishment.

9 A description of the setting and facilities. Nearby attractions may appear in italics.

10 Prices appear in Euros: s – one person, d – two people, t – three people, HB – half board, FB – full board. (See page 11 for further details.)

11 Details of attractions or facilities in the area. The name of and distance from the nearest major town may appear in blue.

12 Further details of facilities at the chambre d'hôtes, or within the immediate vicinity.

13 Additional information, e.g. whether pets are admitted, credit cards (CC) accepted, English spoken, etc.

GENERAL MAP AND KEY

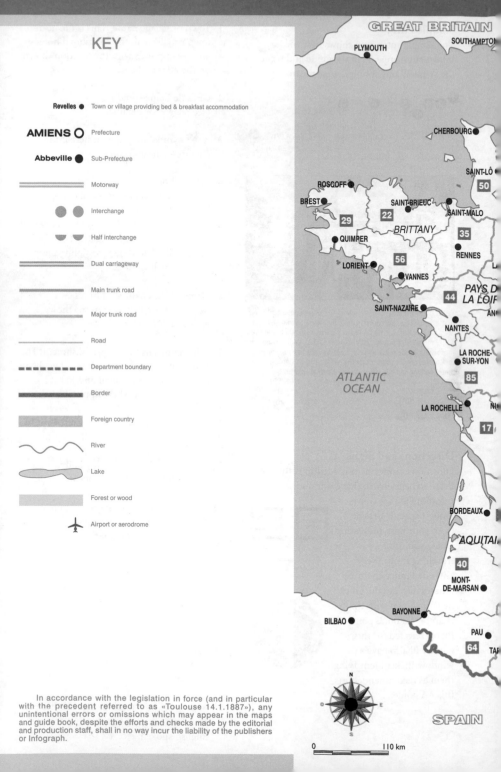

KEY

Revelles ●	Town or village providing bed & breakfast accommodation
AMIENS ○	Prefecture
Abbeville ●	Sub-Prefecture
▬▬▬	Motorway
● ●	Interchange
◗ ◖	Half interchange
▬▬▬	Dual carriageway
▬▬▬	Main trunk road
▬▬▬	Major trunk road
▬▬▬	Road
▬ ▬ ▬	Department boundary
▬▬▬	Border
▬▬▬	Foreign country
～～～	River
⬭	Lake
▬▬▬	Forest or wood
✈	Airport or aerodrome

Staying in a
~ CHAMBRE D'HOTES ~

The French 'chambre d'hôtes' literally means 'bedroom of the host', where you are welcomed as a guest in someone's home. We use the term 'chambre d'hôtes' throughout this guide and refer to the owners of the houses you can stay in as hosts. All the places in this guide are privately-owned, family homes run by hosts who will welcome you as part of the family and be pleased to help you get to know their local area.

Although the chambre d'hôtes philosophy is similar to that of bed and breakfast in the UK, family homes in France may offer different facilities and services to what you might expect in your own home. Chambres d'hôtes come in all shapes and sizes, from rural farmhouses and village inns, to beautiful manor houses and impressive châteaux with acres of garden parkland. You might find yourself staying with a farmer and his family or in some cases with a viscount and viscountess. We give you the names of your hosts in this guide so that you can start to get to know them from the moment you first make contact. You can really make the most of your stay by making friends with your hosts and being a good house guest. We offer some useful tips on French culture and etiquette on page 17.

Gîtes de France Grading ♈♈♈♈

All the chambres d'hôtes in this book are inspected, assessed and given a grade by Gîtes de France. The grading is the *épis* or 'ear of corn' which appears as a symbol for each entry in the guide; for simplicity we refer to this as the grade or grading rather than the number of *épis*. Gîtes de France grades over 8,000 chambres d'hôtes with a grade from 1 up to 4. For this guide we have selected those with the higher grades of 3 and 4, with between three and six rooms. Apart from the guides published in France by Gîtes de France, this guide is the only chambres d'hôtes guide authorised by Gîtes de France to use its logo and its *épis* grading.

The Gîtes de France grading varies according to the style of architecture and the setting, the level of comfort and the services provided, and is shown to give you a general indication of the different standards of the chambres d'hôtes. At grade 3 you can expect 'a high level of comfort', while at grade 4 you can expect to enjoy 'exceptional levels of comfort, in residences of character in outstanding settings'. Whatever the grade, your hosts' priority is to make sure you enjoy your stay.

Gîtes de France standards and facilities for rooms

Chambre d'hôtes rooms in this guide all have fully fitted private bathrooms, however these may not always be en suite. They will have a bath or shower, washbasin and wc. We try to describe the facilities in each entry. French bathrooms may be as full of character as the house. Do not expect them to be fantastically modern; sometimes French showers don't have shower curtains. Rooms are cleaned daily (for long stays, bedlinen is changed at least once a week and towels etc. twice a week).

Breakfast

Breakfast is always included in the price shown. This gives you the chance to try local specialities according to your hosts' individual style, which may include home-made bread, jams, home-baked pastries, local cheese and dairy products and local *charcuterie* (cold meats).

Table d'hôtes evening meals

Like chambre d'hôtes, 'table d'hôtes' means sharing your host's table for an evening meal, usually 'en famille'. You may be joined by other guests and members of the host family. Approximately one third of the chambres d'hôtes in this guide offer an evening meal shown by this symbol ❗️. Table d'hôtes meals are only offered to resident guests. Some chambres d'hôtes may have a 'ferme-auberge' (country inn or restaurant); this will be indicated in the guide entry.

Meal arrangements

If you wish to have meals with your hosts during your stay you will need to let them know in advance. It is best to ask when you make your booking, especially if you want dinner on the night you arrive. Table d'hôtes can be a flexible arrangement; you can opt for one meal only or full-board. If you have not booked in advance you may be able to make arrangements with your hosts a day in advance or each morning of your stay; ask about this when you book to be sure. There may be particular days when table d'hôtes meals are not available so do ask about this too to avoid disappointment. If you book dinner and then cannot make it back to the house in time, do telephone to let the hosts know. Meal times will vary from around 7-9pm; if you wish to eat at a particular time discuss this with your host at the start of your stay, particularly if you have children with you.

Prices

Dinner prices given in the guide are an indication of the cost of the whole meal: starter, main course, cheese and/or dessert, coffee and beverage. Children's meal rates may be available, check when booking. Some chambres d'hôtes may offer special rates for full board.

Alternative arrangements

If dinner is not available at your chambre d'hôtes your hosts will be able to advise you of the best local restaurants or inns, where you can enjoy traditional or regional French cooking. Entries mention if there is a restaurant nearby. Local restaurants generally close one day a week, and may not take orders after 9pm.

Children's rooms and facilities

Some owners may provide an extra bed for children in your room, others offer family rooms or suites with connecting rooms. Additional children's facilities may be mentioned in the guide description. Check with the owners when you book that your requirements can be met.

Taking pets

Information on the pet policy appears in the entry under NOTES. If you are taking your dog or cat, make sure you let the owners know in advance. You can't take a cat or dog that is under three months old to France, and 'pitbull' type dogs are prohibited. You will need a certificate from your vet, dated less than 10 days before departure, confirming that the animal has lived from birth (or the last six months) in a rabies free country, such as the UK.

Room prices

Room prices shown are per night, and may vary depending on the number of people sharing the room. Room prices always include breakfast. Please bear in mind that prices may change during the currency of this guide. Some chambres d'hôtes offer discounts for longer stays or for children, so it is worth asking when booking. Additional price information may appear in the description. Tourist tax (*taxe de séjour*) is collected locally in France. The gazetteer entry states if your hosts will ask you to pay this. Tourist tax is charged per person per day.

Currency

Prices in the guide are given in Euros. Euro banknotes and coins were introduced on 1 January 2002. After 17 February, francs were no longer legal tender, but old national currency notes can be changed at the Post Office, banks and the Bank of France until 30 June 2002. After 30 June 2002, coins in francs can be exchanged at the Treasury or the Bank of France for another 3 years, and notes for another 10.

1 Euro = 6.56FF.   £1 = 1.61 Euros
Correct at time of going to press

Payment

Check which payment methods are acceptable when booking. Most chambres d'hôtes will expect payment in cash, some may accept credit cards but these may incur additional charges.

Arrival times

If you are going to be later arriving than you anticipated, please do telephone to let your hosts know, otherwise they may let your room to someone else. Most chambres d'hôtes expect guests to arrive from 4pm onwards. If you have to cancel your booking, let the owners know immediately.

Complaints

Most common problems arise from a simple misunderstanding so we strongly urge you to take up any issues with your host at the time, in the spirit of 'entente cordiale'. The AA or Gîtes de France are unfortunately not able to make your holiday any more enjoyable after the event so please don't suffer in silence only to complain later. Of course we are anxious to hear about serious problems which may arise and these will also be forwarded to Gîtes de France for their assessment. If you wish to contact the AA about a complaint arising from using this guide, please write to the Editor, Bed & Breakfast in France, AA Hotel Services, Fanum House, Basing View, Basingstoke, Hampshire, RG21 4EA. The AA cannot undertake to obtain compensation or to enter into correspondence.

How to book a
~ *CHAMBRE D'HOTES* ~

It is always best to make your reservations in advance. Many of the places in this guide are in popular areas and are quite small, so they may get booked up quickly. Details of public and school holidays are provided on page 16.

Contacting your hosts for information and to make a booking (see also sample letters)

Each entry in the guide gives you the name of your hosts and the location of the chambre d'hôtes. The address, telephone, fax and e-mail given will usually be for your hosts; however, in some cases Gîtes de France regional offices run a reservation service (SR) and this number may appear instead of, or as an alternative to, the host's number. Many hosts speak English and this is indicated in the entry under NOTES. If you prefer to contact your hosts by telephone, remember that France is an hour ahead of the UK. A brief description of the setting and facilities is provided in the entry. We recommend that you ask for a brochure or further information when you contact an establishment.

You might like to ask a number of questions before you make your booking. Here is a checklist to help you:

- Have they got availability for the dates you require?
- Have they got the right combination of rooms/beds for your party?
- Have you asked about special rates for children/meals?
- Do you want to book any evening meals?
- Do you understand the prices and what is included?
- Have you explained any special requirements e.g. vegetarian food?
- Have you asked about any activities you are interested in e.g. golf, horse-riding?

Confirming your booking

In many cases you will be asked for written confirmation and/or a deposit. An agreement may also be drawn up (usual for longer stays); a copy will be sent out to you to complete and return. Do check the details carefully to ensure that you have the correct dates and the types of rooms and beds that you require in particular. You should also have the agreed price and information on payment methods. It is a good idea to make a note of any special requirements on the written confirmation or in your booking letter to avoid any confusion.

Sample Booking Letters

Establishment
address in full
with postcode
and country

Your address
in full with
postcode and
country

Date

Dear M/Mme X

I am writing to ask you to send me your brochure, or further information about your chambre d'hôtes, which I found in the AA/Gîtes de France Bed & Breakfast in France Guide.

I look forward to hearing from you.

Thank you for your help.

Yours sincerely

Your name

Establishment
address in full
with postcode
and country

Your address
in full with
postcode and
country

Date

Dear M/Mme X

Thank you for sending me your brochure. I would like to reserve ... (single/double) room(s) with private bath/shower and WC, for the nights of (dates). We are a party of ..., comprising ... adults and ... child(ren) aged .../ under ... years. We would require a cot in the parents' room. Do you have any rooms available at that time?

I would also like to book table d'hôtes for (number of adults/children) on (date).

Do you offer any discounts for children and/or longer stays? Will I be able to pay by credit card?

We will be travelling from (place), please can you send me directions?

I look forward to hearing from you.

Yours sincerely

Your name

Establishment
address in full
with postcode
and country

Your address
in full with
postcode and
country

Date

Monsieur/Madame

Je vous serais reconnaissant de me faire parvenir votre brochure ou des renseignements sur votre chambre d'hôtes, que j'ai vu dans le guide AA/Gîtes de France Bed & Breakfast in France.

J'attends vos renseignements et vous remercie par avance.

Je vous prie d'agréer, Monsieur/Madame, l'expression de mes sentiments distingués.

Your name

Establishment
address in full
with postcode
and country

Your address
in full with
postcode and
country

Date

Monsieur/Madame

Je vous remercie pour votre brochure. Je voudrais réserver ... chambre(s) pour (une personne/deux personnes) avec salle de bain/salle d'eau et WC privés, du (date) jusqu'au (date). Nous sommes ..., ... adulte(s), et ... enfant(s) de ... ans/moins de ... ans. Nous voudrions un lit d'enfant dans la chambre des parents. Est-ce que vous avez des chambres disponibles pour ces nuits?

Je voudrais aussi réserver une table d'hôtes pour ... adulte(s) et ... enfant(s) le soir du (date).

Est-ce qu'il y a la possibilité d'un tarif réduit pour les enfants ou pour un séjour prolongé? Est-ce que vous acceptez les cartes de crédit?

Nous partirons de (place); je vous serais reconnaissant de me communiquer l'itinéraire?

En attendant vos renseignements, je vous prie d'agréer, Monsieur/Madame, l'expression de mes sentiments distingués.

Your name

Travelling in
~ FRANCE ~

Motoring

Documentation You should carry your full valid national driving licence or International Driving Permit (IDP), the vehicle registration document, certificate of motor insurance and a letter of authorisation from the owner if the vehicle is not registered in your name. Your vehicle should display the approved standard design International Distinguishing Sign (IDS), for example 'GB' for UK residents. Cycle racks should not obscure your number plate or IDS.

Rules of the road Drive on the right and overtake on the left. Traffic coming from the right has priority (*priorité à droite*), unless signs say otherwise. The *priorité* rule no longer applies at roundabouts, which means you give way to cars already on the roundabout. The minimum age to drive in France is 18, and no one is allowed to drive on a provisional licence.

Lights Right-hand drive cars need headlamp beam converters (available as kits) to divert the beam away from drivers of oncoming left-hand vehicles. Motorists must carry a warning triangle and are advised to carry a set of replacement bulbs, as it is illegal to drive with faulty lights.

Speed limits In built-up areas 50 kph (31 mph); outside built-up areas 90 kph (55 mph), or 80 kph (49 mph) in wet conditions; dual carriageways with a central reservation 110 kph (69 mph) or 100 kph (62 mph) in wet conditions; motorways 130 kph (80 mph) or 110 kph (69 mph) in wet conditions. Minimum speed on the Paris Périphérique is 80 kph (49 mph); on other urban motorways 110 kph (69 mph). In fog the speed limit on all roads is 50 kph (31 mph). Drivers who have held a licence for less than two years must observe the reduced speed limits at all times.

Seatbelts must be worn by the driver and the front and back-seat passengers.

Drink Maximum permissible alcohol levels are very low (0.05 per cent) and random breath tests are frequent. It is wiser not to drink at all if you will be driving.

Motorways France has more than 8,000 km of motorways (*autoroutes*), indicated on maps as A followed by a number. Most of these are toll roads. Prices per km vary and you can pay by cash or credit card at the exit booth (*péage*). Autoroutes in France are usually much quieter than motorways in Britain, and have resting areas (*aire de repos*) every 20 km or so.

Alternative routes Country roads offer a more picturesque, if slower, alternative to the autoroute. Although *routes nationales* (indicated by the letter N before the road number) are generally very good, they can become congested in places. Look for roads signed *itinéraire bis* to avoid trouble spots. The Bison Futé map shows these routes; copies are available from the French Tourist Office. You can also plan your route on the AA website *www.theAA.com*.

Car hire You will need your driver's licence and preferably an IDP. You may be asked to show your passport.

Eurotunnel run a 24-hour drive-on train service through the Channel Tunnel, from Folkestone to Calais, UK telephone 08705 353535.

Motoring websites
www.theAA.com
(route planning, motoring advice, traffic information, insurance and much more)

www.autoroutes.fr
(information on motorways in France – road works, tolls, etc.)

www.sytadin.tm.fr
(traffic reports around Paris)

www.franceguide.com
(information on motoring in France)

Fuel Petrol stations in France no longer sell leaded petrol, which has been replaced with a substitute unleaded petrol that can be used in vehicles that normally use leaded fuel. Unleaded (*sans plomb*) may be found as 98 octane, 95 octane, 'super plus' or 'premium'. Diesel is generally known as *gas oil/gazole*.

Motoring essentials AA shops at Dover sell Five Star Insurance, personal insurance including ski insurance, and a wide range of maps, atlases and guides. Motoring abroad essentials such as beam converters and warning triangles can also be purchased here and international driving permits can be obtained. AA shops give a 5% discount off all merchandise to AA members.

AA Shops
Travelcentre, Eastern Docks Terminal, Dover
Telephone 01304 208122
Eurotunnel passenger terminal, Dover
(access only on day of travel with ticket)
Telephone 01303 273576

Train Travel

There is an extensive rail network in France. It is advisable to book popular routes (e.g. Paris-Lyon) well in advance. You can travel direct from London Waterloo or Ashford, Kent, to Paris or Lille on the Eurostar passenger service. Eurostar also offers direct services to Disneyland Paris and the French Alps. Many other destinations can be reached by taking the high-speed TGV from Paris or Lille. For further information and bookings contact Rail Europe on 08705 848 848 or see your local travel agent. When booking accommodation check that it is accessible by train if this is your main method of transport.

Train websites
www.eurostar.co.uk   www.eurotunnel.com
www.raileurope.co.uk

Ferry Travel

Ferries operate regularly between France and Britain, for foot passengers as well as cars. Services are subject to seasonal variations; check with your travel agent in advance.

Ferry websites
www.condorferries.co.uk *(Condor Ferries)*
www.brittanyferries.com *(Brittany Ferries)*
www.hoverspeed.co.uk *(Hoverspeed Fast Ferries)*
www.poportsmouth.com *(P&O Portsmouth)*
www.posl.com *(P&O Stena Line)*
www.seafrance.com *(SeaFrance)*

Air Travel

The international airports for Paris are Roissy-Charles de Gaulle and Orly Sud and the national airline, Air France, has a very extensive domestic network operating out of both. Other airports used for direct scheduled flights include Bordeaux, Lyon, Marseille, Nantes, Nice, Strasbourg and Toulouse. Check with your travel agent for other possibilities, including fly-drive options.

Airline websites
www.airfrance.co.uk *(Air France)*
www.britishairways.com *(British Airways and GB Airways)*
www.flybmi.com *(British Midland)*
www.buzzaway.com *(Buzz)*
www.go-fly.com *(Go)*
www.ryanair.com *(Ryanair)*

Student and Youth Travel

If you are under 26, you can apply for one of a variety of reasonably priced cards which give discounts on accommodation, meals and travel. You will need identification and a photo for all of them. The International Student Card (ISIC) also entitles you to cheaper museum entry and beds in university residences. Contact your local students' union or student travel office for an application form, or print one out from the ISIC website (www.isiccard.com). Proof of your full-time student status is required. ISIC also issue International Youth Travel Cards, sometimes known as the GO 25 Card, to anyone under the age of 25. Contact ISIC Mail Order, Louis Pearlman Centre, Goulten Street, Hull HU3 4DL. A booklet, Youth Tourism, is available free of charge from the French Tourist Office (www.franceguide.com).

Useful
~ *INFORMATION* ~

School holidays 2002-2003
Holidays marked * are staggered across France between the dates shown.

Christmas – 22 December 2001 to 7 January 2002
Spring half term* – 2 February to 4 March 2002
Easter* – 30 March to 29 April 2002
Summer – 29 June to 4 September 2002
Autumn half term – 26 Oct to 4 November 2002
Christmas – 21 December 2002 to 6 January 2003
Spring half term* – 8 February to 10 March 2003

Public holidays 2002
New Year's Day – *1 January*
Easter Sunday and Monday – *31 March & 1 April*
Labour Day – *1 May*
VE Day – *8 May*
Ascension Day – *9 May*
Whitsunday and Monday – *19 & 20 May*
Bastille Day – *14 July*
Assumption Day – *15 August*
All Saints' Day – *1 November*
Remembrance Day – *11 November*
Christmas Day – *25 December*

Shopping and business hours
Banks:
9am–noon/ 2–4pm weekdays, and closed either Saturday or Monday. Banks close early the day before a public holiday.
Post Offices:
8am–7pm weekdays, 8am–noon Saturdays.
Food shops/supermarkets:
7am–6.30 or 7.30pm
Other shops:
9 or 10am–6.30 or 7.30pm. Many shops close all or half-day Monday. Some food shops (bakers in particular) may open Sunday morning. Shops in the provinces usually close for lunch between 12 and 2pm. Hypermarkets are often open until 9 or 10pm Monday to Saturday (many close on Monday morning). Tourist offices can give you local times.

Telephones
French telephone numbers are 10 digits *(9 from the UK as you drop the initial 0).*
To dial France from the UK – dial 0033 *(international access code)*, then the number minus the first 0.
To call the UK from France – dial 0044 *(international access code)* then the UK number minus the first 0.
To call the US and Canada from France – dial 001 *(international access code)* then the normal phone number.

Payphones are plentiful, and usually take phone cards *(télécartes)*, which you can buy in newsagents *(tabacs)* and post offices. Some payphones in cities will take credit cards.

Mobiles
Arrange international access with your network service provider before you go.

Tourist information There are 5,000 local Offices de Tourisme and Syndicats d'initiative. They can give advice on accommodation, transport, restaurants and entertainment.

Water You can drink the water unless it says EAU NON POTABLE.

British consulate
18 bis, rue d'Anjou, 75008 Paris
Tel (1) 44 51 31 00, Fax (1) 44 51 31 27
Open Mon–Fri 9.30am–12.30pm, 2.30–5pm
There are also Consulates in Bordeaux, Lille, Lyon and Marseilles.

Credit cards Make sure you take your bank's 24-hour credit card contact number with you. Cash can be withdrawn from many cash dispensing machines using your UK pin number – check that the machine displays the appropriate symbol.

Medical treatment and health insurance If you regularly take certain medicines do make sure that you have a sufficient supply for your stay before travelling. If for health reasons you carry drugs or appliances (such as a hypodermic syringe), a letter from your doctor explaining the condition and treatment required may save you from any difficulties in entering France. Before travelling, make sure you are covered by insurance for emergency medical and dental treatment as a minimum. Before taking out extra insurance check whether your homeowner or medical insurance covers travel abroad. Many European countries have reciprocal agreements for medical treatments and will require EU citizens to obtain a validated E111 form before travel. You should not rely exclusively on this, however, and personal travel insurance is advisable.

Emergency numbers
Fire 18, Police 17, Ambulance (SAMU) 15
Operator 13, Directory Enquiries 12

Etiquette and cultural differences
Although your hosts will want you to feel welcome during your stay, don't forget that you are guests in their home. It is polite to notify them if you're going to arrive earlier or later than arranged. Even if your French is limited to a few textbook phrases, do make the effort to use what you know; your hosts will appreciate your efforts, even if it is just a friendly *bonjour* or *au revoir* as you enter or leave the premises. If your French is good enough to hold a conversation, do remember that you should never use the familiar *tu* over the more formal *vous*, unless invited to do so.

When entering a shop, it is courteous to greet the assistant with *bonjour, monsieur/ madame/mademoiselle*. Generally, a woman in her twenties or older is addressed as madame, while a younger woman is addressed as mademoiselle. Use these forms of address to attract the attention of a waiter in a restaurant; never shout *garçon!*

Table etiquette is important to the French but a little common sense should be all you need to get by. When eating with your hosts don't be surprised if you are served several separate courses rather than one main dish with accompaniments. You may be asked to keep your plate. It is polite to place your cutlery at each side of your plate when you finish, rather than together in the middle. It is usual to drink wine or mineral water with a meal, rather than a fizzy drink or coffee. In a restaurant, service is usually included (look out for the words *service compris* on the menu or bill) but people generally leave a few coins on the table as they leave. You will probably need to prompt the waiter to bring your bill; dining out is rarely a hurried affair and most waiters will take the cue from you as to when you're ready to leave.

Food for thought
~ IN FRANCE ~

For many of us the lure of France lies mainly in the food. Browsing the rich bounty of the open-air markets, making the early morning pilgrimage to the boulangerie, stumbling across the most unassuming of village restaurants serving earthy regional cooking for the price of a cinema ticket. It's what we love most about France. Aren't these the memories we treasure most from our trips across La Manche? Isn't it this that keeps calling us back? Well, here's a disturbing thought. Imagine France without French cuisine. A horrible prospect, but it's one that is clearly worrying the French. There is an awful lot of culinary agonising going on across the Channel. Food in France rises way above mere sustenance: it has a spiritual element, it brings people together around the table, it's a fundamental part of the soul of the nation and it's seen as being in danger. Globalisation and urbanisation are widely perceived as urgent threats to the traditional French way of eating – so much so that a Roquefort producing sheep farmer from the south who went on trial for wrecking a McDonalds construction site has become a national icon. The prospect of a nation converted to TV dinners and fast-food outlets is a spectre keeping more than a few French politicians awake at night.

The influences of the bordering countries are found in the sausages, sauerkraut and pâtés of Alsace and the spiciness of Basque cookery in the southwest. As you travel through the country you still witness a mosaic of local traditions and specialities unrivalled in their diversity. There is still an enormous amount to savour and the fact that even small French towns continue to sustain lively markets, with stall after stall of enticing fresh produce, is evidence enough that although much has changed, much remains the same.

In the French kitchen one basic tenet still dominates. Good food comes from good ingredients treated lovingly and with respect. Whilst that philosophy remains we can sleep easily in our beds and continue to savour the aromas of our jaunts across the Channel.

Many of the places in this book serve dinner. There you will find ample evidence that the heart of French cooking still beats strongly. Make the most of them.

So should we be worried too?

In a sense the soul-searching is not new. Forty years ago it was the prospect of the high street supermarket that was raising similar concerns in France. The supermarkets duly arrived, but in quite a different manifestation from our own. They are not dominated by aisle after aisle of convenience foods, the fish counters are a joy of variety and freshness, vegetables with flavour are not restricted to the premium price packs, cheese counters boast wheel after wheel of local offerings, whole cured hams hang in racks.

So, perhaps we should be reassured by the anxieties of the French. Evidently it's not too late and at least it shows they're aware of what they might lose, and let's face it, there's an awful lot to lose.

Despite the ready availability of frozen, canned and processed foods, it's still true to say that the French eat to a pattern dictated by the regions and the seasons. The culture of French provincial cooking, passed down through the generations, still pervades the average French kitchen and nowhere is it more apparent than in the home. The cooking of Normandy is still characterised by Calvados, cream and apples, Burgundy by red wine and the mustard of Dijon, the South by the abundance of seafood, garlic and olive oil.

Index of
~ *REGIONS* ~

ALSACE-LORRAINE

BAS-RHIN

BETSCHDORF

♦♦♦♦ Chambre d'hôtes Christian KRUMEICH
23 rue des Potiers, 67660 BETSCHDORF
☎ 03 88 54 40 56　🖷 03 88 54 47 67
Four bedrooms in the home of a potter. One grade 3 double room with private bathroom facilities on the landing. Two grade 4 twin rooms, one with a kitchen and a TV. Each room has private bathroom facilities. There is a lounge, a garden with outdoor furniture and a covered parking area. Pottery courses can be arranged. Open all year.
PRICES: s €26-€38; d €34-€53; extra person €13　**NEARBY:** Horse riding (10km) Theme park (10km) Fishing (1km) Swimming pool (1km) Stretch of water (10km) Hiking (1km) Cross-country skiing (30km) Downhill skiing (30km) Tennis (1km) Bicycle hire (3km) Railway station (8km) SOULTZ SOUS FORETS　**NOTES:** No pets

BLAESHEIM

♦♦♦ A l'Arc en Ciel Anne SCHADT
57 rue du Maréchal Foch, 67113 BLAESHEIM
☎ 03 88 68 93 37 & SR : 03 88 75 56 50　🖷 03 88 59 97 75
Six en suite bedrooms in the outbuildings of an old Alsace farm dating from 1839. There is one twin, one double, and two triple rooms, plus one triple room and a further double room with two single beds on the second level. On the ground floor there are two double rooms, one with access for the less mobile. Breakfast is served in the dining room. Flower filled courtyard with garden furniture, swing and table tennis. Open all year.
PRICES: s €37-€43; d €44-€50; t €55-€59; extra person €7
ON SITE: Hiking Tennis　**NEARBY:** Horse riding (2km) Theme park (18km) Fishing (3km) Swimming pool (4km) Stretch of water (2km) Bicycle hire (8km) Railway station (6km) GEISPOLSHEIM (4km)
NOTES: Pets admitted Minimum 2 night stay CC English spoken

BOERSCH

♦♦♦ Bienvenue Willkommen Alain TAUBERT
3 route de Rosheim, 67530 BOERSCH
☎ 03 88 95 93 06 & SR : 03 88 75 56 50　🖷 03 88 95 99 98
e-mail: alisnata@tpgnet.net
In an adjoining house to the owners' residence, situated on the edge of a wine growing town near Obernai. On the second floor, there are two triple rooms. On the first floor there is a twin room with a double and a single bed. Each room has its own bathroom. Breakfast is served in the dining room. There is also a lounge area with a bookcase available to guests. The panoramic garden has outdoor furniture and parking facilities. Open all year.
PRICES: s €35; d €42; t €54　**ON SITE:** Fishing Hiking Tennis
NEARBY: Horse riding (5km) Theme park (30km) Swimming pool (5km) Stretch of water (20km) Cross-country skiing (15km) Downhill skiing (15km) Bicycle hire (3km) Railway station (5km) ROSHEIM (4km)
NOTES: No pets CC English spoken

CLEEBOURG

♦♦♦ 🍴 Chambre d'hôtes Anne KLEIN
59 rue Principale, 67160 CLEEBOURG　☎ 03 88 94 50 95
Situated in the centre of a small traditional wine-growing village on the ground floor of the owners' house. There is one family room with a double and a single bed, one double room and one twin

room. Each room has its own bathroom facilities. A camp bed is also available. Breakfast is served in a traditionally decorated room. Meals are available, with Alsace specialities. There is an enclosed courtyard, garden with furniture, barbecue and parking facilities. Half board 59 euros for two people. Open all year.
PRICES: s €26; d €38; t €50; dinner €12　**ON SITE:** Hiking
NEARBY: Horse riding (6km) Theme park (16km) Fishing (10km) Swimming pool (4km) Stretch of water (13km) Tennis (10km) Bicycle hire (10km) Railway station (10km) Shops (7km) WISSEMBOURG (10km)
NOTES: No pets Minimum 2 night stay

DAMBACH-LA-VILLE

♦♦♦ Chambre d'hôtes Michel NARTZ
12 place du Marché, 67650 DAMBACH-LA-VILLE
☎ 03 88 92 41 11　🖷 03 88 92 63 01
A 17th-century vineyard property, situated in the town centre. There are three double rooms, one with a lounge area, one twin room and one single room, each with separate bathroom facilities. Breakfast is served in a small tavern, with traditional food during the summer. There is a 5% discount for stays of more than three nights. Tourist tax is included. The property also has a small wine-tasting cellar. Open 1 April - 20 December.
PRICES: s €35; d €40-€46; extra person €9　**ON SITE:** Wine tasting Fishing Hiking Tennis Bicycle hire　**NEARBY:** Horse riding (15km) Theme park (10km) Swimming pool (7km) Stretch of water (15km) BARR (9km)　**NOTES:** No pets

DIEBOLSHEIM

♦♦♦ Chambre d'hôtes Charles LAUBACHER
27 rue de l'Eglise, 67230 DIEBOLSHEIM
☎ 03 88 74 67 06
Two flower-covered houses situated in the village. There are two double rooms, each with a shower, one twin room with full bathroom facilities and one twin room with a private bathroom on the landing. There are two further en suite bedrooms on the first floor of the owners' house. One double room with a balcony and one with two double beds. Breakfast is served in the glass-covered terrace. Courtyard, garden, orchard and parking. Open all year.
PRICES: s €21; d €30　**ON SITE:** Fishing Hiking Tennis Bicycle hire
NEARBY: Horse riding (8km) Theme park (10km) Swimming pool (15km) Stretch of water (5km) Railway station (15km) MARCKOLSHEIM (13km)　**NOTES:** Pets admitted

DIEFFENBACH-AU-VAL

♦♦♦ ❤ Les Trois Pierres Albert GEIGER
2 route de Neuve Eglise, 67220 DIEFFENBACH-AU-VAL
☎ 03 88 85 69 02 & SR : 03 88 75 56 50　🖷 03 88 85 62 03
e-mail: geiger@les3pierres.com　www.les3pierres.com
Guest rooms on the first floor of the owners' house, situated on the edge of a quiet village. There are three double rooms each with a TV point and private bathroom. Breakfast is served in a private guest room, which also has a lounge area and fireplace. A cot is available. Garden area with furniture and covered parking. Reduced price for stays over three nights. Open all year.
PRICES: s €42; d €52; extra person €16　**ON SITE:** Hiking
NEARBY: Theme park (20km) Fishing (2km) Swimming pool (4km) Cross-country skiing (26km) Downhill skiing (25km) Tennis (4km) Bicycle hire (4km) Railway station (10km) Shops (4km) VILLE (4km)
NOTES: No pets CC

continued

ALSACE-LORRAINE

DRACHENBRONN

🍴 🐓 **Chambre d'hôtes** Philippe FINCK
Ferme-Auberge des 7 Fontaines, 67160 DRACHENBRONN
☎ 03 88 94 50 90 📠 03 88 94 54 57
An old oil press situated in wooded surroundings. There are two
rooms for four people, two triple rooms and one double room
each with its own bathroom facilities. Seminar room and six other
rooms available, three of which are at the nearby auberge, where
you can also dine. There is a shared garden area with furniture,
table tennis, a sauna and parking. Open all year.
PRICES: s €34; d €46; t €63; extra person €11; HB €36; FB €45
ON SITE: Swimming pool Hiking **NEARBY:** Horse riding (3km) Theme
park (12km) Fishing (10km) Stretch of water (10km) Tennis (1km) Bicycle
hire (6km) Railway station (7km) Shops (7km) Restaurant nearby
SOULTZ SOUS FORETS (7km) **NOTES:** Pets admitted

DUPPIGHEIM

🍴 **Chambre d'hôtes** Jean-Jacques SCHAEFFER
2 rue des Roses, Restaurant Au Schaefferhof,
67120 DUPPIGHEIM
☎ 03 88 50 70 81 📠 03 88 50 70 81
On the first floor of a half-timbered farm building, above a
restaurant. There are three double rooms and three triple rooms.
Each room has private bathroom facilities and a TV point. There is
a large area with a boules pitch, a swing, table tennis, table
football and parking facilities. Meals are available, with specialities
from Alsace. Open all year.
PRICES: s €32; d €40; t €47; extra person €9 **ON SITE:** Children's play
area **NEARBY:** Horse riding (10km) Theme park (14km) Swimming pool
(1km) Stretch of water (8km) Hiking (10km) Cross-country skiing (20km)
Downhill skiing (20km) Tennis (1km) Bicycle hire (6km) Railway station
(2km) Restaurant nearby GEISPOLSHEIM (13km) **NOTES:** No pets

HEILIGENSTEIN

🍴 **Chambre d'hôtes** Charles BOCH
6 rue Principale, 67140 HEILIGENSTEIN
☎ 03 88 08 41 26 📠 03 88 08 58 25
A pretty wine maker's house, situated in a vineyard. There are
three double rooms, one with a balcony. All bedrooms have
private bathroom. Extra bed available. Excellent breakfasts are
served in a private dining room. Pot luck meals possible. There is a
garden area with furniture, table tennis and parking. Open all year.
PRICES: d €40; extra person €9 **ON SITE:** Hiking Cross-country skiing
Bicycle hire **NEARBY:** Horse riding (10km) Swimming pool (10km)
Stretch of water (15km) Downhill skiing (20km) Tennis (2km) Railway
station (2km) BARR (2km) **NOTES:** No pets

HOERDT

🍴 **Le Landhome** René et Dorothée STOLL
23 route de la Wantzenau, 67720 HOERDT
☎ 03 88 51 72 29 & 06 08 25 01 51 📠 03 90 29 00 79
Six guest rooms situated in a town with many half-timbered
houses. Five rooms are in an adjoining house to the owners'
residence and one room is located in the owner's house. On the
ground floor of the adjacent house is a dining room and lounge
with cable TV. There are three double rooms on the first floor, one
double room and one twin room on the second floor, and one
twin room in the owner's house. Each room has a telephone and
its own bathroom; one bedroom has a kitchen. Enclosed garden
with furniture and parking. Golf 3km. Open all year.
PRICES: s €38; d €47; extra person €7 **NEARBY:** Horse riding (12km)
Theme park (30km) Fishing (1km) Swimming pool (10km) Stretch of
water (8km) Hiking (1km) Tennis (1km) Railway station (1km) Shops
(1km) BRUMATH (8km) **NOTES:** No pets Minimum 2 night stay English
spoken

HUNSPACH

🍴 **Chambre d'hôtes** MAISON UNGERER
3 route de Hoffen, 67250 HUNSPACH
☎ 03 88 80 59 39 📠 03 88 80 41 46
e-mail: maison-ungerer@wanadoo.fr

This renovated old farm building offers a ground-floor twin room,
and on the first floor there are two further twin rooms. Each room
has bathroom facilities, a kitchen and a lounge area. It is possible
to cater for two additional people. Breakfast is served in the
reserved dining room. There is a shared garden with barbecue,
table tennis and garden furniture. Bike hire is available. There is a
reduction for children and for stays of more than two nights. Open
all year except in July and August.
PRICES: s €27-€30; d €38-€45; t €63 **ON SITE:** Hiking Tennis Bicycle
hire **NEARBY:** Horse riding (6km) Theme park (15km) Fishing (15km)
Swimming pool (6km) Stretch of water (20km) Railway station (2km)
Shops (4km) SOULTZ SOUS FORETS (6km) **NOTES:** Pets admitted CC
English spoken

KUTZENHAUSEN

🍴 **La Vieille Grange** Héléna TRONCY
2 rue des Rossignols, 67250 OBERKUTZENHAUSEN
☎ 03 88 80 79 48 📠 03 88 80 79 48
Three warm, subtly decorated guest rooms are arranged in a
charming barn which adjoins the owners' house, just 100m from a
forest and situated in a small, quiet hamlet of several half-
timbered houses. The property has antique furniture and features
a boudoir grand piano and elaborate woodwork. There is one
double room, which also has a single bed and a lounge. And two
further double rooms. Each room has its own bathroom facilities.
The property has a landscaped flower-filled garden with a covered
terrace; a 100-year-old vine shades the enclosed courtyard.
Parking is available. Open 1 April - 31 December.
PRICES: s €46-€49; d €52-€59; t €67 **NEARBY:** Horse riding (5km)
Theme park (6km) Fishing (4km) Swimming pool (5km) Stretch of water
(20km) Hiking (1km) Tennis (1km) Bicycle hire (2km) Railway station
(4km) Shops (4km) SOULTZ SOUS FORETS (4km) **NOTES:** No pets
English spoken

MAISONSGOUTTE

🍴 **Chambre d'hôtes** Jean-Luc HERRMANN
18 rue Wagenbach, 67220 MAISONSGOUTTE
☎ 03 88 57 22 01
These guest rooms are situated in a quiet village on the first floor
of an adjoining house to the owners' residence. There is one triple
room and three double rooms, each with own bathroom facilities.
The enclosed, shared garden has a barbecue. Parking is available.
Open all year.
PRICES: s €24; d €38; t €53 **ON SITE:** Hiking **NEARBY:** Swimming
pool (3km) Cross-country skiing (20km) Downhill skiing (20km) Tennis
(3km) Bicycle hire (3km) Railway station (17km) VILLE (3km)
NOTES: No pets

MEMMELSHOFFEN

♦♦♦ Chambre d'hôtes S'KAEMMERLE

5 rue de Lembach, 67250 MEMMELSHOFFEN
☎ 03 88 80 50 39 & 03 88 80 62 97 📠 03 88 80 64 01
Four typically Alsace-decorated guest rooms in an adjoining house
to the owners' residence. On the first floor there are three double
rooms, one with a small lounge area. The ground floor has one
double room with wheelchair access and one single room. Each
room has its own bathroom facilities and a TV. Breakfast is served
in a dining room reserved for guests. There is a summer terrace,
enclosed garden with furniture under a parasol and a barbecue.
Private parking is available in the courtyard. Open all year.
PRICES: s €47; d €58; t €74 **ON SITE:** Hiking Bicycle hire
NEARBY: Horse riding (2km) Theme park (12km) Fishing (5km)
Swimming pool (2km) Tennis (3km) Railway station (3km) Shops (2km)
SOULTZ SOUS FORETS (3km) **NOTES:** No pets Minimum 2 night stay

MERKWILLER-PECHELBRONN

♦♦♦ Chambre d'hôtes Thomas LIMMACHER

7 A, route de Lobsann, Résidence Les Helions,
67250 MERKWILLER-PECHELBRONN
☎ 03 88 80 90 96 & 03 88 80 78 61 📠 03 88 80 75 20
On the second floor of the owners' house in a quiet village in a
wooded park on the edge of a brook. There is one double room,
two single rooms and a family room with one double and two
single beds. Each room has its own bathroom facilities. Breakfast is
served in an Alsace-decorated room, or on the terrace. There is
garden furniture, reclining seats, a swing and parking available.
The price for four people is 90 euros. Open all year.
PRICES: s €30-€50; d €37-€58; t €75; extra person €12
ON SITE: Children's play area Hiking Tennis **NEARBY:** Horse riding
(6km) Theme park (4km) Fishing (5km) Swimming pool (5km) Stretch
of water (12km) Bicycle hire (6km) Railway station (6km) SOULTZ SOUS
FORETS (5km) **NOTES:** No pets Minimum 2 night stay English spoken

MITTELBERGHEIM

♦♦♦ |◯| Gîte de la Tulipe Jacqueline DOLDER

15 chemin du Holzweg, 67140 MITTELBERGHEIM
☎ 03 88 08 15 23 📠 03 88 08 54 11

On the first floor of the owners' house situated on the edge of a
quiet village and vineyard. There are three double rooms and two
triple rooms, each with bathroom facilities. Breakfast is served in
the dining room or on the terrace. There is a shared garden,
barbecue, covered swimming pool and parking. There is also a
small chalet with washing facilities and a kitchenette. Reductions for
stays during the week, arriving on a Saturday, are 20% between
01/11 - 31/03 and 10% between 01/04 - 30/10. Open all year.
PRICES: s €40; d €43; t €57; extra person €14; HB €40
ON SITE: Swimming pool Hiking Bicycle hire **NEARBY:** Horse riding
(3km) Theme park (17km) Fishing (1km) Stretch of water (15km) Cross-
country skiing (12km) Downhill skiing (12km) Tennis (1km) Railway
station (1km) BARR (1km) **NOTES:** Pets admitted

NEUBOIS

♦♦♦ |◯| L'Altenberg Richarde MOSSER

4 rue de l'Altenberg, 67220 NEUBOIS
☎ 03 88 85 60 56 📠 03 88 85 60 56
A typical Alsace house adjoining the owners' residence in quiet
surroundings with good views over the village. There is one room
with one double bed and two single beds, one twin room and on
the first floor there is a triple room and a twin room with a double
and a single bed. Each room has its own bathroom facilities and a
TV point. Breakfast is served in the dining room. Meals are
available, with Alsace specialities. There is a shared kitchen,
veranda with a reading area and TV, garden furniture, swing and
parking. Reductions of 10% for stays of one week. Open all year.
PRICES: s €38; d €45; t €59; extra person €14; HB €38
ON SITE: Children's play area Hiking **NEARBY:** Horse riding (15km)
Theme park (45km) Swimming pool (6km) Stretch of water (15km)
Cross-country skiing (15km) Downhill skiing (15km) Tennis (6km) Bicycle
hire (6km) Railway station (12km) Shops (6km) VILLE (6km)
NOTES: Pets admitted Minimum 2 night stay English spoken

NOTHALTEN

♦♦♦ Chambre d'hôtes Bernard EGELE

144 route du Vin, 67680 NOTHALTEN
☎ 03 88 92 48 21
On the first floor of the owners' house, on the edge of a wine-
making village. There is one room with a double bed and a bunk
bed, one double with an extra bed and TV point, and one further
double. All have private bathroom facilities. There is a rustic cellar
for breakfasts and quiet evenings. A kitchen is also available to
guests. Furniture is provided in the garden along with a terrace,
barbecue porch and parking. The price for four people is 55 euros.
There is a reduced price from the third night, which is 35 euros for
two people, 44 euros for three people or 49 euros for four people.
Small animals welcome. Open all year.
PRICES: s €32; d €38; t €47 **ON SITE:** Children's play area Hiking
Bicycle hire **NEARBY:** Horse riding (15km) Theme park (25km) Fishing
(8km) Swimming pool (15km) Stretch of water (15km) Cross-country
skiing (35km) Downhill skiing (35km) Tennis (8km) Railway station (3km)
Shops (3km) BARR (6km) **NOTES:** No pets (except small animals)

♦♦♦ Chambre d'hôtes Roland GEYER

148 route du Vin, 67680 NOTHALTEN
☎ 03 88 92 46 82 & 06 08 03 08 02 📠 03 88 92 63 19
Three rooms in a wine grower's house situated in the heart of the
vineyard on the edge of the village. One double room, with an
adjoining room for two people, one twin room with a balcony and
one further double room with a balcony. Each room has its own
bathroom, kitchen and TV point. Breakfast is served in the guest
lounge or on the terrace. Garden furniture and a barbecue are
provided. Shared garden and parking. Open all year.
PRICES: d €40; t €54-€69 **ON SITE:** Hiking Bicycle hire
NEARBY: Horse riding (15km) Theme park (25km) Fishing (8km)
Swimming pool (15km) Stretch of water (15km) Cross-country skiing
(35km) Downhill skiing (35km) Tennis (8km) Railway station (3km)
Shops (3km) BARR (6km) **NOTES:** No pets

OTTROTT

♦♦♦ Chambre d'hôtes Marie-Dominique MAURER

11 route d'Obernai, Roedel, 67530 OTTROTT
☎ 03 88 95 80 12
A traditional house with a sunny courtyard. Three double rooms,
one triple room and one street-level room with one double and
one bunk bed. Each room has its own bathroom facilities and a TV
point. Breakfast is served in a traditionally decorated Alsace room
reserved for guests. There is a boules pitch, small farmyard, swing,
garden and parking. Supplements for animals. Open all year.

continued

23

PRICES: d €40-€44 ON SITE: Children's play area Hiking Tennis Bicycle hire NEARBY: Horse riding (3km) Theme park (30km) Fishing (2km) Swimming pool (3km) Stretch of water (25km) Cross-country skiing (20km) Downhill skiing (20km) Railway station (4km) ROSHEIM (5km) NOTES: Pets admitted

RANRUPT

♥♥♥ Chambre d'hôtes Laurence FERRY
10 rue Principale, 67420 RANRUPT
☎ 03 88 47 24 71 📠 03 88 47 20 45
A small tavern near forests and Champ de Feu. There are two adjoining double rooms and one room with a double and two single beds. Each has its own bathroom. There is a TV and reading area; swings, a telephone, table tennis, garden furniture and parking. Reduction starting from the third night. Open all year.
PRICES: s €21; d €35; extra person €14; HB €33
ON SITE: Children's play area Hiking Bicycle hire NEARBY: Horse riding (1km) Theme park (25km) Fishing (5km) Swimming pool (11km) Stretch of water (1km) Cross-country skiing (11km) Downhill skiing (11km) Tennis (10km) Railway station (5km) Shops (11km) Restaurant nearby SAALES (10km) NOTES: Pets admitted English spoken

SCHERWILLER

♥♥♥ ¡Ô¡ Chambre d'hôtes Simone SAVA
29 route des Romains, 67750 SCHERWILLER
☎ 03 88 92 84 74 & SR : 03 88 75 56 50 📠 03 88 92 84 74
Guestrooms on the first and second floor of the owners' house, situated on the edge of a vineyard. There are two double rooms with TV and video and private bathroom facilities. It also has a relaxing veranda with a jacuzzi. Large garden with furniture, indoor pool open June-September, and table tennis. Open all year.
PRICES: s €46; d €53-€59; extra person €15; dinner €15
NEARBY: Swimming pool (5km) Hiking (2km) Tennis (5km) Railway station (3km) SELESTAT (5km) NOTES: No pets CC English spoken

SEEBACH

♥♥♥ ¡Ô¡ Chambre d'hôtes Liliane TROG
132 rue des Eglises, 67160 SEEBACH
☎ 03 88 94 74 99 📠 03 88 94 74 99
An old half-timbered farm situated in a traditional village. There is one room with a double and three single beds and one twin room. Each has its own bathroom. There is an enclosed courtyard with garden furniture and table tennis. Reductions are available from the second night. Children's meals cost 7 euros. Table d'hôte meals can be arranged; drinks are not included in the price. Four people sharing 66 euros. Open all year.
PRICES: s €24; d €53; dinner €11 ON SITE: Hiking Tennis NEARBY: Horse riding (1km) Theme park (15km) Fishing (15km) Swimming pool (10km) Stretch of water (15km) Bicycle hire (4km) Railway station (3km) WISSEMBOURG (8km) NOTES: No pets

WACKENBACH

♥♥♥ Chambre d'hôtes Claude BESNARD
16 rue Rain, 67130 WACKENBACH
☎ 03 88 97 11 08
A first floor guest room situated on the GR5 hiking trail on the edge of a forest. There are two grade 1 bedrooms, one double and one triple. Both have a wc and shared bathroom facilities. There are two grade 3 rooms, one double and one triple, each with private bathroom facilities. There is a garden area. Open all year.
PRICES: s €18-€21; d €26-€33; t €37-€42 ON SITE: Fishing Hiking NEARBY: Horse riding (4km) Theme park (3km) Swimming pool (3km) Cross-country skiing (7km) Downhill skiing (20km) Tennis (3km) Bicycle hire (3km) Railway station (3km) Shops (2km) SCHIRMECK (3km) NOTES: Pets admitted

AMMERSCHWIHR

♥♥♥ Chambre d'hôtes André THOMANN-DESMAREST
2, rue des Ponts en pierre, 68770 AMMERSCHWIHR
☎ 03 89 47 32 83 📠 03 89 47 32 83
This former wine-producing farm, in typical 16th-century Alsace style, is peacefully situated in a village near a forest. It has three rooms, each with private shower room and wc. The first has a double bed, bunk beds, and a cot, with a fridge on the landing: €50 per night. The second has a double bed and a child's bed: €45 per night and the third has a double bed and a cot, and TV: €45 per night. There is a guests' sitting room, parking, and an interior courtyard. Four persons, per night: €70. Reduction of 10% for two nights and 20% for four nights and more, except for school holidays, weekends and public holidays. Open all year.
PRICES: d €50; t €60 ON SITE: Fishing Hiking Tennis NEARBY: Horse riding (12km) Golf (4km) Swimming pool (2km) Cross-country skiing (20km) Downhill skiing (20km) Railway station (8km) KAYSERSBERG (2km) NOTES: Pets admitted

♥♥♥ Chambre d'hôtes Guy THOMAS
41, Grand rue, 68770 AMMERSCHWIHR
☎ 03 89 78 23 90 📠 03 89 47 18 90
e-mail: thomas.guy@free.fr   http://thomas.guy.free.fr

This traditional village house has, on the ground floor, two two-person rooms; on the first floor one room for 2-4 people and one two-person room. All rooms have private shower room, wc, and kitchenette. Sitting room and lounge available. Central heating, parking, garden, courtyard, barbecue, swing, table tennis, garden room, sauna, and fitness room. Golf at Ammerschwihr.
PRICES: s €38; d €41-€44; t €46-€49; extra person €8
ON SITE: Children's play area Hiking Tennis NEARBY: Horse riding (4km) Golf (4km) Fishing (1km) Swimming pool (2km) Bicycle hire (1km) Railway station (8km) KAYSERSBERG (4km) NOTES: Pets admitted

BEBLENHEIM

♥♥♥ Chambre d'hôtes Christine COLAIANNI
41, rue de Hoen, 68980 BEBLENHEIM
☎ 03 89 47 82 52 📠 03 89 47 98 29
The owners live in this centrally heated house, peacefully situated with fine views of a vineyard. All rooms have air conditioning. On the first floor are two rooms, one with double bed and private bathroom and wc, the second with double bed and single bed with separate shower room, handbasin and wc. Fridge. A fold-up bed is also available. Breakfast may be taken in the dining room or on the veranda. Courtyard, private parking, and garage for bicycles.
PRICES: d €44; t €57; extra person €12 ON SITE: Hiking Bicycle hire NEARBY: Golf (5km) Swimming pool (5km) Cross-country skiing (20km) Downhill skiing (20km) Tennis (1km) Railway station (10km) KAYSERSBERG NOTES: No pets

EGUISHEIM

♦♦♦ Chambre d'hôtes Christiane GASCHY

3, rue des Fleurs, 68420 EGUISHEIM

☎ 03 89 23 69 09 📠 03 89 23 69 09

This house is peacefully situated close to the edge of the village. First floor: one twin-bedded room, one double room, and one double room with adjoining single room. All rooms have TV, handbasin, shower and wc. Fridge on the landing. Breakfast is served on the veranda, with a view of three châteaux. Parking in enclosed courtyard. Air conditioning in summer. Open all year.

PRICES: s €32; d €39; t €49 **ON SITE:** Hiking Tennis **NEARBY:** Horse riding (3km) Golf (20km) Fishing (5km) Swimming pool (5km) Cross-country skiing (25km) Railway station (5km) WINTZENHEIM (5km) **NOTES:** No pets

♦♦♦ Chambre d'hôtes Marthe HERTZ

3, rue du Riesling, 68420 EGUISHEIM

☎ 03 89 23 67 74 📠 03 89 23 67 74

This character house is situated in the heart of the village. Three double rooms, one twin room, one triple room. Guests may take breakfast in the living room, on a beautiful veranda with garden views, or, in fine weather, on the terrace. Open March to Dec.

PRICES: s €39; d €54; t €69 **NEARBY:** Horse riding (6km) Golf (20km) Fishing (1km) Swimming pool (1km) Tennis (10km) Railway station (2km) WINTZENHEIM (5km) **NOTES:** No pets Minimum 2 night stay English spoken

♦♦♦ Chambre d'hôtes Monique FREUDENREICH

4, Cour Unterlinden, 68420 EGUISHEIM

☎ 03 89 23 16 44 📠 03 89 23 16 44

This 18th-century house is situated in the heart of the village. Three rooms are available, each with a double bed and the possibility of adding one or two single beds. TV, shower, wc and handbasin in each room. Living room with kitchenette and fridge. Central heating. Parking in private courtyard. Open all year.

PRICES: s €31; d €39; t €46 **ON SITE:** Fishing Swimming pool **NEARBY:** Horse riding (6km) Tennis (10km) Railway station (2km) WINTZENHEIM (10km) **NOTES:** No pets English spoken

♦♦♦ Chambre d'hôtes Jean-Pierre BOMBENGER

8, rue du Bassin, 68420 EGUISHEIM

☎ 03 89 23 13 12 📠 03 89 23 13 12

This modern house is close to the centre of the village. Two double rooms with private shower room and wc, one room with one double and one single bed, with shared wc and shower room. There is a lounge, and a dining room in which breakfast is served. Garden, courtyard, barbecue, terrace, swing. Open all year.

PRICES: s €26–€33; d €34–€40; t €42–€48 **ON SITE:** Children's play area Bicycle hire **NEARBY:** Horse riding (5km) Golf (25km) Fishing (5km) Swimming pool (5km) Hiking (1km) Cross-country skiing (15km) Downhill skiing (15km) Tennis (1km) Railway station (7km) WINTZENHEIM (5km) **NOTES:** No pets English spoken

GUEBERSCHWIHR

♦♦♦ Chambre d'hôtes Christiane SCHERB

1, route de Rouffach, 68420 GUEBERSCHWIHR

☎ 03 89 49 33 70 & 03 89 49 21 05 📠 03 89 49 33 70

On a wine-making estate, these comfortable rooms each have shower, wc and handbasin. First floor: one twin room, two double rooms. Second floor: two rooms each with one double and one single bed. Microwave and fridge. Breakfast is served on the veranda with views over the vineyard and the plain of Alsace. Garden. Open all year.

PRICES: s €35; d €45–€50; t €60–€65; extra person €10 **ON SITE:** Fishing Hiking **NEARBY:** Horse riding (4km) Swimming pool (4km) Tennis (4km) Bicycle hire (4km) Railway station (4km) ROUFFACH **NOTES:** No pets

♦♦♦ Chambre d'hôtes Gilberte SCHNEIDER

42 rue du Nord, 68420 GUEBERSCHWIHR

☎ 03 89 49 25 79 📠 03 89 49 25 79

This wine-making estate offers three very comfortable double rooms, each with shower, wc, handbasin and kitchenette. Large courtyard, private parking, terraces with seating and panoramic views over the vineyard and the forest. Reductions for more than three and more than six nights. Open all year.

PRICES: s €51–€55; d €55–€60 **ON SITE:** Hiking **NEARBY:** Swimming pool (10km) Cross-country skiing (10km) Tennis (5km) Railway station (3km) (7km) **NOTES:** No pets

GUEMAR

♦♦♦ Chambre d'hôtes Ernest UMBDENSTOCK

20, route de Selestat, 68970 GUEMAR

☎ 03 89 71 82 72

This centrally heated house in the centre of the village has two twin-bedded rooms and one room with two single beds and a third single bed above. All rooms have private shower room and wc and balcony, and additional beds are available. There is a sitting room for guests, and a shared fridge. Large courtyard, lawn, swing, garden room. Picnic baskets available. Forest 1 km away; fishing available. Open 1 April to 15 November.

PRICES: s €27; d €37; t €48; extra person €10 **ON SITE:** Children's play area **NEARBY:** Horse riding (5km) Swimming pool (2km) Tennis (2km) Railway station (5km) RIBEAUVILLE (5km) **NOTES:** No pets

HOLTZWIHR

♦♦♦ Chambre d'hôtes Liliane MEYER

1, rue de la 5e D.B., 68320 HOLTZWIHR

☎ 03 89 47 42 11 📠 03 89 47 42 11

This centrally heated, terraced house has a garden area and three two-person rooms, one three-person room, and one four-person room; all rooms have private shower, handbasin, wc, kitchenette and TV. Child beds are available. Access for less mobile guests to all rooms, with assistance. Guests' sitting room, shady terraces and barbecue, games area, lawn, and private parking. The forest is within 600m. Restaurant in village. Open all year.

PRICES: d €41; t €53; extra person €11 **ON SITE:** Children's play area Hiking Bicycle hire **NEARBY:** Horse riding (3km) Golf (8km) Fishing (2km) Swimming pool (5km) Cross-country skiing (15km) Downhill skiing (15km) Tennis (5km) Railway station (6km) ANDOLSHEIM (5km) **NOTES:** Pets admitted English spoken

HUNAWIHR

♦♦♦ Chambre d'hôtes Frédérique SEILER

3, rue du Nord, 68150 HUNAWIHR

☎ 03 89 73 70 19 📠 03 89 73 70 19

This former wine-maker's house, in the heart of the village, offers five very comfortable rooms, each with private shower room and wc. Three rooms have a private kitchenette, and one of these rooms has a sofa bed. There is one two-person room and one room for two people and one child. The grounds are enclosed and private, with garden room, barbecue, and courtyard. Open all year except 15-30 November, and March.

PRICES: d €41–€53; extra person €15 **ON SITE:** Fishing **NEARBY:** Swimming pool (2km) Tennis (7km) Railway station (7km) RIBEAUVILLE (4km) **NOTES:** Pets admitted English spoken

HUSSEREN-LES-CHATEAUX

♦♦♦ Chambre d'hôtes Gilles SCHNEIDER

10, rue du Hagueneck, 68420 HUSSEREN-LES-CHATEAUX

☎ 03 89 86 45 04 & 06 03 83 79 23 📠 03 89 86 45 04

e-mail: couette-café@wanadoo.fr

Four rooms are available on the ground floor of this new house,

continued

peacefully situated at the foot of the three châteaux of Eguisheim. Two rooms (one double and one twin) have private shower, handbasin and wc; two rooms (both double) share a shower room with two handbasins, one shower and a wc; one of these rooms has a kitchenette area and fridge. All rooms have TV. Guests' breakfast room, terrace, garden and parking. Open all year.
PRICES: s €30; d €38 **ON SITE:** Hiking Bicycle hire **NEARBY:** Golf (10km) Swimming pool (6km) Cross-country skiing (25km) Downhill skiing (25km) Tennis (5km) Railway station (7km) Shops (2km) WINTZENHEIM (3km) **NOTES:** No pets

HUSSEREN-WESSERLING

♦♦♦ Chambre d'hôtes Yvonne HERRGOTT
4, rue de la gare, 68470 HUSSEREN-WESSERLING
☎ 03 89 38 79 69 📠 03 89 38 78 92
www.chez.com/herrgott/
This beautiful flower surrounded property has a separate guest entrance. One room with double and single bed, and one twin-bedded room both have a private shower room and kitchen area. One adjoining room has two single beds. Two further twin-bedded rooms have a living/kitchen area and private bathroom and wc. Central heating. Garden room and heated covered swimming pool (closed 1 Nov to 1 Mar). Buffet-style breakfast. Open all year.
PRICES: d €43-€48 **ON SITE:** Swimming pool Hiking Bicycle hire **NEARBY:** Horse riding (1km) Golf (15km) Fishing (10km) Cross-country skiing (14km) Tennis (1km) Shops (2km) SAINT-AMARIN (4km) **NOTES:** No pets

KATZENTHAL

♦♦♦ Chambre d'hôtes C et Angèle AMREIN
128, rue des Trois Epis, 68230 KATZENTHAL
☎ 03 89 27 48 85 📠 03 89 27 35 18
e-mail: gites.framboises@wanadoo.fr
This centrally heated house is peacefully situated at the heart of the vineyard, close to the forest. It has two rooms each with one double and one single bed, and one room with three single beds. All rooms have TV, and private bathroom and wc. Courtyard; self-catering gîte also available.
PRICES: s €31; d €41; t €49; extra person €5 **ON SITE:** Hiking Bicycle hire **NEARBY:** Horse riding (8km) Golf (3km) Swimming pool (5km) Downhill skiing (20km) Tennis (5km) Railway station (6km) KAYSERSBERG (4km) **NOTES:** Pets admitted English spoken

KAYSERSBERG

♦♦♦ Chambre d'hôtes Daniel et M-T PICAVET
104, route de Lapoutroie, 68240 KAYSERSBERG
☎ 03 89 47 15 14 📠 03 89 47 39 36
This mansion borders the road, at the edge of the town, with a large park bordering the forest. The rooms - three grade 2 and two grade 3 - are on the first floor. Two double rooms, each with private handbasin and wc and shared bathroom. One double room with TV, private bath and wc. One large twin with TV, and private shower and wc. Two twin doubles (sleep four) with sitting room, TV, handbasin, bath and wc. Open all year.
PRICES: s €31; d €40-€48; t €63; extra person €8 **NEARBY:** Golf (5km) Fishing (1km) Swimming pool (5km) Cross-country skiing (15km) Downhill skiing (15km) Tennis (1km) Railway station (12km) KAYSERSBERG (1km) **NOTES:** Pets admitted English spoken

---

For further information on these and
other chambres d'hôtes, consult
the Gîtes de France website
www.gites-de-france.fr

MITTELWIHR

♦♦♦ Domaine du Bouxhof François EDEL
68630 MITTELWIHR
☎ 03 89 47 93 67 📠 03 89 47 84 82
The home of a wine-grower, this centrally heated house in the heart of the vineyard is listed as a historic monument. One twin-bedded room (child bed available), one double room and one twin room. All rooms have private shower, handbasin, wc, hairdryer and TV. Fridge. Garden room, parking. Open all year, except January.
PRICES: d €44; t €53 **ON SITE:** Fishing Hiking Bicycle hire **NEARBY:** Golf (5km) Swimming pool (3km) Cross-country skiing (10km) Downhill skiing (18km) Tennis (2km) Railway station (2km) KAYSERSBERG (12km) **NOTES:** No pets English spoken

MUNWILLER

♦♦♦ Chambre d'hôtes Yvonne REYMANN
17, rue Principale, 68250 MUNWILLER
☎ 03 89 49 68 66 & 06 87 36 47 15
Rouffach 6 km. Peacefully situated in open country, in a small village 5km from the Route des Vins, this house offers three comfortable rooms on the first floor of a farm outbuilding with a separate entrance. Rooms 1 (with one double and a single bed) and 2 (three singles beds) are duplex, with a kitchen area and small sitting room. Room 3 has two single beds. All rooms have a handbasin, shower, wc, TV and fridge. Kitchenette, washing machine and dryer available at a supplement. Central heating, barbecue, parking in an enclosed courtyard, garden room. Breakfast is served on the terrace or in the lounge. Reduced rates for stays of three nights or more.
PRICES: s €30; d €38; t €46; extra person €8 **ON SITE:** Hiking **NEARBY:** Horse riding (5km) Golf (5km) Fishing (5km) Swimming pool (5km) Cross-country skiing (25km) Downhill skiing (25km) Tennis (5km) Railway station (5km) Shops (2km) ENSISHEIM (8km) **NOTES:** No pets

OLTINGUE

♦♦♦ Huttingue Antoine THOMAS
Moulin de Huttingue, 68480 OLTINGUE
☎ 03 89 40 72 91 & 03 89 40 72 91 📠 03 89 07 31 01
This former mill, dating from the 17th century, is on the French-Swiss border in the Jura-Alsacien, near a forest. It offers four two-person rooms, each with private shower room. Separate entrance, living room and lounge. Open from March to December.
PRICES: s €40; d €49; t €61; extra person €16 **ON SITE:** Fishing **NEARBY:** Horse riding (4km) Swimming pool (6km) Tennis (10km) Railway station (15km) Shops (2km) Restaurant nearby FERRETTE (6km) **NOTES:** No pets English spoken

ORBEY

♦♦♦ ♥ Chambre d'hôtes Fabienne BATOT
33, le Busset, Ferme du Busset, 68370 ORBEY
☎ 03 89 71 22 17 📠 03 89 71 22 17
This farm occupies a calm, green and pleasant spot in the mountains. Ground floor: two double rooms. First floor: two double rooms, one twin-bedded room, one room with double and single bed. All rooms with private shower, handbasin, and wc. Central heating. Garden room, barbecue. Tourist tax payable. Mountain biking nearby, as well as a lodge and a self-catering gîte. Open all year.
PRICES: s €41-€270; d €45; extra person €18 **ON SITE:** Fishing Hiking Cross-country skiing Bicycle hire **NEARBY:** Horse riding (3km) Golf (3km) Swimming pool (10km) Downhill skiing (10km) Tennis (13km) Railway station (25km) Shops (2km) LAPOUTROIE (3km) **NOTES:** No pets English spoken

OSTHEIM

♦♦♦ Chambre d'hôtes Gilbert COTTEL
2, rue de la Gare, Auberge Aux armes d'Ostheim,
68150 OSTHEIM
☎ 03 89 47 91 15 ◻ 03 89 47 86 29
e-mail: ostheim@projet.com www.projet.com/ostheim
This beautiful former Alsace farm has been modernized to provide three centrally heated double rooms, each with shower, wc and private lounge. Guests' dining room. Parking, terrace and garden furniture. An Alsace breakfast is served; evening meals (Alsace specialities) can be arranged on Fridays, Saturdays, and Sundays. Tourist tax payable from May to December. Open from March to mid-November.
PRICES: d €65; t €82 **ON SITE:** Fishing Hiking Bicycle hire
NEARBY: Horse riding (12km) Golf (10km) Swimming pool (5km) Railway station (5km) Restaurant nearby RIBEAUVILLE (4km)
NOTES: No pets English spoken

RIQUEWIHR

♦♦♦ Chambre d'hôtes Gérard SCHMITT
3, chemin des Vignes, 68340 RIQUEWIHR
☎ 03 89 47 89 72
Rooms available on the first floor of the owner's peacefully situated house, which has a garden and views of vineyards, forest and and the village. Two twin-bedded rooms with private handbasin, shower and wc. Electric central heating. Breakfast served in the living room. Open from15 April to December.
PRICES: s €31; d €42; t €54 **ON SITE:** Fishing **NEARBY:** Golf (25km) Swimming pool (2km) Railway station (5km) KAYSERSBERG (12km)
NOTES: No pets

RIXHEIM

♦♦♦♦ Le Clos du Murier Rosa VOLPATTI
42, Grand Rue, 68170 RIXHEIM
☎ 03 89 54 14 81 ◻ 03 89 64 47 08
Mulhouse 6 km. This attractive, restored 16th-century house with enclosed garden is centrally positioned. On the ground floor there is one twin-bedded room with living area. The first floor has one twin-bedded room with living area (one double bed); one double room with living area; and one double room. All rooms have private bathroom, wc, kitchenette, TV and electric central heating. Shared washing machine and dryer. Private parking in an enclosed courtyard; tennis table; bicyles available. Open all year.
PRICES: s €56; d €68; t €84; extra person €22 **ON SITE:** Fishing Hiking **NEARBY:** Horse riding (2km) Golf (10km) Swimming pool (1km) Bicycle hire (1km) Railway station (2km) HABSHEIM (3km)
NOTES: No pets English spoken

RORSCHWIHR

♦♦♦ Chambre d'hôtes Fernande MESCHBERGER
1, rue de la forêt, 68750 RORSCHWIHR
☎ 03 89 73 77 32 ◻ 03 89 73 77 32
This modern house with veranda and garden is peacefully situated, with a view of the Château of Haut-Koenigsbourg. Separate guest entrance. The four double rooms each have private shower and wc. Central heating, fridge. The enclosed veranda and garden room are available for guests to use. Small dogs allowed. Additional bed if required. Open from 15 March to 20 December.
PRICES: s €28; d €37; t €40 **ON SITE:** Fishing Hiking
NEARBY: Swimming pool (3km) Tennis (15km) Bicycle hire (10km) Railway station (7km) Shops (2km) RIBEAUVILLE (3km) **NOTES:** Pets admitted

♦♦♦ Chambre d'hôtes Aimé DINTZER
10, route du Vin, 68750 RORSCHWIHR
☎ 03 89 73 74 48 ◻ 03 89 73 74 48
On the Route des Vins, this house has a separate guest entrance, giving onto the rear of the house with a view of the meadow in the centre of the village. Four double-bedded rooms (two on the ground floor, with balcony, and two on the first floor), each have private shower room and wc. Central heating. Separate dining room. Fridge. Courtyard, parking, garden. Tourist tax included. Open from April to November.
PRICES: s €31; d €38; t €43 **ON SITE:** Fishing **NEARBY:** Swimming pool (2km) Tennis (15km) Bicycle hire (2km) Railway station (7km) RIBEAUVILLE (5km) **NOTES:** Pets admitted

ST-BERNARD

♦♦♦ Chambre d'hôtes Marie-Laure BAIRET
13, rue de l'Eglise, 68720 ST-BERNARD
☎ 03 89 25 44 71
This 19th-century former farm, peacefully situated in beautiful countryside, has been modernized. One twin-bedded room with private bathroom and wc, and two double rooms (each with a sofa bed), with private bathroom and wc. TV and large kitchen available. Garden with furniture and barbecue. Enclosed courtyard, meadow, picnics available. River and lake nearby. Open all year.
PRICES: s €31; d €40; extra person €12 **ON SITE:** Fishing Bicycle hire
NEARBY: Horse riding (10km) Swimming pool (2km) Tennis (15km) Railway station (7km) Shops (5km) ALTKIRCH (6km) **NOTES:** Pets admitted

STE-MARIE-AUX-MINES

♦♦♦ 🐓 Ferme la Fonderie Gabriel DEMOULIN
17, rue Untergrombach, 68160 STE-MARIE-AUX-MINES
☎ 03 89 58 59 51 & 06 83 99 97 29 ◻ 03 89 58 59 51
This restored building, which also includes two self-catering gîtes, occupies a peaceful site on the borders of the forest and close to the river. Two double rooms with private shower room and wc. Electric heating. The communal living room has a TV and kitchen for preparing breakfast. In the owner's house, with separate entrance, TV and central heating, there is one room with a double and a single bed, with separate shower room and wc. Courtyard, car parking, garden furniture. There is a distilling centre where local products can be sampled. Garage. Open all year.
PRICES: d €34-€37; t €46 **ON SITE:** Fishing Hiking **NEARBY:** Golf (5km) Swimming pool (3km) Cross-country skiing (6km) Downhill skiing (12km) Railway station (22km) SAINTE-MARIE-AUX-MINES (1km)
NOTES: No pets

THANNENKIRCH

♦♦♦ Chambre d'hôtes René DUMOULIN
15, rue Ste-Anne, 68590 THANNENKIRCH
☎ 03 89 73 12 07
This house close to the forest, in a calm, fresh setting, offers three two-person rooms, each with shower and wc, and one two-person room with private shower, bath and wc. All rooms have a telephone. Terrace, garden meadow, private parking. Sitting room with TV. Tourist tax payable.
PRICES: d €37-€40 **ON SITE:** Hiking **NEARBY:** Golf (10km) Swimming pool (10km) Railway station (10km) RIBEAUVILLE (9km)
NOTES: No pets

TROIS-EPIS

♦♦♦ La Cheneraie Francine RINN
16 chemin du Galtz, Trois-Epis, 68410
NIEDERMORSCHWIHR
☎ 03 89 49 82 34 ◻ 03 89 49 86 70

continued

ALSACE-LORRAINE

Francine Rinn offers guests a traditional Alsace welcome, in this late 19th-century mansion in parkland. Five cosy double rooms (each with private shower room and wc), a large panelled drawing room, and a dining room where generous buffet breakfasts are served. Open April to October or by arrangement at other times.
PRICES: s €46; d €48–€61 **ON SITE:** Hiking Tennis Bicycle hire
NEARBY: Horse riding (5km) Golf (5km) Fishing (9km) Swimming pool (9km) Cross-country skiing (5km) Downhill skiing (20km) Railway station (13km) KAYSERSBERG (9km) **NOTES:** No pets English spoken

MEURTHE-ET-MOSELLE

BELLEAU

IIII IOI Château de Morey Anne-Marie KARST
54610 BELLEAU
☎ 03 83 31 50 98 & SR : 03 83 93 34 91
🖹 03 83 31 50 98 http://www.chateaudemorey.com
This renovated 16th-century château is beautifully situated with views across the valley. The private swimming pool is in a park with centuries-old trees, bordering a forest. It offers five spacious rooms including a family suite, each with one double bed and one single if required. Living area with TV and video, private bathroom. Games room, library, private parking, stables, mountain bikes. Open all year.
PRICES: s €44; d €53; extra person €12; dinner €15
ON SITE: Forest Hiking **NEARBY:** Horse riding (5km) Fishing (5km) Swimming pool (10km) Stretch of water (5km) Water sports (5km) Tennis (10km) Shops (5km) NOMENY (11km) **NOTES:** Pets admitted English spoken

CHARENCY-VEZIN

IIII IOI Chambre d'hôtes Viviane JAKIRCEVIC
4, rue Coquibut, 54260 CHARENCY-VEZIN
☎ 03 82 26 66 26 & SR : 03 83 93 34 91 🖹 03 82 26 66 26
e-mail: chambreshotes@wanadoo.fr
http://perso.wanadoo.fr/chambreshotes54/
At the gateway to Luxembourg and Belgium, this restored period house dating from 1804 has three furnished guest rooms, of which two have an adjoining sitting area. Fitted kitchen, dining room, recreation room on the veranda. Terrace, garden, and enclosed parking area. Child's bed available on request.
PRICES: s €31; d €39; t €55; extra person €16; dinner €13
ON SITE: Forest Fishing Stretch of water Hiking **NEARBY:** Horse riding (5km) Swimming pool (5km) Water sports (5km) Tennis (5km) LONGUYON (11km) **NOTES:** No pets English spoken

CIREY-SUR-VEZOUZE

IIII IOI Chambre d'hôtes Monique BOUVERY
18, rue du Val, 54480 CIREY-SUR-VEZOUZE
☎ 03 83 42 58 38 🖹 03 83 42 58 38
A mansion house at the foot of the Vosges Mountains has five first-floor guest rooms, each sleeping two or three and with private bathroom and wc. Lounge with fireplace, billiard room, sitting room, TV; office with telephone, and Minitel available. Secure parking. The owners can suggest walking routes. Open all year.
PRICES: s €34; d €46; t €56; extra person €12; HB €41 **ON SITE:** Forest Fishing Stretch of water Hiking Tennis **NEARBY:** Horse riding (2km) Swimming pool (12km) Water sports (15km) LUNEVILLE (39km)
NOTES: No pets English spoken

DOMMARTIN-SOUS-AMANCE

IIII ❦ IOI Chambre d'hôtes
H & Marinette GRANDIDIER
Ferme de Montheu, 54770 DOMMARTIN-SOUS-AMANCE
☎ 03 83 31 17 37 & SR : 03 83 93 34 91 🖹 03 83 31 17 37
In open countryside in relaxing, delightful surroundings in a

picturesque area with many valleys, 8km from Nancy. This restored farmhouse has four spacious en suite rooms, tastefully decorated and furnished with antiques. There is one ground-floor room and three first-floor rooms. Child's bed and additional single bed available. Lounge, library, TV, fridge, microwave. Guests can visit the farm and sample regional products. Open all year.
PRICES: s €32; d €40; t €47; extra person €11; dinner €15
ON SITE: Hiking **NEARBY:** Horse riding (1km) Forest (2km) Fishing (6km) Swimming pool (6km) Stretch of water (6km) Water sports (20km) Tennis (3km) Shops (2km) NANCY-EST (9km) **NOTES:** Pets admitted English spoken

EPLY

III ❦ IOI Chambre d'hôtes Edith & J Marie FRANCOIS
14, rue St Christophe, Gaec les Verts Paturages, 54610 EPLY
☎ 03 83 31 30 85 & SR : 03 83 93 34 91 🖹 03 83 31 30 85
This converted barn is in the centre of the village, where peace and relaxation are assured. Ground floor: two double rooms with private shower room and wc. First floor: one triple room, private shower room and wc. Cot available. Table d'hôte. Secluded garden, sitting room, lounge. Visit the farm. Open all year.
PRICES: s €30; d €38; t €46; extra person €11; dinner €12
ON SITE: Forest Hiking **NEARBY:** Horse riding (2km) Fishing (1km) Swimming pool (12km) Stretch of water (1km) Water sports (30km) Tennis (5km) Shops (5km) Restaurant nearby NOMENY (5km)
NOTES: No pets

HATRIZE

IIII Chambre d'hôtes Roger & Micheline ARIZZI
la Trembloisiere, 54800 HATRIZE
☎ 03 82 33 14 30 & SR : 03 83 93 34 91 🖹 03 82 20 15 55
A family smallholding of 2 hectares situated outside the village. The house is furnished and decorated with care. Huge sitting room with terrace, lawn, and garden with trees. Four rooms, each with private bathroom and wc. Numerous restaurants within 5km. Close to the Regional Nature Park of Lorraine and Metz.
PRICES: s €38; d €45; t €60 **ON SITE:** Forest Fishing Stretch of water Hiking **NEARBY:** Horse riding (5km) Swimming pool (5km) Water sports (20km) Tennis (5km) Shops (5km) BRIEY (8km)
NOTES: No pets English spoken

LEMAINVILLE

IIII IOI Chambre d'hôtes François RICHART
22, Grande rue, 54740 LEMAINVILLE
☎ 03 83 25 54 51 & SR : 03 83 93 34 91
This old Lorraine house has three first-floor guest rooms, each with private, separate bath/shower room and wc. Cot available. Lounge, fireplace, library, video. Terrace, courtyard, parking.
PRICES: s €27; d €37; t €46; extra person €12; dinner €15
ON SITE: Fishing Stretch of water Hiking **NEARBY:** Forest (6km) Swimming pool (10km) Water sports (6km) Tennis (2km) Shops (3km) HAROUE (5km) **NOTES:** Pets admitted English spoken

MAIZIERES

IIII IOI Chambre d'hôtes Laurent COTEL
69, rue Carnot, 54550 MAIZIERES
☎ 03 83 52 75 57 & SR : 03 83 93 34 91
Three guest rooms are available in an attractive house, furnished in country style in a peaceful setting. Ground floor: two rooms, each with private bathroom and wc; first floor: one room with private shower room and wc. Guest sitting room, secluded garden.
PRICES: s €28; d €39; t €46; extra person €10; dinner €13
ON SITE: Forest Hiking **NEARBY:** Horse riding (10km) Fishing (5km) Swimming pool (5km) Stretch of water (5km) Water sports (40km) Tennis (5km) NANCY (16km) **NOTES:** Pets admitted

continued

STE-GENEVIEVE

♦♦♦ ❦ ⎮◯⎮ Chambre d'hôtes
Marc & Véronique GIGLEUX
4, route de Bezaumont, 54700 STE-GENEVIEVE
☎ 03 83 82 25 55 & SR : 03 83 93 34 91 ⎙ 03 83 82 25 55
An 18th-century Lorraine farmhouse, peacefully situated
overlooking the Moselle Valley, has three spacious furnished
rooms, and a large garden with views. Lounge, TV, telephone.
Tennis and boules in the village. Nearby museum and abbey.
Regional cuisine using local produce. Open all year.
PRICES: s €31; d €38; t €46; extra person €11; dinner €12
ON SITE: Forest Hiking Tennis **NEARBY:** Horse riding (7km) Fishing
(4km) Swimming pool (6km) Stretch of water (4km) Water sports (7km)
Shops (6km) Restaurant nearby PONT-A-MOUSSON (8km) **NOTES:** No
pets English spoken

VIRECOURT

♦♦♦ Les Marguerites Manuela & François BEYEL
14, rue de la Republique, 54290 VIRECOURT
☎ 03 83 72 54 20 & SR : 03 83 93 34 91 ⎙ 03 83 72 54 20
Three spacious rooms in a renovated country house at the
gateway to the Vosges Mountains, each with TV and private
shower room and wc. Lounge with tourist information, dining
room. Courtyard garden, garden room, games area, table tennis.
Bicycles. Separate entrance. Children up to 10 years: €8. Skiing
and restaurants one hour away. Walking routes can be suggested,
following way-marked paths. Open all year.
PRICES: s €30; d €38; t €49; extra person €12 **ON SITE:** Forest Fishing
Stretch of water Hiking **NEARBY:** Horse riding (15km) Swimming pool
(20km) Water sports (20km) Tennis (1km) Railway station (1km) BAYON
(1km) **NOTES:** No pets

MEUSE

ANCEMONT

♦♦♦ ⎮◯⎮ Château de Labessière René EICHENAUER
Ancemont, 55320 DIEUE-SUR-MEUSE
☎ 03 29 85 70 21 ⎙ 03 29 87 61 60
e-mail: rene.eichenauer@wanadoo.fr

Four rooms in an 18th-century chateau with period furniture with
a Louis XV-style salon and beautiful Louis XVI dining room. Two
rooms each sleep three, with TV and private shower and wc. Suite
sleeping four to six (two adults and 2-4 children), with shower
room and wc. Table d'hôte menu, and drinks included in half-
board. Garage. Suite sleeping four: €91.47. Reduced prices for
children. Fly-fishing within 6 km. Animals allowed by prior
agreement. Open all year.
PRICES: s €60; d €70; t €80; extra person €10; HB €60; dinner €25
ON SITE: Horse riding Swimming pool **NEARBY:** Forest (1km) Fishing
(10km) Tennis (2km) Sailing (10km) Railway station (10km) Shops (2km)
NOTES: No pets English spoken

AZANNES

♦♦♦ Les Benezières François FAZZARI
9 route de Mangiennes, 55150 AZANNES
☎ 03 29 85 61 88 ⎙ 03 29 85 61 88
Damvillers 8 km. Verdun 19 km. Situated in a peaceful village this
establishment offers: ground floor: the Blue Suite, grade 2, two
double beds, one single on request, private shower room and wc:
the Pink Room, grade 3, one double bed), en suite shower and wc;
first floor: Green Room, grade 3, one double bed, en suite shower
and wc. Garden furniture, terrace. Garage, private parking. Visit
nearby Verdun and the festival of traditional crafts in Azannes in
May. Open all year.
PRICES: s €29-€37; d €37-€45; t €54; extra person €14 **ON SITE:** Horse
riding Forest **NEARBY:** Golf (25km) Fishing (4km) Swimming pool
(19km) Tennis (4km) Railway station (19km) Shops (9km) **NOTES:** No
pets

GUSSAINVILLE

♦♦♦ ⎮◯⎮ Chambre d'hôtes C & Francis LEFORT
2 avenue de Gussainville, 'La Starava', 55400 GUSSAINVILLE
☎ 03 29 87 24 29 ⎙ 03 29 87 24 29

Verdun (Battlefields) 25 km. Lac de Madine (bathing) 30 km.
Farmhouse dating from 1838, in a small, peaceful village. Three
spacious rooms, each in a different style. Two double rooms, one
triple, each with TV and en suite bathroom and wc. Evening meals
of typical Lorraine cuisine are available by booking. Lounge and
dining room, each with a fireplace. Garden room, barbecue,
open-air games area, private parking. Open all year.
PRICES: s €33; d €40; t €48; extra person €8; dinner €19
ON SITE: Horse riding Fishing **NEARBY:** Forest (4km) Railway station
(5km) Shops (5km) **NOTES:** Pets admitted English spoken

RONVAUX

♦♦♦ ⎮◯⎮ Le Logis des Côtes Marie-José WURTZ
4 rue Basse, 55160 RONVAUX
☎ 03 29 87 32 21 ⎙ 03 29 87 32 21
e-mail: wurtzmariejose@minitel.net
Fresnes-en-Woëvre 5 km. Verdun & Etain 15 km. Situated in a
small village at the foot of the Côtes de Meuse, near Verdun and
the battlefields. First floor of an old Lorraine house: one triple
room, with private shower room and wc; two double rooms (extra
bed available) with private shower room and wc. Dining room with
fireplace. Lounge. Garden reserved for guests. Table d'hôte menu
available (booking required). Bicycles available for hire. Recreation
centres and fly-fishing nearby. Open from Easter to end of
October.
PRICES: s €30; d €39; t €47; extra person €10; dinner €17
ON SITE: Forest **NEARBY:** Bathing (5km) Horse riding (5km) Golf
(25km) Fishing (5km) Swimming pool (15km) Tennis (5km) Sailing
(25km) Railway station (15km) Shops (2km) **NOTES:** Pets admitted
English spoken

ST-MAURICE-LES-GUSSAINVILLE

♦♦♦ ⟨○⟩ Ferme des Vales Ghislaine VALENTIN
Saint-Maurice-les-Gussainville, 55400 ETAIN
☎ 03 29 87 12 91 📠 03 29 87 18 59
On the first floor of a former agricultural building, four double rooms, each with en suite bathroom and wc. Sitting room reserved for guests. Garden, garden room, children's climbing frame. Billiards, swimming pool, table tennis. Table d'hôte menu by prior arrangement. Lake, swimming, fishing, tennis; horse-riding, golf nearby. Open all year except February school holidays.
PRICES: s €33; d €40; extra person €8; HB €42–€63; dinner €19
ON SITE: Children's play area Forest **NEARBY:** Bathing (5km) Horse riding (3km) Golf (25km) Fishing (1km) Swimming pool (20km) Tennis (4km) Sailing (25km) Railway station (4km) Shops (4km) **NOTES:** No pets English spoken

THILLOMBOIS

♦♦♦ ⟨○⟩ Le Clos Du Pausa Lise TANCHON
Rue du Château, 55260 THILLOMBOIS
☎ 03 29 75 07 85 📠 03 29 75 00 72
Large character house offering three rooms with park views. Ground floor: two spacious rooms sleeping two or three. Mini-bar, private shower and wc. First floor: one very comfortable suite, tastefully decorated, with TV, telephone and with private bathroom and wc. Coffee and tea-making facilities. Lounge with satellite TV. Shaded garden, garden room. Bicycles. Barbecues. Meals available on request. Fly-fishing on an attractive stretch of river nearby. Supplement payable for animals €8.
PRICES: s €46; d €60–€70; extra person €8; dinner €25 **ON SITE:** Forest Fishing **NEARBY:** Bathing (25km) Golf (25km) Sailing (25km) Railway station (30km) Shops (15km) **NOTES:** Pets admitted English spoken

MOSELLE

ARRY

♦♦♦ ⟨○⟩ Chambre d'hôtes Roland et Martine OTT
Au Gîte du Passant, 1 rue de la Lobe, 57680 ARRY
☎ 03 87 52 08 93 & 06 86 56 57 02 📠 03 87 52 08 93
Metz 17 km. Nancy 40 km. Pont à Mousson 10 km. This house, one of the oldest in a listed village overlooking the Moselle Valley, in the heart of Lorraine, offers three very comfortable guest rooms in a rural setting. One twin-bedded room, with additional bed if required; one double, with additional bed if required; one double. Each room has shower, washbasin and wc. Lounge with satellite TV; laundry room; dining room; garden, parking. The evening meal (booking essential) features regional specialities and seasonal produce. Children's play area close by.
PRICES: s €42; d €51; extra person €12; dinner €19 **ON SITE:** Forest Hiking **NEARBY:** Bathing (10km) Horse riding (3km) Golf (15km) Fishing (1km) Swimming pool (10km) Railway station (5km) Shops (3km) **NOTES:** Pets admitted

♦♦♦ ⟨○⟩ La Belle Arrygeoise
Angeline et Alain FINANCE-SCHVARTZ
5 Grand'Rue, 57680 ARRY
☎ 03 87 52 83 95 📠 03 87 52 82 97
Metz 19 km. Nancy 35 km. In the heart of a pretty village overlooking the Moselle Valley, this attractive Lorraine house, now tastefully restored, has four charming guest rooms on the first floor, including one family room, each with private bathrooms and wc. Lounge, TV, library, courtyard with garden room, kitchenette, cot, picnic hampers can be arranged. A warm welcome, with meals carefully and generously prepared. Numerous walking routes (GR5 in 5km). Open 1 March to 30 November.
PRICES: s €39; d €46; t €54; extra person €8; dinner €19
ON SITE: Forest Hiking **NEARBY:** Bathing (10km) Horse riding (3km)

Golf (15km) Fishing (1km) Swimming pool (10km) Tennis (3km) Railway station (3km) Shops (3km) **NOTES:** Pets admitted English spoken

ARS-LAQUENEXY

♦♦♦ 🐾 ⟨○⟩ Chambre d'hôtes Camille BIGARE
23, rue Principale, 57530 ARS-LAQUENEXY
☎ 03 87 38 13 88
Three ground-floor rooms are available in a restored house in the local style. Three double beds, one single, one child's bed. Private bathroom and wc. Garden; courtyard; enclosed grounds. Parking space. The Messin region offers numerous tourist attractions. Open all year.
PRICES: s €29; d €39; t €46 **ON SITE:** Hiking Tennis
NEARBY: Bathing (10km) Horse riding (3km) Golf (2km) Swimming pool (7km) Railway station (4km) Shops (2km) **NOTES:** Pets admitted

BERTHELMING

♦♦♦ Chambre d'hôtes Alice et J-C PEIFFER
47 rue Principale, 57930 BERTHELMING
☎ 03 87 07 82 76 📠 03 87 07 86 31
Dabo 25 km. Sarrebourg 11 km. On the edge of Sarre, three rooms with private bathroom and wc. All have double beds; one room has an additional single bed. Two child beds available. Access to park, garden, and garden furniture. Barbecue, kitchenette, children's play area; bicycles available; parking; one garage space available. Fax. Lounge, sitting room, TV, video, hi-fi. Reduction of €3 per night per room from the third night. Open all year.
PRICES: s €31; d €35; t €43 **ON SITE:** Children's play area Fishing Hiking **NEARBY:** Bathing (8km) Horse riding (12km) Forest (1km) Golf (12km) Swimming pool (12km) Tennis (1km) **NOTES:** No pets

CUVRY

♦♦♦ 🐾 Ferme de la Haute Rive J-F et Brigette MORHAIN
57420 CUVRY
☎ 03 87 52 50 08 📠 03 87 52 60 20
Three rooms (two rooms and one suite) on the first floor of a detached house. Four single beds, two doubles. Separate shower rooms and wcs. Lounge, dining room, fireplace, reading area, TV for guests' use. Courtyard, enclosed garden, parking. Restaurant in the next village. Many tourist attractions in this area. Open April to October.
PRICES: s €39; d €46; t €54 **ON SITE:** Hiking **NEARBY:** Bathing (35km) Horse riding (5km) Forest (3km) Golf (3km) Fishing (1km) Swimming pool (6km) Tennis (4km) Railway station (10km) Shops (4km) **NOTES:** No pets English spoken

NIDERVILLER

♦♦♦ ♿ Chambre d'hôtes M et Marinette FETTER
11 rue des Vosges, 57565 NIDERVILLER
☎ 03 87 23 79 96
e-mail: FETTERMarcel@hotmail.com
Restored 18th-century Lorraine house from where guests can enjoy lovely walks in the region north of the Vosges Mountains. Three double guest rooms, one triple room, child's bed available, private shower room and wc. Lounge, kitchenette, terrace, barbecue. Pleasure barge rental available on the Marne-Rhine canal. Open all year.
PRICES: s €27; d €35; t €42 **ON SITE:** Horse riding Forest Fishing Hiking Tennis **NEARBY:** Golf (5km) Swimming pool (5km) Railway station (5km) Restaurant nearby **NOTES:** No pets

continued

RAHLING

¶¶¶ ❦ Chambre d'hôtes Louis et Annie BACH
2 rue du Vieux Moulin, 57410 RAHLING
☎ 03 87 09 86 85

Louis and Annie welcome guests to a traditional Lorrain mill in the heart of the Vosges Mosellanes. Three first-floor guest rooms, each with shower room and wc. TV, kitchenette available. Parking. Tariff reduction for three nights or more (10% reduction except July and August). Open all year.

PRICES: s €24; d €34; t €46 **ON SITE:** Hiking Tennis **NEARBY:** Horse riding (5km) Forest (2km) Golf (20km) Fishing (1km) Swimming pool (5km) Railway station (5km) **NOTES:** No pets

SOLGNE

¶¶¶ ❂ Chambre d'hôtes Pierrette SCHNEIDER
16 rue Alsace Lorraine, 57420 SOLGNE
☎ 03 87 57 72 60 & 03 87 57 70 09

Four guest rooms: the Sloe (two single beds), the Pippin (one double), the Greengage (one double, one single), the Cherry (one double). Each room has TV and private bath/shower room and wc. Organic vegetables. Lounge area. Parking. Half-board available for two people. Open all year.

PRICES: s €29; d €38; t €46 **ON SITE:** Horse riding Hiking Tennis **NEARBY:** Bathing (20km) Forest (1km) Golf (8km) Fishing (12km) Swimming pool (20km) Railway station (12km) **NOTES:** No pets

VAUDONCOURT

¶¶¶ Chambre d'hôtes Sylvie KINTZINGER
4 rue de la Chapelle, 57220 VAUDONCOURT
☎ 03 87 64 07 95 📠 03 87 64 27 97
e-mail: larenardiere@infonie.fr

Metz 17 km. St-Avold 17 km. In a countryside setting this establishment offers three guest rooms, two bathrooms, private wcs; dining room, lounge, TV, fireplace, jacuzzi, sauna. Shaded enclosed garden. Terrace. Swimming pool. Reduced rates for weekly bookings. Open all year.

PRICES: s €31; d €40; t €46 **ON SITE:** Children's play area Forest Fishing Hiking **NEARBY:** Horse riding (6km) Golf (20km) Swimming pool (8km) Tennis (1km) Railway station (20km) Shops (4km) **NOTES:** No pets

---

For further information on these and other chambres d'hôtes, consult the Gîtes de France website
www.gites-de-france.fr

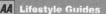

VOSGES

ANOULD

¶¶¶ 🍴 Chambre d'hôtes M-C et J-Yves CONREAUX
563, rue du val de Meurthe, Domaine des Iris, 88650 ANOULD
☎ 03 29 57 01 09 📠 03 29 57 01 09

A spacious home surrounded by 2 hectare grounds, with a fishing lake, bordering a river. Five en suite guest rooms, four with balcony, on the first floor. Each room as follows: double bed and single bed; double bed; double four-poster; one double and one single; one double and two single. Cot available. Central heating. Dining room, lounge, fireplace, TV. Garden swing. Boules. Regional and garden produce. Open all year.

PRICES: s €30; d €38; t €52-€54; extra person €13; dinner €13 **ON SITE:** Fishing **NEARBY:** Horse riding (8km) Forest (1km) Swimming pool (8km) Stretch of water (18km) Hiking (1km) Cross-country skiing (18km) Downhill skiing (13km) Tennis (1km) Spa (58km) Railway station (10km) Shops (1km) SAINT-DIE (10km) **NOTES:** No pets

BULGNEVILLE

¶¶¶ Chambre d'hôtes Benoit BRETON
74, rue des Recollets, 88140 BULGNEVILLE
☎ 03 29 09 21 72 & 06 80 15 00 75 📠 03 29 09 21 72

A large, carefully restored house in the centre of the village. First floor rooms: one double room, two twin rooms, one room with twin beds and one single bed. All rooms with private bathroom and wc, living area, and colour TV. Dining room, kitchen. Central heating. Garden. Twelve km from the thermal spa of Vittel. Reduced tariff for two nights or more. Open all year.

PRICES: s €60; d €65; t €80; extra person €15 **ON SITE:** Fishing Tennis **NEARBY:** Horse riding (10km) Forest (2km) Swimming pool (7km) Stretch of water (7km) Hiking (2km) Spa (7km) Railway station (7km) VITTEL (12km) **NOTES:** Pets admitted English spoken

CELLES-SUR-PLAINE

¶¶¶ 🍴 Chambre d'hôtes Stephane DELBECQUE
40, rue d Alsace, 88110 CELLES-SUR-PLAINE
☎ 03 29 41 20 93 📠 03 29 41 20 93
e-mail: stedel.tourism@wanadoo.fr

Three guest rooms in the owner's house. Room with one double and two single beds. First floor: one double, one room with one double and one single bed; all have a private shower room and wc. The rooms are spacious, well-decorated and well-equipped, and have satellite TV. Cot available. Central heating, telephone, sitting room, recreation area and TV. Grounds. Mountain bikes for hire. Reduced tariff for three nights or more. Meals for children under 10, €7. Animal supplement. Open all year.

PRICES: s €29; d €38; t €47; extra person €9; dinner €11 **ON SITE:** Forest Hiking **NEARBY:** Horse riding (10km) Fishing (1km) Swimming pool (10km) Stretch of water (1km) Cross-country skiing (14km) Downhill skiing (39km) Tennis (1km) Railway station (10km) Shops (1km) RAON L'ETAPE (10km) **NOTES:** Pets admitted English spoken

GERARDMER

⫶◯⫶ & Chalet l'Epinette
Famille POIROT-SCHERRER
70, chemin de la trinité, 88400 GERARDMER
☎ 03 29 63 40 06 & 06 08 61 60 64   ⧄ 03 29 63 40 06
e-mail: epinette@libertysurf.fr

Chalet close to the forest offering six guest rooms. Ground floor: one double room; one room with double four-poster; one double room suitable for less able guests. Dining room with fireplace. First floor: one room with double four-poster, two triple rooms. All rooms have private bath or shower room, wc, TV, balcony or terrace. Cot available. Mezzanine floor: TV, video. Central heating. Spacious grounds. Billiards, sauna, shower, balneotherapy, steam room. Regional cuisine. Open all year except 18 November to 6 December.
PRICES: s €39; d €49-€54; t €67; extra person €13; dinner €15
NEARBY: Horse riding (4km) Forest (1km) Fishing (3km) Swimming pool (2km) Stretch of water (2km) Hiking (1km) Cross-country skiing (3km) Downhill skiing (3km) Tennis (2km) Spa (40km) Railway station (2km) Shops (2km) GERARDMER (2km) **NOTES:** Pets admitted English spoken

LA CHAPELLE-AUX-BOIS

⫶◯⫶ Chambre d'hôtes Marie-Claire CHASSARD
9, les Grands Prés, 88240 LA CHAPELLE-AUX-BOIS
☎ 03 29 36 31 00   ⧄ 03 29 36 31 00
Three comfortable guest rooms on the first floor in a tastefully restored mansion. One twin room, one room with three single beds, one room with one double bed and bunk beds. Dining room and sitting room, colour TV. Spacious grounds, veranda, washing machine available. Very close to the thermal spa of Bains-les-Bains. Fishing in grounds. Self-catering gîtes.
PRICES: s €28; d €38; t €48; extra person €9; dinner €13
ON SITE: Forest Fishing **NEARBY:** Horse riding (4km) Swimming pool (8km) Stretch of water (24km) Hiking (1km) Cross-country skiing (30km) Downhill skiing (59km) Tennis (3km) Spa (3km) Railway station (3km) Shops (3km) BAINS-LES-BAINS (3km) **NOTES:** Pets admitted

NORROY-SUR-VAIR

Chambre d'hôtes Monique et Denis LAURENT
27, grande rue, 88800 NORROY-SUR-VAIR
☎ 03 29 08 21 29 & 06 13 35 02 45   ⧄ 03 29 08 21 29
Five guest rooms in a semi-detached former farmhouse which has been totally renovated. First floor: three double rooms; one twin; one room with one double and one single bed. All rooms with private shower room and wc. All rooms have TV. Guests' dining room; small lounge; kitchen available; central heating; fireplace; library. Reduced rates for three nights or more. Special rates for spa visitors. Open all year.
PRICES: s €30; d €38; t €46 **ON SITE:** Horse riding Forest
NEARBY: Fishing (3km) Swimming pool (3km) Stretch of water (5km) Hiking (1km) Tennis (3km) Spa (3km) Railway station (3km) Shops (3km) VITTEL (3km) **NOTES:** No pets

REMIREMONT

Chambre d'hôtes Sylvie et P KIEFFER
route du Fiscal, 1, le Grand Bienfaisy, 88200 REMIREMONT
☎ 03 29 23 28 20   ⧄ 03 29 23 28 20
e-mail: bienfaisy@aol.com
At the edge of a wood and outside the town of Remiremont. This restored former farmhouse offers three guest rooms. First floor: one room with single bed and double bed; one room with twin beds and sofa bed; each room with TV socket, shower room and wc. Two rooms with one double and three single beds, with bathroom and wc. Lounge, large living room, kitchen area reserved for guests, colour TV. Central heating. Washing machine and dryer. Table tennis and table football. Routes for mountain biking, walking, riding. Tariff for 5 people €92. Open all year.
PRICES: s €29; d €41; t €56; extra person €15 **ON SITE:** Horse riding Forest Swimming pool Hiking Tennis **NEARBY:** Fishing (1km) Stretch of water (30km) Cross-country skiing (8km) Downhill skiing (30km) Spa (11km) Railway station (2km) Shops (2km) REMIREMONT (2km) **NOTES:** No pets English spoken

SAULXURES-LES-BULGNEVILLE

Le Chateau de Bulgneville Andrée SAUMON
6, rue du Château, le château de Saulxures, 88140 SAULXURES-LES-BULGNEVILLE
☎ 03 29 09 21 73
Four attractive guest rooms in a 17th-century house close to the thermal spas of Contrexéville and Vittel. First floor: one double room with fireplace and private shower room and wc. One family suite of two rooms, with one double and two single beds; one twin room; one double room. All rooms with private bathroom and wc. Guests' lounge with TV. Terrace, grounds, swing. Horse-riders welcome. Open all year.
PRICES: s €49; d €58 **ON SITE:** Forest Hiking **NEARBY:** Horse riding (10km) Fishing (1km) Swimming pool (7km) Stretch of water (1km) Tennis (7km) Spa (7km) Railway station (12km) Shops (2km) VITTEL (12km) **NOTES:** Pets admitted

SOULOSSE-SOUS-SAINT-ELOPHE

& La Bienvenue au Pays de Jeanne
J-Luc et M-Josephe KINZELIN
30, rue de l'Eglise, 88630 SOULOSSE-SOUS-ST-ELOPHE
☎ 03 29 06 98 88   ⧄ 03 29 06 98 88
Domrémy 5 km, Grand 15 km. In the heart of the farming area of west Vosges, three guest rooms each with TV and telephone, in the owners' house. Ground floor: one double room, suitable for less able guests, with specially adapted bathroom. Sitting room with fireplace. First floor: one double room and one twin, each with private bathroom and wc. Garage, terrace, central heating. Group/family rates, reduced rates for two nights and more. Children under 8 free. Open all year.
PRICES: s €34; d €44; t €60 **ON SITE:** Fishing **NEARBY:** Horse riding (7km) Forest (1km) Swimming pool (7km) Stretch of water (32km) Hiking (1km) Tennis (7km) Spa (30km) Railway station (7km) NEUFCHATEAU (7km) **NOTES:** Pets admitted English spoken

ST-MICHEL SUR MEURTHE

Chambre d'hôtes Jean-Claude BARETH
390, rue de Brehimont, Ferme du Chenot, 88470 ST-MICHEL SUR MEURTHE
☎ 03 29 58 36 21
Five guest rooms in a restored, former farmhouse in a little village a few kilometres from Saint-Dié. First floor: one double room, one twin room, one room with a double and a single bed. Second floor: two double rooms. All rooms have TV and private shower room and wc. Dining room, lounge area, TV, fireplace. Cot

continued

available. Central heating. Enclosed grounds. Horse-drawn carriage rides possible on summer weekends. Open all year.
PRICES: s €35-€40; d €38-€43; t €50-€55; extra person €12
ON SITE: Fishing **NEARBY:** Horse riding (1km) Forest (1km) Swimming pool (6km) Stretch of water (15km) Hiking (1km) Cross-country skiing (29km) Downhill skiing (32km) Tennis (2km) Spa (90km) Railway station (6km) Shops (1km) SAINT-DIE (6km) **NOTES:** Pets admitted (supplement payable)

VAUDONCOURT

¶¶¶ Chambre d'hôtes Claudine PELLERIN
3, rue Barbazan, 88140 VAUDONCOURT
☎ 03 29 09 23 60 & 06 81 95 00 31 ▤ 03 29 09 23 60
Three guest rooms in a village château on a large estate in the heart of thermal-spa country. First floor: one suite of three rooms (two double and two single beds), one suite of two rooms (one double and two single beds), lounge, balcony. Ground floor: one suite of two rooms (one double and two single beds). All rooms have private shower room and wc. Dining room shared with the owners. Pétanque. Horse riding can be arranged. No smoking. Open all year, except 11 November-31 January.
PRICES: s €61; d €61; t €76; extra person €15 **ON SITE:** Horse riding Forest Hiking **NEARBY:** Fishing (10km) Swimming pool (10km) Stretch of water (10km) Tennis (10km) Spa (10km) Railway station (10km) Shops (2km) VITTEL (10km) **NOTES:** No pets English spoken

VENTRON

¶¶¶ ⏀ Chambre d'hôtes Jean LA SALA
6, route du Frère Joseph, 88310 VENTRON
☎ 03 29 24 13 48
e-mail: jean@couette.com http://www.couette.com/Main.htm
Jean and Woss will welcome their guests like friends and are delighted to introduce you to their beautiful region. On the first floor are five guest rooms. One double room with grade 2 rating; four twin-bedded rooms, one with separate sitting room. All rooms have private shower room and wc across the landing. Generous breakfasts. Washing machine and dryer available. Terrace; barbecue. Skiing locally. Open all year.
PRICES: s €46-€72; d €53-€79; t €91; dinner €15 **ON SITE:** Horse riding Forest Fishing Hiking Cross-country skiing Downhill skiing Tennis **NEARBY:** Swimming pool (12km) Stretch of water (10km) Spa (45km) Railway station (6km) Shops (6km) LA BRESSE (12km) **NOTES:** No pets

⏀
Places with this symbol serve table d'hôtes evening meals - remember to book in advance

AQUITAINE

DORDOGNE

ARCHIGNAC

¶¶¶ ✇ Pouch Serge et Francine BOURGEADE
24590 ARCHIGNAC
☎ 05 53 28 85 02 & SR : 05 53 35 50 01 ▤ 05 53 28 90 93
e-mail/web: see SR Dordogne
Sarlat 18 km. Grottes de Lascaux 15 km. Situated in the Périgord Nord region, this stone house is typical of the region and not far from Montignac, Sarlat and the Vézère Valley. There is one twin bedroom and one double bedroom with a single bed that can be converted into a double (on a mezzanine level). There is a shower room, wc and corner lounge with TV in each bedroom. Outside, there is a terrace and a shady park. The house is in a quiet area and is ideally situated for rambling. Goose and duck patés are available from the house and there is a restaurant nearby. Visa accepted by the Service Reservation. Open 1 April-11 November.
PRICES: s €34; d €40; t €49; extra person €8 **ON SITE:** Children's play area Swimming pool **NEARBY:** Canoeing (15km) Golf (25km) Fishing (3km) Stretch of water (10km) Tennis (8km) Railway station (16km) Shops (6km) **NOTES:** Pets admitted

AUDRIX

¶¶¶ Jeandemai Betty et Olivier PREAUX
Mas Jeandemai, 24260 AUDRIX
☎ 05 53 04 26 96 & SR : 05 53 35 50 01 ▤ 05 53 07 67 96
e-mail: preotel@jeandemai.com ww.resinfrance.com/perigord
Les Eyzies 15 km. This 15th and 17th-century Périgord house lies in 20 hectares of land and dominates Le Bugue area that is bordered by the Vézère and Dordogne Valleys, in the heart of the Périgord Nord. There are two double bedrooms each with shower room or bathroom and wc. Two further bedrooms have a double bed and a

single bed, shower room and wc each. It is also possible to have an extra bed and cot on request. The drawing room with TV is available to guests. An authentic, friendly and tranquil atmosphere is guaranteed. There are restaurants nearby. Visa accepted by the Service Reservation. Open 1 March-31 December.
PRICES: s €40; d €45; t €60; extra person €15 **ON SITE:** Swimming pool **NEARBY:** Bathing (3km) Canoeing (4km) Horse riding (3km) Golf (14km) Fishing (4km) Tennis (3km) Railway station (4km) Shops (4km) **NOTES:** No pets

AZERAT

¶¶¶ Le Var Annie et Claude DELTEL
24210 AZERAT
☎ 05 53 05 28 52 & SR : 05 53 35 50 01 ▤ 05 53 05 28 52
e-mail/web: see SR Dordogne
Grottes de Lascaux 18 km. Châteaux de Hautefort 20 km. Sarlat 40 km. This old farmhouse in the heart of the Perigord countryside, has been restored to offer one double bedroom and four bedrooms for three people (one double bed and one single bed). There is also a cot and each room has a shower room and wc. Downstairs, there is a library and TV. Bicycles available. Awarded a prize at the Cèpes d'Or in 1996. Visa accepted by Service Reservation. Open 1 April to 30 November.
PRICES: s €36; d €43; t €64 **NEARBY:** Bathing (3km) Canoeing (18km) Horse riding (18km) Golf (35km) Fishing (3km) Swimming pool (3km) Stretch of water (10km) Tennis (3km) Railway station (1km) Shops (3km) **NOTES:** No pets

SR Dordogne
e-mail SR: dordogne.perigord.tourisme@wanadoo.fr
web: www.resinfrance.com/perigord/

BAYAC

♦♦♦ ⏸ & La Vergne

Francine PILLEBOUT et Odile CALMETTES
Le Relais de la Vergne, 24150 BAYAC
☎ 05 53 57 83 16 & SR : 05 53 35 50 01 ▤ 05 53 57 83 16
e-mail/web: see SR Dordogne
Monpazier 25 km. Cadouin 15 km. The house is situated in shady grounds, in Le Bergeraçois and right in the centre of regal, historic Périgord. There are three double bedrooms and one twin room, each with bathroom or shower room and wc. There is a further suite with one double bedroom and one twin bedroom, each with a shower room and wc, and access for the less mobile guest. A cot and further bed are also available. Sitting room with TV, table tennis, telephone/fax machine. A stone's throw from the neolilthic sites in the Dordogne Valley. Meals are available on request. Visa accepted by the Service Reservation. Open all year.
PRICES: s €48; d €55; t €69; extra person €80; dinner €20
ON SITE: Swimming pool **NEARBY:** Bathing (10km) Canoeing (20km) Horse riding (12km) Golf (10km) Fishing (3km) Tennis (8km) Railway station (4km) Shops (8km) **NOTES:** Pets admitted English spoken

BRANTOME

♦♦♦ Les Habrans Pierre FALCOZ 24310 BRANTOME

☎ 05 53 05 58 84 & SR : 05 53 35 50 01 ▤ 05 53 05 58 84
e-mail/web: see SR Dordogne
Périgueux, Villars, Bourdeilles and Saint-Jean-de-Côle. A kilometre from Brantôme, Les Habrans is a hidden, 17th-century house with three double bedrooms and two twin bedrooms. An additional bedroom has three large single beds. Each has a bathroom or shower room and wc, and there is a sitting room with TV. This house has a peaceful garden with the River Dronne running alongside. A relaxing spot, in a region famous for its prehistoric history and châteaux. There is a restaurant nearby. Visa accepted by the Service Reservation. Open 1 May to 31 October.
PRICES: s €40; d €49; t €54 **ON SITE:** Children's play area Bathing Fishing Swimming pool Stretch of water **NEARBY:** Canoeing (1km) Horse riding (1km) Golf (26km) Tennis (1km) Railway station (26km) Shops (1km) **NOTES:** Pets admitted English spoken

CARLUX

♦♦♦ La Vigerie Christine & J-Claude PIGEO, 24370 CARLUX

☎ 05 53 28 65 94 & SR 05 53 35 50 01 ▤ 05 53 28 65 95
e-mail/web: see SR Dordogne
Sarlat, Domme 14 km. Beynac 12 km. Situated in nine hectares of parkland, on the edge of the Dordogne River, this property, once a Carthusian monastery dating from 1731, offers spacious bedrooms and refined décor. There are three double bedrooms and one twin bedroom available, each with bathroom or shower room and wc. There is a fireplace in each room and a sitting room for guests. Restaurant nearby. Visa accepted by the Service Reservation. Open all year.
PRICES: s €75; d €80 **ON SITE:** Bathing Fishing Swimming pool **NEARBY:** Canoeing (1km) Horse riding (2km) Golf (14km) Tennis (2km) Railway station (12km) Shops (2km) **NOTES:** No pets English spoken

CENAC

♦♦♦ ♥ ⏸ La Guerinière. Baccas

Brigitte & C DEMASSOUGNE Baccas, 24250 CENAC
☎ 05 53 29 91 97 & SR : 05 53 35 50 01 ▤ 05 53 30 23 89
e-mail/web: see SR Dordogne
Sarlat 12 km. Domme 3 km. La Roque-Gageac 5 km. This 18th-century Périgord monastery is in the middle of ten hectares of traditional parkland. There are three double bedrooms and one twin bedroom and an additional bedroom with a double and single bed. A cot is available on request. Each bedroom has either a bathroom or shower room. A peaceful environment is assured

continued

and there is a wonderful view over Domme. Guests can enjoy the farm produce and traditional cooking prepared by the monks. Open 1 April to 31 October.
PRICES: s €49; d €54; t €68; HB €46-€68; dinner €19
ON SITE: Swimming pool Tennis **NEARBY:** Bathing (2km) Canoeing (2km) Horse riding (3km) Golf (6km) Fishing (2km) Stretch of water (7km) Railway station (12km) Shops (2km) **NOTES:** Pets admitted

CHAMPAGNE-ET-FONTAINE

♦♦♦ ⏸ & Domaine de Puytirel Reine SOUMAGNAC

24320 CHAMPAGNE EN FONTAINE
☎ 05 53 90 90 88 & SR : 05 53 35 50 01 ▤ 05 53 91 64 57
e-mail: puytirel@wanadoo.fr
e-mail/web: see SR Dordogne
Brantôme-Bourdeilles 25 km Situated in the middle of shady parkland with 100-year-old trees, this characterful 19th-century property offers two double bedrooms, both accessible to less mobile guests, and three rooms with both a double and a single bed. Two cots are available, and each bedroom has either a bathroom or shower room with wc. An extra bed is available on request. Family atmosphere ensured. Breakfast of home-made jams and patisseries are served in the house and evening meals are available on reservation. Visa accepted by the Service Reservation. Open all year.
PRICES: s €44; d €54; t €66; extra person €16; HB €46-€63; dinner €19
ON SITE: Children's play area Swimming pool **NEARBY:** Bathing (2km) Canoeing (15km) Horse riding (10km) Golf (20km) Fishing (1km) Tennis (5km) Railway station (35km) Shops (10km) **NOTES:** No pets English spoken

CHAMPNIERS-ET-REILHAC

♦♦♦ ⏸ Baupommier Reine et Dominic FACCINI

24360 CHAMPNIERS ET REILHAC
☎ 05 53 60 55 17 & SR 05 53 35 50 01 ▤ 05 53 60 76 94
e-mail/web: see SR Dordogne
Nontron 18 km. Four double bedrooms and one twin bedroom are available in this small 17th-century farmhouse, in the heart of the Périgord-Limousin Regional Park. Each bedroom has a bathroom or shower room with wc, and each is personalised after a great painter. A child's bed and extra bed are available on request. This area is very peaceful and ideal for horse riding. Meals, made from garden produce, are available by prior arrangement. Visa accepted by the Service Reservation. Open all year.
PRICES: s €38; d €42; extra person €11; dinner €19 **NEARBY:** Bathing (5km) Canoeing (28km) Horse riding (12km) Golf (20km) Fishing (2km) Swimming pool (18km) Stretch of water (5km) Tennis (2km) Railway station (18km) Shops (2km) **NOTES:** Pets admitted English spoken

GAUGEAC

♦♦♦ ♥ ⏸ Tandou Simone & Robert-J VERGNE

24540 GAUGEAC
☎ 05 53 22 62 28 & SR : 05 53 35 50 01 ▤ 05 53 22 62 28
e-mail/web: see SR Dordogne
Château de Biron 1 km. Sarlat and Bergerac 45 km. In the Périgord region, this pretty farm with farmyard animals offers two double bedrooms, one twin bedroom and one bedroom for three people (one double bed and one single bed). There is also a possibility of an extra bed. Each bedroom has a shower room with wc and independent access. The lounge room has a TV and there is a shady terrace. Between Bergerac and Sarlat, this house is near numerous tourist sites, including the Château de Biron (1 km). Local food is served at the family table. Open all year. Visa accepted by Service Reservation.
PRICES: s €36; d €40; t €57; extra person €13; HB €34-€50; FB €48-€64; dinner €14 **NEARBY:** Bathing (2km) Canoeing (20km) Horse riding (2km) Golf (15km) Fishing (1km) Swimming pool (5km) Tennis (2km) Railway station (15km) Shops (2km) **NOTES:** No pets

JOURNIAC

♥♥♥ Les Landettes Annie et André STOCKLOUSER

24260 JOURNIAC
☎ 05 53 54 35 19 & SR : 05 53 35 50 01 📠 05 53 54 35 19
e-mail/web: see SR Dordogne
Les Eyzies 15 km. Périgueux, Sarlat & Bergerac 30 km. This small restored farm in the Vézère Valley offers two double bedrooms and one bedroom with three single beds. An extra bed can be provided. Each bedroom has a shower room, wc and independent access. There is also garden furniture for guest use. This two hectare site in Périgord Noir is near many tourist sites. Visa accepted by the Service Reservation. Open all year.
PRICES: s €40; d €45; t €58; extra person €10 **ON SITE:** Swimming pool **NEARBY:** Bathing (10km) Canoeing (10km) Horse riding (5km) Golf (3km) Fishing (10km) Tennis (10km) Railway station (10km) Shops (10km) **NOTES:** No pets

JUMILHAC-LE-GRAND

♥♥♥ ⚅ ♿ Les Vignes de Chalusset

M SENEE C et CHEDEVILLE
24630 JUMILHAC LE GRAND
☎ 05 53 52 38 25 & SR : 05 53 35 50 01
e-mail/web: see SR Dordogne
Château de Jumilhac Le Grand 4 km. At the heart of the Périgord-Limousin Regional Park, this farm has been restored and now has air conditioning. There are three double bedrooms and a twin bedroom, one with access for the less mobile. An additional bedroom has a double bed and a single bed. There is a shower room and wc with each room. Extra bed available. TV in each bedroom. Sitting room with TV, library and board games. The house is in a peaceful, wooded area with footpaths from the grounds. Evening meals on request. Visa accepted by the Service Reservation. Open all year.
PRICES: s €35; d €40; t €49; extra person €9; HB €34-€49; dinner €14 **ON SITE:** Swimming pool **NEARBY:** Bathing (3km) Canoeing (3km) Horse riding (4km) Golf (50km) Fishing (3km) Tennis (4km) Railway station (5km) Shops (4km) **NOTES:** Pets admitted

LA GONTERIE-BOULOUNEIX

♥♥♥ ⚅ Le Coudert Colette et Claude-Bernard MAGRIN

24310 LA GONTERIE-BOULOUNEIX
☎ 05 53 05 75 30 & SR : 05 53 35 50 01
e-mail/web: see SR Dordogne
Brantôme 6.5 km. Bourdeilles 9 km. There are three double bedrooms in this pretty country farmhouse in the heart of the Périgord Vert region. An extra bed is also available on request. Each bedroom has a private bath or shower room and wc. A warm welcome and calm and relaxation are assured. Visa accepted by the Service Reservation. Open 1 February to 31 December.
PRICES: s €35; d €42; extra person €10; HB €35-€49; dinner €14 **NEARBY:** Bathing (7km) Canoeing (7km) Horse riding (9km) Golf (30km) Fishing (7km) Swimming pool (9km) Tennis (9km) Railway station (34km) Shops (6km) **NOTES:** No pets

LA ROQUE-GAGEAC

♥♥♥ ♥ Le Colombier Martine RIVIERE

La Ferme Fleurie, 24250 LA ROQUE GAGEAC
☎ 05 53 28 33 39 & SR 05 53 35 50 01 📠 05 53 28 29 61
e-mail/web: see SR Dordogne
Sarlat 8 km. Lascaux 30 km. Situated in the Périgord Noir, in the heart of the Dordogne, this farm is built of local stone and guarantees a calm and comfortable setting. There are three double bedrooms and two suites of two double bedrooms. They each have a shower room and wc and an extra bed is available on request. Breakfasts of local patisseries are provided and the farm inn is nearby. €52/4 persons. Visa accepted by the Service

continued

Reservation. Open 1 April to 1 November.
PRICES: s €31; d €37; t €45; extra person €10 **NEARBY:** Bathing (1km) Canoeing (1km) Horse riding (5km) Golf (2km) Fishing (1km) Swimming pool (8km) Tennis (5km) Railway station (8km) Shops (4km) **NOTES:** Pets admitted

LAMONZIE-MONTASTRUC

♥♥♥ ♥ La Barabie M-Jeanne & M-Thérèse ARCHER

24520 LAMONZIE MONTASTRUC
☎ 05 53 23 22 47 & SR : 05 53 35 50 01 📠 05 53 22 81 20
e-mail/web: see SR Dordogne
Dordogne Valley 4 km. Prehistoric sites 10 km. Near to Bergerac, this Périgord farmhouse is situated in a tranquil, shady spot with a terrace. There are two bedrooms with a double bed and single bed and one double bedroom. Each bedroom has a shower room and wc. The sitting room has a TV and board games. Bikes available. A warm, family welcome is guaranteed. Evening meals are available nearby. Visa accepted by the Service Reservation. Open 15 February to 15 November.
PRICES: s €38; d €41; t €55 **ON SITE:** Children's play area **NEARBY:** Canoeing (4km) Horse riding (5km) Golf (3km) Fishing (2km) Swimming pool (10km) Tennis (2km) Railway station (10km) Shops (2km) **NOTES:** No pets

LANQUAIS

♥♥♥ ⚅ Domaine de la Marmette Nadine OSSEDAT

La Crabe, 24150 LANQUAIS
☎ 05 53 24 99 13 & SR : 05 53 35 50 01 📠 05 53 24 11 48
e-mail/web: see SR Dordogne
Bergerac 16 km. Bastide de Monpazier 25 km. In the heart of the Périgord region, this restored 14th-16th century farmhouse is situated in 12 hectares of meadows and protected forests, above the Château de Lanquais. Two double bedrooms, a twin bedroom, one bedroom with a double and one single, and one bedroom with three single beds. Each has a shower room and wc. Cot and extra bed available. Sitting room with TV, library and board games. A warm welcome and peace and quiet assured. Varied evening meals available on reservation. Visa accepted by the Service Reservation. Open all year.
PRICES: s €46; d €52; t €65; extra person €15; HB €48-€68; dinner €22 **ON SITE:** Swimming pool **NEARBY:** Bathing (1km) Canoeing (6km) Horse riding (3km) Golf (12km) Fishing (1km) Tennis (2km) Railway station (4km) Shops (2km) **NOTES:** No pets

LE BUISSON-DE-CADOUIN

♥♥♥ La Feuillantine Geneviève et Jean DONVAL

Lacoste. 24480 LE BUISSON DE CADOUIN
☎ 05 53 23 95 37 & SR : 05 53 35 50 01 📠 05 53 23 95 37
e-mail/web: see SR Dordogne
Sarlat 35 km. Lascaux 25 km. Newly built in traditional Perigord style, this property is situated amidst woodland in the Dordogne Valley and offers a twin, a double and a triple bedroom (one double bed and one single bed). Each has a shower room, wc and independent access from the ground floor. Cot on request. The lounge has a TV and library and there is a terrace and parking area outside. A warm welcome and local information are provided. Restaurant nearby. Visa accepted by the Service Reservation. Open 15 March to 15 October.
PRICES: s €41; d €44; t €54 **NEARBY:** Bathing (1km) Canoeing (1km) Horse riding (5km) Golf (10km) Fishing (1km) Swimming pool (1km) Stretch of water (1km) Tennis (1km) Railway station (1km) Shops (1km) **NOTES:** Pets admitted English spoken

SR Dordogne
e-mail SR: dordogne.perigord.tourisme@wanadoo.fr
web: www.resinfrance.com/perigord/

LE COUX-ET-BIGAROQUE

🏶🏶🏶🏶 La Brunie Ghislaine et Marc OREFICE
24220 LE COUX ET LA BIGAROQUE
☎ 05 53 29 61 42 & SR : 05 53 35 50 01
🖳 05 53 28 62 35 e-mail: marc.orefice@wanadoo.fr
e-mail/web: see SR Dordogne
Villes touristiques : Les Eyzies 10 km and Sarlat 24 km. Beynac 5 km. This comfortable and charming18th-century manor, set in a shady park, offers two double bedrooms, two singles, one twin and one three person room (with one double bed and one single bed). An extra bed is possible on request and each bedroom has a bathroom, wc and independent access. There is also a sitting room with library, and a restaurant nearby. Visa accepted by the Service Reservation. This is a lovely setting in the heart of the Périgord Noir, ideal for exploring the châteaux of the Dordogne. Open all year.
PRICES: d €86; extra person €17 **NEARBY:** Bathing (1km) Canoeing (3km) Horse riding (2km) Golf (6km) Fishing (1km) Swimming pool (3km) Stretch of water (3km) Tennis (1km) Railway station (4km) Shops (1km) **NOTES:** No pets

LISLE

🏶🏶🏶 🍽️ La Picandine Armelle et Olivier LACOURT
24350 LISLE
☎ 05 53 03 41 93 & SR : 05 53 35 50 01 🖳 05 53 03 28 43
e-mail/web: see SR Dordogne
Brantome, Périgueux 20 km In this 18th-century farmhouse with a family atmosphere, there are two double bedrooms and one bedroom with a double bed and a single bed. Another bedroom contains a single bed and a double bed on a mezzanine floor. There is also a suite of two bedrooms (one double bedroom and one twin bedroom). Each bedroom has a bathroom or shower room and wc. Extra single bed and child's bed on request. Sitting room with TV, library, board games, billiard table, terrace and laundry. Total peace can be enjoyed in this countryside location. Evening meals by prior arrangement. Visa accepted by the Service Reservation. Open 1 February to 15 November.
PRICES: s €38; d €44; t €57; extra person €18; HB €39-€54; dinner €16 **ON SITE:** Swimming pool **NEARBY:** Bathing (5km) Canoeing (5km) Horse riding (12km) Golf (12km) Fishing (5km) Tennis (5km) Railway station (20km) Shops (5km) **NOTES:** No pets

MAUZENS-MIREMONT

🏶🏶🏶🏶 🍽️ Forge Neuve Isabelle et Alain BRUNEAU
24260 MAUZENS-MIREMONT
☎ 05 53 08 36 17 & SR : 05 53 35 50 01
🖳 05 53 08 32 95 01
e-mail: bruneau@forgeroy.com
Les Eyzies 12 km. Sarlat 35 km. In the heart of the Périgord Noir region, this 16th-century monastery offers five twin bedrooms each with a safe, mini-bar, shower room and wc. Extra bed or cot provided on request. A suite of two bedrooms (for four people in total) has a private terrace, bathroom, shower room and two wcs. The room rate with breakfast for four people is 227 euros. Sitting room with library area, satellite TV and DVD player. Traditional evening meals or gourmet dinners can be served. There is a billiard room, pool and sauna. This property, on 74 hectares of land, is charming and an ideal place to relax and unwind.
PRICES: d €105; dinner €38 **ON SITE:** Bathing Fishing Swimming pool **NEARBY:** Canoeing (10km) Horse riding (10km) Golf (30km) Railway station (6km) Shops (10km) **NOTES:** Pets admitted CC

CC - credit cards accepted

MENESPLET

🏶🏶🏶 🍽️ ♿ Les Loges M-Dominique & Claude BERTHIER
24700 MENESPLET
☎ 05 53 81 84 39 & SR : 05 53 35 50 01
e-mail/web: see SR Dordogne
Bergerac 35 km. Bordelais vineyards 25 km. Montpon Menesterol 7 km. This house is set in seven hectares of parkland with stables and a stream. There is one twin bedroom and two bedrooms with double bed and single bed. Each has a shower room or bathroom and wc. An extra bed can be provided. Library, board games and TV available. All rooms are accessible to less mobile guests. Lovely garden with furniture and activities for children: volleyball, boules, swings, sandpit, table football and table tennis. Large room in converted barn. Wine route 8 km; forest 3 km. Visa accepted by the Service Reservation. Open all year.
PRICES: s €33; d €42; t €51; extra person €9; HB €35-€47; dinner €14 **ON SITE:** Children's play area **NEARBY:** Bathing (7km) Canoeing (7km) Horse riding (7km) Fishing (3km) Swimming pool (7km) Stretch of water (7km) Tennis (7km) Railway station (7km) Shops (7km) **NOTES:** No pets

MONBAZILLAC

🏶🏶🏶 La Rouquette Françoise & C GAUBUSSEAU
Domaine de la Rouquette, 24240 MONBAZILLAC
☎ 05 53 58 30 60 & SR : 05 53 35 50 01 🖳 05 53 73 20 36
e-mail/web: see SR Dordogne
Bergerac 6 km. Bastides and Valley of the Dordogne 20 km. In this beautiful 18th-19th-century monastery, there are two double bedrooms and three bedrooms with one double and one single bed. Extra bed or cot on request. Each bedroom has a bathroom, wc and independent access. There is a leisure room with a billiard table. Formal gardens with a large terrace and panoramic views over the Dordogne Valley and the Château de Monbazillac. Peace and quiet is assured here in the heart of the wine lands. Restaurant nearby. Visa accepted by the Service Reservation. Open all year.
PRICES: s €65; d €80; t €105; extra person €15 **NEARBY:** Bathing (6km) Canoeing (20km) Horse riding (6km) Golf (5km) Fishing (6km) Swimming pool (6km) Tennis (3km) Railway station (6km) Shops (6km) **NOTES:** Pets admitted English spoken

MONSAGUEL

🏶🏶🏶 Foncarpe Geneviève & Emmanuel FINKEL
24560 MONSAGUEL
☎ 05 53 61 89 92 & SR : 05 53 35 50 01 🖳 05 53 61 89 92
e-mail/web: see SR Dordogne
Monbazillac 8 km. Bergerac 16 km. Issigeac 4 km. In this old restored manor house with wonderful views, there is one double bedroom and two bedrooms with a double bed and a single bed. Extra bed on request. Each room has its own bathroom or shower room and wc. Outside, there is a shady terrace area and garden furniture. Lounge with TV, table tennis and mountain biking available. Near the medieval village of Issigneac and the Château de Monbazillac, on the route of the bastide towns and the Châteaux of Périgord. Visa accepted by the Service Reservation. Open all year (prior reservation necessary out of season).
PRICES: s €38; d €52; t €66; extra person €12 **ON SITE:** Swimming pool **NEARBY:** Bathing (12km) Canoeing (16km) Horse riding (8km) Golf (12km) Fishing (4km) Tennis (4km) Railway station (16km) Shops (4km) **NOTES:** Pets admitted English spoken

MONTCARET

🏶🏶🏶 🌿 🍽️ Fonroque Brigitte FRIED
24230 MONTCARET
☎ 05 53 58 65 83 & SR 05 53 35 50 01 🖳 05 53 58 60 04
e-mail/web: see SR Dordogne
St Michel de Montaigne 2 km. Vignobles du Bordelais 20 km. In

continued

the Montaigne countryside, this large 16th-century wine producer's house is set in 100-year-old parklands. Fonroque welcomes guests to enjoy the peaceful country life. There is one double bedroom, two twin bedrooms and two bedrooms with a double bed and a single bed. Each bedroom has a bathroom or shower room and a cot on request. Open 15 February to 30 November.

PRICES: s €50; d €58; t €77; HB €46-€67; dinner €17 **NEARBY:** Bathing (10km) Canoeing (10km) Horse riding (10km) Golf (20km) Fishing (4km) Tennis (1km) Shops (1km) **NOTES:** Pets admitted English spoken

MONTFERRAND-DU-PERIGORD

♦♦♦ ♥ IOI **Boulègue** Jacqueline & J-Marc BELGARRIC
24440 MONTFERRAND-DU-PERIGORD
☎ 05 53 63 26 42 & SR : 05 53 35 50 01 ▤ 05 53 63 26 42
e-mail/web: see SR Dordogne
Bastide de Monpazier 10 km. Sarlat 48 km. Les Eyzies 35 km. This typical Périgord house lies in the Couze Valley, at the heart of the Bastide region. There are two double bedrooms, one twin bedroom and one single bedroom. Child's bed on request. Each bedroom has a bathroom or shower room and wc. Sitting room with library and TV, and terrace area with garden furniture available. Regional cooking uses vegetables from the garden. Peace and quiet is assured, as is a warm welcome. Near to the GR36 walking route and footpaths; bike hire possible. Visa accepted by the Service Reservation. Open 6 January to 20 December.

PRICES: s €31; d €35; extra person €15; HB €45; dinner €14
NEARBY: Bathing (10km) Canoeing (10km) Horse riding (7km) Golf (10km) Fishing (1km) Swimming pool (12km) Stretch of water (10km) Tennis (5km) Railway station (12km) Shops (6km) **NOTES:** No pets

♦♦♦ ♥ IOI **La Rivière** Sylvie BARRIAT SINICO
24440 MONTFERRAND-DU-PERIGORD
☎ 05 53 63 25 25 & SR : 05 53 35 50 01 ▤ 05 53 63 25 25
e-mail/web: see SR Dordogne
Monpazier 8 km. Sarlat 35 km. This Périgord farm, in the middle of fields and on the route of the bastide towns, offers three double bedrooms and three bedrooms with a double and single bed. A cot and extra bed can be provided on request. Each bedroom has a shower room and a wc. Out of season, cookery courses are available, whilst traditional meals are served at the family table between March and November. There are a number of tourist sites and footpaths nearby. Visa accepted by the Service Reservation. Open 1 March to 15 November.

PRICES: s €30; d €34; t €51; extra person €8; HB €32-€45; dinner €15 **ON SITE:** Fishing **NEARBY:** Bathing (5km) Canoeing (15km) Horse riding (10km) Golf (10km) Tennis (5km) Railway station (15km) Shops (8km) **NOTES:** Pets admitted English spoken

NAILHAC

♦♦♦ ♥ **La Razoire Haute**
M-Madeleine & Daniel BELINGARD, 24390 NAILHAC
☎ 05 53 51 51 74 & SR : 05 53 35 50 01 ▤ 05 53 51 38 29
e-mail/web: see SR Dordogne
Montignac-Lascaux 25 km. Périgueux 40 km. This restored stone house lies in typical Périgord countryside, with a panoramic view over the Château de Hautefort. There are three double bedrooms and two twin bedrooms, each with a shower room and wc. There is a corner sitting room for reading and an information area. The garden has outdoor furniture for guest use. Peace and rest is assured and the location is ideal for walking, mountain biking and visits to the Château de Hautefort and the Musée de la Médecine (medicine museum) 5 km away. Visa accepted by the Service Reservation. Open all year except October.

PRICES: s €31; d €36; dinner €12.20 **NEARBY:** Bathing (5km) Canoeing (25km) Golf (45km) Fishing (5km) Swimming pool (5km) Tennis (5km) Railway station (10km) Shops (5km) Restaurant nearby **NOTES:** Pets admitted English spoken

SR Dordogne
e-mail SR: dordogne.perigord.tourisme@wanadoo.fr
web: www.resinfrance.com/perigord/

PAULIN

♦♦♦ ♥ IOI &. **Le Pech** Catherine STEVAUX
Lou Cantou, 24590 PAULIN
☎ 05 53 30 39 27 & SR: 05 53 35 50 01 ▤ 05 53 30 39 27
e-mail/web: see SR Dordogne
Sarlat 23 km. Montignac/Lascaux Caves 26 km. This is an old, restored blacksmith's forge in the heart of Périgord Nord and near to Quercy; an ideal starting point for visiting the tourist sites of the Dordogne. There are two double bedrooms and two twin bedrooms, each with a shower room and wc. Extra bed on request and evening meals by reservation. Visa cards are accepted by the Service Reservation. Open all year.

PRICES: d €45; extra person €15; dinner €14 **NEARBY:** Horse riding (5km) Golf (15km) Fishing (10km) Tennis (8km) Railway station (25km) Shops (8km) **NOTES:** Pets admitted

PRATS-DE-CARLUX

♦♦♦ ♥ IOI **Les Veyssières** Jeanine ROCHE
24370 PRATS-DE-CARLUX
☎ 05 53 29 81 53 & SR : 05 53 35 50 01 ▤ 05 53 29 81 53
e-mail/web: see SR Dordogne
Sarlat 9 km. Lascaux & Montignac 30 km. There are two double bedrooms and two rooms with a double bed and a single bed, all with shower room with wc and independent access, available at this 18th-century Périgord farm. This is an ideal spot to start on the GR6 hiking route. The farm specialises in rearing fowl for making foie gras. Evening meals using regional specialities are available. Visa accepted by the Service Reservation. Open all year.

PRICES: s €35; d €40; t €51; HB €33-€48; dinner €13 **NEARBY:** Bathing (9km) Canoeing (7km) Horse riding (8km) Golf (8km) Fishing (4km) Swimming pool (8km) Tennis (9km) Railway station (9km) Shops (7km) **NOTES:** No pets English spoken

PROISSANS

♦♦♦ ♥ IOI **Chez Michel** Jeanine et Jacques FUMAT
24200 PROISSANS
☎ 05 53 59 11 79 & SR : 05 53 35 50 01 ▤ 05 53 29 25 39
e-mail/web: see SR Dordogne
Dordogne Valley 12 km. This newly-built country house is near to a farm that produces tobacco, cereal crops, nuts and raises poultry. There are two double bedrooms, a twin bedroom and two bedrooms with a double bed and a single bed. Each bedroom has a shower room and wc. There is a lounge with sitting room area and peace and comfort is guaranteed. Near the many tourist sites and châteaux of the Dordogne. Visa accepted by the Service Reservation. Open 15 March to 15 November.

PRICES: s €34; d €39; t €51; HB €47; dinner €13 **NEARBY:** Bathing (10km) Canoeing (12km) Horse riding (10km) Golf (10km) Fishing (1km) Stretch of water (10km) Tennis (2km) Railway station (25km) Shops (7km) **NOTES:** No pets

♦♦♦ **L'Arche - Les Chanets** Jeannette et Marcel DELEPLACE
24200 PROISSANS
☎ 05 53 29 08 48 & SR : 05 53 35 50 01 ▤ 05 53 29 69 01
e-mail/web: see SR Dordogne
Sarlat 5 km. Lascaux 20 km. This beautiful and charming 18th-century house is in the heart of the Périgord Noir. There are four double bedrooms, each with shower room and wc. Peace and rest are assured in the delightful countryside. Outside, there is a shady terrace, garden furniture, a parking area and a bread oven. Guests will receive a very warm welcome. Restaurant nearby. Visa

continued

AQUITAINE

accepted by the Service Reservation. Open 1 March to 15 November.

PRICES: s €33; d €37; extra person €8 **NEARBY:** Bathing (5km) Canoeing (10km) Horse riding (4km) Golf (5km) Fishing (2km) Swimming pool (5km) Stretch of water (12km) Tennis (5km) Railway station (5km) Shops (5km) **NOTES:** No pets

Les Anglards Isabelle et Thierry VILATTE
24200 PROISSANS
☎ 05 53 29 47 36 & SR : 05 53 35 50 01
e-mail/web: see SR Dordogne

Lascaux 15 km, Sarlat 4 km, Dordogne Valley 10 km In the heart of the Périgord Noir, this old barn has been restored using the local stone. There is one double bedroom and three bedrooms for three people (a double bed and single bed in each); each has a shower room and wc. Cot on request. There is a sitting room with TV, library and open fireplace. Terrace with garden furniture. Private ponds are available for fishing and peace and comfort are assured. Tobacco, corn, asparagus and walnuts are grown on site. Restaurant and farm inn nearby. Visa accepted by the Service Reservation. Open all year.

PRICES: s €34; d €40; t €50; extra person €9 **ON SITE:** Fishing Swimming pool **NEARBY:** Bathing (10km) Canoeing (10km) Horse riding (4km) Golf (5km) Tennis (1km) Railway station (5km) Shops (5km) **NOTES:** No pets

SALIGNAC-EYVIGUES

Moulin de la Garrigue Hélène et Pierre VALLEE
24590 SALIGNAC-EYVIGUES
☎ 05 53 28 84 88 & SR : 05 53 35 50 01
e-mail/web: see SR Dordogne

Sarlat 20 km. Lascaux 30 km. Les Eyzies 30 km. This renovated windmill, dating from 1875, sits on l5 hectares of land. There are four bedrooms, including one on the ground floor (double bedroom with single mezzanine) and an extra bed is available. Each has a shower room, wc and telephone. Outside the terrace is bordered by the small Borrèze River. A farm inn lies nearby and a warm welcome is guaranteed. Visa accepted by the Service Reservation. Open all year.

PRICES: s €40; d €43; t €55; extra person €12 **ON SITE:** Fishing Swimming pool **NEARBY:** Bathing (9km) Canoeing (9km) Horse riding (9km) Golf (9km) Stretch of water (9km) Tennis (2km) Railway station (9km) Shops (9km) **NOTES:** Pets admitted

SARLAT-LA-CANEDA

La Croix d'Allon Nadine et Daniel PERUSIN
24200 SARLAT
☎ 05 53 59 08 44 & SR : 05 53 35 50 24
e-mail/web: see SR Dordogne

Sarlat 2 km. This restored, stone and timber farmhouse lies in a valley in the heart of the Périgord Noir, at the centre of the tourist area of Lascaux, Domme, les Eyzies and Eyrignac. There are two double bedrooms and two single bedrooms at this property, each with shower room and wc. There is independent access to a suite of two bedrooms (one double and one twin), bathroom and wc. The park has garden furniture. Breakfasts of nut bread and home-made jams are served. Visa accepted by the Service Reservation. Open 15 March to 31 December.

PRICES: s €40; d €45; t €60; extra person €10 **ON SITE:** Children's play area Fishing **NEARBY:** Bathing (6km) Canoeing (6km) Horse riding (6km) Golf (3km) Swimming pool (1km) Stretch of water (6km) Tennis (2km) Railway station (3km) Shops (2km) **NOTES:** Pets admitted English spoken

SR Dordogne
e-mail SR: dordogne.perigord.tourisme@wanadoo.fr
web: www.resinfrance.com/perigord/

Pech-Lafaille Monique et Paul MATHIEU
24200 SARLAT
☎ 05 53 59 08 19 & SR : 05 53 35 50 01 ▤ 05 53 59 23 62
e-mail/web: see SR Dordogne

Sarlat 3 km. Lascaux 25 km. This 18th-century Périgord house lies in four hectares of parkland. There are two double bedrooms and two bedrooms with a double bed and single bed. Each bedroom also has a shower room and wc. There is a sitting room with TV and a warm welcome is guaranteed. Outside there is a shady terrace with garden furniture. Restaurant nearby. Visa accepted by the Service Reservation. Open all year.

PRICES: s €35; d €39; t €49 **NEARBY:** Bathing (6km) Canoeing (6km) Horse riding (6km) Golf (6km) Fishing (6km) Swimming pool (2km) Stretch of water (6km) Tennis (3km) Railway station (3km) Shops (2km) **NOTES:** Pets admitted

ST-ANDRE-D'ALLAS

Les Filolies Adrienne et Patrick LANCAUCHEZ
24200 SAINT-ANDRE-D'ALLAS
☎ 05 53 30 31 84 & SR : 05 53 35 50 01 ▤ 05 53 30 31 84
e-mail/web: see SR Dordogne

This old renovated post office lies at the heart of the Périgord Nord within a two-hectare park, bordered by woods and fields. There are two double bedrooms and two bedrooms for three people (two double beds and a single bed). A cot can also be provided and each bedroom has a shower room and wc. Activities available include rambling and cycling. There is private access to the garden and guests may use the outdoor furniture. Nearby there is a restaurant and farm inn. Sarlat and the Dordogne Valley are only 7 km away. Large, varied breakfasts of local produce. Visa accepted by the Service Reservation. Open 30 March to 3 November.

PRICES: s €38; d €42; t €55 **NEARBY:** Bathing (6km) Canoeing (6km) Horse riding (4km) Golf (12km) Fishing (2km) Swimming pool (6km) Tennis (2km) Railway station (8km) Shops (7km) **NOTES:** No pets English spoken

ST-MARTIAL-DE-VALETTE

Domaine de Montagenet Didier DEREIX
24300 PERIGUEUX
☎ 05 53 60 75 18 & SR : 05 53 35 50 01
e-mail/web: see SR Dordogne

Brantôme 15 km. Périgueux 40 km. This 18th-century manor house lies within 70 hectares of land, in the heart of the Périgord Vert and the Périgord-Limousin Regional Park. There is one double bedroom and one three-person bedroom (one double bed and one single bed) each with private bathroom and wc. There is also one two-bedroom suite (one double and one twin) with shower room and wc. Guests can relax around the pool or on the terrace near the pond. After a large breakfast, the children can discover the farm activities (horse and cattle rearing). Visa accepted by the Service Reservation. Open all year.

PRICES: s €46; d €61; t €92; extra person €15 **ON SITE:** Children's play area Fishing Swimming pool Stretch of water **NEARBY:** Bathing (10km) Canoeing (15km) Horse riding (10km) Golf (30km) Tennis (3km) Railway station (40km) Shops (3km) **NOTES:** Pets admitted English spoken

ST-PARDOUX-LA-RIVIERE

La Peyronnie Jeanine et Jacques VANDAMME
24470 SAINT-PARDOUX-LA-RIVIERE
☎ 05 53 60 53 30 & SR : 05 53 35 50 01 ▤ 05 53 60 53 30
e-mail/web: see SR Dordogne

Brantome 25 km. Grottes de Villars 20 km. Périgueux 45 km. This old restored farmhouse lies in a charming hamlet, with a wonderful view over lush countryside. There are three double rooms and one twin room, each with its own shower room and

continued

wc. Downstairs there is a sitting room with TV, library and board games. There is also a terrace area and leafy garden. A relaxing atmosphere is assured and there are many walks to enjoy in the high forests or in the Dronne Valley. There are châteaux nearby and bathing in the pond. Evening meals on request. Visa accepted by the Service Reservation. Open all year.
PRICES: s €28; d €37; HB €35–€44; dinner €16 **NEARBY:** Bathing (10km) Canoeing (15km) Fishing (2km) Swimming pool (10km) Tennis (10km) Railway station (20km) Shops (2km) **NOTES:** No pets

ST-REMY-SUR-LIDOIRE

♥ La Mouthe Marie-Ange CAIGNARD
24700 SAINT-REMY-SUR-LIDOIRE
☎ 05 53 82 15 40 & SR : 05 53 35 50 01   ▤ 05 53 82 15 40
e-mail/web: see SR Dordogne
Bergerac, Monbazillac 30 km, Bordelais vineyards 40 km. Marie-Ange welcomes guests to her house situated between Bergerac and St Emillion. There are two double bedrooms and one twin bedroom, each with shower room and wc. A cot can be provided on request. Each bedroom is comfortable and has individual décor, with private access from the terrace. There are also a library and board games. Situated on 20 hectares of land, between vineyards and forests, with a pond for fishing, there are many footpaths leading from the house. A restaurant, farm inn and stables are nearby. Telephone and fax machine available. Visa accepted by the Service Reservation. Open all year.
PRICES: s €50; d €54 **ON SITE:** Children's play area Horse riding Fishing Swimming pool **NEARBY:** Bathing (8km) Canoeing (11km) Golf (25km) Tennis (3km) Railway station (11km) Shops (4km) **NOTES:** Pets admitted

STE-NATHALENE

La Borie de Latour Anne et Robert RELLO
24200 SAINTE-NATHALENE
☎ 05 53 59 13 41 & SR: 05 53 35 50 01
e-mail/web: see SR Dordogne
Sarlat, Dordogne Valley 10 km. Jardin d'Eyrignac 3 km. Three double bedrooms with a cot, shower room and wc are available in this property. Each bedroom has independent access. There is also a terrace with garden furniture and a parking area. On the walking route, at the heart of the Périgord Noir region, this listed, stone house has wonderful views over the hills. This is an ideal place to discover the numerous tourist and walking routes. There is a farm and inn nearby. Visa accepted by the Service Reservation. Open all year (pre-booking necessary out of season).
PRICES: s €35; d €39 **NEARBY:** Bathing (10km) Canoeing (10km) Horse riding (3km) Golf (25km) Fishing (5km) Swimming pool (10km) Tennis (2km) Railway station (10km) Shops (3km) **NOTES:** No pets English spoken

VAUNAC

♥ Les Guézoux Béatrice et Pierre FOUQUET
24800 VAUNAC
☎ 05 53 62 06 39 & SR : 05 53 35 50 01   ▤ 05 53 62 88 74
Saint-Jean de Côle 12 km. Brantôme 20 km. Périgueux 25 km. This stone farmhouse lies in a lovely, peaceful, wooded area. Guests receive a warm welcome and can learn about snail breeding and tasting. Two double bedrooms and two bedrooms with a double bed and a single bed area are available. Each has a bathroom or shower room and wc. A cot can be provided on request. Large breakfasts feature local produce, home-made jams and nut cakes. There is a shady terrace area and a restaurant nearby. Visa accepted by the Service Reservation. Open all year.
PRICES: s €34; d €38; t €49 **NEARBY:** Bathing (8km) Canoeing (8km) Horse riding (15km) Golf (25km) Fishing (5km) Swimming pool (6km) Tennis (3km) Railway station (8km) Shops (3km) **NOTES:** Pets admitted English spoken

ANDERNOS

Chambre d'hôtes M et Mme BEDEXAGAR
84 avenue Jean Marcel Despagne, 33510 ANDERNOS
☎ 05 56 82 56 73   ▤ 05 56 82 56 73
Bordeaux 40 km. Arcachon 36 km. This old 19th-century grange, near the owners' house, is typical of this area, and lies near the Archachon basin. Breakfast room on the veranda (high chair available). On the first floor, there are two two-person rooms and two three-person rooms with shower room and wc. There is a large, enclosed garden, terrace and parking area. Open all year.
PRICES: s €49; d €53; t €66; extra person €12 **NEARBY:** Bathing (1km) Horse riding (2km) Golf (6km) Sea (7km) Swimming pool (1km) Stretch of water (1km) Tennis (1km) Railway station (10km) Shops (1km) **NOTES:** Pets admitted

Chambre d'hôtes Jacques et Maryse MALFERE
10 boulevard de Verdun, 33510 ANDERNOS
☎ 05 56 82 04 46   ▤ 05 56 82 04 46
This mid 20th-century house is located very near the Archachon beaches, in an enclosed country garden surrounded by beautiful countryside and local architecture. On the ground floor there is a lounge/dining room. On the first floor, there are two themed double bedrooms, each with a bathroom or shower room and wc. One family room for two to four people. Outside there is garden furniture, a barbecue and a summer cooking area with terrace. TV. 10% discount for stays of 4 days or out of season. Open all year.
PRICES: s €49–€59; d €55–€65 **ON SITE:** Swimming pool Fishing (0.15km) **NEARBY:** Horse riding (2km) Golf (5km) Sea (1km) Tennis (2km) Railway station (20km) Shops (1km) **NOTES:** No pets

ARBIS

⊚ Château le Vert Claude IMHOFF
Route d'Escoussans, 33760 ARBIS
☎ 05 56 23 91 49
Targon 4 km. Cadillac 7 km. This 19th-century château is attached to 13th and 16th century buildings in the heart of the Entre-Deux-Mers region and surrounded by a parkland. There is a large twin bedroom with bathroom, wc and TV. There are also two bedrooms with two bunk beds, a bathroom, wc and TV. On the ground floor, with a private entrance, there is a dining/sitting room. It is possible to rent extra reception rooms. In another wing, there is a suite of one double bedroom, a lounge, shower room with hydrojet, wc and TV. Parking. Open all year. Swimming pool on site.
PRICES: d €60–€92; extra person €17; dinner €22 **NEARBY:** Bathing (3km) Fishing (3km) Tennis (2km) Railway station (10km) Shops (4km) **NOTES:** No pets

BLAYE

Chambre d'hôtes Léa GOLIAS
13 rue Prémayac, Villa Prémayac, 33390 BLAYE
☎ 06 07 79 64 05 & 05 57 42 69 05   ▤ 05 57 42 69 09
This 18th-century property is situated in the city of Blayé, near to the Citadel at Vauban and the Gironde estuary. There are four double bedrooms and one twin bedroom each with bathroom, wc and TV. There is also a lounge and tea room. Roman garden and enclosed zen garden. Parking nearby.
PRICES: d €79–€84 **NEARBY:** Bathing (17km) Horse riding (10km) Golf (35km) Sea (70km) Swimming pool (1km) Stretch of water (17km) Tennis (1km) Railway station (20km) **NOTES:** Pets admitted English spoken

⊚ Places with this symbol serve table d'hôtes evening meals - remember to book in advance

BOURG-SUR-GIRONDE

♥♥♥♥ Le Pain-de-Sucre GUERIN
26, Le Pain de Sucre, 33710 BOURG-SUR-GIRONDE
☎ 05 57 68 23 42   🖷 05 57 68 23 42
Vineyards of Côtes de Bourg, citadelle at Blaye 15 km. This
renovated stone house lies in the heart of the wine-growing region
of Côtes de Bourg and is situated on the banks of the Gironde
estuary. On the ground floor there is one double bedroom with
bathroom and wc, a sitting room and dining room. On the first
floor, there are three double rooms and two twin rooms, with
shower and wc. Terrace, garden and parking. Open all year.
PRICES: s €35; d €40; extra person €12   **ON SITE:** Fishing
NEARBY: Bathing (15km) Horse riding (10km) Golf (35km) Swimming
pool (2km) Tennis (2km) Railway station (15km) Shops (2km)
NOTES: No pets

CAPIAN

♥♥♥♥ 🍽 Château Grand Branet Blanche MAINVIELLE
859 Branet Sud, 33550 CAPIAN
☎ 05 56 72 17 30   🖷 05 56 72 36 59

This renovated 17th-century château lies in a large, peaceful,
wooded park. There are five bedrooms with either shower room
or bathroom and wc; two have communal terrace areas. There is
also a sitting room, TV, dining room and gallery area. A cot can be
provided on request. Table tennis and mountain bikes. Evening
meals on reservation. Open all year. Wine tasting.
PRICES: s €37; d €60; t €65; extra person €14; dinner €17
ON SITE: Tennis   **NEARBY:** Bathing (5km) Horse riding (7km) Golf
(30km) Fishing (8km) Swimming pool (7km) Railway station (15km)
Shops (7km)   **NOTES:** No pets

CASTELNAU-DE-MEDOC

♥♥♥♥ Carrat Laurence PERY
Domaine de Carrat, Route de Sainte-Hélène,
33480 CASTELNAU-DE-MEDOC
☎ 05 56 58 24 80
This house has lots of character and is surrounded by woods and
meadows with streams. It is a lovely, calm place to relax. There are
three guest rooms; a twin bedroom with bathroom and wc, a small
suite with a twin bedroom and a small bedroom for two children
with bathroom and wc. On the ground floor, there is a bedroom
with bathroom and wc. A lounge, TV and kitchen for guest use.
Rate for four people: 79 euros.
PRICES: s €41; d €46-€53   **NEARBY:** Bathing (25km) Horse riding (5km)
Golf (10km) Sea (25km) Tennis (2km) Railway station (10km) Shops
(1km)   **NOTES:** Pets admitted English spoken

♥♥♥♥ Le Foulon Danielle DE BARITAULT
Château le Foulon, 33480 CASTELNAU-DE-MEDOC
☎ 05 56 58 20 18   🖷 05 56 58 23 43
Located in a forest, with a park and streams, this château has four
guest rooms with lots of character. One is a double bedroom with

a private bathroom and wc, separate from the room. There are
also two double bedrooms with bathroom and wc. Another suite is
divided into two double bedrooms, a bathroom and wc. Lounge
and dining room. Restaurant 1 km away.
PRICES: s €61; d €69-€77; t €92; extra person €23   **NEARBY:** Bathing
(30km) Horse riding (1km) Golf (15km) Sea (30km) Tennis (1km)
NOTES: No pets

CASTILLON-LA-BATAILLE

♥♥♥♥ ♥ ♿ Robin Pierrette MINTET
33350 CASTILLON-LA-BATAILLE
☎ 05 57 40 20 55   🖷 05 57 40 20 55
This old house is typical of the Gironde region. It has been entirely
restored and is situated on one of many winegrowing estates
stretching over the valleys of the Dordogne and la Lidoire. On the
first floor there is one double bedroom and one twin bedroom,
each with either a bathroom or shower room and wc. On the
ground floor there is one double bedroom with an extra single
bed, shower room and wc, suitable for the less able. There is also
a dining/lounge room and hall area. Garden, terrace and veranda.
Open all year.
PRICES: s €32; d €40; t €56; extra person €14   **NEARBY:** Bathing (8km)
Horse riding (3km) Fishing (3km) Swimming pool (3km) Tennis (3km)
Railway station (3km) Shops (3km)   **NOTES:** No pets English spoken

COUTRAS

♥♥♥♥ Le Baudou Philippe et M-Christine HEFTRE
33230 COUTRAS
☎ 05 57 49 16 33 & 06 86 63 59 48
This restored 18th-century home is situated in four hectares of
parkland, woods, meadows and orchards. On the ground floor
there is a large room with one single bed and one double bed,
shower room, wc and private access. A lounge/dining room with
fireplace. Board games, library and table tennis. On the first floor,
a large room with a double and single bed, bathroom, wc and
independent access. Also a double bedroom with shower and wc.
Terrace and parking. 10% discount after sixth night. Open all year.
PRICES: s €49-€52; d €55-€59; extra person €16   **NEARBY:** Bathing
(16km) Horse riding (3km) Fishing (1km) Swimming pool (3km) Tennis
(1km) Railway station (2km) Shops (1km)   **NOTES:** No pets

EYNESSE

♥♥♥♥ 🍽 Eynesse COLARDELLE
27 La Beysse, aux 3 fontaines, 33220 EYNESSE
☎ 05 57 41 02 28 & 06 80 35 12 32   🖷 05 57 41 02 28
e-mail: colardel@club-internet.fr   www.go.to/aux3fontaines
This 19th-century house in the Dordogne Valley has views over the
vineyards. On the ground floor there is a sitting room with TV,
billiard room, fireplace and dining room. In an annexe there is a
room with a double bed and single bed, shower room, wc and
kitchen area. On the third floor there are three double bedrooms,
each with bathroom or shower room and wc (one is a grade 2
room). There is a further bedroom for 2-4 people (one double bed
and three single beds) with a shower room and wc. Evening meals
on request. Pets admitted under certain conditions. There are large
grounds, an enclosed courtyard, a terrace and garden furniture.
Open all year.
PRICES: s €37-€45; d €46-€54; extra person €14; dinner €16
ON SITE: Swimming pool   **NEARBY:** Horse riding (3km) Golf (15km)
Fishing (1km) Railway station (7km) Shops (1km)   **NOTES:** Pets admitted
English spoken

🍽
Places with this symbol serve table d'hôtes
evening meals - remember to book in advance

continued

♦♦♦♦ ⊙ Le Grand Renom Francine SERAS
Manoir le Grand Renom, 33220 EYNESSE
☎ 05 57 41 02 10 & 06 11 56 34 72
e-mail: augrandrenom@net-up.com //seras.help2.com
St Emilion 28 km. This 19th-century manor house lies amongst the
vines in a shady park. On the ground floor there is a sitting room
and dining room. On the first floor, there are three double
bedrooms and one with three single beds, each with shower room
or bathroom and wc.
PRICES: s €39; d €46-€49; t €60; extra person €16; dinner €20
NEARBY: Horse riding (6km) Golf (15km) Fishing (2km) Swimming pool
(6km) Tennis (6km) Railway station (6km) Bathing (12km) **NOTES:** No
pets CC

FLAUJAGUES

♦♦♦♦ Le Fougueyra Miranda CANAC
Manoir Le Fougueyra, 33350 FLAUJAGUES
☎ 06 87 45 45 81 & 05 57 40 14 33
e-mail: manoir.fougueyra@wanadoo.fr
//perso.wanadoo.fr/didier.canac/
Saint-Emilion 15 km. On the banks of the Dordogne River, this
18th-century manor house is set in parkland. On the ground floor
there are two double bedrooms with either a shower or bathroom
and a wc. There is also a 2-4 person suite with a shower room and
wc, and double and twin beds on the first floor. Each bedroom
looks out onto the Dordogne and has a private entrance. Sitting
room and dining room. Walks from the property, boat and bike for
guest use. Open all year. Four people €88.
PRICES: s €42; d €53-€56; extra person €12 **ON SITE:** Bathing Fishing
Swimming pool Stretch of water Childrens' games **NEARBY:** Horse
riding (6km) Golf (22km) Tennis (6km) Railway station (6km) Shops
(6km) **NOTES:** No pets English spoken

GAJAC-DE-BAZAS

♦♦♦ ❦ Cabirol Xavier DIONIS DU SEJOUR
33430 GAJAC-DE-BAZAS
☎ 05 56 25 15 29 🖺 05 56 25 15 29
Sauternes 15 km. In the heart of the countryside, this restored
18th-century house is typical of the region. On the first floor, there
are four two-person bedrooms, each with a bath or shower room
and wc. On the ground floor, there is a sitting room/dining
room/library leading out onto a terrace. Large country garden.
Parking area. After the fourth night, a 10% reduction. €74-80/4
persons. Games room, billiard table and table tennis. Open all
year (by reservation 15 November to 15 February).
PRICES: d €45-€49 **ON SITE:** Fishing **NEARBY:** Bathing (20km) Horse
riding (4km) Golf (20km) Swimming pool (4km) Tennis (4km) Railway
station (15km) Shops (4km) **NOTES:** No pets English spoken

GENISSAC

♦♦♦♦ Guillaumat Dominique et Francis FULCHI
Domaine de Guillaumat, 33420 GENISSAC
☎ 05 57 24 49 14 & 05 57 51 18 99 🖺 05 57 51 90 69
Saint-Emilion 15 km. Very near to the owners' home, this 17th
century house is peacefully situated in the Dordogne valley, in the
middle of a vineyard. Wonderful views. There are three bedrooms
available, each with private bathroom and wc. The first is a double
bedroom with private entry. Another large twin bedroom has a
lounge area, fireplace and library. Finally, the third bedroom has a
double bed. There is a separate sitting room with TV and open
fireplace and a dining room. Horses may be stabled on request.
Open all year.
PRICES: s €38; d €46; extra person €11 **NEARBY:** Horse riding (10km)
Golf (18km) Fishing (10km) Tennis (2km) Railway station (9km) Shops
(2km) **NOTES:** Pets admitted

LES LEVES-ET-THOUMEYRAGUES

♦♦♦♦ ⊙ Domaine les Jourdis Philippe COMALADA
33220 LES LEVES-ET-THOUMEYRAGUES
☎ 05 57 41 22 35 & 06 72 72 25 30 🖺 05 57 41 22 35
e-mail: COMALADA@net-up.com
www.lesjourdis.com

*Bastide Ste-Foy-la-Grande 7 km. Route des vins and Périgord
20 km.* Originally built in the 16th century and remodelled in
the 18th century, this house lies in 12 hectares of parkland
with wonderful views. The first suite consists of a double
bedroom, lounge (with a double sofa bed) and terrace. The
second suite has one double bed and lounge with two single
beds. A further bedroom has two single beds. Each has a TV
and telephone, private bathroom and wc. There is a dining
room and separate lounge. Outside there is a covered terrace
and many activities: boule, children's games and bikes (for
hire), 4x4 circuits and lessons, boating on the private lake and
rambling. Winetasting weekends. Open all year.
PRICES: s €58-€63; d €67-€75; extra person €14-€22; dinner €22
ON SITE: Children's play area Horse riding Fishing **NEARBY:**
Bathing (7km) Golf (10km) Swimming pool (7km) Tennis (7km)
Railway station (7km) Shops (1km) **NOTES:** No pets English
spoken

LISTRAC-MEDOC

♦♦♦♦ Donissan Maryse MEYRE
Château Cap Léon Veyrin, 33480 LISTRAC-MEDOC
☎ 05 56 58 07 28 🖺 05 56 58 07 50
This refined house has been totally renovated and lies within
vineyards (cru Bourgeois du Médoc). There are five bedrooms for
two people and one bedroom with bathroom and wc. There are
four bedrooms with shower room and wc. There is a large lounge
room and a dining room with a fireplace and TV. Amenities include
a washing machine, barbecue and telephone. You can visit the
owners' wine cellar and taste the wines. There is a forest nearby, a
river 3 km away and a restaurant 2 km away.
PRICES: s €37; d €42; t €54 **ON SITE:** Fishing **NEARBY:** Bathing
(30km) Horse riding (3km) Golf (20km) Sea (25km) Stretch of water
(25km) Railway station (5km) **NOTES:** No pets English spoken

MIOS

♦♦♦♦ Les Tilleuls LAGOUEYTE/COUGET
17 bis rue des Ecoles, 33380 MIOS
☎ 05 56 26 67 85 & 06 14 39 22 54 🖺 05 56 26 49 35
email: gitemios@club-internet.fr http://gitemios.free.fr
Arcachon 20 km. Accommodation is in the old outbuildings of this
manor house, built in the local Arcachon style and dating back to
the start of the last century. On the ground floor, there is a suite of
one double bedroom and one twin bedroom, shower room and
wc. There is also a dining room and wc. On the first floor, there
are two double bedrooms with private shower room and wc each.

continued

AQUITAINE

TV, video and library. Large, tree-lined garden and parking area. 10% discount after the sixth day. The property is situated in a village, in the heart of the Landes de Gascogne Regional Park and near the entrance to the Arcachon Basin. Open 1 May to 1 November.
PRICES: s €38-€43; d €43-€47; t €62; extra person €14 **ON SITE:** Tennis **NEARBY:** Bathing (17km) Horse riding (1km) Golf (15km) Sea (20km) Fishing (1km) Swimming pool (11km) Railway station (4km) Shops (1km) **NOTES:** No pets

NOAILLAC

▦ ℞ ♿ La Tuilerie Claire LABORDE
33190 NOAILLAC
☎ 05 56 71 05 51 ▤ 05 56 71 05 51
e-mail: claire.laborde@libertysurf.fr

In the heart of the countryside, this pretty, restored, 19th century farmhouse has five bedrooms. On the ground floor, there is a twin bedroom, suitable for guests with disabilities, with shower and wc. On the first floor, there is a double bedroom with sofa, bathroom and wc. A further three double bedrooms have a shower room or bathroom and wc each. Sitting room and dining room with TV and fireplace. Evening meals on request. Garden, barbecue, covered terrace and swimming pool. Open all year.
PRICES: s €46; d €52; extra person €19; dinner €20 **ON SITE:** Fishing Swimming pool **NEARBY:** Bathing (15km) Horse riding (1km) Golf (15km) Tennis (4km) Railway station (10km) Shops (6km) **NOTES:** Pets admitted English spoken

PESSAC-SUR-DORDOGNE

▦ ♞ Château de Carbonneau
J & W FRANC DE FERRIERE
33890 PESSAC-SUR-DORDOGNE
☎ 05 57 47 46 46 ▤ 05 57 47 42 26
chateau-carbonneau.com

Situated on a winegrowers' estate, this 16th century chateau has an amazing stained glass window (in the style of Napoleon III) and is surrounded by parkland and vineyards. On the first floor there is one double bedroom with a bathroom and wc. On the ground floor, there is a double with a bathroom and wc. There is also a

lounge and dining room. Very near to the château, there is a pretty dovecote with one twin bedroom, bathroom and wc. Private parking. Open March to November.
PRICES: ; d €60; extra person €15 **ON SITE:** Swimming pool Wine tasting **NEARBY:** Bathing (3km) Horse riding (5km) Golf (20km) Fishing (3km) Tennis (2km) Railway station (12km) **NOTES:** No pets English spoken

PLEINE-SELVE

▦ ♞ Lussan Christian PASTUREAUD
3 Lussan, 33820 PLEINE-SELVE
☎ 05 57 32 74 44 ▤ 05 57 32 95 18
This 18th-century chateau is situated on a winegrower's estate, in the middle of the pilgrim route to Saint-Jacques-de-Compostelle. On the first floor, there is one double bedroom and one room with a double bed and a single bed. There is also a twin bedroom with shower room and wc. On the ground floor, there is a sitting room, TV and dining room. Reduction for longer stays. Wine can be tasted and bought from the chateau and there is a shady garden with shelter outside. Open all year.
PRICES: s €30; d €37; t €48; extra person €12 **NEARBY:** Bathing (8km) Horse riding (6km) Fishing (1km) Swimming pool (6km) Tennis (3km) Railway station (20km) Shops (3km) **NOTES:** Pets admitted

PUJOLS-SUR-CIRON

▦ Les Tauzins-Est Bernard COLON
33210 PUJOLS-SUR-CIRON
☎ 05 56 76 60 13
Four rooms are available in this annexe, close to the owner's house. There are private shower rooms and wcs for each bedroom. There are two bedrooms on the ground floor and two bedrooms on the first floor with a communal terrace area. The building is one of a group of buildings, in a small hamlet, near to a village and in the middle of the Sauterne and Grave vineyards. Private parking is provided and canoeing is available 2km away.
PRICES: d €40 **ON SITE:** Fishing **NEARBY:** Bathing (25km) Horse riding (10km) Golf (10km) Swimming pool (10km) Tennis (4km) Railway station (10km) Shops (10km) **NOTES:** No pets

RIMONS

▦ ℞ Le Grand Boucaud Dominique LEVY
33580 RIMONS
☎ 05 56 71 88 57
There are three guest rooms in this very beautiful renovated old house situated in the middle of undulating countryside. There is a twin bedroom with bathroom and wc and a bedroom with three single beds, shower room and wc. There is a double bedroom (with an extra single bed on a mezzanine level) with shower room, wc and private entrance. There is also a large rustic sitting room and a garden.
PRICES: s €44; d €53; t €63; extra person €9; dinner €18-€30 **ON SITE:** Swimming pool **NEARBY:** Bathing (15km) Tennis (10km) Railway station (29km) **NOTES:** No pets

RIONS

▦ Broustaret SCEA GUILLOT DE SUDUIRAUT
Château du Broustaret, 33410 RIONS
☎ 05 56 62 96 97 ▤ 05 56 62 96 97
www.broustaret.fr
This beautiful house with lots of character is situated in the middle of the countryside on a winegrower's estate, where it is possible to visit the wine cellars. There is a lovely view over the coast, lakes and woods and fishing can be enjoyed nearby. On the first floor, there are five large, light rooms for two to three people. Each has a bath or shower room and wc. There is an entry hall and dining

continued   continued

room for guests and a small kitchen with an annexe room on the first floor for meals. Restaurants 6 km. Reduction for longer stays. Open Easter to 1 Nov.
PRICES: d €40-€45; t €50-€55 **ON SITE:** Fishing Stretch of water **NEARBY:** Swimming pool (5km) Tennis (5km) Railway station (8km) Shops (5km) **NOTES:** No pets

RUCH

♦♦♦ Grand Mounicon Bernadette DEKINDT
6 Grand Mounicon, 33350 RUCH
☎ 05 57 40 78 62
St-Emilion 20 km. Abbaye de Blasimon 3 km. Sauveterre de Guyenne 10 km This old 17th century smallholding, has been entirely restored and overlooks the Grand Mounicon valley, with a pretty view over the surrounding countryside. On the ground floor, there is a bedroom with one double bed, one single bed on a mezzanine floor, shower room and wc. The entrance has been created from a (wine) press house. There is also a wc, sitting/dining room and wood burning stove. On the second floor, there is a bedroom with one double bed and twin beds, shower room and wc. The leisure centre and stretch of water at Blasimon are only 3 km away. Open July to September.
PRICES: s €37; d €43; extra person €12 **ON SITE:** Tennis **NEARBY:** Bathing (3km) Horse riding (10km) Swimming pool (10km) **NOTES:** Pets admitted on request.

ST-BRICE

♦♦♦ ○ Chambre d'hôtes Georgette BARDE
Bourg-Sud, Maison Chevalier, 33540 ST BRICE
☎ 05 56 71 65 22
This old restored house, in the heart of the village, has a terrace and shady parkland. On the first floor, there are three bedrooms with private shower room and wc, TV and telephone. On the ground floor, there is a sitting room and dining room with fireplace. There is a private entrance and parking spaces 50 m away. A 10% reduction applies after the third night. The house is situated on the edge of the D671. Open all year.
PRICES: s €28; d €38; extra person €11; dinner €12 **ON SITE:** Tennis **NEARBY:** Bathing (7km) Golf (25km) Fishing (7km) Swimming pool (5km) Railway station (25km) Shops (7km) **NOTES:** No pets

STE-CROIX-DU-MONT

♦♦♦ ♥ Château Lamarque Thierry DARROMAN
33410 STE-CROIX-DU-MONT
☎ 05 56 76 72 78 & 05 56 62 01 21 ▤ 05 56 76 72 10
e-mail: tsdarroman@clubinternet.fr
This 18th-century monastery is in the heart of the Saint-Croix-du-Mont vineyards, with a view over the Garonne valley. On the first floor, there is a suite of two bedrooms (one has a double bed and the other is a children's room with twin beds), with bathroom, wc and TV. Another suite has two bedrooms with a TV. One bedroom has a double bed, the other bedroom has twin beds, a shower room and wc. On the ground floor, there is a dining room and wc. You can visit the vineyard and taste the wine. Parking and shady terrace. 10% reduction after a week's holiday. Open all year.
PRICES: s €35; d €41 **NEARBY:** Bathing (9km) Horse riding (8km) Golf (8km) Fishing (9km) Swimming pool (6km) Tennis (2km) Railway station (8km) Shops (2km) **NOTES:** No pets

For further information on these and other chambres d'hôtes, consult the Gîtes de France website *www.gites-de-france.fr*

STE-GEMME

♦♦♦ Le Gaboria Mieke BORREMAN
Manoir du Gaboria, 33580 STE-GEMME
☎ 05 56 71 99 57 ▤ 05 56 71 99 58
e-mail: manoir@gaboria.com www.gaboria.com
This 18th-century manor house is in the heart of the Entre-Deux-Mers vineyard, and enjoys a lovely view over the vineyards. There is a covered terrace and garden furniture. On the ground floor, there is a hall, kitchen area (with microwave, washing machine and dishwasher), large lounge/ sitting room with open fireplace and TV. There is a double bedroom with a lounge. On the first floor, there is a double bedroom and a suite with one double bed and twin beds. Shower room and wc with each bedroom.
PRICES: d €61-€76; extra person €16 **ON SITE:** Swimming pool Tennis **NEARBY:** Bathing (10km) Golf (20km) Fishing (4km) Railway station (15km) **NOTES:** No pets

ST-EMILION

♦♦♦ Château Millaud Montlabert Claude BRIEUX
Montlabert, 33330 ST-EMILION
☎ 05 57 24 71 85 ▤ 05 57 24 62 78
On the first floor of this typical Gironde, 18th-century family home, there are three two-person attic rooms with bathroom or shower and wc. A further room for three people has a shower room and wc, a TV and a cot. There is another large room for two people with shower room and wc. Dining room with lounge area and fireplace. First-floor sitting room/library with a TV, a kitchen and a dining room. Two bikes are available. A 6% discount applies after six nights. The house lies on a winegrower's estate, 3km from Saint-Fmilion and 1 km from Pommerol. Wine tasting.
PRICES: s €43; d €46-€49; t €61; extra person €15 **NEARBY:** Horse riding (4km) Fishing (4km) Swimming pool (4km) Tennis (3km) Railway station (4km) Shops (4km) **NOTES:** No pets

♦♦♦ La Gomerie Marie-France FAVARD
Château Meylet, 33330 ST-EMILION
☎ 05 57 24 68 85 ▤ 05 57 24 77 35
This completely renovated, 18th century Gironde house is on a winegrower's estate in the heart of the St-Emilion wine region. There are four character bedrooms with antique furnishings. On the first floor, there is one double bedroom with shower and wc and two bedrooms with a double bed and single bed in each (one is on a mezzanine level). On the ground floor, there is a double bedroom (extra bed possible), a bathroom/shower and wc. Private entrance, day room, sitting room, TV and small kitchen. Stays of three nights and over include use of bicycles, a washing machine, tumbler dryer and an ironing room. Outside, there is a country garden, shady terrace and parking area. Open all year. 8% reduction over 7 nights.
PRICES: s €40-€43; d €45-€53; t €60-€66; extra person €15 **NEARBY:** Bathing (12km) Horse riding (12km) Golf (30km) Fishing (3km) Swimming pool (7km) Tennis (2km) Railway station (3km) **NOTES:** Pets admitted English spoken

STE-TERRE

♦♦♦ Chambre d'hôtes France PRAT
Lavagnac, 33350 STE-TERRE
☎ 05 57 47 13 74 & 06 81 62 42 99 ▤ 05 57 47 12 24
e-mail: france.prat@wanadoo.fr
http://perso.wanadoo.fr/france.prat
Saint-Emilion 9 km. Libourne 10 km. Castillon-la-Bataille 7 km.
This 18th century house is typical of the Gironde region, and is near the Dordogne and the vineyards of St-Emilion, Entre-Deux-Mers and Côtes-de-Castillon. On the first floor, there is a suite (double, and twin on a mezzanine with en suite shower and wc) and a suite with a double bed and twin beds, a bathroom/shower

continued

43

AQUITAINE

and wc (not attached). There is a further bedroom with a single bed and a double bed, shower room and wc. On the ground floor, there is a sitting room with open fireplace, TV and dining room. Outside, there is an enclosed park area and shady parking area. The owner is a watercolour artist and offers lessons. Rate for four people: 89/106 euros. Open all year.
PRICES: s €41; d €52; t €86; extra person €17 **ON SITE:** Fishing **NEARBY:** Bathing (2km) Horse riding (1km) Swimming pool (7km) Tennis (1km) Railway station (8km) Shops (1km) **NOTES:** No pets

♦♦♦ Chambre d'hôtes OPSAHL & MUTIKAINEN
18 chemin de Coubestey, Lavagnac, 33350 STE-TERRE
☎ 05 57 47 13 02
email: sverre.opsahl@waika9.com www.ranska.net/lavagnac
This old house has been entirely renovated whilst maintaining its Gironde style. There are two twin bedrooms and one double bedroom, each with shower room and wc. There is also a sitting/dining room with a fireplace, TV and kitchen area. Outside, there is an enclosed garden, terrace and parking area. The property is situated in a small hamlet, on the banks of the Dordogne, in the heart of the vineyards of Côtes-de-Castillon, St-Emilion and Pomerol. Open 15 April to 30 September.
PRICES: s €31; d €39; extra person €13 **NEARBY:** Bathing (3km) Horse riding (10km) Fishing (3km) Swimming pool (3km) Tennis (3km) Railway station (10km) Shops (3km) **NOTES:** Pets admitted English spoken

ST-FERME

♦♦♦ Manoir de James Michel et Nicole DUBOIS
Route de Sainte-Colombe, 33580 ST-FERME
☎ 05 56 61 69 75 📠 05 56 61 89 78

Three large guest rooms with antique furniture, bathrooms and wc at this 18th-century residence, surrounded by trees with wonderful views over the valleys. It is a peaceful haven amidst ramblers' footpaths and lots of places of cultural interest. The first bedroom, for three to four people, is on the ground floor. On the first floor, the second bedroom sleeps two to three people. Sitting room with fireplace, library and board games. Garage and barbecue area outside. Restaurant 5 km. Table tennis, bathing and rambling. Entre Deux-Mers wine can be tasted on the premises. Visits to wine cellars and vineyards can be organised. A discount of 10% on the whole stay applies after the fifth night.
PRICES: s €46; d €55; t €67; extra person €12 **ON SITE:** Wine tasting Swimming pool **NEARBY:** Bathing (5km) Horse riding (5km) Fishing (4km) Stretch of water (5km) Tennis (5km) Railway station (19km) **NOTES:** Pets admitted

ST-GERMAIN-LA-RIVIERE

♦♦♦ Château de l'Escarderie Bénédicte CLAVERIE
33240 ST-GERMAIN-LA-RIVIERE
☎ 05 57 84 46 28 📠 05 57 84 46 28
e-mail: lescarderie@free.fr lescarderie.free.fr
There are four bedrooms with private bathrooms in this small chateau, in the middle of the Fronsadais coastline. On the first

floor, there is one room for two with balcony and private terrace, and a further two two-people bedrooms. Another bedroom is suitable for three to four people (twin beds). On the ground floor, there is a dining room and lounge leading onto a lovely terrace area. The surrounding parkland is undulating and woody. Walking routes can be followed from the chateau.
PRICES: s €43-€46; d €50-€55; t €69-€73; extra person €18 **NEARBY:** Horse riding (5km) Sea (85km) Fishing (3km) Swimming pool (3km) Stretch of water (4km) Tennis (3km) Railway station (10km) Shops (5km) **NOTES:** No pets

ST-JEAN-DE-BLAIGNAC

♦♦♦ ⅩⅠ Château de Courtebotte Michel MORTEYROL
33420 ST-JEAN-DE-BLAIGNAC
☎ 05 57 84 61 61 & 06 83 07 18 25 📠 05 57 84 68 68
e-mail: michel.morteyrol@wanadoo.fr
www.chateaudecourtebotte.com

This chateau was built under the reign of Henri IV and has parkland and a six-hectare forest, on the banks of the Dordogne. On the first floor, there is a double bedroom with a bathroom, wc and terrace with a lovely view and private access. There are two double bedrooms and one twin bedroom, each with either a bathroom or shower room and wc. There is also a two to four person suite with one double bedroom, a bed/lounge room, bathroom/shower and wc. On the ground floor, there is a hall, dining room, lounge with fireplace, TV and meeting room.
PRICES: s €95-€175; d €100-€180; extra person €35; dinner €45 **ON SITE:** Fishing Swimming pool **NEARBY:** Bathing (1km) Horse riding (1km) Golf (20km) Tennis (1km) Railway station (8km) **NOTES:** No pets

ST-MAGNE-DE-CASTILLON

♦♦♦ Château de Lescaneaut
François FAYTOUT-GARAMOND
33350 ST-MAGNE-DE-CASTILLON
☎ 05 57 40 21 08 & 05 57 40 14 91
This very old house dates back to the 12th and 13th centuries and is typical of the Gironde region with all the charm and family furniture of the original property maintained. The private bathrooms are separate from the four bedrooms in order to maintain the authenticity of the house, but can be found opposite the bedrooms. One large bedroom has two four-poster beds, and three further bedrooms each have double four-poster beds. Open April to end October.
PRICES: s €45; d €54-€57; extra person €7 **NEARBY:** Bathing (10km) Horse riding (2km) Swimming pool (1km) Stretch of water (10km) Tennis (2km) **NOTES:** No pets

♦♦♦ Manegat I DE RICHECOUR ECHENTOPF
21 rue de Mansy, Manegat, 33350 ST-MAGNE DE CASTILLON
☎ 05 57 40 00 49 📠 05 57 40 00 49
St-Emilion 12 km. This 18th century stone house is on the edge of the Dordogne, in the middle of a large garden which lies between

continued

continued

a river and vineyards. There are three twin bedrooms, each with bathroom/shower room and wc. A lounge/dining room is also available for guest use. Private parking is available. Open May to October (other periods by reservation).
PRICES: s €68; d €77 **NEARBY:** Bathing (4km) Horse riding (1km) Golf (10km) Sea (90km) Swimming pool (1km) Stretch of water (4km) Tennis (1km) Railway station (1km) Shops (1km) **NOTES:** No pets English spoken

ST-MARIENS

♦♦♦ Château de Gourdet Daniel et Yvonne CHARTIER
33620 ST-MARIENS
☎ 05 57 58 05 37 & 06 14 42 50 10/06 62 75 41 22

This beautiful 18th-century home lies on the Blaye coast, on a small vineyard. There are five bedrooms for two to three people each, all on the first floor, with a shower room and wc in each one. There is also a dining room and lounge. Horses are reared on this property and there are many walking routes from the house. This is a lovely, calm spot with a beautiful view across vineyards and forests. Open all year.
PRICES: s €35-€45; d €40-€50; extra person €15 **ON SITE:** Horse riding **NEARBY:** Bathing (7km) Fishing (4km) Swimming pool (16km) Tennis (4km) Railway station (2km) **NOTES:** No pets

ST-MARTIN-DE-LAYE

♦♦♦ Gaudard Michel et Josette GARRET
33910 ST-MARTIN-DE-LAYE
☎ 05 57 49 41 37
Libournais and Saint-Emilion vineyards 15 km. This old, restored house is in the middle of the countryside, in a peaceful and verdant setting. There is independent access to the three bedrooms, which include two large rooms for two to three people. (Twin beds can be arranged for 5 euros.) There is also another double. Each bedroom has a bath or shower room and wc. One of the bedrooms is in a pavilion near the owner's house. A kitchen is available and there is a discount of 10% for stays longer than three nights (except July and August). There is a terrace outside and a restaurant 5 km away. Wine tasting. Open mid-April to 10 October.
PRICES: s €29-€40; d €35-€46; extra person €14 **NEARBY:** Fishing (1km) Swimming pool (8km) Tennis (8km) Railway station (15km) **NOTES:** No pets

ST-MARTIN-DE-LERM

♦♦♦ ⧉ La Lézardière Marie-Hélène MATTEI
9 Boimier, 33540 ST-MARTIN-DE-LERM
☎ 05 56 71 30 12 ▨ 05 56 71 30 12
e-mail: lalezardiere@free.fr http://lalezardiere.free.fr
These old stables at a 17th-century smallholding have been entirely restored. On the first floor, there are four bedrooms for 2/3 people with shower room or bathroom and wc each. On the ground floor, there is a sitting room, dining room, library, fireplace, cot and high chair. There is also a table-tennis table,

terrace area, large garden and parking area. The stables are situated opposite the fortified windmills of Loubens and Bagas, halfway between St-Emilion and Sauternes. Childrens meals 10 euros. Open 15 March to 1 November.
PRICES: s €43; d €58; t €73; extra person €15; dinner €16
ON SITE: Bathing Fishing Swimming pool **NEARBY:** Horse riding (1km) Golf (18km) Tennis (6km) Railway station (6km) Shops (6km)
NOTES: Pets admitted English spoken

ST-MICHEL-DE-FRONSAC

♦♦♦ ❦ Clos Saint-Michel Marie-Christine AGUERRE
1 Lariveau, 33126 ST-MICHEL-DE-FRONSAC
☎ 05 57 24 95 81
Saint-Emilion 10 km. Pomerol, Fronsac, Libourne nearby. This old 17th-century house is situated on a small wine-producing property (appellation Fronsac). The guest accommodation is attached to the proprietor's house but has independent access. There are two 2/3 person bedrooms on the first floor, each with private bathroom or shower room and wc. On the ground floor, there is a dining room with a lounge and kitchen area and an open fireplace. There is also a terrace, parking area and private garden. Bordeaux is thirty minutes away. Wines from the estate can be tasted and purchased on site. Open all year.
PRICES: s €50; d €52-€62; t €78; extra person €18 **ON SITE:** Wine tasting **NEARBY:** Horse riding (5km) Fishing (2km) Swimming pool (5km) Tennis (2km) Railway station (8km) Shops (2km) Golf (10km)
NOTES: No pets CC

ST-SEVE

♦♦♦♦ ⧉ Domaine de la Charmaie
France CHAVEROU
33190 ST-SEVE
☎ 05 56 61 10 72 ▨ 05 56 61 10 72
This is a 12th-century manor house. On the first floor, there are two two-person bedrooms, each with a shower room and wc. On the ground floor, there is a twin bedroom with a shower room and wc. There is also a sitting room with a fireplace, dining room, TV, billiard room and library. There is a three-hectare park, walking, horse riding and cycling routes nearby. Open all year.
PRICES: s €49; d €55-€69; dinner €21 **ON SITE:** Wine tasting Swimming pool **NEARBY:** Horse riding (4km) Golf (18km) Fishing (4km) Tennis (4km) Railway station (4km) Shops (4km)
NOTES: No pets English spoken

ST-YZANS DE MEDOC

♦♦♦ ⧉ Chambre d'hôtes Mme POGNOT
5 route de Queyzans, Le Moulin,
33340 ST-YZANS DE MEDOC
☎ 05 56 09 02 80 & 05 56 09 02 80
e-mail: medoc.hote@free.fr http://medoc.hote.free.fr
Pauillac 20 km. Soulac 40 km. This old house has an 18th-century tower and lies in a restored park, at the heart of the Medoc vineyards, within a wine producers' property. There is a sitting/dining room with fireplace and TV, and three beautiful double rooms with private shower rooms and wcs. There is a large terrace and parking area. Open all year.
PRICES: s €47; d €52; HB €92; extra person €16; dinner €20
NEARBY: Horse riding (20km) Sea (25km) Swimming pool (12km) Tennis (3km) Railway station (12km) **NOTES:** No pets English spoken

> Prices are given in Euros €1 = £0.62
> at the time of going to press

continued

AQUITAINE

AQUITAINE

ST-YZANS-DE-MEDOC

¶¶¶ Château La Hourqueyre Corinne BATAILLEY
42, rue de la Hourqueyre, 33340 ST-YZANS-DE-MEDOC
☎ 05 56 09 05 10 & 06 72 88 68 14 ≣ 05 56 09 05 53
e-mail: coribat@net-up.com
Route des Châteaux 1 km. Soulac-sur-Mer 36 km. This is an old
19th-century house on a winegrowing estate, between the river
and the sea, in the heart of the Medoc vineyards. On the ground
floor of this property, there is an entrance hall, sitting room, dining
room, TV and fireplace. On the first floor, there are two double
bedrooms and one twin bedroom, each with shower room or
bathroom and wc. There is an enclosed garden, garage and
parking area. A discount for longer stays. Open March to
November. Hiking, wine tasting.
PRICES: s €35; d €43; extra person €15 **NEARBY:** Bathing (25km)
Horse riding (15km) Sea (25km) Fishing (2km) Swimming pool (10km)
Tennis (2km) Railway station (10km) Shops (1km) **NOTES:** Pets
admitted English spoken

VENDAYS MONTALIVET

¶¶¶ Chambre d'hôtes Max BAHOUGNE
La Cadichonne, 18 le Dehes, 33930 VENDAYS MONTALIVET
☎ 05 56 41 70 54
e-mail: max.bayougne@libertysurf.fr
http://perso.libertysurf.fr/lacadichonne
This beautiful 18th-century, Médocaine-style house is situated in
the heart of the countryside, in the middle of a forest area, in a
large country garden. There are three double bedrooms and two
twin bedrooms, shower room, wc and dining room. Open 1 June
to 30 September.
PRICES: d €53-€61; t €76; extra person €16 **ON SITE:** Swimming pool
NEARBY: Bathing (20km) Horse riding (6km) Golf (50km) Sea (10km)
Stretch of water (20km) Tennis (2km) Railway station (12km) Shops
(2km) Fishing (10km) **NOTES:** No pets English spoken

VERTHEUIL

¶¶¶ ○¶ Château Le Souley Jean-Pierre CHIAMA
33180 VERTHEUIL
☎ 05 56 41 98 76 & SR : 05 56 81 54 23 ≣ 05 56 41 94 87
e-mail: jpchiama@club-internet.fr
http://perso.club-internet.fr/jpchiama
This 19th-century house has been restored but maintains its
country atmosphere. Situated in large grounds, there is a terrace
area with garden furniture and climbing vines, in the middle of the
Médoc vineyard. On the first floor, there are two double
bedrooms, a bathroom or shower room and wc. There is also a
suite with one double bedroom and one twin bedroom, a
bathroom and wc. Dining room, sitting room/library, TV and
fireplace. Another bedroom has a double bed, shower room and
wc and is situated on the ground floor. Evening meals available on
reservation. Open all year.
PRICES: s €42-€45; d €49-€56; t €61-€70; extra person €12; dinner €18
ON SITE: Horse riding **NEARBY:** Sea (20km) Fishing (2km) Swimming
pool (10km) Railway station (10km) **NOTES:** No pets English spoken

LANDES

ANGRESSE

¶¶¶ Ty Boni Bernard et Bab BONIFACE
1831 route de Capbreton, 40150 ANGRESSE
☎ 05 58 43 98 75 ≣ 05 58 43 98 75
Lovely shady garden, rolling down towards a pond and private
swimming pool. There are three pretty bedrooms with private
bathrooms, (two of which have further rooms for two people
attached). The kitchen and washing machine. A garden with
outdoor furniture and a barbecue. 20 minutes from Biarritz and

only five from the beaches. Watersports 4km. Mountain bikes are
available. The rate out of season is €40 for two people. After three
nights the rate is €54. Open all year.
PRICES: d €58; extra person €19 **ON SITE:** Fishing Swimming pool
Stretch of water **NEARBY:** Horse riding (4km) Golf (3km) Tennis (2km)
Sailing (4km) Railway station (8km) Shops (3km) **NOTES:** No pets

BIAUDOS

¶¶¶ ○¶ Carrère Philippe et Jacqueline HARGUES
40390 BIAUDOS
☎ 05 59 56 70 56
This restored 17th-century farm lies in wooded parkland. There are
three very comfortable bedrooms on the ground floor, each with a
private bathroom and wc. Meals can be taken on the covered
terrace area. A relaxing and friendly atmosphere guaranteed.
Evening meals are provided, every day except Sunday out of
season The sea is only 20 km away, and the Biarritz Sea Museum
and Saubusse Nature Reserve are nearby. Open all year.
PRICES: s €36; d €41; t €55; dinner €14 **ON SITE:** Sailing
NEARBY: Horse riding (5km) Golf (20km) Fishing (6km) Swimming
pool (18km) Stretch of water (8km) Tennis (6km) Railway station (18km)
Shops (9km) **NOTES:** Pets admitted English spoken

¶¶¶ ○¶ Ferme Hondouan Pierrette DELBES
40390 BIAUDOS
☎ 05 59 56 70 43 ≣ 05 59 56 79 44
Biarritz 10 km. Capbreton 15 km. Pierrette and Lionel welcome
guests to their renovated Basque farm with its large, tree-lined
garden, where a friendly and peaceful atmosphere is assured.
There are three comfortable bedrooms with private bathrooms.
Sitting room with TV and library. Evening meals are available every
evening except Saturday - the house speciality is Basque fish. The
sea is only 15 km away. Open 20 March to 20 October.
PRICES: s €36; d €41; t €57; extra person €16; dinner €14
NEARBY: Golf (22km) Fishing (12km) Swimming pool (14km) Stretch of
water (10km) Tennis (6km) Sailing (15km) Railway station (15km) Shops
(4km) **NOTES:** No pets

BUANES

¶¶¶ ○¶ Matilon Nicolas et Georgette GOUDINE
40320 BUANES
☎ 05 58 51 12 82 ≣ 05 58 51 12 82
e-mail: nicolas.goudine@wanadoo.fr
Guests are guaranteed a restful stay in this country home, a lovely
18th-century house with a beautiful garden and private swimming
pool. Golf and tennis nearby. Ultra-light planes. There are four
double guest rooms with private bathrooms. Thermal baths of
Eugénie-les-Bains are only 5 km away. Evening meals, using local
produce are available. Open all year except 2 January to 14
February. Holiday tax payable.
PRICES: s €32-€43; d €35-€46; extra person €15; dinner €17
ON SITE: Swimming pool **NEARBY:** Canoeing (18km) Horse riding
(9km) Golf (5km) Fishing (9km) Tennis (1km) Railway station (5km)
Shops (4km) **NOTES:** Pets admitted English spoken

CAMPET-ET-LAMOLERE

¶¶¶ ○¶ Lamolere P et Béatrice DE MONREDON
40090 CAMPET-ET-LAMOLERE
☎ 05 58 06 04 98 ≣ 05 58 06 04 98
e-mail: lamolere@aol.com www.lamolere.com
This beautiful house has lots of character, and lies in the middle of
12 hectares of parkland, bordered by a river. There are four pretty
bedrooms. One has a private shower room and wc. Another has a
private shower, washbasin and wc. There is also a two-bedroom
suite, with shared wc and individual shower room which are only
let to guests who know each other. Evening meals between Friday

continued

continued

& Monday, on reservation between June & September. Out of season, evening meals are available every day. Kennel. Open all year.
PRICES: d €34-€44; extra person €15; dinner €15 **ON SITE:** Fishing **NEARBY:** Canoeing (5km) Horse riding (5km) Golf (10km) Swimming pool (5km) Tennis (5km) Railway station (4km) Shops (4km) **NOTES:** English spoken

GOURBERA

♦♦♦ Les Sables Jacky et Nicole AUBERT
40990 GOURBERA
☎ 05 58 91 51 35 📠 05 58 91 65 42
e-mail: mathieu.aubert@wanadoo.fr
Just twenty minutes from the sea, this typical Landes country home, is set in one hectare of parkland. There are three bedrooms - one is a family suite with a private bathroom and shower room. There is one spacious bedroom with twin beds, bath/shower and wc, and a family suite with electric double bed and another room with double bed. These rooms share a shower room and wc. A kitchen area for guest use. Open all year.
PRICES: d €37-€43; extra person €15 **ON SITE:** Swimming pool **NEARBY:** Horse riding (15km) Golf (30km) Fishing (10km) Stretch of water (10km) Tennis (1km) Sailing (30km) Railway station (12km) Shops (8km) **NOTES:** No pets English spoken

LESPERON

♦♦♦ Chambre d'hôtes Gilles et Nicole GONON
162, allée des Bruyères, 40260 LESPERON
☎ 05 58 89 65 54 📠 05 58 89 65 54
There are three bedrooms with private bathrooms in this home situated in a lovely, calm setting on the edge of a pine wood. Breakfasts are served on a large, communal table. 800 m from the village and two minutes from the beach. Open all year.
PRICES: d €45; extra person €15 **NEARBY:** Canoeing (20km) Horse riding (20km) Golf (25km) Fishing (1km) Swimming pool (15km) Stretch of water (20km) Tennis (1km) Sailing (29km) Railway station (15km) Shops (1km) **NOTES:** No pets

LUE

♦♦♦ l'Oustau Guy et Patricia CASSAGNE
quartier Baxentes, 40210 LUE
☎ 05 58 07 11 58 📠 05 58 07 13 99
This beautiful stone house, with lots of character, lies in an oak forest. There are four bedrooms with independent shower rooms and wc. Breakfast can be enjoyed either outside or in the lounge. A private sitting room for guest use. Restaurant 2km away. The sea and water sports 22km. Rooms available between April and October.
PRICES: s €34; d €41; t €49 **NEARBY:** Canoeing (12km) Horse riding (20km) Golf (20km) Fishing (1km) Swimming pool (8km) Tennis (1km) Sailing (15km) Railway station (7km) Shops (7km) **NOTES:** No pets English spoken

MAYLIS

♦♦♦ ♥ Saint-Germain Jeanine et Jean RECURT
40250 MAYLIS
☎ 05 58 97 72 89 📠 05 58 97 95 21
e-mail: chambre_d_hotes@wanadoo.fr
http://perso.wanadoo.fr/chambresdhotes/
L'Abbaye de Maylis. Guests will be provided with a warm welcome from Jeanine and Jean when visiting this beautiful, 17th-century family farm. Three large bedrooms (for two to three people) with old fireplaces and private bathrooms. Cot available. Kitchen and fridge. Outside, there is garden furniture. Open all year.
PRICES: s €34; d €37; t €49 **NEARBY:** Canoeing (14km) Horse riding

(20km) Golf (10km) Fishing (1km) Swimming pool (10km) Stretch of water (6km) Tennis (10km) Sailing (60km) Railway station (35km) Shops (6km) **NOTES:** No pets

MIMBASTE

♦♦♦ ◯ Capcazal de Pachiou
Colette DUFOURCET-ALBERCA, 40350 MIMBASTE
☎ 05 58 55 30 54 📠 05 58 55 30 54
This Cacazalière house, dating back to 1610, still retains the charm and tradition of a 14th generation family house. A charming atmosphere and excellent cuisine. There are four large bedrooms, each with fireplaces and four-poster beds, bathroom and wc. Outside there is a park and a garage. Open all year.
PRICES: s €38-€53; d €43-€56; dinner €17 **NEARBY:** Horse riding (20km) Golf (35km) Fishing (8km) Swimming pool (8km) Stretch of water (8km) Tennis (8km) Sailing (35km) Railway station (8km) Shops (12km) **NOTES:** Pets admitted English spoken

MIMIZAN

♦♦♦ Chambre d'hôtes Marie PLANTIER
38, avenue du Parc d'Hiver, 40200 MIMIZAN
☎ 05 58 09 03 58 & 06 81 60 46 76 📠 05 58 09 01 47
e-mail: simjan@club-internet.fr
This is a large, Art Deco house where Jean Cocteau found his inspiration, with Louis XV, Louis XVI and Empire furniture, set in two hectares of parkland. There are four bedrooms, each with private bathrooms and double or twin beds. Two of the bedrooms make up a family suite. There are large sitting rooms, a library and TV. 5 km from the sea and the white sand beaches at Mimizan. The rooms are available between 15 April and 15 October. Discounts out of season.
PRICES: s €53-€82; d €85-€100; t €81 **ON SITE:** Swimming pool **NEARBY:** Canoeing (5km) Horse riding (5km) Golf (3km) Fishing (3km) Stretch of water (3km) Tennis (4km) Sailing (5km) Railway station (3km) Shops (20km) **NOTES:** No pets

OUSSE-SUZAN

♦♦♦ ◯ Domaine d'Agès Elisabeth HAYE
40110 OUSSE-SUZAN
☎ 05 58 51 82 28 📠 05 58 51 82 29
e-mail: haye.eeb@wanadoo.fr
This old property lies in the heart of the Landaise forest, surrounded by horses, a swimming pool and old trees. There are four double bedrooms in this house, each with individual bathrooms. Two of these make up a suite, which will only be let to people who know each other. Large breakfasts and reserved evening meals are served in a pretty dining room. Open all year.
PRICES: s €32-€38; d €38-€44; dinner €14 **ON SITE:** Horse riding Swimming pool **NEARBY:** Golf (20km) Stretch of water (10km) Tennis (20km) Sailing (50km) Railway station (5km) Shops (5km) Beach (45km) **NOTES:** No pets English spoken

POUILLON

♦♦♦ Saint-Martin Margrit BUSCHE
Château Saint-Martin, 356 rte de Mimbaste, 40350 POUILLON
☎ 05 58 98 30 17 📠 05 58 98 23 95
Biarritz 50 km. Dax 15 km. This charming, restored château that dates back to the 14th century is situated on the outskirts of a village. It is nestled in the middle of five hectares of wooded parkland with old trees. There is a swimming pool, library and TV for guest use. Open all year.
PRICES: d €41-€58; t €64 **ON SITE:** Swimming pool Stretch of water **NEARBY:** Horse riding (45km) Golf (45km) Fishing (1.5km) Lake (1.5km) Tennis (2km) Sailing (65km) Railway station (13km) Shops (1km) **NOTES:** No pets English spoken

continued

AQUITAINE

SABRES

♦♦♦ Le Plaisy Gwenaelle BACON
40630 SABRES
☎ 05 58 07 50 29 🖥 05 58 07 50 29
Gwenaëlle welcomes guests to this manor house, in the middle of a lovely five-hectare park where peace is guaranteed. There are three bedrooms, each with shower room, and wc. There is a sitting room with TV, heating and a swimming pool. Tennis 3km away. Covered swimming pool, barbecue area, garden furniture. Breakfasts can be taken in the owners' dining room or on the terrace. The sea and water sports are 45km away; mountain biking 1km. The rooms are available between May and October.
PRICES: d €42; t €55 **ON SITE:** Fishing Swimming pool Stretch of water **NEARBY:** Canoeing (1km) Horse riding (3km) Golf (3km) Tennis (3km) Sailing (45km) Railway station (18km) Shops (3km) **NOTES:** No pets English spoken

SAINT-JEAN-DE-MARSACQ

♦♦♦ ⏲ Chambre d'hôtes Patricia HOVNANIAN
100 route du Vicot, 40230 SAINT-JEAN-DE-MARSACQ
☎ 05 58 77 78 17 & 06 82 30 10 31
Sea & Beach 18 km. This old Landes farm has been entirely renovated and sits in a small village. There are three pretty bedrooms with private shower rooms. There is also a beautiful veranda for breakfasts and a private sitting room. Open all year.
PRICES: s €37; d €40; t €52; extra person €14; dinner €14
ON SITE: Canoeing Fishing **NEARBY:** Horse riding (1km) Golf (20km) Swimming pool (7km) Stretch of water (10km) Tennis (3km) Sailing (15km) Railway station (7km) **NOTES:** No pets

SAUBUSSE-LES-BAINS

♦♦♦ Bezincam Claude DOURLET
route de l'Adour, 40180 SAUBUSSE-LES-BAINS
☎ 05 58 57 70 27 🖥 05 58 57 70 27
Bezincam Château is a 19th-century dwelling, in a large park on the edges of the Adour. You will be offered a warm and personal welcome, in an exceptional setting of greenery and quiet. There are three, two person bedrooms with spacious, private bathrooms, that have been tastefully decorated. Situated in the heart of large parkland with old trees, Bezincam is a great place to stay for those who are looking for calmness and relaxation. Open all year.
PRICES: d €60 **NEARBY:** Canoeing (25km) Horse riding (5km) Golf (18km) Fishing (1km) Swimming pool (1km) Tennis (1km) Sailing (18km) Railway station (15km) Shops (1km) **NOTES:** No pets English spoken

SAUGNAC ET MURET

♦♦♦ La Maranne Catherine et Pascal LANDAIS
CD 20E, 40410 LE MURET
☎ 05 58 09 61 71 & 06 84 63 05 11 🖥 05 58 09 61 51
e-mail: la-maranne@wanadoo.fr
Catherine and Pascal offer guests a warm welcome to their manor house in 6 hectares of tree-lined park. There are five guest rooms each with a private bathroom and TV. Cots available on request. There is also a private lounge and sitting room. There is also a jacuzzi, sauna and swimming pool for guest use. Parking is provided and there are restaurants nearby. The rooms are available between February and November.
PRICES: s €46; d €54-€61; t €69; extra person €13 **ON SITE:** Swimming pool Tennis **NEARBY:** Canoeing (6km) Horse riding (11km) Golf (35km) Fishing (5km) Stretch of water (5km) Sailing (30km) Railway station (60km) **NOTES:** No pets English spoken

SEIGNOSSE-BOURG

♦♦♦ ⏲ A l'Orée de la Forét Maria et Claude GIRARD
40510 SEIGNOSSE-BOURG
☎ 05 58 49 81 31 🖥 05 58 49 81 31
e-mail: chambres.hotes.seignosse@wanadoo.fr
//site.wanadoo.fr/loreedelaforet
Hossegor 8 km. Calm and relaxation are guaranteed in this house, in the middle of a pine forest. There are five bedrooms for two, three or four people (two are in a suite), each with private bathroom and private access. Summer kitchen available to guests. Garden. Babies are charged at €8; special price out of season. Evening meals on reservation. Open all year.
PRICES: d €60; extra person €23; dinner €20 **ON SITE:** Children's play area Fishing Swimming pool Stretch of water **NEARBY:** Canoeing (3km) Horse riding (1km) Golf (3km) Tennis (1km) Sailing (4km) Railway station (25km) Shops (1km) **NOTES:** No pets

ST-JUSTIN

♦♦♦ Betjean Marie-Claire VILLENAVE
D933, route de Périgueux, 40240 ST-JUSTIN
☎ 05 58 44 88 42 🖥 05 58 44 67 16
In the middle of the Landes forest, at the crossroads of the St-Jacques-de-Compostelle footpaths and bridleways, this establishment is several centuries old but has been tastefully restored, furnished and decorated. There are two two-person bedrooms with bathroom, shower and a children's room. Several inns nearby. Rooms available between February & November
PRICES: s €37-€40; d €40-€43 **NEARBY:** Canoeing (20km) Horse riding (5km) Golf (12km) Fishing (3km) Swimming pool (12km) Stretch of water (2km) Tennis (3km) Sailing (10km) Railway station (25km) Shops (1km) **NOTES:** No pets English spoken

ST-PAUL-LES-DAX

♦♦♦ l'Aiguade Gérard et Christiane THIENOT
route de la Bretonnière, 40990 ST-PAUL-LES-DAX
☎ 05 58 91 37 10 🖥 05 58 91 37 10
e-mail: laiguade@club-internet.fr www.laiguade.com
Dax 5 km. This large contemporary house lies in a beautiful wooded park, a few minutes from Dax. There are three comfortable, light bedrooms on the ground floor, each with a private bathroom, independent access and a terrace that leads out to the park. Kitchen and barbecue for guests' use. Available between April and October. Reduced price for over two days €43-€50.
PRICES: d €46-€53; extra person €15 **ON SITE:** Swimming pool **NEARBY:** Canoeing (17km) Horse riding (7km) Golf (7km) Fishing (4km) Stretch of water (4km) Tennis (3km) Sailing (30km) Railway station (5km) Shops (3km) Sea (25km) **NOTES:** No pets English spoken

TARNOS

♦♦♦ ✿ Chambre d'hôtes André et Hélène LADEUIX
26 rue Salvador Allende, D181, 40220 TARNOS
☎ 05 59 64 13 95 🖥 05 59 64 13 95
www.enaquitaine.com
Biarritz & Hossegor 13 km. This large, tastefully furnished Basque house, has a swimming pool and is surrounded by a quiet wood. Of the five bedrooms, four are in an annexe and have private bathroom and wc. Also a communal guest room and washing machine for guests' use. Leisure activities include mountain biking, swimming, table tennis and barbecues. Pets are accepted out of season. Open all year.
PRICES: s €38; d €46 **ON SITE:** Children's play area Swimming pool **NEARBY:** Horse riding (5km) Golf (13km) Fishing (5km) Stretch of water (5km) Tennis (1km) Sailing (15km) Railway station (5km) Shops (1km) **NOTES:** English spoken

TOSSE

⚜⚜⚜ Le Bosquet J-Pierre et Monique ARNAUDIN
rue du Hazan, route de St-Vincent de Tyrosse, 40230 TOSSE
☎ 05 58 43 03 40 📠 05 58 43 04 68
This beautiful contemporary house is situated on the outskirts of the village 8km from the beach. Set in nearly 5 hectares of wooded land the property has three pretty, double bedrooms, each with a private terrace, shower room and wc. There is garden furniture, table tennis and private parking. There are many footpaths in the village. Open all year.
PRICES: s €36; d €40; extra person €16 **NEARBY:** Horse riding (5km) Golf (5km) Fishing (3km) Swimming pool (8km) Stretch of water (3km) Tennis (1km) Sailing (8km) Railway station (30km) Shops (4km)
NOTES: No pets

LOT-ET-GARONNE

AIGUILLON

⚜⚜⚜ ◯l Le Baraillot Maryvonne MENGUY
47190 AIGUILLON
☎ 05 53 88 29 92 & 06 09 35 65 37 📠 05 53 88 29 92
e-mail: mary@le_baraillot.com www.le_baraillot.com
Old mansion house offering four bedrooms and one suite, all with en suite facilities. The lounge has TV, hi-fi and board games. There is a swimming pool with jacuzzi, table tennis and bicycle hire. Dishwasher and washing-machine available. Watersports, golf, a theme park and an abbey are nearby. Dinner available on request. Open 1 March to 15 November.
PRICES: s €46; d €50-€58; t €73; extra person €15; HB €79-€87; dinner €14 **ON SITE:** Bathing Swimming pool Hiking **NEARBY:** Horse riding (15km) Golf (20km) Fishing (2km) Tennis (4km) Railway station (4km) Shops (3km)

AURADOU

⚜⚜⚜ ◯l Le Roc Rémi et Françoise COMMANDRE
47140 AURADOU
☎ 05 53 49 16 87 & 06 88 27 97 93 📠 05 53 49 16 87
Penne d'Agenais 6 km. Agen 23 km. Francoise and Remi offer a warm and friendly welcome to their 18th-century home. There are two single 3 rooms, one double and one single with shared bathroom and wc, one family room and another double, both with en suite facilities. South-western cooking and local wines. Price based on four sharing: €68.60. Open all year.
PRICES: s €40-€47; d €43-€50; t €58; extra person €9; HB €43-€52; dinner €17 **ON SITE:** Hiking **NEARBY:** Bathing (10km) Horse riding (10km) Golf (10km) Fishing (5km) Swimming pool (5km) Tennis (4km) Railway station (4km) Shops (6km) **NOTES:** Pets admitted

BALEYSSAGUES

⚜⚜⚜ ◯l Mounica Jocelyne PAZZAGLIA
Domaine du Pech, 47120 BALEYSSAGUES
☎ 05 53 83 33 52 & 06 81 39 46 55
House of character set in 1500 hectares of superb gardens. The comfortable rooms have been renovated exposing beams and flagstones. On the ground floor there are two double rooms and one with a double and a single bed, all with own shower and wc, Small private lounge. Also a separate family suite for four with a large lounge, bathroom and private terrace. Mountain bikes, boules, swings, garden walks, tennis, golf, horseriding. Price for suite: €92. Open all year.
PRICES: s €41; d €46; t €67; extra person €14-€17; HB €30-€37; dinner €16 **ON SITE:** Children's play area Swimming pool **NEARBY:** Bathing (8km) Horse riding (3km) Golf (25km) Fishing (1km) Tennis (3km) Railway station (25km) Shops (3km) **NOTES:** No pets Minimum 2 night stay

BAZENS

⚜⚜⚜ La Molinara Françoise ROULLIES
47130 BAZENS
☎ 05 53 66 62 92 & 05 53 69 43 83
Musée des Automates 10 km. Musée de l'automobile 20 km. Restored 17th-century house located in an 11th-century village said to have inspired Shakespeare's 'Romeo and Juliet'. There are two twin rooms sharing wc and shower, and one large double room with bathroom and wc. A communal pool, a park, and also a castle and art gallery on site. Open all year.
PRICES: s €50-€59; d €59-€69 **ON SITE:** Children's play area Swimming pool Hiking **NEARBY:** Bathing (5km) Horse riding (4km) Golf (20km) Fishing (2km) Tennis (27km) Railway station (3km) Shops (3km) **NOTES:** Pets admitted

BUZET-SUR-BAISE

⚜⚜⚜ ◯l Château de Coustet Alain GELIX
47160 BUZET-SUR-BAISE
☎ 05 53 79 26 60 📠 05 53 79 14 16
e-mail: ccoustet@csi.com www.coustet.com
Laid out over three floors this noble 1882 property built in the style of Napoleon III, is in the heart of the Pays d'Albret, rich with country houses and vineyards. On the first floor there are four individually decorated bedrooms and a duplex suite with en suite facilities. Large families can have two large rooms on the same landing with private entrance. Also a gym and shower room, billiards room and rustic kitchen. Open February to December.
PRICES: s €88; d €105; t €120-€151; extra person €23; dinner €24 **ON SITE:** Fishing Swimming pool **NEARBY:** Bathing (4km) Horse riding (10km) Golf (15km) Tennis (4km) Railway station (5km) Shops (1km) **NOTES:** No pets English spoken

CANCON

⚜⚜⚜ Chanteclair Francis LARRIBEAU
47290 CANCON
☎ 05 53 01 63 34 📠 05 53 41 13 44
Villeneuve-sur-Lot 20 km. Bergerac 40 km (airport). Marmande 40 km. A 19th-century house, 500m from the village, with four guest rooms. On the first floor, two twin and one double room. On the second, a suite with one double and three single beds. All rooms have en suite facilities. There is a sitting room with fireplace and a lounge, a small kitchen and barbecue. Guests can picnic in the park or on the verandah. There is a piano, billiards and bikes. Special off-peak rates. Open all year.
PRICES: s €45; d €60; t €74; extra person €14 **ON SITE:** Swimming pool **NEARBY:** Bathing (4km) Canoeing (10km) Horse riding (7km) Golf (7km) Fishing (2km) Hiking (1km) Tennis (1km) Shops (1km) **NOTES:** No pets

CLAIRAC

⚜⚜⚜ ◯l Caussinat Aimé et Gisèle MASSIAS
47320 CLAIRAC
☎ 05 53 84 22 11 📠 05 53 84 22 11
Accommodation comprises one double and one twin room rated grade 3 with washbasins, sharing bathroom and wc. One twin and two double rooms rated grade 1 with en suite facilities. Table tennis. Half board based on two sharing. Open 15 March to 31 October.
PRICES: s €34-€43; d €37-€46; t €54-€63; extra person €17; HB €65-€73; dinner €14 **ON SITE:** Swimming pool Hiking **NEARBY:** Bathing (2km) Canoeing (1km) Horse riding (20km) Golf (15km) Fishing (2km) Tennis (2km) Railway station (7km) Shops (2km) **NOTES:** No pets

AQUITAINE

COURBIAC

††† ♥ ⭑◎⭑ Château de Rodie Paul HECQUET
47370 COURBIAC
☎ 05 53 40 89 24 📠 05 53 40 89 25
e-mail: Chateau.Rodie@wanadoo.fr

Château de Bonaguil 30 km. Cahors 46 km. Château Rodie is a 13th to 16th-century fortified castle restored to become a warm family home, with vast living rooms and five beautiful bedrooms furnished with antiques. There are three double rooms with private bathrooms; in the round tower a suite with bathroom; in the square tower an en suite double room with private living room and access to the watchtowers. The castle is in an area full of historic, natural and sporting interest. Rodie offers many activities and interests including a bird sanctuary and a rare breed of sheep. 10% discount for six days or more. Open all year.
PRICES: d €70-€100; t €84; extra person €16; dinner €18
ON SITE: Children's play area Swimming pool Hiking
NEARBY: Bathing (5km) Horse riding (15km) Fishing (15km) Tennis (1km) Railway station (40km) Shops (5km) **NOTES:** Pets admitted CC English spoken

DONDAS

††† Gourraud Jean et Myriam MARTY
47470 DONDAS
☎ 05 53 95 43 11 📠 05 53 95 43 11
e-mail: marty.myriam@wanadoo.fr
http://perso.wanadoo.fr/gites.aquitaine/
Abbaye Saint-Maurin 5 km. In Pays de Serres, Jean and Myriam warmly welcome guests to their peaceful 16th-century fortress. On the ground floor one large double room with cot, in a delightful alcove there is a suite with a large double and two twin beds, and another room with a double and a single bed. All accommodation is en suite. Open all year.
PRICES: s €45; d €60; t €75 **ON SITE:** Swimming pool **NEARBY:** Horse riding (8km) Golf (15km) Fishing (8km) Tennis (1km) Railway station (20km) Shops (8km) **NOTES:** Pets admitted English spoken

DOUZAINS

††† ♥ ⭑◎⭑ Le Capy Thérèse JACQUOT
47330 DOUZAINS
☎ 05 53 36 83 68 📠 05 53 36 83 68
e-mail: capy47@aol.com
An 18th-century mansion at the gateway to Périgord offers two double rooms with own bath or shower room, one room for three or four people with bathroom and wc - all garde 2. There is a park, terrace, barbecue, picnic facilities, donkey rides and farmyard animals. Dinner is available on request. Open April to October. Other times by reservation.
PRICES: s €30-€33; d €34-€37; t €43-€46; extra person €10; dinner €11
ON SITE: Children's play area **NEARBY:** Bathing (10km) Horse riding (9km) Golf (18km) Fishing (3km) Swimming pool (4km) Hiking (4km) Tennis (4km) Shops (4km) **NOTES:** Pets admitted

DURAS

††† ⭑◎⭑ & Botte Michel CHAUGIER
47120 DURAS
☎ 05 53 83 81 27 📠 05 53 83 81 27
e-mail: michel.chaugier@wanadoo.fr
Situated between the Dordogne and the vineyards of Bordelais, Duras is known for its castle, its wines and its prunes. This old restored house offers three rooms, one double, one double and single, and one with three single beds. There is one bathroom and two shower rooms, stair-lift, library, verandah, TV, and garden with furniture and outdoor games. Gastronomic dinners on request and picnic hampers for €7. Half board rates based on two sharing. Meals for children under one: €7. Open 1 April to 1 November.
PRICES: s €31; d €40; t €48; extra person €11; HB €58; dinner €14-€24
NEARBY: Bathing (4km) Horse riding (4km) Golf (25km) Fishing (1km) Swimming pool (10km) Tennis (4km) Railway station (25km) Shops (4km) **NOTES:** No pets English spoken

††† ⭑◎⭑ Les Barthes Pamela RYAN
47120 DURAS
☎ 05 53 83 62 54 & 06 72 22 85 42 📠 05 53 83 62 54
An old, restored farmhouse in Guyenne, close to the Dordogne and the Bordelais vineyards, serving breakfast (English if desired) and dinner out on the terrace in the summer. On the ground floor there is a room with a double and a single bed, another double room, both with en suite facilities, and a double room up on the next floor with shower and wc. There is a living and dining room available to guests, central heating and bicycle hire. Gardening is the owners' hobby! Open all year.
PRICES: s €46; d €53; t €63; dinner €15 **ON SITE:** Swimming pool
NEARBY: Bathing (6km) Horse riding (5km) Golf (27km) Fishing (1km) Tennis (8km) Railway station (23km) Shops (5km) **NOTES:** No pets English spoken

GAVAUDUN

††† ⭑◎⭑ Domaine de Majoulassie Guy FEVRY
47150 GAVAUDUN
☎ 05 53 40 34 64 📠 05 53 40 34 64

Monflanquin 10 km. Châteaux de Bonaguil and Biron 15 km. On the borders of a fishing lake, 1km from the village, this restored 17th-century windmill, with a pool, is situated in five hectares. There is a family suite and four rooms on the first floor, each with private bathroom, wc and balcony. There is a TV room with fireplace, a terrace and a park. Dinner is available on request and picnics on site. Boules provided, mountain biking and rock climbing only 1km away. Hunting dogs kept on the estate. Price based on four sharing: €84/99. Open all year.
PRICES: d €46-€54; t €61-€69; extra person €16; dinner €19
ON SITE: Fishing Swimming pool **NEARBY:** Bathing (10km) Horse riding (3km) Golf (30km) Tennis (3km) Shops (10km)
NOTES: Pets admitted English spoken

GREZET-CAVAGNAN

♦♦♦ ﴾O﴿ Château de Malvirade
Joël et Françoise CUVILLIER
Grezet Cavagnan, 47250 BOUGLON
☎ 05 53 20 61 31 & 06 11 60 74 59　📠 05 53 89 25 61
www.chateaux.France.com/malvirade
A castle in 23 hectares with two large Louis XV rooms (Mme de
Pompadour and Mme de Maintenon), two large rooms with
canopied beds (Colbert and Sully), and a suite (Charlotte Rose de
Sacriste), all with a bathroom and wc. There is a small TV room,
reading room, golf course, lake and volleyball. Dinner is available
only if booked the night before. Open 15 April to 30 September.
PRICES: s €53; d €72-€83; t €90-€135; extra person €21; dinner €21-€27
ON SITE: Swimming pool **NEARBY:** Bathing (7km) Canoeing (5km)
Horse riding (10km) Golf (7km) Fishing (2km) Tennis (15km) Railway
station (15km) Shops (7km) **NOTES:** Small pets admitted

LE LAUSSOU

♦♦♦♦ ﴾O﴿ Soubeyrac Claude ROCCA
47150 LE LAUSSOU
☎ 05 53 36 51 34　📠 05 53 36 35 20
This 16th-century manor in two hectares of wooded parkland,
offers a peaceful and romantic stay in a picturesque
panoramic setting. There are four rooms, and one suite with
telephone, balneotherapy baths, shower, multi-jet hydro-
massage and separate wc. There is a Louis XV lounge for
reading and relaxing. Central heating, pool with jet streams, a
lake, table tennis and cycling. Dinner is served in the dining
room or in the courtyard. Open all year.
PRICES: s €73; d €104-€119; t €137; dinner €27
ON SITE: Swimming pool **NEARBY:** Bathing (4km) Horse riding
(4km) Golf (18km) Fishing (1km) Tennis (4km) Shops (4km)
NOTES: No pets

LEVIGNAC-DE-GUYENNE

♦♦♦ La Maison de la halle Leif et Fiona PEDERSEN
47120 LEVIGNAC-DE-GUYENNE
☎ 05 53 94 37 61　📠 05 53 94 37 66
e-mail: maison.de.la.halle@wanadoo.fr
www.lamaisondelahalle.com
Duras 6 km. Saint-Emilion 50 km. Bordeaux 80 km. Interior
designers Leif and Fiona warmly welcome guests to their 19th-
century home in this peaceful fortified village. The three rooms
with one double and three single beds have own private
bathrooms, and breakfast is served on the shaded terrace with
panoramic views of the Drept Valley, or in front of the house.
Open all year.
PRICES: d €69-€76 **NEARBY:** Horse riding (3km) Golf (25km) Fishing
(3km) Swimming pool (16km) Tennis (1km) Railway station (20km)
NOTES: No pets English spoken

LISSE

♦♦♦ ﴾O﴿ Lamarque Nicole et Jacques MENTUY
47170 LISSE
☎ 05 53 65 69 25　📠 05 53 65 32 94
*Nérac-Chateau Henri IV 7 km. Gallo-Roman Ruins 15 km. Mezin 7
km.* Near Nerac in the Albret countryside, Jacques and Nicole
kindly welcome guests to their 17th and 18th-century property
bordering woodland. The two hectares offer forest walks, a non-
chlorinated pool, swings, sandpit, barbecue, terrace with garden
furniture and parasols. There are three rooms with three double
beds and bathrooms, exposed beams and TV. Two of the rooms
open onto terraces with views over the Landes de Gascogne. Open
all year.
PRICES: s €46-€50; d €50-€55; extra person €11; dinner €19

ON SITE: Children's play area Swimming pool Hiking
NEARBY: Bathing (5km) Horse riding (7km) Golf (7km) Fishing (1km)
Tennis (7km) Railway station (7km) Shops (7km) **NOTES:** No pets

MONCAUT

♦♦♦ Domaine de Pouzergues Christiane DOUBESKY
47310 MONCAUT
☎ 05 53 97 53 97　📠 05 53 97 15 25

Agen 10 km. This late 18th-century manor house in a peaceful
setting, 10km from the airport, offers two double rooms with
terraces, one suite with double and twin beds all on the first floor,
and another double room in the attic. All rooms have telephone,
bathroom and kitchenette. There is a library, lounge with TV,
conservatory and also a heated pool. Boat trips on the Baise
Canal, walks in three hectares of park with old and rare trees.
Local drinks tasting. Open 10 January to 23 December.
PRICES: s €61; d €67; t €98; extra person €30 **ON SITE:** Swimming pool
Hiking **NEARBY:** Bathing (10km) Canoeing (20km) Horse riding (4km)
Golf (15km) Fishing (10km) Tennis (4km) Railway station (12km) Shops
(4km) **NOTES:** No pets CC

MONTAGNAC-SUR-LEDE

♦♦♦ ﴾O﴿ Binou Geneviève SEFFALS
47150 MONTAGNAC-SUR-LEDE
☎ 05 53 41 65 57 & 06 83 37 10 26　📠 05 53 41 65 57
☎ SR: 05 53 47 80 87
e-mail: binou-seffals@wanadoo.fr
Binou is a pretty house in a peaceful valley, with three beautiful
rooms with own shower and wc, and TV on request. There is a
living room, flower garden, terrace overlooking the pool, private
entrance and parking. Price of longer stays negotiable. Child's
meal: €8. Open 1 April to 31 October.
PRICES: s €44-€49; d €52-€58; t €65-€71; dinner €14
ON SITE: Swimming pool **NEARBY:** Canoeing (10km) Horse riding
(6km) Golf (25km) Fishing (1km) Tennis (6km) Railway station (12km)
Shops (6km) **NOTES:** No pets

AQUITAINE

continued

MOUSTIER

¶¶¶ ⓘⓄⓘ La Croix-Moustier Jean-Claude PALU
La Croix de Moustier, 47800 MOUSTIER
☎ 05 53 20 21 87 📠 05 53 20 26 33
On the D668, near the village with all amenities, the house offers five rooms with en suite facilities, a private pool, swings and dinner is available on request. The owners are farmers and welcome small pets. There are many walks, fishing on the river or lake, and canoeing nearby. Special off-peak rates. Open all year.
PRICES: s €37; d €41; t €53; extra person €11; HB €30; dinner €12
ON SITE: Children's play area Swimming pool **NEARBY:** Bathing (6km) Horse riding (8km) Golf (20km) Fishing (1km) Hiking (1km) Tennis (8km) Railway station (25km) Shops (1km) **NOTES:** Small pets

NERAC

¶¶¶ ⓘⓄⓘ Le Cauze Isabelle POPE
Domaine du Cauze, 47600 NERAC
☎ 05 53 65 54 44 & 06 70 89 09 20 📠 05 53 65 54 44
e-mail: Cauze.Pope@wanadoo.fr

Parc Walibi 20 km. In a peaceful setting with commanding views, this ancient restored farmhouse, in the middle of wooded parkland, has four double rooms each with shower and wc. The property has a private pool, large terrace with a summer house, large living room with billiards, satellite TV, piano, boules, table tennis and parking. Within a 25km radius there are many walks and places of interest. Meals available on request - lunch €15, dinner €18. Reduced prices if staying three days or more, except in July and August. Open March to October, with possible bookings for November to March.
PRICES: s €43; d €51; t €66; HB €56-€81; dinner €15-€18
ON SITE: Swimming pool **NEARBY:** Bathing (15km) Horse riding (15km) Golf (10km) Fishing (15km) Tennis (2km) Railway station (25km) Shops (2km) **NOTES:** No pets CC English spoken

PUJOLS

¶¶¶ Domaine de Mothis Gérard GUILLUCQ
47300 PUJOLS
☎ 05 53 40 99 29 📠 05 53 40 99 29
e-mail: gerard.guillucq@wanadoo.fr www.gites.pujols.free.fr
A hillside mansion with two and a half hectares overlooking the medieval village of Pujols, one of the most beautiful in France, offers three rooms with two double and two twin beds, shower and wc. There is a private terrace, a pool, table tennis, library, ramblers' walks along the Compostelle pathway. Several outbuildings including a bread oven, pigeon house and wash house. Open all year.
PRICES: d €43-€54 **ON SITE:** Fishing Swimming pool
NEARBY: Horse riding (5km) Golf (18km) Tennis (2km) Railway station (28km) Shops (3km) **NOTES:** No pets English spoken

SALLES

¶¶¶ Pech Gris Bob et Aletta HARRISON
47150 SALLES
☎ 05 53 01 47 76 📠 05 53 40 32 06
Bastide de Monflanquin 10 km. Château de Biron (Dordogne) 8 km. A medieval, fortified farmhouse, newly renovated, in six hectares of park and woodland, offering one suite with two rooms each with bathroom and wc, another suite for three adults and one child with lounge and two double rooms. All rooms have TV. Open 1 May to 31 October.
PRICES: d €76; t €114 **ON SITE:** Swimming pool **NEARBY:** Bathing (10km) Horse riding (3km) Golf (15km) Fishing (10km) Tennis (10km) Railway station (10km) Shops (10km) **NOTES:** No pets English spoken

SAMAZAN

¶¶¶ ⓘⓄⓘ Cantet Jean-Bernard DE LA RAITRIE
Château Cantet, 47250 SAMAZAN
☎ 05 53 20 60 60 & 06 09 86 68 77 📠 05 53 89 63 53
Marmande 10 km. Casteljaloux 12 km. 18th-century manor with a big park offering one suite of two rooms with separate shower and wc, one room with bathroom, wc and dressing room. On the ground floor a double with shower and wc. On-site activities include table tennis, croquet, badminton, French billiards and horse boxes available. Meals provided on request, price for under 12: €9. Price for four sharing: €75. Baby charge: €6. Open all year except from 15 December to 12 January.
PRICES: s €49-€55; d €54-€60; extra person €18; dinner €20
ON SITE: Swimming pool Hiking **NEARBY:** Bathing (12km) Canoeing (5km) Horse riding (6km) Golf (12km) Fishing (2km) Tennis (10km) Shops (3km) **NOTES:** No pets English spoken

ST-EUTROPE-DE-BORN

¶¶¶ 🐓 ⓘⓄⓘ La Fournial Colette AUZERAL
47210 ST-EUTROPE-DE-BORN
☎ 05 53 36 40 98 📠 05 53 36 37 36
www.haut-agenais-perigord.com
Guests here are invited to join the family table and discover the flavours of days gone by with Colette as your magical cook, in the quiet of this soft green countryside. There are ground-floor rooms, one with twin beds (le Rosier Blanc), another with a double and a large single bed (le Marronier) and another with the same facilities plus a cot (la Pruneraie). All rooms have a shower and wc. There is a pool, table tennis, a sheltered terrace, woods, meadows, rambling and farm animals. Open all year except the first two weeks of October.
PRICES: s €37; d €44; t €53; extra person €9; HB €75; dinner €16
ON SITE: Swimming pool **NEARBY:** Bathing (7km) Canoeing (25km) Horse riding (7km) Golf (15km) Fishing (3km) Tennis (5km) Railway station (25km) Shops (5km) **NOTES:** Pets admitted

¶¶¶ ⓘⓄⓘ Le Moulin de Labique Hélène BOULET
47210 ST-EUTROPE-DE-BORN
☎ 05 53 01 63 90 📠 05 53 01 73 17
Near the GR636 at the gates of the Dordogne between Villereal and Montflanquin, this is a group of 18th-century buildings with a windmill. There are three rooms and two suites with private bathrooms and wc. Library, lounges, flower garden, ponds, terrace and a lake. South-western food. Open all year.
PRICES: d €82; t €110-€125; dinner €23 **ON SITE:** Horse riding Fishing Swimming pool **NEARBY:** Bathing (15km) Golf (10km) Tennis (1km) Railway station (19km) Shops (6km) Restaurant nearby **NOTES:** Pets admitted

VIANNE

♦♦♦ Remparts de Jourdain Christiane FERRER
47230 VIANNE
☎ 05 53 65 16 57 📠 05 53 97 36 55
e-mail: ferrer@ambassadeur0147.asso.fr
Parc Walibi 20 km Located in the south-western ramparts of an English 13th-century renovated country house with five en suite double rooms. Breakfast is served in room or out on the terrace. There are restaurants in the village and parking nearby. There is a living room with TV, a games room and a secret walled garden with a terrace. Open 1 April to 31 December.
PRICES: s €40; d €46-€49; extra person €15 **ON SITE:** Fishing Tennis **NEARBY:** Bathing (10km) Horse riding (10km) Golf (5km) Swimming pool (5km) Railway station (5km) **NOTES:** No pets

VILLEREAL

♦♦♦♦ ⁱ◎ⁱ Château de Ricard Sylvia DEGUILHEM
47210 VILLEREAL
☎ 05 53 36 61 02 📠 05 53 36 61 65
A beautiful 19th-century home in the heart of Haut Agenais du Perigord. In the castle there are three large double rooms each with bathroom, wc, TV and telephone. In the outbuildings, two suites each with a large double bed, living room, bathroom, wc and TV. Breakfast is served on the terrace, dinner is available on request, there are lounges, a billiards room, library and two dining rooms. Guests walk in the grounds, fish on the river or pond, use the pool and play tennis. Open 1 May to 30 September.
PRICES: s €76-€107; d €91-€122; t €114-€137; extra person €15; dinner €30 **ON SITE:** Fishing Swimming pool Tennis **NEARBY:** Bathing (1km) Canoeing (20km) Horse riding (5km) Golf (15km) Railway station (30km) Shops (1km) **NOTES:** No pets English spoken

PYRÉNÉES-ATLANTIQUES

AAST

♦♦♦ 🐄 ⁱ◎ⁱ Maison Remy Yves & Jacqueline TUGAYE
64460 AAST
☎ 05 62 32 55 04
Lourdes 25 km. Pau 28 km. The dining room has an open fire, and a welcoming table where meals prepared from own farm produce are served. There are three upstairs rooms tastefully decorated, and with exposed beams, opening out onto the pool and a view of the Pyrenees. Open all year.
PRICES: s €30; d €38; t €46; dinner €12 **ON SITE:** Swimming pool **NEARBY:** Horse riding (15km) Golf (25km) Sea (140km) Stretch of water (10km) Cross-country skiing (30km) Downhill skiing (40km) Tennis (5km) Railway station (22km) Shops (4km) MONTANER (9km) **NOTES:** No pets English spoken

ACCOUS

♦♦♦ L'Oustalet Christine BRUNO
Maison l'Oustalet, Rue Baix, 64490 ACCOUS
☎ 05 59 34 74 39 & SR : 05 59 11 20 64
Col du Somport 25 km. Three rooms in an old Bearnese house located in the heart of the Aspe valley. This imposing medieval property has large rooms, varnished parquet floors, and beautiful fireplaces. The owners will guide you on walks and excursions. Friendly atmosphere. Open all year.
PRICES: s €38; d €46-€49; t €61; extra person €11 **NEARBY:** Horse riding (3km) Swimming pool (25km) Sea (100km) Stretch of water (50km) Cross-country skiing (25km) Downhill skiing (25km) Tennis (25km) **NOTES:** No pets CC English spoken

♦♦♦ Maison l'Arrayade Jean-François LESIRE
L'Arrayade, 64490 ACCOUS
☎ 05 59 34 53 65 📠 05 59 34 53 65
e-mail: jean_françois.leisure@worldonline.fr http://elesire.free.fr
Col du Somport 20 km. Large Bearnese house with sheltered garden in a peaceful village in the Aspe valley region. The house has a kitchenette, television room, laundry, garden furniture and barbecue. There are also restaurants nearby and numerous activities in the village, including mountain biking, paragliding and walking. 10% discount for out of summer stays. Open all year.
PRICES: s €27; d €37 **NEARBY:** Horse riding (5km) Golf (60km) Sea (100km) Stretch of water (50km) Swimming pool (25km) Cross-country skiing (25km) Downhill skiing (25km) Tennis (2km) Railway station (1km) Shops (1km) **NOTES:** Pets admitted

AGNOS

♦♦♦ ⁱ◎ⁱ Château d'Agnos
Heather & Desmond NEARS-CROUCH
64400 AGNOS
☎ 05 59 36 12 52 📠 05 59 36 13 69
e-mail: chateaudagnos@wanadoo.fr
Oloron-Ste-Marie 2 km. Old 15th-century hunting lodge nestled within seven hectares of land bordered by a trout river. The owners are of English origin and are willing to share the rich history of their property. There are five rooms, of which two are suites, a terrace and a large park. Two person suite: €99 Four person suite: €130.
PRICES: s €53-€91; d €58-€99; t €73-€120; HB €69-€91; dinner €18 **ON SITE:** Horse riding **NEARBY:** Golf (40km) Sea (100km) Swimming pool (2km) Stretch of water (10km) Cross-country skiing (45km) Downhill skiing (45km) Railway station (4km) Shops (2km) OLORON-OUEST (2km) **NOTES:** No pets English spoken

AICIRITS

♦♦♦ 🐄 ⁱ◎ⁱ Etchekunenia Arnaud ESCONDEUR
64120 AICIRITS
☎ 05 59 65 65 54 📠 05 59 65 65 54
Situated at the gates of Saint-Palais, a charming city of the Pays Basque between the sea and the mountains, are these five rooms on a working farm. There are two double rooms with two double beds and three twin rooms, a large lounge, corner living room and dining room, separate entrance and meals using farm produce available on request. Open all year.
PRICES: s €27; d €37; t €43; dinner €11 **NEARBY:** Horse riding (1km) Golf (30km) Sea (50km) Swimming pool (1km) Stretch of water (15km) Cross-country skiing (40km) Downhill skiing (55km) Tennis (1km) Railway station (20km) Shops (1km) SAINT-PALAIS (1km) **NOTES:** Pets admitted

AINHICE-MONGELOS

♦♦♦ 🐄 Etxartia Chantal PARIS
64220 AINHICE-MONGELOS
☎ 05 59 37 27 08 & 05 59 37 09 71
In a small village not far from the Spanish border, in the beautiful Cize valley, this Basque-style house has five rooms as well as a living room, TV lounge, kitchenette, verandah, and grounds. Open all year.
PRICES: s €29; d €38; t €49 **NEARBY:** Horse riding (10km) Golf (60km) Sea (60km) Swimming pool (10km) Cross-country skiing (16km) Tennis (10km) Railway station (10km) Shops (10km) SAINT-JEAN-PIED-DE-PORT (9km) **NOTES:** Pets admitted

Aǫᴜɪᴛᴀɪɴᴇ

AQUITAINE (side tab)

ARHANSUS

♥ ⭘ Chambre d'hôtes
Véronique ETCHEGOYHEN
Karikaondoa, 64120 ARHANSUS
☎ 05 59 37 85 65
St-Jean-Pied-de-Port 22 km. Large 18th-century Basque farmhouse with one double room on the ground floor, and one twin and one double upstairs. There are also a living room, a TV lounge, sheltered garden and mountain views. Rambling, biking, clay pigeon shooting, and fishing available nearby. Open all year.
PRICES: s €30; d €38; t €50; dinner €14 **NEARBY:** Horse riding (11km) Sea (60km) Swimming pool (11km) Stretch of water (10km) Cross-country skiing (50km) Downhill skiing (50km) Tennis (12km) Railway station (20km) Shops (12km) **NOTES:** Pets admitted

ASCAIN

♥ Chambre d'hôtes Tina VACQUIE
Galardia, Col de St-Ignace, 64310 ASCAIN
☎ 05 59 54 28 37
Biarritz 18 km. Located at the neck of Saint Ignace at the foot of La Rhune, guests will find peace and fresh air on the beaches and walks. Three rooms are available on the ground and first floor of this pretty Basque house, with living room. Terrace. Open all year.
PRICES: s €38; d €43-€46; t €61; extra person €15 **NEARBY:** Horse riding (5km) Golf (9km) Sea (9km) Swimming pool (3km) Stretch of water (10km) Cross-country skiing (85km) Downhill skiing (150km) Tennis (3km) Railway station (10km) Shops (3km) SAINT-JEAN-DE-LUZ (6km) **NOTES:** No pets

♥ Haranederrea Jean-Louis GRACY
64310 ASCAIN
☎ 05 59 54 00 23
Biarritz et Hendaye 15 km. Spain 10 km. This authentic Basque farmhouse is surrounded by meadows and woods, and has a lounge, library, ping-pong, private walled garden, terrace with flowers, and parking. There are four rooms with own bathroom facilities. Four people for 64 euros.
PRICES: s €38; d €47; t €58 **NEARBY:** Horse riding (3km) Golf (5km) Sea (5km) Swimming pool (1km) Stretch of water (10km) Cross-country skiing (85km) Downhill skiing (150km) Tennis (1km) Railway station (5km) Shops (1km) SAINT-JEAN-DE-LUZ (6km) **NOTES:** Pets admitted

♥ Maison Arrayoa A-Marie et Pierre IBARBURU
64310 ASCAIN
☎ 05 59 54 06 18
Biarritz 15 km.. Near the charming village of Ascain, the coast and the Spanish border, is this four bedroom farmhouse with living room, TV room with fireplace, and car shelter. There are one twin and two double rooms with own bathroom facilities on the first floor. Home produced lamb and duck. Open all year.
PRICES: s €34; d €46; t €53 **NEARBY:** Horse riding (6km) Golf (6km) Sea (6km) Swimming pool (1km) Stretch of water (15km) Cross-country skiing (85km) Downhill skiing (150km) Tennis (1km) Railway station (6km) Shops (1km) SAINT-JEAN-DE-LUZ (6km) **NOTES:** Pets admitted

ASSON

♥ Chambre d'hôtes Lucienne SAINT-PAUL
64800 ASSON
☎ 05 59 71 05 05
Pau 20 km. Grottes de Bétharram 10 km. Lucienne and Jean-Philippe will show guests country living on this working farm, alongside goats, sheep, horses and in well-kept surroundings. With separate entrances, rooms are in the outbuildings of this Bearnese 19th-century farmhouse, all of which open out onto a courtyard. Open all year.
PRICES: s €27; d €35; t €43; extra person €8 **NEARBY:** Horse riding

(5km) Golf (25km) Sea (150km) Swimming pool (7km) Stretch of water (1km) Cross-country skiing (28km) Downhill skiing (45km) Tennis (7km) Railway station (7km) Shops (4km) NAY-OUEST **NOTES:** Pets admitted

AYDIUS

⭘ Chambre d'hôtes Christian et Eliane CATON
La Curette, 64490 AYDIUS
☎ 05 59 34 78 18 ▯ 05 59 34 50 42
e-mail: eliane.et.christian@lacurette.com www.lacurette.com
Col du Somport 25 km. This is a beautiful house overhanging the village of Aydius, high enough to give views of the Aspe valley. Rooms include one double and three single rooms. There are also a living room and lounge shared with the owner, garden furniture, central heating and garage. Half price for children under eight. Open all year. No evening meals on Wednesdays.
PRICES: s €30-€35; d €37-€41; extra person €9; dinner €13
NEARBY: Horse riding (6km) Sea (150km) Swimming pool (20km) Stretch of water (20km) Cross-country skiing (25km) Downhill skiing (25km) Tennis (6km) Railway station (20km) Shops (6km) ACCOUS (10km) **NOTES:** No pets

BARDOS

⭘ Minasantey Jacqueline & J-C. ANICET
64520 BARDOS
☎ 05 59 56 83 40 & 05 59 56 81 13
Bayonne 20 km. Six rooms with TV if requested, are available at this Pays-Basque house on the ground and first floors. There are a large living room, library, TV corner, garden terraces, ping-pong, and electric heating. The house is just outside the village. Open all year.
PRICES: s €29; d €34; t €43; extra person €7; dinner €13
NEARBY: Horse riding (12km) Golf (20km) Sea (25km) Swimming pool (4km) Stretch of water (12km) Cross-country skiing (50km) Tennis (4km) Railway station (20km) **NOTES:** Pets admitted

BIDARRAY

♥ ⭘ Gastanchoanea Marie HARAN
64780 BIDARRAY
☎ 05 59 37 70 37
St-Jean-Pied-de-Port 17 km. An imposing 19th-century Basque farmhouse in a quiet corner surrounded by mountains, on the banks of a river. Home cooking, a reading corner, and a pretty garden are all on offer, along with four rooms for two to three people. In the village you'll find rafting, canoeing, mountain biking and rambling. Meal for children under ten €6. Open 1st February to 15th November.
PRICES: s €32; d €37; t €44; extra person €8; dinner €11
NEARBY: Horse riding (5km) Golf (25km) Sea (40km) Swimming pool (17km) Cross-country skiing (40km) Tennis (17km) Railway station (17km) SAINT-ETIENNE-DE-BAIGORRY (17km) **NOTES:** No pets

BOEIL-BEZING

La Lanne de Bezing Pierre et Myriam MINOT
64510 BOEIL-BEZING
☎ 05 59 53 15 31 & SR : 05 59 11 20 64 ▯ 05 59 53 15 21
e-mail: info@bezing.fr www.bezing.fr
Pau 10 km. Lourdes 25 km. This old restored farmhouse is in a park and close to a village with the Gave running alongside. Rooms include an independent annexe with kitchenette, living and games rooms. Myriam the hostess, will help to organize walking and climbing activities. Open all year.
PRICES: s €32-€37; d €35-€40; extra person €8-€13 **NEARBY:** Horse riding (2km) Golf (18km) Swimming pool (6km) Stretch of water (2km) Cross-country skiing (40km) Downhill skiing (40km) Tennis (1km) Railway station (4km) Shops (3km) NAY-EST (6km) **NOTES:** Pets admitted English spoken

continued

BOSDARROS

Maison Trille Christiane BORDES
Chemin de Labau, 64290 BOSDARROS
☎ 05 59 21 79 51 & SR : 05 59 11 20 64   📠 05 59 21 57 54
e-mail: christiane.bordes@libertysurf.fr
Pau 10 km. A beautiful 18th-century Bearnese house with
inside courtyard and spectacular porch. Peaceful location and
interesting architecture. Rooms have their own entrance and
decorated to a high standard. Refined breakfast and dinner.
Open all year.
PRICES: s €50; d €61; dinner €20-€26 **NEARBY:** Horse riding
(18km) Golf (10km) Sea (100km) Swimming pool (10km) Stretch of
water (40km) Cross-country skiing (50km) Downhill skiing (40km)
Tennis (5km) Railway station (10km) Shops (5km) JURANCON
(9km) **NOTES:** No pets English spoken

BUZY

Chambre d'hôtes Rolande AUGAREILS
6 Place Cazenave, 64260 BUZY
☎ 05 59 21 01 01   📠 05 59 21 01 01
e-mail: rolandeaugareils@wanadoo.fr
Oloron-Ste-Marie 10 km. Laruns 15 km. Five rooms in a farmhouse
located in a village near numerous mountain hikes. Own farm
produce served to the table. Half price for children under seven.
PRICES: s €33; d €46-€49; HB €75-€78; dinner €16
NEARBY: Horse riding (15km) Golf (10km) Sea (100km) Swimming
pool (5km) Stretch of water (15km) Cross-country skiing (50km) Downhill
skiing (35km) Tennis (1km) Railway station (1km) Restaurant nearby
NOTES: No pets

CAME

Bergay Annie PECASTAING, 64520 CAME
☎ 05 59 56 02 79
Bidache 5 km. Biarritz 40 km. Four rooms, one double, in a house
by a river. There are also a guest TV room, kitchenette, balcony,
terrace with outside furniture, barbecue, swings, ping-pong and
central heating. Second child under five free.
PRICES: s €50; d €37; t €46; extra person €8 **ON SITE:** Children's play
area Horse riding **NEARBY:** Golf (15km) Sea (40km) Swimming pool
(5km) Stretch of water (10km) Cross-country skiing (60km) Tennis (5km)
Railway station (40km) Shops (5km) BIDACHE (5km) **NOTES:** No pets

Hayet J-Claude et Evelyne SAUBOT
64520 CAME
☎ 05 59 56 04 52
Four rooms are available at this interesting house at the gates of
Bearn, the Pays-Basque and the Landes. Home produce offered in
a lovely farmhouse. There are a library, TV room, garden furniture,
ping-pong, and central heating. Dinner not served on Sunday
night. Open 15th March to 15th November.
PRICES: d €37; t €46; extra person €9; dinner €13 **NEARBY:** Horse
riding (10km) Golf (40km) Sea (40km) Swimming pool (10km) Tennis
(6km) Railway station (9km) Shops (6km) **NOTES:** No pets

Lamothe Bernard et Elisabeth DARRACQ
Ferme Lamothe, 64520 CAME
☎ 05 59 56 02 73   📠 05 59 56 40 02
e-mail: elisabeth.darracq@wanadoo.fr
Bidache 3 km. Biarritz 40 km. At the gates of the Pays-Basque,
Bearn and Landes, the Lamothe family farmhouse offers two
ground floor and two second floor double rooms. Elisabeth and
Bernard serve some delicious meals. Large garden and central
heating. Open all year.
PRICES: s €36; d €39-€42; extra person €13; dinner €14
NEARBY: Horse riding (6km) Golf (17km) Sea (40km) Swimming pool
(3km) Stretch of water (6km) Cross-country skiing (60km) Downhill skiing

(100km) Tennis (3km) Railway station (35km) Shops (3km) BIDACHE
(3km) **NOTES:** No pets

CAMOU-CIHIGUE

Laminiak Jean-Baptiste AGUER
Aguerria, Ch. Laminiak, 64470 CAMOU-CIHIGUE
☎ 05 59 28 58 80 & 05 59 28 50 85
Gorges de Kakouetta & d'Holzarte 25 km. Forêt d'Iraty 30 km.
Jean-Baptiste, Maiana and their three daughters welcome you to
their tastefully renovated old barn, which has four spacious rooms
with shower. There are many paths for walking and cycling, and
don't forget to ask about the imps of the spring! Open all year.
PRICES: s €35-€37; d €40-€41; extra person €8 **NEARBY:** Horse riding
(5km) Golf (70km) Sea (110km) Swimming pool (10km) Stretch of water
(50km) Cross-country skiing (30km) Downhill skiing (50km) Tennis
(10km) Railway station (60km) Shops (6km) TARDETS (6km)
NOTES: No pets English spoken

COSLEDAA

La Noyeraie Eugène LAUTECAZE
64160 COSLEDAA
☎ 05 59 68 02 90   📠 05 59 68 02 90
Pau 25 km. Lourdes 45 km. This recently built villa is at the
entrance to the village and has a lounge with TV, a garden and
furniture, a shaded terrace, central heating and games. There are
two bedrooms on the ground floor and two more upstairs with
private bathrooms. Guests can walk and fish in the restful
surroundings of the Bearnese countryside. Half price for children
under seven. Open all year.
PRICES: d €30; t €38; HB €27; dinner €13 **NEARBY:** Horse riding
(15km) Golf (25km) Sea (130km) Swimming pool (15km) Stretch of
water (18km) Cross-country skiing (45km) Downhill skiing (45km) Tennis
(5km) Railway station (25km) Shops (15km) LEMBEYE (14km)
NOTES: Pets admitted

ESTIALESCQ

Chambre d'hôtes Jeanne PERICOU
Maison Naba, 64290 ESTIALESCQ
☎ 05 59 39 99 11 & SR : 05 59 11 20 64   📠 05 59 36 14 92
e-mail: maisonnaba@aol.com
www.oloron-ste-marie.com/hote/naba
Oloron-Ste-Marie 5 km. Pau 25 km. Beautiful restored 18th-
century Bearnese farmhouse with four rooms and separate
entrance. In a peaceful rural setting, a shady park with flowers
surrounds the property. Near the valleys of Aspe and Osseau, and
the Soule in the Pays-Basque. Open all year.
PRICES: s €27; d €40; extra person €15 **ON SITE:** Horse riding Stretch
of water Tennis **NEARBY:** Golf (25km) Sea (90km) Swimming pool
(6km) Cross-country skiing (50km) Downhill skiing (50km) Railway
station (6km) Shops (6km) LASSEUBE (6km) **NOTES:** Pets admitted
English spoken

ETCHEBAR

Ibarenborde Viviane BLANCHET
Accès par vallée de Lacarry, 64470 ETCHEBAR
☎ 05 59 28 59 48
A traditional farm in the Soule region houses three pretty rooms,
living room, kitchenette and guest terraces. Situated between
Lacarry and Etchebar, the owners breed Merems horses and
packsaddle mules on the farm. Open all year.
PRICES: s €30; d €35; t €43 **NEARBY:** Horse riding (15km) Golf (50km)
Sea (110km) Swimming pool (13km) Stretch of water (40km) Cross-
country skiing (20km) Downhill skiing (30km) Tennis (13km) Railway
station (25km) Shops (8km) TARDETS (8km) **NOTES:** No pets English
spoken

continued

AQUITAINE

FEAS

♦♦♦♦ ┫◯┣ Chambre d'hôtes Christian PARIS
Quartier du Bas, 64570 FEAS
☎ 05 59 39 01 10
Oloron-Ste-Marie 6 km. Three rooms set in an outbuilding of the property edged by a river in a small village in the valley of Baretous. Grounds, garden furniture, private lake, walks, and mountain biking. The groundsman and fishing monitor will teach or improve your fly-fishing skills. Open all year.
PRICES: s €30; d €37; t €46; extra person €8; dinner €12
ON SITE: Tennis **NEARBY:** Horse riding (6km) Golf (6km) Sea (100km) Swimming pool (6km) Cross-country skiing (20km) Downhill skiing (20km) Railway station (6km) Shops (6km) ARAMITS (6km)
NOTES: Pets admitted

♦♦♦♦ Château de Boues Monique DORNON
Château de Boues, 64570 FEAS
☎ 05 59 39 95 49
Pau 40 km. At the gates of Baretous, not far from the valleys of Aspe and Osseau, this 18th-century castle offers a pleasurable stay at the edge of Bearn and the Pays-Basque. There are four rooms with own entrance, a pool and a beautiful terrace with great views over the countryside. Good location for rambling.
PRICES: s €46; d €56 **ON SITE:** Swimming pool **NEARBY:** Horse riding (15km) Golf (40km) Sea (100km) Stretch of water (20km) Cross-country skiing (40km) Downhill skiing (40km) Tennis (6km) Railway station (6km) Shops (6km) **NOTES:** No pets English spoken

GABAT

♦♦♦♦ ❤ ┫◯┣ Etxebestia Odette SOUVESTE
64120 GABAT
☎ 05 59 65 78 16
St-Jean-Pied-de-Port 20 km. Odette and Jean-Marie offer three rooms in their home in the interior of the Pays-Basque. Meals are mainly made from farm produce. Open all year.
PRICES: s €27; d €35; dinner €12 **NEARBY:** Horse riding (5km) Golf (20km) Sea (60km) Swimming pool (5km) Stretch of water (40km) Cross-country skiing (40km) Downhill skiing (60km) Tennis (5km) Railway station (20km) Shops (5km) SAINT-PALAIS (5km) **NOTES:** Pets admitted

GUICHE

♦♦♦♦ ❤ ┫◯┣ Chambre d'hôtes Jean-Marie LAPLACE
Maison Huntagnères, 64520 GUICHE
☎ 05 59 56 87 48 & 06 80 70 64 90
e-mail: contact@hount.com www.hount.com
Bayonne 30 km. Spain 45 km. This 17th-century farmhouse offers a room with its own entrance on the ground floor. The house is surrounded by lovely countryside and a pretty river flows nearby. Ideal for fishing or just relaxing on the bank. Nicole and Jean-Marie offer home cooking and a great sense of humour. Open all year.
PRICES: d €40-€46; extra person €11; dinner €13 **NEARBY:** Horse riding (2km) Golf (35km) Sea (35km) Swimming pool (5km) Stretch of water (2km) Cross-country skiing (65km) Downhill skiing (95km) Tennis (1km) Railway station (12km) Shops (1km) BIDACHE (5km)
NOTES: No pets English spoken

HASPARREN

♦♦♦♦ ❤ Haramburua Clara BONNAL
64240 HASPARREN
☎ 05 59 29 14 30 & SR : 05 59 11 20 64
e-mail: haramburua@wanadoo.fr
Cambo-les-Bains (thermes) 10 km. Biarritz 30 km. Bayonne 25 km. Basque farmhouse dated 1886 offering four rooms, two of

which are suitable for families, on the first floor. After breakfast facing the Rhune between the sea and the mountain, guests may take a walk, making the most of the green pastures of the Pays-Basque. Open all year. €76 for four people.
PRICES: s €46-€53; d €46-€53; t €64 **NEARBY:** Horse riding (12km) Golf (35km) Sea (35km) Swimming pool (2km) Stretch of water (20km) Tennis (2km) Railway station (10km) Shops (2km) HASPARREN (2km)
NOTES: No pets CC English spoken

HAUT-DE-BOSDARROS

♦♦♦♦ ┫◯┣ Loutares Béatrice DE MONTEVERDE-PUCHEU
Ferme Loutares, 64800 HAUT-DE-BOSDARROS
☎ 05 59 71 20 60 ▤ 05 59 71 26 67

Pau airport 20 km. Gan 9 km. Bearnese 18th-century Loutares house with six rooms in a park which has terraces with panoramic views over the Pyrenees. The charming interior has large rooms with fireplaces, billiards, and TV room, while outside are a pool, ponies, and a filled quarry.
PRICES: s €38; d €49; t €59; extra person €11; dinner €14-€15
ON SITE: Swimming pool **NEARBY:** Horse riding (10km) Golf (20km) Sea (100km) Stretch of water (30km) Cross-country skiing (40km) Downhill skiing (40km) Tennis (5km) Railway station (10km) Shops (7km)
NOTES: Pets admitted

IRISSARRY

♦♦♦♦ ❤ Chambre d'hôtes Pierre ETCHEBEHERE
Herriesta, 64780 IRISSARRY
☎ 05 59 37 67 22
St-Jean-Pied-de-Port 18 km. If you are searching a relaxing holiday, this 16th-century farmhouse is ideal. Three rooms on the ground floor with own entrance and a chance to share in Pierre's passion for agriculture and breeding animals. The village is crossed by the Chemins of St Jacques de Compostelle. Open all year.
PRICES: s €27; d €37; extra person €9 **NEARBY:** Horse riding (1km) Sea (48km) Swimming pool (18km) Stretch of water (3km) Cross-country skiing (40km) Tennis (1km) Railway station (18km) Shops (1km) IHOLDY (6km) **NOTES:** No pets English spoken

ISESTE

♦♦♦♦ Chambre d'hôtes Liliane et Jean ASNAR
4 av. Georges Messier, 64260 ISESTE
☎ 05 59 05 71 51 ▤ 05 59 05 71 51
Gourette (ski resort) & Petit Train d'Artouste 20 km. Three double rooms on the ground floor of a large old manor house in the valley of Osseau. Liliane and Jean are friendly hosts who offer an ample breakfast. An ideal location for those who like to relax under the trees. Open all year.
PRICES: s €35; d €38; extra person €12 **ON SITE:** Stretch of water **NEARBY:** Horse riding (2km) Golf (25km) Sea (120km) Swimming pool (2km) Cross-country skiing (20km) Downhill skiing (20km) Tennis (2km) Railway station (2km) ARUDY (1km) **NOTES:** No pets

continued

ISPOURE

♥ Chambre d'hôtes M. et Mme MOURGUY
Ferme Etxeberria, 64220 ISPOURE
☎ 05 59 37 06 23
Near the village, this beautiful house has a lovely terrace where large breakfasts are served. There are four rooms with mezzanine and separate entrance. The breathtaking view of the Irouleguy vineyard will enhance the taste of this famous Basque wine, and the owners will no doubt introduce you to their mules! Open all year.
PRICES: d €39; extra person €13 **NEARBY:** Horse riding (10km) Golf (40km) Sea (50km) Swimming pool (1km) Stretch of water (4km) Cross-country skiing (30km) Tennis (1km) Railway station (1km) Shops (1km) SAINT-JEAN-PIED-DE-PORT (1km) **NOTES:** No pets English spoken

ISSOR

♥ ❍ Chambre d'hôtes Françoise CAZAURANG
Micalet, 64570 ISSOR
☎ 05 59 34 43 96 & SR : 05 59 11 20 64 🖹 05 59 34 49 56
Oloron-Ste-Marie 20 km. Four upstairs rooms in a Bearnese converted grange, with two lounges, TV, open fire, two terraces with furniture and fantastic panoramic views of the surrounding mountains. Plenty of outdoor and mountain leisure activities are available. On site boar raising farm. Open all year.
PRICES: s €38; d €43-€52; t €56-€65; extra person €13; HB €35; dinner €14 **NEARBY:** Horse riding (11km) Golf (80km) Sea (80km) Swimming pool (10km) Stretch of water (20km) Cross-country skiing (25km) Downhill skiing (27km) Tennis (10km) Railway station (14km) Shops (5km) **NOTES:** No pets

ISTURITZ

❍ Urruti Zaharria Isabelle AIROLDI
64240 ISTURITZ
☎ 05 59 29 45 98 🖹 05 59 29 14 53
e-mail: urruti.zaharia@wanadoo.fr www.urruti-zaharria.fr
Expect a warm welcome at this spacious 11th-century house. There is one bedroom and suite with large double beds upstairs. Oak beams, living room, library and games room, fireplace and terrace where Isabelle will tell local legends of the valley. With the help of her daughter Charlotte and local produce, Isabelle will cook some tasty regional dishes. Open all year.
PRICES: s €40-€46; d €43-€49; t €52-€61; Suite €61-€79; dinner €13-€17 **NEARBY:** Horse riding (15km) Golf (45km) Sea (45km) Swimming pool (10km) Stretch of water (50km) Cross-country skiing (50km) Downhill skiing (100km) Tennis (10km) Railway station (35km) Shops (10km) LA-BASTIDE-CLAIRENCE (10km) **NOTES:** Pets admitted English spoken

ITXASSOU

Soubeleta Marie-Françoise REGERAT
64250 ITXASSOU
☎ 05 59 29 78 64 & 05 59 29 22 34
In this charming village Marie-Françoise welcomes you to her little 17th-century castle surrounded by greenery and cherry trees. Five rooms with breathtaking views over the mountains, a kitchenette, living rooms, antiques and open fire. Open all year.
PRICES: s €35; d €43-€49; extra person €8 **NEARBY:** Horse riding (4km) Golf (15km) Sea (30km) Swimming pool (3km) Stretch of water (15km) Cross-country skiing (60km) Tennis (3km) Railway station (3km) CAMBO-LES-BAINS (3km) **NOTES:** No pets

❍
Places with this symbol serve table d'hôtes evening meals - remember to book in advance

LA BASTIDE-CLAIRENCE

❍ Chambre d'hôtes Gilbert et Valérie FOIX
Rue Notre-Dame, 64240 LA BASTIDE-CLAIRENCE
☎ 05 59 29 18 27 & 06 19 21 21 24 🖹 05 59 29 14 97
e-mail: valérie.et.gilbert.foix@wanadoo.fr.
http://perso.wanadoo.fr/maison.marchand
Biarritz 25 km. A 16th-century house in a listed village integrating the Basque and Gascon cultures, with five rooms all differently decorated (two of which are mezzanine). The friendly hosts offer good food and plenty of advice on how to discover the Pays-Basque and its culture. Evening meals three nights a week. Children's meal €9. Open all year.
PRICES: s €41-€52; d €46-€56; extra person €15; dinner €14-€20 **NEARBY:** Horse riding (6km) Golf (20km) Sea (30km) Swimming pool (1km) Stretch of water (15km) Cross-country skiing (70km) Downhill skiing (100km) Tennis (1km) Railway station (27km) **NOTES:** Pets admitted English spoken

❍ Chambre d'hôtes Sylvianne DARRITCHON
Maison la Croisade, 64240 LA BASTIDE-CLAIRENCE
☎ 05 59 29 68 22 & SR : 05 59 11 20 64 🖹 05 59 29 62 99
Biarritz 25 km. An old coaching inn of St Jacques de Compostelle, this 17th-century building offers breakfast in its magnificent garden. The four guest rooms are upstairs. Guests will enjoy the peace and charm of this family home with its antique furniture, old flagstones, and vast fireplace. The lady of the house offers regional Basque cooking. Meals on request. Open all year.
PRICES: s €43; d €50; t €63; extra person €12; dinner €18 **NEARBY:** Horse riding (8km) Golf (25km) Sea (25km) Swimming pool (4km) Stretch of water (25km) Cross-country skiing (80km) Downhill skiing (80km) Tennis (4km) Railway station (25km) Shops (4km) LA-BASTIDE-CLAIRENCE (4km) **NOTES:** Pets admitted English spoken

❍ Le Clos Gaxen Nathalie ZELLER
64240 LA BASTIDE-CLAIRENCE
☎ 05 59 29 16 44 & SR : 05 59 11 20 64 🖹 05 59 29 16 44
Biarritz 25 km. Nathalie and Christophe welcome you to their 18th-century Basque house where meals are offered at the family table two nights a week. Three rooms are available. The tranquil little valley is very close to a 14th-century listed village. Open all year.
PRICES: s €48; d €50; extra person €15; dinner €15 **NEARBY:** Horse riding (8km) Golf (25km) Sea (25km) Swimming pool (3km) Stretch of water (25km) Cross-country skiing (70km) Downhill skiing (120km) Tennis (3km) Railway station (25km) Shops (2km) LA-BASTIDE-CLAIRENCE (2km) **NOTES:** Pets admitted English spoken

❍ Maison Sainbois Colette HARAMBOURE
64240 LA BASTIDE-CLAIRENCE
☎ 05 59 29 54 20 🖹 05 59 29 55 42
e-mail: sainbois@aol.com www.sainbois.fr
Biarritz 25 km. Near the coast in one of the most beautiful villages in France, is this 17th-century house which offers en suite accommodation for up to twelve people in four bedrooms and one suite. Meals available on request. Open all year.
PRICES: d €69-€90; dinner €23 **ON SITE:** Swimming pool **NEARBY:** Horse riding (6km) Golf (20km) Sea (30km) Stretch of water (15km) Cross-country skiing (70km) Downhill skiing (120km) Tennis (1km) Railway station (27km) **NOTES:** No pets English spoken

LAROIN

Maison Miragou Anne-Marie MARQUE
Chemin de Halet, 64110 LAROIN
☎ 05 59 83 01 19 & SR : 05 59 11 20 64 🖹 05 59 83 01 19
e-mail: miragou@wanadoo.fr
Pau 7 km. Jurançon vineyard nearby . In this small Bearnese village, hidden between the Gave de Pau and the hills of Jurançon,

continued

Anne-Marie will greet you on her old renovated farm in the middle of a wooded garden. There are four rooms with own entrance, private lounge, library, and kitchenette. Also there are games and mountain bikes, and you will be able to taste the famous Jurançon. Open all year.
PRICES: s €31; d €39; t €49; extra person €8 **ON SITE:** Horse riding Stretch of water Tennis **NEARBY:** Golf (1km) Sea (100km) Swimming pool (4km) Cross-country skiing (40km) Downhill skiing (40km) Railway station (7km) JURANCON (4km) **NOTES:** No pets English spoken

LARRAU

Chambre d'hôtes Marcel ACCOCEBERRY
Etxandi, 64560 LARRAU
☎ 05 59 28 60 35
Mauléon 30 km. 17th-century renovated property with three converted rooms, in the heart of a pretty village at the foot of the Orhi peak and the forest of Iraty. Living room with fireplace and TV, heating, garden and terrace. Several walks and hikes round the gorges of Holzarte and Kakueta. Open all year.
PRICES: s €37; d €41; t €46 **NEARBY:** Horse riding (12km) Golf (90km) Sea (90km) Swimming pool (30km) Stretch of water (12km) Cross-country skiing (12km) Downhill skiing (30km) Tennis (12km) Railway station (30km) TARDETS (18km) **NOTES:** No pets

LARUNS

Chambre d'hôtes Anne-Marie CAPDEVIELLE
Quartier Getre, 64440 LARUNS
☎ 05 59 05 46 57 📠 05 59 05 46 57
e-mail: anne_marie.ambielle@wanadoo.fr

Gourette 10 km. Situated in a village in the valley of Osseau, a house with five rooms, overlooking Laruns. Two double rooms on the ground floor and one upstairs, and two family rooms with double and twin beds annexed with own terrace. There is a guest lounge, living room, library, terrace with views, gym and sauna. Walks through the whole of the Pyrenees National Park. Open all year.
PRICES: s €34; d €40; extra person €15; dinner €15 **ON SITE:** Horse riding Swimming pool Tennis **NEARBY:** Golf (50km) Sea (140km) Stretch of water (10km) Cross-country skiing (10km) Downhill skiing (10km) Railway station (40km) Train d'Artouste (10km) **NOTES:** No pets

LASSEUBE

Ferme Dague J-Pierre et Mélina MAUMUS
La Ferme Dague, Chem. Croix de Dague, 64290 LASSEUBE
☎ 05 59 04 27 11 & SR : 05 59 11 20 64 📠 05 59 04 27 11
Pau 18 km. Cave de Jurançon 10 km. Four rooms and one suite are available in the outbuildings of this lovely 18th-century Bearnese farm with its traditional square courtyard. Exceptional views of the Pyrenees can be seen. The farm is on ten hectares of land and is a suitable stop for riders and horses. Babies up to two are free. Open all year.
PRICES: s €40; d €46; extra person €12; suite €76 **ON SITE:** Tennis

NEARBY: Horse riding (10km) Golf (8km) Sea (80km) Swimming pool (6km) Stretch of water (6km) Cross-country skiing (30km) Downhill skiing (45km) Railway station (11km) Shops (1km) LASSEUBE (1km) **NOTES:** Pets admitted English spoken

Maison Rances Amy Isabelle BROWNE
Quartier Rey, 64290 LASSEUBE
☎ 05 59 04 26 37 & SR : 05 59 11 20 64
e-mail: missbrowne@wanadoo.fr
Pau 25 km. Oloron 15 km. This beautiful Bearnese farm from the 18th-century has an inside courtyard and pool. Through a separate entrance there is one room on the ground floor and four upstairs with splendid views over the Pyrenees. Guests can relax under the shade of the walnut tree or in the blossoming bower of the garden. Open all year.
PRICES: s €39; d €48-€60; t €60-€71; dinner €20
ON SITE: Swimming pool **NEARBY:** Horse riding (8km) Golf (10km) Sea (100km) Stretch of water (6km) Cross-country skiing (30km) Downhill skiing (45km) Tennis (2km) Railway station (12km) Shops (2km) LASSEUBE (2km) **NOTES:** No pets English spoken

LAY-LAMIDOU

La Grange de Georges
Georges LABERDESQUE
64190 LAY-LAMIDOU
☎ 05 59 66 50 45 & SR : 05 59 11 20 64 📠 05 59 66 24 11
e-mail: lagrangedegeorges@wanadoo.fr
Oloron-Ste-Marie 15 km. Georges and Babeth welcome you to their recently restored grange at the heart of a small village in the valley of Gave d'Oloron. Guests will enjoy the friendly atmosphere and the table full of home-grown foie gras, duck, lamb and vegetables. On site you can horse ride and cycle. There are also ping-pong, piano, games, a portico and a large terrace. Open all year.
PRICES: s €29; d €37; extra person €8; dinner €13 **ON SITE:** Children's play area Horse riding **NEARBY:** Golf (15km) Sea (80km) Swimming pool (4km) Stretch of water (20km) Cross-country skiing (50km) Downhill skiing (50km) Tennis (4km) Railway station (20km) Shops (5km) NAVARRENX (4km) **NOTES:** Pets admitted

LECUMBERRY

Chambre d'hôtes Jean-Pierre JACQUES
Ur-Aldea, 64220 LECUMBERRY
☎ 05 59 37 24 18 & SR : 05 59 11 20 64 📠 05 59 37 24 42
e-mail: contact@augredesvents.com
www.gredesvents@wanadoo.fr
Maite and Jean-Pierre will greet you in their old restored property edged by a river at the foot of the forest of Iraty. They will cook you up some south-western specialties, and if you have time you could fly over the Basse Navarre in a hot air balloon. Open all year.
PRICES: d €45-€54; extra person €9; dinner €19 **NEARBY:** Horse riding (20km) Golf (50km) Sea (50km) Swimming pool (7km) Stretch of water (20km) Cross-country skiing (20km) Downhill skiing (70km) Tennis (7km) Railway station (7km) Shops (7km) SAINT-JEAN-PIED-DE-PORT (7km) **NOTES:** No pets English spoken

LOUHOSSOA

Chambre d'hôtes Krystel & Philippe MALLOR
Domaine Silencenia, 64250 LOUHOSSOA
☎ 05 59 93 35 60 & SR : 05 59 11 20 64 📠 05 59 93 35 60
e-mail: mallor.krystel@wanadoo.fr
http://perso.wanadoo.fr/silencenia
Biarritz & St-Jean-Pied-de-Port 25 km. Dating from 1881, this charming mansion is surrounded by three hectares of parkland with a small lake at the foot of the Basque mountains. Guests can

continued   continued

make use of the sauna, private pool, and rowing machine, or visit the cellar. Open all year.

PRICES: s €55; d €60; extra person €15; dinner €20 **NEARBY:** Horse riding (6km) Golf (10km) Sea (25km) Swimming pool (6km) Stretch of water (15km) Cross-country skiing (60km) Downhill skiing (150km) Tennis (3km) Railway station (8km) Shops (6km) ESPELETTE (6km) **NOTES:** No pets English spoken

LUCQ-DE-BEARN

♥ ⑴ Chambre d'hôtes Marie LAVIE
Quartier Auronce, 64360 LUCQ-DE-BEARN
☎ 05 59 39 18 39 & SR : 05 59 11 20 64 🖹 05 59 36 06 48
Oloron-Ste-Marie 5 km. Pau 40 km. Marie and her family welcome you to their pretty Bearnese farm at the junction of the valleys of Aspe, Osseau and Baretous. You can join in with vegetable picking in the garden and make the most of the cooking expertise of the lady of the house, who will serve up house chicken and fruit charlottes. Open all year. €53 for four people.
PRICES: s €30; d €37; t €46; dinner €13 **NEARBY:** Horse riding (5km) Golf (40km) Sea (100km) Swimming pool (5km) Stretch of water (4km) Cross-country skiing (60km) Downhill skiing (60km) Tennis (5km) Railway station (5km) Shops (5km) MONEIN (14km) **NOTES:** Pets admitted

MONEIN

♥ ⑴ Chambre d'hôtes Marie-José NOUSTY
Maison Canterou, Quartier Laquidée, 64360 MONEIN
☎ 05 59 21 41 38 & SR : 05 59 11 20 64 🖹 05 59 21 28 96

Pau and Oloron-Ste-Marie 20 km. Daniel and Marie-Jo offer a friendly welcome to their lovely Bearnese farm with enclosed courtyard along the wine routes of Jurancon. There are five bedrooms that are both comfortable and peaceful. Daniel will gladly show you his vines, while Marie-Jo will lay the table out on the terrace. Open all year.
PRICES: s €34-€41; d €43-€51; t €53-€61; dinner €15 **NEARBY:** Horse riding (5km) Golf (15km) Sea (80km) Swimming pool (3km) Stretch of water (15km) Cross-country skiing (60km) Downhill skiing (60km) Tennis (3km) Railway station (15km) Shops (5km) **NOTES:** Pets admitted English spoken

MONSEGUR

⑴ Maison Cap Blanc Francine MAUMY
64460 MONSEGUR
☎ 05 59 81 54 52 & SR : 05 59 11 20 64 🖹 05 59 81 54 52
e-mail: Maumy.Francine@wanadoo.fr
Château de Montaner 7 km. Madiran Vineyards 20 km. Monségur is near the Madiran and Gers vineyards, twenty minutes from the venue of the Marciac Jazz Festival. The rooms are in a separate house and guests may use the lounge with library, TV, shaded garden with pool and private terrace. There are also fishing trips out on the lake. Open all year.
PRICES: s €45; d €50; t €55; extra person €15; dinner €18
ON SITE: Swimming pool Tennis **NEARBY:** Horse riding (1km) Golf (20km) Sea (140km) Stretch of water (7km) Cross-country skiing (70km) Downhill skiing (70km) Railway station (18km) Shops (1km) MONTANER (7km) **NOTES:** No pets English spoken

MONTORY

⑴ Sallenave J-Pierre & Jeanine RUATA
Maison Sallenave, Route de Haux, 64470 MONTORY
☎ 05 59 28 59 69
Gorges de Kakuetta 15 km. On the edge of Bearn, three rooms in an old farmhouse two and a half kilometres from the village. Expect a warm welcome, and traditional cooking using local produce. A good location near some exquisite sights, Kakueta, Holzarte, Arbailles forest, Arguibelle rock and rambling paths. Open all year.
PRICES: s €34; d €38; t €50; HB €30; dinner €13 **NEARBY:** Horse riding (5km) Golf (70km) Sea (90km) Swimming pool (10km) Stretch of water (50km) Cross-country skiing (25km) Downhill skiing (35km) Tennis (10km) Railway station (25km) Shops (6km) TARDETS (6km) **NOTES:** Pets admitted

MORLANNE

⑴ Manoir d'Argeles Rose-Marie JEHLE-LECONTE
64370 MORLANNE
☎ 05 59 81 44 07 & 05 59 81 42 47 🖹 05 59 81 42 47
e-mail: manoirdargeles@aol.com
www.manoir-d-argeles.bellerose.com

Château de Morlanne 500 m. Pau 23 km. A 17th-century mansion at the edge of one of the loveliest villages of Bearn, this is a peaceful place with panoramic views. Contemporary paintings and sculpture fill the rooms, and guests have use of a pool, living room with fireplace and grand piano, ping-pong and bowling green. Imaginative menu. Children under seven €8. Open all year.
PRICES: s €37-€46; d €43-€52; t €67; extra person €16; dinner €16
ON SITE: Swimming pool **NEARBY:** Horse riding (23km) Golf (30km) Sea (80km) Stretch of water (23km) Cross-country skiing (80km) Downhill skiing (80km) Tennis (10km) Railway station (23km) Shops (10km) ARZACQ (12km) **NOTES:** No pets English spoken

OSSES

♦♦♦ ❧ ⦿ Maison Gaztenania Pierrette JAUNARENA
64780 OSSES
☎ 05 59 37 78 21
A lovely converted Basque barn, with well-decorated, comfortable rooms. Farmers Pierrette and Jean-Paul will show you the cheese making process from sheep's milk and invite you to their dining table on Tuesdays, Thursdays and Fridays from May to September. Open all year.
PRICES: d €37; extra person €12; dinner €14 **NEARBY:** Horse riding (1km) Golf (30km) Sea (40km) Swimming pool (8km) Stretch of water (10km) Cross-country skiing (45km) Downhill skiing (75km) Railway station (2km) Shops (8km) SAINT-ETIENNE-DE-BAIGORRY (8km)
NOTES: No pets English spoken

PAGOLLE

♦♦♦ ⦿ Elichondoa Michèle WALTHER
64120 PAGOLLE
☎ 05 59 65 65 34 & SR : 05 59 11 20 64
e-mail: jean.walter@online.fr
At the entrance of a small pastoral village surrounded by hills, are these four rooms including one suite for five, with bread and home-made jams for breakfast, and good home-cooking around the big table for dinner. You will find the authentic Basque interior, the crossing paths of St Jacques, the walks, and mountain biking. Open all year.
PRICES: s €38; d €41; t €52; extra person €11; dinner €15
NEARBY: Horse riding (15km) Golf (80km) Sea (70km) Swimming pool (12km) Stretch of water (28km) Cross-country skiing (55km) Downhill skiing (65km) Tennis (12km) Railway station (32km) Shops (12km) SAINT-PALAIS (15km) **NOTES:** Pets admitted English spoken

POEY-D'OLORON

♦♦♦ ❧ ⦿ Chambre d'hôtes Thierry CIVIT
64400 POEY-D'OLORON
☎ 05 59 39 59 93 & SR : 05 59 11 20 64 🖷 05 59 39 59 93
e-mail: civit.earl@wanadoo.fr http://perso.wanadoo.fr/civit

Oloron-Ste-Marie 10 km. Thierry and Odile invite you to the outbuildings of their 19th-century mansion house, offering two ground and two upstairs rooms. The park's greenery and tranquillity, the pool, and meals prepared with home-grown farm produce all make for a peaceful break. Open all year.
PRICES: s €30; d €41; t €53; extra person €9; dinner €15
ON SITE: Swimming pool **NEARBY:** Horse riding (4km) Golf (25km) Sea (80km) Stretch of water (7km) Cross-country skiing (60km) Downhill skiing (60km) Tennis (10km) Railway station (10km) Shops (10km) OLORON-EST (10km) **NOTES:** Pets admitted

> Ask the proprietor for directions
> when booking

PONTIACQ-VILLEPINTE

♦♦♦ ❧ ⦿ Chambre d'hôtes Michel et Nicole VIGNOLO
Route de Montaner, 64460 PONTIACQ-VILLEPINTE
☎ 05 59 81 91 45
Pau 35 km. Lourdes 30 km. Michel and Nicole have three rooms in their lovely Bearnese home near Lourdes and the Hautes Pyrenees, with views onto a park. The dining table is made up from own farm produce. Friendly atmosphere. Open all year.
PRICES: s €30; d €34; extra person €12; dinner €13 **NEARBY:** Horse riding (4km) Golf (25km) Sea (70km) Swimming pool (10km) Stretch of water (2km) Cross-country skiing (50km) Downhill skiing (70km) Tennis (5km) Railway station (25km) Shops (10km) **NOTES:** Pets admitted

SALIES-DE-BEARN

♦♦♦ ⦿ Chambre d'hôtes Hélène CAMOUGRAND
Maison Léchémia, Quartier du Bois, 64270 SALIES-DE-BEARN
☎ 05 59 38 08 55 & SR : 05 59 11 20 64
Sauveterre-de-Béarn 10 km. Find the good life at Lechemia, on the woody hillsides of the salt city, at this 16th-century family house. In the converted grange near the old press, or under the chestnut trees, Helene explores the flavours of rural cooking over firewood. Open all year. €70 for four people. Sleeps 8.
PRICES: d €46; dinner €15 **NEARBY:** Horse riding (3km) Golf (3km) Sea (50km) Swimming pool (3km) Stretch of water (15km) Cross-country skiing (70km) Downhill skiing (70km) Tennis (3km) Railway station (6km) Shops (3km) SALIES-DE-BEARN (3km) **NOTES:** Pets admitted

♦♦♦ ⦿ La Closerie du Guilhat Marie-Christine POTIRON
Quartier du Guilhat, 64270 SALIES-DE-BEARN
☎ 05 59 38 08 80 & SR : 05 59 11 20 64 🖷 05 59 38 08 80
e-mail: guilhat@club-internet.fr

In a green oasis, Marie-Christine runs this old and serene Bearnese mansion. A park, golf, fishing, nursery and casino are nearby. Around the table guests will enjoy good regional cuisine. Open all year.
PRICES: s €38-€46; d €46-€52; t €60; extra person €12; dinner €15
NEARBY: Horse riding (3km) Golf (3km) Sea (50km) Swimming pool (3km) Stretch of water (15km) Cross-country skiing (70km) Downhill skiing (70km) Tennis (3km) Railway station (6km) Shops (4km) SALIES-DE-BEARN (4km) **NOTES:** No pets English spoken

SARE

♦♦♦ ⦿ Errotaldekoborda Murielle DAUX
Route des Ventas, 64310 SARE
☎ 05 59 54 29 77 & SR : 05 59 11 20 64
e-mail: murielle.daux@libertysurf.fr
St-Jean-de-Luz 15 km. Spain 3 km. 18th-century Basque farmhouse with whitewashed walls. Murielle offers four rooms and breakfast by the fire or under the shade of the fig tree. There are walks, mountain biking and four by four paths and in autumn a chance to do some pigeon shooting. Meals available out of season. Open all year. Child under 12 sharing with parents €12.

continued

PRICES: s €38; d €46-€49; extra person €11; dinner €15
NEARBY: Horse riding (3km) Golf (16km) Sea (16km) Swimming pool (3km) Stretch of water (11km) Cross-country skiing (80km) Downhill skiing (150km) Tennis (3km) Railway station (16km) Shops (1km) ESPELETTE (14km) **NOTES:** Pets admitted English spoken

⁙ ۞ Larochoincoborda Jacques BERTHON
Quartier Lehenbiscaye, 64310 SARE
☎ 05 59 54 22 32
St-Jean-de-Luz 15 km. Little train of the Rhune 2 km. This is an authentic 18th-century Basque farmhouse at the end of a long path, on the banks of the Rhune, with three rooms. Breakfast is served inside or out on the terrace with views of the mountains. Walks and official hiking paths nearby. Meals available out of season. Open all year.
PRICES: s €55; d €55; t €77; dinner €15 **NEARBY:** Horse riding (3km) Golf (15km) Sea (15km) Swimming pool (3km) Stretch of water (10km) Cross-country skiing (80km) Downhill skiing (150km) Tennis (3km) Railway station (15km) Shops (3km) ESPELETTE (14km) **NOTES:** No pets

⁙ ۞ Maison Ttakoinnenborda
Alain et Mary ARRIETA
64310 SARE
☎ 05 59 47 51 42 & SR : 05 59 11 20 64
e-mail: alain-et-mary.arrieta@wanadoo.fr
http://ttakoinnenborda.ifrance.com
St-Jean-de-Luz 15 km. Characterful 17th-century house at the riverside in a rural settings with four rooms. Meals are available on certain nights of the week consisting of fresh farm produce and daily home-baked bread. Open all year.
PRICES: s €38; d €44; t €53; extra person €11; dinner €14
NEARBY: Horse riding (5km) Golf (17km) Sea (17km) Swimming pool (4km) Stretch of water (12km) Cross-country skiing (80km) Downhill skiing (150km) Tennis (4km) Railway station (17km) Shops (2km) ESPELETTE (14km) **NOTES:** No pets English spoken

⁙ Olahbidea Anne-Marie FAGOAGA
64310 SARE
☎ 05 59 54 21 85 & SR : 05 59 11 20 64
🖨 05 59 47 50 41
www.basquexplorer.com/olhabidea
St-Jean-de-Luz 15 km. Sare is probably one of the most typical villages of the Pays-Basque. Your hosts Anne-Marie and her family welcome you to their beautiful home. There are three rooms and a suite, living room, dining room, separate entrance, garden and terraces. Open March to November.
PRICES: s €46; d €53-€61; suite €105 **ON SITE:** Horse riding **NEARBY:** Golf (14km) Sea (15km) Swimming pool (2km) Stretch of water (8km) Cross-country skiing (80km) Downhill skiing (150km) Tennis (2km) Railway station (14km) Shops (2km) ESPELETTE (14km) **NOTES:** No pets

⁙ Uhartea Amaia et Michel ECHEVESTE
Quartier Elbarun, 64310 SARE
☎ 05 59 54 25 30 & 06 20 44 54 97 🖨 05 59 54 24 86
e-mail: echeveste.michel@club-internet.fr
St-Jean-de-Luz 12 km. Little train of the Rhune 3 km. There are four bedrooms in this authentic 15th-century Basque farmhouse, as well as a living room, lounge and kitchenette. At the foot of Louis XIV's fort and the mountain of the Rhune, guests can take walks, go hunting and fishing, or have a round of golf. Open all year.
PRICES: d €46-€49; t €61 **NEARBY:** Horse riding (3km) Golf (12km) Sea (12km) Swimming pool (2km) Stretch of water (10km) Cross-country skiing (80km) Downhill skiing (150km) Tennis (2km) Railway station (12km) Shops (2km) ESPELETTE (14km) **NOTES:** No pets

SAUCEDE

⁙ ۞ Chambre d'hôte du Vieux Moulin
Brigitte BAYAUD
Rue Principale, 64400 SAUCEDE
☎ 05 59 34 37 21 & SR : 05 59 11 20 64
Navarrenx 8 km. Oloron-Ste-Marie 12 km. Three rooms in an old restored windmill, well decorated, spacious and comfortable. At breakfast you'll find breathtaking views of the river and the beach on the opposite bank, and great for fishermen looking for salmon. Don't hesitate to ask your hosts about the history of their ancestors, and of this building with its ancient wheels.
PRICES: s €34; d €40; t €52-€61; suite €69; dinner €14 **NEARBY:** Horse riding (5km) Golf (40km) Sea (80km) Swimming pool (9km) Stretch of water (20km) Cross-country skiing (80km) Downhill skiing (80km) Tennis (9km) Railway station (10km) Shops (10km) OLORON-EST (10km) **NOTES:** Pets admitted

SERRES-CASTET

⁙ Le Peyret P. DE STAMPA
Chemin de Pau, Maison le Peyret, 64121 SERRES-CASTET
☎ 05 59 33 11 92 & SR : 05 59 11 20 64 🖨 05 59 33 98 02
Pau 10 km. At the summit of Serres-Castet, Le Peyret has breathtaking views of the Pyrenees, a park, a communal living room and a small kitchen area for guest use. In an outbuilding there are five spacious and comfortable rooms with own entrance and disabled access. This 18th-century property has all the characteristics of Bearn architecture, chimney stacks and skylights in the roof, small window panes and a lovely pigeon coop. Open all year.
PRICES: s €53-€61; d €61-€69 **NEARBY:** Horse riding (4km) Golf (10km) Sea (100km) Swimming pool (4km) Stretch of water (4km) Cross-country skiing (50km) Downhill skiing (50km) Tennis (4km) Railway station (10km) Shops (4km) **NOTES:** No pets

SOURAIDE

⁙ 🐦 Erieutania Jeanine LARRE
64250 SOURAIDE
☎ 05 59 93 85 40
St-Jean-de-Luz and Biarritz 20 km. San Sebastian 40 km. Spain 8 km. Jeanine and Bernard, dairy farmers, offer you two doubles and one room for three, heating, dining room, TV and own entrance. Open 1st February to 30th November.
PRICES: s €35; d €38; t €49 **NEARBY:** Horse riding (3km) Golf (1km) Sea (20km) Swimming pool (1km) Stretch of water (5km) Cross-country skiing (50km) Tennis (1km) Railway station (20km) Shops (1km) ESPELETTE (3km) **NOTES:** No pets

STE-ENGRACE

⁙ ۞ Chambre d'hôtes Ambroise BURGUBURU
Maison Elichalt, 64560 SAINTE-ENGRACE
☎ 05 59 28 61 63 🖨 05 59 28 75 54
Gorges of Kakuetta 5 km and Holzarte 15 km. Four rooms with shower and one with bathroom, private parking at the foot of the mountain, this typical Basque house offers stunning views over the Ehujarre gorges. This charming village has an exceptional 11th-century Norman church. Ambroise and Madeleine invite guests to their ample dining table. Open all year.
PRICES: s €34; d €38; HB €31; dinner €12 **NEARBY:** Horse riding (18km) Golf (100km) Sea (120km) Swimming pool (33km) Cross-country skiing (11km) Downhill skiing (11km) Tennis (10km) Railway station (50km) Shops (18km) TARDETS (18km) **NOTES:** No pets

🐦Places with this symbol are farmhouses

ST-ESTEBEN

¶¶¶ ❤ Jaureguia Annie DURRUTY
64640 SAINT-ESTEBEN
☎ 05 59 29 65 34

Hasparren 10 km. Isturitz and Oxocelaya caves 5 km. 13th-century stately home, now a dairy farm, with four large rooms (three double, one three-quarter and two single beds) upstairs. There are also lounge, TV, fireplace, and garden with furniture available. A hilly region at the heart of the Pays-Basque, half way between the sea and the mountains, with plenty of walking. Price reduction for stays longer than three nights. Open all year.
PRICES: s €30; d €37; t €46; extra person €8 **NEARBY:** Horse riding (10km) Golf (40km) Sea (40km) Swimming pool (10km) Stretch of water (30km) Cross-country skiing (45km) Downhill skiing (40km) Tennis (10km) Railway station (40km) Shops (10km) HASPARREN (10km)
NOTES: Pets admitted

ST-ETIENNE-DE-BAIGORRY

¶¶¶¶ Château d'Etchaux Line PIERNE
64430 SAINT-ETIENNE-DE-BAIGORRY
☎ 05 59 37 48 58 & SR : 05 59 11 20 64
🖹 05 59 59 01 90

Six rooms and one suite set in an 11th-century castle which dominates the village of St-Etienne-de-Baigorry, in a park of hundred year old trees with a river, offering relaxation and peace. A large communal living room and terrace are also available. Open all year.
PRICES: d €76-€120; extra person €8 **NEARBY:** Horse riding (15km) Golf (30km) Sea (50km) Swimming pool (2km) Stretch of water (10km) Cross-country skiing (45km) Downhill skiing (80km) Tennis (2km) Railway station (10km) Shops (1km) SAINT-ETIENNE-DE-BAIGORRY (1km) **NOTES:** Pets admitted English spoken

¶¶¶ ❤ ÎOÎ Inda Agnès DORRE-GOROSTIAGUE
Maison Inda, Quartier Occos,
64430 SAINT-ETIENNE-DE-BAIGORRY
☎ 05 59 37 43 16

At the heart of the Irouleguy vineyard, this 1724 Basque farm houses a spacious family home where the lady of the house serves up delicious local specialties made from home-grown produce. No dinner on Sunday nights. Children under ten:-€18.
PRICES: s €27; d €38; t €53; dinner €14 **NEARBY:** Horse riding (15km) Golf (45km) Sea (60km) Swimming pool (1km) Stretch of water (10km) Cross-country skiing (35km) Downhill skiing (100km) Tennis (1km) Railway station (1km) Shops (1km) SAINT-ETIENNE-DE-BAIGORRY (1km)
NOTES: No pets

¶¶¶ ❤ Yaureguia Daniel HARGAIN
Quartier Urdos, 64430 SAINT-ETIENNE-DE-BAIGORRY
☎ 05 59 37 49 72 & SR : 05 59 11 20 64
e-mail: hargain.daniel@wanadoo.fr

The old Albret family home, this 16th-century house has three large rooms. At the foot of the Cretes of Iparla in a protected area, you'll find yourselves at the start of several trails. Daniel, owner and mountain guide, will be happy to advise you on the best routes. Open all year.
PRICES: d €53-€61 **NEARBY:** Horse riding (35km) Golf (50km) Sea (50km) Swimming pool (1km) Stretch of water (35km) Cross-country skiing (40km) Downhill skiing (80km) Tennis (1km) Railway station (10km) Shops (1km) SAINT-ETIENNE-DE-BAIGORRY (1km) **NOTES:** No pets

ST-GLADIE

¶¶¶ ÎOÎ Chambre d'hôtes Jacques et Janine ROMEFORT
Lou Guit, Qu. Arrive, 64390 ST-GLADIE
☎ 05 59 38 97 38 & SR : 05 59 11 20 64 🖹 05 59 38 97 38
e-mail: jj.romefort@wanadoo.fr www.bearn-gaves.com
Salies-de-Béarn 10 km. Charming 15th-century Bearnese farm, tastefully done up with old furniture, paintings and beautiful fabrics. Janine and Jacques invite guests to their poolside in a flowered park, and to table with south-western style cooking. Open all year.
PRICES: s €50; d €58; suite €69-€84; dinner €23 **ON SITE:** Swimming pool **NEARBY:** Horse riding (10km) Golf (10km) Sea (70km) Stretch of water (25km) Cross-country skiing (80km) Downhill skiing (80km) Tennis (5km) Railway station (25km) Shops (5km) SAUVETERRE-DE-BEARN (5km) **NOTES:** No pets English spoken

See advert on opposite page

ST-JEAN-PIED-DE-PORT

¶¶¶ Chambre d'hôtes Clara et Jean GARICOITZ
Chemin de Taillapalde, 64220 SAINT-JEAN-PIED-DE-PORT
☎ 05 59 37 06 46
Spain 5 km. Four upstairs rooms in a Basque house with separate entrance, library, terrace, patio and barbecue. Your hosts are happy to share their knowledge of the area and help you discover the heart of the Pays-Basque. Open all year.
PRICES: d €38; t €50 **NEARBY:** Golf (40km) Sea (60km) Swimming pool (1km) Cross-country skiing (30km) Tennis (1km) Railway station (1km) Shops (1km) SAINT-JEAN-PIED-DE-PORT (1km) **NOTES:** No pets English spoken

ST-MICHEL

¶¶¶ ❤ Altzia Marie-Claire AHAMENDABURU
64220 SAINT-MICHEL
☎ 05 59 37 24 90
Just outside a small village, this renovated farmhouse has three rooms, and sits on the path of St Jacques de Compostelle. Marie-Claire will welcome you to her home and take great pleasure in sharing her knowledge of local culture and heritage. Open all year.
PRICES: d €38 **NEARBY:** Horse riding (2km) Golf (60km) Sea (60km) Swimming pool (2km) Cross-country skiing (30km) Tennis (2km) Railway station (2km) Shops (2km) SAINT-JEAN-PIED-DE-PORT (2km)
NOTES: Pets admitted

¶¶¶ ❤ ÎOÎ Ferme Ithurburia
Jeanne OURTIAGUE-PARIS, 64220 SAINT-MICHEL
☎ 05 59 37 11 17
Located on a path of St Jacques de Compostelle, this farmhouse dominates the valley of St-Jean-Pied-de-Port. There are five rooms, one en suite, all running off a gallery with a great view. All have rooms with mezzanines. Guests have use of a private entrance, kitchenette, library, TV and large communal room.
PRICES: s €30; d €38; t €50; extra person €11; dinner €14
NEARBY: Horse riding (5km) Golf (40km) Sea (65km) Swimming pool (5km) Stretch of water (7km) Cross-country skiing (30km) Tennis (5km) Railway station (5km) Shops (5km) SAINT-JEAN-PIED-DE-PORT (5km)
NOTES: No pets

Prices are given in Euros €1 = £0.62
at the time of going to press

ST-PEE-SUR-NIVELLE

♦♦♦♦ ❧ Bidachuna Isabelle ORMAZABAL
RD 3, 64310 SAINT-PEE-SUR-NIVELLE
☎ 05 59 54 56 22 📠 05 59 47 31 00
Biarritz 15 km. St-Jean-de-Luz 20 km. At the edge of a
protected forest, facing the Pyrenees, is Bidachuna, a 19th-
century walled farm huddled set in quiet surroundings. A
charming home. Open all year.
PRICES: s €84; d €92 **NEARBY:** Horse riding (6km) Golf (4km)
Sea (15km) Swimming pool (15km) Stretch of water (3km) Tennis
(6km) Railway station (15km) Shops (6km) USTARITZ (7km)
NOTES: No pets English spoken

♦♦♦ ⏃ Ferme Uxondoa M. POULET
Quartier Elbarron, 64310 SAINT-PEE-SUR-NIVELLE
☎ 05 59 54 46 27 & 06 85 87 84 75
St-Jean-de-Luz 9 km. Three spacious rooms upstairs and two suites
for three with terraces are on offer at this renovated country
farmhouse. Complete with stone, beams, baked earth and white-
washing offering warmth and modern comforts in natural settings
and six hectares of land at the edge of the Nivelle. Breakfast with
homemade jams and meals made from farm produce. Only ten
minutes from the ocean. Open all year.
PRICES: s €50-€65; d €54-€69; t €77; dinner €13-€19 **NEARBY:** Horse
riding (2km) Golf (9km) Sea (9km) Swimming pool (4km) Stretch of
water (2km) Tennis (2km) Railway station (9km) Shops (2km) USTARITZ
(7km) **NOTES:** No pets

SUHESCUN

♦♦♦ ⏃ Chambre d'hôtes Maité SARAGUETA
Gordagia, 64780 SUHESCUN
☎ 05 59 37 60 93
St-Jean-Pied-de-Port 11 km. Guests have use of their own
entrance, kitchenette and living room, TV, central heating,
sheltered garden and terrace. Two rooms with double and twin
beds, and another with two double beds. Meals on request except
on Sundays. Numerous trailpaths. Open all year. €61 for four
people.
PRICES: s €30; d €37; dinner €12 **NEARBY:** Horse riding (5km) Golf
(50km) Sea (50km) Swimming pool (11km) Stretch of water (10km)
Cross-country skiing (40km) Tennis (11km) Railway station (11km) Shops
(5km) **NOTES:** No pets

URCUIT

♦♦♦ ⏃ Relais Linague Marie BLEAU
64990 URCUIT
☎ 05 59 42 97 97 & SR : 05 59 11 20 64
Bayonne 12 km. Five rooms in a beautiful blue-timbered Basque
house with restored furniture and fabrics a few minutes from the
Basque hills. An ideal spot for riders and horse lovers. There are
magnificent views of the surroundings from the terrace where
breakfast is served. Full meals on request three nights a week out
of season. Open all year.
PRICES: s €46; d €50-€54; extra person €15; dinner €15
ON SITE: Swimming pool Tennis **NEARBY:** Horse riding (15km) Golf
(15km) Sea (15km) Stretch of water (20km) Railway station (12km)
SAINT-PIERRE-D'IRUBE (9km) **NOTES:** No pets

> For further information on these and
> other chambres d'hôtes, consult
> the Gîtes de France website
> *www.gites-de-france.fr*

Lou Guit
Quartier Arrive
64390 Saint Gladie

A totally renovated typical Béarnaise farm, part dating back to the
16thC. The garden is enclosed by trees and can be enjoyed at its
best in the spring and summer with several varieties of perfumed
flowers. A warm welcome from your hosts Jacques and Janine who
will do their best to please you. The house is full of colour with
painting by friends. Two pretty bedrooms and one suite with access
to the swimming pool. After your day, you can enjoy a wonderful
meal cooked by a superb chef and share the experiences of the
other guests. Here the atmosphere is happy, enthusiastic and lively,
all part of every day life. Come as a guest and leave as a friend.
Tel/Fax: 05 59 38 97 38
Email: jj.romefort@wanadoo.fr
Web: http://perso.wanadoo.fr/chambresdhotes-lou.guit

USTARITZ

♦♦♦ Bereterraenea Nicole SINDERA
Quartier Arrauntz, 64480 USTARITZ
☎ 05 59 93 05 13 & SR : 05 59 11 20 64 📠 05 59 93 27 70
e-mail: bereter.nicole@wanadoo.fr
Biarritz 10 km. Bayonne 6 km. Only ten minutes from the ocean,
Bereterraenea offers ground floor and upstairs rooms with their
own entrance await. This is a 17th-century coaching-inn,
overlooking forests and rivers. On your arrival cider is offered.
Open all year.
PRICES: s €40-€43; d €44-€47; extra person €13 **NEARBY:** Horse riding
(5km) Golf (2km) Sea (10km) Swimming pool (4km) Stretch of water
(10km) Cross-country skiing (70km) Downhill skiing (100km) Tennis
(4km) Railway station (7km) USTARITZ (4km) **NOTES:** No pets English
spoken

VILLEFRANQUE

♦♦♦ Chambre d'hôtes Thierry JOLY et Marie
Kurutcheta, Quartier Bas, 64990 VILLEFRANQUE
☎ 05 59 44 98 27 & SR : 05 59 11 20 64
Bayonne 5 km. Biarritz 8 km. In his comfortable house ten
minutes from the beach, Thierry offers you five themed rooms,
sharing his interest in travel (Indonesia, Africa, South America, the
sea and mountains). In couples or *en famille*, you can stretch out
by the pool, play ball on the private front wall, have a game of
billiards or ping-pong, or simply let the hosts choose your daily
itinerary: hills, Spain, Bearn, Landes. Open all year.
PRICES: s €46; d €49-€57; extra person €11 **NEARBY:** Horse riding
(5km) Golf (10km) Sea (10km) Swimming pool (5km) Stretch of water
(15km) Cross-country skiing (70km) Downhill skiing (100km) Tennis
(3km) Railway station (5km) Shops (3km) SAINT-PIERRE-D'IRUBE (5km)
NOTES: No pets

ALLIER

AUDES

¶¶¶ ❦ |◎| Roueron Jacques & Véronique SION
Domaine de Roueron, 03190 AUDES
☎ 04 70 06 00 59 📠 04 70 06 16 81
e-mail: jv.sion@wanadoo.fr
www.goecities.com/jvsion/index.html
Montluçon 13 km. A Bourbonnais stables beautifully restored. On
the ground floor are a breakfast room, a lounge and fireplace. On
the first floor are a family room (one double and three single beds
with bath and wc) and a triple room, a twin room and two family
rooms (one with twin beds and a child bed and one with double
bed and cot) each with a private shower and wc. Tourist tax
included, discount for stays of over three days. Open all year.
PRICES: s €31; d €40; t €52; extra person €12; dinner €13
ON SITE: Fishing **NEARBY:** Canoeing (25km) Golf (6km) Swimming
pool (15km) Stretch of water (26km) Tennis (3km) Sailing (26km) Bicycle
hire (18km) Railway station (10km) Shops (3km) **NOTES:** Pets admitted

BESSAY-SUR-ALLIER

¶¶¶ |◎| Les Neufonds Catherine LOHEZIC
03340 BESSAY-SUR-ALLIER
☎ 04 70 43 05 33 📠 04 70 43 05 33
Moulins 15 km. In this refurbished Bourbonnais property are a
ground-floor double room and a first-floor family room with a
double bed and two children's beds. There are two rooms with
independent access which can be linked - one on the ground floor
with twin beds and a couch, and one twin room on the first floor.
All rooms have private facilities. Rooms are non-smoking. Lounge
and library. Table d'hôte meals served if booked. Kitchenette
available on request. Walking trails. Discounts from 2nd night and
longer stays can be negotiated. Please call between 9.00 and 16.00
or after 20.00. Open July to Sept. Other periods by reservation.
PRICES: s €25-€35; d €30-€45; t €55; extra person €15; dinner €15
NEARBY: Canoeing (14km) Golf (10km) Fishing (2km) Swimming pool
(14km) Stretch of water (14km) Tennis (2km) Bicycle hire (14km) Railway
station (12km) Shops (2km) **NOTES:** No pets English spoken

BUXIERES-LES-MINES

¶¶¶ ❦ |◎| Renière Geneviève BREGEOT
03440 BUXIERES-LES-MINES
☎ 04 70 66 00 13 📠 04 70 66 00 13
A working farm next to a private forest with enclosed garden and
shaded park, grazing for horses, fishing and picnic areas. On the
first floor are a double and a twin room. On the ground floor are a
shared lounge with fireplace and dining room. In a separate
building, refurbished in local stone and wood, are a double room
and a family room with one double and one single bed. All rooms
have private bath or shower and wc. Washing machine available.
Table d'hôte meals on reservation. 10% discount from the fourth
night. Walking trails start from the farm and a Palaeontological site
is 3.5 km away. Open all year.
PRICES: s €30; d €35; t €43; extra person €8; dinner €11-€13
ON SITE: Children's play area Fishing **NEARBY:** Canoeing (45km) Golf
(30km) Swimming pool (11km) Stretch of water (6km) Tennis (4km)
Sailing (6km) Bicycle hire (6km) Railway station (30km) Shops (4km)
BOURBON L'ARCHAMBAULT (15km) **NOTES:** No pets

CHAMBERAT

¶¶¶ La Bergerat Simone MEIER
03370 CHAMBERAT
☎ 04 70 06 39 82 & 04 70 06 34 54
e-mail: labergerat@aol.com
Montluçon 20 km. Three big guest rooms (one grade 2) in a large,
interesting house set in a big park. On the first floor is a double
room with bath and wc and a double room with washbasin and a
separate, private shower and wc. On the second floor is a family
room with six single beds, private shower and wc. An extra person
can be accommodated. Facilities include a lounge and sitting room
with fireplace, tennis and table tennis, garden furniture, bicycles,
barbecue, parking. Try an introduction to pottery. Open from 31
March to 3 November.
PRICES: s €30; d €38-€46; t €53-€61; extra person €15 **ON SITE:** Tennis
Bicycle hire **NEARBY:** Canoeing (20km) Golf (20km) Fishing (2km)
Swimming pool (20km) Stretch of water (10km) Sailing (20km) Railway
station (20km) Shops (9km) HURIEL (9km) **NOTES:** Pets admitted
English spoken

CHANTELLE

¶¶¶ |◎| La Croix St-Urbain Nicole et Guy CLAUS
03140 CHANTELLE
☎ 04 70 56 66 25 📠 04 70 56 69 85
e-mail: guyclaus@wanadoo.fr http://sturbain.multimania.fr
Gannat 15 km. In the owner's restored Bourbonnais farmhouse
are three spacious attic rooms. One double with shower and wc,
one family with a double and a single bed, shower and wc and
one family room with a double and two single beds, spa bath and
wc. Lounge and table d'hôte meals by reservation. Open views
over the woods and countryside. Open all year.
PRICES: s €30-€37; d €40-€46; t €50-€56; extra person €11; dinner €15
ON SITE: Swimming pool Bicycle hire **NEARBY:** Canoeing (18km) Golf
(37km) Fishing (1km) Stretch of water (18km) Tennis (1km) Sailing
(32km) Railway station (23km) Shops (1km) **NOTES:** Pets admitted
English spoken

CHARROUX

¶¶¶¶ La Maison du Prince de Conde
Jon et Jeannine SPEER
Place d'Armes, 03140 CHARROUX
☎ 04 70 56 81 36 & 06 88 71 10 59 📠 04 70 56 81 36
e-mail: jspeer@club-internet.fr
www.charroux.com or www.val-de-sioule.com
The house of the Prince de Condé, an old 13th/18th- century
hunting lodge, in a medieval *cité* classed as one of France's
beautiful villages. Five rooms on two floors, with a duplex in
one of the fortified towers. One double room with bath and
wc, one 18th-century double room and three other double
rooms each with a private bath (three are spa baths) and wc.
TV available. Library, lounge with fireplace, dining room in the
13th-century cellar. Enclosed wooded garden. Non-smoking
house. Two restaurants in the village. Open all year.
PRICES: s €38-€46; d €61-€76; t €76-€83; extra person €15
NEARBY: Canoeing (15km) Golf (20km) Fishing (4km) Swimming
pool (12km) Stretch of water (4km) Tennis (6km) Sailing (20km)
Bicycle hire (12km) Railway station (12km) Restaurant nearby
CHANTELLE (6km) **NOTES:** No pets CC English spoken

CHATEL-DE-NEUVRE

♯♯♯ 🍴 Les Quatre Vents
Philippe BOUQUET DES CHAUX
03500 CHATEL-DE-NEUVRE
☎ 04 70 42 09 89 & 06 07 56 89 70 📠 04 70 42 09 89
e-mail: ladivelle@wanadoo.fr
Moulins 18 km. Vichy 37 km. St-Pourçain-sur-Sioule 12 km. A 19th-century house in the heart of the Bourbonnais with six rooms. Four rooms contain a double and a single bed, one room contains a double and two single beds and there is one double room - all with a private shower and wc. Lounge, dining room and sitting room with library and television are available. Table d'hôte meals on reservation. There is a large green space in the Vignoble St-Pourçinois on the edge of the Val d'Allier. Nearby: 11th-century church, viewpoint over the Val d'Allier, hunting (1 km), go-karting (13 km) and aerial sports (23 km). Open all year.
PRICES: s €32; d €41; t €52; extra person €11; dinner €12
NEARBY: Canoeing (1km) Golf (15km) Fishing (1km) Swimming pool (12km) Stretch of water (37km) Tennis (1km) Sailing (37km) Bicycle hire (1km) Railway station (16km) LE MONTET (22km) **NOTES:** Pets admitted English spoken

CHOUVIGNY

♯♯♯ 🍴 La Chouvignotte Karine et Pascal TAVIGNOT
03450 CHOUVIGNY
☎ 04 70 90 91 91 📠 04 70 90 91 91
e-mail: chouvignotte@wanadoo.fr
www.multimania.com/chouvignotte
Gannat 16 km. Against the sheer rockface of the Sioule gorge, on the banks of a river prized by fishermen, this stone-built house offers three first-floor rooms. Two contain a mezzanine, a double and a single bed and one room has three single beds, each has a private shower and wc. In a separate building, ideal for a holiday, is a sitting area and shower/wc on the ground floor and a bedroom on the first floor with a double and two single beds. An extra bed can be provided. There is a terrace, garden, lawn and private access to the river. Table d'hôte meals can be provided if reserved. Open all year.
PRICES: s €35; d €40; t €50; extra person €10; dinner €15
ON SITE: Canoeing Fishing **NEARBY:** Golf (25km) Swimming pool (20km) Stretch of water (10km) Tennis (10km) Bicycle hire (10km) Railway station (25km) Shops (10km) EBREUIL (10km) **NOTES:** Pets admitted English spoken

COULANDON

♯♯♯ 🍴 La Grande Poterie
Jean-Claude POMPON
03000 COULANDON
☎ 04 70 44 30 39 & 06 68 22 20 73
Souvigny 4 km. Next to the owner's house is an old restored barn, which has been beautifully decorated and tastefully refurbished with antique and modern furniture. There are a double, a twin and a family room (with a double and a single bed) each with a private shower and wc. A cot is available. Facilities include a lounge, a dining room, terrace, trail bikes and the owner's swimming pool. Table d'hôte meals available if booked in advance. The forest is 400m away and there is an animal sanctuary and walking trails nearby. Open all year.
PRICES: s €36; d €49-€54; t €55; extra person €13; dinner €14-€19
ON SITE: Swimming pool Bicycle hire **NEARBY:** Canoeing (8km) Golf (10km) Fishing (2km) Stretch of water (8km) Tennis (4km) Sailing (10km) Railway station (8km) Shops (4km) MOULINS (8km)
NOTES: Pets admitted

COUZON

♯♯♯ 🐓 🍴 Manoir de la Beaume
E.A.R.L. MANOIR DE LA BEAUME
(Mme BIEWER-BARRITAUD), La Beaume, 03160 COUZON
☎ 04 70 66 22 74 📠 04 70 66 22 74
e-mail: labeaume@wanadoo.fr http://www.labeaume.fr.fm
Moulins 22 km. Bourbon l'Archambault 12 km. Forêt de Tronçais 30 km. On the Allier horse riding trail is this 17th-century, small manor house on an equestrian farm. There is a ground floor room with a queen bed and a single bed, bathroom and wc. On the first floor are three further rooms. One with a double bed and double couch, bath, shower and wc. One double room and one twin room, both with shower and wc. A cot is available. There is a lounge, dining room and open fire. There are walks, rides, riding lessons, pony trekking (lessons) and Pony Club (BEES 1). Open all year.
PRICES: s €34-€49; d €41-€56; t €56-€64; dinner €14
NEARBY: Canoeing (25km) Golf (25km) Fishing (1km) Swimming pool (12km) Stretch of water (25km) Tennis (12km) Sailing (30km) Bicycle hire (22km) Railway station (22km) Shops (12km) LURCY LEVIS (22km)
NOTES: Pets admitted English spoken

DEUX-CHAISES

♯♯♯ 🍴 Château de Longeville Nicole BEAUREGARD
03240 DEUX-CHAISES
☎ 04 70 47 32 91 📠 04 70 47 33 84
Montmarault 8 km. Four-poster beds in a 19th-century château surrounded by woods and parkland with ancient trees. Two rooms are grade 3 and two are grade 2. Two are in Louis XIV/XV style and one is in 18th-century style, all with double beds and private bath and wc. There is a suite in country style with a double and a single bed, bath and wc. Dinner is served by candlelight. Facilities include a lounge and dining room, television, music, board games and cards and a fish pond. Open all year.
PRICES: s €61; d €69; t €84; extra person €15; dinner €38
ON SITE: Fishing **NEARBY:** Canoeing (25km) Golf (30km) Swimming pool (23km) Stretch of water (28km) Tennis (1km) Sailing (28km) Bicycle hire (30km) Railway station (35km) Shops (1km) LE MONTET (4km) **NOTES:** No pets English spoken

DIOU

♯♯♯ Les Grandjeans Françoise et Claude DAGNNET
Les Quatre Saisons, 03290 DIOU
☎ 04 70 42 91 16
Four first-floor rooms in a renovated old barn. One double, one double with a cot, one with a double and a single bed and one with a double and two single beds - each room has a shower and wc. There is a lounge and dining room for guests only and a large courtyard. Evening meals may be arranged. Additional guests 12 euros; and children from 3 years 5.5 euros. Open from 1 April to end October.
PRICES: s €27; d €37; extra person €12 **ON SITE:** Fishing
NEARBY: Canoeing (2km) Golf (30km) Swimming pool (2km) Stretch of water (16km) Tennis (3km) Sailing (16km) Bicycle hire (35km) Railway station (3km) Shops (3km) DOMPIERRE-SUR-BESBRE (3km)
NOTES: Pets admitted

EBREUIL

♯♯♯ 🍴 Chavagnat Anne-Marie/Christian BOUTONNET
03450 EBREUIL
☎ 04 70 90 73 56 & 06 70 65 06 45 📠 04 70 90 73 56
http://www.multimania.com/chavagnat/
Gannat 12 km. A fully restored old farmhouse in a hamlet overlooking the countryside. One room with a double and a single bed, one room with a double and twin beds each with private

continued

shower room and wc. A room with two double beds, bath and wc and a large room with a double bed and two double sofa beds. There is a lounge, sitting room, library, terrace and garden furniture, also a holiday cottage to let. Half board is 410 euros a week for two. Open all year.
PRICES: s €34; d €38; t €49; extra person €11; dinner €13
ON SITE: Children's play area **NEARBY:** Canoeing (2km) Golf (30km) Fishing (2km) Swimming pool (12km) Stretch of water (2km) Tennis (2km) Sailing (30km) Bicycle hire (2km) Railway station (12km) Shops (2km) EBREUIL (2km) **NOTES:** Pets admitted

FLEURIEL

♦♦♦ ◎| Le Corgenay Manuela et Louis STERCKX
03140 FLEURIEL
☎ 04 70 56 94 12 🖷 04 70 56 90 88
Vichy 30 km. St-Pourçain-sur-Sioule 14 km. A completely restored 1820s house on a working farm with rooms on the first and second floors. Superb views over the Bourbonnais and Puys mountains. One twin room with bath and wc, two double rooms with shower and wc, and two rooms with king-sized beds, bath and wc. There are a shared lounge, dining room and library. Table d'hôte meals must be booked in advance. There is also a jacuzzi, terrace and veranda and garden furniture. Pets may be booked in, kennels available. Open from 28 March to 4 November (other periods on reservation).
PRICES: s €43-€53; d €48-€73; extra person €15; dinner €15
ON SITE: Swimming pool **NEARBY:** Canoeing (30km) Golf (15km) Fishing (8km) Stretch of water (30km) Tennis (8km) Sailing (30km) Bicycle hire (12km) Railway station (30km) Shops (8km) CHANTELLE (8km) **NOTES:** Pets by arrangement only English spoken

GOUISE

♦♦♦ ◎| ♿ Les Rubis Jean-Louis et Irmine HUOT
03340 GOUISE
☎ 04 70 43 12 70 🖷 04 70 43 12 70
Moulins 20 km. Vichy 40 km. Four rooms in the converted outbuildings of a 19th-century property. One double room with disabled access, shower and wc. A twin room, a room with two double beds and a room with a double and a single bed all with shower and wc. Day room, garden and garden furniture set aside for guests. Table d'hôte meals can be booked in school holidays only. There is a kitchenette available. Open all year.
PRICES: d €37; t €43; dinner €11 **NEARBY:** Canoeing (20km) Golf (12km) Fishing (8km) Swimming pool (18km) Stretch of water (18km) Tennis (6km) Bicycle hire (20km) Railway station (20km) Shops (6km) NEUILLY LE REAL (6km) **NOTES:** No pets English spoken

HURIEL

♦♦♦ Malvaux - La Chapelaude Nathalie et Pascal NICOLAS
Les Malvaux, La Chapelaude, 03380 HURIEL
☎ 04 70 06 44 09
Montluçon 10 km. In a hamlet near the village of La Chapelaude, on the first floor of a barn conversion next to the family home, there are three rooms for two, three or four people, each with a private shower and wc. Cot available. On the ground floor is a large lounge with open fire, a library and kitchenette. Outside is a large lawned courtyard, garden furniture, barbecue, parking and stabling for horses. Tourist tax is included in the price. Restaurants are less than 1 km away. Open all year.
PRICES: s €31; d €40; t €50; extra person €10 **NEARBY:** Canoeing (14km) Golf (18km) Fishing (7km) Swimming pool (10km) Stretch of water (10km) Tennis (2km) Sailing (14km) Bicycle hire (7km) Railway station (10km) Shops (2km) Restaurant nearby (7km) **NOTES:** Pets admitted English spoken

LA FERTE-HAUTERIVE

♦♦♦♦ ◎| Demeure de Hauterive
Jérome et Annick LEFEBVRE
03340 LA FERTE-HAUTERIVE
☎ 04 70 43 04 85 & 06 23 12 27 00 🖷 04 70 43 00 62
www.demeure-hauterive.com

Moulins 20 km. St-Pourçain-sur-Sioule 12 km. A big house, typical of the Sologne Bourbonnais, in a large park enclosed by walls. One room on the ground floor with a double and a single bed, bath and wc. On the first floor a double room, a room with a double and a single bed and a two-room suite with four single beds and extra bed available, shower and wc for each room. Indoors are a dining room, lounge and billiard room, outside are a terrace, garage, summerhouses and ornamental ponds. Pets may be accepted and there are kennels. Open all year.
PRICES: s €50; d €67-€73; t €82-€88; dinner €17-€23
ON SITE: Tennis Bicycle hire **NEARBY:** Canoeing (12km) Golf (12km) Fishing (1km) Swimming pool (10km) Stretch of water (20km) Railway station (20km) Shops (20km) NEUILLY LE REAL (17km) **NOTES:** Pets admitted English spoken

LE BREUIL

♦♦♦ ◎| La Tuile à Loups
Christophe ALVERGNAT CARRIOT
03120 LE BREUIL
☎ 04 70 99 24 91 🖷 04 70 99 24 91
e-mail: christophe.alvergnat@wanadoo.fr www.tuile-a-loups.com
Vichy 22 km. La Tuile à Loups is an 18th-century house set in a shady park in the Bourbonnais Mountains. Five rooms are available: one double, two with a double and a single bed, and one triple, all with private shower and wc and one double room with private bath and wc. An extra bed is available. Guests may use the lounge, television, dining room, library, winter garden and French billiards. Open all year.
PRICES: s €38; d €38-€46; extra person €11; dinner €14
ON SITE: Swimming pool Bicycle hire **NEARBY:** Canoeing (29km) Golf (29km) Fishing (2km) Stretch of water (29km) Tennis (8km) Sailing (29km) Railway station (29km) Shops (5km) LAPALISSE (8km) **NOTES:** Pets admitted English spoken

LE PIN

♦♦♦ 🐾 ◎| Chambre d'hôtes Michèle et Alain DECERLE
La Noux, 03130 LE PIN
☎ 04 70 55 62 62 🖷 04 70 55 65 51
A working farm with rooms on the first floor of the owner's house. One room with three single beds, two twin rooms and one double room. Each room has a bathroom and wc. The owner's lounge with fireplace is for guest use and meals are based on the farm produce. There is a lake on site. Open all year.
PRICES: s €27; d €37; t €46; extra person €9; dinner €14
ON SITE: Fishing **NEARBY:** Canoeing (15km) Golf (15km) Swimming

continued

pool (15km) Stretch of water (23km) Tennis (10km) Bicycle hire (21km)
Railway station (15km) Shops (10km) LE DONJON (10km) **NOTES:** Pets
admitted English spoken

LE THEIL

♦♦♦ ⏴◯⏵ **Château du Max** Dominique PESSAR-MAZET
03240 LE THEIL
☎ 04 70 42 35 23
Three guest rooms in a separate wing of the 13th-15th-century
Château du Max, surrounded by a moat. One suite consists of two
rooms with two double four-poster beds, a shower and wc. One
room with two single four-poster beds, bath and wc and one
double room in the château tower with bath and wc. Additional
beds are available. The lounge and dining room are shared with
the owners. Guests may walk the grounds and woods and fish in
the moat. Open all year.
PRICES: s €61; d €69; t €76; extra person €8; dinner €15-€23
ON SITE: Fishing **NEARBY:** Canoeing (35km) Golf (35km) Swimming
pool (15km) Stretch of water (40km) Tennis (5km) Bicycle hire (35km)
Railway station (35km) Shops (15km) LE MONTET (15km) **NOTES:** Pets
admitted

LOUROUX-DE-BEAUNE

♦♦♦ ⏴◯⏵ **L'Etang du Champfournier**
Eric JALLET & Laurent FAUDEMER
Les Roumeaux, 03600 LOUROUX-DE-BEAUNE
☎ 04 70 64 95 04 & 06 84 48 88 37 🖷 04 70 64 95 04
Montluçon 30 km. In the heart of a large wooded area with a
private pond, Eric and Laurent welcome you to an old farm
guesthouse. There is one twin room and three double rooms each
with a private shower room and wc. Other facilities include a
lounge, sitting room, large terrace, parking and garden furniture.
Trail bikes are available for local trips and table d'hôte meals are
served at weekends. Open all year.
PRICES: s €35; d €41; dinner €17 **ON SITE:** Fishing
NEARBY: Canoeing (60km) Golf (30km) Swimming pool (18km) Stretch
of water (10km) Tennis (8km) Bicycle hire (8km) Railway station (18km)
Shops (18km) MONTMARAULT (8km) **NOTES:** No pets English spoken

LURCY-LEVIS

♦♦♦ 💚 **Grand-Veau** Solange et Claude VANNEAU
03320 LURCY-LEVIS
☎ 04 70 67 83 95 🖷 04 70 67 80 80
Forêt de Tronçais 5 km. Three first-floor rooms in a 19th-century
Bourbonnais house on a farm. One room contains a double and a
single bed, one is a double and one a twin - each with a private
shower and wc. There is a communal small lounge and a library, a
shaded garden and lounge. Open all year.
PRICES: s €27; d €35; t €46; extra person €11 **NEARBY:** Canoeing
(45km) Golf (35km) Fishing (5km) Swimming pool (25km) Stretch of
water (10km) Tennis (5km) Sailing (10km) Bicycle hire (5km) Railway
station (45km) Shops (5km) BOURBON L'ARCHAMBAULT (25km)
NOTES: Pets admitted English spoken

LUSIGNY

♦♦♦ **Les Laurents** Frédéric BIRON
03230 LUSIGNY
☎ 04 70 42 41 83 🖷 04 70 42 41 83
e-mail: fred.biron@wanadoo.fr
*Moulins 12 km. Bourbon-Lancy 18 km. Le Pal amusement park 20
km.* Four guest rooms in a renovated 19th-century château. A two-
room suite with two double and one single beds, private shower
room and wc. Two double rooms with private bathrooms and wcs,
one double room with private shower room and wc. Dining room,
lounge and extensive grounds. Open from April to October.

MARIOL

♦♦♦ ⏴◯⏵ **Les Breuils** Catherine ARNAUD
03270 MARIOL
☎ 04 70 41 00 03 🖷 04 70 41 00 12
e-mail: canayma@wanadoo.fr
Vichy 15 km. Thiers 20 km. Five guest rooms in a completely
renovated house of character. Two twin rooms, one double room
and one room with a double and a single bed. Each room has a
private shower or bath and wc. Extra beds and a cot are available.
The owner's lounge and dining room is made available to guests.
There is also a washing machine, large shady patio, garden
furniture, parking and barbeque. Pets may be accepted if booked.
There are discounts out of season after the fourth night and for
groups. Children's meals €7. Open all year.
PRICES: s €31; d €39-€44; t €52; extra person €6; dinner €13
ON SITE: Fishing Bicycle hire **NEARBY:** Canoeing (15km) Golf (15km)
Swimming pool (5km) Tennis (2km) Sailing (15km) Railway station
(15km) Shops (3km) CUSSET (15km) **NOTES:** Pets admitted English
spoken

MEAULNE

♦♦♦ ⏴◯⏵ **Domaine de Bellevue** Jean-Marc COUDRY
SCEA de Diège, 03360 MEAULNE
☎ 04 70 06 24 40
e-mail: scea-diege@nat.fr
Five rooms in a Renaissance-style château built in the time of
Napoleon III, set in a landscaped garden, enclosed by a wall. There
is a double room with separate bath and wc, a double room with
bath and wc, a twin room with shower and wc and a room with a
double and a single bed, bath and wc. Some rooms can
communicate. The owner's lounge, sitting room and library are
made available to guests. It is an equestrian property and rides
can be booked in the Forêt de Tronçais. Open all year.
PRICES: s €34-€46; d €46-€61; t €58-€69; extra person €8; dinner €14
NEARBY: Canoeing (2km) Golf (2km) Fishing (2km) Swimming pool
(7km) Stretch of water (6km) Tennis (3km) Sailing (6km) Bicycle hire
(3km) Railway station (18km) Shops (1km) Restaurant nearby CERILLY
(12km) **NOTES:** Pets admitted English spoken

MONTEIGNET-L'ANDELOT

♦♦♦ ⏴◯⏵ **LA MARIVOLE** Annick SUPPLISSON
Le Bourg, 03800 MONTEIGNET-L'ANDELOT
☎ 04 70 90 58 53 🖷 04 70 90 58 53
e-mail: annick.supplisson@wanadoo.fr
Four rooms on the ground and first floors of this lovely house near
Andelot and a village. Two twin rooms, one double room and one
room with a double and a single bed - all with a private shower or
bath and wc. The owners share the lounge and dining room with
guests. There are large shaded grounds, a terrace and garden
furniture, table tennis and bikes for guests to use. Open all year.
PRICES: s €30-€37; d €38-€45; t €48-€54; extra person €10; dinner €12
ON SITE: Children's play area Bicycle hire **NEARBY:** Canoeing (15km)
Golf (7km) Fishing (5km) Swimming pool (8km) Stretch of water (17km)
Tennis (8km) Sailing (17km) Railway station (6km) Shops (7km)
GANNAT (7km) **NOTES:** Pets admitted

> ⏴◯⏵ Places with this symbol serve table d'hôtes
> evening meals - remember to book in advance

continued

PRICES: s €38; d €53; t €61 **NEARBY:** Canoeing (12km) Golf (10km)
Fishing (3km) Swimming pool (12km) Stretch of water (18km) Tennis
(1km) Sailing (18km) Bicycle hire (12km) Railway station (10km) Shops
(1km) CHEVAGNES (3km) **NOTES:** Pets admitted

MONTILLY

⊪ ⁅◉⁆ Manoir des Herards Pierrette et Rémi BLOCH
Les Herards, 03000 MONTILLY
☎ 04 70 46 51 26 & 06 89 26 71 71
Bourbon l'Archambault 15 km. A 17th-century manor house
belonging to a painter. There are two first floor rooms with
independent access through a 15th-century tower, each with
private bath and wc - one double room and one with a double and
a single bed. There is also a ground floor double room with bath
and wc. The bedrooms are no smoking. Shared lounge and dining
room. Table tennis, fishing and garden furniture for use on the
terrace and in the grounds. Table d'hôte meals must be booked in
advance. Painting and drawing lessons available. Tourist tax
payable. Open 1 April to end October.
PRICES: s €42; d €46-€53; t €69; dinner €15 **ON SITE:** Fishing
NEARBY: Canoeing (7km) Golf (12km) Swimming pool (7km) Stretch
of water (10km) Tennis (1km) Bicycle hire (7km) Railway station (7km)
Shops (7km) MOULINS (7km) **NOTES:** No pets English spoken

MONTMARAULT

⊪ ⁕ ⁅◉⁆ Concize Eric DU BOULET
03390 MONTMARAULT
☎ 04 70 07 60 22 & 04 70 07 40 38 ▤ 04 70 02 90 54
Montluçon 35 km. In a separate wing of the owner's home are two
rooms with double and single beds, one with bath and wc, one
with shower and wc. On the second floor of the owner's house is a
twin room with shower and wc. A cot is available. A lounge and
dining room are kept for guests. Table d'hôte meals must be
booked in advance. There is a large garden with a barbecue. Open
31 March to 29 September.
PRICES: s €27; d €35; t €43; dinner €12 **ON SITE:** Children's play area
Swimming pool Tennis **NEARBY:** Canoeing (15km) Golf (35km) Fishing
(2km) Stretch of water (26km) Sailing (26km) Bicycle hire (31km)
Railway station (35km) Shops (2km) MONTMARAULT (2km)
NOTES: Pets admitted English spoken

NOYANT-D'ALLIER

⊪ ⁕ ⁅◉⁆ Les Jobineaux
Caroline & J-Dominique CARRELET
03210 NOYANT-D'ALLIER
☎ 04 70 47 29 71 & 06 60 72 73 48 ▤ 04 70 47 29 71
Moulins 20 km. Souvigny 9 km. Five rooms on a dairy farm in the
Bourbonnais countryside near Souvigny. There are beautiful views
and it is ideal for holidays with family and friends. Each room has
a shower and wc and four are grade 3, one is grade 2. Large,
shared lounge with open fire, table tennis, table football, trail bikes
and guests can take part in the milking. Horse riders welcome. Ask
about group and extended stay prices. Open all year.
PRICES: s €30; d €37; t €48; dinner €11 **ON SITE:** Fishing
NEARBY: Golf (25km) Swimming pool (13km) Stretch of water (25km)
Tennis (3km) Sailing (25km) Bicycle hire (10km) Railway station (21km)
Shops (3km) BOURBON L ARCHAMBAULT (15km) **NOTES:** Pets
admitted English spoken

PARAY-LE-FRESIL

⊪ ⁕ ⁅◉⁆ Le Château Esmeralda DE TRACY
03230 PARAY-LE-FRESIL
☎ 04 70 43 68 02 & 04 70 43 42 36 ▤ 04 70 43 11 74
On the first floor of a château of local brick are two double rooms
and a twin room, each with bath, wc and television. Cots are
available. The day room and lounge are shared with the owners.
Table d'hôte meals must be booked in advance. There is table
tennis on site as well as large grounds, a swimming pool, stabling
and hunting. Open all year.
PRICES: s €46; d €69; t €76; extra person €8; dinner €23-€30

ON SITE: Swimming pool **NEARBY:** Golf (25km) Fishing (2km) Stretch
of water (15km) Tennis (7km) Sailing (15km) Bicycle hire (25km) Railway
station (25km) Shops (1km) CHEVAGNES (7km) **NOTES:** Pets admitted

PARAY-SOUS-BRIAILLES

⊪ ⁕ ⁅◉⁆ Les Caissons Michèle et Gérard MAUSSAN
Route de Marcenat, 03500 PARAY-SOUS-BRIAILLES
☎ 04 70 45 03 00 & 04 70 45 12 52
Moulins 35 km. Vichy 22 km. Right in the countryside in the heart
of a traditional farm are three annexe rooms: two with two double
beds and one with a double, two singles and a cot. Each room has
a private bath and wc. There is also a lounge, library and
kitchenette, a large green open area, garden furniture, barbecue
and car port. An equestrian property, bicycles for hire. Table
d'hôte meals can be booked. For two adults and one child (15 yrs)
€49 and for two adults and two children €56. There are go-karts 6
km away. Open all year.
PRICES: s €37; d €40; extra person €14; dinner €14 **ON SITE:** Children's
play area Stretch of water **NEARBY:** Canoeing (22km) Golf (5km)
Fishing (2km) Swimming pool (7km) Tennis (3km) Sailing (20km)
Bicycle hire (6km) Railway station (10km) Shops (6km) SAINT POURCAIN
SUR SIOULE (6km) **NOTES:** Pets admitted English spoken

POUZY-MESANGY

⊪ ⁕ ⁅◉⁆ Le Plaix Claire et Georges RAUCAZ
Manoir Le Plaix, Pouzy Mesangy, 03320 LURCY-LEVIS
☎ 04 70 66 24 06 ▤ 04 70 66 25 82

Georges and Claire welcome you to their 16th-century manor
house on a farm near forests and rivers. There are five rooms for
two to three people with private shower or bath and wc and a
private entrance through tower stairs. A kitchenette is available but
table d'hôte meals must be reserved. Weekly rates. Facilities in the
summer include pétanque, table tennis, barbeque and trails for
walkers and cyclists. Stabling and fishing on site. Open all year.
PRICES: s €34; d €34-€40; t €52-€55; extra person €15; dinner €15
ON SITE: Children's play area Fishing **NEARBY:** Canoeing (30km) Golf
(30km) Swimming pool (15km) Stretch of water (5km) Tennis (5km)
Bicycle hire (7km) Railway station (35km) Shops (4km) BOURBON
L'ARCHAMBAULT (15km) **NOTES:** Pets admitted English spoken

SERVILLY

⊪ ⁅◉⁆ Les Vieux-Chînes Elisabeth COTTON
03120 SERVILLY
☎ 04 70 99 07 53
e-mail: cotton.elisabeth@free.fr
Lapalisse 7.5 km. Vichy 25 km. Six rooms with views over the
Monts de la Madeleine on the first and second floors of a large
house. There are three double rooms and one room with a double
and a single bed, each with private bath and wc, and a suite of two
rooms with two double beds and a bath, shower and wc. Cots
available. There is a lounge, sitting room, library, games room and

continued

continued

sauna (for extra charge) and table d'hôte meals which must be booked in advance. Shaded, enclosed grounds, terrace. Tourist tax is payable and pets may be accepted by reservation. Open from March to October, other periods by reservation.

PRICES: s €30-€43; d €46-€53; t €8; extra person €17

NEARBY: Canoeing (25km) Golf (25km) Fishing (4km) Swimming pool (8km) Stretch of water (25km) Tennis (5km) Sailing (30km) Bicycle hire (8km) Railway station (25km) Shops (5km) LAPALISSE (8km)

NOTES: Pets admitted English spoken

ST-AUBIN-LE-MONIAL

ꟿ ꙮ ⦿ La Gare Anne-Marie et Louis MERCIER
03160 ST-AUBIN-LE-MONIAL
☎ 04 70 67 00 20

Four rooms in a Bourbonnais house. On the first floor are a room with alcove containing three single beds, shower and wc, a suite of two rooms with two double beds and a single bed, room for an extra bed, bath and wc and one room with a double and a single bed, shower and wc. On the ground floor is a double room with shower and wc. Guests have sole use of a lounge and dining room. A washing machine and telephone are available. Table d'hôte meals available if reserved. There is a garage, a shaded green area and a forest. Open all year.

PRICES: s €29; d €36; t €46; extra person €9; dinner €10-€13

NEARBY: Canoeing (15km) Golf (40km) Fishing (2km) Swimming pool (7km) Stretch of water (15km) Tennis (15km) Sailing (15km) Bicycle hire (15km) Railway station (25km) Shops (3km) BOURBON L'ARCHAMBAULT (7km) **NOTES:** Pets admitted

ST-BONNET-DE-ROCHEFORT

ꟿ ꙮ ⦿ Rochefort Philippe et Sabine BONNAL
03800 ST-BONNET-ROCHEFORT
☎ 04 70 58 57 26 & 06 84 04 70 62 ▤ 04 70 58 57 26
e-mail: alaferme@multimania.com
http://www.multimania.com/alaferme/

Ebreuil 4 km. Five guest rooms on the ground and first floors of a farm near the Gorges de la Sioule. Two rooms have a private entrance. All the rooms have a double and a single bed with private shower room and wc. The owner's lounge, sitting room and library are available for guests to use. Table d'hôte meals must be booked. The grounds offer a swimming pool, garden furniture and barbecue. Horse riders may be accommodated. Open all year.

PRICES: s €34; d €40; t €49; extra person €11; dinner €14

ON SITE: Children's play area Swimming pool **NEARBY:** Canoeing (4km) Golf (30km) Fishing (1km) Stretch of water (4km) Tennis (4km) Sailing (30km) Bicycle hire (4km) Railway station (10km) Shops (4km) GANNAT (10km) **NOTES:** Pets admitted English spoken

ST-BONNET-TRONCAIS

ꟿ ⦿ La Beaume Jehan et Laurence DE POMYERS
03360 ST-BONNET-TRONCAIS
☎ 04 70 06 83 76 ▤ 04 70 06 13 46

An old smithy in the Forêt de Tronçais. In the main house are two twin rooms and a suite of two rooms with a double and a single bed. Each room has a bath or shower and a wc. In a nearby outbuilding are a double room with shower and wc and a twin room with bath and wc. The lounge is shared with the owners. Table d'hôte meals available if booked in advance. There are guided walks in the forest. Discounts for stays of two nights of 5%, for three or four nights of 10%, for five nights or more or 15%. Meals for long-stay guests €12. Open all year.

PRICES: s €29; d €35; t €46; extra person €12; dinner €13

NEARBY: Fishing (1km) Swimming pool (30km) Stretch of water (1km) Tennis (1km) Sailing (1km) Bicycle hire (1km) Railway station (20km) Shops (1km) CERILLY (12km) **NOTES:** No pets English spoken

ST-DIDIER-EN-DONJON

ꟿ ꙮ ⦿ Les Dibois Mirjam et Yves LAGARDETTE
03130 ST-DIDIER-EN-DONJON
☎ 04 70 55 63 58 & 06 73 50 43 63
e-mail: lagardette.y@infonie.fr

Three rooms in a converted sheepfold next to the owner's house. One twin room, one room with one double and two single beds and one room with one double and one single bed. Each room has a bath and wc. Two of the rooms have a private terrace and the dining room and lounge are reserved for guests. There is parking, and a swimming pool suitable for children and adults. Open all year.

PRICES: s €29; d €37; t €44; extra person €8; dinner €13

ON SITE: Fishing Swimming pool Bicycle hire **NEARBY:** Canoeing (20km) Golf (20km) Stretch of water (20km) Tennis (5km) Railway station (25km) Shops (5km) LE DONJON (5km) **NOTES:** Pets admitted English spoken

ST-GERAND-LE-PUY

ꟿ ⦿ Demeure des Payratons
Christianne POULET
03150 ST-GERAND-LE-PUY
☎ 04 70 99 82 44

Lapalisse 10 km. Vichy 20 km. An 18th-century house with antique furniture from Louis XI, XV, Directoire and Empire, and shaded grounds. The rooms are on the first floor and consist of a double with bath and wc, a double with shower and wc, a room with three single beds, bath and wc and a suite of two rooms with a double and two single beds, bath and wc, a double room in Louis XV with bath and wc. Television is available and pets may be accepted by reservation. The lounge and dining room are shared. Open all year.

PRICES: s €41-€56; d €61; t €76; extra person €15; dinner €18

NEARBY: Fishing (8km) Swimming pool (8km) Stretch of water (20km) Tennis (1km) Sailing (20km) Bicycle hire (10km) Railway station (20km) Shops (1km) VARENNES SUR ALLIER (8km)

NOTES: No pets CC

ST-GERMAIN-DE-SALLES

ꟿ ⦿ Chambre d'hôtes Elisabeth et Bart GIELENS
1 allée des Gandins, 03140 ST-GERMAIN-DE-SALLES
☎ 04 70 56 80 75 ▤ 04 70 56 80 75
e-mail: lesgandins@wanadoo.fr www.domainelesgandins.com

Gannat 10 km. Three rooms on the first floor of a typical Bourbonnais mansion set in an enclosed, wooded park on the banks of the River Sioule. The rooms have their own entrance, two are doubles, one contains three single beds and they all have a shower room and wc. There is a lounge reserved for guests. There are also three self-catering cottages and camping for ten tents on site. Open all year.

PRICES: s €35; d €44; t €55; dinner €15 **ON SITE:** Fishing

NEARBY: Canoeing (20km) Golf (12km) Swimming pool (10km) Stretch of water (20km) Tennis (6km) Sailing (30km) Bicycle hire (10km) Railway station (10km) Shops (10km) Restaurant nearby CHANTELLE (13km)

NOTES: No pets English spoken

ST-PLAISIR

ꟿ ꙮ La Prée Lucette et Lionel DROUET
03160 ST-PLAISIR
☎ 04 70 67 01 39 ▤ 04 70 67 01 39

On a farm in bloom overlooking the countryside four rooms on the first floor of the owner's house. Two double rooms and one room with two double beds all with private shower and wc. One family suite with two rooms, two double beds and private shower and wc - not en suite. The lounge with television is reserved for

continued

AUVERGNE

guests. There is a boules ground and table tennis and a lake. Riders may be accommodated. Open all year.
PRICES: s €29; d €35-€37; t €40-€44; extra person €9
ON SITE: Fishing Stretch of water **NEARBY:** Swimming pool (11km) Tennis (2km) Sailing (22km) Bicycle hire (22km) Railway station (32km) Shops (11km) Restaurant nearby BOURBON L'ARCHAMBAULT (11km)
NOTES: No pets

ST-PRIEST-EN-MURAT

⳾ ⳾ ⎢⌀⎢ La Charvière
Henny ENGELS
03390 ST-PRIEST-EN-MURAT
☎ 04 70 07 38 24 🖹 04 70 02 91 27
e-mail: robert.engels@wanadoo.fr
A Dutch family welcome you to their restored farmhouse. Three rooms on the first floor: a double room and a room with a double and a single bed, both with shower and wc. A room with two double beds, bath, shower and wc. The lounge with open fire is shared and there is a terrace. Self-catering cottages and camping are on site. Open all year.
PRICES: s €23; d €36; t €46; extra person €8; dinner €14
ON SITE: Children's play area Swimming pool **NEARBY:** Canoeing (30km) Golf (30km) Fishing (5km) Stretch of water (14km) Tennis (5km) Sailing (14km) Bicycle hire (25km) Railway station (30km) Shops (5km) MONTMARAULT (7km) **NOTES:** Pets admitted English spoken

THIEL-SUR-ACOLIN

⳾ ⳾ ⎢⌀⎢ Domaine des Domes
Sylviane et Eric SCHUELLER
03230 THIEL-SUR-ACOLIN
☎ 04 70 42 54 28 🖹 04 70 42 54 28
Parc Le Pal 7 km. Moulins-Montbeugny Aerodrome 12 km. Four rooms in a renovated farm outbuilding. One twin room, one double room, one room with four single beds and one room with a double and a single bed - each room has a shower and wc. The lounge is reserved for guests. There is a covered terrace, a barbecue and a shaded courtyard. Livery stables on site. Alsace specialities can be provided on request. Discovery weekends between October and March. Open all year.
PRICES: s €27; d €35; t €44; extra person €9; dinner €13
ON SITE: Swimming pool **NEARBY:** Canoeing (9km) Golf (15km) Fishing (1km) Stretch of water (23km) Tennis (2km) Sailing (23km) Bicycle hire (9km) Railway station (2km) Shops (2km) CHEVAGNES (9km) **NOTES:** Pets admitted

TRONGET

⳾ ⳾ ⎢⌀⎢ La Roche
Olivier et Michèle BAES
03240 TRONGET
☎ 04 70 47 16 43
Souvigny 18 km. Montmarault 16 km. Moulins 30 km. Three rooms in a Bourbonnais farm surrounded by fields and woods. One room with a double bed and a child's bed, shower room and wc. One room with a double and a single bed, shower room and wc and a further double room. The dining room is shared with the owners and meals are made with farm produce. Guests are welcome to join in the life of the farm. Open all year.
PRICES: s €30; d €36; t €48; extra person €12; dinner €13
NEARBY: Canoeing (20km) Golf (40km) Fishing (4km) Swimming pool (20km) Stretch of water (4km) Tennis (4km) Sailing (25km) Bicycle hire (25km) Railway station (30km) Shops (4km) LE MONTET (5km)
NOTES: No pets English spoken

VALIGNAT

⳾⳾⳾⳾ L'Ormet Pierre et Patricia LAEDERICH
RD183, 03330 VALIGNAT
☎ 04 70 58 57 23 🖹 04 70 58 54 36
e-mail: lormet@wanadoo.fr http://ormet.multimania.com

Facing the Puy-de-Dôme and the Montagne Bourbonnaise is this unique house in wooded grounds with three guest rooms. The owner will be delighted to show you his three miniature railways, of different gauges, that circle the garden and grounds. The house is non-smoking and is a good starting point for walks. Two rooms contain a double and a single bed and one is a twin room, they all have a private bath and wc. Open all year and from 1 October to 30 April on reservation.
PRICES: s €47-€67; d €55-€75; t €71-€91 **ON SITE:** Swimming pool **NEARBY:** Canoeing (7km) Golf (25km) Fishing (7km) Stretch of water (7km) Tennis (5km) Sailing (35km) Bicycle hire (7km) Railway station (6km) Shops (5km) EBREUIL (7km) **NOTES:** No pets English spoken

VERNEIX

⳾⳾⳾⳾ ⎢⌀⎢ Château de Fragne
Martine DE MONTAIGNAC LEROY
03190 VERNEIX
☎ 04 70 07 88 10 🖹 04 70 07 83 73
First floor rooms in an 18th-century family château. There are two double rooms, one single room and two suites consisting of two rooms with a double and a single bed. Every room has a bathroom and wc. There is a sitting room and a lounge with period furniture, a large terrace, and spacious shaded grounds. Pets may be accepted by reservation. Price for the two room suites is €150 per night. Open from 1 May to 15 October.
PRICES: ; d €113; t €172; dinner €50 **ON SITE:** Fishing
NEARBY: Swimming pool (15km) Stretch of water (25km) Tennis (15km) Sailing (25km) Bicycle hire (20km) Railway station (13km) Shops (15km) MONTLUCON (15km) **NOTES:** Pets admitted CC English spoken

VERNEUIL-EN-BOURBONNAIS

♥♥♥ ⎜◯⎜ Demeure de Chaumejean Catherine SARRAZIN
03500 VERNEUIL-EN-BOURBONNAIS
☎ 04 70 45 53 92 📠 04 70 45 53 92
A 19th-century house just 500m from the village with five first floor rooms. Two twin rooms, two rooms with three single beds and one double room all with a shower and wc. An additional bed is available for €9. There is a lounge, sitting room and library and shaded grounds and a ceramic gallery and workshop. The house is non-smoking and offers organic breakfasts and table d'hôte meals if reserved. There is a restaurant 500 m away. Book a themed stay at full board. Price for five days €220. Winter reservations taken. Open 1 February to 31 December.
PRICES: s €30; d €43; t €55; FB €44; dinner €13 **NEARBY:** Canoeing (35km) Golf (8km) Fishing (5km) Swimming pool (5km) Stretch of water (30km) Tennis (5km) Sailing (30km) Bicycle hire (15km) Railway station (28km) Shops (5km) SAINT POURCAIN SUR SIOULE (5km) **NOTES:** No pets English spoken

VILLEFRANCHE D'ALLIER

♥♥♥ ⎜◯⎜ Chambre d'hôtes Dominique SIWIEC
23 avenue Louis Pasteur, 03430 VILLEFRANCHE-D'ALLIER
☎ 04 70 07 46 62 📠 04 70 07 46 62
e-mail: dom.hotes@wanadoo.fr
The owners run a small bar in the village centre in this 19th-century Bourbonnais house with guest rooms on the first floor. There is a family suite with two separate rooms each with a double bed, one with a bathroom and wc and one with a washbasin and wc. There is also a twin room with shower room and wc and a room with one double and two single beds, shower room and wc. The dining room is shared and there is a garage, garden and courtyard. Open all year.
PRICES: s €29; d €40; t €49; extra person €10; dinner €12 **ON SITE:** Tennis **NEARBY:** Golf (15km) Fishing (15km) Swimming pool (9km) Stretch of water (18km) Sailing (18km) Bicycle hire (18km) MONTMARAULT (12km) **NOTES:** No pets

YGRANDE

♥♥♥ ♥ Les Ferrons Agnès et Henri VREL
03160 YGRANDE
☎ 04 70 66 31 67 📠 04 70 66 32 64
Forêt de Tronçais 12 km. A large 19th-century house in its own grounds with three first floor rooms: one suite of two rooms with a double and two single beds, a double room and a room with one double and one single bed. All the rooms have a private shower and wc. In an annexe there is a double room with shower room and wc. Meals may be provided. Guests have sole use of a lounge, television and library. Washing machine and cot available. A stable and field for horses are on site and the house is near the Allier equestrian rides. Open all year.
PRICES: s €32; d €40; t €50 **NEARBY:** Fishing (4km) Swimming pool (13km) Stretch of water (4km) Tennis (3km) Sailing (4km) Bicycle hire (4km) Railway station (32km) Shops (3km) BOURBON L'ARCHAMBAULT (10km) **NOTES:** No pets

CANTAL

ANGLARDS DE SALERS

♥♥♥ ⎜◯⎜ Le Bourg Gerard & Francette RIBES
ferme auberge les Sorbiers, 15380 ANGLARDS DE SALERS
☎ 04 71 40 02 87
Six rooms on the first floor of a house near to the owners' home. Two rooms with double and single bed, one twin room and three double rooms with private shower and wcs. The dining room and lounge are for guest use with a library and fireplace. There is an enclosed garden with furniture. Discounts offered for children. The ground floor serves as a ferme auberge at weekends. Salers and Mauriac 8 km away. Open Easter to end September.
PRICES: s €34; d €37; t €44; dinner €13 **ON SITE:** Hiking Tennis **NEARBY:** Horse riding (8km) Fishing (1km) Swimming pool (8km) Cross-country skiing (12km) Sailing (8km) Railway station (8km) Restaurant nearby SALERS (8km) **NOTES:** No pets

APCHON

♥♥♥ L'Oustadou Paulette DERVIN
15400 APCHON
☎ 04 71 78 19 70
Three rooms in the owner's house, two of which have their own entrance. There are two ground floor and one first floor room; two are doubles and one a twin. Each room has a private bathroom and wc. The heating is electric and there is a garden. Restaurants in Apchon and Cheylade (7km), shops in Riom es Montagnes. Puy Mary 20km, Parc des Volcans, Aurillac 60km, Clermont Ferrand 90 km. Out of season telephone number 03.26.82.50.46. Open school holidays and from mid-May to end September.
PRICES: s €26; d €35 **ON SITE:** Hiking **NEARBY:** Horse riding (6km) Fishing (6km) Swimming pool (6km) Cross-country skiing (5km) Tennis (6km) Railway station (35km) Shops (6km) RIOM ES MONTAGNES (6km) **NOTES:** Pets admitted English spoken

ARPAJON SUR CERE

♥♥♥ ⎜◯⎜ Le Cambon Jacqueline & Angelo LENA
15130 ARPAJON SUR CERE
☎ 04 71 63 52 49
A calm and peaceful spot in open countryside. There are three rooms on the top floor of the owner's house, two doubles and one twin with a private lounge and extra bed available. Each room has a TV socket. There are private bathroom facilities, a shared day room with TV, heating, courtyard, and enclosed garden. Discounts are available for stays of four nights or more. Aurillac 5km away, the Monts du Chantal, châteaux, museums, Roman sites and golf 3km away.
PRICES: s €34; d €40-€43; dinner €12 **ON SITE:** Fishing Hiking **NEARBY:** Horse riding (2km) Swimming pool (5km) Cross-country skiing (40km) Downhill skiing (40km) Tennis (2km) Sailing (15km) Railway station (3km) Shops (3km) AURILLAC (5km) **NOTES:** No pets

BADAILHAC

♥♥♥ ♥ ⎜◯⎜ Calmejane Jean François TROUPEL
15800 BADAILHAC
☎ 04 71 62 47 54 📠 04 71 62 47 54
Overlooking a remarkable valley panorama, the three rooms are in a building separate from the owner's house. Each room has a double and a single bed with shower room and private wcs. There is electric heating, a communal lounge, a terrace with furniture, a courtyard and table d'hote meals. Vic sur Cère is 10 km away, or tour the Monts du Chantal. Open all year by reservation.
PRICES: d €35; t €49; dinner €10 **ON SITE:** Hiking **NEARBY:** Horse riding (10km) Fishing (8km) Swimming pool (10km) Cross-country skiing (15km) Tennis (7km) Sailing (50km) Railway station (10km) Shops (10km) VIC SUR CERE (10km) **NOTES:** No pets

♥♥♥ ♥ ⎜◯⎜ La Calsade Jean MORZIERES
15800 BADAILHAC
☎ 04 71 47 40 54
In a small hamlet near Badailhac this farming couple welcome you to their newly restored, centrally heated, house. Two double rooms on the first floor and a family room on the second floor containing a double and a single bed with private shower rooms and wcs, and a TV point in each room. The lounge, shared with the owners, has a fireplace and TV. There is a terrace and courtyard. Vic sur Cère and Polminhac 12 km. Aurillac 20 km, Le Lioran 20 km.

continued

continued

PRICES: s €42; d €44; t €53; dinner €10 **ON SITE:** Hiking
NEARBY: Horse riding (10km) Fishing (3km) Swimming pool (12km)
Cross-country skiing (15km) Downhill skiing (30km) Tennis (12km)
Railway station (12km) Shops (12km) VIC SUR CERE (12km)
NOTES: No pets

BEAULIEU

♦♦♦ ☙ ⁜ Le Bourg Sylvie, Philippe & Cathy EYZAT
15270 BEAULIEU
☎ 04 71 40 34 46 ▧ 04 71 40 34 46
e-mail: CATHY.EYZAT@wanadoo.fr
Enjoying views over the lakes and Monts du Cantal and the
Château de Val, the five rooms include two doubles, three rooms
have mezzanines that can accommodate an extra bed - one of
these contains a double bed, the other two are twins. Facilities
include private shower rooms and wcs, dining room, sitting room
with TV and glass-fronted heater, fridge, table tennis, enclosed
garden with furniture and barbecue. Out of season discounts are
available. There is a restaurant in the town. Lanobre 4 km. Bort les
Orgues 10 km. Open all year by reservation.
PRICES: d €32-€40; t €39-€44; dinner €11 **ON SITE:** Hiking
NEARBY: Horse riding (10km) Fishing (1km) Swimming pool (10km)
Cross-country skiing (20km) Tennis (4km) Sailing (4km) Railway station
(10km) Shops (4km) CHAMPS SUR TARENTAINE (20km) **NOTES:** Pets
admitted

CHALIERS

♦♦♦ ☙ ⁜ La Besse Michel SIQUIER
15320 CHALIERS
☎ 04 71 23 48 80 & 06 80 05 37 85
A small farm on the fringes of Cantal, Lozère and Haute Loire. Five
rooms are in an adjoining barn. All have independent access with
beds on a mezzanine. Two contain a double and single bed, three
are doubles - with private shower rooms and wcs. Extra beds
available. The communal lounge has an open fire - where food is
prepared - and TV. Electric heating. Courtyard, garden and terrace.
Twelve minutes from the N9 and the A75. Near the GR34, the
Vallée de la Truyère, the Ecomusée de la Margeride, Aubrac, Monts
du Cantal and Saint Flour. Open all year.
PRICES: s €37-€40; d €43-€46; t €58-€61; dinner €12 **ON SITE:** Fishing
Hiking **NEARBY:** Horse riding (7km) Swimming pool (10km) Cross-
country skiing (20km) Downhill skiing (30km) Tennis (10km) Sailing
(14km) Railway station (20km) Shops (10km) RUYNES EN MARGERIDE
(12km) **NOTES:** Pets admitted

CHAMPS SUR TARENTAINE

♦♦♦ ⁜ Merigot Jean & Odette GERARD
Camping de l'Etang, 15270 CHAMPS SUR TARENTAINE
☎ 04 71 78 71 36 ▧ 04 71 78 71 36
e-mail: merigot@auvergne-vacances.com
Five rooms in the owners' farmhouse where table d'hôte meals
feature local specialities. On the second floor are two family rooms
- with a double and a single bed - and one double room. Each has
its own shower room and wc. There are two rooms on the ground
floor, one grade 2 room, containing a double and a single bed,
and a double room with a shared shower room and wc in the
corridor. Central heating, open fire, TV and telephone. Garden with
games, pétanque, footpaths, seating, private pond and fishing.
There is camping on the farm. Discounts available out of season.
Nearby attractions include a festival in Champs sur Tarentaine.
PRICES: d €31-€38; dinner €13 **ON SITE:** Children's play area Fishing
Hiking **NEARBY:** Horse riding (7km) Swimming pool (5km) Cross-
country skiing (20km) Downhill skiing (30km) Tennis (5km) Sailing (4km)
Railway station (12km) Shops (5km) CHAMPS SUR TARENTAINE (5km)
NOTES: No pets

CHAUDES AIGUES

♦♦♦ ⁜ La Fouilhouse Marc CHALMETON
15110 CHAUDES AIGUES
☎ 04 71 23 58 15 & 04 71 23 51 16
Three rooms with independent access in an interesting house. One
double room is on the first floor, and two doubles are on the
second floor. An extra bed is available. There are private shower
rooms and wcs, central heating, a communal dining room, a guest
only lounge with TV. The garden has seating and tables. Nearby
are the springs of Chaudes-Aigues, Garabit, Monts d'Aubrac,
Laguiole and Saint-Flour.
PRICES: s €28; d €37; t €48; dinner €12 **NEARBY:** Horse riding (20km)
Fishing (1km) Swimming pool (3km) Hiking (3km) Cross-country skiing
(14km) Tennis (3km) Sailing (20km) Railway station (35km) Shops (3km)
CHAUDES AIGUES (3km) **NOTES:** No pets

CONDAT

♦♦♦ ☙ ⁜ Le Veysset Veronique PHELUT
15190 CONDAT
☎ 04 71 78 62 96
e-mail: veronique.phelut@libertysurf.fr
Four rooms with their own entrances and private shower rooms
and wcs - two doubles and two family. Dining room, electric
heating, and garden. During Apr, May, Sep and Oct table d'hôte
meals are offered, during June, July and Aug the kitchen is
available to guests. Host specialises in growing strawberries,
raspberries and blueberries. 3 km from Condat, 6 km from the
Lastioules Dam and the Lac de la Crégut. Open Easter to 1
November.
PRICES: s €28; d €37; t €46; dinner €11 **ON SITE:** Hiking
NEARBY: Horse riding (1km) Fishing (3km) Swimming pool (3km)
Tennis (3km) Sailing (6km) Railway station (18km) Shops (3km)
CONDAT (3km) **NOTES:** No pets

FRIDEFONT

♦♦♦ ☙ ⁜ Le Bourg Gilbert et Josette CHASSANY
15110 FRIDEFONT
☎ 04 71 23 56 10 ▧ 04 71 23 59 89
e-mail: chassany@terre-net.fr
Enjoy the view over the Plomb du Cantal from this interesting
house. There are four rooms: one double; one with a double and
a single bed; a room with three single beds; and one double room
with a sofa bed, private lounge. All rooms come with private
facilities. Courtyard, dining room, shared lounge, fireplace, TV
available. Discounts available out of season and for children. There
is a ferme auberge on the ground floor. Nearby: St-Flour (30 km),
Garabit, Château d'Alleuze, dams, climbing, Gorges du Bès, Portes
de l'Aubrac and Margeride.
PRICES: s €27; d €37; t €49; dinner €10 **ON SITE:** Hiking
NEARBY: Horse riding (30km) Fishing (3km) Swimming pool (13km)
Cross-country skiing (20km) Tennis (13km) Sailing (3km) Railway station
(30km) Shops (13km) Restaurant nearby CHAUDES AIGUES (13km)
NOTES: No pets

GIOU DE MAMOU

♦♦♦ ⁜ Barathe Pierre & Isabelle BRETON
15130 GIOU DE MAMOU
☎ 04 71 64 61 72
e-mail: barathe3@wanadoo.fr
A beautiful mansion built in 1777 set in a large, peaceful estate
surrounded by small valleys. All five, centrally heated, rooms have
private shower rooms and wcs and period furniture. There are
four double rooms and one family room with a double and two
single beds. Traditional cooking uses vegetables from the garden.
Discounts for children. Nearby are Puy Mary, Salers, Monts du

continued

Cantal, Plomb du Cantal, Laguiole, Conques. Golf course 5km away and snowboarding at Super-Lioran in February.
PRICES: d €41; dinner €11 **ON SITE:** Fishing Hiking **NEARBY:** Horse riding (5km) Swimming pool (9km) Cross-country skiing (30km) Downhill skiing (30km) Railway station (8km) Shops (8km) AURILLAC (8km)
NOTES: No pets

JALEYRAC

♦♦♦ ♥ ⒪⚬ Bourriannes J.C & M.CLaire CHARBONNEL
15200 JALEYRAC
☎ 04 71 69 73 75
Three rooms are available on the first floor of the owner's house. A grade 3 double, two grade 2 rooms, one double and one twin. All three have private shower rooms and wcs. Dining room and lounge with TV and fireplace are shared. There is electric heating, grounds, bread oven and table d'hote meals must be reserved. Child discounts available. Nearby are Monts du Cantal and Salers.
PRICES: s €30; d €35-€37; dinner €10 **NEARBY:** Horse riding (4km) Fishing (1km) Swimming pool (3km) Hiking (5km) Tennis (3km) Sailing (15km) Railway station (3km) Shops (3km) MAURIAC (3km)
NOTES: No pets

♦♦♦ ♥ ⒪⚬ La Salterie Alain & Mireille CHAVAROCHE
15200 JALEYRAC
☎ 04 71 69 72 55
Three rooms in a building adjoining the owner's house. Two rooms contain a double bed and a single bed on a mezzanine. The other room is a twin and an extra bed is available. Private shower room and wc, communal lounge, central heating. Guests have access to a fridge and microwave, and the grounds with garden furniture. Out of season discounts. Climbing or microlighting nearby, or visit Salers 20km, Puy Mary, Le Falgoux and Monts du Sancy.
PRICES: s €31; d €37; t €46; dinner €9 **NEARBY:** Horse riding (10km) Fishing (2km) Swimming pool (7km) Cross-country skiing (25km) Tennis (7km) Railway station (7km) Shops (7km) MAURIAC (7km) **NOTES:** No pets

JOURSAC

♦♦♦ ⒪⚬ Recoules Alain NICOLLEAU
15170 JOURSAC
☎ 04 71 20 59 12 📠 04 71 20 59 12
This typical farmhouse is south of Cézallier with a view of the Massif Cantalien. There are five first-floor rooms with independent access. One has a queen size bed and two rooms have three single beds with room for an extra bed, one family room with a double and a single bed and one double room. Private shower rooms and wcs. Shared dining room with a cantou and alcove, and lounge. Library, garden, electric heating and regional cooking. Group reductions out of season. Nearby: Neussargues (7 km), and Murat (18 km). Open all year by reservation.
PRICES: s €30; d €40; t €52; dinner €11 **ON SITE:** Hiking
NEARBY: Horse riding (15km) Fishing (5km) Swimming pool (17km) Cross-country skiing (15km) Tennis (10km) Railway station (7km) Shops (7km) ALLANCHE (10km) **NOTES:** Pets admitted

JUNHAC

♦♦♦ ⒪⚬ Le Bourg POUJADES J.C. & VIGIER C
les Tilleuls, 15120 JUNHAC
☎ 04 71 49 24 70
Five rooms in a house with character set in a park full of flowers and trees. On the first floor is a twin room, and a room with double bed and single bed. Private, unconnected shower rooms and wcs. On the second floor are a twin room, a triple room and a double with private shower rooms and wcs. Oil heating, communal

dining room and lounge. Regional home cooking using garden grown vegetables. Local to Monts du Cantal, Salers, Conques, Laguiole, Montsalvy 5km, Vallée du Lot 10km and Aurillac 30km. Open 1 May to 30 September.
PRICES: s €34; d €43; t €53; dinner €13 **ON SITE:** Hiking
NEARBY: Horse riding (25km) Fishing (1km) Swimming pool (5km) Tennis (5km) Railway station (30km) Shops (5km) MONTSALVY (5km)
NOTES: No pets

LA CHAPELLE D'ALAGNON

♦♦♦ ⒪⚬ Gaspard Denis et Joelle MEDARD
15300 LA CHAPELLE D'ALAGNON
☎ 04 71 20 01 91
Four charming rooms in this old farmhouse at the heart of Cantal. The hamlet is on the fringes of Alagnon and has pretty views. Three double rooms and one twin with private shower rooms and wcs. Guests have sole use of the dining room and lounge, and access to a telephone. Meals are served table d'hôte. Central heating. Attractions include the Grandval Dam, the Maison de la faune and the Monts du Cantal. Mountain biking (4 km), Murat (4 km), Super Lioran (12 km) and Garabit (25 km).
PRICES: s €30; d €38; dinner €10 **ON SITE:** Fishing Hiking
NEARBY: Horse riding (7km) Swimming pool (4km) Cross-country skiing (12km) Downhill skiing (12km) Tennis (4km) Sailing (30km) Railway station (4km) Shops (4km) MURAT (4km) **NOTES:** Pets admitted

LADINHAC

♦♦♦ ♥ ⒪⚬ Valette E Gilberte COMBELLES JOSETTE
15120 LADINHAC
☎ 04 71 47 80 33 & 06 75 34 48 46 📠 04 71 47 80 16
e-mail: combellesm@aol.com
As well as six b&b rooms, this countryside farm offers self-catering cottages, camping, guest accommodation, farmhouse produce and regional cooking. Five of the rooms are grade 3 in an annexe with level access. One double room, three triple rooms and one twin room. On the ground floor of the house is a grade 2 double room. All rooms have private facilities and a TV socket. Washing machine, fridge, gas cooker, private terrace with furniture, garden and field, games area and managed pond. Nearby are Montsalvy 7km, Aurillac 20km, Vallée du Lot, Conques, Gorges de la Truyère, Monts du Cantal.
PRICES: ; d €38-€41; dinner €10 **ON SITE:** Children's play area Fishing
NEARBY: Horse riding (5km) Swimming pool (7km) Tennis (7km) Railway station (20km) Shops (2km) Restaurant nearby MONTSALVY (7km) **NOTES:** Pets admitted

LE CLAUX

♦♦♦ ⒪⚬ Le Bourg Catherine AGUTTES
les Voyageurs, 15400 LE CLAUX
☎ 04 71 78 93 01 📠 04 71 78 93 01
e-mail: Voyageurs@puy-mary.com http://www.puy-mary.com
Four rooms in the owner's home at the foot of Puy Mary. Meals are taken table d'hôte. There are two double rooms and two family rooms with a double and a single bed, all with private shower and wcs. Communal dining room, central heating, seating area, shaded terrace and petanque. Guests have access to a washing machine. Discounts for out of season bookings. Go paragliding, cross-country skiing, walking (GR400, PR) and trail biking, or see the chamois. Nearby: Riom Es Montagnes (17 km) and Murat (23 km). Open all year.
PRICES: s €32; d €40; t €52; dinner €13 **ON SITE:** Fishing Hiking Cross-country skiing Tennis **NEARBY:** Horse riding (17km) Swimming pool (17km) Railway station (17km) MURAT (34km) **NOTES:** No pets

continued

LE FALGOUX

♥♥♥ 🍴 La Michie Colette JACQUIER-SUPERSAC
3 avenue Gambetta, 15000 AURILLAC
☎ 04 71 69 54 36 & 04 71 45 40 54

Five rooms in a large, impressive house. The three doubles on the first floor have private shower rooms and wcs. The two suites in the attic are family rooms with seating areas and private shower rooms and wcs. One has a double room and a single room and the other consists of two twin rooms. Lounge shared with the owner. Open fire, central heating, table d'hôte meals and use of the grounds. There are shops in Falgoux. Nearby: Vallée du Mars, the Cirque du Falgoux, Puy Mary, Salers and the GR400.
PRICES: s €46–€54; d €46–€54; t €61; dinner €16 **ON SITE:** Fishing Hiking Tennis **NEARBY:** Horse riding (25km) Swimming pool (28km) Cross-country skiing (4km) Sailing (40km) Railway station (28km) SALERS (13km) **NOTES:** No pets

LE VIGEAN

♥♥♥ ♥ 🍴 Lasbordes Daniel & Chantal CHAMBON
Earl de Lasbordes, 15200 LE VIGEAN
☎ 04 71 40 01 59
e-mail: chantal.et.daniel.chambon@wanadoo.fr

Five rooms in the owners' house on a farm between Mauriac and Anglards de Salers. Two double bedded rooms, two twin rooms and one room with a double and a single bed. An additional bed is available. All rooms have private facilities. The table d'hote meals are served in a communal room with fireplace and seating area. There is central heating, a TV, a terrace, and a calm, shady park. Discounts for children under 10. Microlights 3km, Mauriac 5km, Salers 15km, Monts du Cantal. Open all year by reservation.
PRICES: s €35; d €40; t €49; dinner €10 **ON SITE:** Fishing Hiking **NEARBY:** Horse riding (3km) Swimming pool (5km) Cross-country skiing (25km) Tennis (5km) Railway station (5km) Shops (5km) MAURIAC (5km) **NOTES:** No pets

LEYNHAC

♥♥♥ ♥ Martory J. Marie & Jeanine CAUMON
15600 LEYNHAC
☎ 04 71 49 10 47 📠 04 71 49 14 61
e-mail: jean-mariecaumon@wanadoo.fr

A renovated 1808 barn on a cattle farm offering six rooms with own entrance and a terrace and private shower rooms and wcs. Two double rooms, one double room with a kitchenette, two rooms with a double bed, a single bed and a kitchenette and one room with a double and a single bed. Dining room and lounge shared with the owner. Courtyard and garden, games room, bicycle hire and rides in a pony and cart, swimming pool. Out of season discounts available. Near Conques, Figeac, Rocamadour, Rodez, Laguiole, and Salers. Open all year.
PRICES: s €27–€32; d €37–€41; t €46–€50 **ON SITE:** Swimming pool Hiking **NEARBY:** Horse riding (3km) Fishing (1km) Tennis (3km) Sailing (45km) Railway station (10km) Shops (10km) MAURS (10km)
NOTES: Pets admitted

LIEUTADES

♥♥♥ ♥ 🍴 Le Bourg Denise GILIBERT-DEVORS
Esclauzet, 15110 LIEUTADES
☎ 04 71 73 83 16 📠 04 71 73 82 36

This friendly house offers four centrally heated rooms on the first and second floors. There are two double rooms and two family rooms with a double and a single bed and a cot is available. Each room has its own shower room and wc. There is a communal lounge with TV, library, video and board games. Outside are pétanque, badminton and garden furniture.
PRICES: s €30; d €40; t €55; dinner €10 **ON SITE:** Children's play area

Hiking Tennis **NEARBY:** Horse riding (18km) Fishing (3km) Swimming pool (5km) Cross-country skiing (7km) Sailing (20km) Railway station (50km) Shops (15km) CHAUDES AIGUES (15km) **NOTES:** Pets admitted

LORCIERES

♥♥♥ 🍴 Le Bourg Clement & Odette COUTAREL
15320 LORCIERES
☎ 04 71 23 49 79 & 04 71 78 06 19

Odette and Clément Coutarel welcome you to their family home and will introduce you to local life and the best walks and places to visit. The four rooms are on the first floor with level access. Two of the rooms contain a double and a single bed, one room is a double and one a twin, all with their own shower room and wc. The communal lounge has an alcove and *cantou*. The table d'hôte meals offer a range of local specialities such as *truffade* and *aligot*.
PRICES: s €34; d €40; t €53; dinner €12 **ON SITE:** Fishing Hiking **NEARBY:** Horse riding (5km) Swimming pool (9km) Cross-country skiing (40km) Tennis (9km) Sailing (14km) Railway station (20km) Shops (9km) RUYNES EN MARGERIDE (10km) **NOTES:** No pets

MAURS

♥♥♥ ♥ 🍴 La Drulhe Annie et Michel SEYROLLES
15600 MAURS
☎ 04 71 49 07 33 📠 04 71 49 07 33

A recently renovated house on a cattle farm. Four rooms are in an annexe with a lounge and terrace. Two double rooms on the ground floor, one with an additional single bed, both with private bathrooms and wcs. On the first floor is a room with double bed - cot and changing table available - and a room with one double and one single bed. Each room has its own shower room and wc. Electric heating, courtyard and garden. Shops 5km. Nearby: the lakes of Figeac and Tolerme and the Vallée du Lot. Open all year.
PRICES: s €28; d €37; t €50; dinner €11 **ON SITE:** Hiking **NEARBY:** Horse riding (10km) Fishing (1km) Swimming pool (5km) Tennis (5km) Sailing (15km) Railway station (5km) Shops (5km) MAURS (5km) **NOTES:** Pets admitted

ORADOUR

♥♥♥ 🍴 La Roseraie Brigitte DUSSUELLE
le Bourg, 15260 ORADOUR
☎ 04 71 23 92 43 📠 04 71 23 94 55
e-mail: laroseraie@bigfoot.com

La Roseraie is a 19th-century house in wooded parkland with three rooms on the second floor. One room has a queen size bed and en suite bath and wc, a double and a twin have private wc and shower. The dining room and lounge, with fireplace, are shared. Central heating. Washing machine and cot available. Table d'hôte meals must be reserved. Shops in Pierrefort. Places to visit include Chaudes Aigues at 30km, Gorges de la Truyère, Plomb du Cantal and the Viaduc de Garabit. Open 15 March to 15 November.
PRICES: s €32; d €38; dinner €12 **ON SITE:** Hiking **NEARBY:** Horse riding (15km) Fishing (3km) Swimming pool (9km) Cross-country skiing (7km) Downhill skiing (28km) Tennis (9km) Sailing (17km) Railway station (25km) Shops (9km) PIERREFORT (9km) **NOTES:** No pets English spoken

♥♥♥ Lieuriac Gerard WEIL & Catherine GIRAUD
15260 ORADOUR
☎ 04 71 23 39 78
e-mail: GWherisson@aol.com

An interesting house with panoramic views. Rooms have their own entrance. On the ground floor of the owners' house is a grade 2 double room with a private, small shower room and shared wc. There are three further rooms with mezzanines and their own shower rooms and wcs. One is a double room, one a twin and one

continued   continued

room has a double bed, a single bed and an additional bed available. Guest lounge with fireplace and a kitchenette looking out over the courtyard. Central heating and washing machine. Orchard with seating. Nearby: hot springs, Neuvéglise, Chaudes Aigues, the Gorges de la Truyère, Pierrefort (11 km).
PRICES: s €27-€29; d €30-€36; t €43　**ON SITE:** Hiking
NEARBY: Horse riding (12km)　Fishing (12km)　Swimming pool (11km)　Cross-country skiing (7km)　Tennis (11km)　Sailing (20km)　Railway station (22km)　Shops (11km)　PIERREFORT (12km)　**NOTES:** No pets

PERS

▥ ❦ Viescamp Charles et Janine LACAZE
ferme accueil de Viescamp, 15290 PERS
☎ 04 71 62 25 14　📠 04 71 62 28 66
Five rooms in a 19th-century barn on a farm that also offers a self-catering cottage, flats and camping. Three double rooms with an additional single bed and two twin rooms each with a shower room and wc and electric heating. Lounge with fireplace, games room, kitchenette, reading room, garden, meadow, playground, covered shelter and private lake. Also a swimming pool on site, farm goods for sale, stabling for horses, water sports and footpaths. The river is 500 m away and nearby are the Barrage de Saint Etienne Cantalès. Le Rouget is 4km and Aurillac 22km. Discounts during low season.
PRICES: s €31; d €40; t €55　**ON SITE:** Children's play area　Fishing　Swimming pool　**NEARBY:** Horse riding (6km)　Hiking (1km)　Cross-country skiing (60km)　Downhill skiing (60km)　Tennis (5km)　Sailing (4km)　Railway station (4km)　Shops (4km)　SAINT-MAMET (10km)　**NOTES:** No pets

POLMINHAC

▥ Costes-Bas Nicolas & Nathalie TRICHEREAU
15800 POLMINHAC
☎ 04 71 43 17 84 & 06 07 37 05 98
e-mail: estive@free.fr http://estive.free.fr/site.web/index.htm
On the edge of the Coyan plateau, overlooking a small valley, is this charming 19th-century barn. Four rooms: Azur, Fruitee and Ocean with a double and single bed in each, or Champetre with a double bed and a cot. Each has a private shower room, wc and electric heating. Shared lounge and kitchen. Also a swimming pool, walks, fishing, hunting. Shops and restaurants are 5km away. Vic/Cère 9km. Super-Lioran 29km. Open all year.
PRICES: s €38; d €43; t €53　**ON SITE:** Swimming pool　Hiking
NEARBY: Horse riding (7km)　Fishing (5km)　Cross-country skiing (29km)　Downhill skiing (29km)　Tennis (5km)　Sailing (20km)　Railway station (10km)　Shops (5km)　VIC SUR CERE (9km)　**NOTES:** No pets

ROFFIAC

▥ Le Bourg Jean Louis & Josette BROUARD
15100 ROFFIAC
☎ 04 71 60 45 75
Three rooms with a private entrance in the owners' house. Two doubles, one room with two single beds, each with their own bathroom and wc and central heating. The lounge is reserved for guests and there is a terrace and garden. There is a farmhouse hotel 300m away. Visit the Viaduc de Garabit, Château d'Alleuze, Château du Saillant and Chaudes Aigues, 30km. Open all year.
PRICES: s €35; d €40　**ON SITE:** Fishing　Hiking　**NEARBY:** Horse riding (3km)　Swimming pool (3km)　Cross-country skiing (30km)　Downhill skiing (30km)　Tennis (3km)　Sailing (15km)　Railway station (3km)　Shops (3km)　SAINT FLOUR (3km)　**NOTES:** No pets

▥ ❦ ⍥ Mazerat Mado & Raymond BERGAUD
le Ruisselet, 15100 ROFFIAC
☎ 04 71 60 11 33　📠 04 71 60 38 64
Five rooms on a farm in a house adjoining the owners'. Four grade 3 rooms with electric heating. Two rooms with mezzanine

containing a double and a single bed, one double room and one twin room. One grade 1 room with a double and a single bed. Each room has a private shower room and wc. The lounge has TV, and open fire and a library. Dining room. Child discount available. On site are a ferme auberge and camping, children's games, and a garden with seating. The popular city of St-Flour is 4 km away, or visit the Sailhant waterfall and the Viaduc de Garabit.
PRICES: ; d €41; dinner €12　**ON SITE:** Children's play area　Fishing
NEARBY: Horse riding (4km)　Swimming pool (4km)　Cross-country skiing (14km)　Tennis (4km)　Sailing (18km)　Railway station (4km)　Shops (4km)　Restaurant nearby　SAINT FLOUR (4km)　**NOTES:** Pets admitted

SAIGNES

▥ La Vigne Colette CHANET
15240 SAIGNES
☎ 04 71 40 61 02 & 06 73 08 67 20　📠 04 71 40 61 02
Five rooms in an 18th-century mansion. Two grade 3 double bedded rooms, along with two grade 2 rooms, one double, and one family suite with two double bedded rooms. All have private shower rooms. Central heating. Dining room and lounge with TV. Access to a kitchenette and washing machine. Courtyard and enclosed garden with furniture, shady park, private swimming pool, table tennis and camping. Out of season discounts. Local festivals in summer, three restaurants within 300 m, trail bike hire, châteaux and churches, the Parc des Volcans and Bort Les Orgues.
PRICES: s €30; d €40-€41　**ON SITE:** Swimming pool　**NEARBY:** Horse riding (8km)　Fishing (2km)　Hiking (1km)　Tennis (1km)　Sailing (8km)　Railway station (8km)　Shops (1km)　SAIGNES (1km)　**NOTES:** Pets admitted

SAINT CERNIN

▥ ❦ Lamourio Paul & Solange FEREROL
15310 SAINT CERNIN
☎ 04 71 47 67 37　📠 04 71 47 67 37
Three double rooms in an annexe to the owners' house on a farm. Private bathrooms with wc. Lounge for guests, with TV and telephone. Garden with seating. Food is available 4km away in St Cernin. Visit Tournemire 6km, Salers 20km or Mauriac 25km. Open all year.
PRICES: d €38　**ON SITE:** Fishing　Hiking　**NEARBY:** Horse riding (4km)　Swimming pool (10km)　Cross-country skiing (20km)　Tennis (4km)　Railway station (25km)　Shops (4km)　SAINT-CERNIN (4km)　**NOTES:** No pets

SAINT ETIENNE DE CARLAT

▥ ⍥ Lou Ferradou Jacky BALLEUX
Caizac, 15130 SAINT ETIENNE DE CARLAT
☎ 04 71 62 42 37　📠 04 71 62 42 37
e-mail: fballeux@m6net.fr
This traditional, stone-built Auvergne house offers a warm welcome. Three rooms are on the first floor of a renovated annexe, one is a large room with a double and two single beds. There are also a double room and a twin room, while on the ground floor are a double room and a room with a double and two single beds. All have private facilities. Dining room has fireplace and seating. There is a lounge in an old barn. Table tennis. Visit the local châteaux, Monts du Cantal, Vallée de la Cère, 12km or Aurillac 15km. Open all year.
PRICES: d €38-€43; dinner €11　**ON SITE:** Fishing　Hiking
NEARBY: Horse riding (10km)　Swimming pool (12km)　Cross-country skiing (20km)　Downhill skiing (40km)　Tennis (10km)　Sailing (30km)　Railway station (15km)　Shops (12km)　VIC SUR CERE (12km)　**NOTES:** No pets

continued

AUVERGNE

SAINT JUST

♨ ♈ Le Saladou Roger FALCON
15320 SAINT JUST
☎ 04 71 73 70 77 📠 04 71 73 70 77
Four rooms on the first floor of the owner's house. Three grade 3 rooms, two containing a double and a single bed and one double room. One grade 2 room with a double and a single bed. All have private facilities. Guests share the dining room with the owner but have sole use of a lounge with TV, fridge, microwave, library and children's games. Electric heating. Games in the garden. Nearby the Viaduc de Garabit and Cirque de Mallet. 15km from St Flour.
PRICES: d €30-€38; t €40-€47 **ON SITE:** Children's play area Hiking
NEARBY: Horse riding (7km) Fishing (1km) Swimming pool (3km) Cross-country skiing (35km) Tennis (3km) Sailing (7km) Railway station (15km) Shops (5km) RUYNES EN MARGERIDE (12km) **NOTES:** Pets admitted

SAINT MARTIN CANTALES

♨ ♈ ⦿ Sept Fons Jean-Louis & Denise CHANUT
15140 SAINT MARTIN CANTALES
☎ 04 71 69 40 58 e-mail: jean-louis.chanut@wanadoo.fr
Stay on the first floor of the owners' lovely property in the heart of the country. Two grade 3 double rooms with private shower room and wc. One of the rooms can also take two single beds for an extra €23. There is also a grade 2 twin room with its own bathroom and wc. Shared dining room and lounge. Central heating. Garden seating. Nearby attractions 10 km to Martin Valmeroux, or visit Salers, the Château d'Anjony and Lac d'Enchanet. Open May to September.
PRICES: s €30; d €35; dinner €11 **ON SITE:** Hiking **NEARBY:** Horse riding (10km) Fishing (2km) Swimming pool (10km) Cross-country skiing (25km) Downhill skiing (70km) Tennis (10km) Sailing (7km) Railway station (20km) Shops (9km) PLEAUX (24km) **NOTES:** No pets

SAINT MARY LE PLAIN

♨ ♈ ⦿ Nozerolles Bernard et Maryse CHALIER
15500 SAINT MARY LE PLAIN
☎ 04 71 23 05 80
Maryse, Bernard and their children welcome guests to three recently decorated rooms in their large house. One room has a double and a single bed, another a double bed and small lounge with a double bed settee. The third room is a double. There are private bathroom facilities and central heating. The living room with open fire is shared. Courtyard, open garden and regional products served at meals. St Flour 18km.
PRICES: s €34; d €40; t €49; dinner €10 **ON SITE:** Hiking
NEARBY: Horse riding (18km) Fishing (3km) Swimming pool (13km) Cross-country skiing (35km) Tennis (13km) Sailing (30km) Railway station (18km) Shops (13km) MASSIAC (13km) **NOTES:** Pets admitted

SAINT PROJET DE SALERS

♨ Le Bourg Thérèse CHAMBON
15140 SAINT PROJET DE SALERS
☎ 04 71 69 23 01
A family welcome in the heart of the Parc des Volcans. Three rooms with a private entrance on the top floor of the owner's house. Two are doubles, while the third has a double and a single bed. All have private facilities. Sitting room reserved for guests with a kitchenette and another lounge with open fire shared with the owners. Facilities include heating, a terrace, a courtyard, and a garden. Out of season discounts are available. Visit the Vallée de la Bertrande and Monts du Cantal. Open 1 May to 30 October.
PRICES: s €27; d €34; t €46 **ON SITE:** Fishing Hiking **NEARBY:** Horse riding (10km) Swimming pool (15km) Cross-country skiing (10km) Tennis (15km) Sailing (25km) Railway station (30km) SALERS (14km) **NOTES:** No pets

SALERS

♨ Chambre d'hôtes Emmanuel BRAY
avenue de Barrouze, 15140 SALERS
☎ 04 71 40 78 08
Three large rooms in an early 19th-century house, renovated in 2000, at the heart of the medieval city. All three rooms contain a double bed and have private shower rooms and wc, one room has a sitting area. The dining room has a TV and fireplace. Terrace and garden. Homemade jam served at breakfast with *bourriols* and farmhouse butter. Discounts for children, and during low season.
PRICES: s €30-€38; d €37-€44 **ON SITE:** Hiking Tennis
NEARBY: Horse riding (10km) Fishing (3km) Swimming pool (8km) Cross-country skiing (10km) Railway station (18km) SALERS **NOTES:** Pets admitted English spoken

♨ Le Bourg Philippe PRUDENT
rue des Nobles, 15140 SALERS
☎ 04 71 40 75 34 📠 04 71 40 75 36
18th-century house in a medieval city with six double rooms that have a private entrance. Two rooms will take an extra bed. Small, private shower rooms and wcs. The communal dining room has an open fire. The garden enjoys some splendid views. Local facilities include climbing, museum, exhibitions and restaurants in the village. Puy Mary and Mauriac 18km.
PRICES: s €34; d €37; t €47 **ON SITE:** Hiking Tennis **NEARBY:** Horse riding (10km) Fishing (3km) Swimming pool (8km) Cross-country skiing (10km) Railway station (18km) SALERS **NOTES:** Pets admitted

♨ Chambre d'hôtes Jean Pierre VANTAL
route du Puy Mary, 15140 SALERS
☎ 04 71 40 74 02 📠 04 71 40 74 02
e-mail: eliane.vantal@wanadoo.fr
Four rooms with their own entrance on the first floor of the owner's house. A double, a twin room, a double bedded room and a room with a double and a single bed. All have private facilities. Dayroom and lounge with TV. Seating in the garden, children's games and private parking. Tourist tax is included in the price. Nearby are crafts, museums, exhibitions, walk the GR400 or visit Puy Mary. Monts du Cantal.
PRICES: s €36-€39; d €40-€44; t €50 **ON SITE:** Children's play area Hiking **NEARBY:** Horse riding (8km) Fishing (5km) Swimming pool (11km) Cross-country skiing (8km) Tennis (1km) Railway station (18km) Shops (1km) SALERS (1km) **NOTES:** Pets admitted

VEBRET

♨ ⦿ Cheyssac Muguette REBIERE
15240 VEBRET
☎ 04 71 40 21 83
Two grade 3 rooms, one double with access through the owner's house. The other contains a double bed and a double bed settee, and has its own entrance. There are three grade 2 rooms on the first floor. One contains a double and a single bed, while the other two are doubles. All rooms have private facilities. Shared dining room and lounge with fireplace and TV. Kitchenette available. Garden furniture, barbecue and children's games. Out of season discounts. Visit Bort-les-Orgues (5 km), Château de Val and the dam.
PRICES: s €30; d €34-€38; t €46; dinner €9 **ON SITE:** Children's play area Fishing Hiking **NEARBY:** Horse riding (5km) Swimming pool (5km) Tennis (5km) Sailing (6km) Railway station (5km) Shops (5km) SAIGNES (10km) **NOTES:** Pets admitted

♨ ♈ ⦿ Verchalles Guy & Simone GALVAING
15240 VEBRET
☎ 04 71 40 21 58 & 04 71 40 24 20
e-mail: guy-galvaing@wanadoo.fr
Six guest rooms including two grade 2 rooms on the first floor: one double, and one containing a double and a single bed. There

continued

are four grade 3 rooms in an annexe: one double room, and three rooms containing a double and a single bed. All have private facilities. Shared lounge with TV, library, fireplace, central heating, a terrace, grounds with garden furniture and private swimming pool. Children's toys, table tennis, trail bike hire, camping on the farm, and a washing machine. Supplement payable for pets, discounts available for children and out of season. Nearby are Bort-les-Orgues (5 km) and Château de Val.
PRICES: d €43; t €52; dinner €10 **ON SITE:** Children's play area Swimming pool Tennis **NEARBY:** Horse riding (10km) Fishing (1km) Sailing (10km) Railway station (5km) Shops (3km) SAIGNES (8km) **NOTES:** Pets admitted

VIC SUR CERE

♦♦♦ ♥ ⭕ **La Prade** Auguste & Noelle DELRIEU
15800 VIC SUR CERE
☎ 04 71 47 51 64
Three grade 3 rooms in a 14th-century farmhouse. One double room, one room with a double and a single bed and one suite with two double bedded rooms. Private bathroom facilities. One grade 2 double room with private shower room and wc nearby. There is heating, telephone, TV, open fire, library, garden, and play area. Family cooking offering regional dishes and home made jams for breakfast. Discounts for children. Aurillac is 20km away and there are numerous waterfalls to visit, the Vallée de la Cère and the Monts du Cantal, health resort and spa of Vic Sur Cère.
PRICES: d €40; dinner €11 **ON SITE:** Children's play area Fishing Hiking **NEARBY:** Horse riding (1km) Swimming pool (1km) Cross-country skiing (5km) Downhill skiing (17km) Tennis (1km) Railway station (1km) Shops (1km) **NOTES:** No pets

HAUTE-LOIRE

ALLEGRE

♦♦♦ ⭕ **L'Ancienne Baronnie**
Stéphanie et Fabien CHARREYRE
5 place du Marchédial, 43270 ALLEGRE
☎ 04 71 00 22 44 ▤ 04 71 00 22 44
La Chaise Dieu 10 km. Le Puy en Velay 25 km. This typical 15th-century building, with elegant, antique furniture, is situated between the gorges of the Loire and the stunning countryside of the Allier region. There are five bedrooms with private bathrooms: two double bedrooms and three bedrooms with a lounge; one with an open fireplace and a balcony. Small lounge area with TV and a large dining room with an open fireplace. Open all year.
PRICES: d €35-€45; dinner €15 **ON SITE:** Children's play area Hiking **NEARBY:** Horse riding (9km) Fishing (5km) Swimming pool (5km) Cross-country skiing (1km) Railway station (20km) **NOTES:** Pets admitted English spoken

ALLY

♦♦♦ ♥ ⭕ **Chambre d'hôtes**
Paul et Marie MASSEBOEUF
43380 ALLY
☎ 04 71 76 78 34
Near the Allier gorges, in the peaceful windmill country between Velay and the volcanic Puy area, this house is on a farm. The hosts, Marie and Paul, provide a warm welcome and meals using produce straight from the farm and garden. All the bedrooms have private bathrooms and there is a communal eating area with open fireplace, a library, lounge and covered terrace. There are discounts for meals for children under ten. The rate for four people is 49 Euros. Accommodation is available all year.
PRICES: s €26; d €32; t €40; extra person €9; dinner €11 **ON SITE:** Fishing Hiking **NEARBY:** Bathing (10km) Horse riding (15km) Swimming pool (22km) Tennis (22km) Railway station (22km) **NOTES:** Pets admitted

BAINS

♦♦♦ ♥ ⭕ **Chambre d'hôtes** Patricia et Daniel RAVEYRE
Route du Puy, 43370 BAINS
☎ 04 71 57 51 79 & 06 83 59 93 47
In a village, at the heart of the volcanic region, Patricia and Daniel offer you a warm welcome. Their renovated home is full of character and is situated on the outskirts of a market town. All of the bedrooms have a bathroom, wc and TV. Outside there is a garden and private parking. Fresh farm produce is offered and the young owners are happy to help guests discover and get the most out of this beautiful region. The property is near the Saint-Jacques-de-Compostelle pilgrimage route. Open all year.
PRICES: s €24; d €30; t €37; dinner €11 **ON SITE:** Hiking Cross-country skiing Tennis **NEARBY:** Bathing (12km) Horse riding (6km) Fishing (12km) Swimming pool (10km) Railway station (10km) **NOTES:** Pets admitted English spoken

♦♦♦ ⭕ **Fay** Caroline DE RANCOURT
43370 BAINS
☎ 04 71 57 55 19 ▤ 04 71 57 55 19
Le Puy-en-Velay 12 km. In the volcanic Velay region, known for its remarkable volcanic craters, lakes and picturesque villages, this carefully preserved country house is full of character and situated in a lovely village. All bedrooms are non smoking, have en suite bathrooms and antique furniture. There is also a lounge and open fireplace. Traditional cooking is available and outside there are horseboxes, a park, and garage. Pick up of walkers and luggage can be arranged on request and discounts are available for off-peak holidays. Open all year (reservation is recommended).
PRICES: s €27; d €34; t €38; dinner €13 **ON SITE:** Hiking **NEARBY:** Bathing (15km) Horse riding (13km) Fishing (13km) Swimming pool (13km) Cross-country skiing (13km) Railway station (12km) Shops (2km) Golf (7km) **NOTES:** No pets English spoken

♦♦♦ ♥ **Jalasset** Marcel et Monique PELISSE
43370 BAINS
☎ 04 71 57 52 72 ▤ 04 71 57 52 84
This restored farmhouse can be found deep in the countryside, in a small, peaceful hamlet. There are two double bedrooms, a room for three and one for four: all with shower rooms and wc. The lounge has a TV, book library and open fireplace. Outside, there is a garden, parking area, and play area. Meals can be ordered and are made from farm produce. There are also restaurants just 1km away. The house is situated in the volcanic Velay region near Livradois-Foez. Open all year.
PRICES: s €24; d €30; t €37; extra person €6 **ON SITE:** Hiking Cross-country skiing **NEARBY:** Bathing (12km) Horse riding (1km) Fishing (5km) Swimming pool (9km) Tennis (1km) Railway station (12km) Shops (1km) **NOTES:** Pets admitted

BLESLE

♦♦♦ ⭕ **Bousselargues** Michel et Gisèle LUBIN
43450 BLESLE
☎ 04 71 76 27 38 ▤ 04 71 76 27 38
Brioude 20 km. Massiac 8 km. This tiny village, near Blesle, is a typical Cezallier village and is classed as one of the most beautiful in France. The building is a restored winegrower's house, with two bedrooms for three people and one grade 2, double bedroom for four people. There is also a lounge with open fireplace and a dining room. Outside, there are terraces and a parking area. Open all year (reservations necessary from 14th November - 1st April).
PRICES: s €35; d €40; extra person €8; dinner €12 **ON SITE:** Children's play area Fishing Hiking **NEARBY:** Bathing (20km) Horse riding (4km) Swimming pool (8km) Cross-country skiing (10km) Railway station (8km) Shops (4km) **NOTES:** No pets English spoken

AUVERGNE

BOISSET

♥ Le Ponteil André et Catherine PONCET
43500 BOISSET
☎ 04 71 61 31 91 🖹 04 71 75 25 04
Le Puy-en-Velay 25 km. La Chaise Dieu 32 km. In a house attached to the owners' house, in a lovely forest area well known for its variety of wild fruit and mushrooms. Each bedroom has its own bathroom and there is a communal lounge with a kitchen area. Outside, there is a terrace and farm produce is available. Ideal for relaxation, rambling and fishing. There is also a restaurant 1km away. Open all year.
PRICES: s €27; d €34; t €43 **ON SITE:** Hiking Tennis
NEARBY: Bathing (8km) Horse riding (8km) Fishing (2km) Swimming pool (9km) Railway station (28km) Shops (5km) **NOTES:** Pets admitted

BONNEVAL

ℂℂℂ ⏃⏃ Chambre d'hôtes Catherine HAYS
43160 BONNEVAL
☎ 04 71 00 07 47
This old inn has been restored by an English couple who are artists. Catherine and William guarantee a very convivial stay in this picturesque village of Parc Livradois/Forez. Each bedroom has its own wc and shower room - one is a suite. There are also two, communal rooms each with open fireplace. A large terrace area and garden, providing beautiful countryside views. The imposing abbey La Chaise-Dieu, famous for its prestigious music festival, is nearby and looks down over the forests. The house is available from 1st April to 1st November: in winter, weekends and on bank holidays, groups are preferred.
PRICES: s €41; d €48-€53; extra person €15; dinner €19
ON SITE: Fishing Hiking **NEARBY:** Bathing (6km) Horse riding (6km) Cross-country skiing (6km) Tennis (7km) Railway station (40km) Shops (5km) **NOTES:** Pets admitted English spoken

BOURNONCLE-SAINT-PIERRE

ℂℂℂ ♥ ⏃⏃ ⛦ Bard Bernard & Christiane CHAZELLE
43360 BOURNONCLE-SAINT-PIERRE
☎ 04 71 76 01 12 🖹 04 71 76 01 12
This modern house has bedrooms with en suite bathroom on the first and ground floors. Communal lounge room with open fireplace and TV. Terrace, garden and car parking area. Discount for children's meals (under nine) €6.1. The owners speak some English. Nearby Briode is known for the magnificent Roman basilica of Auvergne, the Maison du Saumon (salmon museum) and the old quarters, and also worth exploring are the picturesque gorges of Allier and Allagnon. Farm produce available. Open 15 March to 13 October.
PRICES: s €27; d €38; t €46; extra person €12; dinner €11
ON SITE: Hiking **NEARBY:** Bathing (10km) Horse riding (12km) Fishing (7km) Swimming pool (7km) Railway station (4km) Shops (4km)
NOTES: Pets admitted

CHANTEUGES

ℂℂℂ ⏃⏃ Chambre d'hôtes Marloes DER KINDEREN
43300 CHANTEUGES
☎ 04 71 74 01 91
e-mail: mail@artedu.nl www.artedu.nl
Le Puy-en-Velay 40 km. Gorges de l'Allier 1 km. This beautifully renovated, 15th-century house lies at the foot of the Roman abbey. With lots of character, this building was built from a 12th/13th - century cellar. There are a number of spacious rooms available, each with private bathroom and antique furniture. Lounge room with open fireplace; garden and terrace outside with a wonderful view over the village and Allier region. Creative art workshops available for individuals or groups. There are a number of Roman

churches in the gorges of Allier and the area is known for salmon and the river's rushing white water. Evening meals available on request. Open April to November (group bookings necessary in winter).
PRICES: s €69-€76; d €69-€91 **ON SITE:** Fishing Hiking
NEARBY: Bathing (1km) Horse riding (5km) Swimming pool (5km) Railway station (5km) Shops (5km) **NOTES:** No pets English spoken

CHASPINHAC

ℂℂℂ ⏅⏅ LA PARAVENT Daniel et Chantal CLAVEL
43700 CHASPINHAC
☎ 04 71 03 54 75 🖹 04 71 03 54 75
This house has lots of character and is an ideal spot for relaxation, as it lies in a lovely position near le Puy-en-Velay, with wonderful views over the Puy basin. The spacious, contemporary bedrooms each have a lounge area and a bathroom. There is a leisure room, library and a large garden. There is a restaurant 200m away and patchwork courses are held in November, and between January and March (closed on Sunday evenings). Open all year.
PRICES: d €46; extra person €9 **ON SITE:** Hiking **NEARBY:** Bathing (5km) Horse riding (2km) Fishing (4km) Swimming pool (5km) Tennis (4km) Railway station (10km) Shops (4km) **NOTES:** No pets

CHASPUZAC

ℂℂℂ ⏅⏅ Chambre d'hôtes Robert PILLAY
43320 CHASPUZAC
☎ 04 71 08 68 50 🖹 04 71 08 68 85
e-mail: robert.pillay@wanadoo.fr
This 1678 restored farmhouse with lots of character lies in a village at the heart of the volcanic region of Puy-en-Velay. There are two double bedrooms, one bedroom for three and two bedrooms for four, each with private bathrooms. Other rooms include a lounge with a beautiful old, open fireplace and a dining/kitchen room. Outside, there is an enclosed courtyard. Robert, the owner, is a passionate rambler and will be happy to create tasty meals for you and help you to enjoy the surrounding area. Aerial sports possible (1 km). Open all year.
PRICES: s €25; d €33; t €41; extra person €8; dinner €12
ON SITE: Hiking **NEARBY:** Bathing (10km) Horse riding (8km) Fishing (7km) Swimming pool (10km) Cross-country skiing (8km) Tennis (10km) Railway station (10km) Shops (2km) **NOTES:** Pets admitted English spoken

CHOMELIX

ℂℂℂ ⏃⏃ Fournac Monique et Raymond DAUDEL
43500 CHOMELIX
☎ 04 71 03 62 62
In a completely restored building, next to the owners' house, this property is in the forests in the southern part of the Livradois/Forez Park. Music lovers will be interested in the festivals nearby: the Chaise-Dieu music festival (end of August/beginning of September) is 17km away and Craponne country music festival (end of July) is 10km away. Each bedroom has a private bathroom. In addition, there is a dining room with fireplace, lounge room and terrace. A farm, inn and restaurants are only 3km away. Open 15 July to 15 September.
PRICES: d €36; t €47 **ON SITE:** Hiking **NEARBY:** Swimming pool (7km) Tennis (3km) Railway station (30km) Shops (3km) **NOTES:** No pets

COHADE

ℂℂℂ ⏃⏃ ⏅⏅ Chambre d'hôtes
Pierre et Roselyne CURABET
43100 COHADE
☎ 04 71 50 28 50 🖹 04 71 74 82 20

continued

continued

AUVERGNE

Accommodation is provided in a building next to the owners' farmhouse. There is a lounge with fireplace and TV, a dining room, kitchen and terrace. Farm produce is available on this mixed farm, which specialises in cattle farming. The owners speak some English and Dutch. Meals are available on request. Open all year.
PRICES: s €30; d €38-€45; t €50-€55; extra person €5-€10; dinner €11 **ON SITE:** Hiking **NEARBY:** Bathing (5km) Horse riding (1km) Fishing (1km) Swimming pool (5km) Tennis (5km) Railway station (4km) Shops (4km) **NOTES:** Pets admitted

CRAPONNE-SUR-ARZON

▦ La Crapounette Marie-Claude ROUYER
Doulioux, 43500 CRAPONNE-SUR-ARZON
☎ 04 71 03 20 32 🖹 04 71 03 20 32
La Chaise-Dieu 15 km. Le Puy en Velay 36 km. This beautiful restored, stone farmhouse is situated in the Livradois Forez Park. The area is well known for its music festival, country music festival (in July), lava flow formations and numerous walking routes. There are three bedrooms with private bathrooms and a big lounge with fireplace, television area, library and board games. There is also a garden with children's play area. Open beginning July to end August only. Sleeps nine.
PRICES: s €38; d €46-€53; extra person €12-€15 **ON SITE:** Children's play area Hiking **NEARBY:** Horse riding (12km) Fishing (2km) Swimming pool (2km) Railway station (20km) Shops (2km) **NOTES:** No pets

▦ ⚈ Paulagnac Béate KNOP
43500 CRAPONNE-SUR-ARZON
☎ 04 71 03 26 37 🖹 04 71 03 26 37
e-mail: celivier@infonie.fr

La Chaise-Dieu 20 km. Le Puy-en-Velay 40 km. This beautifully restored, welcoming house, which lies in the Livradois-Forez Park, near La Chaise-Dieu (famous for its music festival) contains two bedrooms with en suite bathrooms and three bedrooms with separate private bathrooms. There is a lounge with fireplace, TV, library, piano, and board games. The huge terrace is the ideal spot for relaxation, and regional, international and vegetarian meals can be prepared on request. Open all year.
PRICES: s €40; d €48; extra person €12; dinner €19 **ON SITE:** Wine tasting Children's play area Hiking **NEARBY:** Bathing (4km) Horse riding (4km) Fishing (2km) Swimming pool (2km) Railway station (25km) **NOTES:** No pets CC English spoken

FAY-SUR-LIGNON

▦ ⚈ ⚈ Abries T BOUTARIN et B DESAGE
43430 FAY-SUR-LIGNON
☎ 04 71 59 56 66 🖹 04 71 56 31 89
This restored stone house is situated on a goat farm and offers bedrooms, each with a private bathroom. There is also a dining room, lounge and library and a terrace outside. Thérèse and Bernard offer you a warm welcome to their house and will be happy to help you enjoy this region. Evening meals and farm produce are available on request. Open all year.
PRICES: s €30; d €40; t €50; extra person €10; dinner €14 **ON SITE:** Fishing Hiking **NEARBY:** Bathing (8km) Horse riding (1km) Swimming pool (25km) Cross-country skiing (8km) Tennis (8km) Railway station (40km) Shops (5km) **NOTES:** Pets admitted English spoken

GREZES

▦ ⚈ ⚈ Bugeac Paul et Martine CUBIZOLLE
43170 GREZES
☎ 04 71 74 45 30 🖹 04 71 74 45 30
Accommodation is available on this small dairy farm, in the heart of Gevaudan. There are two double beds and seven single beds; four of these are enclosed in a separate room. Each bedroom has a private shower room and wc. There is also a lounge, dining room and a charming garden. This old farm is typical of the region with its mix of austere granite and warm wood. Bread, salamis, meat, vegetables, cheeses, jams, honey are all served as specialities of the house. Open all year.
PRICES: d €34; t €43; dinner €11 **ON SITE:** Fishing Hiking **NEARBY:** Bathing (10km) Horse riding (10km) Swimming pool (10km) Tennis (10km) Railway station (25km) Shops (10km) **NOTES:** No pets English spoken

JULLIANGES

▦ ▦ Chambre d'hôtes Michele MEJEAN
Domaine de la Valette, 43500 JULLIANGES
☎ 04 71 03 23 35 & 06 08 28 32 52
A pleasurable stay is guaranteed, in the calm atmosphere of this amazing 19th century, granite manor house, with its large open fireplace in the drawing room and antique furniture. Outside there is a tree and flower-lined park. The spacious bedrooms each have a private bathroom (two of the bedrooms are suites). Large lounge with open fireplace. Drawing room and library. Kitchen and garage available for guest use, as is the TV and a covered parking area. Meals and food can be provided. The property is located between Forez, Auvergne and Velay. Reservations in advance in school holidays.
PRICES: s €56; d €64; extra person €18 **ON SITE:** Hiking Tennis **NEARBY:** Bathing (12km) Horse riding (12km) Fishing (2km) Swimming pool (8km) Cross-country skiing (12km) Restaurant nearby **NOTES:** Pets admitted English spoken

LA CHAISE-DIEU

▦ ⚈ Chambre d'hôtes Jacqueline CHAILLY
Rue Marchedial, La Jacquerolle, 43160 LA CHAISE-DIEU
☎ 04 71 00 07 52
In the Livradois Forez Park, near the famous Chaise-Dieu Abbey, this house has been entirely renovated and is full of character. There are five bedrooms, three of which have private bathrooms and two with separate private shower rooms. All rooms are no smoking. Lounge with open fireplace. Dining room and piano. Terrace area. Picnics and main meals can be prepared on request and a large breakfast of local produce can also be provided. Prestigious music festival held at the abbey nearby. Open all year; outside the high season (July and August) the 7th night is free of charge.
PRICES: s €40; d €49; t €63; extra person €15; dinner €19 **ON SITE:** Hiking Cross-country skiing Tennis **NEARBY:** Bathing (1km) Horse riding (1km) Fishing (1km) Railway station (40km) **NOTES:** No pets English spoken

CC - credit cards accepted

continued

AUVERGNE

LAPTE

⚒ 🐓 🍽 ♿ Les Brus de Verne
Auguste et Josette MOUNIER
43200 LAPTE
☎ 04 71 59 38 30   📠 04 71 59 38 30
In a peaceful village setting, this restored old farmhouse, is linked
to the owners' house. There are five comfortable bedrooms with
private bathrooms (one bedroom has a mezzanine level). There is
also a large communal room with fireplace and a small kitchen.
Outside there is a courtyard and a terrace. This forest region is
ideal for rambling and is near many tourist routes. Open all year.
PRICES: d €37; t €46; extra person €9; dinner €12 **ON SITE:** Hiking
Cross-country skiing **NEARBY:** Bathing (10km) Horse riding (5km)
Fishing (2km) Swimming pool (10km) Tennis (2km) Railway station
(25km) Shops (6km) **NOTES:** Pets admitted English spoken

LAVAUDIEU

⚒ Chambre d'hôtes Marie ROBERT
43100 LAVAUDIEU
☎ 04 71 76 45 04 & 04 71 50 24 85
In this restored house, linked to the owners' house, there are a
number of twin/double bedrooms with private bathrooms. In
addition, there is a dining room with a lounge area. There is an
amazing panoramic view from the property and two restaurants
on site. The peaceful old fortified village is next to the clear waters
of the Sénouire and surrounded by meadows and wooded
hillsides. The village offers many attractions: the winemakers'
houses, picturesque streets, a Benedictine abbey, a museum,
cloisters and stained-glass windows. Check in any time after 6 pm.
Open between Easter and 15 October.
PRICES: s €40; d €45 **ON SITE:** Fishing Hiking **NEARBY:** Bathing
(9km) Horse riding (5km) Swimming pool (9km) Railway station (9km)
Shops (5km) **NOTES:** No pets

LE BOUCHET-SAINT-NICOLAS

⚒ 🍽 Chambre d'hôtes Augustin et Andrée REYNAUD
43510 LE BOUCHET-SAINT-NICOLAS
☎ 04 71 57 31 91   📠 04 71 57 31 13
This restored house in a village, close to the amazing volcanic area
of Lac du Bouchet, has three guest rooms (one with a mezzanine
area) with private bathrooms. There is also a lounge, dining room
and balcony and a courtyard in front of a garage. Nearby is the
cultivation area for Puy lentils and the Stevenson walking route.
Open all year.
PRICES: s €29; d €34; t €38; extra person €3; dinner €10
ON SITE: Hiking **NEARBY:** Bathing (2km) Horse riding (10km) Fishing
(2km) Swimming pool (15km) Cross-country skiing (2km) Tennis (10km)
Railway station (20km) **NOTES:** Pets admitted

LES ESTABLES

⚒ 🐓 🍽 ♿ Chamard
Bruno et Karine TOMOZYK-HERRY
Les Ecuries du Mézenc, 43150 LES ESTABLES
☎ 04 71 08 30 53   📠 04 71 08 30 53
This typical stone country house has a magnificent view over
Mézenc and the Cévennes. All the guest rooms have private
bathrooms and there is a lounge with kitchen area and dining
room. There is a large outdoor garden and the house is ideally
situated for rambling, tennis and cross-country skiing. Feel relaxed
in the open air or enjoy the local heritage. The house is situated in
the picturesque northern area of Mézenc. Open all year.
PRICES: s €30; d €37; t €44; extra person €7; dinner €13
ON SITE: Hiking Cross-country skiing **NEARBY:** Bathing (10km) Horse
riding (3km) Fishing (3km) Swimming pool (15km) Tennis (3km) Railway
station (35km) Shops (4km) **NOTES:** Pets admitted English spoken

⚒ 🍽 ♿ La Vacheresse Gilles FOURCADE
La Bartette, 43150 LES ESTABLES
☎ 04 71 08 31 70   📠 04 71 08 31 70
This 100-year-old, stone house was totally restored in 1994. Near
Mézenc and on the edge of a stream, this small farm inn offers
several bedrooms. Each has a private bathroom; two have a
mezzanine area. Dining room with open fireplace and a lounge
and library. Local produce available. Many activities available at
the farm and an educational farm centre with Lapland reindeer is
only 200 m away. Discounts are available for children sharing with
their parents and for week-long holidays and stays of over two
nights, out of season. Open all year.
PRICES: s €29; d €45; t €63; extra person €16; dinner €14
ON SITE: Fishing Hiking **NEARBY:** Horse riding (5km) Cross-country
skiing (4km) Railway station (30km) Shops (4km) **NOTES:** Pets admitted
English spoken

LISSAC

⚒ 🐓 🍽 ♿ Freycenet Alain et Nicole SIGAUD
Route de Darsac, 43350 LISSAC
☎ 04 71 57 02 97
This is a new house on a farm. The bedrooms each have a private
bathroom (one is suitable for less mobile guests). Communal
room with fireplace and TV. Outside there is a garden looking out
onto the Velay plateaus. Nicole and Alain offer their farm produce
and will be pleased to help guests make the most of the region.
The dairy herd is kept 2.5 km away and Puy lentils are grown on
the farm. Open all year.
PRICES: s €23; d €30; t €38; dinner €9 **ON SITE:** Hiking
NEARBY: Bathing (6km) Horse riding (6km) Fishing (4km) Swimming
pool (18km) Cross-country skiing (15km) Tennis (6km) Railway station
(1km) Shops (1km) **NOTES:** Pets admitted

LORLANGES

⚒ 🐓 🍽 Lachaud J-Claude et Suzanne BOUDON
43360 LORLANGES
☎ 04 71 76 03 03   📠 04 71 76 03 03
In a hamlet, this renovated farm contains two grade 3 bedrooms
with private bathrooms and three bedrooms with mezzanine levels
(not yet graded). There is also a lounge and drawing room with
fireplace. Outside, there is a garden, terrace area, children's play
area and parking area in an enclosed courtyard. Fishing is possible
in the private lake and camping is also available on the farm. This
hamlet is in the Allier/Margeride region. Open all year.
PRICES: d €45; extra person €10; dinner €11 **ON SITE:** Fishing Hiking
NEARBY: Bathing (9km) Horse riding (9km) Swimming pool (9km)
Tennis (9km) **NOTES:** Pets admitted

MALVALETTE

⚒ 🐓 🍽 La Combe Dany et Jean-Marc BUFARD
43210 MALVALETTE
☎ 04 71 66 77 30 & 06 81 66 48 44
Saint-Etienne 25 km. Le Puy-en-Velay 65 km. This new house is
situated on a goat farm in a small village on the edge of the
Auvergne region. Each bedroom has a private bathroom. There
are private entrances on the ground floor to three bedrooms (with
a mezzanine) for four people and two bedrooms for two people.
Outside there is a covered terrace and an enclosed courtyard. This
is a lively area, with a number of tourist attractions nearby and
ideal for rambling or horse riding. The price for four people is 52
euros. Open all year.
PRICES: s €29; d €38; extra person €8; dinner €12 **ON SITE:** Hiking
NEARBY: Bathing (7km) Horse riding (3km) Fishing (2km) Swimming
pool (8km) Railway station (8km) Shops (8km) **NOTES:** Pets admitted
English spoken

MOUDEYRES

⚐⚐⚐ 🐓 🍴 Le Moulinou Lucia et Bertrand GABORIAUD
43150 MOUDEYRES
☎ 04 71 08 30 52

This welcoming property has a warm family atmosphere. There are five bedrooms with lots of character and a private shower room and wc in each. There is also a drawing room and lounge with a huge fireplace. Outside, there is a terrace, enclosed courtyard and private parking area. The body of the building is a typical 18th-century Mézenc farm. It is situated on a volcanic plateau with peaceful pastures. In winter guests can warm themselves in front of the fire, maybe after a day's skiing, and in the spring and summer there is an abundance of wild flowers to enjoy. Pets admitted on request. Jacuzzi available. Open all year.

PRICES: s €28; d €36-€39; t €45; extra person €5; dinner €13
ON SITE: Fishing Hiking **NEARBY:** Bathing (10km) Horse riding (7km) Swimming pool (10km) Cross-country skiing (5km) Tennis (5km) Railway station (25km) Shops (5km) **NOTES:** Pets admitted English spoken

POLIGNAC

⚐⚐⚐ 🍴 Chambre d'hôtes
Dominique et Patrick CHEVALIER
Chemin de Ridet, La Gourmantine, 43000 POLIGNAC
☎ 04 71 05 94 29

Le Puy-en-Velay 5 km, start of Saint-Jacques de Compostelle. This beautifully restored 18th-century, stone farmhouse lies in the heart of a delightful, quiet village. There is one family room for four people with two bedrooms and a private bathroom. The bedrooms are no smoking. There are also a lounge, dining room with fireplace and an upright piano. Outside, there is an enclosed garden and a terrace area with a beautiful view over the blue expanse of the Cévennes massif and Mézenc. The house is set in old woodland, at the foot of the 10th-century, feudal fortress (150m away). Freshly baked bread is served, and also organic wine. Golf is available 8 km away. Open all year.

PRICES: s €45-€53; d €45-€53; t €61-€69; extra person €13; dinner €18
ON SITE: Wine tasting Hiking Tennis **NEARBY:** Bathing (5km) Horse riding (5km) Fishing (4km) Swimming pool (5km) Railway station (6km) Shops (5km) **NOTES:** No pets English spoken

RETOURNAC

⚐⚐⚐ 🐓 Les Revers Béatrice et J-Pierre CHEVALIER
43130 RETOURNAC
☎ 04 71 59 42 81   🖷 04 71 59 42 81

This restored farm lies in the middle of the countryside. There are four bedrooms (two have a mezzanine level), each with bathroom and wc. There is a large lounge room with an open fireplace, TV and library and large garden. Farm produce is also available on the farm. The surrounding countryside is made up of picturesque valleys and some of the oldest Loire châteaux and remarkable Roman churches. Horse riding can be organised by arrangement. Open April to end September.

PRICES: s €27; d €37; t €47; extra person €11   **ON SITE:** Horse riding Hiking **NEARBY:** Bathing (7km) Fishing (7km) Swimming pool (7km) Cross-country skiing (25km) Tennis (7km) Railway station (7km) Shops (7km) **NOTES:** No pets English spoken

SAINT-DIDIER-EN-VELAY

⚐⚐⚐ 🍴 Au delà des bois Laura et Guy FRANC
Montcoudiol, 43140 SAINT-DIDIER-EN-VELAY
☎ 04 71 61 08 09   🖷 04 71 61 08 09
e-mail: maloufr@free.fr

le Puy en Velay. This typical 17th-century farm is situated in a small hamlet in the middle of the forest. Three bedrooms each have a private bathroom. In the large communal room there is a kitchen area and fireplace. Outside, there is a children's play area, a terrace and a large garden. Lots of activities are available in this rural, wooded region. Laura and Guy, the dynamic young owners, have given each room a theme (the lace maker, the boot maker, the harvester) and are happy to help guests discover this region. Open all year.

PRICES: s €28; d €37; t €46; extra person €9; dinner €13
ON SITE: Hiking **NEARBY:** Horse riding (2km) Fishing (1km) Swimming pool (3km) Railway station (20km) Shops (4km)
NOTES: Pets admitted

SANSSAC-L'EGLISE

⚐⚐⚐ 🐓 🍴 Lonnac Patrick et Florence LIABEUF
43320 SANSSAC-L'EGLISE
☎ 04 71 08 64 15

In the middle of the countryside and in the heart of a small quiet village, this old, restored farmhouse, has bedrooms with private bathrooms available. The dining room lounge has a fireplace and there is also a TV. Outside there is an enclosed courtyard and a terrace area. Nearby: Puy lentil growing area, the amazing volcanic craters, lovely villages and the chateaux of Saint-Vidal and Rochelambert. Open all year except between 15 December and 1 January.

PRICES: s €29; d €38; t €46; extra person €8; dinner €11
ON SITE: Hiking **NEARBY:** Bathing (15km) Horse riding (8km) Fishing (2km) Swimming pool (8km) Cross-country skiing (5km) Railway station (12km) Shops (2km) **NOTES:** Pets admitted

SAUGUES

⚐⚐⚐ 🐓 🍴 Chambre d'hôtes Jacky et Brigitte MARTINS
Rue des Roches, 43170 SAUGUES
☎ 04 71 77 83 45

This welcoming new house offers bedrooms with private bathrooms. There is also a lounge, and kitchen, and outside the courtyard leads onto a terrace area. The property is situated on the Saint-Jacques de Compostelle walking route (GR65), in the heart of the Margeride, in 'wild nut' country. There are many charming, small villages to discover. Meals based on produce from the farm and garden can be supplied on request. Open 15 March to 15 November.

PRICES: s €25; d €33; dinner €10 **ON SITE:** Fishing Hiking **NEARBY:** Bathing (1km) Horse riding (1km) Cross-country skiing (20km) Tennis (1km) Railway station (16km) Shops (1km) **NOTES:** Pets admitted

⚐⚐⚐ 🍴 Chambre d'hôtes Pierre GAUTHIER
Les Gabales, Route du Puy, 43170 SAUGUES
☎ 04 71 77 86 92   🖷 04 71 77 86 92
e-mail: pierrelesgabales@wanadoo.fr www.lesgabales.com
Le Puy-en-Velay and Saint-Flour 45 km. This 1930s manor house is on the route from Saint-Jacques de Compostelle. Each bedroom has a private bathroom. There are two suites (four people in each), each with a different style. The lounge has a library and

continued   *continued*

there is a dining room. Outside there is a terrace, leading onto parkland where there are a number of walking routes. The half board tariff varies depending on the number of people per room and there are special rates for children (depending on age). All bedrooms are no smoking. This is granite countryside, a fitting home for the Beast of Gévaudan (a local legend). Open all year by reservation only.
PRICES: s €31; d €39-€41; t €54; extra person €15; HB €44; dinner €15
ON SITE: Hiking **NEARBY:** Bathing (1km) Horse riding (1km) Fishing (1km) Swimming pool (1km) Cross-country skiing (20km) Railway station (20km) **NOTES:** Pets admitted English spoken

♦♦♦ ○| Le Rouve Jean-Pierre & Hélène BLANC
43170 SAUGUES
☎ 04 71 77 64 15 📠 04 71 77 83 84
This house, with lovely countryside views, is set in two hectares of land on the outskirts of a village. On the ground floor, there are bedrooms with private bathrooms and independent entrances. There is also a communal room and a terrace with a large open courtyard and parking area. Evening meals can be provided. Saugues, the small, lively town on the Saint-Jacques-de-Compostelle route, is nearby. This area is known as 'wild nut' country, dotted with small, quiet, charming villages and granite houses. Open all year.
PRICES: d €37; dinner €12 **ON SITE:** Fishing Hiking
NEARBY: Bathing (4km) Horse riding (4km) Cross-country skiing (4km) Railway station (20km) Shops (4km) **NOTES:** Pets admitted

SENEUJOLS

♦♦♦ ○| Chambre d'hôtes Bernard et Colette BOYER
43510 SENEUJOLS
☎ 04 71 03 19 69 📠 04 71 03 19 69
e-mail: sacatez@infonie.fr
The bedrooms in this old, renovated farmhouse all have private bathrooms. In a separate house, there is a kitchenette, communal lounge, library and kitchen area. Communal meals are served in the owners' dining room. Courtyard and terrace outside with garden furniture and children's games. Situated in the heart of the volcanic region, this local stone farmhouse is in a small, very peaceful village near the Bouchet Forest and lake. Horses are welcome and walkers and their luggage can be picked up. Picnics from local or garden produce can be supplied on request. Open 1 March to 15 November.
PRICES: s €25-€26; d €38-€34; t €38-€40; extra person €5-€6; dinner €11-€12 **ON SITE:** Hiking Tennis **NEARBY:** Bathing (8km) Fishing (8km) Swimming pool (12km) Cross-country skiing (5km) Railway station (12km) Shops (5km) **NOTES:** Pets admitted

ST-ARCONS-DE-BARGES

♦♦♦ ○| Le Couvent Alexandra GRISOT
Le Bourg, 43420 ST-ARCONS-DE-BARGES
☎ 04 71 08 28 22 📠 04 71 08 28 22
e-mail: alexandra.grisot@net-up.com
This property is situated in an old 18th-century convent, in the picturesque hamlet of Saint-Arcons-de-Barges with its lovely old church and countryside views. There are five bedrooms for two, three or four people, each with private bathroom. Communal living room with fireplace, lounge, outside courtyard. Meals available on request, including New Year's Eve dinners by arrangement. On the outskirts of the Méjeanne, in the heart of the volcanic Velay region and forest area, this is an ideal place for holidays and weekend breaks. Discount after third night. Open all year.
PRICES: s €29; d €41; t €59; extra person €15; dinner €16
ON SITE: Fishing Hiking **NEARBY:** Horse riding (10km) Swimming pool (15km) Railway station (19km) Shops (5km) **NOTES:** Pets admitted

ST-BEAUZIRE

♦♦♦ ♥ Les Chaumasses Hélène et Dominique CHAZELLE
43100 ST-BEAUZIRE
☎ 04 71 76 81 00 📠 04 71 76 81 00
e-mail: dominique.chazelle@wanadoo.fr
http://perso.wanadoo.fr/chaumasses
Brioude 8 km. Blesle 11 km. This property has comfortable bedrooms with private bathrooms. Each bedroom has a lovely patio and a wonderful view; guests may use the lounge and the garden. The house is near Broude, with its wonderful Roman basilica, and a few kilometres from the superb gorges of Allier with its river and wild salmon. 4km from exit 22 of A75. Open all year.
PRICES: s €35; d €45; t €55; extra person €5 **ON SITE:** Children's play area Hiking Tennis **NEARBY:** Bathing (9km) Horse riding (8km) Fishing (8km) Swimming pool (8km) Railway station (8km) Shops (8km) **NOTES:** No pets English spoken

ST-DIDIER-D'ALLIER

♦♦♦ ♥ ○| La Grangette J AVOINE et P MONTAGNE
43580 ST-DIDIER-D'ALLIER
☎ 04 71 57 24 41
This renovated, isolated farm, lies amongst the magnificent Allier gorges. Two of the bedrooms have a mezzanine level and all have a private bathroom. Living room, library and dining room with kitchen area, courtyard. This is salmon and white-water country with canyoning, rafting and mountain biking available (6 km); and canoeing/kayaking (14 km). In an unrivalled location, this village is perched on the edge of the gorge. Open 1 April to 31 October.
PRICES: s €23; d €30; t €38; extra person €8; dinner €11
ON SITE: Fishing Hiking **NEARBY:** Bathing (7km) Tennis (6km) Railway station (15km) Shops (7km) **NOTES:** Pets admitted English spoken

ST-FRONT

♦♦♦♦ ○| Les Bastides Paul et Nadège COFFY
Les Bastides du Mezenc, 43550 ST-FRONT
☎ 04 71 59 51 57 📠 04 71 59 51 57
In the middle of the countryside, with views over the volcanoes and the high plateaux of Velay, this old country house has been restored in the local style. There are bedrooms for two people and two suites with private bathroom. Sitting room with open fireplace, dining room, library, piano and billiards table. Large garden and terrace area. Paul and Nadège welcome guests into their home at the top of Lauzes. Paul is a professional dog trainer and driver, and also raises horses. Dog driving and horse riding can be arranged. Open all year.
PRICES: s €38; d €61; dinner €23 **ON SITE:** Fishing Hiking Cross-country skiing **NEARBY:** Bathing (4km) Horse riding (7km) Railway station (30km) Shops (5km) **NOTES:** Pets admitted

ST-GENEYS-PRES-ST-PAULIEN

♦♦♦ Bel Air Serge et Annick CHABRIER
43350 ST-GENEYS-PRES-ST-PAULIEN
☎ 04 71 00 45 56
15 km from Puy-en-Velay. This old restored farmhouse is one kilometre from the village in a lovely position. Each bedroom has a private bathroom. There is also a lounge with TV and library, and the large garden has outdoor furniture. Located in the volcanic Velay/Livradois-Forez area, there are several walking routes nearby. The property is available between 1 March and 1 November.
PRICES: s €28; d €32; t €40; extra person €8 **ON SITE:** Children's play area Hiking **NEARBY:** Bathing (7km) Horse riding (5km) Fishing (1km) Swimming pool (4km) Tennis (4km) Railway station (15km) Shops (3km) **NOTES:** Pets admitted

ST-HOSTIEN

♦♦♦ ❍ Les Chazes Pierrette et Jean CHAMBERT
43260 ST-HOSTIEN
☎ 04 71 57 64 16
Pierette and Jean offer you a warm welcome to their isolated farmhouse, at the foot of the Meygal, that has been restored with a lot of care and attention to detail. Each bedroom has a private bathroom. There are two (two person) rooms and one (three person) room. In addition, there is a dining/drawing room with an open fireplace and a library. Outside, there is a large garden area that overlooks the Loire Valley. Evening meals can be provided on request. Jean is happy to help guests discover this area of countryside, throughout the year.
PRICES: s €30; d €38; t €46; dinner €11 **ON SITE:** Fishing Hiking Cross-country skiing **NEARBY:** Bathing (15km) Horse riding (8km) Swimming pool (8km) Tennis (3km) Railway station (18km) Shops (3km) **NOTES:** No pets English spoken

PRICES: s €27; d €37; t €48; extra person €11; dinner €14
ON SITE: Horse riding Hiking **NEARBY:** Fishing (1km) Swimming pool (10km) Railway station (25km) Shops (2km) **NOTES:** Pets admitted English spoken

ST-PIERRE-EYNAC

♦♦♦ ❍ La Chabanade Michelle MIALON-GONOD
Marcilhac, 43260 ST-PIERRE-EYNAC
☎ 04 71 08 44 60
Le Puy-en-Velay 20 km. This isolated house is very peacefully set on the outskirts of the forests, at the foot of the Meygal in an area of volcanoes. There are three bedrooms (two with mezzanine) with private bathroom and wc. There is also a communal room with a corner fireplace, TV and piano. Outside, there is an enclosed courtyard with garden furniture and two hectares of meadow. Impressive views over Mézenc. Local plant/food discovery weekends are held until the end of June with botanical outings, gathering and tasting of plants and making liqueurs, aperitifs and jellys. Guests can enjoy meals made from garden produce and homemade salamis. Open all year.
PRICES: s €30; d €41-€44; t €55-€59; extra person €13; dinner €13-€16
ON SITE: Hiking **NEARBY:** Horse riding (5km) Fishing (3km) Swimming pool (5km) Cross-country skiing (4km) Tennis (5km) Railway station (20km) Shops (5km) **NOTES:** No pets English spoken

♦♦♦ ❍ 🕭 Montoing Michel et Germaine JULIEN
43260 ST-PIERRE-EYNAC
☎ 04 71 03 00 39 & SR : 06 81 29 89 28
This old, restored farm is near Puy-en-Velay. The bedrooms each have a private bathroom and one has a mezzanine area for nine people. There is also a lounge, TV, sitting room area and library. There is a large, enclosed garden attached to the house and a terrace and parking area. There are lots of wide, open spaces in this area of volcanic cones and a rich Roman heritage evident in the churches and museums. Open all year.
PRICES: s €24; d €34; t €43; dinner €11
ON SITE: Hiking **NEARBY:** Bathing (6km) Horse riding (6km) Fishing (6km) Swimming pool (6km) Cross-country skiing (6km) Railway station (12km) Shops (3km) **NOTES:** No pets

ST-VICTOR-MALESCOURS

♦♦♦ ❍ 🕭 La Tourette Zahra et Michel FUCHS
43140 ST-VICTOR-MALESCOURS
☎ 04 77 39 92 98 ▤ 04 77 39 93 16
This 18th-century farm is in the heart of the countryside, near Jonzeiux in the Loire, and is ideal for active people and families. There are five, quiet and comfortable bedrooms, each with a private bathroom. There is also a dining room with open fireplace and an enclosed pond with ducks and fish. Tourist tax is payable from 1st June to 30th September. There are a number of routes and signposted walks from the house. A discount of 10% off the half board rate can be enjoyed between July and August. Open all year.

ST-VINCENT

♦♦♦ ❍ Chalignac Christiane SERRE-LATERRERE
La Buissonnière, 43800 ST-VINCENT
☎ 04 71 08 54 41
Le Puy-en-Velay 17 km. This beautiful and charming dwelling is magnificently situated in large grounds in the Loire gorges, surround by volcanic cones. There are four bedrooms, each with a private bathroom. There is also a music room with an upright piano and a library. All rooms are no smoking. Outside, there is a landscaped garden and private parking. Home-grown produce and savoury meals can be provided. Numerous walks nearby (GR3). Seventh night free out of season (not July or August). Open all year.
PRICES: s €43; d €44-€49; t €58-€62; extra person €14; dinner €18
ON SITE: Wine tasting Hiking **NEARBY:** Bathing (10km) Horse riding (15km) Fishing (1km) Swimming pool (4km) Cross-country skiing (15km) Railway station (1km) Shops (1km) **NOTES:** Pets admitted English spoken

TENCE

♦♦♦ ❍ La Pomme Gérard et Elyane DEYGAS
43190 TENCE
☎ 04 71 59 89 33
This beautifully restored house is situated in large grounds in the middle of the countryside. There are bedrooms with private bathrooms, a lounge with an open fireplace and a drawing room with TV. There is also a terrace, a parking area and a golf-putting course. Gerard and Elyane, the young farmers, offer guests a warm welcome to their comfortable home. Closed 1 October to 1 April, except weekends; and Sundays from 1 September to 1 July, except school holidays. A tourist tax is payable and meals are available on request.
PRICES: s €28; d €38; t €47; extra person €8; dinner €12
ON SITE: Hiking **NEARBY:** Bathing (3km) Horse riding (5km) Fishing (3km) Swimming pool (3km) Tennis (3km) Railway station (17km) Shops (3km) **NOTES:** Pets admitted

VALS-PRES-LE-PUY

♦♦♦ ❤ ❍ Eycenac Philippe & Françoise BESSE
Domaine de Bauzit, 43750 VALS-PRES-LE-PUY
☎ 04 71 03 67 01 ▤ 04 71 03 67 01
Bedrooms with private bathrooms and a communal lounge room with fireplace are provided in this owner-occupied house, near the lovely town of Puy-en-Velay, situated in an unusual volcanic area. There is also a huge garden and the tranquil riverbanks are dotted with remarkable Roman churches and historic relics. In this no-smoking house, half board only is available between July and August. Mountain bikes for hire. Farm produce and home-baked

continued

continued

AUVERGNE

bread are provided and meals are available between 1 April and 15 September (Asian meals once a week). Donkey rides possible between 15 March and 15 October.
PRICES: s €29; d €35; t €46; extra person €9; dinner €13
ON SITE: Hiking **NEARBY:** Bathing (5km) Horse riding (5km) Fishing (5km) Swimming pool (5km) Tennis (3km) Railway station (5km) Shops (3km) **NOTES:** No pets English spoken

VERGEZAC

♦♦♦ ♥ ﾣO︱ Allentin Pierre et M-Thérèse JOURDAIN
43320 VERGEZAC
☎ 04 71 08 66 10 ▤ 04 71 08 04 28
This 19th-century farm specialises in sheep, horses, ponies, donkeys, goats and poultry. The house, in a shady park, has been beautifully restored. Each bedroom has a private bathroom. Lounge room with TV and kitchen with washing machine. Outside, there is a play area and enclosed parking. Farm produce is served at meal times. Stabling available. Ideal for active holidays; children can enjoy pony rides on the farm and there are many mountain biking routes nearby (bikes and mountain bikes can be hired). Aerial sports 6 km away, white-water rafting 12 km. The farm is situated in the volcanic basin of Velay, 13 km from the magnificent site of Puy-en-Velay. Restaurant 3 km. Open all year.
PRICES: s €29; d €35; t €41; dinner €10 **ON SITE:** Horse riding Hiking **NEARBY:** Bathing (15km) Fishing (6km) Swimming pool (12km) Cross-country skiing (7km) Tennis (6km) Railway station (12km) Shops (4km) **NOTES:** Pets admitted

VERNASSAL

♦♦♦ ♥ ﾣO︱ Darsac Robert et Magali VAUCANSON
43270 VERNASSAL
☎ 04 71 57 00 92 ▤ 04 71 57 04 46
This restored 18th-century farm is the oldest house in the village and is built from volcanic stone. All the bedrooms have a private bathroom. Communal lounge with an open fireplace and second-floor library. Terrace area. There is a large tree-lined and enclosed garden next to the house, garden furniture and a private swimming pool, plus a courtyard garden and parking area. Picnics and evening meals provided on request. Activities and attractions nearby include 10-hole mini golf, Puy lentil growing area, remarkable volcanic craters, historic villages and chateaux. The owners' farm is 2 km away. Many footpaths and mountain biking trails. Open 1 May to 15 October.
PRICES: s €44; d €49; extra person €15; dinner €15 **ON SITE:** Children's play area Swimming pool Hiking **NEARBY:** Horse riding (6km) Fishing (1km) Shops (7km) **NOTES:** No pets

VIEILLE-BRIOUDE

♦♦♦ ﾣO︱ Chambre d'hôtes Philippe BOYER
Ermitage Saint-Vincent, Place de l'Eglise,
43100 VIEILLE-BRIOUDE
☎ 04 71 50 96 47
Brioude 5 km. This property is a renovated Presbyterian church situated on the edge of the wonderful Allier gorges, that are dotted with Mediterranian-style villages. The bedrooms, each with a private bathroom, are full of charm and character with lovely views. On the first floor, there is a stained-glass window with benches and deck chairs. There is also a dining room with an open fireplace, library and TV. Outside the terrace area and large garden look out onto Allier. White-water sports, mushroom gathering and picture framing are some of the activities to be enjoyed. Theme weeks can be organised. Open all year.
PRICES: s €33; d €43; t €58; extra person €15; dinner €15
ON SITE: Children's play area Fishing Hiking **NEARBY:** Bathing (5km) Horse riding (5km) Swimming pool (5km) Railway station (5km) Shops (5km) **NOTES:** Pets admitted

♦♦♦ ♥ ﾣO︱ La Coustade Gérard et Anne-Marie CHANTEL
Chemin du Stade, 43100 VIEILLE-BRIOUDE
☎ 04 71 50 25 21 ▤ 04 71 50 20 45
In this newly built house, in the Haut-Allier/Margeride region, there are five bedrooms with bathrooms, all on the ground floor, one of which is suitable for less mobile guests. The sitting room has an open fireplace and TV. There is also a terrace area, a veranda and a large garden with play area. Tourist tax is payable and prices will vary according to the season. Gerard and Anne-Marie, the young farm owners, offer a warm welcome and are be happy to help guests appreciate this region. Open 1 April to 30 October.
PRICES: s €25-€28; d €32-€36; t €37-€41; dinner €11 **ON SITE:** Hiking **NEARBY:** Bathing (1km) Horse riding (3km) Fishing (1km) Swimming pool (3km) Tennis (3km) Railway station (3km) Shops (3km) **NOTES:** Pets admitted

VIELLE-BRIOUDE

♦♦♦ Chambre d'hôtes Verena et Ahmed MEDBOUHI
Le Panorama, Coste Cirgues,
43100 VIELLE-BRIOUDE
☎ 04 71 50 94 35 ▤ 04 71 50 92 45
Brioude 5 km. Gorges de l'Allier 1 km. This spacious modern villa, has a wonderful panoramic view over the Allier Valley. There are three guest rooms on the ground floor, all with bathrooms. One of these is a family room (4-6 people:70 euros) There are private entrances, a lounge, kitchen, a large covered terrace area and garden. Situated in a peaceful spot bordering the Allier gorges, this area is ideal for rambling, bathing and white-water sports. Also situated on numerous tourist trails, it is easy to explore the local heritage and picturesque villages. 800m away there is a restaurant. Open all year.
PRICES: d €45; extra person €15 **ON SITE:** Hiking **NEARBY:** Bathing (1km) Horse riding (5km) Fishing (1km) Swimming pool (5km) Railway station (5km) Shops (5km) **NOTES:** No pets English spoken

AUGEROLLES

♦♦♦ ﾣO︱ La Plaine A-Laure et Frédéric RUFFET
63930 AUGEROLLES
☎ 04 73 53 56 27
http://f.ruffet.free.fr
Aubusson-d'Auvergne 6 km. Courpière 9.5 km. Three guest rooms in a building attached to the owners' house. Bedrooms are on the first floor and consist of two double rooms, and one room with one double and one single bed. All have private shower and wc. There are a lounge, garden and private parking. Six km away is a lake with nature trails and fishing. A Chamina guide is available for walks.
PRICES: s €30; d €38; t €47; extra person €11; dinner €11
ON SITE: Tennis **NEARBY:** Bathing (6km) Horse riding (10km) Swimming pool (10km) Bicycle hire (6km) Railway station (25km) **NOTES:** Pets admitted English spoken

AURIERES

♦♦♦ ﾣO︱ Chambre d'hôtes C et D RANDANNE
Le Bourg, 63210 AURIERES
☎ 04 73 65 67 55 ▤ 04 73 65 67 55
Le Puy-de-Dome 17 km. Le Puy-de-Sancy 27 km. Aydat 9 km. Three rooms in the owners' house. On the ground floor is one room with one double and one single bed and its own terrace. On the first floor are two double rooms. Each room has its own private shower and wc. Sitting room, lounge and private garden. Tourist tax is payable. In the vicinity are the Romanesque church of Orcival, the Col de Guéry, the lac de Guéry, and the Chaîne de Guéry with the Puy-de-Dôme. Watersports & fishing.

continued

PRICES: s €29; d €38; extra person €15; dinner €12 **NEARBY:** Bathing (9km) Horse riding (15km) Swimming pool (24km) Cross-country skiing (8km) Downhill skiing (27km) Tennis (3km) Bicycle hire (13km) Railway station (25km) Shops (13km) **NOTES:** No pets English spoken

AYDAT

♥♥♥ ⅠⓄⅠ Rouillas-Bas Françoise & J-Pierre GOLLIARD
Rue Yvon Chauveix, 63970 AYDAT
☎ 04 73 79 30 44
e-mail: jpf.golliard@wanadoo.fr
Aydat 2 km. Clermont-Ferrand 20.5 km. Four rooms on the first floor of the owners' house, consisting of one room with double bed; one room with twin beds (with communicating door if required); one double room; and one room with one double and one single bed. All rooms have private facilities. A lounge and sitting room with open fire and bread oven, and a snow lodge are available. TV can be supplied on request. A reduction can be made for children under 10, outside school holidays. Tourist tax is payable. Hiking trails and fishing nearby.
PRICES: s €30; d €35; t €44; extra person €10; dinner €12
ON SITE: Tennis **NEARBY:** Bathing (2km) Horse riding (8km) Swimming pool (21km) Cross-country skiing (12km) Downhill skiing (36km) Bicycle hire (2km) **NOTES:** No pets English spoken

BOURG-LASTIC

♥♥♥ Artiges Chantal et Denis DUGAT-BONY
63760 BOURG-LASTIC
☎ 04 73 21 87 39
Le Mont-Dore 33 km. La Bourboule 26 km. Clermont-Ferrand 60 km. Accommodation is in an old family house, now restored. On the first floor is one room with one double and a single bed. On the second floor are one double room, and one room with a double bed and a single bed. All have private bathroom and wc. Guests can use the lounge and kitchenette in the evenings. Courtyard, garden, barbecue, boule pitch and table tennis table available. Restaurants are 2km away. Fishing is available at Chavanon (5km).
PRICES: s €31; d €41; t €52; extra person €11 **NEARBY:** Bathing (12km) Horse riding (12km) Swimming pool (26km) Cross-country skiing (33km) Downhill skiing (33km) Tennis (2km) Bicycle hire (26km) Railway station (26km) Shops (2km) **NOTES:** No pets

CHAMPS

♥♥♥ ⅠⓄⅠ Bel-Air Lilas et Claude GRIENENBERGER
63440 CHAMPS
☎ 04 73 33 06 75
Champs 2 km. Ebreuil 6 km. Gannat 10 km. Four rooms on the first floor of the owners' house consisting of two double bedrooms; one twin bedded room, and one room with a double and a single bed. All rooms have private shower and wc. Guests have use of a dining room, sitting room, courtyard and garden. Table d'hôte meals may be reserved in advance. Reduced rates are given for children under 12 years.
PRICES: s €32; d €41; t €53; extra person €13; HB €29; dinner €14
NEARBY: Bathing (6km) Horse riding (2km) Swimming pool (10km) Tennis (10km) Bicycle hire (6km) Railway station (10km) Shops (4km) **NOTES:** Pets admitted

CHARBONNIERES-LES-VARENNES

♥♥♥ ⅠⓄⅠ La Vedrine Mado et Philippe SAURA
63410 CHARBONNIERES-LES-VARENNES
☎ 04 73 33 82 85 & 06 08 03 24 71
Volvic 8.5 km. Châtel-Guyon 13.5 km. Gour-de-Tazenet 16.5 km. Four guest rooms on the ground floor and upper, attic floor of the owners' house. On the ground floor is one room with one double

and two single beds. On the upper floor are two double bedrooms; and one room with a double and a single bed. All rooms have private shower and wc. Guests may use a sitting room, terrace, and adjacent garden. Reduced weekly rates are available, except in July and August and during school holidays. Table d'hôte meals can be provided at weekends and during school holidays only.
PRICES: s €31; d €35-€39; t €54; extra person €15; dinner €13
NEARBY: Bathing (17km) Horse riding (14km) Swimming pool (14km) Tennis (9km) Railway station (9km) Shops (9km) **NOTES:** No pets English spoken

CLEMENSAT

♥♥♥ ♥ ⅠⓄⅠ Chambre d'hôtes
André et Chantal TRUCHOT
63320 CLEMENSAT
☎ 04 73 71 10 82
St-Nectaire 13 km. Issoire 14 km. Clermont-Ferrand 33 km. Accommodation is offered on the upper floor of a building on a working farm. Two double rooms; one with a double and a single bed; and one with a double and two single beds. All have private facilities. Dining room with fireplace, a covered terrace, courtyard, an adjoining enclosed garden and private parking. Meals can be provided by reservation. Bathing, sailing, windsurfing, canoes, kayaks, and fishing are available at Lac de Chambon (21km).
PRICES: s €29; d €40; extra person €14; dinner €13 **NEARBY:** Bathing (21km) Horse riding (22km) Swimming pool (3km) Cross-country skiing (22km) Downhill skiing (29km) Tennis (3km) Bicycle hire (14km) Shops (5km) Restaurant nearby **NOTES:** No pets

COLLANGES

♥♥♥♥ ⅠⓄⅠ Château de Collanges
Pascale et Denis FELUS
63340 COLLANGES
☎ 04 73 96 47 30 🖷 04 73 96 58 72

Clermont-Ferrand 25 mn. Five rooms, including one family room, on the first floor of a château, consisting of three double rooms; one room with one double and one single bed; and a suite of one double bedroom and one room with one double bed and a single bed. All have private bathroom and wc; one has a jacuzzi. Telephone calls may be received in all rooms. TV can be supplied on request. Table d'hôte meals can be provided if reserved in advance. There is a large wooded park, and table tennis and boules are available.
PRICES: s €79; d €79-€99; extra person €23; dinner €38
ON SITE: Children's play area **NEARBY:** Horse riding (3km) Swimming pool (15km) Tennis (3km) Bicycle hire (15km) Railway station (15km) Shops (3km) **NOTES:** Pets admitted English spoken

> Ask the proprietor for directions
> when booking

continued

COMBRONDE

ᛟᛟᛟ Chambre d'hôtes Lise et André CHEVALIER
105, rue Etienne Clémentel, 63460 COMBRONDE
☎ 04 73 97 16 20 ▤ 04 73 97 16 20
Chatel-Guyon 7 km. Riom 11 km. Clermont-Ferrand 28 km. Four rooms on the first floor of the owners' house. These are two doubles, one room with one double and one single bed, and one twin-bedded room. All have private shower and wc. Dining room, lounge with open fire, a courtyard, a terrace, barbecue and enclosed garden and parking. Restaurants in Combronde.
PRICES: s €35; d €42; extra person €13 **ON SITE:** Tennis
NEARBY: Bathing (9km) Horse riding (7km) Swimming pool (7km) Bicycle hire (7km) Railway station (12km) **NOTES:** No pets

GIAT

ᛟᛟᛟ ❦ Rozery Joëlle BRIQUET-DESBAUX
63620 GIAT
☎ 04 73 21 60 08 & 04 73 21 71 08
Plan d'eau de la Ramade 5 km. Herment 11.5 km. Three bedrooms on the first floor of the owners' house on a working farm. Two double rooms, and one room with one double bed and a single bed. All have private facilities. Dining room, lounge, courtyard, and adjoining garden. Restaurants nearby.
PRICES: s €29; d €37; extra person €12 **NEARBY:** Bathing (5km) Horse riding (4km) Tennis (1km) Bicycle hire (1km) Shops (1km) **NOTES:** Pets admitted

LE MONT-DORE

ᛟᛟᛟ ⏢ Chambre d'hôtes
B et E BERARD ET CHOUKROUN
13, rue Sidoine Apollinaire, 63240 LE MONT-DORE
☎ 04 73 65 25 82 & 06 81 87 66 80 ▤ 04 73 65 24 41
Le Puy-de-Sancy 5 km. La Bourboule 6 km. Five rooms on the first floor of the owners' house. Three rooms for three, and two rooms for two, all with en suite bathroom. Guests have use of a sitting room, library and courtyard. Table d'hôte meals can be reserved in advance. Tourist tax is payable. Mont Dore, a ski resort and spa, is in the Parc des Volcans, which is great walking country.
PRICES: d €54-€61; extra person €16; dinner €17 **ON SITE:** Horse riding Tennis Bicycle hire **NEARBY:** Bathing (17km) Swimming pool (6km) Cross-country skiing (4km) Downhill skiing (5km) **NOTES:** No pets English spoken

ᛟᛟᛟ ❦ ⏢ Le Barbier Chantal et Denis VALLEIX
63240 LE MONT-DORE
☎ 04 73 65 05 77 & 06 11 86 73 87
Four rooms in the proprietors' house. The ground floor has one room with a double bed and a bunk bed for two. On the first floor is one room with one double and one single bed; and two rooms each with a double bed. All rooms have private shower and wc. Guest lounge with open fire and TV, a courtyard and garden. Farm-auberge 'La Golmotte' in an annexe. Tourist tax is payable. Nearby are the spa of Mont Dore, the Puy de Sancy, La Bourbole, and the Parc Fenestre.
PRICES: s €39; d €42; t €53; extra person €11; dinner €14 **NEARBY:** Bathing (14km) Horse riding (3km) Swimming pool (10km) Cross-country skiing (5km) Downhill skiing (6km) Tennis (3km) Bicycle hire (3km) Shops (3km) **NOTES:** No pets

ᛟᛟᛟ Le Genestoux Françoise LARCHER
La Closerie de Manou, 63240 LE MONT-DORE
☎ 04 73 65 26 81 ▤ 04 73 65 58 34
www.mont-dore.com
Le Mont-d'Or 3.5 km. La Bourboule 3.5 km. Five bedrooms (two of which are attic rooms) in the proprietors' 18th-century house. On the first floor are two grade 3 double rooms; and one grade 4 room

with a double and a single bed. On the second floor are two grade 3 attic rooms, one with three single beds, the other with a double bed. All rooms have private shower and wc. Tourist tax is payable. Inn 100m, river 150m. Marked paths for walkers nearby.
PRICES: s €46; d €53-€69; t €69; extra person €15 **NEARBY:** Bathing (21km) Horse riding (4km) Swimming pool (3km) Cross-country skiing (4km) Downhill skiing (8km) Tennis (4km) Bicycle hire (4km) Railway station (3km) Shops (3km) **NOTES:** No pets

LE VERNET-SAINTE-MARGUERITE

ᛟᛟᛟ ⏢ Cluchat Jacqueline & J-Louis BUXEROL
63710 LE VERNET-STE-MARGUERITE
☎ 04 73 88 67 92
Le Mont-Doré 30 km. Besse-et-St-Anastaise 22 km. Four bedrooms in a building attached to the owners' house. On the first floor are two double rooms, and three rooms each with one double and one single bed. All rooms have their own shower and wc. Sitting room, courtyard, and garden. Reduced price meals for children up to 10 years. Tourist tax payable. Murol is 11km away and at Lac d'Aydat (10km) is sailing and sailboarding. St Nectaire 7km.
PRICES: s €29; d €39; t €50; extra person €11; dinner €13 **ON SITE:** Children's play area **NEARBY:** Bathing (10km) Horse riding (10km) Cross-country skiing (8km) Downhill skiing (29km) Tennis (10km) Bicycle hire (10km) Railway station (29km) Shops (11km) **NOTES:** Pets admitted

LES MARTRES-DE-VEYRE

ᛟᛟᛟ Chambre d'hôtes Gerd et Jean STARACE
15 rue St-Martial, 63730 LES MARTRES-DE-VEYRE
☎ 04 73 39 29 49 ▤ 04 73 39 91 97
Cournon 7 km. Vic-le-Comte 7 km. Three rooms in a wing of the proprietors' house. On the first floor are a double with bath, and one room with one double and one single bed and bathroom. On the second floor is a room with a mezzanine floor, and one double and two single beds and bathroom. All have wc. Dining room with open fireplace, lounge with a library, courtyard and balcony. Tariff for 4 persons €76. Canoeing, walking and fishing nearby.
PRICES: s €38; d €46; t €58 **ON SITE:** Tennis Bicycle hire **NEARBY:** Bathing (7km) Horse riding (3km) Swimming pool (7km) **NOTES:** No pets English spoken

MANZAT

ᛟᛟᛟ Les Cheix M-Thérèse & Manuel PEREIRA
63410 MANZAT
☎ 04 73 86 57 74
Chatel-Guyon 14 km. Riom 19 km. Gour-de-Tazenat 3 km. Three bedrooms in a building opposite the owners' house. On the ground floor is a bedroom with a double and a single bed. On the first floor are a room with a double and a single bed; and one double room. All have private facilities. There is a sitting room with open fire, as well as a terrace and garden. Restaurant 1km away. The Fades Besserbe offers bathing, sailing, sailboarding, motor boating, canoeing and fishing.
PRICES: d €41; extra person €14 **NEARBY:** Bathing (3km) Horse riding (8km) Swimming pool (10km) Tennis (1km) Bicycle hire (14km) Railway station (5km) Shops (1km) **NOTES:** No pets

MAREUGHEOL

ᛟᛟᛟ ⏢ Longchamp Catherine MILLOT
Les Etoiles, 63340 MAREUGHEOL
☎ 04 73 71 40 04 ▤ 04 73 71 40 04
Issoire 9 km. Four guest rooms on the first floor of the owners' house, consisting of a double room; a twin bedded room; a room with 3 single beds; and a room with 4 single beds. All have private bathing facilities and wc. Dining room with open fire, lounge with

continued

continued

TV and fireplace, a terrace, courtyard and garden. Meals can be booked in advance. No charge for children under 2. Nearby are Fort de Mareugheol and the Chateau de Villeneuve-Lembron.
PRICES: s €29; d €42; t €55; extra person €13–€14; dinner €15
NEARBY: Swimming pool (9km) Tennis (4km) Bicycle hire (9km) Railway station (9km) Shops (7km) **NOTES:** No pets

MONTAIGUT-EN-COMBRAILLE

⚜⚜⚜ **Chambre d'hôtes** Simone et Paul BOUILLE
La Perriere, 63700 MONTAIGUT-EN-COMBRAILLE
☎ 04 73 85 09 30 🖷 04 73 85 15 83
St-Eloy-les-Mines 4 km. Ayat-sur-Sioule 19 km. Lapeyrouse 6 km.
Three attic bedrooms on the upper floor of the owners' house. These consist of two double rooms; and one twin bedded room, all with en suite bathroom and wc. There is a dining room on the veranda, a lounge, a summer kitchen (barbecue), a terrace, courtyard and garden. Hiking trails are 2km away. A forest, La Prade and Lapeyrouse lakes are nearby.
PRICES: s €34; d €40 **ON SITE:** Tennis **NEARBY:** Bathing (6km) Horse riding (19km) Swimming pool (4km) Bicycle hire (4km) Railway station (4km) **NOTES:** Pets admitted

MONTAIGUT-LE-BLANC

⚜⚜⚜ **Chambre d'hôtes**
Anita et Michel SAUVADET
Le Chastel Montaigu, 63320 MONTAIGUT-LE-BLANC
☎ 04 73 96 28 49 🖷 04 73 96 21 60
Besse and St-Anastaise 19 km. Super-Besse 26 km. Chambon-du-lac 17 km. Five rooms on various floors of this privately owned medieval chateau (11th/15th-century) made up of two rooms with a double and a single bed, one with a terrace; and three double rooms. All rooms have private bathrooms. Central heating. Vaulted sitting room with open fire and lounge. There are terraces; an enclosed garden and secure private parking. Restaurants are 3km away. Reservations must be for two nights minimum in July and August, and must be made in advance in the low season. Sleeps twelve.
PRICES: s €76–€115; d €84–€122; extra person €23
NEARBY: Bathing (17km) Horse riding (10km) Swimming pool (1km) Cross-country skiing (19km) Downhill skiing (26km) Bicycle hire (10km) Railway station (33km) Shops (1km) **NOTES:** No pets

⚜⚜⚜ **Domaine de Chignat** Madeleine et Paul SAUZET
Montaigut le Blanc, 63320 CHAMPEIX
☎ 04 73 96 71 21 🖷 04 73 96 71 21
e-mail: mad.sauzet@libertysurf.fr
St-Nectaire 14 km. Besse and St-Anastaise 21 km. Chambon sur lac 22 km. Accommodation for six persons and one baby in three rooms in the owners' house. There is a double room on the ground floor, and on the first floor are a double room and a room with two single beds and a child's cot. All rooms have private shower, wc and TV. Sitting room with fireplace, terrace and garden. Restaurants 2km, spa town 14km. Guests can participate in a dietary and fitness week but should book in advance.
PRICES: s €33; d €39–€43; extra person €12 **NEARBY:** Bathing (22km) Horse riding (21km) Swimming pool (2km) Cross-country skiing (21km) Downhill skiing (28km) Tennis (2km) Bicycle hire (2km) Railway station (18km) Shops (2km) **NOTES:** Pets admitted

MONTPEYROUX

⚜⚜⚜ **Chambre d'hôtes** Chris et Marcel ASTRUC
Rue du Donjon, 63114 MONTPEYROUX
☎ 04 73 96 69 42 & 06 08 51 81 82 🖷 04 73 96 69 96
Clermont-Ferrand 21.5 km. Issoire 14 km. Five rooms on the first and second floors of the proprietors' house. There is one grade 4 room with double bed and a child's bed, and a small private terrace; one

twin room with terrace; two double rooms, one with terrace; and one grade 4 room with twin beds, and jacuzzi. All rooms have private wc and bathing facilities. Dining room and restaurant on the premises. Lots of local walks and River Allier is 1km away.
PRICES: s €38–€55; d €45–€55; t €57–€66; extra person €13
ON SITE: Tennis **NEARBY:** Bathing (1km) Horse riding (7km) Swimming pool (5km) Cross-country skiing (32km) Downhill skiing (39km) Bicycle hire (14km) Railway station (2km) Shops (2km) **NOTES:** Pets admitted

⚜⚜⚜ **Chambre d'hôtes** Edith et Claude GRENOT
Les Pradets, 63114 MONTPEYROUX
☎ 04 73 96 63 40 🖷 04 73 96 63 40
e-mail: grenot@maison-hotes.com
www.auvergne.maison-hotes.com
Vic-le-Comte 8 km. Super-Besse 39 km. Aydat 24 km. On the first floor of the owners' house, one grade 4 bedroom with two single beds, bathroom and wc; one grade 4 room with a double and a single bed, shower and wc. In a detached pavilion on the same premises, are one grade 3 bedroom with mezzanine and one double and a single bed, bathroom with wc and a terrace. Dining room, lounge with fireplace and piano, and enclosed shady garden. A restaurant is on the premises.
PRICES: d €55–€58; extra person €17 **ON SITE:** Tennis
NEARBY: Bathing (24km) Horse riding (7km) Swimming pool (8km) Cross-country skiing (32km) Downhill skiing (39km) Bicycle hire (14km) Railway station (22km) Shops (2km) **NOTES:** Pets admitted

⚜⚜⚜ **Chambre d'hôtes** Hermann & Jacqueline VOLK
Place de la Croix du Bras, 63114 MONTPEYROUX
☎ 04 73 96 92 26 🖷 04 73 96 92 26
Issoire 14 km. Three guest rooms are available on the first floor of the proprietor's house. One room has twin beds; another has three single beds and balcony; and one is a double room. All have private shower and wc. Bedrooms are non-smoking. Smoking is permitted in the lounge and day-room. Other facilities include library, balcony, tennis court and restaurant. Fishing is available nearby. Aydat Lake has bathing, sailing and sailboarding.
PRICES: s €38–€45; d €45–€53; extra person €12 **ON SITE:** Tennis
NEARBY: Bathing (24km) Horse riding (7km) Swimming pool (8km) Cross-country skiing (32km) Downhill skiing (39km) Bicycle hire (14km) Railway station (22km) Shops (2km) **NOTES:** Pets admitted English spoken

MUROL

⚜⚜⚜ **Beaume le Froid** Janine ROUX
63790 MUROL
☎ 04 73 88 63 63
Château de Murol 4 km. Lac Chambon 5 km. Five bedrooms including a family room in a building on a working farm. On the attic floor is one room with a double and a single bed; one double room; and a family suite of two rooms with one double and two single beds. All rooms have TV, private shower and wc. Dining room and kitchenette, terrace, garden and private parking. A barbecue is available. Out of season reduced rates. Tourist tax is charged. There are restaurants in the village. Free visits can be arranged to the St Nectaire cheese factory.
PRICES: s €30; d €38; t €50; extra person €12 **ON SITE:** Cross-country skiing **NEARBY:** Bathing (5km) Horse riding (6km) Swimming pool (22km) Downhill skiing (12km) Tennis (4km) Bicycle hire (5km) Railway station (34km) Shops (4km) **NOTES:** Pets admitted

NEBOUZAT

⚜⚜⚜ ⧉ **Recoleine** Jocelyne GAUTHIER
63210 NEBOUZAT
☎ 04 73 87 10 34 & 06 89 93 99 54 🖷 04 73 87 10 34
Nebouzat 1.5 km. Ceyssat 7 km. Aydat 9 km. Saulzet-le-Froid 10

continued   *continued*

km. Three guest rooms including a family suite in a building adjoining the owners' house. The family suite on the ground floor consists of two rooms with one double and two single beds, with bathroom and wc. On the first floor is one room with three single beds and a room with one double and one single bed. Both rooms have private shower and wc. There is a sitting room, a terrace and a garden. Table d'hôte meals are available if booked in advance and there is an inn at Recoleine. Tourist tax is charged.
PRICES: s €30; d €40; t €55; extra person €15; dinner €12
NEARBY: Bathing (9km) Horse riding (7km) Swimming pool (17km) Cross-country skiing (10km) Downhill skiing (30km) Tennis (2km) Bicycle hire (10km) Railway station (22km) **NOTES:** No pets

OLBY

♦♦♦ 🐦 Bravant Paul BONY
63210 OLBY
☎ 04 73 87 12 28 🖅 04 73 87 19 00
Le Mont-Dore 38 km. Spa resort 25 km. Five rooms are available in a former farm building close to the owners' house. On the ground floor is one bedroom with one double and one single bed. On the first floor is one room with three single beds; one room with one double and one single bed; and two rooms, each with a mezzanine, one double and a single bed. All rooms have private facilities. A kitchen is available for guests and there is a sitting room with fireplace, a courtyard, an open garden and private parking. Reduced rates are available outside July and August and children under two years are free. There are restaurants at 2km.
PRICES: s €32; d €37; extra person €14 **NEARBY:** Bathing (13km) Horse riding (6km) Swimming pool (18km) Cross-country skiing (17km) Downhill skiing (31km) Tennis (13km) Bicycle hire (9km) Railway station (20km) Shops (2km) **NOTES:** No pets

OLLIERGUES

♦♦♦ 🍴 Chambre d'hôtes Annie-Paule CHALET
19 rue Jean de Lattre de, Tassigny, 63880 OLLIERGUES
☎ 04 73 95 52 10 🖅 04 73 95 59 41
Ambert 19 km. Thiers 31 km. Three family suites on the first and second floors of the proprietor's house. Each suite consists of two rooms with one double and one single bed, private bathroom and wc and a library. There is a sitting room with a library, a terrace, garden and garages.
PRICES: s €30; d €40; extra person €13; dinner €13 **ON SITE:** Tennis
NEARBY: Bathing (16km) Horse riding (16km) Bicycle hire (16km) Railway station (26km) **NOTES:** Pets admitted English spoken

ORCINES

♦♦♦♦ Ternant Catherine PIOLLET
Domaine de Ternant, 63870 ORCINES
☎ 04 73 62 11 20 🖅 04 73 62 29 96
e-mail: domaine.ternant@free.fr
http://domaine.ternant.free.fr
Royat 13 km. Vulcania 5 km. Set in the Auvergne Volcanic regional park near the Puy-de-Dôme site. Five guest rooms on the first floor of a 19th-century family home. One family suite of a double and a twin; one family suite of two rooms with four single beds; two double rooms; and one twin. All rooms have private bathrooms. Guests share with the owner a lounge, billiard room and a dining room. The property has a 10 hectare wooded park and a tennis court. Golf and paragliding nearby. There is a restaurant in the village. 10% reduction after the third night or for the rental of all the rooms.
PRICES: s €58-€73; d €66-€80; extra person €20 **ON SITE:** Tennis
NEARBY: Bathing (30km) Horse riding (5km) Swimming pool (15km) Bicycle hire (12km) Railway station (13km) Shops (4km)
NOTES: No pets English spoken

PERRIER

♦♦♦ Chambre d'hôtes Mireille et Paul GEBRILLAT
Chemin de Siorac, 63500 PERRIER
☎ 04 73 89 15 02 🖅 04 73 55 08 85
e-mail: lequota@club-internet.fr
Issoire 3 km. On the second floor of the owners' 18th-century home are one twin bedroom, and one family suite consisting of two rooms, each with one double and two single beds. On the first floor of the old hay-barn, which has an electric stair lift for those with reduced mobility, there is a twin-bedded room. All have private facilities. On the ground floor of the annex is a common room with kitchenette. Covered terrace, large garden and enclosed parking. Restaurants at Perrier. Rate for the suite is €86.
PRICES: s €40-€45; d €45-€52; extra person €16 **ON SITE:** Tennis
NEARBY: Bathing (28km) Horse riding (3km) Swimming pool (3km) Cross-country skiing (26km) Downhill skiing (33km) Bicycle hire (3km) Railway station (3km) Shops (3km) **NOTES:** Pets admitted

PRONDINES

♦♦♦ 🐦 Vedeux Danielle et André MONNERON
Au Belhetre, 63470 PRONDINES
☎ 04 73 87 84 55 🖅 04 73 87 84 55
Le Mont-Dore 36 km. La Bourboule 31 km. This house on a dairy farm offers a double room, a room with three single beds, and a room with a double and a single bed. All have private facilities. Day room with kitchen corner, terrace, open garden, barbecue and enclosed parking. Reductions can be offered out of season and for longer stays. Restaurants 1km.
PRICES: d €38; t €51; extra person €13 **ON SITE:** Children's play area
NEARBY: Bathing (26km) Horse riding (20km) Cross-country skiing (31km) Downhill skiing (42km) Tennis (8km) Bicycle hire (8km) Shops (8km) **NOTES:** No pets

ROYAT

♦♦♦♦ Château de Charade
Marc et M-Christine GABA
63130 ROYAT
☎ 04 73 35 91 67 🖅 04 73 29 92 09

Laschamps 4 km. Orcines 5 km. Aydat 9 km. Accommodation is in the owners' château. On the first floor are two double rooms; and one family suite consisting of two rooms, each with three single beds. On the second floor is a family suite of two rooms, one with a double and a single bed, the other with a double bed. All rooms have private bathing and wc. Dining room, billiard room and library. Outside in the large garden, are a boules court and private parking. Royat 4km. Tourist tax is charged. 5% reduction for stays of more than two nights.
PRICES: s €60-€69; d €66-€75; extra person €23 **NEARBY:** Bathing (9km) Horse riding (4km) Swimming pool (6km) Cross-country skiing (25km) Downhill skiing (40km) Tennis (4km) Bicycle hire (5km) Railway station (4km) Shops (4km) **NOTES:** No pets English spoken

SAURIER

♦♦♦ ⦿ Rozier Joël RODDE
63320 SAURIER
☎ 04 73 71 22 00   ▤ 04 73 71 24 06
On the attic floor of the owners' farmhouse are two double rooms; two twin rooms; one room with a double and a single bed; and one room with a double and two single beds. All rooms have private shower or bathroom and wc. Two of the rooms can connect. Sitting room with fireplace and TV, terrace and courtyard, garden and private parking. Local free activities:- walking, mountain biking, cross-country skiing with instruction. Weekly rates are available. Children under two years old are free; a €10 supplement is payable for children from two to six years.
PRICES: s €31; d €40; extra person €15; dinner €11 **ON SITE:** Bicycle hire **NEARBY:** Bathing (16km) Horse riding (15km) Swimming pool (12km) Cross-country skiing (15km) Downhill skiing (22km) Tennis (12km) Railway station (19km) Shops (15km) **NOTES:** No pets English spoken

SAUXILLANGES

♦♦♦ ❤ La Haute Limandie
Patricia et J-Claude ANGLARET
63490 SAUXILLANGES
☎ 04 73 96 84 95
Le Vernet-la-Varenne 20 km. Manglieu 6.5 km. Three rooms in the owners' house. One room with double bed and baby's cot is on the ground floor. On the first floor is a room with a double bed and a single bed, and one twin room. All rooms have private shower and wc. Guests have use of a day room with TV and there is a courtyard and open garden. There are restaurants at Sauxillanges (3km).
PRICES: d €34-€37; extra person €12 **NEARBY:** Bathing (20km) Horse riding (7km) Swimming pool (3km) Tennis (3km) Bicycle hire (15km) Railway station (15km) Shops (3km) **NOTES:** No pets

SERMENTIZON

♦♦♦ Chambre d'hôtes Andrée et Marius GROLET
63120 SERMENTIZON
☎ 04 73 53 03 14
Four rooms on the first and second floors of the proprietors' house. On the first floor is one grade 3 twin-bedded room with private bath and wc, and on the second floor is one grade 3 room with a double bed and cot, bathroom and wc; and two grade 2 double rooms with en suite shower and shared wc. There is a dining room, and an adjacent enclosed area with a barbecue. Courpière, Thiers, Billom, the Monts de Livradois, and the Monts du Forez, are within easy reach.
PRICES: s €25-€28; d €28-€32; extra person €10 **ON SITE:** Horse riding **NEARBY:** Bathing (12km) Swimming pool (4km) Tennis (4km) Bicycle hire (12km) Railway station (4km) Shops (4km) **NOTES:** No pets

ST-BONNET-PRES-ORCIVAL

♦♦♦ Château de Voissieux Danielle et John PHILLIPS
63210 ST-BONNET-PRES-ORCIVAL
☎ 04 73 65 81 02   ▤ 04 73 65 81 27
La Bourboule 25 km. Le Mont-Dore 23 km. Three rooms in the British owners' small château. All rooms are doubles, and all have private bathroom and wc. Lounge and dining room. Terrace, private parking and park with walks. A minimum stay of two nights is required in July and August. Tourist tax is payable. There are restaurants 2km away.
PRICES: s €38-€46; d €44-€52 **NEARBY:** Bathing (20km) Horse riding (11km) Cross-country skiing (14km) Downhill skiing (27km) Bicycle hire (6km) Railway station (27km) Shops (2km) **NOTES:** Pets admitted English spoken

♦♦♦ ⦿ Vareilles Thierry et Michelle GAIDIER
63210 ST-BONNET-PRES-ORCIVAL
☎ 04 73 65 87 91
e-mail: gaidier.thierry@wanadoo.fr
La Bourboule 25.5 km. Le Mont-Dore 23 km. Three bedrooms on the first floor of a building adjacent to the proprietors' house. There are two double rooms each with en suite bathroom and wc; and one family room with one double and two single beds, bathroom and wc. Dining room with fireplace, microwave and refrigerator, and lounge, terrace, garden and private parking. Table d'hôte meals. Reduced rates for more than three nights and out of season. Tourist tax is charged. A donkey Margot will carry children or baggage on your walking trips (€30 per day).
PRICES: s €32; d €39; t €51; extra person €11; dinner €12 **ON SITE:** Children's play area **NEARBY:** Bathing (20km) Horse riding (11km) Cross-country skiing (14km) Downhill skiing (27km) Tennis (8km) Bicycle hire (6km) Shops (2km) **NOTES:** Pets admitted English spoken

ST-GERVAIS-D'AUVERGNE

♦♦♦ ⦿ Le Masmont Marion GAUVIN
63390 ST-GERVAIS-D'AUVERGNE
☎ 04 73 85 80 09
e-mail: lemasmont@wanadoo.fr
Viaduc-des-Fades 13.5 km. Clermont-Ferrand 57 km. A family suite in the proprietor's house consists of a double room on the first floor, and a room with three single beds on the second. There is an adjacent shared private shower and wc. On the first floor of another building are two double rooms each with private shower and wc. Dining room in both buildings. Wooded grounds, barbecue. Table d'hôte meals can be booked in advance. A supplement is payable for pets and tourist tax is charged. The Châteauneuf-les-Bains is 10 km away and there is fishing and sailboarding 3 km away.
PRICES: s €30; d €38; extra person €20; dinner €13 **NEARBY:** Bathing (3km) Horse riding (16km) Swimming pool (23km) Tennis (3km) Bicycle hire (3km) Railway station (3km) Shops (3km) **NOTES:** Pets admitted English spoken

♦♦♦ Montarlet Elyane et Jean-René PELLETIER
63390 ST-GERVAIS-D'AUVERGNE
☎ 04 73 85 87 10
e-mail: Montarlet@libertysurf.fr.
Viaduc des Fades 16 km. Gorges de la Sioule 20 km. A building adjoining the owners' house. On the first floor are two double rooms. On the second is an attic room with one double and two single beds. All have private shower and wc. Lounge with fireplace, dining room, garden and private parking. Reduced rates for longer stays. Restaurants at St Gervais d'Auvergne (4km) and Châteauneuf-les-Bains (9km). St Gervais has a lake with sailboarding and fishing. Mountain bikes available for loan.
PRICES: s €31; d €40; extra person €13 **NEARBY:** Bathing (4km) Horse riding (17km) Tennis (4km) Bicycle hire (11km) Railway station (4km) Shops (4km) **NOTES:** Pets admitted English spoken

ST-GERVAZY

♦♦♦ ❤ Chambre d'hôtes Patrick TROUILLER
63340 ST-GERVAZY ☎ 04 73 96 44 51
Clermont-Ferrand 53 km. Four bedrooms in an annexe to the owners' house on a farm. Two are first floor, two second floor and all are twin-bedded and have private shower and wc. On the ground floor is a sitting room/kitchenette reserved for guests. There is private non-enclosed parking. Meals can be obtained at M Trouiller's inn. Children's nightly rate of €19.
PRICES: s €25; d €50; HB €36; FB €47; dinner €11 **ON SITE:** Horse riding **NEARBY:** Swimming pool (7km) Tennis (6km) Railway station (18km) Shops (6km) Restaurant nearby **NOTES:** No pets

ST-IGNAT

♦♦♦♦ Chambre d'hôtes Nicole et Jacques RODRIGUEZ
2 impasse de la Forge, Les Trèfles, 63720 ST-IGNAT
☎ 04 73 33 22 32   📠 04 73 33 22 32
Five rooms in a 19th-century house attached to the owner's house.
There are three double rooms; and two rooms with a double and
a single bed each with their own shower and wc. Guests have use
of a reception room, a sitting room, and games room with books.
Trail bikes are available. Terrace and garage. Restaurants 4km
away and fishing 2km away.
PRICES: s €38; d €43–€48; t €61; extra person €13   **ON SITE:** Bicycle hire
NEARBY: Horse riding (13km)   Swimming pool (13km)   Tennis (4km)
Shops (4km)   **NOTES:** No pets

ST-PIERRE-LE-CHASTEL

♦♦♦♦ IOI Bonnabaud Martine et Joël PARROT
Les Genêts fleuris,
63230 ST-PIERRE-LE-CHASTEL
☎ 04 73 88 75 81   📠 04 73 88 75 81
Pontgibaud 5 km. Three rooms on the first floor of the owners'
former farmhouse. All three rooms have a double and a single bed
and their own shower and wc. Sitting room, terrace and garden.
Meals can be reserved and children's meals are available for the
under-10s at €8. Tourist tax is payable. Reduced rates outside
school holidays. Nearby are the Puy-de-Dôme (paragliding
available), the Parc de Volcans, the Châine des Puys and the Valley
of the Sioule. Activities include hiking, fishing, mountain biking,
riding and hang-gliding.
PRICES: s €33; d €40; t €53; extra person €14; dinner €13
ON SITE: Children's play area   **NEARBY:** Bathing (7km)   Horse riding
(6km)   Swimming pool (28km)   Cross-country skiing (26km)   Tennis (5km)
Bicycle hire (14km)   Railway station (5km)   Shops (5km)   **NOTES:** Pets
admitted

ST-REMY-DE-CHARGNAT

♦♦♦♦ Château de Pasredon
Henriette et Henri MARCHAND
63500 ST-REMY-DE-CHARGNAT
☎ 04 73 71 00 67   📠 04 73 71 08 72
Issoire 8 km. Clermont-Ferrand 39 km. Sauxillanges 6 km.
The rooms are in a château with 2ha of grounds. On the first
floor are a twin bedded room with sitting room, and one
double room with dressing room. On the second floor are one
twin-bedded room with dressing room; one double room with
dressing room; and one double room. All have private
facilities. Dining room, lounge, private tennis court and garage
parking. Restaurants 3km. Château situated between Parc de
Volcans and Parc du Livradois-Forez.
PRICES: s €46–€72; d €61–€87   **ON SITE:** Tennis   **NEARBY:** Horse
riding (8km)   Swimming pool (8km)   Bicycle hire (8km)   Railway
station (8km)   Shops (6km)   **NOTES:** No pets

ST-VICTOR-MONTVIANEIX

♦♦♦ ♥ IOI Dassaud Michel et Joëlle GIRARD
63550 ST-VICTOR-MONTVIANEIX
☎ 04 73 94 38 10
St-Rémy-sur-Durolle 15 km. Accommodation for six people and a
baby in four first floor rooms in a former farm building adjacent to
the owner's house. One room has 3 single beds, two rooms are
doubles, and one room has a double and a single bed. All rooms
have private shower and wc. Garden and private parking. Rates
vary according to season and we offer reductions for children
under 12. Please telephone, between 12.00-13.30 or after 18.00.
Nearby: Thiers, the Vallée de Rouets and the Creux de l'Enfer
contemporary arts centre.

PRICES: d €35; t €49; extra person €14; dinner €12   **NEARBY:** Bathing
(15km)   Horse riding (15km)   Swimming pool (15km)   Tennis (9km)
Railway station (30km)   Shops (15km)   **NOTES:** No pets

TAUVES

♦♦♦ ♥ IOI Escladines Sylvie FEREYROLLES
63690 TAUVES
☎ 04 73 21 13 02 & 04 73 21 10 53
e-mail: sylvie.feyrerolles@wanadoo.fr
Spa resorts La Bourboule 15km and Le Mont-Dore 22km. Guest
rooms on the first floor of a former farmhouse opposite the
owner's home. There are three bedrooms, one with a double, one
with a single bed, and one with three single beds. Two rooms can
communicate. All rooms have private bathroom facilities. Sitting
room with fireplace, games room and a garden. Table d'hôte
meals can be booked in advance and a children's menu is
available. Tourist tax is payable. The Mont-Dores and lakes are
nearby.
PRICES: s €32; d €40–€46; extra person €9–€12; dinner €12
NEARBY: Bathing (9km)   Horse riding (9km)   Swimming pool (15km)
Cross-country skiing (11km)   Downhill skiing (26km)   Tennis (3km)   Bicycle
hire (3km)   Railway station (15km)   Shops (3km)   **NOTES:** No pets
English spoken

TOURS-SUR-MEYMONT

♦♦♦ ♥ IOI Ferme de Pied Froid
Evelyne et Philippe MAJEUNE
63590 TOURS-SUR-MEYMONT
☎ 04 73 70 71 20 & 06 84 28 06 89   📠 04 73 70 71 20
Cunlhat 7 km. In the Parc du Livradois Forez. Accommodation is
on the first floor of a former farm building adjacent to the owner's
house, and consists of a twin room; a double room; and a room
with one double and two single beds, all with en suite shower and
wc. Guests have use of a sitting room with fireplace and an open
garden with table tennis. Table d'hôte meals can be booked. Rates
are reduced from the fourth night. Fishing and walking are
available locally. Tourist tax is charged.
PRICES: s €29; d €37–€39; extra person €12; dinner €11
ON SITE: Children's play area   **NEARBY:** Bathing (7km)   Horse riding
(7km)   Swimming pool (33km)   Tennis (2km)   Bicycle hire (7km)   Shops
(7km)   **NOTES:** No pets

VARENNES-SUR-USSON

♦♦♦♦ Les Baudarts Hélène et Jacques VERDIER
63500 VARENNES-SUR-USSON
☎ 04 73 89 05 51   📠 04 73 89 05 51

Issoire 6 km. Accommodation is in three rooms in the owners'
house. On the ground floor is a family room and lounge, with
four single beds, and a private shower and wc. On the first
floor are two twin bedded rooms one with a lounge, each with
a private bathroom and wc. Guests have the use of a lounge
and dining room with fireplace and library, a garden and

continued   *continued*

AUVERGNE

private parking. Restaurants 2km away. Attractions in the area include Usson, the château of Queen Margot; Le Vernet-la-Varenne (17km), the Château de Parentignat; and Sauxillanges. **PRICES:** s €48; d €58-€69; extra person €19 **NEARBY:** Bathing (17km) Horse riding (6km) Swimming pool (7km) Tennis (6km) Bicycle hire (6km) Railway station (6km) Shops (6km) **NOTES:** No pets English spoken

VERNEUGHEOL

▦ ❦ ▯○▯ Le Glufareix Christiane & Bernard THOMAS
63470 VERNEUGHEOL
☎ 04 73 22 11 40
La Ramade 10 km. Four bedrooms in the owners' house. On the first floor is a family suite with two double and one single bed; and one room with one double and a single bed. On the second floor are one room with two double beds and one room with a double and a single bed. All rooms have private facilities. Lounge, dining room, courtyard, terrace and private parking. No charge for children under 2 years and reduced rates for longer or out of season stays. Table d'hôte meals can be reserved in advance. The nearby observatory of Verneugheol offers lectures on astronomy.
PRICES: s €28-€31; d €36-€39; t €47-€49; extra person €11; dinner €11
NEARBY: Bathing (10km) Horse riding (20km) Tennis (6km) Bicycle hire (6km) Shops (6km) **NOTES:** Pets admitted

VILLOSSANGES

▦ ▯○▯ La Verrerie C et P QUEYRIAUX
La Ferme de l'Etang, 63380 VILLOSSANGES
☎ 04 73 79 71 61
Six rooms in the owner's house attached to a country cottage. On the first floor are a twin bedded room, two rooms with a double and a single bed, and a double room. On the second floor are two double rooms. All come with private facilities. There is a lounge with a mezzanine floor and TV, and on the ground floor a dining room with fireplace. Terrace, garden and private parking. Table d'hote meals can be provided if booked in advance. We have a private lake and you can enjoy your own catch at table. Half-board is available from the fourth day. Closed in February.
continued

PRICES: s €30; d €38; t €50; extra person €12; dinner €12
NEARBY: Bathing (11km) Horse riding (9km) Tennis (3km) Bicycle hire (7km) Railway station (48km) Shops (4km) **NOTES:** No pets

VOLLORE-VILLE

▦▦▦ Chambre d'hôtes
G et M AUBERT-LA FAYETTE
Château de Vollore, 63120 VOLLORE-VILLE
☎ 04 73 53 71 06 ▤ 04 73 53 72 44
Five rooms are available in this château. On the ground floor is a double room. On the first floor are one double room, and one double room with sitting room. On the second floor are two twin bedded rooms. All have private facilities. Guests have the use of a lounge with fireplace, dining room, TV, French billiards, and table tennis. There is a terrace, a large wooded park and a private tennis court. The château is open to the public. Restaurant 6km away.
PRICES: d €95-€190 **ON SITE:** Tennis **NEARBY:** Bathing (4km) Horse riding (8km) Bicycle hire (4km) Railway station (17km) Shops (8km) **NOTES:** Pets admitted English spoken

▦▦▦ ❦ ▯○▯ Le Troulier Arlette et Bernard MOIGNOUX
Le Temps de Vivre, La Bergerie du Troulier,
63120 VOLLORE-VILLE
☎ 04 73 53 71 98
e-mail: troulier@libertysurf.fr
Thiers 20.5 km. Clermont-Ferrand 55 km. Three rooms on the first floor in a farmhouse, consisting of one bedroom with three single beds; and two double rooms. Each has private facilities. Guests have the use of a sitting room with fireplace and library, a large flower garden and a table tennis table. Table d'hôte meals can be provided using our own garden vegetables. In July concerts of classical music are held at Vollore-Ville. Fishing and walking can be enjoyed in the vicinity.
PRICES: s €29; d €37; t €51; extra person €11; dinner €11
NEARBY: Bathing (5km) Horse riding (4km) Swimming pool (12km) Cross-country skiing (20km) Tennis (4km) Bicycle hire (9km) Shops (4km) **NOTES:** Pets admitted

BRITTANY

CÔTES-D'ARMOR

CREHEN

▦▦▦ ▯○▯ La Belle Noë Roselyne SIROS
22130 CREHEN
☎ 02 96 84 08 47 ▤ 02 96 80 41 88
e-mail: info@crehen.com http://www.crehen.com
Cote d'Emeraude, Cap Fréhel 18km. Dinard 15km. St-Malo 25km. This 18th-century house is set apart from the owner's own property. There are three rooms all with en suite bathrooms. On the ground floor is a double room with private patio, upstairs one room with a double and a single bed, and one room with a double and two bunk beds. A lounge is available. Cost for four people: €71. The property is in wooded grounds with a rose garden. Cycling, badminton and table tennis. Parking. 10 minutes from St-Jacut de la Mer and de St Cast le Guildo. Meals can be arranged. Open all year.

PRICES: s €39; d €46; t €58; extra person €13; dinner €19
NEARBY: Golf (8km) Sea (4km) Swimming pool (8km) Hiking (5km) Water sports (6km) Tennis (1km) Railway station (4km) Shops (1km) PLANCOET (4km) **NOTES:** No pets English spoken

♦♦♦ Villa Bellevue Albert EVEN
10 rue du Port, Port du Guildo, 22130 CREHEN
☎ 02 96 41 08 21 ▤ 02 96 41 08 21
Dinan 20km, medieval town. Cap Frehel & Fort La Latte 20km.
This large centrally heated house has sea views and a large
garden. Four double and two twin rooms are available with en
suite facilities. Breakfast is served in the dining room and on the
veranda. A guest sitting room is also offered. Further facilities
include parking, garage, balcony and terrace. Restaurant nearby.
Local attractions: Créhen, Port du Guildo, ruins of the Château du
Guildo, Pleudihen, St Cast and St Malo. Open all year.
PRICES: s €43; d €46; t €61 **ON SITE:** Sea Water sports
NEARBY: Golf (6km) Swimming pool (6km) Hiking (1km) Tennis (2km)
Railway station (25km) PLANCOET (6km) **NOTES:** No pets

DINAN

♦♦♦ Moulin de la Fontaine des Eaux Denis & Elsie NOEL
22100 DINAN
☎ 02 96 87 92 09 ▤ 02 96 87 92 09
e-mail: denisnoel5@aol.com

Dinan: 2km. St-Malo: 29km. Mont St-Michel: 50km. This restored
watermill with pond and garden has five beamed rooms with en
suite facilities. Four double rooms with the possibility of an extra
bed and the large room has one double and two single beds.
Parking is available. Breakfast is served in the sitting room or on
the terrace. Walks in forest, around the harbour and in Dinan,
overlooking the Vallée de Rance. Cost for four people: €77. Tax:
€0.3 per person per day. Open all year except February.
PRICES: s €40; d €46-€61; t €69; extra person €16 **NEARBY:** Golf
(30km) Sea (15km) Swimming pool (1km) Water sports (1km) Tennis
(2km) Railway station (2km) Shops (2km) DINAN (2km) **NOTES:** No
pets CC English spoken

ERQUY

♦♦♦ Le Dreneuf Roselyne GORIN
22430 ERQUY
☎ 02 96 72 10 07 & 06 19 71 86 72 ▤ 02 96 72 10 07
Erquy 4km. Roselyne welcomes you to the annexe of her small
farm, which has two double rooms with en suite bathrooms and a
family suite of two rooms with one double and two single beds.
Cooking facilities are available. Cost for four people: €59. Nearby
are the beaches and cliffs of Cap d'Equay and Cap Fréhel, Mont St
Michel and La Côte de Granit Rose. Guests can walk on part of the
GR34. Open all year.
PRICES: s €32; d €34-€37; t €45-€48 **NEARBY:** Golf (4km) Sea (1km)
Swimming pool (8km) Water sports (1km) Tennis (4km) Railway station
(18km) Shops (2km) PLENEUF-VAL-ANDRE (4km) **NOTES:** No pets

♦♦♦ Les Bruyères Aline DUTEMPLE
Les Ruaux, 22430 ERQUY
☎ 02 96 72 31 59 ▤ 02 96 72 04 68
Erquy. Cap Frehel 15km. Fort La Latte 18km. This establishment
offers five spacious rooms with telephone, terrace, balcony and
private bathrooms in a family unit of two rooms offering a
children's room, a parents' room and three double rooms, one
room having a terrace and balcony. Sitting rooms with fireplace,
TV and a garden. Ideal area for hikers and cyclists. Watersports
and many cultural sites nearby. Cost for four people: €72/82.
Open all year.
PRICES: s €32-€42; d €45-€53; t €60-€70; extra person €16
ON SITE: Hiking **NEARBY:** Golf (10km) Sea (2km) Swimming pool
(12km) Water sports (2km) Tennis (2km) Railway station (25km) Shops
(2km) PLENEUF-VAL-ANDRE (2km) **NOTES:** No pets English spoken

ETABLES-SUR-MER

♦♦♦ La Ville Jacob Florence LE CORVAISIER
22680 ETABLES SUR MER
☎ 02 96 73 32 68 & 06 08 57 28 18 ▤ 02 96 73 32 68
e-mail: CHRIST-FLO@wanadoo.fr
Binic, St-Quay Portrieux. Welcoming farm offering two double
rooms with en suite facilities and a well-equipped kitchen. An
additional double room with en suite facility is available upstairs.
Breakfast is served in the dining room. Garden with terrace,
barbecue and a children's room with bikes for guest use. Walking
and cycling trails nearby. Open all year.
PRICES: s €25; d €33-€40 **ON SITE:** Children's play area Hiking
NEARBY: Golf (2km) Sea (2km) Swimming pool (2km) Water sports
(2km) Tennis (2km) Railway station (2km) Shops (2km) ETABLES-SUR-
MER (2km) **NOTES:** No pets

FREHEL

♦♦♦ Le Relais de Frehel Myriam FOURNEL
La Ville Besnard-Plevenon, 22240 FREHEL
☎ 02 96 41 43 02 ▤ 02 96 41 30 09
e-mail: Myriam.FOURNEL@lerelaisdefrehel.com
www.lerelaisdefrehel.com

Cap Frehel: 2km. Fort La Latte: 3km. Set in La Lande de Fréhel,
this 19th-century stone farmhouse is in two hectares of wooded
parkland. The four rooms all have private bathrooms. There are
two grade 3 double rooms and two grade 2 rooms with one
double and one single bed each. The family unit has two grade 2
rooms, one double room and one single room, both en suite.
Sitting room, dining room, large garden with children's room.
Parking. Tennis court. Cost for four people: €71. Open Easter to 1
November, weekends and school holidays.
PRICES: d €50; extra person €13 **ON SITE:** Children's play area Hiking
Tennis **NEARBY:** Golf (8km) Sea (2km) Swimming pool (17km) Water
sports (2km) Shops (4km) FREHEL (11km) **NOTES:** No pets English
spoken

BRITTANY

GOMENE

♦♦♦♦ ⦿ La Hersonnière d'en Haut
Gérard LE MEAUX, 22230 GOMENE
☎ 02 96 28 48 67   ▤ 02 96 28 48 67
Loudéac 20 km. This 19th-century house is at the heart of
Brittany. There are three rooms, all with private bathrooms.
On the second floor is a twin room, while on the first floor are
a suite with one double and one single bed, and a two room
family suite. Breakfast and evening meals with local dishes
and garden vegetables are served. The sitting room has views
over the lake, where guests can fish. Garden and
conservatory. Cost for four people: €92. Open all year.
PRICES: s €39-€51; d €43-€54; t €75; extra person €22; dinner €18
NEARBY: Golf (5km) Sea (55km) Swimming pool (5km) Tennis
(5km) Railway station (20km) Shops (5km) MERDRIGNAC (5km)
NOTES: No pets English spoken

HENGOAT

♦♦♦♦ ♿ Le Rumain J.François DUYCK
22450 HENGOAT
☎ 02 96 91 30 92 & 06 83 49 18 39   ▤ 02 96 91 30 92
e-mail: jf.duyck@libertysurf.fr
*Tréguier, Pontrieux, Lezardrieux nearby. Cote de la Granit
Rose.* On the site of a 16th-century manor house set in
grassland and woods are these three rooms and a studio with
private bathrooms. The grade 3 studio has disabled access
and one double, one single room and a small kitchen. Living
room with fireplace, library, washing machine and kitchen. On
the first floor are two grade 4 rooms with one double and one
single bed, and one grade 3 double room. Barbecue, stables,
bikes for hire. Out of season special prices: one person: €24-
26; two people: €41-46. Open all year.
PRICES: s €28-€30; d €45-€50; extra person €15   **NEARBY:** Golf
(15km) Sea (15km) Swimming pool (10km) Hiking (5km) Water
sports (15km) Tennis (10km) Railway station (15km) Shops (4km)
LA ROCHE-DERRIEN (4km)   **NOTES:** No pets English spoken

KERBORS

♦♦♦ ⦿ Troezel Vraz J.Marie & Françoise MAYNIER
22610 KERBORS ☎ 02 96 22 89 68   ▤ 02 96 22 90 56
e-mail: troezel.vras@free.fr http://troezel.vras.free.fr/

Kerbors 2km. Five rooms in a 17th-century renovated manor
house set in two hectares. All have private bathrooms. Ground
floor three-room family unit and upper floor, three double rooms
and a three person family room. Extra beds available. Homemade
jams and yoghurt served. Sitting room and library, garden, terrace
and garden room. Children's meals €8. Mountain bikes for hire.
Open April to end of October.
PRICES: s €41-€47; d €47-€52; t €63-€70; extra person €14; dinner €16
NEARBY: Golf (19km) Sea (3km) Swimming pool (10km) Water sports
(3km) Tennis (7km) Railway station (15km) Shops (2km) **NOTES:** No
pets CC English spoken

KERPERT

♦♦♦ Gars-An-Cloarec Pierre LE BRETON
22480 KERPERT
☎ 02 96 24 32 16   ▤ 02 96 24 34 22
Lac de Guerlédan: 20km. This farm in a wooded area offers three
double rooms with optional additional children's bed, all with en
suite bathrooms. Breakfast is served in a room with many
authentic features. Nearby are the 16th-century church of St Pierre
in Kerpert, the 12th-century Abbey of Coat-Malouen, the Chapel of
Guiadet, the charnel and torture chamber at Lanrivain and the
school museum at Bothoa. Open April till the end of October.
PRICES: s €25; d €32; extra person €10 **ON SITE:** Hiking
NEARBY: Sea (40km) Swimming pool (7km) Water sports (10km)
Tennis (2km) Shops (2km) ST-NICOLAS-DU-PELEM **NOTES:** No pets

LANCIEUX

♦♦♦ Les Hortensias Jacqueline COSSON
Villeneuve, 22770 LANCIEUX
☎ 02 96 86 31 15 & 06 70 08 35 29
Cap Frehel, Fort La Latte. Dinard, St-Malo, Cancale, Dinan.
Beautiful 17th-century longbarn, renovated with taste. The seaside
ambiance together with antique furnishings create a warm
atmosphere. Three comfortable, quiet rooms with private
bathrooms. Garden furniture, parking. Seaside resort of Dinard 8
km. Tariff for 4 people: 70 euros. Frémur Valley, magnificent views
from the water tower at Ploubalay. Open all year.
PRICES: s €40; d €48; t €60; extra person €10 **NEARBY:** Golf (4km)
Sea (1km) Swimming pool (10km) Water sports (1km) Tennis (1km)
Shops (1km) PLOUBALAY (20km) **NOTES:** No pets English spoken

LE FAOUET

♦♦♦ Le Rohiou Germaine LE DIUZET
22290 LE FAOUET
☎ 02 96 52 34 99 e-mail: c.lediuzet@infonie.fr
Ile de Bréhat, Paimpol 13km. Pontrieux 7km. Germaine and
Claude offer four rooms with en suite bathrooms at their
farmhouse. The ground floor has one room with one double and
one single bed and one family suite with two grade 2 rooms (one
double and two single beds) with private bathroom. On the first
floor there is one room with a double and a single bed, and one
double room. Sitting room with kitchen, courtyard, and garden.
Cost for four people: €61/64. Open all year.
PRICES: s €31; d €38; t €49-€54; extra person €9 **NEARBY:** Golf (4km)
Sea (10km) Swimming pool (10km) Water sports (14km) Tennis (4km)
Railway station (17km) LANVOLLON (6km) **NOTES:** No pets English
spoken

LEZARDRIEUX

♦♦♦ Chambre d'hôtes M.Yvette GUILLOU
5 rue de Kervoas, 22740 LEZARDRIEUX
☎ 02 96 20 14 53   ▤ 02 96 20 14 53
Sillon du Talbert:10km, Ile de Brehat:15km. Yvette and Robert
welcome you to their renovated former stable on the Sauvage
peninsula. There are four en suite rooms, one with a double and a
single bed. In the owners' house there are two grade 1 twin rooms
with communal bathroom and wc. Large breakfasts, sitting room,
TV, garden, terrace, barbecue, picnic area and garden bowls.
Walking on the GR34 is close by. Open all year.
PRICES: s €34; d €39; extra person €16 **NEARBY:** Sea (3km) Beach
(8km) Swimming pool (8km) Tennis (3km) Railway station (3km) Shops
(3km) LEZARDRIEUX (3km) **NOTES:** No pets

♦♦♦ ♿ Croas Hent Michel CARRIOU
22740 LEZARDRIEUX
☎ 02 96 22 21 82   🖷 02 96 22 21 82
e-mail: michel.CARRIOU@wanadoo.fr
Set on a vegetable farm this family accommodation is in a private annexe. It offers one double bed and twin beds, with private bathroom and wc as well as a well-equipped kitchen area and veranda. In another annexe are four rooms; two on the ground floor with disabled access, private bathroom and wc; one double and one twin room on the first floor both with en suite facilities. Communal veranda and kitchen. Garden. Nearby: Paimpol, Bréhat and beaches. Cost for four people: €77. Open all year.
PRICES: s €37; d €40-€44; t €57-€59; extra person €16
ON SITE: Children's play area   Hiking   **NEARBY:** Golf (15km)   Sea (3km) Swimming pool (7km)   Tennis (2km)   Railway station (7km)   Shops (2km) LEZARDRIEUX (2km)   **NOTES:** No pets   English spoken

---

LOUANNEC

♦♦♦ Le Colombier de Coat Gourhant M & Mme FAJOLLES
22700 LOUANNEC
☎ 02 96 23 29 30
In a private wing of this renovated farm you will find four attic rooms with en suite bathrooms. There are two double rooms, one room with a small double bed and one twin room. Communal sitting room. Breakfast is served at individual tables. Large aquarium, conservatory and parking. Picnics in the grounds are possible. Nearby is the resort of Perros Guirac. Open March to end October, out of season on request.
PRICES: s €40; d €45; extra person €12   **NEARBY:** Golf (10km)   Sea & beach (2.5km)   Swimming pool (2km)   Water sports (2km)   Tennis (3km) Railway station (9km)   Shops (2km)   PERROS-GUIREC (9km)   **NOTES:** No pets   English spoken

---

MERDRIGNAC

♦♦♦ Manoir de la Peignie François-Regis MARIE
22230 MERDRIGNAC
☎ 02 96 28 42 86
Five large rooms are on offer at this old manor house dating from the 13th and 17th centuries. All have en suite bathrooms. Reading room and library, medieval dining room, board games and table tennis. A rural park of 8000 square metres within 10 hectares and barbecue. Restaurant nearby. The forest of La Brocéliande is 20 minutes away; the coast, one hour, and the leisure-park at Landrouet is just five minutes. Open all year.
PRICES: s €38-€46; d €46-€54; extra person €18   **ON SITE:** Swimming pool   Tennis   **NEARBY:** Golf (1km)   Sea (45km)   Water sports (15km) MERDRIGNAC   **NOTES:** Pets admitted by arrangement   English spoken

---

MERLEAC

♦♦♦ ⏇ Kerdaval Colette BEUREL, 22460 MERLEAC
☎ 02 96 28 87 65
Colette and Michel welcome you to their house set between two lakes. On the first floor are one grade 2 room; two grade 3 rooms with bathroom and wc en suite: on the ground floor one grade 2 room where animals are welcome, with private access and en suite facility. Rustic dining room, sitting room with library. Meals are served at the family table. The veranda leads onto a park with deer and birds. Flower garden, and lawns with bowls. Pony riding and bike hire. Four people: €46. Open all year.
PRICES: s €28; d €33; t €43; dinner €12   **NEARBY:** Golf (40km)   Sea (35km)   Swimming pool (20km)   Hiking (1km)   Water sports (15km) Tennis (1km)   Railway station (6km)   Shops (6km)   UZEL (3km)
NOTES: No pets

MONCONTOUR

♦♦♦ ⏇ Chambre d'hôtes Christiane LE RAY
10 place de Penthièvre, 22510 MONCONTOUR
☎ 02 96 73 52 18   🖷 02 96 73 52 18
This 16th-century house offers four bedrooms. The first floor has two rooms with a double and two single beds, one room with a double and a single bed and one double room, all with en suite bathrooms. Sitting room, dining room and kitchen, and outside the yard, the terrace, the garden room and barbecue. Cost for four people: €64. Meals are served on demand for €15 over a four-day period. Children €8. Shops 100m. Open all year.
PRICES: s €31; d €39; t €54; extra person €15; dinner €15
NEARBY: Golf (25km)   Sea (20km)   Swimming pool (1km)   Water sports (20km)   Tennis (1km)   Railway station (17km)   MONCONTOUR
NOTES: Pets admitted

PERROS-GUIREC

♦♦♦ ⏇ Goas ar Ian Nicole et André MICHEL
Louannec, 22700 PERROS-GUIREC
☎ 02 96 49 08 54 & 06 13 60 75 94   🖷 02 96 49 00 29
e-mail: goas-ar-Ian@wanadoo.fr   www.goasarIan.com
At the centre of the Côte du Granit Rose is this restored house set in five hectares. On the ground floor is one double room with separate private bathroom. On the upper floor, four double rooms, two with separate private bathrooms, one with en suite bathroom and one with en suite wc and washbasin. Private parking, a garden room and barbecue are available. Meals can be ordered in advance. Prize-winning garden with trees. 5km from the casino. Open February to October and out of season on request.
PRICES: d €47-€52; extra person €15; dinner €19   **NEARBY:** Golf (5km) Sea (2km)   Swimming pool (5km)   Hiking (2km)   Water sports (2km) Tennis (2km)   Railway station (5km)   Shops (2km)   PERROS-GUIREC (5km)
NOTES: No pets   English spoken

PLELO

♦♦♦ ⏛ ⏇ Le Char à Bancs Famille LAMOUR
Au Char à Bancs, Moulin de la ville Geffroy, 22170 PLELO
☎ 02 96 74 13 63   🖷 02 96 74 13 03
e-mail: charabanc@wanadoo.fr   aucharabanc.com

Four rooms are available in this house, which is also a local museum. All rooms have wc and washbasin and one has a bath. Guest sitting room. Meals are available at the farm inn 500m away costing €14-25. Shetland pony rides for children accompanied by their parents, and fishing are available. Cost for four people: €105. Establishment produces its own electricity. Pedal boats can be hired on the River Leff. Open all summer and weekends by request.
PRICES: s €46-€76; d €60-€82; t €75-€98; extra person €15; dinner €14-€25   **NEARBY:** Golf (10km)   Sea (13km)   Swimming pool (5km)   Water sports (13km)   Tennis (5km)   Railway station (20km)   Shops (2km) Restaurant nearby   CHATELAUDREN (2km)   **NOTES:** No pets   English spoken

PLERIN

♦♦♦ Manoir de Maupertuis Brigitte DUPUY
Tournemine, 22190 PLERIN
☎ 02 96 74 46 08   📠 02 96 33 80 38
Brigitte is your welcoming hostess in this comfortable restful
manor house with its views of the sea. On the first floor are three
rooms with double bed and mezzanine floor for children with
private bathroom. There is TV and wooded one-hectare parkland
with summerhouse and barbecue. A sailing school, horse riding
and walking nearby. Open 1 April until 30 September.
PRICES: d €39-€44; extra person €8-€11 **NEARBY:** Golf (16km) Sea
(1km) Swimming pool (10km) Hiking (1km) Water sports (1km) Tennis
(1km) Railway station (7km) Shops (2km) SAINT-BRIEUC (6km)
NOTES: No pets

PLESLIN-TRIGAVOU

♦♦♦ ⟨◯⟩ Le Val Garance Elizabeth NICOLAS-MOREL
Trebefour, 22490 PLESLIN-TRIGAVOU
☎ 02 96 27 83 57   📠 02 96 27 83 57
e-mail: MRELIMOMOO@aol.com
South-facing accommodation offers four grade 3 rooms: one
double room; two twin rooms; one room with one double and two
single beds all with private facilities and one grade 2 double room
with separate bathroom and wc. Big garden and bikes, shops 1km,
station 9km. Cost for four people: €61. Meals served apart from
Saturdays in July and August. Sitting room with large fireplace.
Nearby sites: Leslin-Trigavou, the barges of Fremur, the field of the
Druids, and the megalithic sites. Open all year.
PRICES: s €34; d €39; t €40; extra person €12; dinner €14
NEARBY: Golf (5km) Sea (9km) Swimming pool (9km) Water sports
(9km) Tennis (9km) Railway station (9km) Shops (1km) DINAN (9km)
NOTES: Pets admitted English spoken

PLEUDIHEN SUR RANCE

♦♦♦ Le Val Hervelin Sylvie BRIGNON
22690 PLEUDIHEN SUR RANCE
☎ 02 96 88 20 99 & SR : 02 96 62 21 73
e-mail: hervelines@hotmail.com
http://www.multimania.com/leshervelines
Dinan 12km, St-Malo 20 km. Four themed rooms are available at
this charming establishment. La Campagnarde sleeps three and
has an en suite bathroom. Two double rooms with en suite
facilities include la Bretonne and Terres Neuvas with its sea blue
décor. La Romantique is ideal for couples. Sitting room and
garden. The Malouine coast is nearby, and there is a forest on the
doorstep. Open all year.
PRICES: s €34; d €39; t €51; extra person €10 **ON SITE:** Hiking Tennis
NEARBY: Golf (7km) Sea (20km) Swimming pool (12km) Water sports
(3km) Railway station (12km) Shops (3km) PLEUDIHEN SUR RANCE
(3km) **NOTES:** Pets admitted

♦♦♦ ⟨◯⟩ La Chesnaie Bernard & Nicole GAUDRY
22690 PLEUDIHEN SUR RANCE
☎ 02 99 58 04 88
Bernard and Nicole welcome you to their former farmhouse.
Upstairs are two grade 3 double rooms with en suite facilities, and
a family room with one double and one single bed, again with en
suite. The dining/sitting room has an open fireplace. Farm produce
is served. Outside are a terrace and prize-winning flower garden as
well as a garden room. Nearby are Pleudihen sur Rance, the apple
and cider museum and the pleasure port of Lyvet. Open all year.
PRICES: d €40; t €56; extra person €9; dinner €13 **NEARBY:** Golf
(10km) Sea (15km) Swimming pool (15km) Water sports (6km) Tennis
(2km) Railway station (15km) Shops (2km) DINAN (9km) **NOTES:** No
pets

♦♦♦ Le Val Hervelin Françoise CHENU
22690 PLEUDIHEN SUR RANCE
☎ 02 96 83 35 61   📠 02 96 83 38 43
In a valley with a view over a lake the annexe to this house has
been renovated and divided to provide two gîtes. One double
room with en suite bathroom, one twin room and one room for
four with a double and two single beds are offered. A cot is
available. The open plan living area provides a kitchen, a sitting
area and an open fire. There is parking and an enclosed courtyard.
Open all year.
PRICES: s €35; d €40; t €55 **ON SITE:** Hiking **NEARBY:** Golf (20km)
Sea (15km) Swimming pool (9km) Water sports (15km) Tennis (3km)
Railway station (9km) Shops (3km) DINAN **NOTES:** Pets admitted

♦♦♦ Manoir de la Pepiniere Jacques VILLAIN
Pont de Cieux, 22690 PLEUDIHEN SUR RANCE
☎ 02 96 83 36 61   📠 02 96 88 26 26
St-Malo: 14km. Pleudihen/Rance: 1km. In a beautiful spot with
views over the marshland of La Rance, this 17th-century manor
house has been completely renovated and is set in extensive
grounds. Upstairs the rooms are decorated with stencils and
consist of three double rooms, one twin room, and one room with
a double and a single bed. Each room has its own bathroom. The
sitting room has a breakfast table that transforms into a billiard
table in the evening. Open all year.
PRICES: s €42; d €49; t €64 **NEARBY:** Golf (14km) Sea (14km)
Swimming pool (10km) Water sports (14km) Tennis (2km) Railway station
(12km) Shops (1km) DINAN (10km) **NOTES:** No pets English spoken

PLEVEN

♦♦♦ ⟨◯⟩ La Rompardais Michelle BLANCHARD
22130 PLEVEN
☎ 02 96 84 43 08
Michelle welcomes you to this renovated 19th-century cottage.
There are four rooms: a double room, and a room with one
double and one single bed, on the first floor. Both have en suite
bathrooms. While on the second floor are two single rooms.
Breakfast is served in the living room or on the veranda. Activities
include mountain biking and fishing. Local sites include the farm
d'Antan at Plédéliac and the medieval castle. 1/2 board is possible
for a stay of more than three days. Open all year.
PRICES: s €33; d €37-€39; t €46-€49; extra person €8; HB €31; dinner
€14 **NEARBY:** Golf (20km) Sea (20km) Swimming pool (17km) Hiking
(1km) Water sports (20km) Tennis (1km) Railway station (17km) Shops
(1km) PLANCOET (7km) **NOTES:** Pets admitted

PLOEZAL

♦♦♦ ❤ Kerleo Roselyne & J. Louis HERVE
FERME DE KERLEO, 22260 PLOEZAL
☎ 02 96 95 65 78   📠 02 96 95 14 63
Paimpol 15km. Roselyne offers four rooms. One is grade 3 with a
double and a single bed and en suite bathroom, another grade 3
room has a double and twin beds and en suite bathroom, and two
grade 1 double rooms have a shared bathroom. All rooms have
private entry. Sitting room and garden. There is also a gîte on the
site. The Côte du Granit Rose is twenty minutes away and the 15th-
century castle of la Roche Jagu is 1km. A steam train goes from
Pontrieux to Paimpol. Open all year.
PRICES: s €29-€35; d €34-€42; extra person €11 **NEARBY:** Golf (15km)
Sea (10km) Swimming pool (15km) Water sports (3km) Tennis (3km)
Railway station (3km) Shops (3km) PONTRIEUX (3km) **NOTES:** No pets

PLOUBAZLANEC

♦♦♦ ⓘOI Ker'Ever Katerine CHABOUD
1 chemin de Kertanouarn, 22620 PLOUBAZLANEC
☎ 02 96 55 82 76 & 06 14 59 56 96
e-mail: jpkchaboud@wanadoo.fr
This beautiful and authentic breton house has been charmingly
restored and offers a warm welcome to three rooms decorated in
English style with en suite facilities. The yellow room has a double
bed, the flax room has a double bed and the green room is a twin.
Outside are a garden and garden room and inside is the guest
sitting room. Take the dinghy out to picnic by the sea on the
islands of Bréhat or sail in the reserve with M. Chaboud. Bicycles
for hire. Open all year.
PRICES: s €42-€46; d €48-€53 **ON SITE:** Hiking **NEARBY:** Sea (1km)
Swimming pool (5km) Water sports (1km) Tennis (2km) Railway station
(5km) Shops (1km) PAIMPOL (3km) **NOTES:** No pets English spoken

PLOUER-SUR-RANCE

♦♦♦ ⓘOI La Renardais Jean & Suzanne ROBINSON
Le Repos, 22490 PLOUER SUR RANCE
☎ 02 96 86 89 81 🖷 02 96 86 99 22
e-mail: Suzanne.Robinson@wanadoo.fr
http://perso.wanadoo.fr/suzanne.robinson.bnb/

Plouer/Rance 2 km. A warm welcome awaits at this elegant stone
house. On the first floor are two rooms each with a double and a
single bed, and on the second floor one double and one twin
room. All rooms have en suite bathrooms. An extra bed is available
if required. Sitting room with open fireplace. On fine days you can
enjoy breakfast in the flower garden. Nearby sites include: Mont-St-
Michel, Cap Fréhel, Dinard, and St Malo. Price for four people:
€83/93. Open all year except January and February.
PRICES: s €46-€56; d €51-€61; t €67-€77; extra person €16; HB €42-€62;
dinner €16-€20 **NEARBY:** Golf (15km) Sea (15km) Swimming pool
(8km) Water sports (8km) Tennis (1km) Railway station (8km) Shops
(1km) DINAN (8km) **NOTES:** No pets English spoken

PLOUGRESCANT

♦♦♦ Chambre d'hôtes Marie-Claude JANVIER
15 rue du Castel Meur, 22820 PLOUGRESCANT
☎ 02 96 92 52 67 & 06 71 07 32 32 🖷 02 96 92 52 67
Marie-Claude offers three rooms for you in a breton house. The
rooms are on the first floor and two have en suite wc and
washbasin while the third has an en suite bathroom. One double
room has a view of the sea; two rooms have a library, one is a
double with extra bed and one is a twin with bathroom. There is a
fridge for your use as well as the sitting room and the patio.
Parking. The airport is at Lannion. Open all year.
PRICES: d €41-€46; t €53 **NEARBY:** Golf (25km) Sea (1km) Swimming
pool (7km) Hiking (1km) Water sports (1km) Tennis (1km) Railway
station (20km) Shops (1km) TREGUIER (6km) **NOTES:** No pets

♦♦♦ Le Tourot Gilles LE BOURDONNEC
2 Kervoazec Hent Tourot, 22820 PLOUGRESCANT
☎ 02 96 92 50 20 & 06 87 52 64 62
Margaux and Gilles welcome guests to this renovated cottage. In
an annexe of their house they have four very spacious double
rooms, two of which have private access. Each room has an en
suite bathroom. Large sitting room, dining room and kitchen can
be used at a cost of €1.55 per day. The farm enjoys a fine sea view
and has a dovecote. Trips on sailing boats and in kayaks available.
Good walking country. There is a tax of €0.5 per person per day.
Open all year.
PRICES: s €36; d €40 **ON SITE:** Sea Hiking Water sports
NEARBY: Golf (22km) Swimming pool (7km) Tennis (2km) Railway
station (30km) Shops (2km) TREGUIER (8km) **NOTES:** No pets English
spoken

PLOUGUENAST

♦♦♦ Garmorin Madelaine LUCAS, 22150 PLOUGUENAST
☎ 02 96 28 70 61 & 06 70 55 96 49
Loudéac: 10km. This neo-breton style house offers three rooms
each with its own bathroom. One room has a double and a single
bed, one room is a twin and the third is a family suite with two
rooms (a double and a single bed in each). Picnics, another gîte
and a campsite are in the grounds. Station 10km, shops 2km and a
restaurant 1.5km. Cost for four people: €48. The property is at the
centre of the Accueil de Loudac. Nearby: Plougenast with a gothic
church dating from the 15th and 16th centuries. Good walking
country.
PRICES: s €28; d €34; t €40 **ON SITE:** Golf **NEARBY:** Sea (35km)
Swimming pool (10km) Hiking (1km) Water sports (30km) Tennis (2km)
Railway station (10km) Shops (2km) PLOUGUENAST (2km) **NOTES:** No
pets

PLOUGUIEL

♦♦♦ La Roche Jaune Claire L'ANTHOEN
4 rue de Lizildry, 22220 PLOUGUIEL
☎ 02 96 92 57 34
Claire offers three rooms two of which are grade 3 double rooms
with seaview and private facilities, and the other is a grade 2
double room on the ground floor, and en suite. An extra bed can
be provided. Breakfast is served in the dining room. Parking,
bowls, a large lawn and a garden with sitting area. Only 500m
from the sea. Nearby sites: Paimpol, Ile de Bréhat, Perros Guirec,
Ploumanch. The tourist tax is €0.50 per person per day. Open all
year.
PRICES: s €36; d €40; t €51; extra person €11 **ON SITE:** Hiking
NEARBY: Golf (5km) Sea (1km) Swimming pool (7km) Water sports
(5km) Tennis (5km) Railway station (20km) TREGUIER (6km)
NOTES: Pets admitted

PLOUVARA

♦♦♦ Le Château de la Magdeleine Arnaud MORIN
22170 PLOUVARA
☎ 06 22 19 35 06 🖷 02 96 73 86 35
3km Plouvara, 15km Quintin. Situated in a wooded property of 10
hectares, is le Château de la Magdeleine. Four rooms on the first
floor include a family unit for five (one double, one single and
bunk beds) with a private sitting room, TV and separate bathroom.
The three other rooms are double with the option of an additional
bed with en suite wc in each and one with bath. Guests have use
of the kitchen. On the estate is an equestrian centre and there is a
swimming pool 8km away in Quentin. Open all year.
PRICES: s €46; d €51; t €71 **NEARBY:** Sea & beach (23km) Swimming
pool (8km) Water sports (23km) Tennis (9km) Railway station (15km)
Shops (5km) CHATELAUDREN (5km) **NOTES:** No pets

PLUMIEUX

♨ ♥ ⏧ Breil Sable

A.Marie & Dominique GUILLAUME
22210 PLUMIEUX
☎ 02 96 26 77 16 ▤ 02 96 26 66 13
In the annexe next to the farmhouse are three rooms two of which have en suite facilities and a double and a single bed. The other has a bathroom and one double and one single bed. Dining room, sitting room/kitchen with dining area, courtyard, garden, garden room and barbecue. Walking on the banks of the Lié. 15th- and 16th-century churches and the forests of Brocéliande, Loudéac, and Lanouée are nearby. Cost for children under ten years: €10; children over ten years €13. Open all year.
PRICES: s €29; d €36; t €48; extra person €13; dinner €13
NEARBY: Golf (5km) Sea (60km) Swimming pool (5km) Hiking (5km) Water sports (40km) Tennis (5km) Railway station (18km) Shops (8km) LA CHEZE (5km) **NOTES:** No pets

PLURIEN

♨ Guitrel Colette MORIN, 22240 PLURIEN-FREHEL

☎ 02 96 72 35 37
Colette runs this entirely renovated cottage with parking and a flower-filled garden with south-facing terrace. The accommodation is made up of five rooms with en suite facilities. On the ground floor, a family room with one double and two single beds with disabled access, and on the first floor two double and two twin rooms. Breakfast is served in the dining room. 2km from the sea and near Cap Fréhel and Port d'Erquy (Blue Lake). Cost for four people: €54/61. Open 20 March - 15 November.
PRICES: s €27-€35, d €35-€40; t €45-€51 **NEARBY:** Golf (2km) Sea (2km) Swimming pool (15km) Water sports (2km) Tennis (1km) Railway station (20km) Shops (1km) PLENEUF-VAL-ANDRE **NOTES:** No pets

POMMERIT-JAUDY

♨ ⅙ Quillevez Vraz Georges BEAUVERGER

22450 POMMERIT-JAUDY
☎ 02 96 91 35 74 & 02 96 91 52 81
In a cottage near the home of the owner we are offering three rooms - one double and one with one double and one single bed - with private bathroom all with disabled access. A large living room and a kitchen complete the accommodation. Cooking at a cost of 4euros is also possible. Open Easter till the end of October.
PRICES: s €34; d €40; t €50; extra person €11 **NEARBY:** Golf (10km) Sea (15km) Swimming pool (5km) Hiking (3km) Water sports (15km) Tennis (2km) Railway station (20km) Shops (1km) LA ROCHE-DERRIEN (2km) **NOTES:** No pets

PORDIC

♨ Saint Halory Henriette TREHEN

22590 PORDIC
☎ 02 96 79 41 11 & 06 88 28 29 15 ▤ 02 96 79 41 11
St-Brieuc (7km). Port de Binic (3km). St-Quay-Portrieux. This newly renovated cottage is beside the owner's home on a dairy farm. On the ground floor, there is one double room and, on the first floor, a twin room and a family unit with two rooms sleeping four people. All have private bathrooms. Sitting room, dining room, and small kitchen, terrace, lawn, garden room, yard and barbecue. Activities include trailwalking, mountain bike circuits, a velodrome (1km), beaches, the sailing school (2km) and canoeing. Open all year.
PRICES: s €31; d €38; t €54 **ON SITE:** Hiking **NEARBY:** Golf (6km) Sea (2km) Swimming pool (8km) Water sports (2km) Tennis (1km) Railway station (8km) Shops (2km) CHATELAUDREN (6km) **NOTES:** No pets

PRAT

♨ Manoir de Coadelan Jeanne RIOU

22140 PRAT
☎ 02 96 47 00 60 & 02 96 47 02 01
This 16th century manor house is the setting for six rooms. Two rooms for three, and four double rooms. All with en suite. The house has an 8m high menhir by a lovely pond surrounded by flowers. You will see Lannion in the Léguer valley, Perros-Guirec, Tréguier, Paimpol, and Ile de Bréhat. Open April to end October.
PRICES: s €40; d €46; t €58; extra person €12 **NEARBY:** Golf (6km) Sea (15km) Swimming pool (15km) Water sports (15km) Tennis (2km) Railway station (15km) Shops (2km) LA ROCHE-DERRIEN (15km) **NOTES:** No pets

QUEVERT

♨ ⏧ Argenteil Stéphane LESAGE

La Borgnais, 22100 QUEVERT
☎ 02 96 85 46 59
e-mail: argenteil@chez.com http://www.chez.com/argenteil/
Just on the outskirts of Dinan is this unusual country property. On the first floor are three family units for four people each. Retro and Anglais cost €67 for four people and Safari costs €74 for four. Marble bathrooms form part of each unit and all have one double and two single beds. You may prepare your own meals or order meals in advance from your host. Art Nouveau dining room. Costs for a child: €8. The tree-lined grounds run alongside the river Argenteil. Swimming pool, games, fishing and walking. Washing machine, internet access and bicycle hire. Open all year.
PRICES: d €43-€59; t €55-€68; extra person €10; dinner €16
ON SITE: Swimming pool Hiking **NEARBY:** Sea (17km) Water sports (3km) Tennis (1km) Railway station (2km) Shops (2km) DINAN (2km) **NOTES:** Pets admitted English spoken

QUINTIN

♨ La Pommeraie M-Pierre LE LOUET

22800 QUINTIN
☎ 02 96 74 80 09 ▤ 02 96 74 80 09
This quiet detached house is just beside the small town of Quentin which has a character of its own. The accommodation is in three rooms. On the ground floor is a double room with private bathroom and on the first floor there is a twin room with en suite facilities and a family unit of two rooms, a twin and a single with private wc and bathroom. There is garden furniture. Open all year.
PRICES: s €23; d €34; t €46; extra person €13 **NEARBY:** Golf (20km) Sea (20km) Swimming pool (3km) Water sports (20km) Tennis (3km) Railway station (3km) Shops (3km) QUINTIN (3km) **NOTES:** No pets

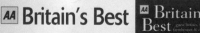
BRITTANY

ST-ALBAN

††† ✿ Malido Huguette LE GRAND
22400 SAINT ALBAN

☎ 02 96 32 94 74 ▯ 02 96 32 92 67

This accommodation is in an annexe of the owner's farmhouse. There are five grade 3 rooms and one grade 2 room, four of the rooms having private access. There are two double rooms, two three-person rooms and a family unit with two rooms, one with balcony. Sitting room with open fireplace, well equipped kitchen and baby-sitting service. Outside is a play area and a leisure park nearby in summer. Nearby are sandy beaches and a local walking trail. Open all year.

PRICES: s €30; d €33-€40; t €45-€52; extra person €13 **NEARBY:** Golf (4km) Sea (4km) Swimming pool (4km) Water sports (4km) Tennis (4km) Railway station (18km) Shops (2km) PLENEUF-VAL-ANDRE (5km)
NOTES: No pets

ST-CARADEC

††† ◯| Goizel Loïc LE MAITRE
22600 SAINT CARADEC

☎ 02 96 25 05 30 & 06 20 15 68 12 ▯ 02 96 25 05 30
e-mail: LOIC.LE-MAITRE@wanadoo.fr

Set on the edge of La Rigole de l'Hilvern, Lucienne and Loïc welcome guests to this pretty cottage on their farm. The accommodation: on the ground floor two double rooms with private facilities (one with a bath), on the first floor two rooms, one with a double and a single bed and one twin room both with private facilities. Meals using local produce are served in a family atmosphere. In summer you can ride in a carriage to the market at Loudéac farm. Open all year.

PRICES: s €29; d €36; t €49; HB €39-€57; dinner €16 **NEARBY:** Golf (10km) Sea (40km) Swimming pool (9km) Water sports (40km) Tennis (2km) Railway station (9km) Shops (2km) LOUDEAC (9km)
NOTES: No pets

ST-DONAN

††† ✿ ◯| La Ville Suzanne Michel CORBEL
le Cheval et le Paysan, 22800 ST-DONAN

☎ 02 96 73 95 03 & 06 86 78 07 62 ▯ 02 96 73 86 41
e-mail: CorbelM@wanadoo.fr

Micheline and Michel welcome you to two double guestrooms with en suite bathrooms in an extension of their home. On the ground floor there is a small communal kitchen. In a separate annexe is a family suite with cooking alcove, sitting room with open fireplace, a double room and a twin room with bathroom. Cost for four people: €58. Meals use local produce. Garden and barbecue. Horses may be stabled and there is a nearby donkey museum.

PRICES: s €31; d €35-€43; t €51; dinner €16 **NEARBY:** Golf (25km) Sea (12km) Swimming pool (10km) Hiking (1km) Water sports (2km) Tennis (3km) Railway station (10km) Shops (3km) SAINT-BRIEUC **NOTES:** No pets

ST-JUVAT

††† Les Effourneaux Thierry HADJAL
22630 ST-JUVAT

☎ 02 96 88 17 52 ▯ 02 96 88 17 52
e-mail: effourneaux@wanadoo.fr
http://perso.wanadoo.fr/leseffourneaux/

Near the village of St Juvat, lies this 19th-century restored house of Falun stone with its hundred year old trees. Two spacious double rooms furnished in traditional style with en suite bathrooms and one double room with en suite shower are offered. There is a relaxing lounge with terrace and bicycles are available for your use. Private parking. Nearby: beaches, walking trails and water sports. Open all year with prior booking.

PRICES: s €36-€40; d €43-€48 **NEARBY:** Golf (30km) Sea (30km) Swimming pool (10km) Tennis (10km) Railway station (10km) Shops (1km) EVRAN **NOTES:** No pets English spoken

ST-LORMEL

††† ◯| La Pastourelle Evelyne LEDE
22130 SAINT LORMEL

☎ 02 96 84 03 77 ▯ 02 96 84 03 77

Evelyne welcomes you to this lovely cottage with outdoor sitting area, lawn and games. Only a few kilometres from the beaches of the emerald coast with Cap Fréhel, Fort-La-Latte, St Malo, and Dinan. Four double rooms with shower and one double room with bath, and one family unit on the first floor with two rooms and bathroom. The cottage is well presented with fine porcelain and beautiful furniture, and with stone walls in the sitting and dining rooms. Open all year.

PRICES: s €37; d €39-€41; t €51-€53; extra person €13; HB €32; dinner €15 **ON SITE:** Children's play area **NEARBY:** Golf (10km) Sea (10km) Swimming pool (23km) Water sports (10km) Tennis (10km) Railway station (4km) Shops (1km) PLANCOET (4km) **NOTES:** No pets

ST-POTAN

††† ◯| Bonn Vie Denise GUILLAUME
22550 SAINT-POTAN

☎ 02 96 41 02 91 ▯ 02 96 41 10 54

By the sea and with all the charm of the country this family property has three rooms with bathroom: one double room, and two rooms with one double and one single bed. Breakfast is served with produce from the dairy farm. Picnics in the large garden and organised walks can be arranged. Meals are served on Monday, Wednesday and Friday or Saturday. Open all year.

PRICES: s €32; d €38; t €49; extra person €11; dinner €13
NEARBY: Golf (4km) Sea (4km) Swimming pool (4km) Water sports (4km) Tennis (4km) Railway station (20km) Shops (1km) MATIGNON
NOTES: No pets

ST-QUAY-PERROS

†††† ◯| Manoir de Kéringant Evelyne GUERY
22700 ST QUAY-PERROS

☎ 02 96 48 81 86 ▯ 02 96 48 73 50
e-mail: manoir.keringant@wanadoo.fr
http://perso.wanadoo.fr/keringant

Evelyne and André welcome you to their charming 14th-15th-century manor house. On the first floor are three double rooms with bathrooms, and one grade 3 room with narrow double bed, also with bathroom. Dairy produce, pancakes, home-made cake, jams, local biscuits, and fruit juice for breakfast. Sitting room with TV and library. Courtyard and garden with trees and flowers. The area is near Port de Porros Guirec with its beaches, and the sea coast of the Côte de Granit Rose. Closed in January unless booked in advance.

PRICES: s €71; d €58-€75; t €104; dinner €26 **NEARBY:** Golf (10km) Sea (3km) Swimming pool (3km) Hiking (5km) Water sports (3km) Tennis (3km) Railway station (3km) Shops (3km) PERROS-GUIREC **NOTES:** No pets

TREGROM

††† ◯| L'Ancien Presbytere Nicole DE MORCHOVEN
22420 TREGROM

☎ 02 96 47 94 15 ▯ 02 96 47 94 15

Château de Rosambo, Château de Kergrist. This 17th &18th-century presbytery has been tastefully furnished and is set in a village in the heart of the Tréguer area. Three rooms are on offer here all with private bathroom or shower room and a garden. 800m from the river, airport 25km. 10% reduction for guests who

continued

continued

stay more than three nights out of season. Near Lannion, the Château de la Roche Jagu, and Tréguer with the circuit of Ajoncs d'Or. Open all year.

PRICES: s €45; d €50; dinner €20 **NEARBY:** Golf (28km) Sea (20km) Swimming pool (28km) Water sports (20km) Tennis (1km) Railway station (7km) PLOUARET (7km) **NOTES:** Pets admitted English spoken

TREGUIER

⚜⚜⚜ **Tara** Guy & Malou ARHANT
31 rue Ernest Renan, 22220 TREGUIER
☎ 02 96 92 15 28

Paimpol and Lannion: 18km. Malou and Guy welcome guests to this 16th-century house in the capital of Trégor. There are five rooms, all with en suite facilities. Four double rooms on the first floor can have an additional bed, and on the ground floor one three bedded room has disabled access. Breakfast is at the communal table of the period dining room and there is a small kitchen and dining area. Parking in the garden. Cost for four people: €80. Open all year with reservation.
PRICES: s €42; d €50; t €67; extra person €17 **NEARBY:** Golf (20km) Sea (1km) Swimming pool (1km) Water sports (4km) Tennis (1km) Railway station (18km) TREGUIER **NOTES:** No pets English spoken

TRELEVERN

⚜⚜⚜ **Le Launay** Christian LEROY
La Ferme de l'Etang, 22660 TRELEVERN
☎ 02 96 91 70 44　📠 02 96 91 79 96
Liliane and Christian offer four rooms in their 19th-century cottage on a large property with a pond. On the first floor are three rooms with one double and one single bed and one double room all with en suite bathrooms. Breakfast may be served in the dining room or garden. Babies are welcome. Fax, garden room, table tennis and hire of bicycles. From here you can visit the Côte de Granit Rose, the reserve of the seven islands and Bréhat on the GR34. Open all year.
PRICES: s €38-€44; d €47-€54; t €61-€68; extra person €15 **NEARBY:** Golf (20km) Sea (4km) Swimming pool (14km) Hiking (4km) Water sports (4km) Tennis (3km) Railway station (15km) Shops (4km) PERROS-GUIREC (14km) **NOTES:** No pets

TREMEREUC

⚜⚜⚜ **Chambre d'hôtes** Gérard DELEPINE
25 la Ville Patouard, 22490 TREMEREUC
☎ 02 96 27 88 29
Cap Fréhel, Dinan: 13 km. Three rooms are available at this private detached property with a shady garden. On the first floor are two double rooms and one room with a double and a single bed, all with private bathroom. Guests have use of the kitchen. Sitting room, barbecue and parking. Local activities include volleyball, football, basketball, golf, horse riding, mountain biking and walking. Guests can enjoy the joys of both countryside and the sea between the Vallée du Frémur and de la Rance taking you to Dinan. Open all year.
PRICES: s €35; d €40; t €55; extra person €15 **ON SITE:** Hiking Tennis **NEARBY:** Golf (1km) Sea (8km) Swimming pool (7km) Water sports (8km) Railway station (13km) Shops (1km) PLOUBALAY (13km) **NOTES:** No pets English spoken

TRESSAINT-LANVALLAY

⚜⚜⚜ 🐓 🍴 **La Ville Ameline**
Huguette & Yvon LEMARCHAND
22100 TRESSAINT-LANVALLAY
☎ 02 96 39 33 69　📠 02 96 39 33 69
e-mail: lemarchand.huguette@wanadoo.fr
www.perso.wanadoo.fr/lavilleamelinechambres
Huguette and Yvon welcome guests to their farm near the magnificent Vallée de la Ronce and close to the emerald coast and to the town of Dinan. The accommodation is in three family units with two rooms for four people each, and one additional double room all with private bathroom. There is also a dining room. Outside is a large park with trees and a vast lawn. Garden furniture, a play area and bowls. Cost for four people: €58; 1/2 board €32. Open all year.
PRICES: s €32; d €38; t €49; extra person €11; HB €32; dinner €13 **ON SITE:** Children's play area **NEARBY:** Golf (15km) Sea (25km) Swimming pool (3km) Water sports (25km) Tennis (2km) Railway station (4km) Shops (2km) DINAN (3km) **NOTES:** No pets

TREVE

⚜⚜⚜ 🐓 🍴 **Le Bois d'en Haut** Paulette et Jean DONNIO
22600 TREVE
☎ 02 96 25 44 53
Lac de Guerlédan & Bosméléac nearby. On the ground floor of this renovated house on a horse-breeding farm, we have four rooms with a small kitchen and separate entrance. There are two double rooms with communal sitting room and fireplace, bathroom and wc; for 2/3 people, one grade 2 room with wc and two double rooms with bathroom all with sitting room. Set in grounds of one hectare the garden offers a barbecue, a sitting area and games. Cost for four people: €60. Open all year.
PRICES: s €24; d €34-€37; t €50; extra person €12; dinner €12 **ON SITE:** Hiking **NEARBY:** Golf (20km) Sea (35km) Swimming pool (4km) Water sports (20km) Tennis (4km) Railway station (4km) Shops (2km) LOUDEAC (4km) **NOTES:** No pets

UZEL

⚜⚜⚜ 🐓 🍴 **Bizoin** Marie Annick CADORET
22460 UZEL
☎ 02 96 28 81 24 & 06 74 55 84 68　📠 02 96 26 28 42
Mur de Bretagne 12km. The accommodation on this charming farm is in two grade 2 rooms with one double room and one room with a double and a single bed and two grade 3 rooms with one double room and one room with one double and one single bed. All have en suite bathrooms. Dining room, kitchen, courtyard, terrace and garden furniture. Evening meals are served. Pony club

continued

7km. Local sites: Lac du Bosméléac and Quintin. Cost for four people: €52 1/2 board for two people €57. Open all year.
PRICES: s €31; d €34; t €43; extra person €10; HB €57; dinner €12
ON SITE: Hiking **NEARBY:** Golf (40km) Sea (35km) Swimming pool (18km) Water sports (12km) Tennis (3km) Railway station (3km) UZEL (3km) **NOTES:** Pets admitted

YFFINIAC

♥ La Fontaine Menard
François & Josiane PENNORS
22120 YFFINIAC
☎ 02 96 72 66 68 & 06 89 24 38 73 ▤ 02 96 72 66 63
e-mail: fpennors@infonie.fr
Moncontour: 12km. Val André: 15km. Your hosts welcome guests to this annexe of an old restored stone manor. Accommodation is on two floors including a large room with a double and two single beds on the ground floor, and three rooms on the first floor, one room with a double and a single bed and two double rooms. All rooms have their own bathrooms. Price for four people is €69. Kitchen, sitting room, washing machine, terrace with barbecue and a courtyard. Animals are welcome by prior arrangement. Walking trails 2km, hippodrome 800m, and ice rink 4km. Open all year.
PRICES: s €42; d €45; t €57; extra person €12 **NEARBY:** Golf (8km) Sea (6km) Swimming pool (6km) Water sports (6km) Tennis (6km) Railway station (8km) Shops (3km) SAINT-BRIEUC (6km) **NOTES:** Pets admitted English spoken

♥ Les Villes Hervé Elisabeth JOUAN
22120 YFFINIAC
☎ 02 96 72 50 31
Hillion 7km. There are two grade 3 rooms - a double and a twin - with private bathroom and one grade 2 twin room with wash hand basin and bath. WC is separate. Breakfast is served with farm produce. Large garden with terrace, garden room and barbecue. You can fish in the river only 500m from the farm. We are between Cap Fréhel and Perros Guirec, which is an ideal walking area. Open May to September and weekends all year.
PRICES: s €30; d €38; t €49; extra person €11 **NEARBY:** Golf (10km) Sea (6km) Swimming pool (8km) Hiking (1km) Water sports (15km) Tennis (2km) Railway station (10km) Shops (2km) SAINT-BRIEUC (7km) **NOTES:** No pets

Le Grenier Marie Reine LOQUIN
route de Plédran, 22120 YFFINIAC
☎ 02 96 72 64 55 & 06 19 90 95 82 ▤ 02 96 72 68 74
e-mail: le.grenier@wanadoo.fr http://www.le.grenier.com
Val André et Moncontour 15km. Fernand and Marie-Reine welcome guests to this large house on a farm. There is a family unit with bathroom, double room with bathroom and a room for three people with bathroom and a cooking area. Sitting room, dining room and barbecue. The garden has a children's play area. The house is half way between Cap Fréhel and la Côte de Granit Rose. There are bicycles for touring the area. Cost for four people is €61. Open all year.
PRICES: s €32; d €34-€37; t €49 **ON SITE:** Children's play area **NEARBY:** Golf (10km) Sea (8km) Swimming pool (8km) Hiking (4km) Water sports (10km) Tennis (4km) Railway station (8km) Shops (3km) SAINT-BRIEUC (8km) **NOTES:** No pets English spoken

ARGOL

♥ La Fontaine Blanche Yves MEVEL
29560 ARGOL
☎ 02 98 27 78 13
At the entrance to the Presqu'île de Crozon, ten minutes from the beaches, Marie-Céline and Yves offer you three bedrooms on the first floor of their farmhouse. On the first floor, there is one double bedroom with a shower room and wc, one bedroom with a double bed, a single bedroom with shower room and wc and a twin bedroom with bathroom and wc. Lounge area for guest use. Walks nearby. Museum of L'Abbaye de Landevennec 8 km. Hang-gliding at Menez-Hom 7 km. Open all year.
PRICES: s €34; d €40; t €52 **NEARBY:** Bathing (7km) Horse riding (10km) Golf (40km) Sea (7km) Fishing (2km) Swimming pool (20km) Hiking (2km) Water sports (7km) Tennis (7km) Bicycle hire (15km) Railway station (20km) Shops (3km) CROZON (16km) **NOTES:** No pets

ARZANO

Château de Kerlarec Michel BELLIN
29300 ARZANO
☎ 02 98 71 75 06 & 06 08 52 39 04
Discover the refined atmosphere of the elegant Château de Kerlarec and savour a time gone by. Set in a green park, a few paces from the ocean, the large, relaxing bedrooms have been individually decorated. There are two double bedrooms on the first floor and three doubles and a twin on the second. All rooms have a bathroom and wc. Lounges with fireplaces. Park with lake, tennis court and swimming pool. Permanent exhibitions are held in the gallery with 19th-century windows. Large breakfasts. Seafood platters and crêpe dinners served on reservation. Ask proprietor for directions Open all year.
PRICES: d €73-€88; extra person €27 **ON SITE:** Swimming pool Tennis **NEARBY:** Bathing (15km) Horse riding (15km) Golf (15km) Sea (10km) Fishing (3km) Hiking (1km) Water sports (10km) Railway station (7km) Shops (3km) QUIMPERLE (7km) **NOTES:** No pets English spoken

BANNALEC

♥ Sainte Anne Nicole & Jean René CHRISTIEN
29380 BANNALEC
☎ 02 98 39 53 44 & 06 85 20 56 25 ▤ 02 98 39 53 54
e-mail: jrchristien@wanadoo.fr
Charming, tranquil house at the gateway to Cornouaille, ten minutes from Pont-Aven and Quimperlé and twenty minutes from Quimper and Concarneau. Nicole, Jean René and their children welcome you to the relaxing, verdant countryside of their farm. There are three comfortable, individual bedrooms, each with shower room and wc. On the ground floor, there is bedroom with a double and a single bed. On the first floor, there are double and twin bedrooms. Lounge room with fireplace and TV, washing machine and high chair. Kitchen available on request. Garden with furniture. Country walking footpaths nearby.
PRICES: d €41; t €53; extra person €10 **ON SITE:** Hiking **NEARBY:** Bathing (20km) Golf (20km) Sea (20km) Fishing (5km) Swimming pool (15km) Water sports (20km) Tennis (1km) Bicycle hire (3km) Railway station (3km) Shops (3km) QUIMPERLE (15km) **NOTES:** No pets English spoken

BRASPARTS

♥♥♥ ⓘ◎ⓘ Domaine de Rugornou Vras Romy CHAUSSY
29190 BRASPARTS
☎ 02 98 81 46 27 & 06 82 91 37 36

In this region of legends, between mountains and sea, Romy welcomes you to a stone longbarn, in a verdant setting overlooking the town of Brasparts. There are four pretty bedrooms: three double bedrooms and one twin bedroom, each with independent access, shower room and wc. Fireplace, TV, garden with garden furniture and terrace. Lounge room, gazebo. Evening meals available on reservation. Walking footpaths from the house, close to the Parc Naturel Régional d'Armorique. Open all year.

PRICES: s €34; d €41; t €52; dinner €14 **ON SITE:** Hiking
NEARBY: Bathing (35km) Horse riding (1km) Golf (40km) Sea (35km) Fishing (2km) Swimming pool (15km) Water sports (15km) Tennis (2km) Bicycle hire (1km) Railway station (15km) Shops (2km) PLEYBEN (10km)
NOTES: No pets English spoken

CAST

♥♥♥ ♥ ⓘ◎ⓘ Kernir Madeleine PHILIPPE, 29150 CAST
☎ 02 98 73 54 31 🗏 02 98 73 61 07
e-mail: contact@kernir.com http://www.kernir.com

At the heart of this livestock farm, near the bay of Douarnenez and Locronan, Pierre and Madeleine welcome you to share their love of the region and their comfortable, tastefully restored longbarn, with its typical Breton reception room and fireplace. There is a twin bedroom on the ground floor of the main house. In an annexe house: one twin room on the ground floor and, on the first floor, two double bedrooms with a single bed on a mezzanine level, and a further twin bedroom. Each bedroom has a shower room and wc. There is a TV in the two sitting rooms and a garden with terrace area. Evening meals served on reservation.

PRICES: d €43; t €58; extra person €15; dinner €16 **ON SITE:** Hiking
NEARBY: Bathing (7km) Horse riding (5km) Golf (35km) Sea (7km) Fishing (7km) Swimming pool (9km) Water sports (7km) Tennis (3km) Railway station (9km) Shops (3km) CHATEAULIN (10km) **NOTES:** No pets English spoken

CLEDER

♥♥♥ ♥ Coz-Milin François & Annie MOYSAN
29233 CLEDER
☎ 02 98 69 42 16 🗏 02 98 69 42 16

Surrounded by a flower garden, this house on a vegetable-growing farm is full of character. Situated 1 km from the beaches, the coastal paths, a park and watersports, there are three rooms available on the first floor: one double bedroom and one twin with shower room and private wc. There is a further double bedroom with bathroom and wc. All bedrooms are no smoking. Cot available on request. You can use the large lounge room with TV where you will be served a large breakfast of homemade crêpes, and Breton gateaux. St-Pol-de-Léon 10 km, Roscoff is 15km away. Open Easter to end Septmber.

PRICES: s €35; d €43 **NEARBY:** Bathing (1km) Horse riding (2km) Golf (12km) Sea (1km) Fishing (1km) Water sports (1km) Tennis (1km) Railway station (10km) Shops (3km) SAINT POL DE LEON (10km)
NOTES: No pets

CROZON

♥♥♥ Saint Hernot Didier MOYSAN
Village de Saint Hernot, 29160 CROZON
☎ 02 98 27 25 80 & 06 81 52 85 39 🗏 02 98 27 25 80

The Moysans welcome you to their very comfortable house in the village of Saint Hernot. From here, you can discover Morgat and the Cap de la Chèvre. A large breakfast is served in the lounge, and the sitting room and three of the bedrooms offer impressive

continued

views over the sea. The four bedrooms are situated in an annexe building: a twin on the ground floor, and two doubles and a family suite on the first floor, all with shower rooms and wc. TV in lounge, garden with garden furniture, barbecue and terrace area.
PRICES: s €42; d €47; t €65; extra person €18 **ON SITE:** Hiking
NEARBY: Bathing (1km) Horse riding (10km) Sea (1km) Fishing (1km) Water sports (4km) Tennis (4km) Bicycle hire (4km) Railway station (60km) Shops (4km) CROZON (7km) **NOTES:** No pets

DINEAULT

♥♥♥ ♥ Rolzac'h Anne-Marie L'HARIDON
29150 DINEAULT
☎ 02 98 86 22 09

In a flower-filled, restful spot on a small restored farm in the Aulne valley, Anne-Marie and André offer you four bedrooms with shower rooms and wc. On the ground floor, 'Emilie' and 'Anaïs' have double beds and 'Elise' has twin beds. On the first floor, 'Iris' has a double bed and a private lounge room with fridge. It is possible to use the kitchen and there are private gardens for exploring Cot on request. Garden with furniture and barbecue area. Closed November to February.

PRICES: s €34-€35; d €38-€41 **NEARBY:** Bathing (12km) Horse riding (3km) Golf (30km) Sea (12km) Fishing (3km) Swimming pool (3km) Hiking (1km) Water sports (12km) Tennis (3km) Bicycle hire (3km) Railway station (2km) Shops (3km) CHATEAULIN (8km) **NOTES:** No pets

DOUARNENEZ

♥♥♥ Manoir de Kervent Marie-Paule LEFLOCH
29100 DOUARNENEZ
☎ 02 98 92 04 90 🗏 02 98 92 04 90

Although this manor house is near the Douarnenez exit, it lies in full countryside in a flower-filled park. Two double bedrooms, one with extra single bed, one family room with a double and twin beds, and one twin room. Each a shower room and wc and a cot can be provided on request. Breakfast of Breton specialities served in the light and spacious dining room. This is an arable farm and there are many footpaths on the property; guidebooks on the region can be provided. Table tennis and croquet. Tourist tax charged in the summer.

PRICES: s €35; d €40-€43; t €52-€64 **NEARBY:** Bathing (3km) Horse riding (3km) Golf (30km) Sea (2km) Fishing (2km) Swimming pool (3km) Hiking (5km) Water sports (3km) Tennis (3km) Bicycle hire (2km) Railway station (25km) Shops (2km) DOUARNENEZ (1km) **NOTES:** Pets admitted

EDERN

♥♥♥ ♥ Kergadiou Jacqueline CHAUSSEC
29510 EDERN
☎ 02 98 57 90 50
e-mail: chaussec@terre-net.fr

Near to Quimper and 30 minutes form the Douarnenez bays, this welcoming old dairy farm is situated at the heart of the verdant countryside. In this family home, there are three bedrooms for guest use. On the garden level, there is a suite: one double bedroom, one single bedroom, a bathroom, wc and fridge and a lounge opening onto a flower-lined terrace. On the ground floor, there is a single bedroom with a bathroom and wc. On the first floor, there is a double bed, a single bed, bathroom and wc. Nearby: Parish Close of Plyben, Trévarez park and château, walks along the Aulne, Quimper, Locronan, Crozan.

PRICES: s €26; d €39-€42; t €46-€49 **ON SITE:** Fishing Hiking Bicycle hire **NEARBY:** Bathing (28km) Horse riding (15km) Sea (28km) Swimming pool (10km) Water sports (28km) Tennis (3km) Railway station (25km) Shops (3km) BRIEC DE L'ODET (5km) **NOTES:** No pets English spoken

ELLIANT

♯♯♯ ♥ Quelennec Monique LE BERRE

☎ 02 98 59 10 43 & 06 72 78 28 49

Ten minutes from Quimper and 8 km from the expressway, in the heart of the countryside, this welcoming 1945 family home offers four individual bedrooms, all on the first floor: three double bedrooms with shower room and wc and one double bedroom with a single bed, bathroom and wc. Lounge/sitting room with TV, kitchen. Horses and riders welcome. The house is ideally located for long walks and enjoyment of the sea. The Quimper and Concarneau countryside has a wonderful historic and natural heritage: Chapel of Kerdévot 5 km, the site of Stangala, megaliths and old manors are all close by. Price reductions out of season.
PRICES: s €34; d €39; t €49 **ON SITE:** Fishing Hiking
NEARBY: Bathing (22km) Horse riding (8km) Golf (25km) Sea (22km) Swimming pool (8km) Water sports (13km) Tennis (8km) Railway station (10km) Shops (9km) QUIMPER (13km) **NOTES:** No pets

GUIPAVAS

♯♯♯ La Châtaigneraie Michelle MORVAN

Kéraveloc, 29490 GUIPAVAS
☎ 02 98 41 52 68 ▤ 02 98 41 48 40
e-mail: la-chataigneraie@wanadoo.fr
http://site.voila.fr/la.chataigneraie

La Châtaigneraie offers three bedrooms in a spacious house. On the ground floor, there are two double bedrooms (extra bed possible), one with shower room and one with bathroom. Each has a TV. On the first floor, there is a suite of one double and one twin bedroom with a shower room, wc and TV. Large mezzanine area in the library room and a billiard room. Use of kitchen and garage. Terrace with a panoramic view over the botanical garden. Views over the boat harbour, Rade de Brest. Wooded park with games, garden furniture and a barbecue. Direct access to Vallon de Stangalac'h (footpaths). Moulin Blanc beach, Brest and Océanopolis five minutes away. Heated swimming pool and solarium available during high season.
PRICES: s €35-€38; d €41-€44; t €57-€60; extra person €13
ON SITE: Swimming pool Hiking **NEARBY:** Bathing (2km) Horse riding (10km) Golf (10km) Sea (2km) Fishing (2km) Water sports (2km) Tennis (4km) Bicycle hire (5km) Railway station (4km) Shops (3km) BREST (2km) **NOTES:** No pets English spoken

ILE-DE-BATZ

♯♯♯ ♥ Chambre d'hôtes Marie Pierre PRIGENT

Bourg, 29253 ILE DE BATZ
☎ 02 98 61 76 91

Your hosts will help you discover traditional Breton life in their ancestral home with antique furniture, next to the farm and opposite the sea. On the first floor: double bedroom with shower room and wc. The family room has a bathroom and separate wc, a double bed and twin beds. On the second floor: one double and

one twin bedroom, both with shower room and wc. Dining room, sitting room with fireplace and TV. Small garden with furniture. The port of Roscoff is close by; from there you can cross to Ile-de-Batz in only 15 minutes. The house is in a market town, five minutes from the landing stage, next to the church. Open 1 March to 15 November.
PRICES: s €35; d €50; t €60 **ON SITE:** Bathing Sea Fishing Hiking Water sports Bicycle hire **NEARBY:** Horse riding (2km) ROSCOFF **NOTES:** No pets

KERLAZ

♯♯♯ ♥ Chambre d'hôtes Michel & Cathy KERVOALEN

Lanevry, 29100 KERLAZ
☎ 02 98 92 85 49 ▤ 02 98 92 85 49

Discover the charms of the countryside, close to the sea (350 m). Cathy and Michel welcome you to the dairy farm with their two horses. There are beautiful views of Douarnenez bay, the fishing port, the Locronan mountains and Ménez Hom. Four bedrooms with private shower rooms and wcs. On the first floor, there are two double bedrooms and one twin bedroom. On the second floor, there is a family room with a double bed and twin beds. Independent access, sitting room. Garden furniture and barbecue. Billiard room, table tennis. Horses welcome. Open all year; reduced rates out of season.
PRICES: s €38; d €43; t €58 **ON SITE:** Hiking **NEARBY:** Bathing (1km) Horse riding (5km) Golf (25km) Sea (1km) Fishing (3km) Swimming pool (3km) Water sports (5km) Tennis (2km) Bicycle hire (3km) Railway station (20km) Shops (2km) DOUARNENEZ (5km) **NOTES:** No pets

♯♯♯ Chambre d'hôtes René & Josy GUEGUEN - GONIDEC

Lanevry, 29100 KERLAZ
☎ 02 98 92 14 87 ▤ 02 98 92 23 55
e-mail: info@lanevry.com www.lanevry.com

Between Douarnenez fishing port and the small town of Locronan, Josy and Ren welcome you to their restored farmhouse opposite the pretty bay of Douarnenez, set in a flower garden in a lovely verdant area. Relax in the bedrooms and listen the sea. On the first floor, 'La ville d'Y's' has a view of the sea and a double bed, 'Tristan' has twin beds and 'Korrigan' has a double bed. On the ground floor, 'Gradlon' and 'Iseult' have double beds. Each has a private bathroom. Large breakfasts feature regional specialities. Use of kitchen allowed, out of season. Lounge with TV and garden furniture. Reduced rates out of season. Winner of the first prize in the département's flower competition in 2000.
PRICES: d €45; €40 low season **NEARBY:** Bathing (1km) Horse riding (5km) Golf (20km) Sea (1km) Fishing (1km) Swimming pool (2km) Water sports (5km) Tennis (2km) Bicycle hire (3km) Railway station (20km) Shops (2km) DOUARNENEZ (5km) **NOTES:** No pets English spoken

♥
Places with this symbol are farmhouses

continued

BRITTANY

KERNILIS

♨ 🐦 Chambre d'hôtes Dona & Jo UGUEN
Route de Kerbrat, 29260 KERNILIS
☎ 02 98 25 54 02 🖷 02 98 25 54 02

Dona and Jo welcome you to their dairy farm, near the Aber Wrac'h valley, where the land meets the sea. There is independent access to the three guest bedrooms on the first floor of their house. The first has a double bed, the second twin beds, and the third has three singles. Each bedroom has a private bath or shower room and wc. Extra bed on request. Sitting room and TV, kitchen, garden with furniture and bikes. Plouguerneau is 7 km away and Brest is 23 km. Open all year.

PRICES: d €37; t €47; extra person €10 **ON SITE:** Tennis Bicycle hire **NEARBY:** Bathing (7km) Horse riding (10km) Golf (25km) Sea (7km) Fishing (1km) Swimming pool (8km) Hiking (2km) Water sports (7km) Railway station (22km) 8 KM DE LESNEVEN (8km) **NOTES:** Pets admitted

LAMPAUL-GUIMILIAU

♨ Chambre d'hôtes Odile & Jean Marc PUCHOIS
26, Revirez, 29400 LAMPAUL-GUIMILAU
☎ 02 98 68 62 02 & 06 67 03 93 26 🖷 02 98 68 62 02

This property is in the heart of the Pays des Enclos Paroissiaux (parish closes), ideal for discovering the north Finistère region. There are two double bedrooms and one twin bedroom, with shower rooms, wc and TV. There is a corner lounge in one of the bedrooms. Fridge and cot available. Garden with furniture, barbecue and enclosed private parking. Odile and Jean-Marc can suggest walks in the region. Four bikes available at no charge. The GR380 is nearby and the Gallimard guidebook and various detailed maps are provided. Restaurant 1.5 km. Open all year.

PRICES: s €30; d €39 **ON SITE:** Bicycle hire **NEARBY:** Bathing (20km) Horse riding (5km) Sea (20km) Fishing (2km) Swimming pool (5km) Hiking (2km) Water sports (15km) Tennis (2km) Railway station (5km) Shops (2km) LANDIVISIAU (5km) **NOTES:** Pets admitted English spoken

LANHOUARNEAU

♨ 🐓 Kergollay Alexis & M. France QUEGUINEUR
29430 LANHOUARNEAU
☎ 02 98 61 47 35 & 06 12 64 76 24 🖷 02 98 61 82 81

In the heart of this vegetable-growing farm, in a calm and flower-filled setting, Marie-France and Alexis offer a warm welcome. On the ground floor, there is a double bedroom with a shower room and wc. On the first floor, there is a double bedroom, shower room and wc. Another bedroom has twin beds, and a bathroom and wc. TV, terrace, garden with furniture. Crêperie and restaurant nearby. Numerous tourist routes in the surrounding area. Beach 8 km. Roscoff ferry 20 km. Open all year.

PRICES: s €33; d €40; extra person €11 **ON SITE:** Fishing Hiking Bicycle hire **NEARBY:** Bathing (8km) Horse riding (8km) Sea (8km) Swimming pool (9km) Water sports (8km) Tennis (1km) Railway station (20km) Shops (1km) ROSCOFF (20km) **NOTES:** No pets

LANILDULT

♨ Chambre d'hôtes Dominique & Anne LE TARNEC
4, hent Kergaradoc, 29840 LANILDULT
☎ 02 98 04 38 41

This small, tranquil village runs the length of the Aber Ildut. This beautiful, stone house overlooks the countryside and the sea. The four guest rooms are decorated in a nautical theme. On the ground floor, there are two double bedrooms with shower room and wc. On the first floor, there is a twin bedroom, shower room and wc, and a bedroom with a four-poster bed, bathroom and wc. There is an open fireplace in the lounge room and a private sitting room with a TV and library. Huge, enclosed garden with garden furniture. Baby equipment and bike hire available. Footpaths and a small stream nearby. Boat trips to the Ile d'Ouessant from the port in July and August.

PRICES: d €44; extra person €15 **ON SITE:** Hiking Bicycle hire **NEARBY:** Bathing (3km) Horse riding (6km) Golf (8km) Sea (3km) Fishing (3km) Swimming pool (20km) Water sports (3km) Tennis (2km) Railway station (23km) Shops (2km) PLOUDALMEZEAU (12km) **NOTES:** No pets English spoken

LANNILIS

♨ Chambre d'hôtes Robert CREACH
Saint Alphonse, 29870 LANNILIS
☎ 02 98 04 14 13

There are three bedrooms in this annexe to the owners' house. Each has a shower room, wc and TV. On the ground floor, there is a double bedroom with a corner lounge, and a twin with corner lounge. On the first floor, there is a twin bedroom (grade 2). Kitchen available. Sitting room with a veranda in the owners' house. Garden with garden furniture, games room with table tennis and billiards.

PRICES: s €27; d €35-€38; t €52 **ON SITE:** Hiking **NEARBY:** Bathing (4km) Horse riding (5km) Sea (4km) Fishing (1km) Swimming pool (12km) Water sports (4km) Tennis (1km) Bicycle hire (1km) Railway station (20km) Shops (1km) BREST (20km) **NOTES:** Pets admitted

LE JUCH

♨ 🐓 Kersantec Yvette RENEVOT
29100 LE JUCH
☎ 02 98 74 71 36 & 06 86 91 93 65

Yvette and René welcome you to their house, which is not far from a dairy farm and surrounded by a lovely flower garden, where you can enjoy calm and relaxation. There are three double bedrooms (one on the ground floor), each with private bath or shower room and wc. A breakfast featuring homemade jams is served in the garden. TV and games for the children. Garden and furniture. Walking, tennis and horse riding possible. Beaches and the port museum are nearby. Open all year.

PRICES: s €31; d €39 **ON SITE:** Children's play area **NEARBY:** Bathing (7km) Horse riding (10km) Golf (20km) Sea (7km) Fishing (7km) Swimming pool (7km) Hiking (4km) Water sports (7km) Tennis (4km) Bicycle hire (7km) Railway station (14km) Shops (2km) DOUARNENEZ (6km) **NOTES:** No pets

Use the atlas at the back of the guide to locate your chambre d'hôtes

🍽

Places with this symbol serve table d'hôtes evening meals - remember to book in advance

♦♦♦ ❧ Le Carbon Anne-Marie YOUINOU
29100 LE JUCH
☎ 02 98 92 21 08 & 06 85 28 10 11
A warm welcome awaits in this farmhouse, with its large flower courtyard, surrounded by gardens. There are three bedrooms in this old house: two doubles and one single, each with a shower room and private wc. There is also a family room with two doubles, one single, a bathroom and wc. Cot on request. TV, garden and garden furniture. Large, homemade breakfasts served in a beautiful Breton room. Restaurant, beach and coastal footpaths 3 km. The rate for five people is 66 euros. Open all year.
PRICES: s €30; d €39; t €48 **ON SITE:** Hiking **NEARBY:** Bathing (3km) Horse riding (6km) Golf (25km) Sea (3km) Fishing (3km) Swimming pool (4km) Water sports (5km) Tennis (4km) Railway station (25km) Shops (4km) DOUARNENEZ (6km) **NOTES:** No pets English spoken

LE TREHOU

♦♦♦ ⏀ Mescouez Elisabeth SOUBIGOU
29450 LE TREHOU
☎ 02 98 68 86 79 & 02 98 68 83 39 📠 02 98 68 86 79
e-mail: elisabeth.soubigou@libertysurf.fr
This flat is ideally located for exploring the *enclos parroissiaux* of the Monts d'Arée and the coast. There are four bedrooms with lots of character and private bathrooms in this beautiful country house, restored in a 1900 style. On the first floor, there are two double bedrooms. On the second floor, there is a twin bedroom and a double bedroom. Evening meals, based on local produce, are served on reservation (except 15 July to 15 August). Breakfasts of homemade crêpes and gateaux. Sitting room with TV and library, kitchen. On a farm, this manor house looks out onto an enclosed garden with shade, flowers and garden furniture. Private tennis court.
PRICES: s €36-€38; d €42-€45; dinner €15 **ON SITE:** Hiking Tennis **NEARBY:** Bathing (35km) Horse riding (10km) Golf (12km) Sea (15km) Fishing (2km) Swimming pool (5km) Water sports (10km) Railway station (12km) Shops (5km) LANDERNEAU (12km) **NOTES:** No pets English spoken

LOC-EGUINER-SAINT-THEGONNEC

♦♦♦ ❧ ⏀ Ty Dreux Annie MARTIN
29410 LOC EGUINER SAINT THEGONNEC
☎ 02 98 78 08 21 📠 02 98 78 01 69
e-mail: ty-dreux@club-internet.fr
In the middle of the countryside, and 7 km from St Thégonnec, in the heart of the *enclos paroissiaux* countryside, you will find Ty Dreux, an old weaver's farmhouse. Cut off from all traffic, you will enjoy the lovely tranquillity of Annie and Jean's farm and the warmth of their welcome. There are four bedrooms on the first and second floor: two double bedrooms, one single bedroom and two twin bedrooms, each with a shower room and wc. Unique in Finistère, there is a permanent exhibition of Breton costumes on display. Generous breakfasts will be served in the rustic sitting room. Veranda and large garden. Use of kitchen possible. Evening meals from homemade farm produce can be served at weekends and in school holidays.
PRICES: s €34; d €43; t €53; dinner €17 **ON SITE:** Hiking **NEARBY:** Bathing (18km) Horse riding (8km) Golf (20km) Sea (18km) Fishing (5km) Swimming pool (5km) Water sports (5km) Tennis (6km) Bicycle hire (4km) Railway station (18km) Shops (4km) MORLAIX (18km) **NOTES:** No pets

LOCRONAN

♦♦♦ ❧ Rodou glaz Fernand JAIN
29180 LOCRONAN
☎ 02 98 73 52 41 & 02 98 91 70 15 📠 02 98 51 83 71
e-mail: philippe-camus@club-internet.fr
One kilometre from Locronan, this is one of the most beautiful villages in France, in the centre of the Pointe du Raz and the Presqu'île de Crozon. You will be warmly welcomed in this large restored home, surrounded by a lovely flower garden. On the first floor there is a double bedroom and a twin bedroom, and a family room with a double and twin beds. On the second floor there are two double bedrooms. All have TV and private bathrooms. Large breakfasts are carefully prepared and served either in the airy lounge or on the veranda. You will love Locronan's undeniable charm, its great character, its arts and craft activities and its shops. Walks in the forest or on the fine sandy beaches of Douarnenez Bay (5 minutes away).
PRICES: s €35; d €42; t €56; extra person €15 **ON SITE:** Hiking **NEARBY:** Bathing (5km) Horse riding (10km) Sea (5km) Fishing (10km) Swimming pool (10km) Water sports (10km) Tennis (2km) Bicycle hire (2km) Railway station (15km) Shops (2km) QUIMPER (19km) **NOTES:** No pets English spoken

MAHALON

♦♦♦ ❧ Kerantum Anne OLIER
29790 MAHALON
☎ 02 98 74 51 93 & 02 98 74 58 04 📠 02 98 74 51 93
On the outskirts of Cap Sizun, on the Pointe du Raz road, this place is ideally situated for the Douarnenez and Audierne bays. There are three large, comfortable bedrooms with independent entrances: two doubles, a single and a twin. There is a shower room and wc in each bedroom. In this old farmhouse, in the middle of the country, you will enjoy calm and relaxation. Sitting room, courtyard, parking space, lawn, garden furniture, barbecue and table tennis. Use of kitchen possible. Rate for four people: 60-63 euros. Open all year.
PRICES: s €35; d €40; t €50-€53 **ON SITE:** Fishing Hiking **NEARBY:** Bathing (10km) Horse riding (8km) Golf (10km) Sea (10km) Swimming pool (10km) Water sports (10km) Tennis (10km) Bicycle hire (10km) Railway station (25km) Shops (3km) DOUARNENEZ (10km) **NOTES:** Pets admitted English spoken

PEUMERIT

♦♦♦ ❧ Lespurit-Coat Georges L'HELGOUALC'H
29710 PEUMERIT
☎ 02 98 82 92 27
In the Bigouden countryside, there are several welcoming bedrooms on this restored farm, in a longbarn annexe. On the ground floor, there is a double bedroom with shower room and wc. On the first floor, there are two double bedrooms, one single bedroom and one twin bedroom, with a shower room and wc for each bedroom. Breakfast is served in a communal room with fireplace. There is a terrace, garden, garden furniture and barbecue.
PRICES: s €38; d €50; t €58 **ON SITE:** Hiking **NEARBY:** Bathing (4km) Horse riding (6km) Golf (22km) Sea (4km) Fishing (2km) Swimming pool (12km) Water sports (15km) Tennis (1km) Bicycle hire (3km) Railway station (18km) Shops (1km) PLONEOUR LANVERN (6km) **NOTES:** Pets admitted English spoken

PLOGASTEL-SAINT-GERMAIN

⊞ ⥂ Kerguernou Jean Marie LE HENAFF
29710 PLOGASTEL SAINT GERMAIN
☎ 02 98 54 56 30 ▨ 02 98 54 57 00
The Le Hénaff family welcome you to their dairy farm, in a lovely calm setting. Five hundred metres from the departmental road, relax and unwind in an old renovated longbarn, near the owner's house. On the ground floor, there are two double bedrooms, whilst on the first floor, there are two double bedrooms and one twin bedroom. There is a shower room and wc for each bedroom and a lounge with fireplace. Kitchen available to guests. Garden, barbecue and play area. Beach 10 km.
PRICES: s €30; d €40; t €50 **ON SITE:** Fishing **NEARBY:** Bathing (10km) Horse riding (6km) Golf (23km) Sea (10km) Swimming pool (18km) Hiking (5km) Water sports (17km) Tennis (5km) Bicycle hire (10km) Railway station (18km) Shops (5km) QUIMPER (15km)
NOTES: No pets

PLOGOFF

⊞ ⥂ ⎮◎⎮ Ferme de Kerguidy Izella
Annick & Jean Noël LE BARS
29770 PLOGOFF
☎ 02 98 70 35 60 ▨ 02 98 70 34 09
e-mail: Jean-Noel.LE-BARS@wanadoo.fr
Five kilometres from the Pointe du Raz, Annick and Jean Noel welcome you to their farmhouse set in a valley. On the ground floor, there is a double bedroom and a twin bedroom, accessible for the less mobile. On the first floor, there are three, double bedrooms, one twin bedroom, and a single bedroom, each with shower room and wc and independent access. Lounge room with library, TV and games. Evening meals on request (except Sundays and holidays), based on farm produce. Enclosed garden, garden furniture and a terrace. Cot on request. Reduced prices out of season. Open all year.
PRICES: d €38; t €50; extra person €12; dinner €13 **ON SITE:** Hiking **NEARBY:** Bathing (3km) Horse riding (1km) Golf (15km) Sea (1km) Fishing (2km) Swimming pool (28km) Water sports (12km) Tennis (1km) Bicycle hire (1km) Railway station (53km) Shops (1km) AUDIERNE (15km) **NOTES:** Pets admitted

⊞ ⎮◎⎮ Kerhuret Jean Paul GANNE
29770 PLOGOFF
☎ 02 98 70 34 85
In this coastal village, 2 km from the Pointe du Raz, Marie Rose and Jean Paul welcome you to their old farmhouse, which is calm and comfortable. There are independent entrances to the five bedrooms on the ground floor, each with its own bath or shower room and wc: three doubles, one double with twin beds on a mezzannine, and one double with a single mezzanine bed and lounge. There is also a separate lounge with a fireplace. Evening meals on request, featuring farm products or local produce (smoked salmon, fish paté, langoustines, rabbit paté etc.) Courtyard, garden with garden furniture and a play area. Cot on request. Diving 1 km.
PRICES: s €30; d €35; t €46; dinner €15 **NEARBY:** Bathing (1km) Horse riding (1km) Golf (15km) Sea (1km) Fishing (1km) Hiking (1km) Water sports (10km) Tennis (2km) Bicycle hire (1km) Shops (2km) AUDIERNE (10km) **NOTES:** Pets admitted

⊞ Lescoff René LE CORRE
Rue des hirondelles, 29770 PLOGOFF
☎ 02 98 70 38 24
One kilometre from the famous Pointe du Raz, just off the main road, there are three ground-floor bedrooms in this old, renovated farmhouse, each with independent access. One bedroom has twin beds and there are two double bedrooms, each with a shower room and wc. Lounge with TV and telephone. Enclosed garden,

terrace, garden furniture and private parking. Open all year.
PRICES: d €38-€40; extra person €12 **ON SITE:** Wine tasting **NEARBY:** Bathing (1km) Horse riding (3km) Golf (50km) Sea (1km) Fishing (1km) Swimming pool (28km) Hiking (1km) Water sports (1km) Tennis (3km) Bicycle hire (3km) Railway station (50km) Shops (2km) AUDIERNE (15km) **NOTES:** Pets admitted English spoken

PLOMEUR

⊞ ⎮◎⎮ La Chaumière de Keraluic
Luis & Irène GOMEZ-CENTURION
Keraluic, 29120 PLOMEUR
☎ 02 98 82 10 22 ▨ 02 98 82 10 22
In the heart of Bigouden country, close to the sea, Irène and Luis welcome you to their restored traditional farmhouse and will help you discover their region. The warm, comfortable bedrooms are situated in a beautiful detached cottage There are three bedrooms on the first floor: two twin bedrooms and one double bedroom, with private shower rooms and wcs. There are also two bedrooms on the ground floor: one double bedroom and one twin bedroom, with private bathrooms, wcs and a terrace area. Lounge with fireplace. Evening meals are occasionally provided. Camping in the fields next to the house is possible (max. 25 places). Walks, fishing harbours and beaches nearby. Sofabed available on request. Open all year.
PRICES: d €48-€60; t €61-€73; dinner €19 **ON SITE:** Hiking Bicycle hire **NEARBY:** Bathing (6km) Horse riding (5km) Golf (15km) Sea (6km) Fishing (3km) Swimming pool (3km) Water sports (7km) Tennis (3km) Railway station (20km) Shops (2km) PONT L'ABBE (3km) **NOTES:** Pets admitted English spoken

PLOMODIERN

⊞ ⥂ ♿ Sainte-Marie du Menez Hom Michelle JACQ
29550 PLOMODIERN
☎ 02 98 81 54 41 & 06 08 63 68 99 ▨ 02 98 81 59 20
e-mail: michelle.jacq@infonie.fr
Michelle welcomes you to her dairy farm, at the crossroads of Presqu'île de Crozon and the Pointe du Raz, at the foot of the Menez Hom (330m). In this longbarn, there are two gîtes and four guest rooms. On the ground floor, there is one double bedroom and one twin room, which is accessible to the less mobile. On the first floor, there is a double bedroom with a single bed on a mezzanine level. A further room contains a double bed and twin beds on a mezzanine. Each room has a shower room and wc. Sitting room for guest use and the kitchen may be used in the evening. Terrace and garden furniture. Electric heating. Crêperie 100 m.
PRICES: d €43; t €56 **ON SITE:** Hiking **NEARBY:** Bathing (5km) Horse riding (1km) Golf (32km) Sea (5km) Fishing (1km) Swimming pool (11km) Water sports (5km) Tennis (3km) Bicycle hire (10km) Railway station (11km) Shops (3km) CHATEAULIN (12km) **NOTES:** No pets English spoken

PLOUEGAT-MOYSAN

⊞ ⥂ ⎮◎⎮ Pen an Néac'h
Famille THOMAS ET SCARELLA
29650 PLOUEGAT MOYSAN
☎ 02 98 79 20 15 ▨ 02 98 79 22 73
This beautiful detached 1950s house lies in the middle of a large park with a magnificent view over undulating countryside. The house is very comfortable and contains rustic style furniture. On the first floor, there are two family rooms with twin beds and a double bed, and on the second floor there are two twin bedrooms. Each room has a shower room and wc. Fireplace, TV, telephone, washing machine, baby equipment and garden with furniture. Terrace, lounge room, gazebo and garage. Baby sitting, cooking and bike hire can be arranged on request. There is a farm inn on site. Half board 37 euros. Open all year.

continued   continued

PRICES: d €40; FB €37; dinner €16 **ON SITE:** Hiking
NEARBY: Bathing (12km) Horse riding (6km) Golf (20km) Sea (12km)
Fishing (1km) Swimming pool (15km) Water sports (15km) Tennis (6km)
Bicycle hire (6km) Railway station (15km) Shops (1km) GUERLESQUIN
(6km) **NOTES:** Pets admitted

PLOUENAN

▥ ❦ Lopreden Allain & Sylvie CAZUC
29420 PLOUENAN
☎ 02 98 69 50 62 🖷 02 98 69 50 02
This farm is typical of the region. Allain and Sylvie offer you three
large bedrooms in an old longbarn built of local stone. There are
two double bedrooms and one twin bedroom, each with a shower
room and wc. This is a lovely relaxing, family setting with a flower
garden, children's play area and footpaths from the house, leading
to the forest (1 km) and the sea (8 km). Use of kitchen on request.
Open March to October.
PRICES: s €32; d €37; extra person €10 **ON SITE:** Hiking
NEARBY: Bathing (8km) Horse riding (3km) Golf (10km) Sea (8km)
Fishing (8km) Swimming pool (8km) Water sports (8km) Tennis (3km)
Bicycle hire (8km) Railway station (15km) Shops (3km) ROSCOFF (12km)
NOTES: Pets admitted English spoken

PLOUGAR

▥ ❦ Keramis Jean Vincent &Yvonne LOUSSAUT
29440 PLOUGAR
☎ 02 98 68 56 21 & 02 98 68 54 26 🖷 02 98 68 56 21
Between the sea and the *pays des enclos paroissiaux* (parish
closes), there are three bedrooms at this recently built home,
situated in the middle of the countryside. On the ground floor,
there is a double bedroom (extra bed on request), and a double
with an additional single bed. On the first floor, there is a double
bedroom with a single bed. All have bath or shower rooms and
wcs. Lovely garden, parking space and barbecue. Breakfasts served
in the lounge/sitting room with its open fireplace. TV and games
provided. Nearby: restaurant, crêperie, stretch of water. The house
lies near the historic site of the Chateau de Kerjean (D30).
PRICES: s €30; d €40; extra person €10 **ON SITE:** Hiking
NEARBY: Bathing (13km) Horse riding (12km) Sea (13km) Fishing
(5km) Swimming pool (12km) Water sports (13km) Tennis (5km) Bicycle
hire (12km) Railway station (12km) Shops (2km) LANDIVISIAU (12km)
NOTES: No pets

PLOUGASNOU

▥ Merdy Bras Chantal & Gilbert FILY
29630 PLOUGASNOU
☎ 02 98 67 34 12
Chantal and Gilbert welcome you to their restored longbarn, 3 km
from the sea, between the pink granite coast and Roscoff. There
are three guest rooms with independent entrances on the ground
floor. One family room with a double bed on a mezzanine and
twin beds. Another room has a double bed and the third room is a
twin bedroom. Each bedroom has a shower room and wc. Extra
bed provided on request. Large lounge with TV. Kitchen may be
used. Tree and flower lined garden with garden furniture. Coastal
footpaths 3 km.
PRICES: s €31; d €37; t €46 **NEARBY:** Bathing (3km) Horse riding
(3km) Sea (3km) Fishing (2km) Hiking (3km) Water sports (4km) Tennis
(1km) Railway station (20km) Shops (2km) MORLAIX (20km)
NOTES: No pets

> Prices are given in Euros
> €1 = £0.62
> at the time of going to press

PLOUGONVELIN

▥▥▥ Keryel Monique SALIOU
29217 PLOUGONVELIN
☎ 02 98 48 33 35 & 06 62 06 33 35
e-mail: saliou.monique@wanadoo.fr
Guest rooms in an annexe of the main house. Three bedrooms on
the ground floor, each with shower rooms and a wc: one double
bedroom, one twin bedroom and one family suite with a double
bed and twin beds. On the first floor there is a family suite with a
double bed, twin beds a shower room, a bathroom and two wcs.
Garden with furniture and a terrace area. Baby sitting service.
Camping possible in the farm grounds. Plougonvelin, Finistère
point, the Trez Hir with its microclimate, and the picturesque sites
of the Pointe Saint Mathier, and Bertheaume Fort are all nearby.
Coastal footpath 10 km, Le Conquet, the fishing port, and the
departure point for the Molène and Ouessant islands all 4 km
away. Open all year.
PRICES: d €43; t €61; extra person €10 **ON SITE:** Hiking
NEARBY: Bathing (3km) Horse riding (1km) Golf (15km) Sea (2km)
Fishing (2km) Swimming pool (3km) Water sports (3km) Tennis (2km)
Bicycle hire (4km) Railway station (20km) Shops (2km) BREST (20km)
NOTES: No pets

PLOUIDER

▥▥▥ ❦ Kermabon Thérèse CORBE
29260 PLOUIDER
☎ 02 98 25 40 28
There are four guest rooms in this country location with views of
the sea: one double bedroom in the owner's home, and three
others in a renovated farmhouse nearby. Of these, there is a
double on the ground floor, and a double bedroom with
mezzanine level on the first floor. A further twin room has a view
of the sea. Each bedroom has a private bathroom. The kitchen
may be used and there is a communal sitting room with a
fireplace. Beautiful walks along the seashore. Land yachting
possible nearby. Bird sanctuary 2 km. Restaurants and shops
nearby. Airport 30 km.
PRICES: d €40; extra person €12 **ON SITE:** Hiking **NEARBY:** Bathing
(3km) Horse riding (4km) Golf (25km) Sea (2km) Fishing (2km)
Swimming pool (5km) Water sports (4km) Tennis (2km) Bicycle hire
(3km) Railway station (20km) Shops (3km) LESNEVEN (5km)
NOTES: Pets admitted English spoken

▥▥▥ ❦ 🍴 Kersehen Claudine ROUE
29260 PLOUIDER
☎ 02 98 25 40 41 & 06 81 04 10 87
e-mail: Claudine.Roue@wanadoo.fr
The owners welcome you to their farmhouse. On the first floor,
there are three double bedrooms, each with private bath or
shower room and wc. Cot available on request. Lounge, TV and
library. Large garden with furniture, children's swing and bikes.
Meals are 14 euros (8 euros for children under ten), available on
reservation. Land yachting.
PRICES: d €38; extra person €10; dinner €14 **ON SITE:** Hiking Bicycle
hire **NEARBY:** Bathing (3km) Horse riding (3km) Sea (3km) Fishing
(3km) Swimming pool (5km) Water sports (5km) Tennis (1km) Railway
station (20km) Shops (2km) LESNEVEN (6km) **NOTES:** Pets admitted
English spoken

PLOUIGNEAU

▥▥▥▥ Manoir de Lanleya André MARREC
29610 PLOUIGNEAU
☎ 02 98 79 94 15 🖷 02 98 79 94 15
e-mail: manoir.lanleya@libertysurf.fr
http://www.multimania.com/lanleya
Lanleya Manor, with its intriguing legends, lies between

continued

Morlaix Bay and the pink granite coast. On the ground floor, there is a dining/sitting room with a fireplace and rustic furniture. On a 'half floor', there is a double bedroom, whilst the first floor is reached by a 16th-century granite staircase and contains a bedroom with a double bed, a single bed, cot and a huge pink granite fireplace. A further bedroom has a double bed and a cot. A stone staircase leads up to the second floor in a watchtower. Here there are two double bedrooms. On the same floor, there is a sitting room in a 16th-century tower. Shower room and wc in each bedroom.
PRICES: s €44; d €55; t €78 **ON SITE:** Fishing Hiking **NEARBY:** Bathing (10km) Horse riding (3km) Golf (12km) Sea (10km) Swimming pool (10km) Water sports (17km) Tennis (6km) Bicycle hire (6km) Railway station (8km) Shops (6km) MORLAIX (7km) **NOTES:** No pets

PLOUNEOUR-MENEZ

🏵 🐄 🍴 Domaine de Lanhéric
Catherine & Patrick BERTHIER
29410 PLOUNEOUR MENEZ
☎ 02 98 78 01 53 & 06 61 33 75 54 📠 02 98 78 06 30
e-mail: lanheric@wanadoo.fr

At the gateway of the Amorique regional park, and less than 30 minutes from the sea, Catherine and Patrick welcome you to their large 18th-century longbarn in a lovely verdant and calm setting. On the first floor, there is a bedroom with a double and a single bed (extra bed possible) and a twin room. There is a further twin room in a second building (extra bed possible). All rooms have a shower room and wc. Large sitting room with fireplace. Lounge with library of guidebooks, cards, games and TV. Garden furniture and washing machine provided. Numerous walks around the, the, Arée mountains and along the seashore. Evening meals using local produce provided on request. Half-board accommodation available. Off-peak rates given on request. Open all year.
PRICES: s €37-€40; d €42-€48; t €55-€58; extra person €10; dinner €15 **ON SITE:** Hiking **NEARBY:** Bathing (25km) Horse riding (10km) Golf (25km) Sea (25km) Fishing (25km) Swimming pool (4km) Water sports (25km) Tennis (4km) Bicycle hire (4km) Railway station (15km) Shops (4km) MORLAIX (15km) **NOTES:** Pets admitted English spoken

PLOURIN-LES-MORLAIX

🏵 🐄 Lestrezec Patrick HELARY
29600 PLOURIN LES MORLAIX
☎ 02 98 72 53 55 📠 02 98 72 53 55
This dairy farm is at the foot of the Arée mountains. There are three bedrooms, decorated with passion and charm. One is on the ground floor and has a private bathroom. There are also two double bedrooms and a twin bedroom. The Helary family welcome you to this simple granite, Breton house, with large bay windows, looking onto the country garden. Large lounge and sitting room with fireplace. Kitchen. Reduced rates October to April (on reservation).

PRICES: d €50 **ON SITE:** Fishing Hiking **NEARBY:** Bathing (20km) Horse riding (10km) Golf (14km) Sea (10km) Swimming pool (10km) Water sports (20km) Tennis (4km) Bicycle hire (10km) Railway station (10km) Shops (4km) MORLAIX (10km) **NOTES:** No pets English spoken

PLOUVIEN

🏵 Croas Eugan Maurice & Denise LE JEUNE
29860 PLOUVIEN
☎ 02 98 40 96 46 📠 02 98 40 96 46
Denise and Maurice Le Jeune welcome you to their property in North Finistère, at the centre of the Abers region and the 'Côte des légendes'. There is independent access to the three bedrooms. The first and second have double beds and private bathrooms (the second one is a grade 2 bedroom and has a wc on the landing). The third bedroom has twin beds, a bathroom, sitting room and TV. Use of kitchen. Fireplace, TV and dining room. Electric heating. Open all year.
PRICES: s €32; d €35-€46; t €55 **ON SITE:** Hiking Bicycle hire **NEARBY:** Bathing (10km) Horse riding (6km) Golf (10km) Sea (10km) Fishing (5km) Swimming pool (10km) Water sports (10km) Tennis (2km) Railway station (18km) Shops (2km) BREST (18km) **NOTES:** No pets

PLOUZANE

🏵 🐄 🍴 ♿ Lézavarn Christiane PHILIPOT
29280 PLOUZANE
☎ 02 98 48 41 28 📠 02 98 48 93 29
Christianne and Yvon welcome you to their pig and dairy farm. There is independent access to the four bedrooms available in an annexe building. Three are doubles, one accessible to the less mobile, and the other is a twin. All have TV, telephone and private facilities. Extra bed possible. There is also a grade 2 family room in the owners' house with a double bed and twin beds, a shower room and a separate, private wc. Kitchen available, washing machine. Gazebo with table tennis, table football and billiards, play area. You can visit the farm. Evening meals possible except on Sundays, free for children under four. Brest is ten minutes away. Open all year.
PRICES: s €35; d €50; t €62; extra person €10; HB €40; dinner €15 **NEARBY:** Bathing (8km) Horse riding (5km) Golf (10km) Sea (8km) Swimming pool (12km) Hiking (5km) Water sports (3km) Tennis (3km) Bicycle hire (10km) Railway station (15km) Shops (3km) BREST (8km) **NOTES:** Pets admitted

PLOZEVET

🏵 Kérongard Divisquin Claudine TREPOS
29710 PLOZEVET
☎ 02 98 54 31 09
In the heart of the Audierne Bay, Claudine and Ernest welcome you to their home in the middle of a small, calm village, opposite the ocean and 30 km from the Pointe Du Raz, the Pointe de Penmarc'h and Bénodet, Quimper and Locronan. There are three light bedrooms on the first floor with independent access: two doubles and a twin, with a shower room and a wc in each. On the ground floor, there is a large Breton room, where you can enjoy a generous breakfast of homemade crêpes and Breton gateaux. TV, fridge, garden furniture and boule pitch. Beach and footpaths 1 km. Restaurant 2 km. Varying rates depending on length of stay.
PRICES: s €38; d €43 **ON SITE:** Hiking **NEARBY:** Bathing (1km) Horse riding (8km) Golf (25km) Sea (1km) Fishing (1km) Swimming pool (15km) Water sports (10km) Tennis (4km) Bicycle hire (4km) Railway station (25km) Shops (4km) PONT L'ABBE (15km) **NOTES:** No pets

continued

▦ |◎| **Lesneut** Evelyne BOURDIC
29710 PLOZEVET
☎ 02 98 54 34 33 🖷 02 98 54 35 71
e-mail: evelyne.bourdic@wanadoo.fr
http://perso.wanadoo.fr/evelyne.bourdic
This 18th-century farm is situated on the Pointe du Raz road, 2 km
from the sea. On the edge of a calm hamlet, there is a view of the
sea from the garden. There are four non-smoking comfortable
bedrooms. There are three ground-floor bedrooms in the
longbarn, each with bathroom and wc. In a second building, there
is a family suite for four people, occupying the whole of the first
floor, with a bathroom and wc. Large lounge and sitting room with
chimney, library and TV. Washing machine, tumble dryer, fridge.
Evening meals featuring seafood and garden produce are served
in a peaceful setting. Garden furniture and picnic area in the
orchard.
PRICES: s €43; d €46-€49; t €56; dinner €16 **ON SITE:** Hiking
NEARBY: Bathing (2km) Horse riding (2km) Golf (30km) Sea (2km)
Fishing (2km) Swimming pool (17km) Water sports (8km) Tennis (3km)
Bicycle hire (2km) Railway station (25km) Shops (2krn) QUIMPER (23km)
NOTES: No pets English spoken

PONT-AVEN

▦ **Kermentec** Véronique LAROUR
29930 PONT AVEN
☎ 02 98 06 07 60
High up in Pont Aven, two minutes from the 'city of painters' and
two steps from the 'Bois d'amour', Mme Larour offers you a warm
welcome to her pretty stone house. There are three bedrooms
available, one twin and two doubles, each with a shower room
and wc. Large lounge with a corner seating area. Kitchen available.
Extra bed on request. Breakfasts can be served in the open air or
next to the fireplace. Tranquil countryside with lovely walks near
the beaches. Quimper, Locronan, Concarneau and many acitivites
nearby.
PRICES: d €41; t €53; extra person €12 **ON SITE:** Hiking
NEARBY: Bathing (10km) Horse riding (1km) Golf (25km) Sea (5km)
Fishing (1km) Swimming pool (15km) Water sports (7km) Tennis (1km)
Bicycle hire (15km) Railway station (18km) **NOTES:** No pets

POULLAN-SUR-MER

▦▦ **Manoir de Kerdanet**
Sid & Monique NEDJAR
29100 POULLAN SUR MER
☎ 02 98 74 59 03 & 06 75 24 07 84 🖷 02 98 74 59 03
e-mail: manoir.kernadet@wanadoo.fr
This 15th-century manor house nestles in the hollow of a
verdant valley. As with all beautiful, stately homes of this
period, there is a large lake occupying pride of place in the
three hectare park. Stone stairs lead up to a period bedroom
on the first floor with a fireplace and a four-poster bed. In the
sitting room on the ground floor, there is a carved stone
fireplace, where shields of the former lords of the manor are
displayed. There are two double bedrooms with bathroom
and wc, and a bedroom/sitting room suite with a double and
twin beds, bathroom, shower and wc. All the bedrooms are
no smoking.
PRICES: d €90-€115; extra person €15 **ON SITE:** Hiking
NEARBY: Bathing (5km) Horse riding (4km) Golf (30km) Sea
(5km) Fishing (5km) Swimming pool (6km) Water sports (5km)
Tennis (5km) Bicycle hire (7km) Railway station (30km) Shops (2km)
DOUARNENEZ (7km) **NOTES:** No pets English spoken

POULLAOUEN

▦ ❦ |◎| **Goasvennou** Ghislaine DEGRYSE-BRIAND
Les Tilleuls, 29246 POULLAOUEN
☎ 02 98 93 57 63
In the centre of Brittany, less than thirty minutes from the sea and
near to Huelgoat, 'the forest of 1001 legends', you be warmly
welcomed to this green, tranquil setting. There is a small pond and
a large flower garden on this beautiful property, where you can
immerse yourself in farm life. There are four double bedrooms,
each with a shower room and wc. Cot and baby equipment
available. Garden with furniture and terrace. From the house, you
can enjoy walks, mountain biking and 4x4 driving. Outdoor play
area for the children. Picnic baskets can be prepared on request.
PRICES: s €35; d €41; extra person €10; dinner €15 **ON SITE:** Hiking
Bicycle hire **NEARBY:** Bathing (40km) Horse riding (3km) Golf (6km)
Sea (30km) Fishing (1km) Swimming pool (5km) Water sports (40km)
Tennis (4km) Railway station (10km) Shops (4km) HUELGOAT (10km)
NOTES: No pets English spoken

QUEMENEVEN

▦ ❦ |◎| **Nanclic** P & M JEZEQUEL - DULIEU
29180 QUEMENEVEN
☎ 02 98 73 51 86 🖷 02 98 73 51 86
e-mail: P.Dulieu.Jezequel@wanadoo.fr
In the heart of the Cournouaille countryside, 2 km from
characterful Locronan and 2.5 km from Plonévez Porzay, Martine
and Patrick welcome you to their dairy farm. On the first
floor, there are four guest rooms: two doubles, one twin, and one
room with a single and a double bedroom, each with shower
room and wc. Lounge with fireplace and TV. Baby equipment
available. Garden with garden furniture, terrace, barbecue and a
gazebo. Evening meals on reservation, except July and August.
Open all year.
PRICES: s €35; d €42; t €57; dinner €16 **NEARBY:** Bathing (6km) Horse
riding (2km) Golf (16km) Sea (6km) Fishing (6km) Swimming pool
(12km) Hiking (1km) Water sports (12km) Tennis (2km) Railway station
(8km) Shops (2km) LOCRONAN (2km) **NOTES:** No pets English
spoken

QUIMPER

▦ |◎| **Le Logis du Stang** Annie HERVE
Stang Youenn, 29000 QUIMPER
☎ 06 81 55 73 83 & 02 98 52 00 55 🖷 02 98 52 00 55
e-mail: logis-du-stang@wanadoo.fr
Welcome to Cournouaille, in the middle of the countryside, ten
minutes from the old town of Quimper. This 19th-century manor
house at Ergué-Armel is on the cider route. There is a twin
bedroom with shower room and wc on the first floor and two
family rooms in a separate longbarn close by. In these ground-
floor rooms, there are two double beds leading onto private
terraces and two single beds on a mezzanine level, with a shower
room, wc, TV and telephone. Large garden with high stone walls.
PRICES: s €40; d €54; t €67-€74; dinner €15 **NEARBY:** Bathing (12km)
Horse riding (9km) Golf (15km) Sea (12km) Fishing (5km) Swimming
pool (5km) Water sports (12km) Tennis (5km) Bicycle hire (3km) Railway
station (5km) Shops (2km) QUIMPER (2km) **NOTES:** No pets English
spoken

RIEC-SUR-BELON

▦ ❦ |◎| **Le Rest** Rémy & Martine GUILLOU
29340 RIEC SUR BELON
☎ 02 98 06 92 98
Martine and Rémy welcome you to their farm. Near to their home,
there is a 19th-century stone building with four bedrooms on the
first floor: three doubles and one single, each with shower room

continued

and wc. On the ground floor, there is a large room where large, tasty breakfasts and evening meals (on reservation) are served. Lounge area with TV. Large play area for children and a garden with furniture. Open all year.

PRICES: d €39; t €50; dinner €15 **ON SITE:** Children's play area **NEARBY:** Bathing (12km) Horse riding (2km) Golf (30km) Sea (4km) Fishing (1km) Swimming pool (10km) Hiking (6km) Water sports (6km) Tennis (3km) Bicycle hire (3km) Railway station (10km) Shops (3km) PONT AVEN (6km) **NOTES:** No pets

ROSNOEN

♥♥♥ ♥ ♿ Le Seillou Marie Thérèse LE PAPE
29590 ROSNOEN
☎ 02 98 81 92 21 ▤ 02 98 81 07 14

The Le Pape family welcome you to this typically Breton farm. There are six bedrooms above the farm and in an annexe: four doubles, one twin and a ground-floor double with a single bed; each has either a shower or bathroom, wc and private lounge area. Garden with furniture and play area. Set back from the D791, on the Presqu'île de Crozon crossroads and 300 m from the Rade de Brest, you will enjoy a relaxing stay. Meals of farm produce and homemade crêpes served on reservation. Half board possible. Outside there is a park for relaxation or children's play. From Faou, take the direction of Crozon for 6km. Follow the signs 'Ferme-auberge du Seillou'. Open all year.

PRICES: s €37; d €43; t €57; HB €35 **ON SITE:** Sea Fishing Hiking **NEARBY:** Bathing (15km) Horse riding (10km) Golf (25km) Swimming pool (20km) Water sports (18km) Tennis (5km) Bicycle hire (3km) Railway station (15km) Shops (6km) Restaurant nearby LE FAOU (5km) **NOTES:** No pets English spoken

ROSPORDEN

♥♥♥ Kerantou Monique BERNARD
29140 ROSPORDEN-KERNEVEL
☎ 02 98 59 27 79 ▤ 02 98 59 27 79

Six guest rooms in old farm buildings, close to the owners' home, 2 km from Rosporden and 15 km from Concarneau and Pont-Aven. Christian and Monique will help you discover Breton traditions. There are three double rooms, two twin rooms and a family room with a double bed and two single beds. Bath or shower room in each bedroom. Kitchen, sitting room, garden with furniture, barbecue, covered area and games. Walks from the house. Fishing 2 km. Baby sitting service. Open all year.

PRICES: s €30; d €38; extra person €10 **ON SITE:** Hiking **NEARBY:** Bathing (15km) Horse riding (10km) Golf (18km) Sea (15km) Fishing (2km) Swimming pool (9km) Water sports (15km) Tennis (3km) Bicycle hire (3km) Railway station (3km) Shops (2km) CONCARNEAU (14km) **NOTES:** Pets admitted English spoken

♥♥♥ ♥ Manoir de Coat Canton Diana SIMON
Grand bois, 29140 ROSPORDEN
☎ 02 98 66 31 24

The Coat Canton Manor house dates from between the 13th and 17th centuries; you will be warmly welcomed in this historic, rural setting. There are four very comfortable guest bedrooms in the renovated longbarn: two ground-floor doubles, and a family room on the first floor with a double and twin beds. Each room has a shower room and wc. Baby-sitting can be arranged. TV, telephone, washing machine, garden with furniture. Visits to the private museum and horse riding lessons on site. Fifteen minutes by car to the beach, Concarneau port, Quimper and Pont Aven ('the city of painters').

PRICES: s €40; d €45; t €60 **ON SITE:** Horse riding Hiking **NEARBY:** Bathing (13km) Golf (10km) Sea (13km) Fishing (1km) Swimming pool (1km) Water sports (13km) Tennis (1km) Bicycle hire (1km) Railway station (1km) Shops (1km) QUIMPER (15km) **NOTES:** No pets English spoken

SANTEC

♥♥♥♥ Chambre d'hôtes Annick STEPHAN
361, route du Dossen, Brenesquen, 29250 SANTEC
☎ 02 98 29 70 45 ▤ 02 98 29 70 45

Annick welcomes you to this rustic style house, with its windows surrounded by pink granite, located between the countryside and the sea. On the ground floor, there is a double bedroom with a TV, while on the first floor, there is independent access to two doubles and one twin bedroom, a sitting room, TV and cardphone. Each bedroom has a bath or shower room and wc. Dining room with fireplace and view over the garden, where generous breakfasts are served. Enclosed garden with arbour, garden furniture and barbecue. Beach 1.5 km (windsurfing, sailing and other watersports). Only 6 km from Roscoff, the location is handy for trips to the île Batz. Crêperie and restaurants 1.5 km. Non-smoking bedrooms. Open 1 April to 1 October.

PRICES: s €32; d €38-€40; t €63 **NEARBY:** Bathing (2km) Horse riding (10km) Golf (15km) Sea (2km) Fishing (2km) Swimming pool (3km) Hiking (3km) Water sports (4km) Tennis (5km) Bicycle hire (5km) Railway station (3km) Shops (3km) SAINT POL DE LEON (3km) **NOTES:** No pets

♥♥♥ ❦ Chambre d'hôtes Joël SALOU
295 route de Poulmavic, 29250 SANTEC
☎ 02 98 29 40 15 & 02 98 29 41 60

Three guest rooms in two houses annexed to the owners' house. On the first floor of the first building, there is a double bedroom and a single bedroom with TV; both have shower rooms and wcs. On the ground floor, there is a communal lounge room with a fireplace. In the second building, there is a bedroom with a double bed on a mezzanine, whilst on the ground floor, there is a box bed with a shower room and wc. All the bedrooms are themed with antique furniture and waxed parquet floors, with coordinating furnishings. Television. Garden with furniture and terrace. Evening meals on reservation; half board possible. Open all year.

PRICES: s €33; d €42; t €51; HB €57; dinner €20 **ON SITE:** Bathing Sea Fishing Hiking **NEARBY:** Horse riding (10km) Golf (10km) Swimming pool (4km) Water sports (3km) Tennis (2km) Bicycle hire (5km) Railway station (20km) Shops (3km) SAINT POL DE LEON (5km) **NOTES:** No pets

♥♥♥ Chambre d'hôtes Marie Pierre RIVOALLON
183 route du Dossen, 29250 SANTEC
☎ 02 98 29 70 65 & 02 98 29 74 98
e-mail: mariepierre.rivoallon@wanadoo.fr

Marie Pierre offers you a warm welcome to her typically Breton home, in a green, tranquil setting. On the ground floor, there is a family suite of two bedrooms (a double and a twin), separated by a partition, with a bathroom and wc. On the first floor, there are two twin bedrooms with a shower room, wc and TV, and a further twin bedroom with a separate bathroom and wc. Cot available. Flower garden with furniture, terrace, barbecue and parking area. A large beach is only 1.5 km away, where you can enjoy land yachting, sea kayaking and surfing. Forest walks. Creperie and several restaurants nearby. Roscoff 6 km. Open all year.

PRICES: s €32; d €38-€40; t €63; extra person €12 **ON SITE:** Wine tasting **NEARBY:** Bathing (2km) Horse riding (15km) Golf (15km) Sea (2km) Fishing (2km) Swimming pool (3km) Hiking (1km) Water sports (5km) Tennis (5km) Bicycle hire (5km) Railway station (3km) Shops (3km) SAINT POL DE LEON (3km) **NOTES:** No pets English spoken

---

❦
Places with this symbol serve table d'hôtes
evening meals - remember to book in advance

SCAER

ᛃᛃᛃ 🕊 Ti Penn at Kerloaï Louis & Thérèse PENN
Kerloaï, 29390 SCAER
☎ 02 98 59 42 60 🖹 02 98 59 05 67
e-mail: lan.guillou@wanadoo.fr
Thérèse and Louis welcome you to Ti Penn at Kerloaï, situated between Armor (the sea region) and Argoat (the wood region). After a nice, calm evening, you can enjoy a large breakfast in the large lounge, around the central fireplace. There are five bedrooms, each with shower room and wc: four doubles and one twin. Lovely garden. Breton is spoken and Scaër is very central. From here you can visit Pont Aven, Concarneau, Quimper and discover inner Brittany. Open all year.
PRICES: s €36; d €40 **NEARBY:** Bathing (20km) Horse riding (15km) Golf (15km) Sea (20km) Fishing (4km) Swimming pool (4km) Hiking (4km) Water sports (20km) Tennis (4km) Bicycle hire (4km) Railway station (10km) Shops (4km) ROSPORDEN (14km) **NOTES:** No pets English spoken

SCRIGNAC

ᛃᛃᛃ 🕊 🍴 Le Cloître Lionel COTONNEC
29640 SCRIGNAC
☎ 02 98 78 23 17
This old renovated farmhouse is situated near to the cattle and dairy farm of the owners. There are three guest bedrooms with double beds, shower room and wc. You will enjoy the lovely family atmosphere and tranquillity around the stretch of water and flower garden outside. In the woods, around the farm, you will be able to enjoy activities, such as walking, fishing and nature discovery. Baby sitting can be arranged and there is a telephone.
PRICES: s €34; d €38; t €53; dinner €13 **ON SITE:** Wine tasting Hiking **NEARBY:** Bathing (30km) Horse riding (15km) Golf (7km) Sea (30km) Fishing (1km) Swimming pool (15km) Water sports (15km) Tennis (7km) Bicycle hire (15km) Railway station (15km) Shops (7km) HUELGOAT (15km) **NOTES:** Pets admitted English spoken

ST-ELOY-HANVEC

ᛃᛃᛃ 🕊 🍴 Kerivoal Nicole LE LANN
29460 SAINT ELOY HANVEC
☎ 02 98 25 86 14 🖹 02 98 25 86 14
A beautiful group of farm buildings, typical of the Mont Arrée region. There is a south-facing flower garden with a lovely view over a wooded valley and trout river. In an independent building, there are two guest bedrooms on the first floor, one double and one twin, both with shower room and wc. Lounge with fireplace and TV. Kitchen available. Attached to the owners' house, there is independent access to a family room with a double bed, twin beds on a mezzanine, a bathroom, wc, TV and fridge. Garden with furniture, barbecue and portico. Evening meals available on request.
PRICES: s €30; d €40-€43; t €60; dinner €14 **ON SITE:** Fishing Hiking **NEARBY:** Bathing (20km) Horse riding (8km) Golf (15km) Sea (10km) Swimming pool (10km) Water sports (10km) Tennis (3km) Bicycle hire (10km) Railway station (17km) Shops (6km) DAOULAS (10km) **NOTES:** No pets English spoken

ST-MARTIN-DES-CHAMPS

ᛃᛃᛃ 🕊 Kereliza Marie-Noëlle ABIVEN
29600 SAINT-MARTIN-DES-CHAMPS
☎ 02 98 88 27 18
Marie-Noëlle and Christian welcome you to their charming renovated 19th-century manor house. There are five lovely bedrooms, all equipped with either a shower room or a bathroom, and wc. There are two twin bedrooms, and two double bedrooms and another room with a double bed and a single bed. Situated on a farm, with a large flower garden, private parking is provided. There is also a sitting room, with television, kitchen, table tennis, billiards and baby equipment available. Restaurant 1 km. Open all year.
PRICES: s €26; d €38; t €46 **NEARBY:** Bathing (10km) Horse riding (10km) Sea (3km) Fishing (3km) Swimming pool (5km) Water sports (10km) Tennis (2km) Bicycle hire (2km) Railway station (2km) Shops (1km) MORLAIX (3km) **NOTES:** Pets admitted English spoken

ST-THEGONNEC

ᛃᛃᛃ 🍴 Chambres d'hôtes Christine PRIGENT
18, rue Lividic, Ar presbital coz, 29410 SAINT THEGONNEC
☎ 02 98 79 45 62 🖹 02 98 79 48 47
In the heart of the *enclos paroissiaux* and the Arrée mountains, this house was the Presbyterian church of Saint Thégonnec for two centuries. There are six spacious, comfortable bedrooms: three doubles, two twins and one room with a double and a single bed. Each bedroom has a private bathroom. The owners are happy to provide suggestions for a personalised visit to Brittany. Bicycles can be hired on site. Parking. Crêperie, restaurants and shops within 300 m. Discount after two nights. Evening meals using local specialities and regional produce available on reservation.
PRICES: s €35-€38; d €41-€44; t €55-€58; extra person €14; dinner €14 **ON SITE:** Hiking Tennis Bicycle hire **NEARBY:** Bathing (20km) Horse riding (10km) Golf (12km) Sea (14km) Fishing (1km) Swimming pool (6km) Water sports (20km) Railway station (12km) Shops (1km) MORLAIX (10km) **NOTES:** No pets English spoken

ST-THONAN

ᛃᛃᛃ 🕊 Veuleury Marie Jo EDERN
29800 SAINT THONAN
☎ 02 98 20 26 99 & 02 98 20 22 95 🖹 02 98 20 27 13
e-mail: marie-jo.edern@wanadoo.fr
In this large, recently built house, Marie Jo offers three bedrooms, two of which are family rooms, situated on the first floor. Also available for guest use: sitting room, terrace and garden with furniture. One family suite is made up of three bedrooms containing a double bed, twin beds, and a sitting room. There is also a bedroom with twin beds and a single bed, and a further double room. Each bedroom has a shower room, wc and telephone (takes France Telecom phone cards). Central heating. Kitchen available. Independent guest entrance. Two self-catering gîtes also available. Footpath and Chapelle St-Herbot 200 m. Reduced rates between September and June, and for holidays of a week or more. Anti-allergy bed linen provided. Visit to pig farm. Sports teams welcome. Open all year.
PRICES: s €25-€35; d €37-€45; t €55-€60; extra person €18 **NEARBY:** Bathing (20km) Horse riding (6km) Golf (9km) Sea (15km) Fishing (6km) Swimming pool (6km) Water sports (20km) Tennis (3km) Railway station (5km) Shops (3km) LANDERNEAU (6km) **NOTES:** No pets

ST-YVI

ᛃᛃᛃ Kervren Odile LE GALL
29140 SAINT-YVI
☎ 02 98 94 70 34 🖹 02 98 94 81 19
Near to Quimper, Concarneau, Bénodet and Pont-Aven, Odile welcomes you to a longbarn on a 19th-century farm, 2.5 km from the town. There are six guest bedrooms: four double bedrooms and two twin bedrooms. All have a shower room and wc. Large breakfasts served. Lovely parkland with panoramic views. Sitting room with a fireplace. Kitchen. Shops, tennis court, swimming pool and river (for fishing) five minutes away. Beach and golf course fifteen minutes away. Walks nearby. Quimper airport twenty minutes away. Open all year.

continued

continued

PRICES: s €34; d €40 **ON SITE:** Hiking **NEARBY:** Bathing (10km) Horse riding (5km) Golf (10km) Sea (10km) Fishing (8km) Swimming pool (5km) Water sports (20km) Tennis (5km) Railway station (10km) Shops (2km) QUIMPER (13km) **NOTES:** Pets admitted

TOURC'H

▓▓▓ 🍴 Le Bourg Rémy & Odette LE BOURHIS
Ti ar Vourc'hized, 29140 TOURC'H
☎ 02 98 59 15 42 📠 02 98 59 01 41
Odette and Rémy welcome you to their large house in the town of Tourc'h, opposite the 16th-century church. Situated between Concarneau and the Trévarez Chateau, in open countryside. There are four guest rooms on the first floor: two doubles and two twins, each with a TV, bathroom or shower room and wc. Large dining room, sitting room and an enclosed garden with a terrace. Evening meals made from farm produce (duck paté and poultry) are available. Farm 2 km away on the other side of the valley. Shops close by. Open 15 June to 15 September.
PRICES: d €40; dinner €14 **ON SITE:** Hiking **NEARBY:** Bathing (20km) Horse riding (6km) Golf (30km) Sea (20km) Fishing (1km) Swimming pool (7km) Water sports (20km) Tennis (7km) Railway station (7km) ROSPORDEN (7km) **NOTES:** No pets

ILLE-ET-VILAINE
BAGUER-MORVAN

▓▓▓ 🍴 Chambre d'hôtes Bernard et Geneviève MABILE
Malouinière de Launay Blot, Baguer Morvan,
35120 DOL-DE-BRETAGNE
☎ 02 99 48 07 48 & SR : 02 99 78 47 57 📠 02 99 80 94 47
www.pays-de-dol.com

There are three bedrooms in this 17th century St Malo property. There is one bedroom for three people, a main bedroom for four and another bedroom for three. All bedrooms have private bathrooms and wcs. There is a lounge and a sitting room for guests. Outside, there is a large, wooded park, fishing is possible in the moats of the manor house and bikes can be hired on site. The property is very near the tourist spots of Mont-St-Michel, Saint-Malo, Dinard and Dinan. Evening meals are available on reservation (except July, August and bank holidays).

PRICES: s €46; d €54-€61; t €73-€81; extra person €20; dinner €22-€25 **NEARBY:** Horse riding (6km) Forest (10km) Golf (4km) Swimming pool (10km) Tennis (2km) Sailing (20km) **NOTES:** No pets

▓▓▓ Les Sageais Maurice et Yvonne PAPAIL
Baguer Morvan, 35120 DOL-DE-BRETAGNE
☎ 02 99 80 90 45 & SR : 02 99 78 47 57
Mont St-Michel Bay 10 km. St-Malo & Dinan 25 km. Combourg 10 km. This restored, stone house, lies in wooded, green countryside. There are two family suites, each containing two bedrooms, in this house. There is one double bedroom with a private bathroom. A kitchen is also available for guest use. There is a lounge/dining room with fireplace and library on a mezzanine level. Outside, there are landscaped grounds with garden furniture and children's games. Private parking is provided and you will receive a warm welcome and generous breakfasts. The rooms are available throughout the year and the rate for four people is 61/67 Euros.
PRICES: s €30; d €35-€38; t €53 **ON SITE:** Children's play area **NEARBY:** Horse riding (2km) Golf (2km) Swimming pool (10km) Tennis (3km) Railway station (5km) Shops (5km) **NOTES:** No pets

BAINS-SUR-OUST

▓▓▓ Chambre d'hôtes Marie ROBERT
rue de la Fosse Piquet, 35600 BAINS-SUR-OUST
☎ 02 99 91 60 10 & 06 03 87 50 78
Redon & Gacilly 5 km. In the heart of a small rural, well known tourist village, known for the Ile au Pies, this modern house lies amongst large flowery, country grounds. There are three bedrooms for two people, each with a bathroom. There is a terrace with garden furniture and inside there is a lounge/sitting room for guest use. A farm inn is 1.5km away and the beaches and sea of the Atlantic coast are only an hour away. The rooms are available throughout the year.
PRICES: s €30; d €38; t €50 **NEARBY:** Horse riding (1km) Sea (50km) Swimming pool (6km) Tennis (1km) Railway station (5km) **NOTES:** No pets

BETTON

▓▓▓ 🐓 Bas Cheneze Roger et Odile BESNIER
35830 BETTON
☎ 02 99 55 82 92 & SR : 02 99 78 47 57 📠 02 99 55 31 44
Mont Saint-Michel 55 km. Rennes 10 km. Odile and Roger, welcome you to their pretty, rural farmhouse, in lovely verdant countryside. On the ground floor, there is a family suite with a very spacious mezzanine level, that opens onto two terraces. This suite is made up of a bathroom, double bed, three single beds and a kitchen area. On the first floor, there is another family suite with two bedrooms: a double bed, cot and twin beds, bathroom and wc. There are two extra double bedrooms and one twin bedroom, each with shower room and wc. A lounge, sitting room with fireplace and kitchen with fridge are also available for guest use. Generous breakfasts are served in the lounge. Outside there are terraces and garden furniture, a play area, a volleyball pitch and animal park. Fishing in a private pond and walking are also possible from the site. Open all year.
PRICES: s €26-€29; d €31-€38; t €46-€49; extra person €11; 4 people €53-€60 **ON SITE:** Children's play area **NEARBY:** Bathing (55km) Horse riding (3km) Forest (5km) Golf (10km) Swimming pool (10km) Stretch of water (3km) Tennis (3km) Railway station (2km) Shops (3km) Sailing (15km) **NOTES:** No pets

For further information on these and other chambres d'hôtes, consult the Gîtes de France website *www.gites-de-france.fr*

continued

BILLE

♦♦♦ Chambre d'hôtes Stéphanie ROUSSEL
Mesauboin, 35133 BILLE

☎ 02 99 97 61 57 & SR : 02 99 78 47 57   📠 02 99 97 50 76
There are five guest bedrooms in this 17th century manor house with turret and chapel, in the middle of the countryside. There are two two-person bedrooms, one bedroom for three people and two bedrooms for four. Each bedroom has a private bathroom and wc. There is a lounge room and play area outside. The rate for four people is 56 euros.
PRICES: s €28; d €36; t €46; dinner €13   **NEARBY:** Bathing (80km) Horse riding (10km) Forest (10km) Golf (25km) Sea (65km) Swimming pool (10km) Tennis (2km) Restaurant nearby   **NOTES:** Pets admitted CC English spoken

BONNEMAIN

♦♦♦ Rocher Cordier Brigitte et Colin ADAMS
Colibri, 35270 BONNEMAIN

☎ 02 99 73 45 45 & SR : 02 99 78 47 57   📠 02 99 73 45 45
Dinan 22 km. Saint-Malo & Mont Saint-Michel 30 km. There are two double bedrooms and one triple bedroom, each with private bathroom, on the first floor of this renovated, granite, country house. There is a lounge/ sitting room, TV and open fireplace. Outside there are large grounds with a small wood, children's games and a barbeque. Bikes can be hired on site and the house is near to two golf courses and a cricket pitch. Open all year.
PRICES: s €29; d €37-€40; t €49; extra person €9   **ON SITE:** Children's play area   **NEARBY:** Bathing (25km) Horse riding (6km) Forest (6km) Golf (5km) Sea (20km) Swimming pool (8km) Stretch of water (2km) Hiking (5km) Tennis (1km) Sailing (25km) Railway station (1km) Shops (1km)   **NOTES:** No pets English spoken

CANCALE

♦♦♦ 🍽 La Gaudichais Marc LOISEL
Les Oyats, 35260 CANCALE

☎ 02 99 89 73 61 & SR : 02 99 78 47 57   📠 02 99 89 73 61
e-mail: lesoyats@club-internet.fr
Saint-Malo 12 km. Mont Saint-Michel 35 km. This old renovated farm, offers two, triple bedrooms and two, four people rooms with an extra bed on request. Each bedroom has a shower room and wc. There is a lounge/ sitting room, reading room and TV. A cot and childcare items are available. There is also a garden, with play area for children. Mountain bikes can be hired on site. Evening meals are available on reservation, on Tuesdays and Thursdays. The rate for four people is 62/68 Euros. Ten minutes form the beach, the fine sands of "Verger" and the footpaths of the GR34 walking route, which follows the coast. Tel. 06.60.89.81.54 (owner's mobile). Open all year.
PRICES: s €34-€37; d €42-€45; t €53-€58; extra person €10; dinner €14   **ON SITE:** Children's play area   **NEARBY:** Bathing (1km) Horse riding (6km) Golf (30km) Sea (1km) Swimming pool (15km) Stretch of water (3km) Hiking (1km) Tennis (3km) Sailing (3km) Railway station (12km) Shops (2km)   **NOTES:** No pets

CHAUVIGNE

♦♦♦ 🐏 🍽 La Haunaie Aimée et Jean COUDRAY
35490 CHAUVIGNE

☎ 02 99 97 77 19 & SR : 02 99 78 47 57   📠 02 99 95 02 09
Mont Saint-Michel 35 km. Fougères 20 km. There are two double bedrooms and one triple bedroom with private bathroom. There is a sitting room with TV and a shady garden with garden furniture and children's play area. This old, renovated house, has a garden and large flowery courtyard and is in the middle of the countryside. You will be offered a warm welcome and the property is available throughout the year.

PRICES: s €23; d €34; t €46; dinner €12   **ON SITE:** Children's play area
NEARBY: Horse riding (10km) Swimming pool (23km) Railway station (40km) Shops (4km)   **NOTES:** Pets admitted

CHERRUEIX

♦♦♦ 🐏 Chambre d'hôtes Marie-Madeleine GLEMOT
Hamelinais, 35120 CHERRUEIX

☎ 02 99 48 95 26 & 06 17 47 53 49   📠 02 99 48 89 23
This property is situated between Mont Saint Michel and St Malo. Marie-Madeleine offers you a warm and personalised room, in her old, restored house, surrounded by a small park with flowers and shade. There are two, double bedrooms and one triple bedroom. There are also two, four person bedrooms with a mezzanine level. Each bedroom has a private bathroom and there is a lounge/ sitting room with an old, granite, open fireplace. Outside, there is a terrace and private parking. The rate for four people is 65 euros.
PRICES: d €35-€40; extra person €12   **NEARBY:** Bathing (15km) Golf (8km) Sea (4km) Swimming pool (18km) Hiking (4km) Tennis (4km) Sailing (4km)   **NOTES:** No pets

♦♦♦ Chambre d'hôtes Victor CAUQUELIN
167 les Grandes Grèves, route de Sainte-Anne, 35120 CHERRUEIX

☎ 02 99 48 97 67 & SR : 02 99 78 47 57 & 06 75 56 01 27
There are four (2-4 people) guest rooms available in this property, each with private bathroom. Breakfasts are served on the veranda, with a panoramic view overlooking the sea. There is a kitchen, garden and private parking and blossoms running along the Duchesse Anne dike, 1.5km from the tourist route of Pontorson/ St Malo by the coast. Victor welcomes you to his house, in the bay of Mont St Michel. In order to respect the comfort of the non smokers, no smoking is allowed in the house.
PRICES: s €28; d €36-€39; t €47   **NEARBY:** Horse riding (2km) Forest (2km) Swimming pool (20km) Tennis (2km) Railway station (2km)   **NOTES:** No pets

♦♦♦ 🐏 La Croix Gaillot Michel TAILLEBOIS
35120 CHERRUEIX

☎ 02 99 48 90 44 & SR : 02 99 78 47 57

Between Mont St Michel and St Malo, at Cherrueix (capital of land-sailing), Michel and Marie-France welcome you to their home and offer you five bedrooms in their stone 19th-century house. There are three double bedrooms and two triple bedrooms, each with private bathroom. There is also a lounge/sitting room with TV and possible use of the kitchen. Outside there is a lovely garden with garden furniture and private parking. Reduced rates are charged in low and mid season. The rooms are available throughout the year.
PRICES: s €34; d €39; t €48   **NEARBY:** Bathing (15km) Horse riding (2km) Golf (15km) Sea (2km) Swimming pool (7km) Tennis (2km) Sailing (15km) Railway station (7km) Shops (2km)   **NOTES:** No pets

continued

♦♦♦ La Pichardière Valérie ZIMMERMANN
35120 CHERRUEIX
☎ 02 99 48 83 82 & SR : 02 99 78 47 57　📠 02 99 48 80 01
www.baie-Saintmichel.com
This old house lies on the coast. There is one bedroom with a double bed and four single beds, shower room and wc. There is another bedroom with two double beds, a shower room and wc. Two further bedrooms, have double beds, shower room and wc. There is a lounge, sitting room with colour TV and fireplace and large terrace area, for guests. This house is near to the Saint-Anne Chapel.
PRICES: s €29; d €37; t €49; extra person €12　**ON SITE:** Sea　**NEARBY:** Horse riding (3km) Forest (5km) Golf (18km) Swimming pool (20km) Tennis (3km) Railway station (10km) Shops (3km)　**NOTES:** No pets

♦♦♦ ⭐ Le Lac Stéphane et Corinne DEGRAEVE
124 rue du Han, 35120 CHERRUEIX
☎ 02 99 48 93 77
e-mail: corinne-degraeve@wanadoo.fr
www.perso.wanadoo.fr/le-lac/
Half way between Mont St Michel and St Malo, you will love the hospitality shown in this 19th century bretonne home, situated near the sea shore and the bay of Mont Saint Michel, with access direct to the walking route around the sea wall (GR34). There are two bedrooms overlooking the sea. Each bedroom is prettily decorated and has a private bathroom. Another double bedroom is on the ground floor, and is accessible to guests with disabilities. There are three double bedrooms on the first floor and an extra bed may be provided on the ground floor. On the first floor, there is also a lounge room and library with a view over the sea. The dining room, on the ground floor, has an open fireplace. Generous breakfasts are provided on reservation and evening meals are served, using local produce. There is a country garden and garden furniture outside and private parking on site. The house is no smoking. Open all year.
PRICES: s €37; d €45; t €60; extra person €15; dinner €16　**ON SITE:** Sea
NEARBY: Horse riding (3km) Golf (18km) Swimming pool (20km) Tennis (2km) Railway station (8km) Shops (2km)　**NOTES:** No pets English spoken

♦♦♦ Chambres d'hôtes Jean-Paul GRASSER
136 Les Grandes Grèves, 35120 CHERRUEIX
☎ 02 99 48 81 28 & SR : 02 99 78 47 57　📠 02 99 48 81 28
Saint-Malo & Mont Saint-Michel 20 km. Both of these double bedrooms have a sea view and private bathroom. There is an extra family room for four with a private bathroom. A lounge room and sitting room are also available for use. Outside there is a terrace with garden furniture. Large breakfasts are served and the sea and bay of Mont Saint Michel are only 100m away. This is a comfortable and welcoming breton home. Land-sailing is possible and the property is available between April and October.
PRICES: s €31; d €36-€42; t €48-€54　**ON SITE:** Sea Swimming pool
NEARBY: Bathing (2km) Horse riding (3km) Golf (18km) Stretch of water (3km) Tennis (3km) Sailing (3km) Railway station (10km) Shops (3km)　**NOTES:** No pets English spoken

DOL-DE-BRETAGNE

♦♦♦ ⭐ Chambre d'hôtes
Catherine COSTARD-SOULABAILLE
La Begaudière, Mont-Dol, 35120 DOL-DE-BRETAGNE
☎ 02 99 48 20 04 & SR : 02 99 78 47 57　📠 02 99 48 20 04
e-mail: bonds@club-internet.fr www.begaudiere.com
There are five bedrooms in this house with lots of character on the edge of a river: two double bedrooms with bathroom and one triple bedroom with bathroom. A further two four-person, split-level bedrooms have bathrooms. Lounge with fireplace. Garden and terrace overlooking tree-lined parkland. The rate for four people is 61 euros. Open all year.

PRICES: d €39; t €50; extra person €11; dinner €16　**NEARBY:** Bathing (20km) Horse riding (5km) Golf (10km) Sea (8km) Swimming pool (2km) Hiking (8km) Tennis (1km) Railway station (2km) Shops (1km)　**NOTES:** Pets admitted English spoken

♦♦♦ 🐝 Haute Lande Riekus et Ineke RENTING
35120 DOL-DE-BRETAGNE
☎ 02 99 48 07 02 & SR : 02 99 78 47 57

There are two double bedrooms and one triple bedroom, each with private bathroom, in this old 17th-century manor house with a garden and lawn. There is also a lounge/sitting room. Outside there is a terrace area with garden furniture. The house is situated on a farm, near to numerous towns and tourist sites: Dol, Dinan, Saint Malo, Mont Saint-Michel, Combourg. The rate for four people is 50 euros and the property is available throughout the year.
PRICES: s €35; d €38; t €45　**NEARBY:** Horse riding (3km) Forest (10km) Golf (3km) Swimming pool (15km) Stretch of water (20km) Hiking (10km) Tennis (3km) Railway station (3km) Shops (3km)　**NOTES:** No pets English spoken

♦♦♦ 🐓 l'Aunay Begasse Alain RONCIER
35120 DOL-DE-BRETAGNE
☎ 02 99 48 16 93 & SR : 02 99 78 47 57

There is a double bedroom and two triple bedrooms in this house. Each bedroom has a bathroom and there is a breakfast room, where large breakfasts are served, a sitting room and TV. Fishing can be enjoyed, 1km away. Mayvonne and Alain are your

continued　　　　　　　　　　　　　　　　　　*continued*

welcoming hosts at this stone, country house, with its lovely flower
garden and easy friendly ambience.
PRICES: s €31; d €36; t €46; extra person €11 **NEARBY:** Horse riding
(7km) Forest (7km) Golf (7km) Swimming pool (1km) Tennis (1km)
NOTES: No pets

ESSE

♦♦♦ La Roche aux Fées Béatrice ROZE-SANTOS
35150 ESSE
☎ 02 99 47 73 84 & 06 07 06 04 22 ▤ 02 99 44 50 79
e-mail: relais-des-fees@wanadoo.fr www.roche-aux-fees.com
Vitré 25 km. Four bedrooms on the first floor of the owner's
house are available. There are three, two people rooms and one,
four person room, each with a bathroom. Generous breakfasts are
served using homemade produce. Outside, there is a terrace with
garden furniture. A rate of 60 euros for four people is charged.
Just a few steps from the largest dolemen in Brittany (the Fées
Rock), Béatrice and Johnny, welcome you to their home which is
full of character, in the heart of the hamlet. Attached to an inn, you
can enjoy local produce and there are a number of spectacles that
take place around the Roche aux Fées in the summer. Open all
year.
PRICES: s €30; d €40; t €52; extra person €10; HB €15
ON SITE: Children's play area **NEARBY:** Horse riding (15km) Swimming
pool (15km) Tennis (3km) Railway station (3km) Shops (3km) Restaurant
nearby **NOTES:** Pets admitted English spoken

GAHARD

♦♦♦ La Rogerie André et Angèle HOUDUSSE
Le Bourg, 35490 GAHARD
☎ 02 99 39 50 17 & SR : 02 99 78 47 57
Mont Saint-Michel 40 km. There are three bedrooms available in
this stone house with grounds (and garden furniture) attached. On
the ground floor, there is a bedroom for three people, with private
bathroom. On the first floor, there is a bedroom for two and one
for three, with a private bathroom. An extra bed is possible on
request. There is a lounge/sitting room with fireplace and the
kitchen may be used. Fishing can be enjoyed 6km away and there
is a pony club on site.
PRICES: s €25; d €32; t €40 **ON SITE:** Horse riding **NEARBY:** Forest
(1km) Golf (30km) Swimming pool (10km) Stretch of water (10km)
Hiking (2km) Sailing (10km) **NOTES:** Pets admitted

♦♦♦ ♥ |◎| Chambre d'hôtes
Victor & Anne-Marie DUGUEPEROUX
Le Viviers, 35490 GAHARD
☎ 02 99 39 50 19 & SR : 02 99 78 47 57 ▤ 02 99 39 50 19
This house is full of character and situated in a verdant setting,
attached to a dairy farm, between Rennes and Mont-St-Michel.
There are four bedrooms on the first floor: two two-person rooms
and two three-person rooms, each with private bathroom. There is
also a possibility of an extra bed. There is a lounge/drawing room
with TV for guest use. Evening meals are available on request and
there is a garden, with kids play area and terrace. Fishing can be
enjoyed 6km away and hiking is possible from the property. The
rooms are available throughout the year.
PRICES: s €30; d €34-€40; t €46-€56; extra person €9-€12; dinner €11-
€15 **ON SITE:** Children's play area **NEARBY:** Bathing (60km) Horse
riding (1km) Forest (2km) Golf (30km) Sea (40km) Swimming pool
(10km) Stretch of water (8km) Hiking (1km) Tennis (1km) Sailing (8km)
Railway station (12km) Shops (1km) **NOTES:** Pets admitted

♦♦♦ Haut Bignonet Jules et Odile VAUGON
35490 GAHARD
☎ 02 99 55 26 20 & SR : 02 99 78 47 57
Mont Saint-Michel 40 km. In the countryside, this pretty house,
has a lovely flower filled garden, is very calm and near a wood

and forests. There are two, three people rooms, each with private
bathroom. There is also a double bedroom with private bathroom.
There is a lounge/sitting room with TV and the kitchen may be
used. Outside there is a landscaped garden. The rate for four
people is 62 euros.
PRICES: s €33; d €40; t €51 **NEARBY:** Bathing (60km) Horse riding
(3km) Forest (1km) Golf (30km) Sea (40km) Swimming pool (11km)
Stretch of water (15km) Hiking (1km) Tennis (3km) Sailing (15km)
Railway station (11km) Shops (4km) **NOTES:** No pets Minimum 2 night
stay

GUIPRY

♦♦♦ |◎| La Bouetelaie Marie-Hélène PUIG
35480 GUIPRY
☎ 02 99 34 76 12 & 06 14 43 84 80 ▤ 02 99 34 75 34
Guipry 2,5 km. Redon 25 km. On the first floor of this house, there
are two, double bedrooms, and one, four person bedroom, each
with private shower room and wc. There is also a sitting room with
library and TV. Generous breakfasts and evening meals, based on
local produce, can be provided. The house is in a large, wooded,
enclosed parkland with children's play area, a terrace and garden
furniture. 100m from the banks of Vilaine, the house is in Guipry, a
holiday resort with lots of activities in the summer. Also ten
minutes for Loheac village and the automobile museum. The
house is available throughout the year.
PRICES: s €35; d €43; t €52; extra person €9; dinner €15
ON SITE: Children's play area Forest Hiking **NEARBY:** Bathing (45km)
Horse riding (5km) Sea (45km) Swimming pool (3km) Tennis (3km)
Railway station (3km) Shops (3km) **NOTES:** No pets English spoken

♦♦♦ La Crépinière Yves et Christine AUVRAY
29 avenue du Port, 35480 GUIPRY
☎ 02 99 34 24 34 & 06 15 21 72 04 ▤ 02 99 34 24 54
e-mail: yves.auvray@wanadoo.fr
Redon 25 km. A beautiful building with lots of character, this
house lies within 6000m² of wood and flower filled parkland.
There are several spacious and tastefully decorated bedrooms,
looking over the park, in this house. The first bedroom has a suite
of one double bed (which can be converted to twin beds) and a
sitting room with armchairs. There are also two, two people
bedrooms, each with bathrooms or shower rooms. There is a
dining room and sitting room, both with fireplaces. There is also a
terrace with garden furniture. In the Vilaine region, this house is in
the middle of a summer holiday resort. Near Guipry port and in a
village with lots of summer activities: (open air swimming pool,
tennis, footpaths, hiking and horse riding routes and local parties).
Open all year.
PRICES: s €35-€49; d €43-€61; extra person €9 **NEARBY:** Horse riding
(1km) Golf (30km) Sea (45km) Swimming pool (1km) Tennis (1km)
Railway station (3km) Shops (1km) **NOTES:** No pets English spoken

HIREL

♦♦♦ Chambre d'hôtes Marlène et Michel HARDOUIN
10 rue du Domaine, 35120 HIREL
☎ 02 99 48 95 61 & SR : 02 99 78 47 57
e-mail: HardouinM@wanadoo.fr
Saint-Malo 15 km. Mont Saint-Michel 30 km. This rural house is
near the sea (Mont Saint-Michel bay). On the first floor, there are
four, two people bedrooms with private bathrooms. Another
bedroom is suitable for four people and has private bathroom.
There is a lounge area, reading area and sitting room/lounge with
TV. Extra beds may be available on request. Outside there is a
garden and private parking. The rate for four people is 50 euros.
PRICES: s €31; d €35; t €41-€44 **ON SITE:** Tennis **NEARBY:** Horse
riding (4km) Golf (15km) Swimming pool (15km) Stretch of water (25km)
Railway station (8km) **NOTES:** Pets admitted

continued

LA BOUSSAC

♦♦♦ ○ Moulin de Bregain Mary-Anne BRIAND
35120 LA BOUSSAC
☎ 02 99 80 05 29 & SR : 02 99 78 47 57 📠 02 99 80 06 22
There is one bedroom for two people, one bedroom for four
people and one bedroom for three, each with private bathroom, in
this house. There is a lounge/sitting room with board games.
There is also a gym and outside there are ponies. This old
renovated water mill, lies within parkland that has a pond for
fishing and a lovely wood. The area is ideal for walking. Picnics
and meals can be prepared, in the maisonette on the edge of the
lake. Owner's number (mobile): 06.82.18.72.70.
PRICES: s €30; d €38; t €46; extra person €8; dinner €13
ON SITE: Forest Stretch of water Hiking **NEARBY:** Horse riding (6km)
Golf (8km) Tennis (3km) Shops (3km) **NOTES:** Pets admitted English
spoken

LA CHAPELLE-AUX-FILTZMEENS

♦♦♦ Le Chat Fauve Pascal PERRAULT
Le Bourg, 35190 LA CHAPELLE-AUX-FILTZMEENS
☎ 02 99 45 23 81 & SR : 02 99 78 47 57 📠 02 99 45 25 84
e-mail: pascal.perrault@wanadoo.fr
www.perso.wanadoo.fr/kerlan/index.htm
In the heart of Chateaubriand country (Combourg) and less than
half an hour from the Emerald Coast and from Mont-St-Michel,
this beautiful dwelling has retained lots of character from the 19th
century. Situated in the heart of a village, there are two, triple
bedrooms, one double bedroom and one, four person bedroom,
each with private bathrooms. There is a lounge, sitting room, TV
and library and the rate for four people is 53 Euros. There is a
country garden with garden furniture outside. A communal kitchen
can also be used. Maryse and Pascal offer you a warm welcome
and can offer Tai Chi (chuan) classes and sophrologie, in July and
August. The rooms are available throughout the year.
PRICES: s €38; d €38; t €46; extra person €7 **NEARBY:** Bathing (30km)
Horse riding (3km) Forest (15km) Golf (15km) Sea (30km) Swimming
pool (6km) Stretch of water (6km) Tennis (4km) **NOTES:** Pets admitted
English spoken

LA SELLE-EN-COGLES

♦♦♦ La Totinais Jean-Louis AOUSTIN
35460 LA SELLE-EN-COGLES
☎ 02 99 98 64 69 & SR : 02 99 78 47 57
Mont Saint-Michel 35 km. Fougères 15 km. There are two double
bedrooms and one triple bedroom, all with private bathrooms, in
this 18th-century property, within one hectare of wooded and
flower lined, parkland. There is a separate sitting room with fire
place and garden furniture outside. The rate for four people is
€72. The house is available between Easter and the end of
October.
PRICES: s €35; d €43; t €60; extra person €16 **NEARBY:** Horse riding
(15km) Forest (17km) Golf (45km) Sea (45km) Swimming pool (17km)
Stretch of water (4km) Tennis (2km) Railway station (15km) **NOTES:** No
pets English spoken

> Use the atlas at the back of the guide to
> locate your chambre d'hôtes

> Ask the proprietor for directions
> when booking

LE TRONCHET

♦♦♦♦ Le Baillage Catherine SCALART
35540 LE TRONCHET
☎ 02 99 58 17 98 📠 02 99 58 17 97
e-mail: info@lebaillage.com www.lebaillage.com

Saint-Malo 20 km. Dinan 10 km. Mont Saint-Michel 25 km.
Catherine welcomes you to her beautiful home, full of
character, where the bedrooms are large and beautifully
decorated. There are three double bedrooms with TV,
bathrooms and private wcs. There is also a sitting room and a
lounge with an open fireplace. A lovely terrace outside, has
garden furniture. You will enjoy the charm of this property
and the opportunity to relax. You can enjoy golf in Le Tronchet
or the forest in Mesnil. Open all the year on reservation only.
PRICES: s €45-€55; d €49-€60; t €70-€73; extra person €14
ON SITE: Golf **NEARBY:** Bathing (20km) Horse riding (1km) Sea
(20km) Swimming pool (6km) Tennis (1km) Railway station (10km)
NOTES: No pets CC

MARCILLE-RAOUL

♦♦♦ 🐓 ○ Chambre d'hôtes Louis et Annick RAULT
Le Petit Plessix, 35560 MARCILLE-RAOUL
☎ 02 99 73 60 62 & SR : 02 99 78 47 57 📠 02 99 73 60 62

Mont Saint-Michel 30 km. Combourg 10 km. This house offers a
four-person bedroom with private bathroom and a communicating
bedroom with one double bed and twin beds, each with private
bathrooms. Another bedroom has a double bed and a sofa bed for
two, with private bathroom. Two further bedrooms have a double
bed and private bathroom. There is also a lounge/sitting room.
Outside, there is a lawn/garden furniture and barbecue. A kitchen
can also be used. Evening meals by reservation, apart from
Saturdays and Sundays. You can visit the farm or go fishing 3km
away. Restaurant 1km. The rate for four people is 50 euros. Open
all year.
PRICES: s €31; d €35; t €45; extra person €11; dinner €15
ON SITE: Children's play area **NEARBY:** Bathing (40km) Horse riding
(9km) Forest (4km) Golf (18km) Sea (30km) Swimming pool (9km)
Stretch of water (4km) Hiking (12km) Tennis (1km) Sailing (3km) Railway
station (10km) Shops (1km) **NOTES:** Pets admitted

MINIAC-MORVAN

🏳🏳🏳 📷 Estival Tina et Malcolm KINZETT
La Ville Blanche, 35540 MINIAC-MORVAN
☎ 02 96 83 33 30 📠 02 99 88 26 56
e-mail: kinzett@worldonline.fr

Saint-Malo 15 km. Mont-Saint-Michel 40 km. Dinan 8 km. Near the banks of the Rance, Tina and Malcolm welcome you to their stone house, with large flower garden and large grounds, terrace and garden furniture. There is a family suite of two bedrooms (one double bedroom and a twin bedroom), a shower room and wc. There are also three double bedrooms with private bathrooms. Another double bedroom has a private bathroom on the landing. Breakfasts and meals are served in the dining room or on the summer terrace. Tina will cook you meals from homemade and local produce. Open 1 March to 15 November. Other periods are available on request.

PRICES: s €39; d €46-€49; t €84-€90; extra person €15; dinner €14-€18 **NEARBY:** Forest (8km) Golf (8km) Sea (15km) Swimming pool (10km) Stretch of water (8km) Hiking (15km) Tennis (3km) Railway station (4km) Shops (3km) **NOTES:** No pets CC English spoken

MONTAUBAN-DE-BRETAGNE

🏳🏳🏳 📷 Les Camelias Maryvonne BOSI
35360 MONTAUBAN-DE-BRETAGNE
☎ 02 99 06 39 89

Rennes 30 km. Madame Bosi welcome you to her wonderful, home surrounded by large enclosed parkland of old trees. There are four spacious bedrooms which are tastefully decorated, (two double bedrooms and two triple bedrooms), each with private bathroom. There is a sitting room for guest use, a TV and games room with billiard table, chess and board games. Large breakfasts are served from homemade produce (crêpes, tarts, jams and Breton dishes). In the heart of the Brocéliande area, on the crossroads between Rennes and St Brieuc, this is an ideal place for discovering both the north and south of Brittany. You are 8km from the leisure area of Trémelin (watersports). The house is available throughout the year.

PRICES: s €37; d €37-€40; t €52-€56; dinner €17 **NEARBY:** Bathing (60km) Horse riding (8km) Sea (60km) Swimming pool (20km) Tennis (1km) Sailing (8km) **NOTES:** Pets admitted

MONTERFIL

🏳🏳🏳 Le Logis Yann et Fanny TENIN
35160 MONTERFIL
☎ 02 99 07 43 27 & 06 08 48 58 60 📠 02 99 07 43 27

Yann and Fanny welcome you to their home - typical of the area. There is one triple bedroom with a bathroom and wc. There are also two double bedrooms with private wcs. There is a dining room for guest use and large breakfasts are served from organic food and local fruit jams. The house is prettily decorated and fitted out and lies in the middle of an old wooded park. There is a stretch of water on site and walking can also be enjoyed. The Paimpont forest is ten minutes away and you are in the Brocéliande region. The Domain de Tremelin is ten minutes away (watersports, bathing etc.) Open all year.

PRICES: s €30; d €40; t €50; extra person €9 **ON SITE:** Children's play area Forest **NEARBY:** Horse riding (1km) Golf (25km) Swimming pool (9km) Tennis (1km) Railway station (9km) Shops (1km) **NOTES:** No pets English spoken

NOYAL-SUR-VILAINE

🏳🏳🏳 💜 Le Val Froment Michel et Edith LEHUGER
35530 NOYAL-SUR-VILAINE
☎ 02 99 00 66 29 & 06 88 01 05 85 📠 02 99 00 57 37

Rennes 10 km. Vitré 25 km. There are two double bedrooms with shower rooms and wc available in this property. There is also one triple bedroom with a shower room and wc. The lounge/sitting room has a fireplace and kitchen area. There is also a terrace with garden furniture. An extra bed or cot is available on request. In a lovely, green setting, this is a restored home where Edith and Michel welcome you for one night or a holiday. You can learn about their farming life and also enjoy the farm produce served at breakfast. Open all year.

PRICES: s €33; d €38; t €46; extra person €8 **NEARBY:** Bathing (70km) Horse riding (5km) Golf (5km) Sea (70km) Swimming pool (6km) Tennis (1km) Sailing (6km) Railway station (1km) Shops (1km) **NOTES:** No pets English spoken

PAIMPONT

🏳🏳🏳🏳 La Corne de Cerf Annie et Robert MORVAN
Le Cannée, 35380 PAIMPONT
☎ 02 99 07 84 19 & SR : 02 99 78 47 57

There are three prettily decorated bedrooms on the first floor of this house. Two are triples and one is a double bedroom, each with private bathroom. There is a lounge with fireplace and sitting room for guest use. A park with garden furniture and terrace are also attached to the house. The house has lots of character and is situated in the heart of the Brocéliande forest. One of the bedrooms can sleep four people. Relaxing day rooms include sitting room, fireplace, and library. Outside, there is a forest with a number of footpaths and hiking routes. Open all year, except January.

PRICES: s €39; d €46; t €57; extra person €11 **ON SITE:** Forest **NEARBY:** Horse riding (6km) Swimming pool (12km) Stretch of water (2km) Tennis (2km) Sailing (2km) Shops (2km) **NOTES:** No pets

🏳🏳🏳 Manoir de la Ruisselée Christine HERMENIER
35380 PAIMPONT
☎ 02 99 06 85 94 & 06 84 61 50 30

Paimpont 5 km. Plélan-le-Grand 1 km. There are three beautifully decorated, bedrooms in this 18th-century manor house. There is one, two person bedroom with a bathroom and wc. There is also a bedroom for two with shower room and wc. There is a sitting room for guests and a summer garden for large breakfasts. 500m from the Brocéliande forest, the rate for four people is 76Euros. This pretty manor house is situated in a wood and flower adorned park. Christine welcomes you to this remarkable site, covered with forests and countryside, near to Pélan-le-Grand, where there is an open air swimming pool for young children. The rooms are available throughout the year.

PRICES: s €43; d €46; t €69 **NEARBY:** Horse riding (5km) Forest (1km) Sea (60km) Swimming pool (2km) Tennis (2km) Railway station (25km) Shops (1km) **NOTES:** Pets admitted English spoken

💜 Places with this symbol are farmhouses

continued

BRITTANY

PIRE-SUR-SEICHE

✦ ❤ ⍥ Les Epinays René COLLEU
35150 PIRE-SUR-SEICHE
☎ 02 99 00 01 16 & SR : 02 99 78 47 57

There are three double bedrooms and one triple bedroom with private shower, wc and washbasin, fitted out for comfort and charm in this restored 18th century longère, amongst flower adorned grounds. There is a large lounge/sitting room with a fireplace. One of the rooms is accessible to less able people. The house is in a small valley and evening meals are available on request. Telephone number of the owner: 06.12.02.38.22 (mobile). The rooms are available throughout the year.

PRICES: s €26-€35; d €40; t €52; dinner €16 **ON SITE:** Stretch of water **NEARBY:** Horse riding (25km) Golf (12km) Swimming pool (10km) Tennis (6km) Railway station (12km) **NOTES:** No pets

PLEINE-FOUGERES

✦ ❤ La Cotardière Gérard et Isabelle HERVE
La Cotardière, 35610 PLEINE-FOUGERES
☎ 02 99 48 55 92 & SR : 02 99 78 47 57

Mont Saint-Michel 10 km. Pontorson, Dol, Saint-Malo 35 km. This 16th-century manor house lies on a working farm and has one two-person bedroom with a fireplace, one three-person bedroom and one four-person bedroom, with fireplace. There are private bathrooms in each. There is also a sitting room and parkland with animals and kids' games. Around the property, there are fields, woods, a stretch of water for fishing and boating. River 1km. Open all year.

PRICES: s €28; d €36; t €44; extra person €8 **NEARBY:** Horse riding (8km) Forest (10km) Golf (15km) Swimming pool (17km) Tennis (2km) **NOTES:** No pets English spoken

PLEUGUENEUC

✦ Lézard Tranquille Julie de LORGERIL
35720 PLEUGUENEUC
☎ 02 99 69 40 36 & SR : 02 99 78 47 57

Saint-Malo 25. Mont Saint-Michel 40 km. Dinan 15 km. This magnificent property is situated in the grounds of the 17th-century Bourbansais château. There are five bedrooms, each with private bathrooms and wc. There is a TV and lounge/sitting room with fireplace. There is direct access to the chateau, its parkland, zoo. Table tennis and bikes are available.

PRICES: s €37; d €44; t €53 **ON SITE:** Horse riding Forest Hiking **NEARBY:** Golf (10km) Swimming pool (15km) Stretch of water (15km) Tennis (1km) Sailing (15km) Railway station (15km) **NOTES:** Pets admitted

ROZ-LANDRIEUX

✦ Chambre d'hôtes Maryvonne ROGER
La Grande Rivière, 35120 ROZ-LANDRIEUX
☎ 02 99 48 18 25 & SR : 02 99 78 47 57

Saint-Malo 15 km. Mont Saint-Michel 20 km. There are three double bedrooms with private bathrooms in this modern house. There is a lounge and sitting room, a terrace and garden furniture, and a lawn and flowers.

PRICES: s €24; d €30-€33; t €38-€41 **NEARBY:** Bathing (15km) Horse riding (1km) Golf (6km) Sea (8km) Swimming pool (15km) Tennis (1km) Sailing (15km) Railway station (3km) Shops (1km) **NOTES:** Pets admitted

✦ ⍥ Manoir de la Mettrie Marie-Claude JOURDAN
35120 ROZ-LANDRIEUX
☎ 02 99 48 29 21 & SR : 02 99 78 47 57 📠 02 99 48 29 21

Mont Saint-Michel, Saint-Malo & Dinan 20 km. There are three double bedrooms and two bedrooms for three/four people, each with bathroom, in this magnificent 13th and 16th century manor

house. Lounge room, reading room and sitting room with TV. Garden with furniture and children's play area. Open all year.

PRICES: s €34; d €37-€46; t €46; dinner €15 **ON SITE:** Children's play area **NEARBY:** Horse riding (1km) Forest (7km) Golf (4km) Swimming pool (4km) Stretch of water (3km) Tennis (1km) Railway station (3km) Shops (3km) **NOTES:** No pets CC

✦ Petite Rivière Geneviève ROBIDOU
35120 ROZ-LANDRIEUX
☎ 02 99 48 15 64 & SR : 02 99 78 47 57

Mont Saint-Michel 30 km. St-Malo & Dinan 20 km. Dol-de-Bretagne 5 km. This old renovated house is situated amongst green countryside, in the bay of Mont Saint-Michel. There are two double bedrooms and a triple bedroom, each with private bathrooms. There is also a lounge room and a courtyard with lawn, flowers and garden furniture.

PRICES: s €29; d €34; t €42 **NEARBY:** Horse riding (4km) Forest (7km) Golf (6km) Swimming pool (4km) Stretch of water (5km) Tennis (1km) Railway station (7km) Shops (1km) **NOTES:** No pets

ROZ-SUR-COUESNON

✦ Chambre d'hôtes Hélène GILLET
Val Saint-Revert, 35610 ROZ-SUR-COUESNON
☎ 02 99 80 27 85 & SR : 02 99 78 47 57 📠 02 99 80 20 57

Mont Saint-Michel 8 km. Saint-Malo 25 km. There are five bedrooms in this 18th-century house, with a view over Mt-St-Michel. Each bedroom has a private bathroom, and each sleeps two or three people. Two have a panoramic view over Mont-St-Michel. There is a four person bedroom, with a terrace and a panoramic view. Enclosed garden, lounge/sitting room and TV. Cooking is possible on site, fishing can be enjoyed 8 km away and land-sailing 10km away. Four people/€53.

PRICES: s €27; d €35-€38; t €46 **NEARBY:** Tennis (7km) Sailing (10km) Railway station (7km) Shops (1km) **NOTES:** No pets

✦ La Bergerie Jacky PIEL
La Poultière, 35610 ROZ-SUR-COUESNON
☎ 02 99 80 29 68 & SR : 02 99 78 47 57 📠 02 99 80 29 68

This is a large 17th and 18th century property, built in granite.

continued

continued

There are five bedrooms for between two and four people. Each bedroom has a private bathroom. There is a lounge/ sitting room and kitchen area, all for guest use. There is also a lawn and private parking. The house is situated in Mont Saint-Michel bay, between Cancale and Mont-Saint-Michel. The rate for four people is 53 euros.
PRICES: s €35-€39; d €39-€43; t €46-€49; extra person €8
NEARBY: Horse riding (9km) Forest (10km) Golf (13km) Swimming pool (18km) Stretch of water (8km) Tennis (9km) Railway station (8km)
NOTES: Pets admitted English spoken

♥ La Roselière Bernard et Odile MOUBECHE
35610 ROZ-SUR-COUESNON
☎ 02 99 80 22 05 & SR : 02 99 78 47 57   📠 02 99 80 22 05
Mont Saint-Michel 8 km. Saint-Malo 25 km. This is a 16th century house, owned by Odile and Bernard, who produce foie gras paté. There is one bedroom for three people, suitable for guests with disabilities, and with a private bathroom. There are also two three-people bedrooms and two four-people bedrooms, all with private bathrooms. There is a lounge with TV and food can be provided on request. Outside, there is a courtyard and private garden. The rate for four people is 53 euros. The house is on the tourist route, (Pontorson, Saint Malo on the coast) and the river is only 7km away. Open all year, except between 1 October and 1 March.
PRICES: s €30; d €35-€41; t €46   **NEARBY:** Horse riding (2km) Forest (8km) Golf (15km) Swimming pool (20km) Tennis (1km) Railway station (15km) Shops (1km) **NOTES:** Pets admitted

ST-BRIAC-SUR-MER

Le Clos du Pont Martin Daniel COUPLIERE
35800 ST-BRIAC-SUR-MER
☎ 02 99 88 38 07 & SR : 02 99 78 47 57   📠 02 99 88 05 48
e-mail: info@briac.com   www.briac.com

Dinard 8 km. Saint-Malo 12 km. On the ground floor of this building, there is one double bedroom (can be used for four people), with private bathroom, TV and a terrace with sun loungers. On the first floor, there is a double bedroom (can sleep four) with private bathroom, TV and lounge area. A further double bedroom has a TV and private bathroom. All the bedrooms have a mini bar. There is also a lounge with fireplace, a garage and private parking. This house is furnished with antiques and decorated with taste. In the park, there is a canopied area, garden furniture, sun loungers and a barbecue. The house has character and is situated in an enclosed, tree and flower lined park where it is possible to find calm and rest. The property is available throughout the year.
PRICES: d €43-€50; t €58-€65; extra person €15 **ON SITE:** Hiking
NEARBY: Bathing (2km) Horse riding (6km) Golf (3km) Sea (2km) Swimming pool (3km) Stretch of water (2km) Tennis (1km) Sailing (2km) Railway station (12km) Shops (2km) **NOTES:** No pets

Manoir de la Duchée Jean-François STENOU
35800 ST-BRIAC-SUR-MER
☎ 02 99 88 00 02 & SR : 02 99 78 47 57
📠 02 99 88 92 57
http://Pro.wanadoo.fr/manoir.duchée/
Dinard 8 km. Saint-Malo 12 km. This 17th century manor house lies within a wooded and flower lined park. There are two double bedrooms, two suites and a duplex room. Each bedroom has a TV, private bathroom and hair dryer. The sitting room can be used by the guests and contains a library area and art gallery (paintings, sculptures etc.) This is a lovely setting. The building has lots of character and contains antique furniture. Breakfasts are served in the winter garden. The rate for four people is 84 euros.
PRICES: s €46; d €61-€76; t €76; extra person €15 **ON SITE:** Horse riding Hiking **NEARBY:** Golf (3km) Swimming pool (3km) Tennis (1km) Sailing (3km) Railway station (12km) Shops (3km)
NOTES: No pets

ST-COULOMB

La Haute Ville Enoux René THOMAS
35350 ST-COULOMB
☎ 02 99 89 04 79 & SR : 02 99 78 47 57   📠 02 99 89 04 79
This modern house is situated within flower lined, shady grounds, near the sea (900m from the Duguelin cove). On the first floor, there is a double bedroom and two triple bedrooms. There is also a five person bedroom. Each bedroom has a private wc. There is a lounge/ sitting room with TV and a terrace. Saint Malo is within easy reach, as is the rest of the Emerald coast. The beach is within walking distance. The rate for four people is 65 euros, the rate for five people is 77 euros. The property is available between Easter and 15 September.
PRICES: s €35; d €40; t €52 **NEARBY:** Horse riding (3km) Golf (20km) Swimming pool (10km) Stretch of water (3km) Tennis (1km) Sailing (1km) Railway station (10km) Shops (1km) **NOTES:** Pets admitted English spoken

See advert on opposite page

La Marette Emile LIMPALER
La Guimorais, 35350 ST-COULOMB
☎ 02 99 89 00 46 & SR : 02 99 78 47 57
Saint-Malo 9 km. Josephine and Emile welcome you to the their country house, half way between Cancale and Saint Malo. There is one double bedroom and two triple bedrooms, each with private bathrooms, in this house. There is also a sitting room/lounge room and a garden with a lawn. There is private parking and you can reach the beach easily by foot as the property is situated on the Emerald Coast. The house is available throughout the year.
PRICES: s €35; d €40; t €50 **NEARBY:** Bathing (1km) Horse riding (2km) Golf (10km) Sea (1km) Swimming pool (7km) Stretch of water (2km) Tennis (2km) Sailing (1km) Railway station (9km) **NOTES:** No pets

Le Hindre Catherine ROBIN
35350 ST-COULOMB
☎ 02 99 89 08 25 & SR : 02 99 78 47 57   📠 02 99 89 08 25
Saint-Malo 10 km. Cancele 3km. There are four double bedrooms and one bedroom for four people, each with private bathroom, in this old, renovated, house, with large garden. There is a sitting room/lounge with open fireplace and a kitchen area. The rate for four people is 61 euros. Tel. 06.63.48.23.30 (mobile). The property is available throughout the year.
PRICES: s €35; d €42; t €53 **ON SITE:** Horse riding **NEARBY:** Bathing (3km) Golf (15km) Sea (3km) Swimming pool (8km) Stretch of water (3km) Tennis (2km) Sailing (3km) Railway station (8km) Shops (2km)
NOTES: No pets English spoken

STE-MARIE-DE-REDON

♦♦♦ l'Aumonerie Régine ROLLO VAN DE VYVER
Ti Kezeg Ar Sav Eol, 35600 STE-MARIE-DE-REDON
☎ 02 99 72 05 34 & 06 77 62 84 14
Redon 6 km. You will receive a warm welcome to this 18th-century
home, situated in a country park, planted with exotic plants. There is
a family suite of one double bedroom and one twin bedroom, and a
twin bedroom; each bedroom has a shower room and wc. There is
a lounge room with TV and outside there is parkland with a terrace,
veranda, garden chairs, sun loungers and a barbecue, all for guest
use. This is an ideal stopover point; a traditional country home built
upon the remains of the Redon abbey. The house lies on the
borders of the large swamps and is south facing. Open all year.
PRICES: s €34; d €43; t €55; extra person €12 **ON SITE:** Hiking
NEARBY: Bathing (6km) Horse riding (5km) Forest (1km) Golf (30km)
Sea (50km) Swimming pool (5km) Stretch of water (1km) Tennis (5km)
Sailing (8km) Railway station (6km) Shops (4km) **NOTES:** No pets
English spoken

ST-MALO

♦♦♦ ♥ ⭐◯ Goeletterie Quelmer Raymonde TREVILLY
35400 ST-MALO
☎ 02 99 81 92 64 & SR : 02 99 78 47 57 📠 02 99 82 27 01
Saint-Malo 4 km. There are four double bedrooms and one
bedroom for four/five people in this house with lots of character,
on the banks of the Rance. Each bedroom has a private bathroom
and two of the bedrooms have a lovely view. The property is
situated in a calm and relaxing area. There is a sitting room with
open fireplace and TV and a play area. The port is only 4km away
and there are several footpaths on site. The property is available
throughout the year.
PRICES: s €38-€42; d €42-€47; t €58; extra person €11; dinner €11-€16
ON SITE: Children's play area **NEARBY:** Horse riding (3km) Forest
(10km) Swimming pool (4km) Tennis (4km) Railway station (5km) Shops
(2km) **NOTES:** No pets

♦♦♦ Le Gué Joëlle COQUIL
La Petite Ville Mallet, 35400 ST-MALO
☎ 02 99 81 75 62 📠 02 99 81 75 62
Saint-Malo 5 mn. Your hostesses welcome you to their Breton
home, in wooded and flower lined parkland. There is one double
bedroom, one triple bedroom and a family suite of two bedrooms
(one twin bedroom and one double bedroom and one extra single
bed). Each bedroom has a private bathroom and there is a lounge
area with a library. Outside, there is a terrace area with garden
furniture, where the large homemade breakfasts are served. From
Saint-Malo you can reach the Channel Islands and Mont-Saint-
Michel which is less than an hour away. The house is available
throughout the year.
PRICES: s €45; d €51; t €63 **NEARBY:** Horse riding (1km) Forest
(20km) Golf (10km) Sea (2km) Swimming pool (3km) Hiking (1km)
Tennis (3km) Sailing (2km) Railway station (5km) Shops (1km)
NOTES: Pets admitted   *See advert on this page*

♦♦♦ Les Croix Gibouins Maryline BASLE
Parame, 35400 ST-MALO
☎ 02 99 81 12 41 & SR : 02 99 78 47 57 📠 02 99 81 12 41
Situated on the outskirts of Saint Malo, 2km away, there are four
guest bedrooms on the first floor of this 16th century country
home. There is one double bedroom, one bedroom for four
people and two communicating bedrooms for four people. Each
bedroom has a private bathroom. There is also a sitting
room/lounge. Outside, there is a terrace with garden furniture and
private parking. The rate for four people is €61. Open all year.
PRICES: s €34; d €40-€46; t €54 **NEARBY:** Horse riding (4km) Forest
(6km) Golf (10km) Swimming pool (4km) Hiking (4km) Tennis (4km)
Railway station (5km) Shops (2km) **NOTES:** Pets admitted English spoken

ST-MELOIR-DES-ONDES

🐓 **Langavan** Loïc COLLIN
35350 ST-MELOIR-DES-ONDES
☎ 02 99 89 22 92 & SR : 02 99 78 47 57
This is a renovated 18th century barn with a terrace (view of the sea and the Mont Saint-Michel bay). There are two double bedrooms and three bedrooms for four people (one is accessible to guests with disabilities). Each bedroom has a private bathroom. There is also a dining room and terrace area with a view of the sea. Outside there is a garden with a lawn. The rate for four people is 58 euros. Open April to November.
PRICES: s €28; d €39; t €50 **ON SITE:** Children's play area Horse riding Sea Hiking **NEARBY:** Forest (25km) Golf (25km) Swimming pool (12km) Stretch of water (8km) Tennis (5km) Sailing (5km) Railway station (12km) Shops (5km) **NOTES:** Pets admitted

🐓 **Le Parc** Pierre et Sylvie PILORGE
35350 ST-MELOIR-DES-ONDES
☎ 02 99 89 12 39 & SR : 02 99 78 47 57

Sylvie and Pierre welcome you to their farmhouse, four kilometres from the sea. There are four bedrooms available, each with private bathroom. There is also a sitting room with TV. The dining room also has a TV. Extra beds are available on request and there is a play area outside.
PRICES: s €33; d €40; t €49 **ON SITE:** Children's play area
NEARBY: Horse riding (3km) Golf (25km) Sea (4km) Swimming pool (6km) Stretch of water (25km) Tennis (6km) Sailing (6km) Railway station (5km) Shops (3km) **NOTES:** No pets

🐓 **Le Pont Prim** Marie-Joseph BOUTIER
35350 ST-MELOIR-DES-ONDES
☎ 02 99 89 13 05 & SR : 02 99 78 47 57 📠 02 99 89 13 05
This individual house is surrounded by a tree-lined garden. On the ground floor, there are two double bedrooms with private bathrooms. On the first floor, there is a family suite of two separate bedrooms (for four people), each with private bathroom. There is a lounge/ sitting room and kitchen and a play area for children. This is a lovely calm setting, near the Emerald coast. There is independent access to each bedroom and a lawn with garden furniture. The rate for four people is 62 euros. Open all year. Tel. 06.07.75.56.76. (mobile).
PRICES: s €29; d €36 **ON SITE:** Children's play area Horse riding
NEARBY: Bathing (5km) Forest (10km) Golf (10km) Sea (5km) Swimming pool (4km) Stretch of water (5km) Hiking (2km) Tennis (2km) Sailing (5km) Railway station (4km) Shops (2km) **NOTES:** No pets

🐓 **Le Tertre Nande** Madeleine LOCHET
Le Tertre Nande, 35350 ST-MELOIR-DES-ONDES
☎ 02 99 89 10 86 & SR : 02 99 78 47 57
Near the sea (Mont Saint-Michel bay), between St-Malo and Cancale, Madeleine welcomes guests to the 16th-century farmhouse with donkeys and cows. There is one triple bedroom with private bathroom and two double bedrooms with private bathrooms. There is a kitchen area in one bedroom and a sitting

room with open fireplace, and a lounge/sitting room used by guests and the owner. Outside, there is a terrace area and a south-facing garden. The rate for four people is €61.
PRICES: s €30; d €38-€46; t €49; extra person €12 **NEARBY:** Horse riding (1km) Forest (20km) Golf (20km) Swimming pool (5km) Hiking (20km) Tennis (1km) Sailing (5km) Railway station (3km) Shops (3km) **NOTES:** Pets admitted

ST-OUEN-LA-ROUERIE

🐓 **Chambre d'hôtes** Thérèse et François LEGROS
La Morissais, 35460 ST-OUEN-LA-ROUERIE
☎ 02 99 98 38 80 & SR : 02 99 78 47 57
e-mail: morissais@free.fr
Mont Saint-Michel 16 km. Fougères 26 km. Saint-Malo 45 km. This beautiful house has been carefully renovated in stone. There are five bedrooms: four double bedrooms and one for three or four people. Each bedroom has a private bathroom, microwave, fridge and private entrance. The house is surrounded by flowers and there is a lawn with garden furniture. There is a forest with a stretch of water 12km away. Open all year. The rate for four people is €56.
PRICES: s €27-€30; d €32-€35; t €41-€49; extra person €9
NEARBY: Horse riding (12km) Forest (12km) Swimming pool (20km) Hiking (12km) Tennis (8km) **NOTES:** No pets

ST-PERE

🐓 **La Ville Hermessan** LE BIHAN
35430 ST-PERE
☎ 02 99 58 22 02 & SR : 02 99 78 47 57 📠 02 99 58 22 02
e-mail: laville-hermessan@free.fr
Saint-Malo 7 km. Marie-Claude and Marcel offer a warm welcome to their 18th-century home, in its rural and restful setting. There are two, triple bedrooms, a shower room and private wc. There are also two double bedrooms with shower rooms and private wcs. In addition, there is a dining room and lounge. There is central heating and a 1.5 hectare park with large lawns and garden furniture. Private parking is also available. Nearby, there are lots of tourist sites, such as Cancale, Dol-de-Bretagne, Combourg and Mont Saint-Michel. Bikes, golf putting, horse riding and boules nearby. Oven baked bread is provided and the property is available between 15th March and 15th December.
PRICES: s €34-€37; d €38-€43; t €49-€55 **NEARBY:** Horse riding (10km) Forest (5km) Golf (15km) Swimming pool (8km) Stretch of water (5km) Tennis (1km) Sailing (5km) Railway station (10km) Shops (1km) **NOTES:** No pets English spoken

ST-PIERRE-DE-PLESGUEN

🐓 🍴 **Les Petites Chapelles** Nadine DUHAMEL-RAUX
35720 ST-PIERRE-DE-PLESGUEN
☎ 02 99 73 84 34 & SR : 02 99 78 47 57 📠 02 99 73 70 28
Saint-Malo and beaches 25 km. Mont-Saint-Michel 40 km. Dinan 15 km. This beautiful, granite, country house is situated 5km from Saint-Pierre. There are two double bedrooms and one bedroom for four people. Each bedroom has a private bathroom. There is also a large, guest sitting room, with TV, games, fireplace, piano and library. Outside, there is a garden with outdoor furniture. There is also a small pond. Evening meals are available on request.
PRICES: s €28; d €35; t €50; dinner €12 **ON SITE:** Hiking
NEARBY: Bathing (25km) Horse riding (10km) Golf (10km) Sea (25km) Swimming pool (15km) Tennis (2km) Sailing (2km) Railway station (15km) Shops (2km) **NOTES:** Pets admitted English spoken

🐓
Places with this symbol are farmhouses

continued

ST-SULIAC

††† Les Mouettes Isabelle ROUVRAIS
Grande Rue, 35430 ST-SULIAC
☎ 02 99 58 30 41 & SR : 02 99 78 47 57 ▤ 02 99 58 39 41
Saint-Malo 10 km. Dinard 12 km. This 19th-century house with an enclosed garden, is 150m from the port of St-Suliac, (a protected village, classed as the most beautiful village in France). There is one double bedroom with a private bathroom, accessible to disabled. There are also three double bedrooms and a twin bedroom each with bathrooms. A river is two kilometres away and a port is ten minutes away.
PRICES: s €33-€39; d €38-€44 **NEARBY:** Horse riding (15km) Forest (5km) Golf (10km) Sea (1km) Swimming pool (15km) Stretch of water (1km) Tennis (1km) Sailing (1km) Railway station (10km)
NOTES: No pets CC

VEZIN-LE-COQUET

††† 🐓 La Touche Thebault
Marie-Annick & Pierrick LOUAPRE
35132 VEZIN-LE-COQUET
☎ 02 99 60 19 74 & SR : 02 99 78 47 57 ▤ 02 99 60 10 79
Five minutes from Rennes, this farm is owned by Marie-Annick, Pierrick and their children. Their renovated home is beautifully decorated and offers a warm atmosphere. One bedroom for two people and one bedroom for four people on the ground floor. On the first floor, there is a family room with a mezzanine level, sleeping five people. There is also a family suite of two bedrooms for five people and a possible extra bed. Each bedroom has a private bathroom and a kitchen area with fridge and a washing machine. A lounge/sitting room is available for guest use. Calm and relaxation is assured in this home. Reduction in the room rate, after the fourth night. Garden with children's play area. Open all year.
PRICES: s €29; d €35-€40; t €45-€50; extra person €10-€15
ON SITE: Children's play area **NEARBY:** Horse riding (3km) Forest (15km) Golf (10km) Swimming pool (5km) Stretch of water (8km) Tennis (2km) Sailing (8km) Railway station (10km) Shops (2km) **NOTES:** Pets admitted

††† 🐓 Le Rouvray Michel THOUANEL
35132 VEZIN-LE-COQUET
☎ 02 99 64 56 38 & SR : 02 99 78 47 57 ▤ 02 99 64 56 38
There are two double bedrooms, two triple bedrooms and one double bedroom, accessible to the less able in this renovated house near Rennes, in the heart of Brittany. Each bedroom has a private bathroom. There is a sitting room/ lounge room with TV. There is also a lovely garden with flowers and garden furniture. A 10% reduction is available after the fourth night. Tel. 06.84.93.01.38 (mobile). Open all year.
PRICES: s €30; d €35-€40; t €42-€50 **NEARBY:** Horse riding (1km) Forest (25km) Golf (2km) Swimming pool (4km) Tennis (4km) Railway station (3km) Shops (1km) **NOTES:** No pets

AMBON

††† Le Listy d'en Bas Jean & Patricia COELIS
56190 AMBON
☎ 02 97 41 04 33 ▤ 02 97 41 04 33
e-mail: jeancoelis@hotmail.com

Damgan 3 km. Muzillac 5 km. A warm welcome awaits at Jean and Patricia's renovated longhouse 1.5 km from Ambon and 10km from hiking trail 34. The first floor has four double bedrooms, three with en suite bathroom/wc and one with en suite shower-room/wc. The dining room and lounge are reserved for guests. There is a garden with furniture/barbecue and fishing is available in the private lake. Kitchen facilities are provided at an extra cost of five euros per day. Open from May until September
PRICES: s €35-€40; d €40-€44; extra person €10 **NEARBY:** Bathing (3km) Horse riding (7km) Golf (20km) Sea (3km) Fishing (3km) Swimming pool (25km) Hiking (10km) Water sports (3km) Tennis (2km) Railway station (25km) Shops (2km) DAMGAN (3km) **NOTES:** No pets English spoken

AURAY

††† Les Evocelles Paul MUET
26 rue du Pont Neuf, 56400 AURAY
☎ 02 97 56 42 03 ▤ 02 97 50 83 99
Auray 0.5 km. Vannes 15 km. Situated in a quiet area of central Auray and only 10 km from hiking trail 34, this detached house provides three first floor double bedrooms, all with en suite bathroom/wc, central heating and colour TV. There is an enclosed garden with furniture, a private pool and a parking area. Open from 1 June until 15 September.
PRICES: d €36; t €51 **ON SITE:** Swimming pool **NEARBY:** Bathing (12km) Horse riding (10km) Golf (10km) Sea (12km) Fishing (2km) Hiking (10km) Water sports (12km) Tennis (1km) Railway station (1km) Shops (1km) AURAY (1km) **NOTES:** No pets

BAUD

††† Kersommer Alice ROBIC
56150 BAUD
☎ 02 97 51 08 02 ▤ 02 97 51 08 02
Quistinic 15 km. Hennebont 20 km. Madame Robic's detached house of character is situated on a farm close to another house. It offers one room sleeping three people and three double bedrooms, each with en suite shower-room/wc, and one of which is situated on the ground floor. Facilities include a lounge, TV, dining room, washing machine and garden furniture. Open from 1 April until 15 November.
PRICES: s €35; d €41; t €56 **NEARBY:** Bathing (30km) Horse riding (7km) Golf (20km) Sea (30km) Fishing (3km) Swimming pool (2km) Water sports (5km) Tennis (2km) Railway station (25km) Shops (1km) BAUD (1km) **NOTES:** Pets admitted

BELZ

♦♦♦ **Kercadoret** Jean-François ROLLAND
Route de Ninezur, 56550 BELZ
☎ 02 97 55 44 01
Auray 14 km. Erdeven 7 km. Only 50 metres from the Ria d'Etel and 5km from hiking trails 34 and 341, this secluded traditional house has five bedrooms, all with en suite shower-room and wc: one room sleeping three on the ground floor, one single, two double and one room sleeping three on the first floor. Guests may use the lounge with TV, also the garden with furniture and barbecue, table tennis and boules. Optional facilities include use of the kitchen at €4 per day and washing machine at €3 per load. Open all year.
PRICES: s €32; d €40-€43; t €49-€52; extra person €9-€12
NEARBY: Bathing (5km) Horse riding (6km) Golf (5km) Sea (3km) Fishing (4km) Swimming pool (12km) Hiking (5km) Water sports (5km) Tennis (1km) Railway station (10km) Shops (1km) AURAY **NOTES:** No pets English spoken

BERNE

♦♦♦ **Marta** Isabelle HELLO-BREGARDIS
56240 BERNE
☎ 02 97 34 28 58 📠 02 97 34 28 58
Le Faouet 15 km. Plouay 10 km. In a rural setting 30 minutes from the coast, Isabelle's detached house provides the following accommodation: two ground floor rooms sleeping three, and four first floor double rooms, each with en suite shower-room/wc. A hairdryer and a cot are also available. Kitchen has a washing machine, microwave, refrigerator and freezer. Lounge with TV. Guests can relax in the garden that has furniture, swing, table tennis and heated private pool. Fishing and forest walks nearby. Parking. Reductions of up to 20% apply in all months except July and August. Open all year.
PRICES: s €34; d €41; t €52; extra person €9 **ON SITE:** Children's play area Swimming pool **NEARBY:** Bathing (25km) Horse riding (9km) Golf (20km) Sea (25km) Fishing (2km) Hiking (1km) Water sports (10km) Tennis (1km) Railway station (25km) Shops (5km) LORIENT (9km) **NOTES:** No pets English spoken

BRANDERION

♦♦♦ **L'Hermine** Mouche ZETUNIAN
Route d'Hennebont, 56700 BRANDERION
☎ 02 97 32 96 17
Hennebont 5 km. Port-Louis 12 km. Situated one kilometre from Brandérion and surrounded by five acres of woodland, Madame Zetunian's charming house has three double guest rooms, one with en suite shower/wc and two with en suite bathroom/wc. Guests are welcome to relax in the lounge and the garden. Hiking trail 34E is within ten km. Open all year.
PRICES: d €45 **NEARBY:** Bathing (12km) Horse riding (3km) Golf (25km) Sea (12km) Fishing (1km) Swimming pool (15km) Hiking (10km) Water sports (5km) Tennis (1km) Railway station (5km) Shops (1km) HENNEBONT (5km) **NOTES:** No pets English spoken

BRANDIVY

♦♦♦ **Kerdréan** Gilles DEMAIS
Domaine de Kerdréan, 56390 BRANDIVY
☎ 02 97 56 12 50 & 06 08 06 92 81 📠 02 97 56 10 52
e-mail: domaine.de.kerdrean@wanadoo.fr
http://www.gîtes-de-france-morbihan.com/kerdrean
Auray (Port de St-Goustan) 15 km. Bieuzy 7 km. The Demais family's superb wooded estate, incorporating two cottages and a longhouse, provides a peaceful and comfortable retreat. On the first floor there are three grade 3 double rooms (double or twin beds), two with en suite bathroom/wc, one with en suite shower-

room/wc, and one grade 2 double room with en suite shower-room and separate ground floor wc. Facilities include lounge, open fireplace, colour TV, piano, books and a large garden with furniture. Hiking trail 38 is 7km away. Open all year.

PRICES: s €28-€34; d €34-€45; extra person €15 **NEARBY:** Bathing (20km) Horse riding (10km) Golf (20km) Sea (20km) Fishing (2km) Swimming pool (10km) Hiking (7km) Water sports (20km) Tennis (2km) Railway station (15km) Shops (2km) GRAND-CHAMP (9km) **NOTES:** Pets admitted English spoken

CARNAC

♦♦♦ **L'Alcyone** Marie France ALLAIN-BALSAN
Impasse de Beaumer, 56340 CARNAC
☎ 02 97 52 78 11 & 06 68 31 43 17
Carnac 0.6 km. Auray 8 km. Madame Allain-Balsan's detached house is set in secluded, enclosed gardens and lies within one kilometre of hiking trail 341 and only 500 metres from the sea. Local recreational facilities include thalassotherapy at Carnac-Plage and a casino. There are five double bedrooms, all with en suite bathroom/wc, telephone and optional TV. There is also a lounge with TV and a terrace with garden furniture. Reduced rates apply in June and September (49 euros). July/August rate: 53 euros. Low season rate: 43 euros. Open all year.
PRICES: d €46-€53; extra person €15 **NEARBY:** Bathing (1km) Horse riding (1km) Golf (6km) Sea (1km) Fishing (1km) Swimming pool (2km) Hiking (1km) Water sports (1km) Tennis (1km) Railway station (8km) Shops (1km) AURAY **NOTES:** Pets admitted English spoken

♦♦♦ **Le Lac** Evelyne AUDIC
56340 CARNAC
☎ 02 97 55 78 75
Carnac 0.1 km. Vannes 15 km. Situated on the banks of the River Crach, with fine views of the Sound, Madame Audic's detached house provides the following accommodation: one ground floor double room with en suite bathroom/wc (€42) ; three first floor rooms comprising one grade 3 double room (€39), one grade 2 double room (€36) and one family room sleeping up to four people. All rooms have en suite shower-room/wc. Facilities include a comfortable lounge with TV, garden, terrace with furniture, microwave and refrigerator. Hiking trail nearby. Open from 15 March until 30 September.
PRICES: s €34; d €36-€42; t €53; extra person €12 **ON SITE:** Fishing **NEARBY:** Bathing (3km) Horse riding (2km) Golf (10km) Sea (3km) Swimming pool (6km) Hiking (10km) Water sports (3km) Tennis (3km) Railway station (12km) Shops (3km) AURAY (15km) **NOTES:** No pets

♦♦♦ **Ty-Me-Mamm** Anne-Sophie DANIEL
Quelvezin, 56340 CARNAC
☎ 02 97 52 45 87 & 06 89 07 24 57
Carnac 5 km. La Trinité-sur-Mer 5 km. Idyllically situated in the Carnac countryside, Anne-Sophie Daniel's house offers four guest rooms: on the ground floor there is a double bedroom with en suite shower-room/wc and on the first floor there are two double

continued   continued

rooms and one room sleeping three, all with en suite shower-room/wc. A lounge with open fireplace is also available. Breakfast is served in a separate room reserved for guests, which also has a TV. Guests are welcome to use the large garden and furniture. Open all year.

PRICES: s €34; d €41; t €52; extra person €11 **NEARBY:** Bathing (7km) Horse riding (5km) Golf (7km) Sea (7km) Fishing (7km) Swimming pool (10km) Water sports (7km) Tennis (5km) Railway station (10km) Shops (5km) AURAY (10km) **NOTES:** Pets admitted English spoken

CRACH

††† Kergoët Hélène KERVADEC
56950 CRACH
☎ 02 97 55 06 91
Auray 10 km. La Trinité-sur-Mer 5 km. This attractive detached house has five guest rooms with a separate entrance. There are two ground floor double rooms with en suite shower-room/wc and three first floor rooms, two sleeping three people, each with en suite bathroom/wc and one double with en suite shower-room/wc. Kitchen facilities are available at a cost of €2 per day. There is a lounge with TV and a garden with furniture. Open all year.

PRICES: s €27; d €36; t €44 **NEARBY:** Bathing (7km) Horse riding (7km) Golf (10km) Sea (7km) Fishing (1km) Swimming pool (7km) Water sports (7km) Tennis (3km) Railway station (10km) Shops (3km) AURAY (6km) **NOTES:** Pets admitted English spoken

††† Keruzerh-Brigitte Nelly FRAVALO
56950 CRACH
☎ 02 97 56 47 62
Auray 2 km. La Trinité sur-Mer 5 km. Madame Fravalo's sunny, detached house provides the following accommodation on the ground floor: one room sleeping three with its own entrance off the terrace, which has an en suite shower-room/wc, and one double room with TV and en suite bathroom/wc; on the first floor, one double room with TV and en suite bathroom/wc, one double room with TV and en suite shower-room/wc. Kitchen, lounge, library, terrace with garden furniture, garden with barbecue and private parking. Open all year.

PRICES: s €26; d €34; t €41 **NEARBY:** Bathing (10km) Horse riding (8km) Golf (8km) Sea (10km) Fishing (10km) Swimming pool (3km) Water sports (10km) Tennis (6km) Railway station (3km) Shops (2km) AURAY (2km) **NOTES:** Pets admitted

††† Kerzuc Michel & Andrée ELHIAR
56950 CRACH
☎ 02 97 55 03 41
Auray 10 km. La Trinité-sur-Mer 5 km. Monsieur and Madame Elhiar's charming detached house offers three double guest rooms on the first floor, two with en suite shower-room/wc and one grade 2 room with separate bathroom/wc. The dining room, lounge, terrace and a large garden with furniture are at their guests' disposal. Open all year.

PRICES: s €29; d €39; extra person €16 **NEARBY:** Bathing (5km) Horse riding (7km) Golf (10km) Sea (5km) Fishing (2km) Swimming pool (6km) Water sports (5km) Tennis (2km) Railway station (8km) Shops (1km) AURAY **NOTES:** Pets admitted

ELVEN

††† Kergonan Nadine FRENKEL
56250 ELVEN
☎ 02 97 53 37 59 & 06 80 23 57 09 📠 02 97 53 37 59
e-mail: nd1frenkel@aol.com
Elven 5 km. Vannes 14 km. Nadine and Denis welcome guests in one wing of their rural house. Ground floor guest rooms have a separate entrance. There are three double bedrooms, two with en suite bathroom/wc and one with en suite shower-room/wc. On the

first floor, and with its own entrance, there is one family room with en suite shower-room/wc, sleeping up to four people (€69 for four). Dining room with TV. Other facilities include microwave, refrigerator, cot, table tennis table, garden furniture and a porch. Storage is available for bicycles and motorcycles. Open from mid-March until mid-November.

PRICES: s €39; d €44; t €55; extra person €12 **ON SITE:** Children's play area **NEARBY:** Bathing (20km) Horse riding (8km) Golf (20km) Sea (20km) Fishing (1km) Swimming pool (20km) Water sports (20km) Tennis (2km) Railway station (14km) Shops (2km) VANNES (14km) **NOTES:** No pets English spoken

ERDEVEN

††† Manémeur Pascale ARRADON
56410 ERDEVEN
☎ 02 97 55 93 69 & 06 15 66 79 95 📠 02 97 55 93 69
e-mail: parradon@aol.com
Erdeven 4 km. Auray 15 km. Pascale provides accommodation in a charming 17th-century village house close to her own home. There are five double rooms, two on the ground floor and three on the first floor, all with en suite shower-room/wc. All rooms have separate access to the garden. Facilities include use of the dining room, terrace with garden furniture, parking and use of the kitchen (€4). Open all year.

PRICES: s €39; d €45; extra person €13 **NEARBY:** Bathing (4km) Horse riding (4km) Golf (6km) Sea (4km) Fishing (4km) Swimming pool (15km) Water sports (6km) Tennis (4km) Railway station (15km) Shops (1km) ERDEVEN (1km) **NOTES:** No pets English spoken

ETEL

††† ⫟⊙⫟ L'Amirauté Vony PERSON
9, rue Amiral Schwerer, 56410 ETEL
☎ 02 97 55 48 59 & 06 20 70 84 62 📠 02 97 55 47 31
e-mail: mail@amiraute-etel.com www.amiraute-etel.com
A warm welcome awaits at Didier and Vony Person's house, which is situated at the mouth of the Ria. On the first floor there are five guest rooms: three grade 2 double rooms, one with separate shower-room /wc and two with en suite shower-room/wc; two grade 2 rooms sleeping three with separate shower-room/wc. Guests have their own entrance and lounge and are free to use the garden. Breakfast is served in the dining room. Hiking trails 34 and 341 are nearby. Open all year.

PRICES: s €42; d €46; t €60; dinner €17 **ON SITE:** Bathing Sea Fishing **NEARBY:** Horse riding (6km) Golf (7km) Swimming pool (12km) Hiking (5km) Water sports (1km) Tennis (1km) Railway station (18km) ETEL **NOTES:** No pets

GUEHENNO

††† Les Chimères Robert & Florence BLANCHARD
3 rue St-Pierre, 56420 GUEHENNO
☎ 02 97 42 30 14 & 06 67 17 94 92 📠 02 97 42 30 14
e-mail: leschimeres@club-internet.fr
Josselin 10 km. Florence and Robert invite you to their charming house, in Guéhenno, a Breton heritage site. There are four guest rooms, reached via a separate entrance: one twin-bedded room suitable for less able guests; two split-level rooms sleeping three with traditional Breton box beds; and one split-level family room. All have en suite shower room/wc. A cot and other baby requirements are available. Shared use of a kitchen (€3 per day) and a washing machine (€4 per day). Garden has a picnic area, play area and parking. Open all year.

PRICES: s €30; d €38; t €50; extra person €12 **ON SITE:** Children's play area **NEARBY:** Bathing (37km) Horse riding (15km) Golf (18km) Sea (37km) Fishing (5km) Swimming pool (5km) Hiking (6km) Water sports (18km) Tennis (5km) Railway station (25km) JOSSELIN (8km) **NOTES:** Pets admitted English spoken

continued

BRITTANY

GUER

ᴴᴴᴴ ᶦᴼᶦ La Biliais Albert & Christine CHOTARD
56380 GUER
☎ 02 97 75 74 84 📄 02 97 75 81 22

Guer (Vallée de l'Aff) 2 km. Situated only 10km from the Forest of Brocéliande and the megalithic site of Monteneuf, Christine and Albert's imposing house offers five bedrooms, all with en suite shower-room/wc. On the ground floor there is a double room with access for less mobile guests. On the first floor there are two double rooms and one room sleeping three. Other facilities: large garden, verandah, lounge with fireplace, garage, table tennis, outdoor games including boules and palets, board games and a permanent exhibition of old artefacts. Open all year.
PRICES: s €39; d €46; t €58; extra person €13; dinner €15
NEARBY: Bathing (60km) Horse riding (20km) Golf (20km) Sea (60km) Fishing (3km) Swimming pool (5km) Water sports (20km) Tennis (5km) Railway station (40km) Shops (5km) PLOERMEL (20km) **NOTES:** No pets

GUIDEL

ᴴᴴᴴ Ty Horses Robert HAMON
Le Rouho - Route de Locmaria, 56520 GUIDEL
☎ 02 97 65 97 37

Pont-Scorff 10 km. Ploemeur 10 km. Monsieur and Madame Hamon provide accommodation in two houses situated in private parkland at Guidel. An annexe with its own entrance contains four guest rooms for three people, two on the ground floor and two on the first floor, all with en suite shower-room/wc. In the main house there is a double bedroom with separate shower-room/wc nearby. Breakfast is served in the TV room/ verandah. Garden with outdoor furniture. Kitchen facilities €5 per day. Horse riding breaks are also offered. Open all year.
PRICES: s €37; d €43-€46; t €58; extra person €12 **NEARBY:** Bathing (5km) Horse riding (4km) Golf (8km) Sea (5km) Fishing (1km) Swimming pool (10km) Hiking (8km) Water sports (5km) Tennis (4km) Railway station (15km) Shops (4km) LORIENT (6km) **NOTES:** Pets admitted English spoken

INZINZAC-LOCHRIST

ᴴᴴᴴ Le Ty-Mat Penquesten Catherine SPENCE
Penquesten, 56650 INZINZAC-LOCHRIST
☎ 02 97 36 89 26 📄 02 97 36 89 26
e-mail: ty-mat@wanadoo.fr pro.wanadoo.fr/ty-mat/
Hennebont 5 km. Port-Louis 20 km. Madame Spence's 18th/19th-century house is situated in seven and a half acres of parkland in the Blavet valley. It has four first floor guest rooms, two doubles and two rooms sleeping three, all with en suite bathroom/wc. Guests are free to relax in the living room or to watch TV in the lounge. Hiking trail 341 is within easy striking distance. Open all year.
PRICES: d €49; t €64; extra person €15 **NEARBY:** Bathing (22km) Horse riding (5km) Golf (15km) Sea (22km) Fishing (2km) Swimming

pool (15km) Hiking (1km) Water sports (4km) Tennis (12km) Railway station (8km) Shops (4km) HENNEBONT (2km) **NOTES:** No pets English spoken

JOSSELIN

ᴴᴴᴴ La Butte St-Laurent Jean GUYOT
56120 JOSSELIN
☎ 02 97 22 22 09 & 06 14 44 74 63 📄 02 97 73 90 10
e-mail: chez.guyot@wanadoo.fr www.chambres-bretagne.com

Josselin 0.5 km. Ploermel 10 km. The detached house of Jean and Marie Guyot is 500 metres from the town, in shady grounds providing walks and a play area. Panoramic views of the Oust valley and the Château de Josselin. Accommodation comprises one room sleeping three with en suite shower-room/wc, one double room with en suite bathroom/wc, two grade 2 double rooms, one with separate shower-room/wc, one with separate bathroom/wc. There is a reduction of €5 per night on bookings of three nights or more. Open from 1 May until 30 September.
PRICES: s €41-€44; d €46-€49; t €64; extra person €12
ON SITE: Children's play area **NEARBY:** Bathing (45km) Horse riding (5km) Golf (12km) Sea (45km) Fishing (1km) Swimming pool (10km) Water sports (8km) Tennis (1km) Railway station (45km) Shops (1km) JOSSELIN **NOTES:** No pets English spoken

LA CROIX-HELLEAN/JOSSELIN

ᴴᴴᴴ ✆ Les Hortensias Monique & Hervé NICOLAS
La Ville Robert, 56120 LA CROIX-HELLEAN
☎ 02 97 75 64 37 & 06 81 90 05 75 📄 02 97 75 64 37
e-mail: nicolasmo@wanadoo.fr
http://www.geocities.com/h_m_nicolas
Josselin 2.5 km. Forêt de Brocéliande 10 km. In a wing of their lovingly restored old house, Monique and Hervé offer ground floor accommodation comprising one double room with en suite shower-room/wc and kitchen area, which is accessed directly from the terrace, and two first floor rooms sleeping three, each with en suite shower-room/wc and kitchen area. The garden, outdoor furniture, barbecue, table tennis table and lounge/veranda with TV are all available for guests' use. Hiking trail 37 is only 2km from the house. Open all year.
PRICES: d €38; extra person €12 **NEARBY:** Bathing (45km) Horse riding (1km) Golf (11km) Sea (45km) Fishing (3km) Swimming pool (8km) Hiking (2km) Water sports (11km) Tennis (3km) Railway station (45km) Shops (3km) JOSSELIN (2.5km) **NOTES:** Pets admitted English spoken

LA TRINITE-SUR-MER

ᴴᴴᴴ Kervilor Rolland & Sylviane BAGAGLIA
61 rue du Latz, 56470 LA TRINITE-SUR-MER
☎ 02 97 30 18 65 📄 02 97 30 18 65
Port of Trinité-sur-Mer 1.5 km. Situated in peaceful pine forests, this comfortable house allows guests to enjoy both a rural and a coastal setting. There is one ground floor double room with en suite bathroom/wc, lounge and TV and on the first floor there are

continued   *continued*

BRITTANY

two further rooms, one accommodating three people with en suite bathroom/wc and lounge area, and a family room sleeping up to four people with en suite shower-room/wc. Garden furniture and a table tennis table are available in the large wooded garden. Private parking. Open all year.
PRICES: d €58-€61; extra person €15 **NEARBY:** Bathing (2km) Horse riding (3km) Golf (7km) Sea (2km) Fishing (1km) Swimming pool (6km) Water sports (1km) Tennis (2km) Railway station (10km) Shops (1km) CARNAC (5km) **NOTES:** No pets English spoken

LARMOR-PLAGE

▓▓▓ Villa les Camélias Paulette ALLANO
9, rue des Roseaux, 56260 LARMOR-PLAGE
☎ 02 97 65 50 67
Lorient 3 km. Ploemeur 10 km. Situated on the coast road, Madame Allano's large detached house provides one single and five double guest rooms. On the ground floor there is one grade 2 room with separate shower-room/wc and one room with en suite bathroom/wc. On the first floor there are three rooms with en suite shower-room/wc and one grade 2 room with separate shower-room/wc. Lounge with TV, garden, terrace, free use of the kitchen from June to September and private parking. Hiking trail 34 is 5km. Open all year (except 25/09 to 05/10).
PRICES: s €35-€38; d €38-€43 **ON SITE:** Bathing Sea Fishing Water sports **NEARBY:** Horse riding (1km) Golf (5km) Swimming pool (3km) Hiking (5km) Tennis (1km) Railway station (3km) Shops (1km) LORIENT (5km) **NOTES:** No pets

LE COURS

▓▓▓ Le Moulin du Pont de Molac Véronique RESTOIN
Kermelin, 56230 LE COURS
☎ 02 97 67 52 40 & 06 18 92 50 79 ☐ 02 97 67 52 40
Rochefort-en-Terre 15 km. Questembert 10 Km. Véronique extends a warm welcome at her 18th-century mill on the banks of the River Arz, 1.5 km from le cours, a gite in the process of being renovated. On the first floor, and on two levels, there are three double rooms and one room sleeping three, all with en suite shower-room/wc. The owner's longhouse provides one double ground floor bedroom with a separate entrance and en suite bathroom/wc. Breakfast is served in the mill. There is a garden, not enclosed, extending to the river. Open all year.
PRICES: s €38; d €43; t €61; extra person €12 **ON SITE:** Fishing **NEARBY:** Bathing (30km) Horse riding (5km) Golf (25km) Sea (30km) Swimming pool (12km) Water sports (15km) Tennis (10km) Railway station (12km) Shops (2km) QUESTEMBERT (12km) **NOTES:** No pets

LOCMARIAQUER

▓▓▓ La Tykoumad Michelle COUDRAY
2 impasse de la Ruche, 56740 LOCMARIAQUER
☎ 02 97 53 33 16 & 06 72 28 76 18 ☐ 02 97 57 33 16
La Trinité-sur-Mer 7 km. Auray 12 km. La Tykoumad is only five minutes from the port. There are two grade 2 guest rooms on the first floor, one family room sleeping up to four people, and the other a double room, both rooms having separate shower-room/wc. An annexe houses three grade 3 rooms: two double rooms and one sleeping three people, all with en suite shower-room/wc. A lounge overlooking the garden is reserved for guests. Also available: refrigerator, microwave and VCR. Open from 16 March until 6 October and from 26 October until 11 November.
PRICES: d €42-€45; extra person €10-€15 **ON SITE:** Water sports Tennis **NEARBY:** Bathing (1km) Horse riding (12km) Golf (15km) Sea (1km) Fishing (1km) Swimming pool (12km) Railway station (15km) LA TRINITE-SUR-MER (7km) **NOTES:** No pets English spoken

LOCOAL-MENDON

▓▓▓ Kerohan Jean-François LE NY
56550 LOCOAL-MENDON
☎ 02 97 24 65 08
Auray 8 km. Belz 5 km. Located on an old farm in its own grounds, this charming house owned by Monsieur and Madame Ny provides the following accommodation: on the first floor, one family room sleeping up to five people with separate shower-room/wc and one double room with en suite bathroom/wc; on the second floor, one double room with en suite shower-room/wc. Facilities: living room, lounge with fireplace, TV and VCR, refrigerator, and use of the barbecue and garden furniture. Small pets are allowed. Open from 1 April until 15 October.
PRICES: s €30; d €40; extra person €12-€21 **NEARBY:** Bathing (12km) Horse riding (12km) Golf (6km) Sea (6km) Fishing (6km) Swimming pool (12km) Water sports (12km) Tennis (3km) Railway station (8km) Shops (3km) AURAY (8km) **NOTES:** No pets

▓▓▓ 🐓 🍽 Kervihern Gabriel & M.-Thérèse MAHO
56550 LOCOAL-MENDON
☎ 02 97 24 64 09 ☐ 02 97 24 64 09
http://www.gites-de-france-morbihan.com/kervihern

Auray 10 km. Belz 5 km. This 17th-century house situated on farmland close to the Etel Ria is owned by Marie-Thérèse and Gabriel. They have five guest rooms (one on the ground floor), four doubles and one room sleeping three, each with en suite shower-room/wc. A separate family room with en suite shower-room/wc is also available in a renovated barn, providing four beds (single or dual king). Table d'hôte dinners are prepared with fresh farm produce. A TV lounge is reserved for guests. Other facilities: washing machine, garden furniture, bicycles and table tennis. Open all year.
PRICES: d €38-€41; t €53-€56; extra person €14; HB €66-€69; dinner €14 **ON SITE:** Children's play area **NEARBY:** Bathing (12km) Horse riding (10km) Golf (5km) Sea (5km) Fishing (5km) Swimming pool (10km) Hiking (7km) Water sports (12km) Tennis (2km) Railway station (10km) Shops (2km) VANNES (15km) **NOTES:** No pets English spoken

▓▓▓ 🍽 Manescouarn Jean & Edith NICOLAS
56550 LOCOAL-MENDON
☎ 02 97 24 65 18
Auray 11 km. Belz 5 km. Edith and Jean welcome guests to a renovated farm complex adjoining their house. There is one ground floor double bedroom with en suite shower-room/wc and the first floor has three double rooms, each with either en suite shower-room/wc or bathroom/wc and one family room sleeping two to five people with en suite shower-room/wc. Dining room, lounge with open fireplace and TV are reserved for guests, who may also use the garden and garden furniture. Sample Edith and Jean's culinary delights at their table d'hôte dinners. Open all year.
PRICES: s €34; d €41; t €56; extra person €15; dinner €14 **NEARBY:** Bathing (7km) Horse riding (7km) Golf (2km) Sea (7km) Fishing (7km) Swimming pool (11km) Water sports (7km) Tennis (3km) Railway station (11km) Shops (3km) AURAY (11km) **NOTES:** Pets admitted

MALANSAC

⁂ Manoir de St-Fiacre Roger & Denise GOAPPER
56220 MALANSAC
☎ 02 97 43 43 90 & 06 07 55 64 89   📠 02 97 43 43 40
La Gacilly 15 Km. Monsieur and Madame Goapper provide
accommodation in one wing of their 17th-century manor house,
which is surrounded by landscaped, wooded parkland. On the
ground floor is one double room with en suite bathroom/wc, on
the second one family room with en suite bathroom/wc and
separate shower-room/wc, on the third floor there is a room
sleeping three with en suite bathroom/wc. An annexe contains two
bedrooms, each sleeping three, one on the ground floor with
lounge and en suite bathroom/wc and another with identical
facilities on the first floor, accessed via an exterior staircase. Living
room/TV and garden with furniture. Open all year.
PRICES: d €61-€77; extra person €16 **NEARBY:** Bathing (25km) Horse
riding (5km) Golf (5km) Sea (25km) Fishing (1km) Swimming pool
(25km) Water sports (1km) Tennis (1km) Railway station (4km) Shops
(2km) ROCHEFORT EN TERRE (1.5km) **NOTES:** No pets

See advert on opposite page

MELRAND

⁂ ⏏ Quénetevec Marie-Thérèse CHAUVEL
56310 MELRAND
☎ 02 97 27 72 82 & 06 83 75 08 52   📠 02 97 27 72 82
www.gites-de-france-morbihan.com/quenetevec
Quistinic 6 km." This typical Breton house is situated in landscaped
grounds traversed by a trout stream. On the first floor Madame
Chauvel provides one family room with en suite shower-room/wc
and one double room with en suite bathroom/wc. Another double
room with en suite shower-room/wc is on the ground floor.
Garden furniture, toboggan, volleyball net, table tennis table and
fitness equipment are available, as well as a swimming pool.
Hiking trail 341 10km. Open from 15 March until 2 November.
PRICES: s €34-€38; d €41-€46; t €56; extra person €15; HB €37; dinner
€16 **ON SITE:** Children's play area Swimming pool **NEARBY:** Bathing
(45km) Horse riding (2km) Golf (4km) Sea (45km) Fishing (5km) Hiking
(10km) Water sports (5km) Tennis (5km) Railway station (30km) Shops
(5km) PONTIVY (10km) **NOTES:** No pets

MENEAC

⁂ Manoir de Bellouan Emilienne BELLAMY
56490 MENEAC
☎ 02 97 93 35 57   📠 02 97 93 35 57
Alfred and Emilienne welcome guests to this 17th-century manor
house set in five acres of natural woodland. On the first floor there
is one traditionally furnished double guest room, two further
double rooms (one at €38, the other at €46), and one room
sleeping three (€46). All rooms have en suite shower room and
wc. Living room and lounge. Independent kitchen facilities are
available at €4.5 per day. Open from Easter until early November.
PRICES: d €38-€61; extra person €15 **NEARBY:** Bathing (65km) Horse
riding (20km) Golf (25km) Sea (65km) Fishing (1km) Swimming pool
(10km) Hiking (25km) Water sports (20km) Tennis (2km) Railway station
(60km) Shops (1km) PLOERMEL (20km) **NOTES:** Pets admitted

MESLAN

⁂ Roscalet Marie-France JAMBOU
Roscalet, 56320 MESLAN
☎ 02 97 34 24 13   📠 02 97 34 24 13
http://www.gites-de-france-morbihan.com/roscalet
Le Faouet 10 km. Plouay 10 km. Madame Jambou offers complete
peace and quiet in a traditional house reserved entirely for guests,
which has its own private garden with furniture. There are five
bedrooms, each with en suite shower-room/wc: on the ground

floor there is one twin-bedded room, one room sleeping three and
a lounge with open fireplace. On the first floor there are three
double bedrooms and a mezzanine with books/TV. Hiking trails
34E and 38 are within five km. Open from 1 April until 31 October.

PRICES: s €35; d €40-€43; t €56; extra person €11 **NEARBY:** Bathing
(30km) Horse riding (15km) Golf (20km) Sea (30km) Fishing (1km)
Swimming pool (8km) Hiking (5km) Water sports (12km) Tennis (4km)
Railway station (15km) Shops (4km) LORIENT (10km)
NOTES: No pets

MOHON

⁂ ⏏ La Charbonnière Marylène FOUR
Bodegat, 56490 MOHON
☎ 02 97 93 96 80   📠 02 97 93 97 41
Josselin 10 km. This house of character is situated only 500 metres
from the Bronze Age town of Mohon and close to the Lanouée
Forest. Hiking trail 37 is within 10km. Madame Four provides four
double guest rooms, one on the ground floor and three on the
first floor, all with en suite shower-room/wc. There is a living room
with open fireplace, a TV lounge and a large garden with furniture.
Pony-trekking is available at €15 for the first hour and thereafter
€10 per hour. Open all year.
PRICES: s €28; d €37; dinner €13 **ON SITE:** Horse riding Fishing
NEARBY: Bathing (50km) Golf (17km) Sea (50km) Swimming pool
(15km) Hiking (10km) Water sports (17km) Tennis (1km) Railway station
(17km) Shops (1.5km) JOSSELIN (10km) **NOTES:** Pets admitted English
spoken

NIVILLAC

⁂ ⏏ Au Fil de l'Eau Michel & Maryse ARNOU
Port de Folleux, 56130 NIVILLAC
☎ 02 99 90 96 61 & SR : 02 97 56 48 12   📠 02 99 90 96 61
www.gites-de-france-morbihan.com/folleux/
La Roche-Bernard 7 km. La Baule 30 mn. Situated in a landscaped
garden on the banks of the River Vilaine, this old stone house is
run by Maryse and Michel who provide accommodation accessed
via a private entrance. Two first floor double rooms and one
ground floor room sleeping three. All rooms have en suite shower-
room/wc. Verandah, garden furniture, loungers and barbecue.
River trips in the owners' boat can be arranged and the nearby
restaurant provides a free ferry service. Local attractions include a
marina and La Roche Bernard. Table d'hôte dinners may be
booked four nights a week. Open Easter to early November.
PRICES: s €40-€43; d €43-€45; t €60; dinner €15 **ON SITE:** Fishing
Water sports **NEARBY:** Bathing (25km) Horse riding (5km) Golf (15km)
Sea (25km) Swimming pool (5km) Hiking (6km) Tennis (5km) Railway
station (30km) Shops (5km) LA ROCHE-BERNARD (7km) **NOTES:** No
pets English spoken

> ⏏ Places with this symbol serve table d'hôtes
> evening meals - remember to book in advance

continued

♯♯♯ ❦ |◯| Le Moulin du Couedic Joseph CHESNIN
St-Cry, 56130 NIVILLAC
☎ 02 99 90 62 47 ▯ 02 99 90 62 47
La Roche-Bernard 12 km. Barrage d'Arzal 15 km. Marie-Pierre and Joseph Chesnin provide accommodation on their farm in four bedrooms, which have a private entrance. One double room is situated on the ground floor and on the first floor there are two double rooms and one room sleeping three. All rooms have en suite shower-room/wc. Lounge with open fireplace, colour TV and VCR. Garden furniture and boules. Rates are dependent on the number of nights booked. Dinner is available as an extra every evening except Sunday. Open all year except Christmas and New Year.
PRICES: d €35-€37; t €37-€41; extra person €13; HB €65-€69; dinner €14
ON SITE: Children's play area **NEARBY:** Bathing (30km) Horse riding (9km) Golf (15km) Sea (30km) Fishing (2km) Swimming pool (9km) Hiking (11km) Water sports (12km) Tennis (8km) Railway station (22km) Shops (8km) LA ROCHE-BERNARD (12km)
NOTES: No pets

PLOEMEL

♯♯♯♯ Kerimel Babeth & Pierre MALHERBE
56400 PLOEMEL
☎ 02 97 56 84 72 & 06 07 58 63 20 ▯ 02 97 56 84 72
e-mail: elisabeth.malherbe@wanadoo.fr
Auray 6 km. Erdeven 8 km. This complex of 17th-century cottages is 7km from the coast and 2km from St. Laurent golf course. On the first floor, Babeth and Pierre have four guest rooms, two doubles and two sleeping three people. Bed sizes range from single to dual king. All rooms have en suite shower-room/wc, a hairdryer and a kettle. There is a guest lounge with TV/VCR, books and board games. A refrigerator is also available. Guests are free to use the garden furniture. Open all year.
PRICES: ; d €60-€68; t €88; extra person €20 **NEARBY:** Bathing (7km) Horse riding (3km) Golf (2km) Sea (7km) Fishing (7km) Swimming pool (7km) Hiking (3km) Water sports (7km) Tennis (1km) Railway station (6km) Shops (1km) AURAY (6km)
NOTES: No pets English spoken

PLOEMEUR

♯♯♯ Chapelle Sainte Anne Christiane LE LORREC
3 bis rue de St-Deron, 56270 PLOEMEUR
☎ 02 97 86 10 25 & 06 72 70 76 48
e-mail: chrislelorrec@aol.com
http://www.gites-de-france-morbihan.com/deron
Fort Bloqué Ploemeur 4 km. Guidel 8 km Only 4km from the beaches and close to the aquatic leisure centre, Océanis, this is also an ideal area for walking. On the first floor of the main house there is a room sleeping three with en suite shower-room/wc. An annexe provides one ground floor double room with en suite shower-room/wc, and one first floor double room with en suite bathroom/wc. Books, TV, garden with furniture and a barbecue. There is a 5% reduction on bookings of five consecutive days and over. Open all year except for certain dates in February.
PRICES: s €35; d €41; t €53 **NEARBY:** Bathing (4km) Horse riding (3km) Golf (1km) Sea (4km) Fishing (4km) Swimming pool (2km) Hiking (4km) Water sports (8km) Tennis (1km) Railway station (7km) LORIENT (7km) **NOTES:** No pets

> For further information on these and
> other chambres d'hôtes, consult
> the Gîtes de France website
> *www.gites-de-france.fr*

Mr et Mme GOAPPER – Bed & Breakfast

"Manoir de Saint-Fiacre"

56 220 MALANSAC (Rochefort-en-Terre)
Tel: 02.97.43.43.90 – Fax: 02.97.43.43.40

Built in the XVII century and situated in its own grounds of 6500 m², the manor offers five bedrooms with varied facilities. Facilities include one ground floor double bedroom en-suite, a family en-suite room for four people with its own separate bathroom and an en-suite bedroom for three people with its own access via an external staircase and features a mezzanine floor. Guest lounge is available with television and games. A large patio offers good views and access to the extensive garden.
4 km from Rochefort-en-Terre, city of character.

PLOUGOUMELEN

♯♯♯ Cahire Arsène TROCHERY
56400 PLOUGOUMELEN
☎ 02 97 57 91 18
e-mail: trochery@leschaumieres.com
http://www.leschaumieres.com
Auray 5 km. Vannes 10 km. Located within a conservation area, Monsieur Trochery's group of 17th-century cottages offers four spacious, traditionally furnished rooms each with a separate entrance, lounge area and en suite shower-room/wc. The ground floor and the first floor each provide one double guest room and one room sleeping three. A garden with furniture and a terrace are available for guests. Open from February until December (except 5-15 March).
PRICES: d €44-€58; extra person €11-€15 **NEARBY:** Bathing (10km) Horse riding (1km) Golf (3km) Sea (10km) Fishing (10km) Swimming pool (6km) Hiking (3km) Water sports (6km) Tennis (1km) Railway station (6km) Shops (3km) AURAY (6km) **NOTES:** No pets

PLOUHARNEL

♯♯♯ Kercroc Serge ROUSSEAU
56340 PLOUHARNEL
☎ 02 97 52 32 40 & 06 86 04 72 51
Auray 10 km. Carnac 5 km. Monsieur Rousseau's detached house in a quiet village cul-de-sac 0.8km from Plouharnel has one ground floor double bedroom with en suite bathroom/wc and two first floor guest rooms: one double with en suite shower-room/wc and one family room sleeping up to five people with separate bathroom/wc. Dining room, lounge area with open fireplace and TV, terrace and enclosed garden. Open all year.
PRICES: s €32; d €37-€40; t €49; extra person €8-€12 **ON SITE:** Sea Fishing **NEARBY:** Bathing (2km) Horse riding (5km) Golf (7km) Swimming pool (12km) Water sports (2km) Tennis (1km) Railway station (12km) Shops (1km) CARNAC (5km) **NOTES:** No pets English spoken

♦♦♦ Kerzivienne Gilbert LE BARON

Kerzivienne, 56340 PLOUHARNEL
☎ 02 97 52 31 44 & 06 78 54 72 47
Auray 12 km. Carnac 5 km. Monsieur and Madame Le Baron provide accommodation for up to seven people in their detached house situated between Carnac and Quiberon. On the first floor there are two grade 3 double rooms with en suite shower-room/wc and sea views, also one grade 2 room sleeping three with a separate shower-room/wc. TV lounge, garden with garden furniture, barbecue and table tennis table. Hiking trails 34 and 341 are within 1.5 km. Open from March until November.
PRICES: ; d €39-€41; t €49; extra person €11　**NEARBY:** Bathing (2km) Horse riding (3km) Golf (6km) Sea (1km) Fishing (2km) Swimming pool (12km) Hiking (2km) Water sports (3km) Tennis (1km) Railway station (12km) Shops (1km) CARNAC (5km)　**NOTES:** No pets English-spoken

PLUMELIN

♦♦♦ Gostrevel Dominique CAPPY

Gostrevel, 56500 PLUMELIN
☎ 02 97 44 20 92 & 06 70 43 97 54
Baud 10 km. This pleasant detached house situated 4km from Plumelin and 7km from Locminé provides the following first floor accommodation : one family room sleeping up to four people and one room for three, both with en suite shower-room/wc; one grade 2 double room with separate shower-room/wc. Situated in the heart of the Morbihan region, Locminé is the ideal base from which to explore the many tourist, leisure and cultural sites nearby. Hiking trail 341 is 16 km away. Open all year.
PRICES: s €37; d €45; t €59; extra person €14　**NEARBY:** Bathing (45km) Horse riding (10km) Golf (25km) Sea (45km) Fishing (12km) Swimming pool (7km) Hiking (16km) Water sports (35km) Tennis (3km) Railway station (35km) Shops (4km) LOCMINE (7km)　**NOTES:** No pets

PLUMERGAT

♦♦♦ Kerthomas Joseph JACQ

56400 PLUMERGAT
☎ 02 97 57 70 11 　🖷 02 97 57 70 11
e-mail: marie-claire-jacq@wanadoo.fr
www.gites-de-france-morbihan.com/kerthomas
Auray 10 km. Vannes 12 km. Monsieur and Madame Jacq provide accommodation for up to seven people in their quiet, detached house 2km from Ste.- Anne-d'Auray. Of the three guest rooms situated on the first floor, one double and one room sleeping three are grade 3 with en suite shower-room/wc and one is a grade 2 double room with separate shower-room/wc. Other facilities include a living room/lounge with TV, a kitchen and an enclosed 3.5 hectare garden with furniture and a barbecue. Hiking trail 38 is within 10km. Open all year.
PRICES: s €30; d €38; t €50; extra person €12　**NEARBY:** Bathing (15km) Horse riding (4km) Golf (15km) Sea (15km) Fishing (10km) Swimming pool (10km) Hiking (10km) Water sports (15km) Tennis (2km) Railway station (10km) Shops (2km) AURAY (10km)　**NOTES:** Pets admitted

PLUVIGNER

♦♦♦ ⭐ Chaumière de Kerréo Gérard & Nelly GREVES

56330 PLUVIGNER
☎ 02 97 50 90 48 & SR : 02 97 56 48 12 　🖷 02 97 50 90 69
www.gites-de-france-morbihan.com/kerreo
Auray 15 km. Vannes 20 km. Nelly and Gérard welcome guests to their 17th-century cottage, which has five double guest rooms, four with en suite shower-room/wc and one with en suite bathroom/wc. Guests will appreciate the peaceful, rural location, the authentic interior of the cottage, and the landscaped gardens. However, the highlight of the visit will undoubtedly be the meals, prepared by a former cookery teacher. Open all year. .

PRICES: s €38-€41; d €46-€50; extra person €11; dinner €17
NEARBY: Bathing (20km) Horse riding (6km) Golf (15km) Sea (20km) Fishing (10km) Swimming pool (20km) Water sports (20km) Tennis (7km) Railway station (16km) Shops (7km) AURAY (20km)　**NOTES:** No pets English spoken

♦♦♦ Kerdavid Duchentil Marie-Claire COLLET

56330 PLUVIGNER ☎ 02 97 56 00 59 & 06 08 57 05 00
www.gites-de-france-morbihan.com/kerdavid

Auray 15 km. Vannes 25 km. This traditional longhouse enjoys a rural location close to a gîte in large, shady grounds. Madame Collet provides four ground floor double bedrooms and one family room, each with private entrance and en suite shower-room/wc. A kitchen, lounge, living room, TV, garden with furniture and barbecue are at her guests' disposal and there is a private lake for fishing. Numerous historic sites, the Gulf of Morbihan, beaches and forests are all within easy reach. Open all year.
PRICES: s €35; d €41; t €56　**NEARBY:** Bathing (25km) Horse riding (3km) Golf (13km) Sea (25km) Fishing (3km) Swimming pool (13km) Hiking (3km) Water sports (18km) Tennis (13km) Railway station (15km) Shops (5km) PLUVIGNER (5km)　**NOTES:** Pets admitted

PONTIVY/NEULLIAC

♦♦♦ La Bretonnière Adèle MILOUX

Bel-Air, 56300 NEULLIAC/PONTIVY
☎ 02 97 39 62 48 & 06 86 65 86 04 　🖷 02 97 39 62 48
www.gites-de-france-morbihan.com/bretonniere
Pontivy 5 km. Loudeac 20 km. In her detached house at Neuillac, Madame Miloux offers the following accommodation: one grade 3 double room with en suite bathroom/wc, one grade 2 double room with separate bathroom/wc one further double room with en suite shower-room/wc and one grade 3 room sleeping three with en suite shower-room/wc. Facilities include a lounge with open fireplace, a 3 hectare enclosed garden and a set of boules. Hiking trail 37 is only 3km away. Open all year. Booking essential.
PRICES: ; d €37; t €47; extra person €11　**NEARBY:** Bathing (50km) Horse riding (2km) Golf (3km) Sea (50km) Fishing (3km) Swimming pool (3km) Hiking (3km) Water sports (10km) Tennis (3km) Railway station (50km) Shops (3km) PONTIVY (5km)　**NOTES:** No pets English spoken

continued

BRITTANY

QUEVEN

♦♦♦ Le Mané Marie-Louise KERMABON
Route de Kerdual, 56530 QUEVEN ☎ 02 97 84 83 20
This verdant, two-acre setting is close to Lorient and within easy reach of beaches, Val Quéven golf course and Pont-Scorff zoo. On the first floor Madame Kermabon provides a family suite with one double bedroom and one room sleeping two children with separate bathroom/wc. There is also one grade 2 double room with separate shower-room/wc. On the ground floor there is a double room with en suite bathroom/wc. TV lounge, terrace with garden furniture and ample parking. Hiking trails 34E and 38E are 1km away. Open all year.
PRICES: s €34; d €37-€40; t €52; extra person €12 **NEARBY:** Bathing (6km) Horse riding (3km) Golf (3km) Sea (6km) Fishing (3km) Swimming pool (1km) Hiking (1km) Water sports (3km) Tennis (2km) Railway station (2km) Shops (1km) LORIENT (2km) **NOTES:** No pets English spoken

RIANTEC

♦♦♦ Kervassal WATINE
56670 RIANTEC ☎ 02 97 33 58 66 📠 02 97 33 49 47
e-mail: gonzague.watine@wanadoo.fr
Port-Louis (Citadelle) 5 km. Plouhinec (Entre Etel et l'océan) 5 km.
In a rural village setting and close to beaches, Maya Watine offers the following accommodation in her 17th-century cottage: three spacious first floor rooms, all with en suite shower-room/wc, one double room and two rooms for three people. On the ground floor there is a lounge reserved for guests and a TV is also available. Garden furniture is provided, so that visitors can enjoy the abundance of flowers in the large garden. Open March to October.
PRICES: ; d €49; t €64 **NEARBY:** Bathing (4km) Horse riding (3km) Golf (18km) Sea (4km) Fishing (2km) Swimming pool (3km) Hiking (10km) Water sports (4km) Tennis (2km) Railway station (12km) Shops (2km) PORT-LOUIS (4km) **NOTES:** No pets English spoken

RIEUX

♦♦♦ La Maison Mavette Joël DRAPKIN
56350 RIEUX
☎ 02 99 91 95 69 & 06 08 35 63 07 📠 02 99 91 95 69
e-mail: joël.drapkin@wanadoo.fr
Redon 10 km. La Gacilly 20 km. Joël Drapkin's renovated coaching inn, situated 3km from Rieux and overlooking the River Vilaine, offers one double room with en suite shower-room/wc, one grade 2 double room with separate bathroom/wc and one room sleeping three people with en suite shower-room/wc. Guests may use the kitchen at an extra cost of €10 per day. Other facilities: guest lounge with books and billiard table, large garden with furniture and a barbecue. Hiking trail 39 is 0.5km away. Open all year. Booking is essential out of season.
PRICES: s €38; d €40-€48; t €58; extra person €15 **NEARBY:** Bathing (35km) Horse riding (5km) Golf (8km) Sea (35km) Fishing (4km) Swimming pool (6km) Hiking (1km) Water sports (4km) Tennis (5km) Railway station (8km) Shops (3km) REDON (7km) **NOTES:** No pets English spoken

ROCHEFORT-EN-TERRE

♦♦♦ Chambre d'hôtes Yvon LE BIHAN
Rue Candre, 56220 ROCHEFORT-EN-TERRE
☎ 02 97 43 35 44 📠 02 97 43 30 79
In the heart of Rochefort en Terre, Monsieur and Madame Le Bihan welcome guests to their spacious house, part of which has been converted into a helioscopic museum. There are five first floor guest rooms with a private entrance, comprising two double rooms with views over the valley and three split-level rooms, each accommodating three people. All rooms have en suite

bathroom/wc and two breakfast rooms are provided. Local attractions include a lake with water sports. Open all year.
PRICES: s €40; d €46-€61; t €76; extra person €15 **ON SITE:** Hiking **NEARBY:** Bathing (30km) Horse riding (2km) Golf (7km) Sea (30km) Fishing (2km) Swimming pool (10km) Water sports (2km) Tennis (2km) Railway station (10km) ROCHEFORT-EN-TERRE **NOTES:** No pets English spoken

RUFFIAC

♦♦♦ 🐓 Ferme de Rangera Gilbert COUEDELO
Rangera, 56140 RUFFIAC
☎ 02 97 93 72 18 📠 02 97 93 72 18

Malestroit 6 km. La Gacilly 15 km. In their converted holiday farmhouse with adjoining gîte, Monsieur and Madame Couedelo offer one ground floor double guest room and two first floor rooms sleeping three, all with en suite shower-room/wc. Facilities include a living room/TV lounge, a microwave and a garden with furniture, barbecue and boules. Accommodation comprising one double room and one room for three people, both with en suite shower-room/wc is also available in the Conduelos' own house. Hiking trail 347 8km. Open from 15 February until 15 November.
PRICES: s €30; d €37; t €46; extra person €9 **NEARBY:** Bathing (40km) Horse riding (6km) Golf (25km) Sea (40km) Fishing (3km) Swimming pool (8km) Hiking (8km) Water sports (18km) Tennis (2km) Railway station (30km) Shops (2km) MALESTROIT (6km) **NOTES:** No pets

SARZEAU

♦♦♦ Kerblay Jacques COLIN
Route de St-Jacques, 56370 SARZEAU
☎ 02 97 48 05 51
Sarzeau 1.5 km. Vannes 22 km. Monsieur Colin's detached house offers five spacious double rooms with en suite shower-room/wc on the first floor and on the ground floor, one double room with en suite bathroom/wc. Breakfast is served in the huge living room, which has an open fireplace. Guests are at liberty to use all garden facilities. Parking is available. Open from June until September, and during the French school holidays.
PRICES: s €42; d €46-€50; extra person €10 **NEARBY:** Bathing (2km) Horse riding (5km) Golf (5km) Sea (2km) Fishing (2km) Swimming pool (22km) Water sports (2km) Tennis (2km) Railway station (22km) Shops (2km) SARZEAU (2km) **NOTES:** No pets English spoken

ST-JEAN-BREVELAY

♦♦♦ Kermarquer Etienne & Annie PICAUD
Route de Locminé, 56660 ST-JEAN-BREVELAY
☎ 02 97 60 31 61
Locmine 10 km. Vannes 30 km. Monsieur and Madame Picaud provide bed and breakfast accommodation adjoining a small inn, comprising two ground floor double rooms with a private entrance and each with en suite shower-room/wc. A family room sleeping up to four people is also available in an annexe. There is a garden

continued   *continued*

with a terrace and furniture. Meals at the inn can be provided on request. Hiking trail 38 is within 1.5km. Open all year.
PRICES: s €34; d €37; t €55; extra person €12 **ON SITE:** Fishing
NEARBY: Bathing (30km) Horse riding (15km) Golf (50km) Sea (30km) Swimming pool (10km) Hiking (2km) Water sports (30km) Tennis (2km) Railway station (20km) Shops (2km) LOCMINE (10km) **NOTES:** Pets admitted English spoken

ST-PHILIBERT

♦♦♦ KERNIVILIT Christine GOUZER
17 route de Quéhan, 56470 ST-PHILIBERT
☎ 02 97 55 17 78 📠 02 97 30 04 11
e-mail: fgouzer@club-internet.fr
http://www.gites-de-france-morbihan.com/kerivaud/
La Trinité-sur-Mer (Port) 2 km. Auray (Port de St-Goustan) 8 km.
Madame Gouzer's oyster farm affords panoramic views of the River Crach. There are three guest rooms on the ground floor, accessed via a separate entrance, each having en suite shower-room/wc. There is one double room, one room for three with kitchenette and one family room with kitchenette accommodating up to four people. A lounge area, a garden with terrace and furniture are at guests' disposal. Open all year.
PRICES: s €40; d €46-€55; t €55-€63; extra person €11 **ON SITE:** Sea Fishing Water sports **NEARBY:** Bathing (2km) Horse riding (6km) Golf (7km) Swimming pool (7km) Tennis (2km) Railway station (8km) Shops (2km) LA TRINITE-SUR-MER (2km) **NOTES:** Pets admitted English spoken

SULNIAC

♦♦♦ ⚫|O| Quiban Arlette SEIBERT-SANDT
56250 SULNIAC
☎ 02 97 53 29 05 & 06 85 38 49 75 📠 02 97 53 29 05
e-mail: daniel-flahaut@wanadoo.fr
www.gites-de-france-morbihan.com/quiban
Questembert 5 km. Vannes 16 km. Arlette and Daniel provide bed and breakfast accommodation on the ground floor of their charming house. There are three double rooms, one with en suite bathroom/wc and two with en suite shower-room/wc. Breakfast is served on the verandah and guests are free to enjoy the abundance of flowers and trees in the attractive enclosed garden, where furniture is provided. Evening meals are available on request. Open all year.
PRICES: s €37; d €45; extra person €13; dinner €15 **NEARBY:** Bathing (20km) Horse riding (2km) Golf (25km) Sea (20km) Fishing (5km) Swimming pool (8km) Hiking (20km) Water sports (20km) Tennis (2km) Railway station (16km) Shops (2km) VANNES (16km) **NOTES:** No pets English spoken

SURZUR

♦♦♦ Le Petit Kerbocen Claude GAUGENDAU
56450 SURZUR
☎ 02 97 42 00 75 & 06 82 06 58 55 📠 02 97 42 00 75
Sarzeau 10 km. Vannes 15 km. In a restored annexe of their house on a working farm, Monsieur and Madame Gaugendau offer accommodation in four double rooms and two rooms sleeping three, all with en suite shower-room/wc. Facilities include a TV lounge, a cot, children's games and free use of the kitchen. Hiking trail 34 is 6km away. Open all year.
PRICES: s €30-€34; d €37-€41; t €49-€53; extra person €12
ON SITE: Children's play area **NEARBY:** Bathing (9km) Horse riding (8km) Golf (15km) Sea (9km) Fishing (6km) Swimming pool (13km) Hiking (6km) Water sports (8km) Tennis (1km) Railway station (16km) Shops (1km) VANNES (13km) **NOTES:** Pets admitted

THEHILLAC

♦♦♦ Chambre d'hôtes Danièle BROSSIER
7 rue St-Michel, 56130 THEHILLAC
☎ 02 99 90 24 16 & 06 70 40 73 00 📠 02 99 90 24 16
e-mail: chambres-hotes-d-brossier@wanadoo.fr
Redon 10 km. Accommodation for eight in three grade 3 double rooms with en suite bathroom/wc and one grade 2 double room with separate bathroom/wc. Living room with open fireplace and TV, video library and drawing room. The shady garden has a gazebo. Other facilities include a barbecue, parking and bicycle/motorcycle storage. Madame Brossier is an expert on local traditional music, dance and costume. Open 30 March to 30 September (other months on request).
PRICES: s €38; d €44; extra person €15 **NEARBY:** Bathing (35km) Horse riding (12km) Golf (10km) Sea (35km) Fishing (2km) Swimming pool (15km) Hiking (12km) Water sports (5km) Tennis (1km) Railway station (12km) Shops (3km) LA ROCHE BERNARD (15km) **NOTES:** Pets admitted English spoken

THEIX

♦♦♦ Le Bézit Gérard LE BOURSICAULT
Allée Ty Er Beleg, 56450 THEIX
☎ 02 97 43 13 75 & 06 86 23 08 82
Vannes 10 km. Muzillac 15 km. This 17th-century farm is near the Gulf of Morbihan and close to hiking trail 34. On the first floor, accessed via a separate entrance, are two grade 2 double bedrooms, each with en suite shower-room/wc. Lounge, TV and garden with furniture. In the mansion house there is one first floor grade 3 double room with en suite bathroom/wc at €43 for two people; at the same price, and on the second floor, is another grade 3 double room with en suite shower-room/wc. Living room with TV is provided and guests may share kitchen facilities at an extra cost of €5 per day. Open all year.
PRICES: d €37-€43; extra person €16 **NEARBY:** Bathing (12km) Horse riding (15km) Golf (14km) Sea (12km) Fishing (2km) Swimming pool (8km) Hiking (1km) Water sports (12km) Tennis (2km) Railway station (8km) Shops (2km) VANNES (8km) **NOTES:** No pets English spoken

♦♦♦ Le Petit Clérigo Guy LE GRUYERE
56450 THEIX
☎ 02 97 43 03 66
Vannes 10 km. Muzillac 15 km. This detached house is situated on a farm and offers three guest rooms with a private entrance, also a garden with furniture. Two ground floor double rooms and one first floor double room, all with en suite shower-room/wc. Hiking trail 34 is within 14 km. Open March to end October.
PRICES: s €29; d €35 **NEARBY:** Bathing (15km) Horse riding (20km) Golf (20km) Sea (15km) Fishing (4km) Swimming pool (10km) Hiking (14km) Water sports (12km) Tennis (1km) Railway station (10km) Shops (1km) VANNES (10km) **NOTES:** No pets

BRITTANY

BURGUNDY

CÔTE-D'OR

AIGNAY-LE-DUC

Chambre d'hôtes Claude et Myriam BONNEFOY
la Demoiselle, rue sous les Vieilles Halles,
21510 AIGNAY-LE-DUC
☎ 03 80 93 90 07 📠 03 80 93 90 07
e-mail: Myriam.Bonnefoy@wanadoo.fr
The 18th-century mansion is characterised by its rendering, which is specific to this region. There are fine views of the village with its 13th-century church. The four rooms have a private entrance. There are three double bedrooms and one triple room, each with en suite shower-room/wc. A cot is also available. Central heating, lounge with TV and library. Evening meals are available on request and are served in the living room. Garden with barn. Contact establishment for directions. Open all year.
PRICES: s €29; d €37; t €46; dinner €14 **NEARBY:** Bathing (14km) Forest (1km) Golf (15km) Swimming pool (34km) Tennis (11km) Railway station (34km) CHATILLON-SUR-SEINE (34km) **NOTES:** Pets admitted

AISY-SOUS-THIL

Les Forges Daniel et Françoise GIROUDEAU
21390 AISY-SOUS-THIL
☎ 03 80 64 53 86
e-mail: dangiroudeau@aol.com
Situated on an old farm in the heart of the countryside, the four bedrooms, each accommodating up to three people, are equipped with en suite shower-room/wc. Guests are welcome to use the kitchen and the living room with open fireplace. Safe storage is provided for bicycles and motorcycles and private parking is available for cars. The nearest A6 motorway exit is at Bierre-les-Semur (5km). Open all year.
PRICES: s €34; d €40; t €46; extra person €10 **NEARBY:** Bathing (10km) Rock climbing (18km) Forest (1km) Golf (5km) Swimming pool (11km) Tennis (1km) Railway station (30km) Shops (2km) SEMUR-EN-AUXOIS (13km) **NOTES:** No pets English spoken

ATHEE (COTE D'OR)

Chambre d'hôtes Gilbert MILLIERE
17 rue Serpentiere, 21130 ATHEE
☎ 03 80 37 36 33
Enjoying a peaceful, rural location with views of the 3.5 hectare garden or of a courtyard planted with trees, this old farmhouse offers three ground floor guest rooms, one of which is classified grade 2, all with private entrance and en suite shower-room/wc. Facilities include central heating, a living room, a lounge, an open fireplace, games, shady terraces, floral displays, three secure garages and table d'hôte meals on request. The nearest motorway exit is at Soirans (6 km) Open all year.
PRICES: s €28; d €31; t €38-€46; extra person €7; dinner €15
ON SITE: Children's play area **NEARBY:** Bathing (4km) Rock climbing (20km) Forest (1km) Golf (20km) Swimming pool (3km) Tennis (6km) Railway station (4km) Shops (1km) AUXONNE (5km) **NOTES:** Pets admitted

Les Laurentides Michelle ROYER-COTTIN
27 rue du Centre, 21130 ATHEE
☎ 03 80 31 00 25
The four bedrooms form part of an old farm dating back to the 19th-century. There is one grade 2 room sleeping up to three

people, also two grade 3 double rooms and one grade 3 room sleeping three. All rooms have en suite shower-room/wc. Electric heating, living room, lounge with TV, fully equipped kitchen, private parking and garden. Table d'hôte meals may be booked at weekends and public holidays, and there is a restaurant within 2km. The nearest motorway exit is at Soirans (6km). Open all year.
PRICES: s €30; d €41; t €50; extra person €11; dinner €17
NEARBY: Bathing (4km) Forest (2km) Golf (30km) Swimming pool (4km) Tennis (4km) Railway station (4km) Shops (4km) DIJON (28km) **NOTES:** Pets admitted

AUXEY-DURESSES

Chateau de Melin Helene et Arnaud DERATS
21190 AUXEY-DURESSES
☎ 03 80 21 21 19 📠 03 80 21 21 72
http://www.chateaudemelin.com
This 16th-century château lies in the heart of a Beaune vineyard, where guests are welcome to taste and buy wines from the estate The accommodation comprises one double guest room, also two adjoining rooms, one double and the other twin-bedded, all with en suite shower-room/wc. The property has central heating, a lounge, a terrace, parking and five acres of land with a small lake. There is a restaurant within 2km. The nearest motorway exit is at Beaune. Open all year.
PRICES: s €65; d €85-€100; t €115; extra person €15
NEARBY: Bathing (8km) Rock climbing (6km) Forest (1km) Golf (13km) Swimming pool (9km) Tennis (2km) Railway station (12km) Shops (4km) BEAUNE (9km) **NOTES:** Pets admitted English spoken

BAUBIGNY

Chambre d'hôtes Marie et Gerard FUSSI
au Village, 21340 BAUBIGNY
☎ 03 80 21 84 66 📠 03 80 21 84 66
e-mail: gerard.fussi@wanadoo.fr
Set in the heart of a vineyard with fine panoramic views, the three guest rooms, each accommodating up to five people, all open directly on to a terrace and spacious grounds. A guest dining room and lounge, a kitchenette, a TV and parking are provided and there is a restaurant only 800 metres away. Hiking trails are also close by. Between 15/9 and 30/6 there is a 10% reduction on four consecutive nights and over. The nearest motorway exit is at Beaune. Open all year.
PRICES: s €38; d €41; t €50; extra person €9-€14 **ON SITE:** Forest **NEARBY:** Bathing (6km) Rock climbing (5km) Golf (16km) Swimming pool (6km) Tennis (1km) Railway station (13km) Shops (7km) BEAUNE (15km) **NOTES:** No pets English spoken

continued

BURGUNDY

BAUBIGNY (ORCHES)

▦ Orches François & Blandine ROCAULT
21340 BAUBIGNY
☎ 03 80 21 78 72 ▤ 03 80 21 85 95
e-mail: francois.blandine.rocault@wanadoo.fr
http://www.Francois-Blandine-Rocault.com
This winegrowers' house is situated at the foot of some cliffs on a vineyard overlooking the hamlet. There are five guest rooms, three double and two rooms sleeping three, each with en suite shower-room/wc. Facilities include central heating, a living room, a garden and parking. Wine-tasting tours of the vineyard are available for guests. The nearest motorway exit is at Beaune. Open all year.
PRICES: s €37; d €46; t €53 NEARBY: Bathing (7km) Rock climbing (4km) Forest (1km) Golf (15km) Swimming pool (7km) Tennis (2km) Railway station (15km) Shops (3km) BEAUNE (15km) NOTES: No pets CC English spoken

BEAUNE (LA MONTAGNE)

▦ ⍾ Chambre d'hôtes Elisabeth SEROUART
la Montagne, chemin du Dessus de Bressandes, 21200 BEAUNE
☎ 03 80 22 93 50 e-mail: maisonbressandes@multimania.com
http://www.multimania.com/maisonbressandes/
This large, welcoming house has a unique view of the vineyard and the town of Beaune. The accommodation comprises one suite and two other guest rooms, all tastefully furnished and with en suite bathroom/wc. Central heating, TV, lounge and library. Spacious grounds with parking and swimming pool surrounded by garden. Table d'hôte meals are available on request and there is an inn within 500 metres of the house. The nearest motorway exit is at Beaune-Nord. Open 1 March to 30 November.
PRICES: d €55-€69; t €85; dinner €19 ON SITE: Swimming pool
NEARBY: Bathing (8km) Forest (1km) Golf (5km) Tennis (3km) Railway station (3km) Shops (2km) BEAUNE (3km) NOTES: No pets English spoken

▦ Les Tilleuls Christine MARTIN
La Terre d'Or, la Montagne - rue Izembart,
21200 BEAUNE
☎ 03 80 25 90 90 & 06 85 08 62 14 ▤ 03 80 25 90 99
e-mail: jlmartin@laterredor.com http://www.laterredor.com
Only two minutes from Beaune and in an idyllic position amidst trees and birds overlooking the vineyard, Les Tilleuls is a contemporary, welcoming house with a huge lounge, a kitchenette, books, a TV, and central heating. It offers five guest rooms, all with either en suite bathroom or shower-room/wc. Parking and a garage are available and guests will particularly appreciate the swimming pool and 13th-century gardens. The nearest motorway exit is at Beaune-Sud. Open all year.
PRICES: ; d €170-€215 ON SITE: Forest Swimming pool
NEARBY: Bathing (25km) Rock climbing (10km) Golf (6km) Tennis (2km) Railway station (4km) Shops (2km) BEAUNE (3km)
NOTES: No pets English spoken

BELLENOT-SOUS-POUILLY

▦ ⍾ Chambre d'hôtes Martine DENIS
21320 BELLENOT-SOUS-POUILLY ☎ 03 80 90 71 82
e-mail: mrdenis@club.internet.fr
Two double guest rooms are situated in a traditional house adjoining the owners' property. Facilities include en suite bathroom or shower-room/wc, a kitchenette, a lounge, central heating, a TV and books. There is also one guest room sleeping up to four people in a small 18th-century house, with shower-room/wc and a kitchenette. Garden with parking. Table d'hôte meals are provided on request and there is a restaurant within two kilometres. Some English and German is spoken. Nearest motorway exit Pouilly-en-Auxois. Open all year.

PRICES: s €30; d €37; t €46; extra person €9; dinner €13
ON SITE: Forest NEARBY: Bathing (6km) Rock climbing (15km) Golf (3km) Swimming pool (12km) Tennis (2km) Railway station (45km) Shops (2km) POUILLY-EN-AUXOIS (2km) NOTES: No pets

BOUILLAND

▦ Chambre d'hôtes Marie-Christine RUSSO
rue Josserand, 21420 BOUILLAND
☎ 03 80 21 59 56 ▤ 03 80 26 13 03
e-mail: russo.bouilland@wanadoo.fr
http://perso.wanadoo.fr/russo.bouilland/
Situated in a large, peaceful garden on the banks of a river, this old, renovated property provides, via a separate entrance: two adjoining grade 3 rooms, one a double, the other a twin room, with en suite shower-room/wc and a living room; an apartment comprising a living room, a kitchenette, a shower-room/wc and a mezzanine area with one double and one single bed. The nearest motorway exit is at Savigny-les-Beaune. Open all year.
PRICES: d €43; extra person €15-€18 ON SITE: Rock climbing Forest Tennis NEARBY: Bathing (15km) Golf (20km) Swimming pool (15km) Railway station (15km) Shops (10km) SAVIGNY-LES-BEAUNE (10km)
NOTES: No pets English spoken

BOUSSENOIS

▦ ⍾ Chambre d'hôtes Christiane GROSJEAN
Grande rue, 21260 BOUSSENOIS
☎ 03 80 75 56 21 ▤ 03 80 75 56 21
Guests are guaranteed a warm welcome at this old winegrowers' house situated between Dijon and Langres in the 'Land of the Three Rivers'. Three comfortable rooms are provided, each with en suite shower-room/wc, together with a living room/TV, a garden, a garage and generous, imaginative table d'hôte meals on request. The nearest motorway exit is at Til-Châtel. Open all year.
PRICES: s €28; d €38; t €48; dinner €14 NEARBY: Bathing (20km) Forest (1km) Golf (35km) Swimming pool (5km) Tennis (5km) Railway station (20km) Shops (5km) SELONGEY (5km) NOTES: Pets admitted

BUSSY-LE-GRAND

▦ Entre Cour et Jardin Roger et Colette LANG
rue de la Montagne, 21150 BUSSY-LE-GRAND
☎ 03 80 96 98 51

A complete wing of this 17th-century listed property is reserved for guests. Guests will have at their disposal a large lounge with French-style ceiling and open fireplace, a bathroom/wc and a suite of three bedrooms furnished with antique furniture. The property also boasts award-winning terraced gardens and superb views over the Auxois valleys. The nearest A6 motorway exit is at Bierre-les Semur. Open 15 April to 15 October.
PRICES: d €76; t €99; extra person €23 NEARBY: Bathing (20km) Rock climbing (10km) Forest (1km) Golf (40km) Swimming pool (10km) Tennis (7km) Railway station (14km) Shops (7km) VENAREY-LES-LAUMES (7km) NOTES: No pets English spoken

continued

CHAMBOEUF

♦♦♦ Chambre d'hôtes Christiane & Dominique MONCEAU
les Sarguenotes, rue de Dijon, 21220 CHAMBOEUF
☎ 03 80 51 84 65 & 06 20 51 75 32 📠 03 80 49 77 24
Situated on the edge of a wood in an elevated position, this
beautiful house has panoramic views of Mont Vergy. There are five
double bedrooms, each with en suite bathroom or shower-
room/wc, all opening out on to a terrace and large garden. Living
room, lounge, TV and kitchen area. Central heating. Nearest
motorway exit Dijon-Sud-Chenôve. Open all year.
PRICES: s €38-€42; d €46-€47; extra person €15 **ON SITE:** Forest
NEARBY: Bathing (14km) Rock climbing (8km) Golf (28km) Swimming
pool (8km) Tennis (6km) Railway station (14km) Shops (6km) GEVREY-
CHAMBERTIN (6km) **NOTES:** Small pets admitted

CHANCEAUX

♦♦♦ Chambre d'hôtes Gaby & Raymonde BLAISE
32 Grande Rue, 21440 CHANCEAUX
☎ 03 80 35 02 70 📠 03 80 35 08 83
This former chapel is in the heart of a quiet village close to
woodland. It contains one double bedroom and two adjoining
family rooms for up to four people. Facilities include an en suite
bathroom or shower-room/wc, a living room with open fireplace, a
lounge, a TV, a kitchen area, heating and a covered terrace. A
special offer of four nights for the price of three is available. Access
is easy via motorway exits Sombernon or Til-Châtel. Open all year.
PRICES: s €28; d €34; t €49 **ON SITE:** Tennis **NEARBY:** Bathing
(20km) Rock climbing (25km) Forest (1km) Golf (20km) Swimming pool
(15km) Railway station (25km) SAINT-SEINE-L'ABBAYE (12km)
NOTES: No pets

CHATEAUNEUF-EN-AUXOIS

♦♦♦ Chambre d'hôtes Annie BAGATELLE
rue des Moutons, 21320 CHATEAUNEUF-EN-AUXOIS
☎ 03 80 49 21 00 📠 03 80 49 21 49
e-mail: jean-michel.bagatelle@wanadoo.fr
This former shepherd's cottage is situated in the heart of a
medieval village renowned for its 12th-15th century château and its
quaint houses. It offers four rooms, each accommodating up to
four guests, with mezzanine and en suite shower-room/wc. A living
room, a garden and parking are available and the village has a
choice of restaurants. The Burgundy Canal and public footpaths
are nearby. The nearest motorway exit is at Pouilly-en-Auxois.
Open all year except local school holidays in February.
PRICES: s €40-€50; d €46-€58; t €54-€66; extra person €8
ON SITE: Forest **NEARBY:** Bathing (1km) Rock climbing (30km) Golf
(12km) Tennis (5km) Shops (10km) POUILLY-EN-AUXOIS (10km)
NOTES: No pets English spoken

CHAUDENAY-LE-CHATEAU

♦♦♦ ⁱⓄⁱ Le Cottage du Chateau Claudette TOUFLAN
21360 CHAUDENAY-LE-CHATEAU
☎ 03 80 20 00 43 & 06 70 58 92 81 📠 03 80 20 01 93
e-mail: le.cottage@libertysurf.fr
This peaceful, detached cottage is located on the edge of a forest
close to hiking, equestrian and mountain bike trails. It offers four
large guest rooms, all accommodating up to five people. Each
room has a private entrance, a terrace, satellite TV and en suite
shower-room/wc. There is a living room, a kitchen area and a
garden with panoramic views of the surrounding countryside.
Secure parking and garage. Local facilities: go-karting (12km), lake
for bathing, and a zoo (25km). Open all year.
PRICES: d €44-€52; t €55-€63; extra person €11; dinner €18
NEARBY: Bathing (8km) Rock climbing (15km) Forest (1km) Golf
(15km) Swimming pool (15km) Tennis (5km) Railway station (30km)

Shops (2km) DIJON/BEAUNE (30km) **NOTES:** Pets admitted English
spoken

CHOREY-LES-BEAUNE

♦♦♦ Chambre d'hôtes Henri & Marie-Claire DESCHAMPS
l'Escale des Grands Crus, 15 rue d'Aloxe Corton,
21200 CHOREY-LES-BEAUNE
☎ 03 80 24 08 13 📠 03 80 24 08 01
e-mail: henri.deschamps@wanadoo.fr
These six guest rooms are right in the heart of the vineyards. They
comprise five double rooms and one room sleeping three people,
all with en suite shower-room/wc. A lounge with TV, central
heating a garden and a garage are available. The bedrooms and
breakfast room are non-smoking areas. There is a restaurant
within 3km. The nearest motorway exit is at Beaune-Nord. Open 1
March to 30 November.
PRICES: s €38; d €43; t €58 **NEARBY:** Bathing (3km) Rock climbing
(12km) Forest (3km) Golf (6km) Swimming pool (3km) Tennis (3km)
Railway station (3km) Shops (3km) BEAUNE (3km) **NOTES:** No pets

♦♦♦♦ Le Château François GERMAIN
21200 CHOREY-LES-BEAUNE
☎ 03 80 22 06 05 📠 03 80 24 03 93
e-mail: chateau-de-chorey@wanadoo.fr
http://www.chateau-de-chorey-les-beaune.fr
The six guest rooms boast a fine setting in a 13th-17th-century
château owned by a family of winegrowers. There are two
double rooms, three rooms accommodating three people and
a suite for four people, all with en suite bathroom/wc and
telephone. Guests are welcome to use the living room, lounge
and terrace, also to sample and purchase the estate's wines.
There is a restaurant nearby. The nearest motorway exit is at
Beaune-Nord. Open Easter to end November.
PRICES: s €130-€145; d €140-€155; t €170-€185 **NEARBY:** Bathing
(3km) Rock climbing (15km) Forest (2km) Golf (6km) Swimming
pool (3km) Tennis (1km) Railway station (3km) Shops (3km)
BEAUNE (3km) **NOTES:** Pets admitted English spoken

CLAMEREY (PONT-ROYAL)

♦♦♦ La Maison du Canal
Pont Royal, 21490 CLAMEREY
☎ 03 80 64 62 65 📠 03 80 64 65 72
Located beside an attractive port on the Burgundy Canal, this
beautifully restored house offers six bedrooms, each
accommodating either two or three people and with en suite
bathroom/wc. There is a living room with a typically Burgundian
fireplace and a TV, electric heating and a stone terrace with garden
furniture affording a panoramic view of wooded valleys. Parking is
available. Only small pets are permitted. The nearest motorway
exit is at Bierre-les-Semur.
PRICES: s €34; d €43; t €52 **ON SITE:** Bathing **NEARBY:** Forest (8km)
Golf (9km) Swimming pool (4km) Tennis (4km) Railway station (15km)
SEMUR-EN-AUXOIS (12km) **NOTES:** Pets admitted

continued

BURGUNDY

COLOMBIER

▦ ◎ Chambre d'hôtes Yvette BROCARD
21360 COLOMBIER
☎ 03 80 33 03 41 & 06 12 57 23 16
The five guest rooms are situated in a quiet little village in a stone house separate from that of the owner. It offers three double rooms and two rooms sleeping three, all with en suite bathroom or shower-room/wc. Electric heating, a living room with open fireplace, a lounge and a kitchen area are also available. Outside there is a parking area, a meadow and stables. Local inn 9km. The nearest motorway exit is at Pouilly-en-Auxois. Open all year.
PRICES: s €32; d €40-€43; t €56; dinner €16 **NEARBY:** Bathing (15km) Rock climbing (12km) Forest (1km) Golf (30km) Swimming pool (25km) Tennis (7km) Railway station (25km) Shops (9km) BLIGNY-SUR-OUCHE (9km) **NOTES:** No pets

CORBERON

▦ L'ormeraie Alain et Chantal BALMELLE
rue des Ormes, 21250 CORBERON
☎ 03 80 26 53 19 ▤ 03 80 26 54 20
e-mail: cab.abc@wanadoo.fr
Peace is assured in this five-acre setting. The imposing 18th-century house situated on the edge of the village provides three charming guest rooms, one with a double bed and two with a double and a single bed. All rooms have en suite shower room, and a lounge and central heating are available. Restaurants are available either on the premises or in Beaune. The nearest motorway exit is at Beaune et Seurre. Open May to October.
PRICES: s €60; d €64; t €83; extra person €19 **NEARBY:** Bathing (10km) Forest (1km) Golf (9km) Swimming pool (13km) Tennis (5km) Railway station (13km) BEAUNE/NUITS-SAINT-GEORGES (13km) **NOTES:** No pets English spoken

CORCELLES-LES-MONTS

▦ Chambre d'hôtes Gisele BERGERY
9 bis rue du chateau, 21160 CORCELLES-LES-MONTS
☎ 03 80 42 92 36
e-mail: thierry.bergery@wanadoo.fr
http://www.fransurf.com./dijon/contrées-ournès
The four garden-level guest rooms are located in a quiet village 8km from Dijon. There are three double rooms, two of which are linked, and one room for three people. Each room is equipped with en suite shower-room/wc, TV and central heating. An enclosed garden with a courtyard and a parking area are available for guests. There is a restaurant 6km away. The nearest motorway exits are at Velars-sur-Ouche and Dijon-Sud/Longvic.
PRICES: s €46; d €54-€61; t €70; extra person €12 **NEARBY:** Bathing (10km) Rock climbing (8km) Forest (1km) Golf (15km) Swimming pool (8km) Tennis (5km) Railway station (8km) Shops (6km) DIJON (8km) **NOTES:** No pets English spoken

CORROMBLES

▦ Chambre d'hôtes Roger et Nicole ICHES
1 rue de la Planche, 21460 CORROMBLES
☎ 03 80 96 48 67 ▤ 03 80 96 30 62
e-mail: rogeriches@libertysurf.fr
http://perso.libertysurf.fr/les4saisons
The five guest rooms, each accommodating three people and each with mezzanine and shower-room/wc, are housed within the barn of a renovated old farmhouse. Facilities include electric heating, a communal living room with a kitchen area and TV, a garden, a garage and a private access with parking. Hiking and cycle trails are close by and mountain bikes are available. The nearest motorway exits are at Bierre-les-Semur and Avallon. Open all year.
PRICES: s €35; d €43; t €55; extra person €12 **NEARBY:** Bathing (2km)

Rock climbing (6km) Forest (2km) Golf (20km) Swimming pool (2km) Tennis (2km) Railway station (25km) Shops (2km) SEMUR-EN-AUXOIS (10km) **NOTES:** No pets

COURBAN

▦ ◎ Le Château Pierre VANDENDRIESSCHE
21520 COURBAN
☎ 03 80 93 78 69 & 06 09 62 51 77 ▤ 03 80 93 79 23
e-mail: chateau.decourban@wanadoo.fr
http://www.chateaudecourban.fr
This beautiful old house is in a secluded village 15km north-east of Châtillon-sur-Seine. There are six guest rooms, five double/twin-bedded rooms with en suite shower-room/wc and one double room with en suite bathroom/wc and a couch. Living room, lounge, satellite TV, books, gardens, terraces and swimming pool. Parking. Pets permitted by prior arrangement. The nearest motorway exits are at Ville-sous-la-Ferté or Chaumont-Semontiers. Open all year.
PRICES: s €53-€115; d €53-€135; t €135; dinner €24
ON SITE: Forest **NEARBY:** Bathing (7km) Golf (20km) Swimming pool (15km) Tennis (7km) Railway station (50km) Shops (7km) MONTIGNY-SUR-AUBE (7km) **NOTES:** Pets admitted English spoken

CURTIL-VERGY

▦ ◎ Le Val de Vergy Brigitte PUVIS DE CHAVANNES
Pelleroy, 21220 CURTIL-VERGY
☎ 03 80 61 41 62 ▤ 03 80 61 41 62
This winegrowers' house dates from the 18th century and boasts a magnificent wine cellar. Three guest rooms enjoy an elevated position right in the heart of the Hautes-Côtes vineyard. There are two triple rooms and one double, all with en suite bathroom/wc. Communal living room with exposed beams and an open fireplace. Central heating, meadow and garden with terrace. Table d'hôte meals twice a week on request. Some English is spoken. Nearest motorway exit Nuits-Saint-Georges. Open 1 April to 1 November.
PRICES: s €37-€43; d €46-€53; t €56-€64; dinner €19 **NEARBY:** Bathing (8km) Rock climbing (15km) Forest (1km) Golf (20km) Tennis (1km) Railway station (8km) Shops (2km) GEVREY-CHAMBERTIN (12km) **NOTES:** Small pets admitted

ECHALOT

▦ ◎ Chambre d'hôtes Rita BONNEFOY
bas du Village, 21510 ECHALOT
☎ 03 80 93 86 84
Two grade 3 guest rooms accommodating three people and one grade 2 double room, all with en suite shower-room/wc are available in this charming house, which also has central heating, a living room, a lounge with TV, a garden with a terrace and a parking area. Meals can be provided on request. The nearest motorway exit is at Til-Châtel. Open all year.
PRICES: s €26; d €36; t €46; dinner €13 **NEARBY:** Bathing (5km) Forest (1km) Golf (6km) Tennis (6km) Railway station (30km) Shops (11km) AIGNAY-LE-DUC (11km) **NOTES:** Pets admitted

ECUTIGNY

▦ ◎ Le Château Patrick et Françoise ROCHET
21360 ECUTIGNY
☎ 03 80 20 19 14 ▤ 03 80 20 19 15
e-mail: info@chateaudecutigny.com
http://www.chateaudecutigny.com
This 12th-17th-century château has six rooms, each accommodating either two or three guests, and one is a complete suite. All rooms are equipped with en suite bathroom or shower-room/wc and TV. A steam room is

continued

continued

available. Central heating, living room and lounge with kitchen area and library. Play area, stable, meadow and garage. Restaurant 4km. The nearest motorway exit is at Beaune. Open all year.

PRICES: s €81-€131; d €82-€182; t €113-€183; extra person €21; dinner €40 **ON SITE:** Tennis **NEARBY:** Bathing (20km) Rock climbing (15km) Forest (3km) Golf (25km) Swimming pool (25km) Railway station (25km) Shops (4km) BLIGNY-SUR-OUCHE (4km) **NOTES:** Pets admitted CC English spoken

EPERNAY-SOUS-GEVREY

♦♦♦ La Vieille Auberge Neil et Pam AITKEN
2 place des Tilleuls, 21220 EPERNAY-SOUS-GEVREY
☎ 03 80 36 61 76 🖷 03 80 36 64 68
e-mail: bacchus.neil@wanadoo.fr

All five guest rooms are located on the first floor of this old inn, which has been restored, and comprise two double rooms, one room sleeping three and two rooms sleeping up to four people. All rooms have en suite bathroom or shower-room and wc. The property has central heating, a lounge, books, a garden and parking facilities. There is a restaurant within six kilometres. The nearest motorway exit is at Nuits-Saint-Georges. Open all year.
PRICES: s €43; d €58; t €67 **NEARBY:** Bathing (6km) Forest (1km) Golf (6km) Swimming pool (6km) Tennis (6km) Railway station (8km) Shops (6km) GEVREY-CHAMBERTIN (8km) **NOTES:** No pets English spoken

FLAGEY-ECHEZEAUX

♦♦♦ Petit Paris Nathalie BUFFEY
6 rue du Petit Paris, Pont Chevalier-Gilly, 21640 FLAGEY-ECHEZEAUX
☎ 03 80 62 84 09 & 03 80 62 83 88
The guest rooms are located in the annexe of a 17th-century house, on the banks of the River Vouge surrounded by parkland. There are four double rooms centred around a large engraving and painting studio, each with en suite bathroom or shower-room/wc. Extra beds are available for children or teenagers. Living room, lounge, books, garden, river and fishpond. Nearest motorway exit Nuits-Saint-Georges. Open all year.

PRICES: s €77; d €77; extra person €15 **NEARBY:** Bathing (5km) Rock climbing (8km) Forest (1km) Golf (15km) Swimming pool (1km) Tennis (1km) Railway station (1km) NUITS-SAINT-GEORGES (5km) **NOTES:** No pets English spoken

FRANCHEVILLE

♦♦♦ Chambre d'hôtes Pierre et Denise DROUOT
21440 FRANCHEVILLE ☎ 03 80 35 01 93 🖷 03 80 35 07 27
Situated in a quiet, wooded area, this large, old house offers three guest rooms, each with en suite shower-room/wc. It also has central heating, a living room, a kitchen, a lounge with open fireplace and TV, parking and a garden with a play area. There is a choice of restaurants nearby, also hiking trails 2 and 7. Reductions for bookings of three nights and over. The nearest motorway exits are at Pouilly-en-Auxois or at Til-Châtel. Open all year.
PRICES: s €30; d €40; t €50 **ON SITE:** Forest Tennis **NEARBY:** Bathing (20km) Rock climbing (20km) Golf (35km) Swimming pool (18km) Railway station (20km) Shops (9km) DIJON (20km) **NOTES:** No pets

GEVREY-CHAMBERTIN

♦♦♦ Chambre d'hôtes Genevieve SYLVAIN
14 rue de l'Eglise, 21220 GEVREY-CHAMBERTIN
☎ 03 80 51 86 39 🖷 03 80 51 86 39
Three guest rooms in a large, plush house situated close to vineyards in the centre of the village. All rooms have either en suite bathroom or shower-room/wc, There is also a dining room and a very pleasant, small garden. The village offers a choice of restaurants and hiking trail 7 is in the vicinity. Some English is spoken. The nearest A6 motorway exits at Nuits-Saint-Georges.
PRICES: s €37; d €47 **NEARBY:** Bathing (5km) Rock climbing (3km) Forest (1km) Golf (15km) Swimming pool (5km) Tennis (2km) Railway station (3km) Shops (1km) DIJON (11km) **NOTES:** No pets

GILLY-LES-CITEAUX

♦♦♦ Chambre d'hôtes André et Sandrine LANAUD
la Closerie de Gilly, 16 avenue Bouchard, 21640 GILLY-LES-CITEAUX
☎ 03 80 62 87 74 🖷 03 80 62 87 74
e-mail: as.lanaud@wanadoo.fr

This historic 18th-century residence is located in a pretty village on the wine-growing slopes. The five spacious and comfortable guest rooms are all decorated and furnished in an elegant, individual style and overlook a garden with 100-year-old trees. Each room has an en suite bathroom/wc. Living room, lounge, TV, central heating, secure parking, play area and mountain bike rental. Local attractions include the vineyard at Vougeot and Cîteaux Abbey (15km). Nearest motorway exit Nuits-Saint-Georges. Open all year.
PRICES: d €70-€85; t €85-€100; extra person €15 **NEARBY:** Bathing (1km) Rock climbing (4km) Forest (2km) Golf (20km) Swimming pool (1km) Tennis (1km) Railway station (1km) NUITS-SAINT-GEORGES (5km) **NOTES:** Small pets by arrangement English spoken

continued

IS-SUR-TILLE

♦♦♦ ⭐ ⚹ Le Vieux Moulin Annie DORAL
6 rue Pierre Perrenet - BP 13, 21120 IS-SUR-TILLE
☎ 03 80 95 02 92 & 06 07 38 70 50 🗎 03 80 95 02 92
This old water-mill situated beside a river offers two double guest
rooms and one room sleeping three people, each with en suite
shower-room/wc. There is also a living room, a lounge with TV,
central heating, a garage and a waterside garden. Table d'hôte
meals are provided on request. A special offer of four nights for
the price of three applies in all months except June, July and
August. The nearest motorway exit is at Til-Châtel. Open all year.
PRICES: s €29; d €35; t €44; extra person €12; dinner €12
ON SITE: Swimming pool Tennis **NEARBY:** Bathing (20km) Forest
(1km) Golf (16km) Railway station (2km) DIJON (20km) **NOTES:** Pets
admitted

LA ROCHE-EN-BRENIL(CHENESAINT)

♦♦♦ ⭐ Chambre d'hôtes Michelle et René LEGRAND
Chenesaint, 21530 LA ROCHE-EN-BRENIL
☎ 03 80 64 79 06 🗎 03 80 64 79 06
e-mail: rene.legrand@free.fr
This tastefully renovated farm is typical of the region and is located
in the Morvan Regional Park. It has two double rooms, two triple
rooms, and a family room for four, all with en suite bathroom/wc.
A cot is available at extra cost. Electric heating, lounge, garden with
play areas, parking and private swimming pool. Table d'hôte meals
are available on request. 10% discount on bookings of one week.
Nearest motorway exit Avallon. Open all year.
PRICES: s €38; d €49; t €64; extra person €15; dinner €12-€20
ON SITE: Forest Swimming pool **NEARBY:** Bathing (6km) Rock
climbing (8km) Golf (15km) Tennis (4km) Railway station (3km) Shops
(3km) SAULIEU (13km) **NOTES:** No pets English spoken

LAMARCHE-SUR-SAONE

♦♦♦ Chambre d'hôtes Martine CLEMENT
15 rue du Pont, 21760 LAMARCHE-SUR-SAONE
☎ 03 80 47 87 69 & 03 80 47 17 04 🗎 03 80 47 40 06
In the heart of the Burgundy countryside and on the banks of the
River Saône, this charming old house provides four guest rooms,
all with en suite bathroom/wc. Facilities include a colourful
courtyard and garden situated in sunny, enclosed grounds, gas
central heating, table football, a variety of games and a private
swimming pool. Restaurants are located 100 metres and three
kilometres away. The nearest motorways are at Soirans or at Arc-
sur-Tille. Open all year.
PRICES: d €46; t €56; extra person €11 **ON SITE:** Bathing Swimming
pool **NEARBY:** Forest (1km) Golf (30km) Tennis (1km) Railway station
(30km) PONTAILLER-SUR-SAONE (4km) **NOTES:** No pets

LONGECOURT-EN-PLAINE

♦♦♦ Chambre d'hôtes Arielle MERLE
22 rue du Murot, 21110 LONGECOURT-EN-PLAINE
☎ 03 80 39 73 68
e-mail: ariellemanu@aol.com
Accommodation is provided in three rooms in a detached house
reserved for guests within a few kilometres of vineyards and Citeaux
Abbey. The private entrance opens into a large living room with a
lounge area. All rooms have en suite shower-room/wc. A kitchen, a
garden and secure parking are also available and there is a full
range of shops in the village. The Canal de Bourgogne runs through
the village, where fishing and cycling are popular local activities.
Nearest motorway exits Crimolois or Longvic. Open all year.
PRICES: s €26; d €36; t €45; extra person €10 **ON SITE:** Tennis
NEARBY: Bathing (6km) Forest (1km) Golf (12km) Swimming pool
(6km) DIJON (14km) **NOTES:** No pets

MARSANNAY-LA-COTE

♦♦♦ Chambre d'hôtes J.Charles & Brigitte VIENNET
34 rue de Mazy, 21160 MARSANNAY-LA-COTE
☎ 03 80 59 83 63 🗎 03 80 59 83 28
e-mail: viennet.Jean-Charles@wanadoo.fr
http://perso.wanadoo.fr/gite.marsannay
These three charming, self-contained guest rooms for either two or
four people are located in an old winegrowers' house in the centre
of a village along the Grands Crus route. Facilities include en suite
shower-room/wc and optional TV in every room. TV lounges, a
garden with mature trees, secure parking and bicycle hire are also
available. Guests are offered a complimentary glass of wine from
the family wine cellar. Restaurant 300m. Nearest motorway exit
Dijon-Sud. Open all year.
PRICES: s €42-€47; d €50-€56; t €67; extra person €11 **NEARBY:** Rock
climbing (2km) Forest (1km) Golf (15km) Swimming pool (3km) Tennis
(1km) Railway station (6km) DIJON (6km) **NOTES:** No pets English
spoken

MAXILLY-SUR-SAONE

♦♦♦ ⭐ Chambre d'hôtes Yves FONTENILLE
2 rue de Talmay, 21270 MAXILLY-SUR-SAONE
☎ 03 80 47 41 95
This old house is situated in a village on the banks of the Saône
and offers the following accommodation: one double and one twin
bedroom, each with shower-room/wc, and one family room
containing one double and two single beds with bathroom/wc.
Facilities: billiard table, juke box, library, living room, lounge with
open fireplace and TV, mountain bikes, tandem, motorboat,
courtyard, parking and green open spaces. A 10% reduction for
bookings of three nights and over. Nearest motorway exit Arc-sur-
Tille. Open all year.
PRICES: s €29; d €38; t €49; extra person €11; dinner €15
NEARBY: Forest (3km) Golf (30km) Swimming pool (10km) Tennis
(3km) PONTAILLER-SUR-SAONE (4km) **NOTES:** No pets

MESSANGES

♦♦♦ Chambre d'hôtes Maire-Louise RUCH
23A, Grande rue, 21220 MESSANGES
☎ 03 80 61 41 29 🗎 03 80 61 48 40
This renovated old house offers five guest rooms, comprising three
grade 1 rooms with either double or twin beds, each with a
washbasin and a shared shower-room/wc. A grade 3 suite contains
two adjoining double rooms, en suite bathroom/wc, a lounge with
TV, a kitchen and a dining room. Central heating, terrace, lawn and
parking. Restaurant 2km and hiking trail 7 is nearby. The nearest
A31 motorway exit is at Nuits-Saint-Georges. Open 1 March to 20
December.
PRICES: s €33; d €37-€51; t €69 **NEARBY:** Bathing (7km) Rock
climbing (10km) Forest (1km) Golf (20km) Swimming pool (7km) Tennis
(7km) Railway station (7km) Shops (2km) NUITS-SAINT-GEORGES (7km)
NOTES: No pets

MESSIGNY-ET-VANTOUX

♦♦♦ Chambre d'hôtes Michel et Annette DESCHAMPS
20 rue de la Maladiere, 21380 MESSIGNY-ET-VANTOUX
☎ 03 80 35 48 54 & 06 21 66 25 94
e-mail: deschamps.annette@wanadoo.fr
This newly constructed house offers five guest rooms, four with en
suite shower-room/wc and one with separate shower-room/wc.
The house has electric heating, a living room, a lounge, a kitchen,
parking and landscaped gardens with 100-year-old trees. Horse-
riding facilities and the Jouvence woods are nearby. The nearest
motorway exit is at Dijon-Nord. Open all year.
PRICES: s €36; d €43; extra person €8 **ON SITE:** Tennis

continued

NEARBY: Forest (1km) Golf (3km) Swimming pool (8km) Railway station (10km) DIJON (8km) **NOTES:** Pets admitted English spoken

MEULSON

₩₩ ⦿ Le Clos Lucotte Simonne DESTEPHANIS
rue Haute, 21510 MEULSON
☎ 03 80 93 85 81 ▤ 03 80 93 85 81
This charming 17th-century property adjoining the owner's house offers three bedrooms, two doubles with a lounge area and one twin room. All rooms have en suite facilities and optional TV. Central heating, dining room and lounge. Garden, parking and private swimming pool. Table d'hôte meals are available on request. 10% reduction on bookings of one week and over. Pets are not allowed in the bedrooms. Some English is spoken. Nearest motorway exit Semur-en-Auxois. Open 15 March to 15 October, and at other times by arrangement.
PRICES: s €38; d €46; HB €44; FB €59; dinner €12-€20 **ON SITE:** Forest Swimming pool **NEARBY:** Golf (18km) Tennis (4km) Railway station (40km) Shops (4km) AIGNAY-LE-DUC (4km) **NOTES:** Pets admitted

MOLPHEY

₩₩ Chambre d'hôtes Didier PASQUET
le Village, 21210 MOLPHEY
☎ 03 80 64 21 94 ▤ 03 80 64 21 94
e-mail: pasquet.didier@wanadoo.fr
The four double guest rooms enjoy a peaceful, verdant setting in an old house, which has fine views of the surrounding countryside. All rooms have en suite shower-room/wc. A living room, a lounge, a kitchen area, parking and a garden are also available and there is a restaurant in the village. Between 15 September and 1 April a reduction of 10% is offered on bookings of one week. The nearest motorway exit is at Avallon. Open all year.
PRICES: s €29; d €37; extra person €9-€18 **NEARBY:** Bathing (8km) Forest (1km) Golf (15km) Swimming pool (8km) Tennis (4km) Railway station (8km) Shops (8km) SAULIEU (10km) **NOTES:** Pets admitted

MONTAGNY-LES-BEAUNE

₩₩ ⦿ Fare-nui Lucien et Brigitte MOREL
4 Rue des Gravieres,
21200 MONTAGNY-LES-BEAUNE
☎ 03 80 24 02 11 ▤ 03 80 22 65 70
This renovated old village farmhouse offers five very spacious rooms, for either two or three people, all with en suite shower-room/wc. The rustic dining room and lounge are slightly exotic in décor. There is an enclosed courtyard and a parking area. The nearest motorway exit is at Beaune. Open all year.
PRICES: s €44; d €54; t €66; dinner €18 **ON SITE:** Bathing Tennis **NEARBY:** Rock climbing (20km) Forest (2km) Golf (4km) Swimming pool (4km) Railway station (3km) Shops (3km) BEAUNE (4km) **NOTES:** No pets CC

MONTCEAU-ECHARNANT

₩₩ ❦ ⦿ Ferme du Pigeonnier
Elisabeth et Bernard LAGRANGE
21360 MONTCEAU-ECHARNANT
☎ 03 80 20 23 23 ▤ 03 80 20 23 23

This attractive house, on a Charollais cattle farm, offers three guest rooms, each with en suite shower-room/wc and a private entrance. There is one double room and one triple room, also two adjoining rooms (one double and two single beds) with their own lounge. Central heating, living room, lounge and garden with parking. Table d'hôte meals need to be booked on Sundays. A reduction of 10% on bookings of four nights or more. A supplement is charged for pets. Nearest motorway exit Beaune. Open all year.
PRICES: s €32; d €41; t €56; extra person €16; dinner €15
ON SITE: Forest **NEARBY:** Bathing (15km) Rock climbing (15km) Golf (20km) Swimming pool (20km) Tennis (3km) Railway station (20km) Shops (6km) BLIGNY-SUR-OUCHE (6km) **NOTES:** Pets admitted CC

MOREY-SAINT-DENIS

₩₩ Caveau Saint-Nicolas
Françoise PALISSES-BEAUMONT
13 rue Haute, 21220 MOREY-SAINT-DENIS
☎ 03 80 58 51 83
Guests are accommodated in a detached property, which has housed generations of winegrowers. It contains three bedrooms, each with en suite shower-room/wc. Living room, lounge area with TV and kitchenette. There is also a studio with separate entrance, providing a double and two single beds, shower-room/wc and kitchen. Central heating. Guests may use the terrace and park at the edge of the vineyard. Wine tasting and wine-buying possible. There is a restaurant in the village. Nearest motorway exit Nuits-Saint-Georges. Open all year.
PRICES: s €38-€43; d €43-€53; t €43-€69; extra person €14
NEARBY: Bathing (2km) Rock climbing (4km) Forest (1km) Golf (14km) Swimming pool (20km) Tennis (2km) Railway station (7km) GEVREY-CHAMBERTIN (4km) **NOTES:** Pets admitted

₩₩ Chambre d'hôtes Jean-Pierre & Eliane DUPREY
34 route des Grands Crus, 21220 MOREY-SAINT-DENIS
☎ 03 80 51 82 89
This winegrowers' house with vineyard views provides the following accommodation: two double guest rooms, each with en suite bathroom/wc (€41) and a family suite of three bedrooms with en suite bathroom/wc (the cost of one room is €41, two rooms €66 and all three rooms €96). Facilities include central heating, a living room, a garden, parking and a restaurant within 500 metres. Breakfast is served in the family wine cellar. The nearest motorway exit is at Nuits-Saint-Georges). Open from February until December.
PRICES: d €41 **NEARBY:** Bathing (2km) Rock climbing (4km) Forest (1km) Golf (20km) Swimming pool (7km) Tennis (2km) Railway station (4km) Shops (4km) GEVREY-CHAMBERTIN (4km) **NOTES:** Pets admitted

NOIRON-SUR-BEZE

♦♦♦ ఈ Chambre d'hôtes Bernard & Bernadette SUBLET
6 route de Blagny, 21310 NOIRON-SUR-BEZE
☎ 03 80 36 79 18 ⊟ 03 80 36 79 18
Three guest rooms are provided in this recently built house, which
has views of the river. All rooms have en suite shower-room/wc
and accommodate either two or three people (one is available for
less mobile guests). Facilities include a kitchen area, a lounge,
books, central heating, a garden and parking. There is a reduction
of 10% on reservations of four nights and over. The nearest
motorway exits are at Arc-sur-Tille or Til-Châtel. Open all year.
PRICES: s €30; d €38; t €49; extra person €12 **NEARBY:** Bathing (5km)
Rock climbing (28km) Forest (1km) Golf (25km) Swimming pool (5km)
Tennis (5km) Railway station (28km) Shops (5km) DIJON (28km)
NOTES: Pets admitted

PLOMBIERES-LES-DIJON

♦♦♦ ⋈ Chambre d'hôtes Colette & J.Claude TOURTET
Chateau Plombieres-les-Dijon,
21370 PLOMBIERES-LES-DIJON
☎ 03 80 45 00 61 ⊟ 03 80 43 29 73
e-mail: chateau-de-plombieres@wanadoo.fr
www.chateauplombieres.com

The six guest rooms, all with en suite bathroom/wc, are located in
a charming 17th-century house furnished with period furniture.
Facilities include large lounges, a partly shared dining room, a
television, a telephone, a garden and parking. A special offer of
four nights for the price of three is available. The nearest
motorway exit is at Plombières-les-Dijon (600m). Open all year.
PRICES: d €53; t €76; extra person €23; HB €46; dinner €21
ON SITE: Tennis **NEARBY:** Bathing (2km) Forest (1km) Golf (8km)
Swimming pool (4km) Railway station (4km) DIJON (4km) **NOTES:** No
pets

PONTAILLER-SUR-SAONE

♦♦♦ ⋈ Les Clematites D et C PITEY-DUCHEMIN
65 rue du 8 Mai 1945, 21270 PONTAILLER-SUR-SAONE
☎ 03 80 36 11 01
e-mail: DANKIKI@wanadoo.fr
http://www.maison-des-clématites.com
Christiane and Daniel Pitey are passionate about painting and
welcome guests to their 17th-century house, which has a garden
that combines English and exotic styles of landscaping. There are
two large guestrooms, each with a lounge area and en suite
bathroom/wc. Lounge with TV, CDs and library. Mountain bike hire
and painting/stained glass courses available. Regional dishes are
provided on request and are served in the dining room or on the
verandah. Nearest motorway exits Soirans or Arc-sur-Tille. Open 15
May to 15 November.
PRICES: d €38-€53; extra person €23; dinner €15 **ON SITE:** Bathing
Tennis **NEARBY:** Forest (1km) Golf (20km) Swimming pool (13km)
Railway station (16km) AUXONNE (13km) **NOTES:** No pets

ROUGEMONT

♦♦♦ La Forge Jean-Luc et Carole BACCHIERI
21500 ROUGEMONT
☎ 03 80 92 35 99 ⊟ 03 80 92 35 99
The three guest rooms, each accommodating up to four people,
are located in a delightful house beside the Canal de Bourgogne in
the Armançon Valley. All rooms have a private entrance, en suite
bathroom/wc and an open fireplace. A living room with books and
TV, a kitchen, central heating, a garden, a courtyard and boat trips
are also available. There is a restaurant three kilometres away. The
nearest motorway exits are at Bierre-sur-Semur or Nitry (30km).
Open all year except 25 and 31 December.
PRICES: s €30; d €40-€44; t €52-€56 **ON SITE:** Bathing Forest
NEARBY: Rock climbing (10km) Golf (30km) Swimming pool (10km)
Tennis (1km) Railway station (10km) Shops (6km) MONTBARD (10km)
NOTES: Pets admitted English spoken

SAINT-BERNARD

♦♦♦ Chambre d'hôtes Jeanne ESMONIN
Paquis de Rolanges, 21700 ST-BERNARD
☎ 03 80 62 81 60 ⊟ 03 80 62 89 14
e-mail: les-rolanges@wanadoo.fr
Jeanne and Daniel welcome guests to this quiet detached building
near their own property: three double bedrooms, each with en
suite shower-room/wc and direct access to the garden via a
terrace with furniture. Parking is available. In their own house
there is a twin-bedded room with en suite bathroom/wc and
electric heating. There is a restaurant within three kilometres. Local
attractions: Cîteaux Abbey, the Vouget vineyard (7km) and the
Nuits-Saint-Georges wine slope. Nearest motorway exit Nuits-
Saint-Georges. Open all year.
PRICES: s €43; d €46-€50; extra person €10-€15 **ON SITE:** Children's
play area **NEARBY:** Bathing (5km) Forest (1km) Golf (23km)
Swimming pool (5km) Tennis (5km) Railway station (7km) Shops (7km)
NUITS-SAINT-GEORGES (7km) **NOTES:** Pets admitted

SALIVES (LARCON)

♦♦♦ ⋎ ⋈ Ferme de Larcon Simone RAMAGET
Larcon, 21580 SALIVES
☎ 03 80 75 60 92 ⊟ 03 80 75 60 92
The five guest rooms, each accommodating two or three people,
are situated on a farm and all are equipped with en suite shower-
room/wc. Facilities include a living room, TV, books, central
heating, a garden with play area and parking. Table d'hôte meals
using farm produce are available. The nearest motorway exits are
at Til-Châtel (30km) or La Ferté (40km). Open all year.
PRICES: s €27; d €38; t €53; HB €30; FB €38; dinner €12 **ON SITE:** Golf
Swimming pool **NEARBY:** Forest (2km) Tennis (5km) Railway station
(30km) Shops (15km) Restaurant nearby AIGNAY-LE-DUC (15km)
NOTES: No pets

SANTENAY-EN-BOURGOGNE

♦♦♦ Chambre d'hôtes Françoise MONIOT
44 grande rue, 21590 SANTENAY-EN-BOURGOGNE
☎ 03 80 20 60 52 ⊟ 03 80 20 60 52
e-mail: moniot@net-up.com
Four guest rooms are located in a charming farmhouse on a
vineyard. There are two double rooms and two triple rooms, all
with en suite bathroom or shower-room/wc and TV. Extra
beds can be supplied. Central heating and a living room are
provided for guests. Hiking trail 7 is close by. The village offers a
choice of restaurants. Nearest motorway exits Beaune-Sud or
Chalon-Nord. Open all year, except during the wine harvest.
PRICES: s €46; d €55; t €64; extra person €9 **NEARBY:** Bathing (1km)
Rock climbing (10km) Forest (1km) Golf (15km) Swimming pool (1km)

continued

BURGUNDY

Tennis (1km) Railway station (5km) NOLAY (10km) **NOTES:** Pets admitted (supplement payable)

♦♦♦♦ ⌷◎⌷ Le Chateau de la Crée
Yves Eric et R REMY-THEVENIN
les Hauts-de-Santenay,
21590 SANTENAY-EN-BOURGOGNE
☎ 03 80 20 62 66 🖷 03 80 20 66 50
e-mail: chateaudelacree@wanadoo.fr

This authentic 18th-century manor house forms part of a family estate at the heart of the Côte de Beaune vineyards. There are four guest rooms, two of which are linked, each with en suite bathroom/wc, TV and telephone. Private drawing rooms, 15th-century vaults and wine cellar, bars and billiard table, garden with tennis and putting green. Table d'hôte meals are available on request. A supplement of €19 is charged for pets, which are not allowed in the bedrooms. Open all year (January and February prior booking only).
PRICES: s €125-€170; d €135-€185; extra person €50-€60; HB €120-€160; dinner €85-€120 **ON SITE:** Tennis **NEARBY:** Bathing (1km) Rock climbing (10km) Forest (1km) Golf (18km) Swimming pool (1km) Railway station (5km) Shops (1km) BEAUNE (18km)
NOTES: Pets admitted Minimum 2 night stay English spoken

SAVIGNY-LES-BEAUNE

♦♦♦ ⌷◎⌷ **Chambre d'hôtes** Christine ROSSIGNOL
16 rue General Leclerc, 21420 SAVIGNY-LES-BEAUNE
☎ 03 80 26 10 47 🖷 03 80 26 11 78
e-mail: christine-rossignol@wanadoo.fr
This charming property is close to the Château of Savigny-les-Beaune. There are two double rooms and one suite for six people, which has wooden panelling, ceiling frescos and hexagonal floor tiles. All rooms are en suite. Breakfast is served in the vaulted cellar. A lounge, a kitchenette and central heating, a shady courtyard, a garage (on request) and secure parking are all provided. Guests are welcome to taste and purchase wine.
PRICES: s €46-€63; d €52-€69; t €69-€99; extra person €18; dinner €18 (by reservation) **NEARBY:** Rock climbing (9km) Forest (1km) Golf (7km) Swimming pool (5km) Tennis (1km) Railway station (5km) BEAUNE (4km) **NOTES:** No pets

SEURRE

♦♦♦ **Chambre d'hôtes** Gilles et Christine VERNAY
15 quai du Midi, 21250 SEURRE ☎ 03 80 20 46 32
Situated on the banks of the River Saône in a pleasant little town, this 18th-century house offers four guest rooms, all with en suite shower-room/wc. Facilities include a guest lounge with TV, central heating, a courtyard and parking. A special offer of four nights for the price of three applies. There is a restaurant within 50 metres. Some English is spoken. The nearest motorway exits are at Seurre or Beaune. Open all year.
PRICES: s €27-€30; d €34-€38 **NEARBY:** Bathing (1km) Rock climbing (20km) Forest (2km) Golf (18km) Swimming pool (1km) Tennis (1km) Railway station (1km) Shops (1km) **NOTES:** No pets

THOISY-LE-DESERT (CERCEY)

♦♦♦ **Chambre d'hôtes** Marie-Josephe MIMEUR
Cergey, 21320 THOISY-LE-DESERT
☎ 03 80 90 88 48 & 06 15 10 52 12 🖷 03 80 90 88 48
The four guest rooms, two of which are linked, are all equipped with en suite shower-room/wc. Central heating, a living room, a veranda, a garden, a garage and parking are available. There is a choice of restaurants within three kilometres. The nearest motorway exit is at Pouilly-en-Auxois. Open all year.
PRICES: s €39; d €47-€50; t €57 **NEARBY:** Bathing (1km) Rock climbing (15km) Forest (2km) Golf (1km) Swimming pool (10km) Tennis (2km) Railway station (35km) Shops (3km) POUILLY-EN-AUXOIS (3km) **NOTES:** No pets

VANDENESSE-EN-AUXOIS

♦♦♦ ⌷◎⌷ **Chambre d'hôtes** Lisa JANSEN BOURNE
Lady A Barge, port du Canal - CIDEX 45,
21320 VANDENESSE-EN-AUXOIS
☎ 03 80 49 26 96 🖷 03 80 49 27 00
The three guest cabins are located on a barge on the Canal de Bourgogne in this medieval town. There is a choice of double or single beds and each cabin has en suite shower-room/wc. Living room, lounge with TV, library and central heating. Table d'hôte meals on request, also horse-drawn carriage rides. Nearest motorway exit Pouilly-en-Auxois. Open 1 February to 30 November.
PRICES: s €40; d €50; dinner €20 **ON SITE:** Forest **NEARBY:** Bathing (3km) Golf (10km) Tennis (7km) Railway station (38km) Shops (7km) POUILLY-EN-AUXOIS (7km) **NOTES:** No pets English spoken

VAUCHIGNON

♦♦♦ ♥ **Chambre d'hôtes** Joel TRUCHOT
le Bout du Monde, 21340 VAUCHIGNON
☎ 03 80 21 80 53 🖷 03 80 21 88 76
This old winegrowers' house, situated in a picturesque valley on a Charollais cattle farm, offers five guest rooms, each sleeping two or three guests. There are three grade 3 rooms with en suite shower-room/wc and one grade 1 family room with separate shower-room/wc. A living room, a lounge with TV, electric heating, a garden, a meadow and stabling facilities are also available. Restaurant 3km, hiking trail 7 close by. Open all year.
PRICES: s €23-€30; d €30-€40; t €38-€49 **ON SITE:** Forest **NEARBY:** Bathing (3km) Rock climbing (1km) Golf (21km) Swimming pool (10km) Tennis (3km) Railway station (20km) Shops (3km) NOLAY (3km) **NOTES:** Pets admitted English spoken

VILLARS-VILLENOTTE

♦♦♦ **Les Langrons** Mary & Roger COLLINS
Villars-Villenotte, 21140 SEMUR-EN-AUXOIS
☎ 03 80 96 65 11 🖷 03 80 97 32 28
There are three large rooms, accommodating either two or three

continued

guests, situated in a newly renovated old farm. All rooms have superb views and are equipped with en suite shower-room/wc. Other facilities include a living room, books, central heating, and a large garden with play area and secure parking. A 10% reduction applies on bookings of two nights (except in July and August). There is a choice of restaurants four kilometres away. The nearest motorway exit is at Bierre-les-Semur. Open all year except Christmas.
PRICES: s €45; d €50; t €65; extra person €15 **NEARBY:** Bathing (5km) Rock climbing (17km) Forest (1km) Golf (34km) Swimming pool (12km) Tennis (4km) Railway station (12km) Shops (4km) SEMUR-EN-AUXOIS (5km) **NOTES:** No pets English spoken

VILLEFERRY

♥♥♥ ﻬ Chambre d'hôtes J. SPENCER MERSKY
le verger sous les Vignes, 21350 VILLEFERRY
☎ 03 80 49 60 04 🖹 03 80 49 60 04
Two guest rooms, each with private terrace and garden, enjoy a secluded position amidst the Auxois hills, with a beautiful view of the undulating countryside. A split-level apartment (€61), with kitchen area and private garden, is also available in a restored old winegrowers' house at the bottom of an orchard. All three guest rooms have en suite facilities and a private entrance. Table d'hôte meals are available on request. The nearest motorway exit is at Bierre-les-Semur. Open all year.
PRICES: s €49-€56; d €53-€61; t €70; extra person €9; dinner €18 **ON SITE:** Forest **NEARBY:** Bathing (15km) Rock climbing (10km) Golf (25km) Swimming pool (1km) Tennis (8km) Railway station (13km) Shops (8km) VITTEAUX (8km) **NOTES:** Pets admitted English spoken

NIÈVRE

ALLUY

♥♥♥ ﻬ Bouteuille Colette et André LEJAULT
Alluy, 58110 CHATILLON-EN-BAZOIS
☎ 03 86 84 06 65 & 06 77 35 01 34 🖹 03 86 84 03 41
e-mail: lejault.c@wanadoo.fr http://perso.wanadoo.fr/bouteuille/
Canal du Nivernais 4 km. Forêt de Vincence 6 km. This attractive house, in its own grounds, has a lounge and kitchen for the use of guests. It has three double rooms with private shower room and wc, and one double room with adjoining child's room with private bathroom and wc. There is a payphone. Cycles and boats can be rented 5 km away, and there is a mountain bike trail. Parking. Restaurants within 5 km. Open all year.
PRICES: s €35-€41; d €43-€55; t €61-€66; extra person €12-€15 **ON SITE:** Hiking **NEARBY:** Horse riding (3km) Forest (1km) Fishing (5km) Swimming pool (5km) Water sports (5km) Tennis (5km) Sailing (15km) Railway station (38km) Shops (5km) CHATILLON EN BAZOIS (5km) **NOTES:** No pets English spoken

BAZOCHES

♥♥♥ ﻬ Domaine Rousseau
Nadine et Philippe PERRIER
58190 BAZOCHES
☎ 03 86 22 16 30 🖹 03 86 22 11 81
e-mail: ferme.auberge@dial.oléane.com
http://www.auberge.bazoches.com
Lake Chaumeçon 20 km. This detached 18th-century mansion overlooking the Château de Basochesis close to the Parc du Morvan, and to Clamecy, Vezelay, and Avallon. The five furnished rooms are on the first floor. Three double rooms and two triple rooms each have central heating and private bathroom facilities. A fourth bed is available at a supplement of 12.20 euros. Table d'hôte available except for Wednesday and Sunday evenings. Beautiful views over surrounding countryside. Open all year; booking necessary.

PRICES: d €39; t €54; extra person €13; dinner €14 **ON SITE:** Forest Hiking **NEARBY:** Horse riding (6km) Fishing (2km) Swimming pool (18km) Place of interest (11km) Water sports (17km) Tennis (8km) Sailing (17km) Railway station (20km) Shops (8km) Restaurant nearby VEZELAY (8km) **NOTES:** No pets

♥♥♥ ﻬ Ferme d'Ecosse Chantal PERRIER
58190 BAZOCHES
☎ 03 86 22 14 57 🖹 03 86 22 14 57
e-mail: fermedecosse@wanadoo.fr
This centrally heated house occupies an agricultural setting at the foot of the Château de Bazoches in Morvan. On the ground floor is an entrance and living room reserved for guests. On the first floor there are two double rooms and one triple room, each with private shower room and wc. There is also a kitchen area and garden. Visit the farm and its Charolais cattle. Signposted walking routes offer superb views over surrounding countryside. A farmhouse inn is within 800m. Open throughout July; booking necessary at other times.
PRICES: s €31; d €36; t €48 **NEARBY:** Horse riding (8km) Forest (1km) Fishing (7km) Swimming pool (22km) Hiking (1km) Place of interest (12km) Water sports (15km) Tennis (12km) Sailing (15km) Railway station (12km) Shops (1km) VEZELAY (12km) **NOTES:** No pets English spoken

CHAUMARD

♥♥♥ ﻬ Le Château Charles VAISSETTE
58120 CHAUMARD
☎ 03 86 78 03 33 🖹 03 86 78 04 94
e-mail: chateauchaumard@minitel.net
Lake Settons 15 km. Mont Beuvray 25 km. In the Nature Park of Morvan, the Château de Chaumard has six guest rooms (four grade 3 rooms and two grade 2). The peaceful garden is set within wooded parkland, with views of the Pannecière Lake. A calm family atmosphere, with table d'hôte available on some evenings. Guests are asked to arrive between 5pm and 7pm. Dogs are allowed if kept on a lead. Riders and horses are welcome. Bathing in the lake within 200m, also grocery store and inn. Open all year.
PRICES: s €44; d €44; t €54; extra person €10; dinner €15-€23 **ON SITE:** Fishing Water sports **NEARBY:** Horse riding (10km) Forest (1km) Swimming pool (5km) Hiking (1km) Tennis (5km) Sailing (15km) Railway station (70km) CHATEAU CHINON (12km) **NOTES:** Pets admitted

COSNE-SUR-LOIRE

♥♥♥ ﻬ ﻬ L'Orée des Vignes Marie-Noëlle KANDIN
Croquant, 58200 ST-PERE
☎ 03 86 28 12 50 🖹 03 86 28 12 50
e-mail: loreedesvignes@wanadoo.fr
www.france-bonjour.com/oree-des-vignes
Sancerre 15 km. Pouilly-sur-Loire 15 km. Marie-Noëlle welcomes guests to this small former farmhouse, now restored, offering five charming and individually furnished rooms, each with private shower/wc. Sitting room with fireplace and piano, bread oven, games room, and terrace with garden furniture. The spacious grounds include a wooded area. Parking. GR 3 hiking trail nearby. Golf course within 10km; meals available by reservation. Farm produce, wine, and mountain bike rental are all available nearby. Seventh night free. Also available for birthdays, family reunions, and foie gras trips. Open all year.
PRICES: s €35; d €45; t €58; extra person €17; dinner €20 **ON SITE:** Hiking **NEARBY:** Horse riding (3km) Forest (25km) Fishing (5km) Swimming pool (2km) Place of interest (1km) Water sports (10km) Tennis (2km) Sailing (10km) Railway station (2km) Shops (2km) COSNE SUR LOIRE (2km) **NOTES:** No pets English spoken

continued

DONZY

⚑ ⏹ Jardins de Belle Rive Laura et Bernard JUSTE
Bagnaux, 58220 DONZY
☎ 03 86 39 42 18 🖹 03 86 39 49 15
This detached and centrally heated house is situated in a pleasant wooded region. It has four comfortable guestrooms on the ground and first floors, each with private bathroom and wc. There is also a guests' sitting room, with pretty views of the garden and countryside. Guests may use the private swimming pool. The valley, with a river, has a first-class restaurant. Open all year.
PRICES: s €37; d €40-€49; t €59; extra person €10; dinner €16
ON SITE: Forest Fishing Swimming pool Hiking **NEARBY:** Horse riding (5km) Water sports (25km) Tennis (2km) Sailing (25km) Railway station (17km) Shops (1km) COSNE SUR LOIRE (17km) **NOTES:** No pets English spoken

FOURS

⚑ ⏹ Chambre d'hôtes Denis PETILLOT
Château Latour, 58250 FOURS
☎ 03 86 50 20 15 🖹 03 86 50 20 15
This attractive house, at the gateway to Morvan, has three double rooms on the first floor, each with private bathroom and wc. On the ground floor there is one twin-bedded room with kitchen area and private bathroom/wc. Guests may use the private swimming pool. Lake and river fishing is available, and the Nivernais Canal is nearby. There are walking routes, and a riding centre in the grounds. Small dogs allowed. Open all year.
PRICES: s €38; d €43-€46; t €55 **ON SITE:** Horse riding Forest Hiking **NEARBY:** Fishing (2km) Swimming pool (7km) Water sports (8km) Tennis (1km) Sailing (8km) Railway station (7km) DECIZE (20km) **NOTES:** No pets English spoken

GUERIGNY

⚑ ⏹ Château de Villemenant
Famille CHESNAIS
58130 GUERIGNY
☎ 03 86 90 93 10 🖹 03 86 90 93 19
e-mail: info@chateau-villemenant.com
http://www.chateau-villemenant.com
The tranquil region of Nivernais, between Burgundy and the Loire Valley, is the setting for this fine 14th-century château, marrying together beautifully the charm and nobility of the Middle Ages and modern comforts. The warm welcome, the sumptuous rooms (four rooms, of which two are suites), and refined cuisine make this a truly relaxing stay. Walking and fishing; the Canal du Nivernais and the Formula 1 circuit at Nevers Magny-Cours are nearby. Open all year.
PRICES: s €79-€100; d €95-€115; t €115-€135; extra person €19; dinner €15-€23 **ON SITE:** Fishing **NEARBY:** Horse riding (15km) Forest (1km) Swimming pool (15km) Hiking (1km) Place of interest (30km) Water sports (45km) Tennis (1km) Sailing (45km) Railway station (15km) Shops (1km) NEVERS (15km) **NOTES:** Pets admitted English spoken

LA FERMETE

⚑ ⏹ Château de Prye
Antoine-Emmanuel et Magdalina DU BOURG DE BOZAS
58160 LA FERMETE
☎ 03 86 58 42 64 🖹 03 86 58 47 64
e-mail: welcome@pryecastle.com
Nevers & F1 Circuit at Magny-Cours 15 km. This château was built and furnished between the 17th and 19th centuries. It is situated in a walled estate of some 160 ha, with stables and with a river running through the grounds - a haven of peace and greenery. It has two suites and two rooms, all with private bath and wc.

Billiards, table tennis, piano, TV, and video are available, together with fishing in the grounds. Wedding days and conferences can be arranged. Open from 15 April to 15 October.
PRICES: s €68; d €68-€85; dinner €22 **ON SITE:** Forest Fishing Hiking **NEARBY:** Horse riding (5km) Swimming pool (5km) Tennis (1km) Railway station (5km) Shops (1km) NEVERS (15km) **NOTES:** No pets CC English spoken

LANTY

⚑ 🐾 Chambre d'hôtes LE MAIRE DE LANTY
Mairie, Le Bourg, 58250 LANTY
☎ 03 86 30 93 22 🖹 03 86 30 93 22
Four double guest rooms are available on the first floor, each with shower room and wc. A sitting room and well-equipped kitchen area are reserved for guests' use, and there is also a library and table tennis. Parking. The shady grounds have superb views. Walking routes can be suggested in the nearby forest area. Farm produce is available nearby. Open all year.
PRICES: s €30; d €40; extra person €8 **ON SITE:** Forest Hiking **NEARBY:** Horse riding (13km) Fishing (3km) Swimming pool (13km) Place of interest (80km) Water sports (25km) Tennis (13km) Sailing (6km) Railway station (4km) Shops (3km) FOURS (8km) **NOTES:** Pets admitted English spoken

MAGNY-COURS

⚑ 🐾 Domaine de Fonsegre Michelle BELLANGER
Fonsegre, 58470 MAGNY-COURS
☎ 03 86 21 28 04 🖹 03 86 21 28 05
This former farm building, completely renovated, is close to the Loire châteaux and a Formula One circuit. Six charming furnished rooms are available: one double room and five twin rooms, each with private shower and wc. There is also a billiards room, sitting room, lounge, conference room, library, and swimming pool. GR hiking trail 3 is within 8 km. Open 1 February to 15 December.
PRICES: s €45; d €51; t €70 **ON SITE:** Swimming pool **NEARBY:** Horse riding (10km) Forest (12km) Fishing (4km) Hiking (8km) Water sports (11km) Tennis (5km) Sailing (55km) Railway station (15km) Shops (4km) NEVERS (15km) **NOTES:** No pets

⚑ 🐾 ⏹ Nioux Sylvie BESSON
58470 MAGNY-COURS
☎ 03 86 58 17 94
This former 18th-century hunting lodge on a Charolais estate has four guest rooms. On the first floor are two double rooms and one twin room, each with private shower and wc. In the ground floor annexe is a family room sleeping five, with kitchen and living area and private shower and wc. The building is centrally heated, and includes keep-fit equipment, a lounge with library and playing cards, etc, table tennis, and games room.
PRICES: s €32; d €40-€44; t €73; extra person €27; dinner €18
NEARBY: Horse riding (15km) Forest (5km) Fishing (7km) Swimming pool (15km) Hiking (7km) Tennis (15km) Sailing (35km) Railway station (15km) Shops (2km) NEVERS (15km) **NOTES:** No pets

MONT-ET-MARRE

⚑ Domaine de Semelin Nicole et Paul DELTOUR
Semelin, 58110 MONT-ET-MARRE
☎ 03 86 84 13 94 🖹 03 86 84 13 94
In peaceful countryside, this house has three charming furnished rooms on the ground floor. One triple room has private shower and wc; one double room has private shower and wc; one twin room has private shower room. Fishing and sailing are available on the Etang de Baye; swimming and tennis, as well as pleasant walks, can be found in Châtillon en Bazois.The estate houses a fine collection of dahlias. Open all year; advance booking required from 1 November to 31 March.

continued　　　　　　　　　　　　　　　　*continued*

BURGUNDY

PRICES: s €31-€42; d €35-€46; t €55; extra person €10 **ON SITE:** Hiking **NEARBY:** Horse riding (5km) Forest (10km) Fishing (10km) Swimming pool (4km) Water sports (10km) Tennis (4km) Sailing (10km) Railway station (25km) Shops (4km) CHATILLON EN BAZOIS (4km) **NOTES:** Pets admitted

ONLAY

♦♦♦ ⏱ Château de Lesvault Stanislas BOS
58370 ONLAY
☎ 03 86 84 32 91 📠 03 86 84 35 78
e-mail: chateau.lesvaults@wanadoo.fr www.chateaulesvault.nl
Five triple rooms are available, each with private bathroom, in this peaceful, parkland setting. There is a sitting room, lounge, fireplace, and terrace. An exhibition of contemporary art, and group bookings can be arranged for seminars or workshops. Table d'hôte available. Walking and mountain bike routes, horse-riding available. There is an equestrian centre nearby. Dogs allowed: 4.60 euros. Open all year except for January and February.
PRICES: s €61; d €72; t €88; extra person €15; dinner €22
ON SITE: Forest Hiking **NEARBY:** Horse riding (12km) Fishing (1km) Swimming pool (5km) Water sports (30km) Tennis (5km) Sailing (30km) Railway station (25km) Shops (5km) MOULINS ENGILBERT (5km)
NOTES: Pets admitted CC English spoken

OUROUER

♦♦♦ Château de Nyon Catherine HENRY
Nyon, 58130 OUROUER
☎ 03 86 58 61 12
F1 Circuit 30 km. This handsome house is surrounded by a country park. It has three double guest rooms, tastefully decorated, with private bathrooms and wcs. There is a dining room and lounge. Non-smoking establishment. There are numerous walks in the forest of Amognes. Near a museum, and Nevers, city of art and history. Reduced rates for stays of three nights and more (49 euros/2 persons). Open all year.
PRICES: s €40; d €52; extra person €16 **ON SITE:** Forest Hiking
NEARBY: Horse riding (4km) Fishing (9km) Swimming pool (9km) Place of interest (43km) Water sports (33km) Tennis (6km) Sailing (33km) Railway station (18km) Shops (9km) NEVERS (15km)
NOTES: No pets

OUROUX-EN-MORVAN

♦♦♦ ⏱ Savault Fabrice BELHAMICI
58230 OUROUX-EN-MORVAN
☎ 03 86 78 25 38
This market town is in the heart of the Morvan area. Three large lakes (Les Settons, Pennecière, and Chaumeçon) are close by. Six double rooms are available, each with shower and wc. The lounge and dining room are on the ground floor. Grounds and parking. Group bookings are possible (up to 24 persons). Open all year.
PRICES: s €28; d €44; HB €34; dinner €12 **ON SITE:** Forest Hiking
NEARBY: Horse riding (15km) Fishing (3km) Tennis (3km) Sailing (15km) Railway station (35km) Shops (3km) MONTSAUCHE (4km)
NOTES: Pets admitted

POUILLY-SUR-LOIRE

♦♦♦ ⏱ La Vieille Auberge FAMILLE FABRE
Charenton, 58150 POUILLY-SUR-LOIRE
☎ 03 86 39 17 98 📠 03 86 39 17 98
This former coaching inn is in the middle of a flower-filled park, in the heart of the vineyard of Pouilly sur Loire, 2 hours from Paris. It has three centrally heated rooms, each with private entrance and shower room/wc. Everything possible is done to ensure relaxation. Various leisure activities can be suggested, including hiking routes (GR 13) and mountain and hybrid bike trails. Fishing and kayak

canoeing can be enjoyed in the Loire nature reserve. Fixed-price weekend for two: 135 euros (2 nights, 2 breakfasts, 2 evening meals). Open all year except 15 November to15 December.
PRICES: s €34; d €40; t €50; dinner €18 **NEARBY:** Horse riding (6km) Forest (2km) Fishing (1km) Swimming pool (13km) Hiking (2km) Place of interest (2km) Tennis (2km) Railway station (2km) Shops (2km) LA CHARITE SUR LOIRE (11km) **NOTES:** Pets admitted

RAVEAU

♦♦♦ 🦃 ⏱ Bois-Dieu
Dominique et J MELLET-MANDARD
58400 RAVEAU
☎ 03 86 69 60 02 📠 03 86 70 23 91
e-mail: leboisdieu@wanadoo.fr www.leboisdieu.com

This family house is close to a farm bordering the forest of Bertranges (10,000 ha), on the pilgrim road of St Jacques de Compostelle. It offers four double rooms with private bath/wc, lounge, library, and sitting room. There is a garden and a small lake. Table d'hôte meals can be booked (except for Sunday evenings), and include farm produce and local wine. Non-smoking rooms. Numerous historic sites and monuments are nearby, as well as the vineyards of Pouilly/Loire and Sancerre. Open from16 March to 15 November.
PRICES: s €42; d €49; dinner €19 **ON SITE:** Forest Fishing Hiking Place of interest **NEARBY:** Horse riding (2km) Swimming pool (6km) Water sports (8km) Tennis (2km) Sailing (40km) Railway station (6km) Shops (6km) LA CHARITE SUR LOIRE (6km) **NOTES:** No pets English spoken

♦♦♦ ⏱ Domaine des Forges Claudine MULLER
Route de la Fontaine, 58400 RAVEAU
☎ 03 86 70 22 96 📠 03 86 70 92 66
e-mail: claudine.muller@wanadoo.fr
www.france-bonjour.com/lavache/
On the site of the royal foundry of La Chaussade (18th century), this manor house has six beautiful and comfortable rooms, as well as dining and reception rooms, sitting room, and library, furnished with a discerning eye to both antique and modern. The peaceful countryside and forest of Bertranges offer absolute calm. Stabling available. The property is on the pilgrim road of St James of Compostella, close to vineyards and to Loire à La Charité, a monastic site and literary town. Table d'hôte available. Open all year; advance booking required.
PRICES: s €54; d €72; t €90; HB €73; FB €88; dinner €20-€23
ON SITE: Forest Swimming pool Hiking **NEARBY:** Horse riding (2km) Fishing (3km) Place of interest (9km) Water sports (5km) Tennis (3km) Sailing (20km) Railway station (5km) Shops (5km) LA CHARITE SUR LOIRE (5km) **NOTES:** Pets admitted English spoken

---

For further information on these and
other chambres d'hôtes, consult
the Gîtes de France website
www.gites-de-france.fr

continued

SEMELAY

♦♦♦ ♥ |◎| Domaine de la Chaume

Pierre et Valérie D'ETE
58360 SEMELAY
☎ 03 86 30 91 23 📠 03 86 30 91 23
The owner of this house, set in open country with superb views,
has four first-floor guest rooms: two double rooms, one 4-person
room with mezzanine floor, and one double room with small
kitchen. All have private shower and wc. Stabling for horses, and
shelter for bikes and cars. Children's games, table tennis and
cycles are available, and there is an equestrian centre within 12km.
There are lots of walks and hiking routes, as well as visits to sites
of historical interest (Mont-Beuvray), caves (Beaune) and an
organic farm. Open all year.
PRICES: s €35; d €40; extra person €6; HB €66; dinner €13
ON SITE: Children's play area Forest Hiking **NEARBY:** Horse riding
(12km) Fishing (2km) Swimming pool (10km) Place of interest (1km)
Water sports (14km) Tennis (10km) Sailing (14km) Railway station (10km)
Shops (2km) SAINT HONORE LES BAINS (10km) **NOTES:** No pets
English spoken

ST-AMAND-EN-PUISAYE

♦♦♦ La Berjatterie René MANNEHEUT

58310 ST-AMAND-EN-PUISAYE
☎ 03 86 39 67 14 📠 03 86 39 65 97
e-mail: manneheut@aol.com
Three km from the pottery region of St-Amand, this house is set
peacefully among flowers and trees. The proprietors offer five
independent rooms: two double rooms, two twin rooms, and one
triple room, each with private bathroom and wc. On the ground
floor is a large sitting room, games room with library, and
television. Parking, extensive grounds. Restaurants are within 3 km,
and several châteaux and museums can be visited close by. The
house is close to the Château of St-Fargeau, with its son et
lumière. Open all year.
PRICES: s €43; d €43; t €51; extra person €9 **NEARBY:** Horse riding
(5km) Forest (5km) Fishing (1km) Swimming pool (19km) Hiking (3km)
Place of interest (29km) Tennis (4km) Sailing (10km) Railway station
(17km) Shops (3km) COSNE SUR LOIRE (19km) **NOTES:** No pets

ST-ANDRE-EN-MORVAN

♦♦♦ ♥ |◎| Villurbain

Lise et famille CARREAU, 58140 ST-ANDRE-EN-MORVAN
☎ 03 86 22 67 08 📠 03 86 22 60 46
www.aubergeetfermeauberge.com
Château de Bazoches 5 km. Vézelay 10 km. Winner of first prize in
the regional floral competition, this house has three first-floor
rooms, each with private bathroom and wc: two double rooms,
and one room with twin beds and children's bunk beds. There is a
ground-floor dining room, children's play equipment, and a
terrace; a farming inn is also on the site. Several lakes are close by.
Open from March to December.
PRICES: s €31-€36; d €35-€40; t €48-€51; extra person €13; dinner €14-
€21 **ON SITE:** Children's play area **NEARBY:** Horse riding (4km) Forest
(1km) Fishing (1km) Swimming pool (15km) Hiking (1km) Water sports
(10km) Tennis (4km) Sailing (17km) Railway station (17km) Shops
(10km) Restaurant nearby LORMES (12km) **NOTES:** No pets English
spoken

ST-ELOI

♦♦♦ ♥ |◎| Domaine de Trangy

Chantal et Guy DE VALMONT
8 route de Trangy, 58000 ST-ELOI
☎ 03 86 37 11 27 📠 03 86 37 18 75
e-mail: gdevalmont@free.fr http://chambreshotestrangy.free.fr

The owner of this late 18th-century house has four rooms available
on the first floor. Two double rooms and two twin, each with
private shower and wc; child bed available. Living room and
library. Meals can be booked. There is a swimming pool, table
tennis, and badminton, as well as a pony club. The house is set in
open countryside, with forested land within 2 km. Open all year.
PRICES: s €38; d €45; t €58; dinner €15 **ON SITE:** Horse riding
Swimming pool **NEARBY:** Forest (2km) Fishing (1km) Hiking (1km)
Water sports (8km) Tennis (6km) Sailing (45km) Railway station (6km)
Shops (3km) NEVERS (6km) **NOTES:** No pets English spoken

ST-GRATIEN-SAVIGNY

♦♦♦ |◎| La Marquise Huguette et Noël PERREAU

58340 ST-GRATIEN-SAVIGNY
☎ 03 86 50 01 02 📠 03 86 50 07 14
e-mail: hcollot@aol.com
Canal du Nivernais 1.5 km. This pretty mansion house has two
furnished suites, each with two double rooms and two twin rooms,
with private bathroom and wc. Also on the first floor is a large
room comprising kitchenette and living/sitting area. Central
heating, TV, telephone, parking, heated swimming pool from May
to October, garden. Loose-boxes for horses available. There are
private tennis facilities within 4 km, and short walks (1 to 5 km)
around the property. Children up to 6 years free. Open all year.
PRICES: s €35; d €46; dinner €15 **ON SITE:** Swimming pool Hiking
NEARBY: Horse riding (10km) Forest (1km) Fishing (1km) Water sports
(3km) Tennis (3km) Sailing (25km) Railway station (4km) Shops (4km)
CERCY LA TOUR (5km) **NOTES:** Pets admitted

ST-HILAIRE-EN-MORVAN

♦♦♦ ♥ La Ferme des Archers Edith CAUMONT

Courcelles, 58120 ST-HILAIRE-EN-MORVAN
☎ 03 86 85 08 90 📠 03 86 85 08 90
This typical Morvan farmhouse, on one level, has been restored to
provide four comfortable guest rooms, one of them accessible to
guests with disabilities, all with superb views and private bath
or shower room and wc. A breakfast room is reserved for guests.
There is an animal park of 20 ha, together with traditional farm
animals. Archery and table tennis available. Close by are the lakes
of the Morvan, the museum and archaeological excavations at
Glux-en-Glenne, and a costume museum at Château-Chinon. Non-
smoking. Open 1 February to 15 November.
PRICES: s €40; d €44; t €56; extra person €5 **NEARBY:** Horse riding
(8km) Forest (1km) Fishing (10km) Swimming pool (7km) Hiking (1km)
Water sports (10km) Tennis (16km) Sailing (10km) Railway station (7km)
Shops (7km) CHATEAU-CHINON (7km) **NOTES:** No pets English spoken

♦♦♦ ♥ Les Chaumottes Paul et Bernadette COLAS

Chaumotte, 58120 ST-HILAIRE-EN-MORVAN
☎ 03 86 85 22 33
e-mail: paul.colas@libertysurf.fr
Lac de Pannecière 12 km. In the heart of the Morvan region, close
to the lakes, this 14th-century manor house in open countryside
has panoramic views of the capital of the region. It has one double
room, one twin room, and one room with double bed and bunk
beds. All rooms have private shower and wc. There is a fireplace
and terrace, children's play equipment, and a lawn. Free fishing is
available on the property. The lake of Pannecière is 12 km away
(swimming, fishing, and pedal). Seventh night free. Open 1 May to
30 September.
PRICES: s €30; d €40; t €50; extra person €10 **ON SITE:** Children's play
area Forest Fishing Hiking **NEARBY:** Horse riding (5km) Swimming
pool (5km) Water sports (12km) Tennis (5km) Sailing (12km) Railway
station (40km) Shops (3km) CHATEAU CHINON (5km) **NOTES:** No pets
English spoken

continued

ST-JEAN-AUX-AMOGNES

♥♥♥ ⦿ Château de Sury Hubert DE FAVERGES
58270 ST-JEAN-AUX-AMOGNES
☎ 03 86 58 60 51 ▤ 03 86 68 90 28
e-mail: sury@terre-net.fr

Three furnished guest rooms are available in a 17th-century château, peacefully situated a few kilometres from Nevers in the region of Amognes. Two double rooms each with TV and private shower/wc; one twin room with separate private bathroom and wc. Nearby attractions include the Formula One circuit at Magny-Cours, the vineyards of Pouilly, Sancerre, and Côteaux du Giennois, and the Nivernais Canal. Mountain bikes can be rented. Open all year.
PRICES: s €39; d €49; t €61; dinner €23 **ON SITE:** Horse riding Forest Hiking **NEARBY:** Fishing (1km) Swimming pool (6km) Tennis (6km) Sailing (18km) Railway station (15km) Shops (6km) NEVERS (15km) **NOTES:** Pets admitted English spoken

TINTURY

♥♥♥ Fleury la Tour Michel GUENY
58110 TINTURY
☎ 03 86 84 12 42 ▤ 03 86 84 12 42
e-mail: fleurylatour@wanadoo.fr
http://perso.wanadoo.fr/fleurylatour
This pretty house is close to, but separate from, the owner's house. It has four centrally heated first-floor rooms: one double room and two triple rooms with private shower/wc, and one triple room with private bathroom/wc. There is a kitchen area, and children's play equipment is available. There is a pony club 5 km away. The property includes a private lake, and offers walks, canoeing, table football, and table tennis. Open all year; booking necessary from 11 November to 31 March.
PRICES: s €35-€43; d €38-€46; t €49-€56; extra person €11 **ON SITE:** Children's play area Forest Fishing Hiking Tennis Sailing **NEARBY:** Horse riding (5km) Swimming pool (12km) Water sports (30km) Railway station (18km) Shops (6km) ROUY (6km) **NOTES:** Pets admitted English spoken

VAUCLAIX

♥♥♥ ✿ ⦿ Les Chaumes Pierre DUMOULIN
58140 VAUCLAIX
☎ 03 86 22 75 37
The Domaine des Chaumes is an organic farming enterprise, with a river on the estate. Five rooms are available: two double rooms (one with private bathroom and wc, one with private shower room and wc) and three rooms sleeping two to three (each with private shower room and wc). Mountain bikes, horse riding, canoeing, and boating are available. Rates reduced by 10 per cent for two nights or more; fifth night free. Open all year; booking necessary.
PRICES: s €38; d €40; t €50; dinner €15 **ON SITE:** Horse riding Fishing Hiking **NEARBY:** Forest (1km) Tennis (7km) Railway station (30km) Shops (7km) LORMES (7km) **NOTES:** Pets admitted

ALLERIOT

♥♥♥ ⦿ Chambre d'hôtes Claudine et Alain FRANCK
Rue de l'Etang Bonnot, 71380 ALLERIOT
☎ 03 85 47 58 58 ▤ 03 85 47 58 58
e-mail: franck-71380@libertysurf.fr
Alain and Claudine invite you to their 18th-century farm on the banks of the Saône. Three guest rooms (four and two people) with private bathrooms and wc. Sitting room for guests. Gourmet discovery weekends can be booked in advance. Huge enclosed wooded grounds. Golf 6 km. Open mid-March to mid-November.
PRICES: s €30; d €38-€43; t €50-€55; extra person €12; dinner €15 **ON SITE:** Fishing Hiking **NEARBY:** Horse riding (2km) Swimming pool (12km) Place of interest (25km) Tennis (6km) Bicycle hire (6km) Railway station (12km) Shops (6km) CHALON-SUR-SAONE (12km) **NOTES:** No pets English spoken

AMANZE

♥♥♥ ⦿ Chambre d'hôtes Marie-Christine PAPERIN
GAEC des Collines, 71800 AMANZE
☎ 03 85 70 66 34 ▤ 03 85 70 63 81
e-mail: philippe.paperin@wanadoo.fr
There are four spacious rooms on offer here in this very old farm building in the heart of Brionnais. One double room, one triple and two rooms for four, one with mezzanine. Individual bathrooms. Communal lounge for visitors. Enclosed grounds. Children's games. Local cycle discovery route. Roman churches. Open 1 April to 1 November.
PRICES: s €34; d €43; t €54; extra person €11; dinner €14 **ON SITE:** Children's play area Hiking **NEARBY:** Horse riding (5km) Fishing (3km) Swimming pool (10km) Stretch of water (10km) Place of interest (50km) Tennis (5km) Bicycle hire (10km) Railway station (10km) Shops (10km) Restaurant nearby LA CLAYETTE (10km) **NOTES:** No pets English spoken

ANZY-LE-DUC

♥♥♥ ⦿ Les Pradelles Laurence SAUCEZ-DUQUESNE
Chemin des Colins, 71110 ANZY-LE-DUC
☎ 03 85 25 26 02 ▤ 03 85 25 26 02
e-mail: laurence.duquesne@wanadoo.fr

On the circuit of the Roman churches of Brionnais. Four family rooms with individual bathrooms. Enormous enclosed wooded grounds. Babysitting if required. Private swimming pool. Meals on request. Open all year.
PRICES: s €43; d €49; extra person €15; dinner €15 **ON SITE:** Swimming pool Hiking Tennis Bicycle hire **NEARBY:** Horse riding (15km) Fishing (1km) Stretch of water (40km) Place of interest (4km) Railway station (20km) Shops (1km) MARCIGNY (4km) **NOTES:** No pets English spoken

AZE

🏠 Chambre d'hôtes Nelly PEULET
Le Bourg, 71260 AZE
☎ 03 85 33 44 20
e-mail: peulet.nelly@wanadoo.fr
http://perso.wanadoo.fr/nelly.peulet/
A village house on a Mâcon vineyard, a few kilometres from Cluny. Four guest rooms for two to four people, with individual access from the garden. Lovely view over the vineyards. Television in each room. Private breakfast room. Terrace. Courtyard and enclosed grounds. Open 15 January to 15 December.
PRICES: s €34; d €43-€49; t €55; extra person €12 ON SITE: Place of interest NEARBY: Horse riding (1km) Forest (1km) Fishing (1km) Swimming pool (1km) Stretch of water (20km) Hiking (1km) Tennis (1km) Bicycle hire (1km) Railway station (20km) CLUNY (12km)
NOTES: No pets

🏠 En Rizerolles Roger BARRY
En Rizerolles, 71260 AZE
☎ 03 85 33 33 26 📠 03 85 33 40 13
e-mail: r.barry.azé@infonie.fr
Five comfortable rooms in a pretty and typical house halfway between Cluny and Mâcon. Each room has shower and wc. Communal room with lounge reserved for guests. Central heating. Balcony, courtyard, terrace and enclosed garden. Golf 5 km, caves 250m. Restaurants around the corner. Open all year.
PRICES: s €33; d €43; t €58; extra person €17 ON SITE: Fishing Swimming pool Hiking Place of interest Tennis NEARBY: Horse riding (1km) Stretch of water (25km) Bicycle hire (17km) Railway station (17km) Shops (1km) CLUNY (12km) NOTES: Pets admitted

BAUDRIERES

🏠 Chambre d'hôtes Arlette VACHET
Le Bourg, 71370 BAUDRIERES
☎ 03 85 47 32 18 & 06 07 49 53 46 📠 03 85 47 41 42
Three guest rooms in a house of character. Double rooms, one with an extra child's bed, each with shower or bath and wc. Television in each room. Garden, parking. Open 15 April to 15 October; out of season on request.
PRICES: s €53-€64; d €58-€69; t €69 ON SITE: Hiking Tennis Bicycle hire NEARBY: Horse riding (12km) Fishing (1km) Swimming pool (12km) Stretch of water (10km) Place of interest (20km) Railway station (18km) Shops (5km) CHALON-SUR-SAONE (18km) NOTES: Pets admitted English spoken

BISSEY-SOUS-CRUCHAUD

🏠 La Combe Jean et Marie-Anne COGNARD
71390 BISSEY-SOUS-CRUCHAUD
☎ 03 85 92 15 40 & 06 81 10 79 07 📠 03 85 92 19 54
Four comfortable rooms on a wine-producing enterprise of the Côte Chalonnaise, 3 km from Buxy. All double rooms, with shower and wc. Breakfast room and lounge reserved exclusively for visitors. Swimming pool. Footpaths and vineyards all around. Open all year.
PRICES: s €38; d €53; extra person €15 ON SITE: Swimming pool Hiking Place of interest NEARBY: Horse riding (8km) Fishing (9km) Stretch of water (15km) Tennis (3km) Bicycle hire (3km) Railway station (15km) Shops (3km) BUXY (3km) NOTES: No pets English spoken

BOURGVILAIN

🏠 Le Moulin des Arbillons C et S DUBOIS-FAVRE
Les Arbillons, 71520 BOURGVILAIN
☎ 03 85 50 82 83 📠 03 85 50 86 32
e-mail: arbillon@club-internet.fr
www.club-internet.fr/perso/arbillon
Near Cluny (8 km) in the outbuildings of an 18th-century mill. Five

rooms with shower or bath and wc. One room accessible to guests with disabilities. Lounge (fireplace, television, video recorder) and breakfast room reserved for guests. Regional wines and crafts are sold in the cellar. Restaurant 300m. Open 1 July to 31 August.
PRICES: s €46-€72; d €53-€72; t €87 ON SITE: Wine tasting Fishing Hiking NEARBY: Horse riding (8km) Swimming pool (8km) Stretch of water (3km) Place of interest (15km) Tennis (8km) Bicycle hire (9km) Railway station (25km) Shops (1km) CLUNY (8km) NOTES: No pets

BRESSE-SUR-GROSNE

🏠 Relais du Vieux Collombier
Elisabeth et Robert CARRETTE
Collombier, 71460 BRESSE-SUR-GROSNE
☎ 03 85 92 58 84 & 03 85 32 56 74 📠 03 85 32 19 76
e-mail: rcarrette@infonie.fr http://perso.infonie.fr/rcarrette
Old freestanding farm building. Large day room reserved for guests. Convivial surroundings. Fully equipped kitchen for visitors' use. Sitting area. Three double rooms, each with bath and wc. Part of the grounds reserved for guests. Cycling and hiking trails. Open 1 April to 31 October.
PRICES: s €43; d €49; t €61 ON SITE: Hiking Bicycle hire NEARBY: Horse riding (4km) Fishing (1km) Swimming pool (8km) Stretch of water (10km) Place of interest (2km) Tennis (1km) Railway station (17km) Shops (6km) SAINT-GENGOUX-LE-NATIONAL (6km) NOTES: No pets

CHARDONNAY

🏠 Champvent Jean-Paul et Régine RULLIERE
71700 CHARDONNAY
☎ 03 85 40 50 23 📠 03 85 40 50 18
Five double rooms on the first floor, one of which has a sitting room and cot (or can take three). Showers and baths, wcs. Private breakfast room. Lounge with open fire. Washing machine. Dish washer. Exhibition room and function room. Shady park and children's games, and outdoor concerts. Two hiking trails around the village. La Boucherette discovery trail 2 km. Parking. Open 1 March to 30 October.
PRICES: s €34; d €44-€46 ON SITE: Children's play area Hiking Place of interest NEARBY: Horse riding (10km) Fishing (5km) Swimming pool (11km) Stretch of water (20km) Tennis (5km) Bicycle hire (7km) Railway station (11km) Shops (5km) TOURNUS (11km) NOTES: Pets admitted English spoken

CHATENAY

🏠 🍽 Lavaux Paulette GELIN
71800 CHATENAY
☎ 03 85 28 08 48 📠 03 85 26 80 66
Five guest rooms in a farmhouse full of character. Each room has access to an outside gallery. Shower or bath and wc in each room. Grounds. Farm produce 500m. Pond. Honey producer in the village. Open Easter to mid-November.
PRICES: s €38; d €46-€53; extra person €9; dinner €11-€18 ON SITE: Fishing Hiking Bicycle hire NEARBY: Horse riding (12km) Swimming pool (8km) Stretch of water (8km) Place of interest (25km) Tennis (8km) Railway station (8km) Shops (4km) Restaurant nearby LA CLAYETTE (8km) NOTES: No pets English spoken

🏠 Les Bassets Bernadette JOLIVET
71800 CHATENAY
☎ 03 85 28 19 51 📠 03 85 26 83 10
Guests have the choice of four really comfortable rooms for two and four people in this old farmhouse. Each has full bathroom facilities. Lounge and sitting room set aside for guests; kitchen area available. Courtyard and enclosed grounds. Many Roman churches and castles nearby. Mountain biking and hiking trails. Farmhouse inn 1 km. Open 1 April to 31 October.

continued   continued

PRICES: s €34; d €42; t €55; extra person €12 **ON SITE:** Hiking
NEARBY: Horse riding (12km) Fishing (2km) Swimming pool (7km)
Stretch of water (7km) Place of interest (30km) Tennis (7km) Bicycle hire
(7km) Railway station (7km) Shops (7km) LA CLAYETTE (7km)
NOTES: No pets

CHEVAGNY-LES-CHEVRIERES

♥♥♥ Chambre d'hôtes Marie-Thérèse MARIN
Le Bourg, 71960 CHEVAGNY-LES-CHEVRIERES
☎ 03 85 34 78 60 ▤ 03 85 20 10 99
e-mail: marie-therese.marin@wanadoo.fr
Three rooms for two or four people in a 17th-century agricultural
house in the heart of the Mâconnais, on the wine and Roman
church trail. Panoramic view over Solutré, Vergisson.. Private
showers and wcs. Courtyard, garden, wine-tasting and wine sales.
Restaurant 100 m. Open all year.
PRICES: s €30; d €46; extra person €12 **ON SITE:** Wine tasting Hiking
NEARBY: Horse riding (1km) Fishing (5km) Swimming pool (5km)
Stretch of water (20km) Place of interest (8km) Tennis (5km) Bicycle hire
(5km) Railway station (5km) MACON (5km) **NOTES:** No pets

DEMIGNY

♥♥♥ Le Meix des Hospices Françoise THIERY
Rue Basse, 71150 DEMIGNY
☎ 03 85 49 98 49
In an old farmhouse once belonging to the Hospices de Beaune,
three large rooms for two to four people (with showers and wcs);
large living room full of character (kitchen area available). Leisure
room (television, books, board games). Barbecue. Well-tended
estate and external areas (pétanque). Nearby vineyard. Restaurant
4 km. Open all year.
PRICES: s €34; d €49; t €61; extra person €12 **ON SITE:** Tennis
NEARBY: Fishing (1km) Swimming pool (7km) Stretch of water (6km)
Hiking (4km) Place of interest (1km) Railway station (7km) BEAUNE
(10km) **NOTES:** Pets admitted English spoken

FLEY

♥♥♥ Chambre d'hôtes Françoise et André DAVID
Le Bourg, 71390 FLEY
☎ 03 85 49 21 85 & 06 07 09 54 81 ▤ 03 85 49 21 85
e-mail: anddavid@club-internet.fr
Three charming, comfortable rooms (one a suite for three people)
in a house in a Chalonnais village. Separate access to rooms. Each
room has shower and wc. Day room and sitting room exclusively
for visitors. Tended enclosed courtyard. Gallery. Walk no. 6 on the
Voie Verte. Open all year except October. Out of season by
booking.
PRICES: s €32; d €45; extra person €21 **ON SITE:** Hiking Place of
interest **NEARBY:** Horse riding (20km) Fishing (3km) Swimming pool
(6km) Stretch of water (15km) Tennis (6km) Bicycle hire (5km) Railway
station (20km) Shops (3km) BUXY (6km) **NOTES:** Pets admitted English
spoken

IGUERANDE

♥♥♥ ⏀ Les Montées Denise et Maurice MARTIN
Outre-Loire, 71340 IGUERANDE
☎ 03 85 84 09 69 ▤ 03 85 84 09 69
e-mail: mart1dmonty@aol.com www.lesmonty.free.fr
Four vast rooms (one ground floor) in an old farmhouse deep in
the Brionnais, a few kilometres from the banks of the Loire. Rustic
décor. Peace and quiet guaranteed. Private shower, bath and wc.
Living room with sitting area. Enclosed shady grounds. Mountain
bike circuit. Airport 20 km. Possible lodging for horses. Meals if
booked. Open all year.
PRICES: s €39; d €45; t €60; dinner €17 **ON SITE:** Hiking

NEARBY: Horse riding (5km) Fishing (1km) Swimming pool (10km)
Place of interest (5km) Tennis (1km) Railway station (22km) Shops (1km)
MARCIGNY (10km) **NOTES:** No pets English spoken

LA GRANDE-VERRIERE

♥♥♥ Les Dues Paul CARE
71990 LA GRANDE-VERRIERE
☎ 03 85 82 50 32
Three very comfortable rooms (one for families) in an old
renovated barn in a hamlet in the Parc du Morvan. Very quiet.
Each room has shower and wc. Breakfast room and living room
reserved for guests. Feel free to relax on the terrace and grounds .
Golf 15 km. Open all year.
PRICES: s €30; d €37; extra person €15 **ON SITE:** Hiking
NEARBY: Horse riding (15km) Fishing (2km) Swimming pool (15km)
Stretch of water (15km) Place of interest (30km) Tennis (15km) Bicycle
hire (3km) Railway station (15km) Shops (3km) AUTUN (15km)
NOTES: Pets admitted

LA GUICHE

♥♥♥ Les Maupoix Nadine SACCHETI
L'Hermitage, 71220 LA GUICHE
☎ 03 85 24 68 55
e-mail: nadine.saccheti@wanadoo.fr
Three rooms in a large, quiet stone house. Two double rooms with
extra child's bed, with shower and wc; one double room with
shower. Dining room, hire television. Wooded park. Horses can be
accommodated in stables or on grass. Restaurant 200m. Open all
year.
PRICES: s €38; d €46; t €53 **NEARBY:** Horse riding (20km) Fishing
(2km) Swimming pool (20km) Stretch of water (2km) Hiking (1km) Place
of interest (20km) Tennis (1km) Railway station (20km) Shops (1km)
CLUNY (20km) **NOTES:** Pets admitted English spoken

LA ROCHE-VINEUSE

♥♥♥ Somméré Eliane HEINEN
Le Tinailler d'Aléane, Somméré,
71960 LA ROCHE-VINEUSE
☎ 03 85 37 80 68 ▤ 03 85 37 80 68
A noteworthy house giving a fine view over the rocks of Solutré
and Vergisson. Two double rooms and one room for two to four
people, all with bath or shower and wc. Lounge. Courtyard and
grounds. Closed parking. On the Lamartinien Circuit. Restaurant 2
km. Open all year.
PRICES: s €30-€33; d €38-€46; extra person €12 **ON SITE:** Hiking
Bicycle hire **NEARBY:** Horse riding (2km) Fishing (2km) Swimming pool
(8km) Stretch of water (15km) Place of interest (1km) Tennis (2km)
Railway station (5km) Shops (2km) MACON (8km) **NOTES:** No pets
English spoken

LA VINEUSE

♥♥♥ La Maitresse Julie SERRES
Le Bourg, 71250 LA VINEUSE
☎ 03 85 59 60 98 ▤ 03 85 59 65 26
e-mail: serres.chris@wanadoo.fr www.netacf.com/maitresse
Five comfortable rooms (one accessible to guests with disabilities),
each with private shower or bathroom and wc. Exceptional site.
Breakfast room for guests. Kitchen available for use. Television in
every room. Enclosed grounds. Private swimming pool. Bikes
available. Meals available Saturday, Sunday, Monday. Open Easter
to 30 September, and on request out of season.

continued

continued

PRICES: s €53; d €61-€76; t €91; extra person €15 **ON SITE:** Swimming pool Hiking Bicycle hire **NEARBY:** Horse riding (2km) Fishing (5km) Stretch of water (19km) Place of interest (15km) Tennis (7km) Railway station (35km) Shops (7km) CLUNY (7km) **NOTES:** No pets English spoken

LAIVES

🎏 La Ruée Nadine FUMAL
71240 LAIVES
☎ 03 85 44 78 63
Let Nadine show you the three guest rooms in her ancient Chalonnais farmhouse. Each room has private shower and wc. Breakfast is served in a huge dining room with lounge area, television and library. Enclosed garden. Open 1 April to 1 November.
PRICES: s €38; d €46 **ON SITE:** Hiking **NEARBY:** Horse riding (6km) Fishing (2km) Swimming pool (3km) Stretch of water (2km) Place of interest (15km) Tennis (3km) Railway station (12km) Shops (3km) SENNECEY-LE-GRAND (3km) **NOTES:** Pets admitted

LAIZY

🎏 🐓 ⦿ La Chassagne Françoise GORLIER
71190 LAIZY
☎ 03 85 82 39 47 📠 03 85 82 39 47
e-mail: françoise.gorlier@wanadoo.fr
Four comfortable rooms in a noteworthy farmhouse. At ground level, a breakfast room and sitting room with television. Four double bedrooms with shower or bath and wc. Terrace and managed grounds. Meals if booked, except Sunday evening. Farm produce. Golf 12 km. Open 15 January to 15 December.
PRICES: s €32; d €40; t €49; extra person €9; dinner €14
ON SITE: Hiking **NEARBY:** Horse riding (5km) Fishing (4km) Swimming pool (12km) Stretch of water (12km) Place of interest (35km) Tennis (4km) Bicycle hire (12km) Railway station (7km) Shops (7km) AUTUN (12km) **NOTES:** No pets English spoken

LE ROUSSET

🎏 Le Grand Fussy Dominique BRUN
71220 LE ROUSSET
☎ 03 85 24 60 26 & 06 07 26 19 22 📠 03 85 24 60 26
A few kilometres from Cluny, in a huge and beautiful 18th-century house surrounded by a large garden, choose from three comfortable rooms, all carefully appointed. Each has a bathroom and wc. Salon, small kitchen and guests' breakfast room. Library. Terrace. Private swimming pool. Open ally ear.
PRICES: s €53; d €59; extra person €12 **ON SITE:** Swimming pool Hiking **NEARBY:** Horse riding (8km) Forest (1km) Fishing (2km) Stretch of water (2km) Place of interest (25km) Tennis (6km) Bicycle hire (15km) Railway station (20km) Shops (6km) MONTCEAU-LES-MINES (15km) **NOTES:** Pets admitted English spoken

MARCIGNY

🎏 Chambre d'hôtes Andrée RICOL
La Musardière, 50 rue de la Tour, 71110 MARCIGNY
☎ 03 85 25 38 54 & 06 08 26 92 14

On the Roman church trail, at the entrance to the village, a 19th-century house of character offers three guest rooms, one with cooking facilities. All have bathroom and wc. Quiet is guaranteed in our lush parkland, well-managed and enclosed. Private swimming pool. Enclosed parking with car shelter. Open all year.
PRICES: s €30-€43; d €46-€50; extra person €18 **ON SITE:** Swimming pool Bicycle hire **NEARBY:** Horse riding (8km) Fishing (2km) Stretch of water (30km) Hiking (1km) Place of interest (15km) Tennis (1km) Railway station (30km) PARAY-LE-MONIAL (25km) **NOTES:** Pets admitted English spoken

🎏 ⦿ Les Recollets Josette BADIN
71110 MARCIGNY
☎ 03 85 25 05 16 📠 03 85 25 06 91
Six guest rooms (each with bathroom and wc) in a house of some character. Lounge, sitting room, television, library, games room. Garden with shaded terrace. Meals if booked. Open all year.
PRICES: s €49; d €72; t €82; extra person €11; dinner €31
ON SITE: Bicycle hire **NEARBY:** Horse riding (3km) Fishing (2km) Swimming pool (1km) Hiking (2km) Place of interest (50km) Tennis (1km) Railway station (20km) Shops (1km) PARAY-LE-MONIAL (25km) **NOTES:** Pets admitted

MAZILLE

🎏 Le Domaine du Vernay Yolande et J-Claude BORY
71250 MAZILLE
☎ 03 85 50 85 51 📠 03 85 50 85 83
e-mail: contact@domaineduvernay.com
www.domaineduvernay.com
In this 18th-century vineyard house, located a few kilometres from Cluny, there are enormous and comfortable upstairs rooms giving charming views over the Lamartinien valley. Each room has bathroom and wc. Communal room with sitting room and open fireplace. Kitchenette for guests' use. Large reception room. Enclosed grounds and courtyard. Garage and parking. Restaurant 1 km. Open all year.
PRICES: s €40-€52; d €50-€62; t €60-€72; extra person €10
ON SITE: Hiking **NEARBY:** Horse riding (2km) Forest (1km) Fishing (1km) Swimming pool (7km) Stretch of water (10km) Place of interest (10km) Tennis (1km) Bicycle hire (7km) Railway station (20km) Shops (1km) CLUNY (7km) **NOTES:** Pets admitted CC English spoken

⦿
Places with this symbol serve table d'hôtes
evening meals - remember to book in advance

MELLECEY

⁴⁴⁴⁴ Le Clos Saint-Martin Kate et Stephan MURRAY-SYKES
71640 MELLECEY ☎ 03 85 45 25 93 🖹 03 85 45 25 93
e-mail: stephan.murraysykes@freesbee.fr

Amongst the vineyards of the Côte Chalonnaise, Kate and Stephan
welcome you to their beautiful property surrounded by an
enclosed wooded park. Six extremely comfortable rooms for two
to four people, all equipped with private bath or shower.
Television, private swimming pool. Non-smoking establishment.
Restaurant 300m. Open 7 January to 22 December.
PRICES: s €69-€120; d €84-€135; t €130-€145; extra person €15-€23
ON SITE: Fishing Swimming pool Hiking Place of interest
NEARBY: Horse riding (2km) Stretch of water (25km) Tennis (1km)
Bicycle hire (10km) Railway station (10km) CHALON-SUR-SAONE (10km)
NOTES: No pets English spoken

MONT-SAINT-VINCENT

⁴⁴⁴⁴ La Croix de Mission Madeleine GONNOT
71300 MONT-SAINT-VINCENT
☎ 03 85 79 81 03
This substantial home is at the village entrance. Splendid views
from the terrace and gardens. Disabled access. On the ground
floor: communal living room with television; one room with twin
beds and disabled facilities. Upstairs four rooms for two or three
people with private bath or shower and wc. Open 1 March to 15
November. Book for dates in closed season.
PRICES: s €41-€44; d €44-€50; t €55-€61 **ON SITE:** Hiking
NEARBY: Horse riding (10km) Fishing (4km) Swimming pool (10km)
Stretch of water (4km) Place of interest (6km) Tennis (5km) Bicycle hire
(10km) Railway station (10km) MONTCEAU-LES-MINES (10km)
NOTES: Pets admitted

MOROGES

⁴⁴⁴⁴ 🍽 L'Orangerie David EADES et Niels LIEROW
Vingelles, 71390 MOROGES
☎ 03 85 47 91 94 🖹 03 85 47 98 49
In a huge country house between vineyards and meadows, choose
from five elegant rooms, each with private bath or shower and wc.
Beautiful day room. Enclosed shady park. Telephone in each room.
Meals can be booked. Open Easter to 1 November.
PRICES: s €55-€80; d €60-€90; t €110; dinner €30 **ON SITE:** Swimming
pool Hiking Place of interest **NEARBY:** Fishing (5km) Stretch of water
(10km) Tennis (2km) Railway station (16km) Shops (2km) GIVRY (8km)
NOTES: No pets English spoken

⁴⁴⁴⁴ 🍽 Moulin Brulé Françoise PAUPE
71390 MOROGES ☎ 03 85 47 90 40 🖹 03 85 47 97 10
e-mail: moulin.brule@wanadoo.fr
In a Chalonnais vineyard, your hostess Françoise welcomes you to
her enormous house, surrounded by a wooded park. Four rooms
for two or three people in the old mill with refined decor. Each

room has shower and wc. Television points. Breakfast room and
salon. Meals can be booked. Restaurant 2 km. Open all year.

PRICES: d €54; t €66; dinner €22 **ON SITE:** Fishing Hiking Place of
interest **NEARBY:** Horse riding (10km) Swimming pool (10km) Stretch of
water (5km) Tennis (2km) Bicycle hire (5km) Railway station (12km)
Shops (5km) CHALON-SUR-SAONE (12km) **NOTES:** No pets English
spoken

PALINGES

⁴⁴⁴⁴ Les Hortensias Michèle AUZEL
71430 PALINGES
☎ 03 85 70 21 34
A house of character in the village centre. One twin room, with
bath and wc; one triple with shower and wc; one double with
washbasin and wc. Lounge, television. Possible use of kitchenette
in separate studio (for three) adjoining owner's house. Shady
terrace, garden, garage, enclosed grounds. Lake for fishing and
bathing. Restaurant in village. Open 15 May to 15 November.
PRICES: d €46-€53; t €76; extra person €23 **ON SITE:** Fishing Hiking
Tennis **NEARBY:** Horse riding (12km) Swimming pool (12km) Railway
station (1km) PARAY-LE-MONIAL (12km) **NOTES:** No pets

POISSON

⁴⁴⁴⁴ 🍽 Château de Martigny Edith DOR
71600 POISSON
☎ 03 85 81 53 21 🖹 03 85 81 59 40
e-mail: château.Martigny@worldonline.fr
www.worldonline.fr/château.Martigny
Four bedrooms in a restored 18th-century castle. Shaded park.
Two double rooms and two triples, and the possibility of a
children's room. All have bathroom and wc. Lounge and sitting
room with television. Garage. Farm produce. Performances and
theatre at the castle. Open 1 April to 1 November.
PRICES: s €69-€91; d €76-€99; t €99; dinner €30 **ON SITE:** Swimming
pool Hiking Bicycle hire **NEARBY:** Horse riding (4km) Fishing (2km)
Stretch of water (4km) Place of interest (40km) Tennis (2km) Railway
station (12km) Shops (12km) PARAY-LE-MONIAL (12km) **NOTES:** Pets
admitted English spoken

⁴⁴⁴⁴ 🍽 Sermaize Maguy et Paul MATHIEU
71600 POISSON
☎ 03 85 81 06 10 🖹 03 85 81 06 10
A 14th-century Charollais hunting lodge offering one family room
(five beds), two double rooms and two triple rooms, each with
shower room and wc. Living room, library. Set out parkland,
courtyard, garage. Restaurant 4km. Meals must be booked. Open
15 March to 11 November.
PRICES: s €42; d €46-€54; t €66; extra person €12; dinner €16
ON SITE: Fishing **NEARBY:** Horse riding (4km) Swimming pool (12km)
Stretch of water (14km) Hiking (1km) Place of interest (50km) Tennis
(4km) Bicycle hire (11km) Railway station (11km) Shops (4km) PARAY-
LE-MONIAL (11km) **NOTES:** Pets admitted English spoken

continued

SALORNAY-SUR-GUYE

Chambre d'hôtes Jean-Pierre FORESTIER
La Salamandre, Le Bourg, 71250 SALORNAY-SUR-GUYE
☎ 03 85 59 91 56 🖷 03 85 59 91 67
e-mail: info@la-salamandre.fr www.la-salamandre.fr

This 18th-century house offers four double rooms and one suite
for three or four. All have shower or bathrooms and wc. Library
and sitting room. Garden and enclosed park. Cycle tracks. The
rooms are no smoking. Closed 15 Jan-15 Feb & 15 Nov-15 Dec.
PRICES: s €53-€70; d €70-€90; t €90; extra person €17; dinner €20
NEARBY: Horse riding (7km) Fishing (2km) Swimming pool (10km)
Hiking (1km) Place of interest (20km) Tennis (1km) CLUNY (10km)
NOTES: No pets

SENNECE-LES-MACON

Le Clos Barault Roger JULLIN
425 rue Vrémontoise, 71000 SENNECE-LES-MACON
☎ 03 85 36 00 12
Three guest rooms in a house of some character 5 km from
Mâcon. Two double rooms with shower room and wc. One
separate room for two to four people, with cot, bath, lounge and
kitchen. Dining room, lounge, television, library. Lovely garden.
Restaurant in village on banks of the Saône. Open all year
PRICES: s €34; d €46; t €66; extra person €14 **ON SITE:** Bicycle hire
NEARBY: Horse riding (5km) Fishing (2km) Swimming pool (5km)
Stretch of water (13km) Hiking (1km) Place of interest (6km) Tennis
(5km) Railway station (6km) MACON (6km) **NOTES:** No pets

SENOZAN

Chambre d'hôtes Susan BADIN
Le Bourg, 71260 SENOZAN
☎ 03 85 36 00 96 🖷 03 85 37 51 09
e-mail: clos.de.leglise@wanadoo.fr

Four guest rooms for two to five people with private bathroom
and wc, in an old restored house. Garden. Private closed parking.
Open all year.

PRICES: s €35; d €46; t €58; extra person €15 **NEARBY:** Horse riding
(1km) Fishing (1km) Swimming pool (8km) Hiking (1km) Place of
interest (4km) Tennis (1km) Bicycle hire (8km) Railway station (8km)
Shops (1km) MACON (8km) **NOTES:** No pets English spoken

SIVIGNON

L'Ecousserie du Bas Jean-Claude GEOFFROY
71220 SIVIGNON
☎ 03 85 59 66 66
Half an hour from the major tourist and cultural sites of south
Burgundy, this family mansion projects calm and relaxation in the
emerald setting of the Monts du Charolais. Guests can enjoy
fishing and the flower garden at the right times of year. Nearby
restaurant. Open all year.
PRICES: s €35-€40; d €46; t €61 **ON SITE:** Swimming pool Hiking
NEARBY: Horse riding (3km) Stretch of water (15km) Place of interest
(20km) Tennis (8km) Bicycle hire (3km) Railway station (20km) Shops
(7km) CLUNY (20km) **NOTES:** No pets English spoken

SOMMANT

Château de Vareilles
D et F WILLEMSEN et FRANSEN
71540 SOMMANT
☎ 03 85 82 67 22 🖷 03 85 82 69 00
e-mail: ch.de.vareilles@wanadoo.fr www.chateaudevareilles.com

Six huge, comfortable double rooms; one suite is adapted for less
able guests, in an early 19th-century house. Each room has private
bathroom and wc. Possible extra beds. Panoramic vista. Lounge,
dining room, library and video room, salon with television and
open fire exclusively for guests. 7 ha park. Terrace. Private
swimming pool. Open all year.
PRICES: s €53; d €69-€84; t €87-€100; extra person €18; dinner €21
ON SITE: Swimming pool Hiking Bicycle hire **NEARBY:** Horse riding
(1km) Fishing (2km) Stretch of water (11km) Place of interest (30km)
Tennis (11km) Railway station (11km) Shops (11km) AUTUN (11km)
NOTES: No pets English spoken

ST-AUBIN-SUR-LOIRE

Château des Lambeys Etienne DE BUSSIERRE
71140 SAINT-AUBIN-SUR-LOIRE
☎ 03 85 53 92 76
Five guest rooms in an 18th-century house on the banks of the
Loire. Each double room has a large bed, bathroom and wc.
Dining room and billiard room are reserved for guests. Huge
shady park. Thermal health spa (Damona at Bourbon-Lancy 5
km). Open 1 April to 31 December.
PRICES: s €49-€64; d €53-€69; t €69-€76; extra person €12; dinner €11-
€23 **ON SITE:** Fishing Hiking **NEARBY:** Horse riding (6km) Swimming
pool (4km) Stretch of water (4km) Place of interest (70km) Tennis (4km)
Bicycle hire (4km) Railway station (30km) Shops (1km) BOURBON-
LANCY (4km) **NOTES:** Pets admitted English spoken

continued

ST-BOIL

♦♦♦ Chaumois Suzanne PERRAUT
71390 SAINT-BOIL
☎ 03 85 44 07 96
Four enormous rooms of considerable comfort in a restored house
in a winegrowing hamlet of Côte Chalonnaise. Each room sleeps
two to three people, with baths and wc. Fully equipped kitchen
area. Sitting room with television point and library. Lounge for use
of guests. Private breakfast room. Interior courtyard. Bathing at
Moulin de Collonges. Open all year.
PRICES: s €30; d €41; t €53; extra person €12   **ON SITE:** Hiking
NEARBY: Horse riding (1km) Fishing (1km) Swimming pool (12km)
Stretch of water (8km) Place of interest (2km) Tennis (4km) Bicycle hire
(1km) Railway station (20km) Shops (4km) ST-GENGOUX-LE-NATIONAL
(4km)   **NOTES:** Pets admitted English spoken

ST-DIDIER-SUR-ARROUX

♦♦♦ Moulin de Bousson Jacqueline DE VALK
71190 SAINT-DIDIER-SUR-ARROUX
☎ 03 85 82 35 07 ▯ 03 85 82 25 41
e-mail: moulin.bousson@wanadoo.fr www.moulinbousson.com
Three guest rooms in an old mill beside the lake with wc and
shower in each room. Extra couch or child's bed may be available.
Living room, lounge and games room reserved for guests. Garden,
tracks and water sports. Resting and leisure area set aside for
visitors. Restaurant 200m. Open all year.
PRICES: s €34; d €44; t €55   **ON SITE:** Fishing Stretch of water Hiking
Bicycle hire   **NEARBY:** Horse riding (3km) Swimming pool (11km) Place
of interest (50km) Tennis (8km) Railway station (8km) Shops (2km)
ETANG-SUR-ARROUX (8km)   **NOTES:** Pets admitted English spoken

ST-FORGEOT

♦♦♦ ⁙◉⁙ Château de Millery Gérard PERRETTE
Millery, 71400 SAINT-FORGEOT   ☎ 03 85 52 18 51

A 19th-century house of character located in a fine shady park. Five
comfortable guest rooms with private shower rooms and wc. The
rooms sleep two or four people. Baby equipment. Breakfast room
and sitting room for guests' use only. Terrace and grounds.
Restaurant 4 km. Meals can be booked. Open 15 April to11
November.
PRICES: s €40; d €49; t €58; extra person €15; dinner €15
ON SITE: Hiking **NEARBY:** Horse riding (4km) Fishing (1km)
Swimming pool (4km) Stretch of water (4km) Place of interest (20km)
Tennis (4km) Bicycle hire (4km) Railway station (4km) Shops (4km)
AUTUN (4km)   **NOTES:** Pets admitted English spoken

ST-GERVAIS-EN-VALLIERE

♦♦♦ ⁙◉⁙ Champseuil Martine LYSSY
71350 SAINT-GERVAIS-EN-VALLIERE
☎ 03 85 91 80 08 ▯ 03 85 91 80 08
e-mail: martine.lyssy-chambres-dhotes@wanadoo.fr

A village house a few kilometres from Beaune and Verdon. Three
rooms which are both quiet and comfortable, with bath and wc.
Breakfast room for guests' use. Courtyard and enclosed garden.
Meals may be booked. Open 15 March to 15 November.
PRICES: s €34; d €50; extra person €18; dinner €18   **ON SITE:** Fishing
NEARBY: Swimming pool (12km) Hiking (1km) Place of interest (7km)
Tennis (12km) Bicycle hire (14km) Railway station (14km) Shops (4km)
BEAUNE (14km)   **NOTES:** No pets English spoken

ST-MAURICE-LES-CHATEAUNEUF

♦♦♦ La Violetterie Madeleine CHARTIER
71740 ST-MAURICE-LES-CHATEAUNEUF
☎ 03 85 26 26 60 ▯ 03 85 26 26 60

This traditional Brionnais home offers double rooms with shower
and wc. Extra bed possible. Dining room and lounge with open
fire, TV and books. Shady garden and courtyard. On the Roman
Church Trail. Antique shops in village. Restaurant 200m. Open 15
March to 11 November.
PRICES: s €37-€40; d €46; t €58; extra person €11   **NEARBY:** Fishing
(1km) Swimming pool (7km) Stretch of water (10km) Hiking (1km)
Tennis (1km) Railway station (7km) Shops (1km) CHAUFFAILLES (7km)
NOTES: No pets English spoken

ST-PIERRE-LE-VIEUX

♦♦♦ ⁙◉⁙ Château des Colettes Corinne et Jacques LORON
Les Colettes, 71520 SAINT-PIERRE-LE-VIEUX
☎ 03 85 50 40 96 ▯ 03 85 50 40 96
Manor house of the 17th century on the borders of Mâconnais and
Beaujolais. Rooms for two or three people with shower room and
wc. Guests' lounge with open fire, television and library. Enclosed
garden. Baby equipment. Meals with themed menus available.
Open all year.
PRICES: s €41-€52; d €46-€57; t €65-€70; extra person €13; dinner €17
ON SITE: Forest Hiking   **NEARBY:** Fishing (1km) Swimming pool (7km)
Stretch of water (10km) Place of interest (12km) Tennis (7km) Bicycle hire
(7km) Railway station (27km) Shops (7km) CLUNY (20km)
NOTES: Pets admitted English spoken

ST-POINT

♦♦♦ Le Domaine Dauphin
C SCHALBURG-CHARPENTIER
71520 SAINT-POINT
☎ 03 85 50 57 87 ▯ 03 85 50 59 57
e-mail: dom-dauphin@wanadoo.fr
Between Mâconnais and Beaujolais, in the Val Lamartine, opposite
the poet's castle, and only 100m from the lake, is located this 16th-
century home. Four guest rooms (one a family room) on the
theme of Lamartine, furnished and decorated with care, all with
bathroom and wc. Communal living room and sitting room with
fireplace. Table tennis. Large courtyard. Reduced prices for
extended stays. Meals if booked. Restaurants 200m and 3 km.
Open all year except 8 January to 8 February.

continued   continued

PRICES: s €46; d €60; extra person €15 **ON SITE:** Fishing Stretch of water Hiking **NEARBY:** Horse riding (3km) Swimming pool (8km) Place of interest (10km) Tennis (1km) Bicycle hire (5km) Railway station (25km) Shops (5km) CLUNY (8km) **NOTES:** Pets admitted English spoken

ST-PRIX

¶¶ ❍ L'Eau Vive Catherine DENIS
71990 SAINT-PRIX
☎ 03 85 82 59 34
e-mail: redenis@club-internet.fr
In the Parc du Morvan, near to Mont Beuvray, Catherine and René have created four comfortable guest rooms, each with bathroom and wc. Salon with open fire for guests. Private pond, walking trails, mountain biking. Archaeological site of Bibracte 6km. 100 km of walking trails. High quality evening meals. Open 29 March to 15 June and 1 July to 3 November.
PRICES: s €36; d €42; t €53; dinner €18 **ON SITE:** Fishing Hiking Bicycle hire **NEARBY:** Horse riding (2km) Swimming pool (21km) Stretch of water (21km) Place of interest (40km) Tennis (4km) Railway station (21km) Shops (4km) AUTUN (21km) **NOTES:** No pets English spoken

ST-SERNIN-DU-PLAIN

¶¶ ❍ Mazenay Thierry et M-Claire VIGOUREUX
71510 SAINT-SERNIN-DU-PLAIN
☎ 03 85 49 62 37 🖷 03 85 49 62 37
www.ch.hotes.mazenay.free.fr
On the Beaune to Cluny wine route, in an old restored house, three comfortable rooms with private bathrooms and wcs. One room sleeps four (one double bed and two singles). Sitting room with television. Kitchen available for use. Separate entrance. Courtyard and enclosed wooded grounds. Bathing 7km. Meals must be booked. Reduction for long stays. Open all year.
PRICES: s €32; d €38-€52; t €52; extra person €14; dinner €15 **ON SITE:** Hiking Place of interest **NEARBY:** Horse riding (12km) Fishing (10km) Swimming pool (7km) Tennis (3km) Railway station (15km) NOLAY-COUCHES (6km) **NOTES:** Pets admitted English spoken

ST-USUGE

¶¶ ❍ Les Chyses Fabienne THEBERT
71500 SAINT-USUGE
☎ 03 85 72 18 12 & 06 89 33 30 51 🖷 03 85 72 18 12
In a typical Bressanne house, four guest rooms laid out in style. Rustic breakfast room and sitting room with TV. One ground floor room sleeps three. Upstairs are two double rooms and a room for four. Private bathrooms and wc. Courtyard, shady enclosed park. Evening meals may be booked. Open all year except May.
PRICES: d €50-€85; t €77-€92; dinner €23 (on reservation) **ON SITE:** Bicycle hire **NEARBY:** Horse riding (2km) Fishing (1km) Swimming pool (8km) Hiking (1km) Tennis (1km) Railway station (7km) Shops (1km) LOUHANS (7km) **NOTES:** No pets

TINTRY

¶¶ ❍ Lusigny Jean-Pierre BERTRAND
71490 TINTRY
☎ 03 85 82 98 98
Between Beaune and Autun, near the vineyards of Couchois. Three charming and spacious guest rooms, one with covered terrace. Each has shower room and wc. Lounge area, gym. Well-tended garden. Meals must be booked. Reduced prices in low season. Open all year.
PRICES: s €32; d €35-€40; t €49; HB €28-€30; dinner €13 **ON SITE:** Hiking Bicycle hire **NEARBY:** Horse riding (10km) Swimming pool (23km) Stretch of water (23km) Place of interest (10km) Tennis (10km) Railway station (23km) Shops (3km) AUTUN (23km) **NOTES:** No pets English spoken

TOURNUS

¶¶ Chambre d'hôtes Françoise DOURNEAU
1 quai de Saône, Marie-Clémentine, 71700 TOURNUS
☎ 03 85 51 04 43 🖷 03 85 51 04 43
e-mail: francoise.dourneau@wanadoo.fr
http://perso.wanadoo.fr/marie.clementine.chambres.hotes/
Three rooms in a house of character on the banks of the Saône. Breakfast room with lounge corner, library, television, reserved for guests. Enormous enclosed shady garden. The bedrooms sleep two or three, and each have private shower and wc. Open 15 March to 2 November. Booking required out of season.
PRICES: s €50; d €60; t €75; extra person €15 **ON SITE:** Fishing **NEARBY:** Horse riding (6km) Swimming pool (1km) Stretch of water (12km) Hiking (2km) Place of interest (2km) Tennis (1km) Bicycle hire (1km) Railway station (1km) MACON (24km) **NOTES:** No pets English spoken

UCHIZY

¶¶ Chambre d'hôtes Annick SALLET
Route de Chardonnay, Domaine de l'Arfentière, 71700 UCHIZY
☎ 03 85 40 50 46 & 06 89 93 02 75 🖷 03 85 40 58 05
Four rooms in a distinctive house on a wine growing estate. Peaceful. The rooms sleep four; three; two plus child; two people. Each room has bath or shower and wc. Cooking area for guests' use, living room, courtyard, games, parking. Winetasting on the premises. Open all year.
PRICES: s €32; d €43; t €55; extra person €13 **ON SITE:** Wine tasting **NEARBY:** Horse riding (15km) Fishing (2km) Swimming pool (10km) Hiking (1km) Place of interest (1km) Tennis (10km) Bicycle hire (10km) Railway station (2km) Shops (1km) TOURNUS (10km) **NOTES:** No pets English spoken

VARENNES-SOUS-DUN

¶¶ ❦ ❍ La Saigne Alain et Michèle DESMURS
71800 VARENNES-SOUS-DUN
☎ 03 85 28 12 79 & 06 84 67 14 81 🖷 03 85 28 12 79
e-mail: michelealaindesmurs@wanadoo.fr
Between meadows and forest, on a traditional Charolais Brionnais agricultural estate, Michèle and Alain provide, in a separate building, three rooms (one a suite for four people) with bath or shower and wc. Kitchen area. Mountain bikes and cycles available. Central heating. Meals (booking required). Open all year.
PRICES: s €32; d €40; t €55; dinner €16 **ON SITE:** Hiking Bicycle hire **NEARBY:** Horse riding (10km) Fishing (2km) Swimming pool (4km) Stretch of water (4km) Place of interest (30km) Tennis (4km) Railway station (4km) Shops (4km) LA CLAYETTE (4km) **NOTES:** No pets English spoken

VEROSVRES

🍴🍴🍴 Le Rocher Roger et Ginette CARETTE
71220 VEROSVRES
☎ 03 85 24 80 53 & 06 83 55 68 16
Three guest rooms on the first floor of a new house, in the birthplace of Ste-Marguerite Marie Alacoque. Panoramic view. Separate access to rooms. Two rooms sleeping two or three people; a suite of two rooms sleeping four or five. Showers and wcs. Communal living room with fireplace and television. Terrace, courtyard, enclosed grounds. Restaurants 3 and 4 km. Open all year.
PRICES: s €35; d €42-€43; extra person €10 **NEARBY:** Horse riding (5km) Fishing (1km) Swimming pool (5km) Hiking (1km) Tennis (5km) Railway station (30km) CHAROLLES (13km) **NOTES:** Pets admitted

VERZE

🍴🍴🍴 Château d'Escolles Yvan et Monique DE POTTER
Escolles, 71960 VERZE
☎ 03 85 33 44 52 & 06 83 36 52 50 🖷 03 85 33 34 80
e-mail: info@gite-escolles.com www.gite-escolles.com
This lovely 17th-century house is right in a Mâconnais vineyard. Huge wooded park. Five upstairs guest rooms: one with seven single beds; one double; one sleeping four in two double beds. Breakfast room. Lounge area reserved for guests. Open all year.
PRICES: s €38; d €60; t €84; extra person €23 **ON SITE:** Hiking Place of interest **NEARBY:** Horse riding (4km) Fishing (3km) Swimming pool (8km) Stretch of water (20km) Tennis (5km) Bicycle hire (14km) Railway station (14km) Shops (3km) MACON (14km) **NOTES:** No pets English spoken

VIRE

🍴🍴🍴 Les Cochets Michèle NOBLET
71260 VIRE
☎ 03 85 33 92 54
Three independent rooms at a village winegrower's house which has been completely renovated. One studio with kitchenette and two double rooms. Showers and wcs. Individual access. Lounge and living room for guests' use. Garden and enclosed courtyard. Golf and lots of leisure opportunities 5 km. Open 1 March to 15 November.
PRICES: s €38; d €46; extra person €14 **ON SITE:** Hiking Place of interest **NEARBY:** Horse riding (5km) Fishing (4km) Swimming pool (7km) Stretch of water (25km) Tennis (7km) Bicycle hire (13km) Railway station (4km) Shops (1km) TOURNUS (13km) **NOTES:** No pets

YONNE

ANCY-LE-FRANC

🍴🍴🍴 Chambre d'hôtes M-P et J-L GUIENNOT
Le Moulin, Chemin de Halage, 89160 ANCY-LE-FRANC
☎ 03 86 75 02 65 🖷 03 86 75 17 97
e-mail: info@moulin-ancy.com http://www.moulin-ancy.com
Situated on an island of two hectares by the palace of Ancy le Franc, this 17th-century windmill on the Bourgogne canal offers four subtle bedrooms, one of which has a private roof terrace, for two to four people. There is a park with horses, patios by the canal, an art gallery and a stained glass window workshop. Fishing, mountain bike hire and regional wines are available. Open 1 April to 31 October.
PRICES: s €49; d €53-€64; t €78 **ON SITE:** Forest Fishing Hiking Place of interest **NEARBY:** Horse riding (15km) Golf (12km) Swimming pool (17km) Tennis (1km) Railway station (1km) Shops (1km) ANCY LE FRANC (1km) **NOTES:** No pets English spoken

BROSSES

🍴🍴🍴 🍽 La Colombière Claude et Noëlle COUJOUR
60 Grande Rue, 89660 BROSSES
☎ 03 86 32 42 34 🖷 03 86 32 42 44
e-mail: la-colombiere@wanadoo.fr
http://www.la-colombiere.com
Situated at the heart of the village in a renovated old house, three bedrooms have private bathroom facilities. In a separate building there is a lounge with a fireplace and a bedroom with private bathroom. In the pigeonry there is one first floor bedroom, with bathroom facilities on the ground floor. Each bedroom has a private balcony. There is also a non-supervised swimming pool and a flower garden. Open all year.
PRICES: s €50-€55; d €55-€60; extra person €25; dinner €25
ON SITE: Forest Swimming pool Hiking **NEARBY:** Horse riding (4km) Fishing (5km) Place of interest (12km) Tennis (5km) Railway station (5km) Shops (5km) VEZELAY (12km) **NOTES:** No pets CC English spoken   *See advert on opposite page*

CHARNY

🍴🍴🍴 🐓 🍽 Ferme du Gué de Plénoise
Daniel et Dominique ACKERMANN
89120 CHARNY
☎ 03 86 63 63 53
Four guestrooms on a working cattle farm in the middle of the countryside on the edge of a river. Each bedroom has a private bathroom. There is a lounge, bookcase and television. Set meals are available on reservation and are free for babies. Toboggan and indoor games are available. Guests can discover the art of milking on site. Walking paths are nearby. There is a weekly car to Paris-Charny. Restaurant 5 km away. Open all year.
PRICES: s €30; d €46; t €58; extra person €12; dinner €17
ON SITE: Children's play area Forest Fishing Hiking **NEARBY:** Horse riding (10km) Golf (30km) Swimming pool (5km) Stretch of water (5km) Place of interest (30km) Tennis (5km) Railway station (40km) Shops (5km) TOUCY (25km) **NOTES:** No pets

CHEVANNES

🍴🍴🍴 🐓 Château de Ribourdin
Claude et Marie-Claude BRODARD
89240 CHEVANNES
☎ 03 86 41 23 16 🖷 03 86 41 23 16
Five bedrooms arranged in the outbuildings of a 16th-century castle in the middle of the country, 300m from the village. Each bedroom has a private bathroom and one has disabled access. A lounge is available to guests. There is a flower garden, non-supervised swimming pool and parking. Shops and a restaurant are 0.4 km away. Mountain bike hire is available. Open all year.
PRICES: s €50; d €57-€65; t €76; extra person €11 **ON SITE:** Swimming pool Hiking **NEARBY:** Horse riding (2km) Forest (3km) Golf (20km) Fishing (7km) Place of interest (7km) Tennis (1km) Railway station (7km) AUXERRE (7km) **NOTES:** No pets English spoken

COLLAN

🍴🍴🍴 🍽 La Marmotte Gilles LECOLLE
2, rue de l'Ecole, 89700 COLLAN
☎ 03 86 55 26 44 🖷 03 86 55 00 08
e-mail: lamarmotte.glecolle@wanadoo.fr
http://www.bonadresse.com/bourgogne/collan.htm
Three bedrooms in an old renovated house in the heart of the village, 6 km from Chablis. There is one twin bedroom on the ground floor and two double bedrooms on the first floor. Each has its own bathroom. Set meals are available on Mondays, Tuesdays and Thursdays from April to September, upon reservation by 5pm the day before. There is parking and a garden for guests' use.

continued

There are also marked footpaths in the surrounding area. Tourist tax supplement applies and there is a supplement of 11 euros for children aged 3-10. Open all year on reservation from 1 November to 31 March.
PRICES: s €34; d €42; t €53; dinner €16 **ON SITE:** Forest Hiking Tennis
NEARBY: Horse riding (8km) Golf (20km) Fishing (6km) Swimming pool (10km) Stretch of water (6km) Place of interest (6km) Railway station (10km) Shops (6km) CHABLIS (6km) **NOTES:** No pets

DANNEMOINE

Chambre d'hôtes Jean-François KUZIO
5 route Paris Genève, La Bichonnière, 89700 DANNEMOINE
☎ 03 86 55 53 56 ▤ 03 86 55 53 56
Guestrooms in a house full of character located in the village in a wine growing region with numerous castles. There are two bedrooms for two people on the first floor, both with private bathrooms. On the second floor there is one bedroom for two people and one triple bedroom, both with bathroom facilities. There is a lounge on the first floor with books and television. The enclosed shaded courtyard has parking available. Open Easter to end September on reservation at least three days before.
PRICES: s €39-€46; d €46-€54; t €61; extra person €10
ON SITE: Fishing Hiking **NEARBY:** Horse riding (10km) Forest (2km) Golf (15km) Swimming pool (7km) Place of interest (7km) Tennis (7km) Railway station (7km) Shops (7km) TONNERRE (7km) **NOTES:** No pets

EGLENY

Chambre d'hôtes Roger et Martine BALTUS
Château d'Egleny, 6 place du Marché, 89240 EGLENY
☎ 03 86 41 08 16 ▤ 03 86 41 14 41
Four guestrooms arranged in an outbuilding at the entrance of the castle of Egleny, in the centre of the village. There are two bedrooms on the first floor and two bedrooms on the second floor, each with private bathroom facilities. There is a lounge with books available to guests. Open Easter to 15 December and at Christmas and New Year's Eve by request.
PRICES: s €36; d €46; t €57 **ON SITE:** Fishing Hiking **NEARBY:** Horse riding (7km) Forest (6km) Golf (10km) Swimming pool (7km) Stretch of water (35km) Place of interest (20km) Tennis (7km) Railway station (20km) Shops (7km) TOUCY (11km) **NOTES:** No pets English spoken

ESCOLIVES-STE-CAMILLE

Chambre d'hôtes Régine BORGNAT
1 rue de l'Eglise, 89290 ESCOLIVES-STE-CAMILLE
☎ 03 86 35 35 28 ▤ 03 86 53 65 00
e-mail: domaineborgnat@wanadoo.fr
A beautiful fortified 17th-century house above caves. There are five bedrooms, all with private bathroom facilities. The bedrooms will sleep up to four people and have independent access. There is a lounge, television and books available to guests. A swimming pool is also available, along with a garden, table tennis and parking. Visits to the caves and tastings are possible. Set meals are available on reservation. Open all year.
PRICES: s €37; d €43-€46; t €52; extra person €9; dinner €20
ON SITE: Wine tasting Swimming pool Hiking Place of interest
NEARBY: Horse riding (4km) Forest (2km) Golf (30km) Fishing (2km) Tennis (2km) Railway station (3km) Shops (3km) AUXERRE (10km)
NOTES: Pets admitted CC English spoken

La Cour Barrée Raymond TRIPOT
12 bis, route de Vaux, 4, rue du canal-La Cour Barrée, 89290 ESCOLIVES-STE-CAMILLE
☎ 03 86 53 35 98 & 06 87 12 56 92 ▤ 03 86 53 35 98
e-mail: rtrip@wanadoo.fr
http://perso.wanadoo.fr/raymond.tripot/

La Colombière
60 Grande rue
89660 Brosses

Centrally situated in the village, La Colombière has been renovated to provide five bedrooms, which were once the ancient stables and pigeon loft. The rooms are very comfortable, have been decorated with charm in harmonising colours, and include antique furniture. A swimming pool is available for guests and the very beautiful garden has won prizes in the area. Your hosts Claude and Noelle welcome you to their home with open arms and will share with you their love of this region.
Tel: 03 86 32 42 34   Fax: 03 86 32 42 44
Email: la-colombiere@wanadoo.fr
Web: la-colombiere.com

A five-bedroom guest house on a farm set in a pretty park. One of the bedrooms is a double room for a family of four. Each bedroom has bathroom facilities and independent access. There is a lounge, TV room, kitchen, books and fireplace. Unsupervised swimming pool. Secure parking, boules pitch, garden, barbecue and table tennis. Open all year.
PRICES: s €32; d €43-€53; t €59; extra person €12 **ON SITE:** Fishing Swimming pool **NEARBY:** Horse riding (20km) Forest (1km) Golf (25km) Hiking (1km) Place of interest (1km) Tennis (1km) Railway station (1km) Shops (1km) AUXERRE (8km) **NOTES:** Pets admitted

FOISSY-SUR-VANNE

Chambre d'hôtes G et G KOHLER-COUVIDET
5 rue du Moulin, 89190 FOISSY-SUR-VANNE
☎ 03 86 86 71 74 ▤ 03 86 86 71 74
http://www.bonadresse.com/Bourgogne/Foissy-sur-van.htm

An old 17th-century mill on the edge of the village on the reach of the Vanne canal. There are five bedrooms each with its own

continued   continued

comfortable bathroom. There is a large room with a grand fireplace and television. A small television room and children's games area is also available. The garden has a barbecue for guests' use. Covered parking area and garage. Fishing is possible. Restaurant 5km. Open 1 April to 31 October, and during the rest of the year on reservation.

PRICES: s €37-€46; d €46-€54; t €54-€64; extra person €9
ON SITE: Fishing Hiking **NEARBY:** Horse riding (20km) Forest (3km) Place of interest (8km) Railway station (23km) Shops (5km) SENS (23km)
NOTES: No pets English spoken

FONTAINES

♥ ◉ La Bruère Guy et Chantal JORRY
89130 FONTAINES
☎ 03 86 74 30 83
Three guestrooms on the first floor of a working cattle-breeding farm, set in the heart of the countryside. There is a lounge with a fireplace, a garden and parking. Open all year.

PRICES: d €38; dinner €14 **ON SITE:** Hiking **NEARBY:** Horse riding (8km) Forest (5km) Fishing (4km) Swimming pool (8km) Place of interest (8km) Tennis (8km) Railway station (32km) Shops (7km) TOUCY (8km) **NOTES:** No pets

GY-L'EVEQUE

♥ ◉ Chambre d'hôtes Martial et Chantal MOYER
2, rue de la Fontaine, 89580 GY-L'EVEQUE
☎ 03 86 41 61 64 📠 03 86 41 74 17

Five guestrooms on the first floor of an old restored building on a working farm. Each bedroom has its own bathroom facilities. There is a lounge with a fireplace. The house is located in a village which is well-known for the Marmot cherry. During May and June, guests are invited to taste and pick the cherries. Hunting is possible during the season. Set meals are available at weekends on reservation. Open all year except January.

PRICES: s €42; d €46-€51; t €55; extra person €14; dinner €20
ON SITE: Forest Hiking Tennis **NEARBY:** Horse riding (4km) Fishing (10km) Swimming pool (10km) Place of interest (4km) Railway station (10km) AUXERRE (10km) **NOTES:** No pets

HAUTERIVE

◉ Chichy Patrick et Annie DESHAYES
1 rue St-Martin, 89250 HAUTERIVE
☎ 03 86 47 74 34 & 06 18 47 49 25 📠 03 86 47 74 34
e-mail: cvf1@wanadoo.fr
Three bedrooms in an outbuilding of an 18th-century vicarage. There is one double bedroom on the ground floor with a bathroom and disabled wc facilities. There is one double bedroom and one triple bedroom on the first floor, both with private bathroom facilities. There is a lounge, corner kitchen and patio available to guests. Set meals on reservation. Also available is a garden, tennis court, table tennis and mountain bike hire. Animals are welcome by arrangement. Open all year.

PRICES: s €30; d €43-€49; t €53-€61; extra person €11; dinner €21
ON SITE: Forest Hiking Tennis **NEARBY:** Horse riding (5km) Fishing (2km) Swimming pool (4km) Stretch of water (7km) Place of interest (12km) Railway station (8km) Shops (4km) SEIGNELAY (4km)
NOTES: Pets admitted English spoken

JOUX-LA-VILLE

Le Clos du Merry Jean-Paul et Maryse GUEUNIOT
4 rue Crété, 89440 JOUX-LA-VILLE
☎ 03 86 33 65 54 📠 03 86 33 61 72
e-mail: closmerry@free.fr
Five guestrooms arranged in an old farm barn. There are three double bedrooms, one has disabled access, and two double bedrooms for families of four or five people. There is independent access to the guestrooms. Over half of this property is landscaped. There is a garden with a patio, a picnic area, a boules pitch and various games. Guided walks are available during high season, for groups of ten to fifteen people. Open all year.

PRICES: s €30; d €40; t €50 **ON SITE:** Children's play area Hiking **NEARBY:** Horse riding (16km) Forest (5km) Fishing (12km) Swimming pool (16km) Place of interest (16km) Tennis (4km) Railway station (16km) Shops (16km) AVALLON (16km) **NOTES:** No pets

LAIN

◉ Art'Monie Jacques et Arlette ELZIERE
6, rue du Bourgelet, 89560 LAIN
☎ 03 86 45 20 39 📠 03 86 45 21 76
e-mail: arlette@artmonie.net http://www.artmonie.net
Five guestrooms in an old Burgundian farm. The bedrooms sleep from two to four people and all have private bathrooms. One bedroom has disabled access. There is a guest lounge and set meals can be provided on Thursdays, Fridays and Saturdays upon reservation by 5pm the day before. Table tennis, a games area and picnic area are also available. Walking, fishing, horse riding and bathing nearby. Animals are welcome by arrangement. Open 1 February to 15 November.

PRICES: s €30; d €38-€41; t €52; dinner €15 **ON SITE:** Children's play area Hiking **NEARBY:** Horse riding (12km) Forest (2km) Fishing (10km) Swimming pool (18km) Stretch of water (20km) Place of interest (11km) Tennis (4km) Railway station (30km) AUXERRE (32km) **NOTES:** Pets admitted English spoken

LEZINNES

Chambre d'hôtes Jean et Madeleine PIEDALLU
5 route d'Argentenay, 89160 LEZINNES
☎ 03 86 75 68 23
A new house of regional character with three bedrooms. Each bedroom has private bathroom facilities. There is a lounge reserved for guests. There is also an enclosed courtyard with parking and a garden shaded by trees. Shops, a restaurant, tennis and a train station are available in the village. The castles of Tanlay and Ancy le Franc are nearby. Open all year.

PRICES: s €35; d €40 **ON SITE:** Fishing Hiking Tennis **NEARBY:** Forest (3km) Golf (8km) Swimming pool (10km) Place of interest (7km) TONNERRE (10km) **NOTES:** No pets

LINDRY

◉ La Vederine Gérard et Eliane BONFANTI
CIDEX 500 - N°28, Chazelles, 89240 LINDRY
☎ 03 86 47 10 86 & 03 86 47 18 78 📠 03 86 47 01 64
An old renovated farm situated in a small, very quiet hamlet. There is one bedroom on the ground floor with disabled access and four bedrooms on the first floor. All bedrooms have private bathrooms. There is a lounge with a fireplace, books and a corner kitchen for guest use. Set meals are available on reservation, except on

continued

continued

Fridays and bank holidays. There is over 8 hectares of land with a garden, boules pitch, patio and parking. Open all year.
PRICES: s €29-€31; d €38-€40; extra person €14-€15; dinner €19
ON SITE: Forest Hiking **NEARBY:** Horse riding (5km) Golf (15km) Fishing (5km) Swimming pool (3km) Place of interest (10km) Tennis (3km) Railway station (15km) Shops (3km) AUXERRE (15km)
NOTES: Pets admitted

LIXY

⫟⫟⫟ ◉ Chambre d'hôtes Alain et Catherine BALOURDET
16 place de la Liberté, 89140 LIXY
☎ 03 86 66 11 39 & 06 86 65 53 87   📠 03 86 66 11 39
e-mail: clos-melusine@infonie.fr
http://perso.infonie.fr/clos-melusine/
An old Burgundian farm in the centre of the village with three guestrooms arranged in a separate barn, built on a 12th-century crypt. Each bedroom has its own bathroom facilities. There is a lounge with books and literature about the surrounding region. Set meals are accompanied by Yonne wines. There is a garden for guests' use. Open all year.
PRICES: s €35; d €41; extra person €11; dinner €17   **ON SITE:** Forest Golf Hiking **NEARBY:** Horse riding (4km) Fishing (10km) Swimming pool (15km) Stretch of water (20km) Place of interest (4km) Tennis (4km) Railway station (10km) Shops (2km) SENS (15km)
NOTES: No pets

MOLAY

⫟⫟⫟ ◉ Le Calounier Pascal et Corinne COLLIN
5 rue de la Fontaine - Arton, 89310 MOLAY
☎ 03 86 82 67 81 & 06 85 84 21 67   📠 03 86 82 67 81
e-mail: info@lecalounier.fr   http://www.lecalounier.fr
This charming house, full of character, is situated in the quiet countryside. There are four bedrooms with private bathroom facilities, of which two are double bedrooms for families of up to five people. One of the bedrooms has disabled access. There is a lounge and rooms with books and games. There is a large garden. Set meals are available and feature regional dishes. Open all year.
PRICES: d €46-€51; t €68; extra person €17; dinner €19
ON SITE: Forest Fishing Hiking **NEARBY:** Horse riding (6km) Swimming pool (19km) Place of interest (7km) Tennis (3km) Railway station (19km) Shops (8km) CHABLIS (16km) **NOTES:** No pets English spoken

NOYERS-SUR-SEREIN

⫟⫟⫟ Château d'Archambault Claude MARIE
Cours, 89310 NOYERS-SUR-SEREIN
☎ 03 86 82 67 55   📠 03 86 82 67 87
e-mail: chateau.darchambault.cmarie@wanadoo.fr
http://www.chateau-archambault.com

Guestrooms in the owners' 19th-century mansion house, amidst a wooded park. There are five bedrooms, all with private bathrooms. Four of the bedrooms are on the first floor and the fifth is on the

second floor. Two of the rooms are doubles, suitable for a family. There is a lounge with a fireplace. The 12th-century village of Noyers-sur-Serein is 1.5 km away. Open all year.
PRICES: d €58-€69; extra person €15 **ON SITE:** Forest Fishing Hiking
NEARBY: Railway station (32km) Shops (2km) NOYERS SUR SEREIN (1.5km) **NOTES:** No pets CC English spoken

SACY

⫟⫟⫟ ◉ Les Vieilles Fontaines Claude et Maryse MOINE
89270 SACY
☎ 03 86 81 51 62 & 06 08 25 55 31   📠 03 86 81 51 62
e-mail: vieillesfontaines@minitel.net
Four guestrooms in a former winemaker's house, located at the heart of a very old Burgundian village. One of the bedrooms is a double, suitable for one family. There is a lounge, kitchen and card phone in an arched cellar on the ground floor. Gastronomic set meals are available with the hosts, Maryse and Claude. There is a garden and parking. Walks and guided visits to the village and church are available on reservation. Open end March to beginning November and during the rest of the year by reservation.
PRICES: s €34; d €44; t €59; extra person €15; dinner €23
ON SITE: Forest Hiking **NEARBY:** Horse riding (25km) Golf (30km) Fishing (7km) Swimming pool (20km) Place of interest (9km) Tennis (7km) Railway station (7km) Shops (7km) AUXERRE (30km)
NOTES: Pets admitted CC English spoken

SAUVIGNY-LE-BEUREAL

⫟⫟⫟ 🐓 ◉ La Forlonge Bernard & Jacqueline NOIROT
5 rue de la Vallée de Beauvoir,
89420 SAUVIGNY-LE-BEUREAL
☎ 03 86 32 53 44 & 03 86 32 58 28   📠 03 86 32 53 44
Five guestrooms in the old attics of an authentic Burgundian farm, situated in the heart of the village. The bedrooms have private bathrooms and central heating. There is a restored old room with an open fireplace. There is a garden, billiards, table tennis and fishing in a private lake. Footpaths in the surrounding area. Open all year.
PRICES: d €44; t €55; extra person €11; dinner €13 **ON SITE:** Forest Fishing Hiking **NEARBY:** Horse riding (5km) Swimming pool (5km) Place of interest (5km) Tennis (5km) Railway station (17km) Shops (2km) AVALLON (17km) **NOTES:** No pets

ST-FARGEAU

⫟⫟⫟ ◉ Chambre d'hôtes J-S et C MOYE
8, rue de l'Hôpital, 89170 ST-FARGEAU
☎ 03 86 74 09 99   📠 03 86 74 09 99
e-mail: christine.moye@wanadoo.fr
Three guestrooms on the first floor of a grand house in the village. All bedrooms have private bathrooms. There is a lounge with a piano. The house has central heating. Also available is a garden with a patio and parking. There is a daily bus between Paris and St-Fargeau. The lake at Bourdon is 3 km away. Open all year.
PRICES: s €46-€49; d €54-€58; extra person €17; dinner €20
ON SITE: Forest Hiking Place of interest Tennis **NEARBY:** Horse riding (3km) Golf (40km) Fishing (3km) Stretch of water (3km) Railway station (35km) SAINT FARGEAU **NOTES:** No pets English spoken

Use the atlas at the back of the guide to
locate your chambre d'hôtes

🐓Places with this symbol are farmhouses

continued

ST-GERMAIN-DES-CHAMPS

♦♦♦ ♦Oi Le Meix Maureen O'SULLIVAN
19 route du Morvan, Le Meix,
89630 ST-GERMAIN-DES-CHAMPS
☎ 03 86 34 27 63 ▤ 03 86 34 24 91
e-mail: Kenmare89@aol.com http://www.harasdekenmare.com

Five guestrooms arranged in a house full of character, set in a small hamlet. The bedrooms are spread over the first and second floor, and all have bathroom facilities and independent access. There is a lounge and two further rooms available, and an enclosed garden and parking. Set meals on reservation. Cookery lessons are available for groups of six people. Local fishing is also possible. Open all year.
PRICES: s €40; d €50; extra person €11; dinner €21 **ON SITE:** Horse riding Forest Hiking **NEARBY:** Fishing (3km) Swimming pool (10km) Stretch of water (5km) Place of interest (15km) Tennis (10km) Railway station (10km) Shops (10km) AVALLON (10km) **NOTES:** Pets admitted CC English spoken

TANNERRE-EN-PUISAYE

♦♦♦ Moulin de la Forge René et Chantal GAGNOT
La Forge, 89350 TANNERRE-EN-PUISAYE
☎ 03 86 45 40 25 ▤ 03 86 45 40 25
e-mail: renegagnot@aol.com
A 14th-century mill set in four hectares of wooded ground with a lake and private swimming pool. There are five bedrooms; one with disabled access. All bedrooms have private bathroom facilities. There is a corner kitchen, a lounge with a fireplace and a covered barbecue for guests' use. Fishing is available on site. Open all year.
PRICES: d €50; t €65 **ON SITE:** Fishing Swimming pool
NEARBY: Horse riding (3km) Forest (3km) Golf (20km) Place of interest (12km) Tennis (1km) Railway station (40km) Shops (6km) SAINT FARGEAU (12km) **NOTES:** Pets admitted

THIZY

♦♦♦ ♦Oi Chambre d'hôtes FRITSCH et Mme BRUN
L'Esperluette, 10 rue Edmé-Marie Cadoux, 89420 THIZY
☎ 03 86 32 04 59 ▤ 03 86 32 04 59
The former house of the sculptor Edme Marie Cadoux is situated on the edge of a picturesque village. There are three bedrooms for two or three people, with bathroom facilities. There is a lounge with a piano and books. The house has a large garden and a shaded park. Set meals are available on reservation. Animals are welcome on request. Open 15 April to end November.
PRICES: s €32-€49; d €43-€52; t €61; dinner €20 **ON SITE:** Hiking
NEARBY: Horse riding (5km) Forest (1km) Golf (45km) Fishing (5km) Swimming pool (15km) Place of interest (15km) Tennis (5km) Railway station (15km) Shops (5km) AVALLON (15km) **NOTES:** Pets admitted English spoken

VALLERY

♦♦♦ ♥ ♦Oi La Margottière Didier et Colette DELIGAND
89150 VALLERY
☎ 03 86 97 57 97 & 03 86 97 70 77 ▤ 03 86 97 53 80
Six guestrooms arranged in a detached Burgundian residence, on the working farm of the 17th-century castle of Conde. The bedrooms have separate bathroom facilities, a telephone and a television. One of the bedrooms has disabled access. The lounge has a 17th-century fireplace. Set meals are available on reservation. There is an enclosed courtyard. Children's games, table tennis and table football. It is possible to hire a reception room with a patio. Open all year.
PRICES: d €61; t €76; dinner €14-€20 **ON SITE:** Children's play area Horse riding Forest Fishing Hiking Place of interest **NEARBY:** Golf (4km) Swimming pool (20km) Stretch of water (12km) Tennis (5km) Railway station (20km) SENS (20km) **NOTES:** No pets English spoken

VENOY

♦♦♦ Chambre d'hôtes Nicole GENEST
Domaine de Ste-Anne, Soleines le Haut, 89290 VENOY
☎ 03 86 94 10 16 ▤ 03 86 94 10 12
e-mail: info@domainesainteanne.com
http://www.domainesainteanne.com
An 18th-century estate with three bedrooms arranged on the first floor. There are two double bedrooms and one triple bedroom, all with bathroom facilities. There is a wooded park with a stream. On the ground floor there is a lounge with a fireplace, television and books and a breakfast room. Parking is available. There is a restaurant 1.2 km away. Open 1 March to 31 October.
PRICES: d €60-€68; t €80; extra person €12 **ON SITE:** Forest Fishing Stretch of water Hiking **NEARBY:** Horse riding (10km) Golf (15km) Swimming pool (8km) Place of interest (4km) Tennis (1km) Railway station (8km) Shops (8km) AUXERRE (8km) **NOTES:** No pets English spoken

VEZANNES

♦♦♦ ♥ ♦Oi Chambre d'hôtes D et E COPIN-RAOULT
1 Grande Rue, 89700 VEZANNES
☎ 03 86 55 14 05 ▤ 03 86 55 35 96
Three guestrooms in a house full of character at a winemaker's residence on the edge of the village. The bedrooms have private bathroom facilities. There is a lounge, television, books and fireplace. Evening meals are available on reservation the day before, except Sundays and Wednesdays. There is a garden. Chablis is 10 km away. Open 1 April to 15 September.
PRICES: s €32; d €42; dinner €16 **NEARBY:** Forest (10km) Golf (20km) Swimming pool (10km) Place of interest (10km) Tennis (10km) Railway station (10km) Shops (10km) TONNERRE (10km) **NOTES:** No pets English spoken

VILLEFARGEAU

♦♦♦♦ ⍟ Les Bruyères
Pierre et Monique JOULLIE
5, allée de Charbuy, 89240 VILLEFARGEAU
☎ 03 86 41 32 82 🖷 03 86 41 28 57
e-mail: infos@petit-manoir-bruyeres.com
http://www.petit-manoir-bruyeres.com
A small manor with a Burgundian roof with glazed tiles,
located in an enclosed shaded flower-filled park. There are
four subtly decorated bedrooms on the first floor, with a
television and large comfortable bathroom in each. Two of the
bedrooms also have a lounge, fireplace and safe. There is a
dining room on the ground floor with a television and
fireplace. On the second floor, there is a room with a
television, video, books and indoor games. Set meals are
available on reservation. There is a garden with outdoor
furniture. Open all year.
PRICES: d €107-€183; dinner €38 **ON SITE:** Forest Hiking
NEARBY: Horse riding (3km) Golf (15km) Fishing (2km)
Swimming pool (7km) Place of interest (6km) Tennis (3km) Railway
station (6km) Shops (3km) AUXERRE (6km) **NOTES:** No pets CC
English spoken

See advert on this page

For further information on these and
other chambres d'hôtes, consult
the Gîtes de France website
www.gites-de-france.fr

CENTRAL FRANCE

CHER

ANNOIX

♦♦♦ ⍟ Ferme du Château Gaillard Alain et Anita MAZE
18340 ANNOIX
☎ 02 48 59 66 59 🖷 02 48 59 81 52
Rooms with individual access in a renovated outbuilding. There is
a two-roomed suite for two people with shower/wc, and a double
room with shower/wc. Dining room/lounge (television, books) for
guests' use. Kitchenette available. Large grassed courtyard with
outdoor furniture. Restaurants 4 and 9 km. One kilometre from the
Bourges RN, the house stands at the entrance to Annoix, a village
at the heart of Champagne Berrichonne. Open all year.
PRICES: s €39; d €41; extra person €14 **ON SITE:** Hiking
NEARBY: Bathing (18km) Horse riding (2km) Fishing (1km) Swimming
pool (9km) Water sports (18km) Tennis (9km) Railway station (18km)
NOTES: Pets admitted English spoken

ARCAY

♦♦♦ Château de Belair Roger et Claudette MAGINIAU
Belair, 18340 ARCAY
☎ 02 48 25 36 72
Six bedrooms (five in Louis XVI-style) in a 19th-century castle
surrounded by a large wooded park, in a hamlet. Double rooms
each with shower, wc and television. One room has an additional
room to accommodate two children while another has a sitting
room with open fire. Lounge and salon. Mountain bike hire and
marked circuits. Restaurant 3 km. Open all year.
PRICES: d €39-€54; extra person €12; dinner €25
ON SITE: Hiking **NEARBY:** Horse riding (14km) Fishing (4km)
Swimming pool (14km) Water sports (14km) Tennis (14km)
NOTES: Pets admitted English spoken

ARDENAIS

♦♦♦ ⍟ La Folie Annick JACQUET
18170 ARDENAIS
☎ 02 48 96 17 59
e-mail: la.folie@wanadoo.fr
http://perso.wanadoo.fr/cher.berry.la.folie
In this 18th-century farmhouse, there is one double room with
shower and wc, and one suite with a double bed and two singles,
again with shower and wc. Separate entry. Lounge/dining room
with TV and open fireplace, and a reading room with documents
about the region and tourist information. Your hostess Annick will
share her knowledge of the countryside and recommend routes of
discovery round the region. Hectare of woods. Naval base at
Sidiailles, river banks, forest, hiking. Open all year; booking
essential in winter.
PRICES: ; d €40-€46; t €70; extra person €13; dinner €15
ON SITE: Hiking **NEARBY:** Bathing (4km) Horse riding (12km) Fishing
(4km) Swimming pool (15km) Water sports (20km) Tennis (4km)
Railway station (13km) **NOTES:** No pets English spoken

continued

||||| ¡©¡ Vilotte Jacques CHAMPENIER
18170 ARDENAIS
☎ 02 48 96 04 96 📠 02 48 96 04 96
Five double rooms in a lovely 19th-century home, all with bathroom and wc. One adjoining room for two with washbasin (€35 supplement). Reception and an area for relaxing with television. Large living room with open fire. Breakfast room. Extensive shady park, rose garden, pond, farm. Meals if booked. Deep in the country, this ancient Roman site will captivate guests with its elegance, harmonious architecture, its quiet and comfort. Your host is the first commercial director of Futuroscope, the fourth generation owner of this family house. Open all year.
PRICES: s €48-€58; d €60-€70; extra person €18; dinner €25
ON SITE: Fishing Hiking **NEARBY:** Bathing (15km) Horse riding (30km) Swimming pool (20km) Water sports (15km) Tennis (5km)
NOTES: Pets admitted English spoken

BEDDES

||||| ¥ ¡©¡ Chambre d'hôtes Jean-Claude AUPETIT
Le Grand Vernet, 18370 BEDDES
☎ 02 48 56 20 31 📠 02 48 56 30 23
A warm welcome awaits at this farmhouse inn on a cattle-rearing and mixed farm. Rooms for one to three persons, all with shower and wc, on the first floor. Small sitting room with television, for guests only. Lavish breakfasts. Wooded garden, outdoor furniture, swimming pool. Local attractions: the Priory Gardens at Orsan, the Alain Fournier School, the Abbey of Noirlac, the Châteaux of Ainay-le-Vieil and Culan, the Valley of George Sand, the vineyard of Châteaumeillant. Open all year.
PRICES: d €40; extra person €8-€12; dinner €13 **ON SITE:** Swimming pool Hiking **NEARBY:** Bathing (23km) Horse riding (15km) Fishing (5km) Water sports (23km) Tennis (4km) Railway station (25km) Shops (4km) Restaurant nearby **NOTES:** No pets English spoken

BELLEVILLE-SUR-LOIRE

||||| Chambre d'hôtes Gery et Christine DE JENLIS
20, route de Beaulieu, 18240 BELLEVILLE-SUR-LOIRE
☎ 02 48 72 49 60 & 06 11 61 41 57 📠 02 48 72 49 60
e-mail: g.de.jenlis@wanadoo.fr
http://perso.wanadoo.fr/de.jenlis/pansard
Cosne-sur-Loire 15 km. Sancerre 25 km. At the edge of Loiret and the Nièvre, these old, renovated stables, set across from the owners' home, now house double guest rooms, all with shower room and wc, all on the first floor. Television lounge, dining room and kitchenette for use by guests. Fine wooded grounds leading to water garden and the canal alongside the Loire. Garden furniture. Restaurant. Open 15 June to 15 September; at other times by reservation.
PRICES: d €37; extra person €13 **ON SITE:** Bathing Horse riding Fishing Swimming pool Hiking Water sports Tennis **NEARBY:** Canoeing (3km) Railway station (15km) **NOTES:** No pets English spoken

BERRY-BOUY

||||| ¥ L'Ermitage Géraud et Laurence DE LA FARGE
18500 BERRY-BOUY
☎ 02 48 26 87 46 📠 02 48 26 03 28
Laurence and Géraud, who run this mixed and cattle farm 6 km west of Bourges, live in a stunning family mansion. They have carefully restored the comfortable guest rooms. Two rooms in a wing of the house and three more upstairs in the adjacent mill. Three double rooms, one sleeping three and one for four, all with bath or shower and wc. All have television. Lounge for guests' exclusive use. Park with 100-year-old trees. Parking. Restaurants 3 km. Open all year.

PRICES: s €38-€41; d €49-€52; extra person €19 **ON SITE:** Fishing Hiking **NEARBY:** Bathing (8km) Horse riding (5km) Swimming pool (5km) Water sports (8km) Tennis (5km) **NOTES:** No pets English spoken

BLANCAFORT

||||| Chambre d'hôtes J et M-Claude HARDY-CALLOT
La Renardière, 21, rue Pierre Juglar, 18410 BLANCAFORT
☎ 02 48 58 40 16 📠 02 48 58 40 16
An 18th-century house opposite the Château de Blancafort. The accommodation comprises 'Bleue d'Aurore' for two people, and 'Grand Maulnes', a suite for two to four, each with shower or bath and wc. Flower-filled park and locked parking. Literary weekends or holidays. Wine discovery tours of Central France and Loire Valley. Tariff €91 for four. Theme weekend €30 to €38. Open April to 11 November.
PRICES: ; d €53; extra person €18 **ON SITE:** Fishing Hiking **NEARBY:** Bathing (15km) Horse riding (7km) Swimming pool (7km) Water sports (15km) Tennis (7km) Railway station (21km) **NOTES:** No pets English spoken

BLET

||||| Château de Blet Michel BIBANOW
18350 BLET
☎ 02 48 74 76 66 & 02 48 74 72 02
One room and two suites on the first floor of this château dating from the 15th and 16th centuries. Large terrace and shaded, 21-hectare park. One double room, a suite for two to four people and a suite for three or four. All have bath, wc and television. Billiard room and small lounge for guests' use. Breakfast room. Garden furniture. Near to Bourges, Noirlac, Sancerre and Nevers. Restaurants 15 km. Open all year.
PRICES: d €70; extra person €27 **ON SITE:** Fishing **NEARBY:** Bathing (25km) Horse riding (15km) Fishing (1km) Swimming pool (15km) Water sports (25km) Tennis (15km) Railway station (15km) **NOTES:** No pets

||||| ¡©¡ Domaine de Chassy
M DE VILDER et F HULSHOF
Chassy, 18350 BLET
☎ 02 48 74 72 47 📠 02 48 74 72 47
e-mail: DOM.dechassy@wanadoo.fr
www.geocities.com/chassyfrance

Bourges 40 km. On the ground floor of an 18th-century house and on the first floor of a 14th-century pigeon-house, three double rooms each with separate access, shower or bathroom and wc. Living room/lounge with open fireplace. Extensive grounds, garden furniture. Meals may be booked. Kennels for animals. Golf 25 km. Bicycles available. The welcoming hosts have completely restored this lovely house, to provide charming comfortable rooms in a quiet and secluded spot. Open 1 April to 31 October.
PRICES: d €40-€55; extra person €16; dinner €19 **ON SITE:** Swimming

continued

continued

pool Hiking **NEARBY:** Bathing (30km) Horse riding (20km) Fishing (15km) Water sports (30km) Tennis (7km) Railway station (40km) Shops (3km) **NOTES:** No pets English spoken

CHARENTON-LAUGERE

La Serre Claude et Claude MOREAU
route de Dun, 18210 CHARENTON-LAUGERE
☎ 02 48 60 75 82 & 06 14 90 23 56 🖹 02 48 60 75 82
Three upstairs rooms in a 100-year-old house, harmoniously combining art-deco and contemporary furnishings. Park and garden with outdoor furniture. Two living rooms and a dining room for guests. Three double rooms with shower and wc. Claude Moreau will share his enthusiasm for topiary and French gardens. Restaurants 3 km. Open 1 April to 30 September, or by reservation.
PRICES: s €53; d €61-€76; extra person €15 **ON SITE:** Fishing Hiking **NEARBY:** Bathing (6km) Horse riding (4km) Swimming pool (15km) Water sports (6km) Tennis (3km) Railway station (15km) Shops (3km) **NOTES:** No pets English spoken

CLEMONT

Chambre d'hôtes Roland et M-José DAUDE
Ferme des Givrys, 18410 CLEMONT
☎ 02 48 58 80 74 🖹 02 48 58 80 74

Rooms for two people, with private facilities, on the ground and first floors of a charming farmhouse in the midst of forests and lakes. Living room/lounge with television. Kennels for dogs and stables for three horses. Many tourist sites near at hand, plus tennis, horse riding, golf, etc. Group rates for eight-ten guests. Fishing in the river and lakes: black bass, trout, carp; wildlife photography and wine trail (Sancerre, Menetou, Quincy). Open all year by reservation.
PRICES: s €46; d €52; extra person €18; dinner €23 **ON SITE:** Fishing Hiking **NEARBY:** Bathing (10km) Horse riding (5km) Water sports (10km) Railway station (34km) Shops (4km) **NOTES:** No pets English spoken

---

🍽️
Places with this symbol serve table d'hôtes
evening meals - remember to book in advance

For further information on these and
other chambres d'hôtes, consult
the Gîtes de France website
www.gites-de-france.fr

COUST

🍽️ **Chambre d'hôtes** Henri VOLCOVICI
Le Haut de Changy, 18210 COUST
☎ 02 48 63 52 84

Guests will be welcomed with a glass of wine at La Madenria, a 19th-century farmhouse with en suite rooms sleeping 2-5 people. One separate room is at ground level and there are two upstairs. Living room/lounge with television. Table tennis room. Lovely flower garden. Nearby sites: Château d'Ainay le Vieil, Abbaye de Noirlac, Jardin du Prieuré d'Orsan. Walking trails in the Forest of Tronçais. Tariff: €85 for five guests. Open 1 April to 15 November, and by booking out of season.
PRICES: s €34; d €42; extra person €15; dinner €18-€23
ON SITE: Hiking **NEARBY:** Bathing (8km) Horse riding (8km) Fishing (8km) Swimming pool (10km) Water sports (8km) Tennis (2km) Railway station (10km) Shops (2km) **NOTES:** Pets admitted English spoken

CREZANCY-EN-SANCERRE

La Maison de Margot Karine et Hubert CHARLON
Reigny, 18300 CREZANCY-EN-SANCERRE
☎ 02 48 79 05 43
e-mail: Chambres.MARGOT@wanadoo.fr
Sancerre 9 km. Cosne-sur-Loire 20 km. Amidst the Sancerre vineyards in a winegrowing village. The comfortable and stylishy decorated rooms include two double rooms and one for two to four guests, each with shower and wc, on the first floor of an old restored barn. Lounge/living room for guests. Terrace, garden furniture, private parking. Walking and cycling routes. Restaurants 7 km. Golf 9 km. Open all year.
PRICES: d €45-€48; extra person €12 **ON SITE:** Hiking
NEARBY: Bathing (14km) Fishing (9km) Swimming pool (9km) Water sports (14km) Tennis (9km) Railway station (20km) Shops (9km)
NOTES: No pets English spoken

EPINEUIL-LE-FLEURIEL

Le Moulin d'Epineuil Pierre et Claude FAYAT
18360 EPINEUIL-LE-FLEURIEL
☎ 02 48 63 03 94
In the home village of writer Alain Fournier, this is a pleasant stopover on a working corn mill. One double room with washbasin, wc and television on the first floor of a large 19th-century building. Guests' dining room and suite for five people (two bedrooms and a sitting room, shower, wc and television) in an extension at the entrance to the house. Kitchen, cycles available for use. Large wooded garden, outdoor furniture. On the river and near the forest. Restaurants 2 and 5 km. Reduced tariff for more than two nights for two rooms. Open all year.
PRICES: d €43; extra person €16 **ON SITE:** Fishing Hiking Tennis
NEARBY: Bathing (10km) Horse riding (5km) Swimming pool (18km) Water sports (15km) Railway station (3km) **NOTES:** No pets

FARGES-EN-SEPTAINE

🏵🏵🏵 Augy Noëlle LEGOFFE et Serge ROUET
7, route du Vieux Moulin, 18800 FARGES-EN-SEPTAINE
☎ 02 48 69 16 01 📠 02 48 69 15 40

Bourges 15 km. A beautiful stone and timber house, restored with taste, that offers comfort and peace and a warm welcome from the proprietors. On the first floor of an outbuilding on this 18th-century farm, one room for two to four people, with shower and wc, and a suite of two rooms for two to four. Cot available. Guests' kitchen. Wooded and flower-filled park, outdoor furniture. Parking and garage. Golf 15 km. Restaurants 2 and 5 km. Open all year.
PRICES: d €39-€43; extra person €15 **ON SITE:** Hiking
NEARBY: Bathing (15km) Horse riding (15km) Swimming pool (11km) Water sports (15km) Tennis (11km) Railway station (15km) Shops (5km)
NOTES: Pets admitted

FOECY

🏵🏵🏵🏵 ⏷ Au Petit Prieuré Pierre DALTON
7, rue de l'Eglise, 18500 FOECY
☎ 02 48 51 01 76
e-mail: aupetit.prieure@laposte.net www.philosophes.com
At the heart of Berry, what was once believed to be a small priory is now a musician's house. There may even be musical performances (piano, violin and flute) during your stay. Enchanting atmosphere and gardens. Three rooms all with shower and wc. On the ground floor, one double with private sitting room. Upstairs in a wing, two double rooms (one which has access to a living room and kitchen area if required). Closed parking. Meals if reserved. Courses in watercolour painting. Open 15 January to 28 December.
PRICES: s €49-€58; d €52-€61; extra person €16-€21; dinner €21
ON SITE: Hiking Tennis **NEARBY:** Bathing (25km) Canoeing (10km) Horse riding (10km) Fishing (4km) Swimming pool (10km) Water sports (25km) Railway station (10km) **NOTES:** No pets English spoken

See advert on opposite page

GRON

🏵🏵🏵 ⏷ Les Chapelles Stéphanie MEFFERT
18800 GRON
☎ 02 48 68 51 49 📠 02 48 68 51 49
Between Sancerre and Bourges, three en suite double rooms with independent access on the first floor of a house adjoining the main house. Wooded and flower-bedecked grounds, garden furniture. Guests' living room/lounge with television. Parking. Restaurant 4 km. Lavish breakfasts. Open all year.
PRICES: s €29; d €39; t €50; extra person €11 **ON SITE:** Hiking
NEARBY: Swimming pool (4km) Tennis (4km) Railway station (30km)
NOTES: Pets admitted English spoken

HENRICHEMONT

🏵🏵🏵 ⏷ Le Lac aux Fées J-Claude et M-Odile MORIN
18250 HENRICHEMONT
☎ 02 48 26 71 23 e-mail: morin.earl@worldonline.fr
Pottery village 3 km. This restored farmhouse has held on to its charming name - The Lake of the Fairies - over the centuries. The guest rooms, all with independent access, are in an extension on the main house. One room for three and one for two to four on the ground floor, beside a small sitting room and kitchen. Upstairs, a kitchenette and lounge area for guests, one double room and one triple. All rooms have shower, wc and television. Wooded grounds, terrace, garden furniture. Restaurants close by. Reduction in tariff over three days. Open all year.
PRICES: ; d €40; extra person €13 **ON SITE:** Bathing Fishing Hiking Tennis **NEARBY:** Horse riding (10km) Swimming pool (12km) Railway station (30km) **NOTES:** No pets CC English spoken

HERRY

🏵🏵🏵 Domaine des Butteaux Martine BELTRAMELLI
Les Butteaux, 18140 HERRY
☎ 02 48 79 54 57 & 02 48 79 56 11 📠 02 48 79 51 03
e-mail: butteaux@online.fr http://butteaux.online.fr
Sancerre 10 km. La Charité 15 km. At the gateway to two notable wine areas, Martine, an artist and framemaker, has given the guest rooms the bewitching names of the perfumes they contain. A 19th-century family mansion on the banks of the Loire, it contains one double room and two rooms for three, each with shower and wc and independent access. Cots available. Living room/lounge for guests. Extensive wooded grounds with swimming pool. Garage, parking. Restaurants 2 km. Open all year.
PRICES: s €43; d €53; t €64; extra person €12 **ON SITE:** Children's play area Hiking **NEARBY:** Horse riding (10km) Fishing (1km) Tennis (2km) Railway station (15km) Shops (5km)
NOTES: No pets English spoken

IVOY-LE-PRE

🏵🏵🏵🏵 Château d'Ivoy J.Gérard et M.France GOUEFFON
18380 IVOY-LE-PRE
☎ 02 48 58 85 01 📠 02 48 58 85 02
e-mail: chateau.divoy@wanadoo.fr
http://perso.wanadoo.fr/chateau.divoy
Aubigny-sur-Nere 20 km. Bourges 30 km. At the edge of Berry and Sologne, at the gateway to Sancerrois, a 17th-century castle, perfect for a weekend stay or longer. Expect a warm but discreet welcome in the comfortable surroundings of a family home with a rich history. On the first floor, five exceedingly comfortable double rooms and a suite for two or three, all with bath or shower and wc. Sitting rooms, library and dining room. Ten hectares of wooded parkland. Kennels available. Golf 14 km. Open all year.
PRICES: ; d €125-€185; extra person €70 **ON SITE:** Fishing Swimming pool Hiking Tennis **NEARBY:** Bathing (5km) Horse riding (25km) Water sports (5km) Railway station (30km)
NOTES: No pets CC English spoken

🏵🏵🏵🏵 ⏷ La Verrerie Etienne et Marie DE SAPORTA
18380 IVOY-LE-PRE
☎ 02 48 58 90 86 📠 02 48 58 92 79
e-mail: desaporta@dactyl-buro.fr
Sancerre 32 km. Aubigny 15 km. Within a nature reserve on the edge of the Forest of Ivoy, this 18th-century forgemaster's house offers guests a cosy interior enhanced by period furniture. A two-roomed suite for two people (bath and wc) with sitting room (video, open fire), and a double room (160cm bed, shower, wc), both on the first floor of a separate building. Dining room for guests. Box garden with three

continued

ornamental lakes. Outdoor furniture and kitchen. Horses welcome (grass and stable). Fly fishing. Reduced rates for over three days. €145/four people. Children free. Open all year.
PRICES: s €70-€90; d €75-€99; t €122; dinner €16-€23
ON SITE: Fishing Hiking **NEARBY:** Bathing (8km) Horse riding (15km) Swimming pool (15km) Water sports (8km) Tennis (6km) Railway station (35km) Shops (3km) **NOTES:** No pets English spoken

JARS

🐓 La Brissauderie Philippe & Madeleine JAY
18260 JARS
☎ 02 48 58 74 94 📠 02 48 58 74 94
e-mail: madeleine.jay@wanadoo.fr
Calm reigns at this mid-Sancerrois house in 10 ha of woods. The comfortable rooms have painted furniture and murals. On the ground floor, one double room ('The Tulips') has a shower and wc. Upstairs: landing and relaxing area, two two-roomed suites ('The Bees' and 'The Sunflowers') for three to six people, with 160cm beds, shower and wc. Day room, lounge with television for guests. Parking. Restaurant 4 km. Substantial breakfast with fresh refined goats' milk cheese from Chavignol. Open all year.
PRICES: s €28; d €31-€37; t €37; extra person €12 **ON SITE:** Hiking
NEARBY: Bathing (2km) Horse riding (5km) Fishing (2km) Swimming pool (12km) Water sports (2km) Tennis (2km) Railway station (22km) Shops (4km) **NOTES:** No pets

LE CHATELET

🍴 Estiveaux Odette DE FAVERGES
18170 LE CHATELET
☎ 02 48 56 22 64
In the heart of Berry, south of the Route Jacques Coeur, 2.5 hours from Paris. Three rooms (double canopy bed) in a striking house in the middle of a large shady park. All have shower and wc. Dining room with wood fire depending on season. Small smoking room with television, library and large living room (non-smoking). Restaurant 1.5 km. Parking. Pond with fishing. Games and keep fit room. Meals if booked. Quiet, comfort and a warm welcome. Open all year - booking required.
PRICES: s €70; d €85-€92; extra person €15-€25; dinner €25-€31
ON SITE: Fishing Hiking **NEARBY:** Bathing (19km) Horse riding (36km) Swimming pool (25km) Water sports (19km) Tennis (2km)
NOTES: No pets

LUNERY

La Vergne Francis et M-Hélène JACQUIER
18400 LUNERY
☎ 02 48 68 01 07 e-mail: lavergne@wanadoo.fr

Marie-Hélène and Francis welcome guests to La Vergne, their 17th-century family home, overlooking the Valley of Cher. Enjoy the comfort, quiet and charm. Six guest rooms in the old outbuildings. Five double rooms and one for four, all with private shower and

Au Petit Prieuré
Tel: +33(0)2.48.51.01.76 Fax: 07092-154125 (from UK)
Email: aupetit.prieure@laposte.net
Web Site: www.philosophes.com
7 rue de l'Église, 18500 FOËCY
An atmosphere of warmth and comfort awaits you all the year round in this former priory in the Berry with its forests, lakes and wine. The rooms are spacious, with double beds, TV and private bathrooms. One is equipped as an apartment with kitchen and living area, and another with four-poster bed and private sitting room. Delicious evening meals with regional produce and wine are served from the excellent kitchen. During the summer there are music and watercolour courses.
Prices: d €52 to €61, including breakfast. Table d'hôte €21.
Nearby: Railway station, fishing, walking, horse riding.
Notes: No pets, no smoking

television. Library. Living room/dining room for guests. Terrace, garden, outdoor furniture. Nearby restaurant. Open all year.
PRICES: ; d €39-€46; extra person €15 **ON SITE:** Hiking
NEARBY: Bathing (10km) Horse riding (10km) Fishing (10km) Swimming pool (25km) Water sports (10km) Tennis (2km) Railway station (25km) Shops (2km) **NOTES:** Pets admitted English spoken

MEHUN-SUR-YEVRE

Les Buissons Jeanne COMPAGNIE-GUIDOT
107, avenue Jean Chatelet, 18500 MEHUN-SUR-YEVRE
☎ 02 48 57 31 22 📠 02 48 57 31 22
Bourges 15 mins. Visitors will find calm in this green corner overhanging the Valley of the Yèvre. The accommodation is comfortable and decorated in the style of the Berry region. Rooms with separate access in outbuildings of a 19th-century farm. Two double rooms and a triple, all with shower and wc. Living room/dining room reserved for guests (reading room and television). Porcelain and art displays. Garden with furniture. Closed parking. Forest. Vineyards 6 km. Cot available. Restaurants in town. Open March to October; booking required.
PRICES: s €40; d €43-€45; extra person €15 **ON SITE:** Fishing Swimming pool Hiking Tennis **NEARBY:** Bathing (20km) Horse riding (4km) Water sports (6km) **NOTES:** No pets English spoken

CC - credit cards accepted

Places with this symbol are farmhouses

continued

MONTIGNY

🏵 ♥ 🍽 Domaine de la Reculée Elisabeth GRESSIN
La Reculée, 18250 MONTIGNY
☎ 02 48 69 59 18 🖷 02 48 69 52 51
e-mail: scarroir@terre-net.fr
Five guest rooms each with separate access on an interesting farm. Double rooms with bath or shower and wc. Television. Mountain bikes available. Dine and relax in the living room with its open fire and antique furniture, opening on to the garden where on fine days the proprietor serves breakfast. 10% reduction for over three nights. Nearby restaurant. No meals on Sunday. Open 15 March to 15 November.
PRICES: s €39; d €46; extra person €15; dinner €18 **ON SITE:** Hiking **NEARBY:** Bathing (26km) Fishing (10km) Swimming pool (26km) Tennis (10km) **NOTES:** Pets admitted English spoken

NEUVY-SUR-BARANGEON

🏵 🍽 Le Bas-Guilly Sylvie MARTIN
18330 NEUVY-SUR-BARANGEON
☎ 02 48 51 64 46
Carefree holidays can be enjoyed at Bas Guilly. Double rooms (one on the ground floor) with shower and wc in a house of some character in the open countryside. Living room with open fireplace, sitting room with cooking area in an adjoining building. Ten hectare park with barbecue area and parking. Meadow and river. Gîte adjacent with seven single rooms. Horses can be accommodated. Fishing, walking on the magnificent pathways of the area. Spend quiet evenings in warm and comfortable rooms. Car essential. Open all year.
PRICES: d €47; extra person €16; dinner €20-€31 **ON SITE:** Bathing Fishing Hiking **NEARBY:** Horse riding (15km) Swimming pool (20km) Water sports (30km) Tennis (20km) **NOTES:** Pets admitted

ORVAL

🏵 🍽 Chambre d'hôtes Marie-Claude DUSSERT
La Tromière, 18200 ORVAL
☎ 02 48 96 47 45
Double rooms in a home of character with a shady park. Living room and lounge for guests. Grounds. Parking. River 500 m; forest 4 km. Two rooms with private shower and common wc. One room with private bathroom and wc. The hostess, Marie-Claude, will serve meals based on seasonal produce, by prior arrangement. Open all year.
PRICES: s €40-€48; d €45-€53; t €56; dinner €16-€17 **ON SITE:** Fishing Hiking **NEARBY:** Bathing (15km) Horse riding (6km) Swimming pool (3km) Water sports (15km) Tennis (2km) **NOTES:** No pets English spoken

PLAIMPIED-GIVAUDINS

🏵 Chambre d'hôtes Régis et Martine VANDAMME
1, rue de l'Abbaye, 18340 PLAIMPIED-GIVAUDINS
☎ 02 48 25 64 28
Bourges 10 km. Rooms on the first floor of a large 19th-century building opposite the 12th-century Roman abbot's house in a quiet little village. Martine will have a warm welcome waiting, and inspire you to discover the area (Bourges cathedral, nuits lumière, the chateaux on the Jacques Coeur trail). One room for three people, two suites for three, and one double room, all with shower and wc. Living room/lounge reserved for guests. Parking, closed courtyard, garden furniture. Restaurant nearby. Open all year.
PRICES: ; d €30-€35; extra person €12 **ON SITE:** Fishing Hiking Tennis **NEARBY:** Bathing (10km) Horse riding (10km) Swimming pool (10km) Water sports (10km) Railway station (10km) **NOTES:** No pets Minimum 2 night stay English spoken

QUINCY

🏵 Domaine du Pressoir Claude et Georgette HOUSSIER
18120 QUINCY
☎ 02 48 51 30 04 & 02 48 51 31 13
Upstairs in a restored 19th-century wine store, two rooms for three, and two for four guests. Each has shower and wc. Huge reception room with television, microwave and fridge. Private fishing, flower garden, outdoor furniture, parking. Separate buildings with cooking facilities (€3/day). Restaurants nearby. Winegrowing business, where guests can visit the cellars and sample the wines of Quincy. Open 1 March to end December.
PRICES: d €40; t €52; extra person €12 **ON SITE:** Wine tasting Bathing Fishing Swimming pool Hiking Tennis **NEARBY:** Horse riding (15km) Water sports (22km) Railway station (15km) Shops (5km) **NOTES:** Pets admitted

RIANS

🏵 ♥ 🍽 La Chaume Yves et Odile PROFFIT
Rians, 18220 LES AIX-D'ANGILLON
☎ 02 48 64 41 58 🖷 02 48 64 29 71
e-mail: proffityve@aol.com

On the way to the Sancerrois in a quiet spot, a warm welcome awaits guests, whether for one night or a long stay. The bedrooms are in an extension to the house, with separate access. Two double rooms, two rooms for three (one is grade 2), and one for four guests. All have private shower and wc. Guests' living room/lounge with television. Cot available. Meals may be booked, except Sunday. Kitchen for guests' use. Open all year.
PRICES: d €42; extra person €15; dinner €16-€18 **ON SITE:** Hiking **NEARBY:** Bathing (20km) Horse riding (25km) Fishing (5km) Swimming pool (4km) Water sports (20km) Tennis (4km) Railway station (20km) Shops (4km) **NOTES:** Pets admitted English spoken

SAULZAIS-LE-POTIER

🏵 🍽 La Truffière D HAMMES et J LEPRAT
18360 SAULZAIS-LE-POTIER
☎ 02 48 63 04 59
A very old house, now restored, surrounded by oaks in a large park. One two room suite with living room area, shower, wc, television, upstairs. On the ground floor one double room with bath and shower. Television lounge for guests. Four hectares of wooded grounds full of animals. Garden furniture. Possible stabling for two horses. GR walking paths nearby. Telephone/fax on request. Meals except Monday and Tuesday. 5-15% discount according to number of rooms and length of stay. Open 1 April to 30 September, at other times by booking.
PRICES: s €45; d €55; extra person €15; dinner €15-€20
ON SITE: Fishing Swimming pool Hiking **NEARBY:** Bathing (4km) Horse riding (20km) Water sports (25km) Tennis (15km) Railway station (15km) Shops (5km) **NOTES:** Pets admitted English spoken

SENS-BEAUJEU

¡¡¡ ÍÖÍ Les Bergères Ana et Antonio MONTENEGRO
18300 SENS-BEAUJEU
☎ 02 48 58 78 89
Sancerre 15 km. Cosne-sur-Loire 25 km. On first and ground floors of an old barn next to the main house, with separate entrance, three double rooms with bath and wc. Lounge and small kitchen reserved for guests. Botanical garden, terrace, outdoor furniture, sun loungers. Sauna available. Volleyball, table tennis. Golf 15 km. Restaurants 5 km. In the Pays Fort, near Sancerre. Visit Château de Boucard, and local vineyards. Children €9. Open all year.
PRICES: d €44; t €49; dinner €15–€18 **ON SITE:** Hiking
NEARBY: Bathing (5km)　Horse riding (5km)　Fishing (10km)　Swimming pool (15km)　Water sports (10km)　Tennis (5km)　Railway station (25km)　Shops (5km)　**NOTES:** No pets

SIDIAILLES

¡¡¡ ÍÖÍ La Fosse-Ronde Gilberte U GARIH et M. CARLI
18270 SIDIAILLES
☎ 02 48 56 61 25　🖷 02 48 56 61 25
e-mail: carligarih@wanadoo.fr

Between the medieval town of Culan and the Roman Oppidum of Chateaumeillant on the Route Jacques Coeur. Three double rooms upstairs in this renovated house, each with bath and shower. Living room/lounge. Television. Open fires. Large grassed grounds. Terrace, outdoor furniture, parking. Animals welcome, kept in kennels. Meals if booked. At Culan: castle-forts, restaurants. Possible tours on request. Children will enjoy the farm animals. Open all year.
PRICES: d €35–€42; extra person €12; dinner €10–€14 **ON SITE:** Hiking
NEARBY: Bathing (5km)　Canoeing (5km)　Horse riding (7km)　Fishing (5km)　Swimming pool (28km)　Water sports (5km)　Tennis (3km)　Railway station (28km)　Shops (3km)　**NOTES:** Pets admitted　English spoken

ST-BAUDEL

¡¡¡ 🐓 Parassay F CARTERON et C DUCLUZEAUD
18160 ST-BAUDEL
☎ 02 48 60 14 18 & 02 48 60 00 81
Guests will find here comfort, quiet and hospitality. Four double rooms with shower/wc in an old building on an isolated farm. Grounds with pond, garden furniture, children's games. Lounge/dining room with television and open fire for guests. Several châteaux nearby. Leisure area by the Arnon with picnic site 3 km. For a long stay, the seventh night is free. Open all year.
PRICES: s €33; d €37–€39; extra person €13 **ON SITE:** Children's play area　Hiking **NEARBY:** Bathing (7km)　Horse riding (10km)　Fishing (3km)　Swimming pool (24km)　Water sports (7km)　Tennis (7km)　Railway station (9km)　Shops (2km)　**NOTES:** No pets　Minimum 2 night stay　English spoken

ST-ELOY-DE-GY

¡¡¡ La Grande Mouline Jean et Chantal MALOT
Bourgneuf, 18110 ST-ELOY-DE-GY
☎ 02 48 25 40 44　🖷 02 48 25 40 44
Very old house where the welcome is genuine, and where guests can discover the quiet and pleasure of the countryside. Enjoy a summer stroll in the forest and the warmth of an open fire in winter. The rooms are on the ground floors of the main house and a large outbuilding. Two rooms for four guests, each with mezzanine and small lounge, shower and wc (one has a bath as well). One room for two to four people, with bath and wc. One apartment for three plus two. One room for three with shower and wc. Sitting room/library. Sitting/dining room. Games. Television. Bikes available. Terrace, garden furniture. Open all year.
PRICES: s €35; d €40; t €50; extra person €10 **ON SITE:** Hiking
NEARBY: Bathing (13km)　Horse riding (11km)　Fishing (1km)　Swimming pool (11km)　Water sports (13km)　Tennis (11km)　**NOTES:** No pets　English spoken

ST-GEORGES-SUR-LA-PREE

¡¡¡ Chambre d'hôtes Jacqueline et Daniel LEFEVRE
10, chemin des Menoux,
18100 ST-GEORGES-SUR-LA-PREE
☎ 02 48 52 00 51 & 06 80 84 22 39
Jacqueline and Daniel welcome visitors to their guest house that is situated on the way to the Sologne. Double rooms, each with shower or bath and wc, upstairs in a renovated 17th-century farmhouse. Dining/living room (with open fire) for guests' use. Parking, courtyard, extensive grounds and terrace. Garden furniture. Possibility of television in rooms. Bikes at guests' disposal. Restaurant 8 km. Open all year.
PRICES: s €29; d €37; t €46; extra person €11 **ON SITE:** Hiking
NEARBY: Horse riding (15km)　Swimming pool (15km)　Tennis (2km)　Railway station (15km)　Shops (2km)　**NOTES:** No pets

ST-GERMAIN-DU-PUY

¡¡¡ 🌿 Jacquelin Irène et Jean-Paul JOLLY
18390 ST-GERMAIN-DU-PUY
☎ 02 48 30 84 97　🖷 02 48 30 61 37

Bourges 5 km. Double rooms (some with 160cm beds) with shower or bath and wc, television, independent access and lounge area on first and ground floors. The rooms are in the 15th-century main house or one of the outbuildings. Kitchen available. Wooded park, garden furniture. At the gateway to the Bourges, guests will enjoy the peace of the country in this beautiful farmhouse and its rural setting. Open all year.
PRICES: s €42; d €46; t €61; extra person €15 **ON SITE:** Hiking
NEARBY: Bathing (7km)　Horse riding (7km)　Fishing (7km)　Swimming pool (1km)　Water sports (7km)　Tennis (1km)　Railway station (7km)　Shops (1km)　**NOTES:** No pets　English spoken

THENIOUX

♦♦♦ Le Petit-Nançay J et M BARDIOT-JOBLEAU
5, route de Genouilly, 18100 THENIOUX
☎ 02 48 52 01 58 📠 02 48 52 01 58
e-mail: bardiot-jobleau@libertysurf.fr
Five rooms, two at ground level, each with separate entry, in 15th-century farm buildings. The rooms accommodate two to four people and each has shower and wc. Communal living room. Two sitting rooms, library and cooking area at guests' disposal. Indoor and outdoor kitchen with barbecue. Swimming pool. Restaurant at hand. Open all year.
PRICES: s €34; d €38-€42; t €48-€52; extra person €10-€14
ON SITE: Fishing Swimming pool Hiking Tennis **NEARBY:** Bathing (2km) Horse riding (7km) Water sports (2km) **NOTES:** No pets English spoken

VIGNOUX-SOUS-LES-AIX

♦♦♦ i⊙i La Petite Noue J-F et D GILBERT
18110 VIGNOUX-SOUS-LES-AIX
☎ 02 48 64 56 55
Vineyards of Menetou-Salon 5 km. 10 mn from Bourges. Guests will enjoy the beauty of this restored farmhouse, the hospitality of the owners, and the comfort they offer. Rooms for two or three people, each with shower and wc, on the first floor of a 19th-century farmhouse. Large wooded grounds with ornamental lake. Terrace with garden furniture. Living room/lounge with open fire and television. Near the châteaux on the Route Jacques Coeur. Open all year.
PRICES: s €31; d €36-€39; t €46; extra person €11; dinner €14
ON SITE: Hiking **NEARBY:** Bathing (12km) Horse riding (12km) Fishing (3km) Swimming pool (12km) Water sports (12km) Tennis (12km) Railway station (12km) Shops (1km) **NOTES:** Pets admitted

VIGNOUX-SUR-BARANGEON

♦♦♦ Villemenard J et M GREAU
18500 VIGNOUX-SUR-BARANGEON
☎ 02 48 51 53 40 📠 02 48 51 58 77

A charming property in a peaceful setting. At the gateway to the Sologne, it is a large 19th-century bourgeois house built on an ancient site. Six rooms (three doubles, two for three visitors and one for four). Dining room available to guests. Wooded park and river and ponds (fishing and boating). Garden furniture. Many restaurants nearby. Open all year.
PRICES: d €40-€44; extra person €14 **ON SITE:** Fishing Hiking **NEARBY:** Horse riding (7km) Swimming pool (5km) Water sports (25km) Tennis (5km) Railway station (5km) Shops (8km) **NOTES:** No pets English spoken

> Prices are given in Euros €1 = £0.62
> at the time of going to press

BAILLEAU-L'EVEQUE

♦♦♦ ♥ i⊙i Levesville Bruno et Nathalie VASSEUR
Avenue du Château, 28300 BAILLEAU-L'EVEQUE
☎ 02 37 22 97 02 📠 02 37 22 97 02
Large farmhouse, with a bedroom consisting of two adjoining twin rooms on the first floor, each has a private shower room and wc. Two double rooms with space for an extra bed, each with a private bathroom and wc. The ground floor has a living room for the guests' exclusive use. All rooms are non-smoking. There is a garage and access to the garden. Situated in a peaceful area. Open all year.
PRICES: s €38; d €45-€55; extra person €15; dinner €15
NEARBY: Horse riding (5km) Fishing (3km) Swimming pool (8km) Tennis (8km) Railway station (10km) Shops (3km) **NOTES:** No pets English spoken

CLOYES

♦♦♦ ♥ Ferme du Carrefour Dominique et Odile CLICHY
Ferme du Carrefour, 28220 CLOYES
☎ 02 37 98 53 10 📠 02 37 98 53 10
In a country hamlet, Odile and Dominique offer three comfortable bedrooms on their farm, situated 1km from the main village in the area. One double room, another double room with a small adjoining single room, a twin room plus supplementary single bed, each room has a private shower room and wc. Living/dining room, with colour TV available for the guests. Patio, parking, table tennis. Open all year.
PRICES: s €30; d €37; t €45 **NEARBY:** Canoeing (2km) Horse riding (10km) Fishing (1km) Swimming pool (10km) Tennis (1km) Sailing (2km) Bicycle hire (14km) Railway station (1km) Shops (1km)
NOTES: No pets

DANGEAU

♦♦♦ i⊙i Bouthonvilliers Thérèse et Richard DE VERDUN
28160 DANGEAU
☎ 02 37 96 77 04
Bouthonvilliers is situated at the border between Beauce and Perche. One double room and one twin room. Also a suite made up of a double room and a single room. Each bedroom has a private bathroom and wc. Reservations for set evening meals available. Châteaux of the Loire and many leisure facilities are close by. Open all year.
PRICES: s €53; d €99; t €145; extra person €22; dinner €43
ON SITE: Fishing Bicycle hire **NEARBY:** Canoeing (7km) Horse riding (7km) Swimming pool (7km) Tennis (5km) Railway station (7km) Shops (5km) **NOTES:** Pets admitted English spoken

LA BOURDINIERE-ST-LOUP

♦♦♦ Le Temple Marcel et Marguerite GUIARD
3, route Nationale 10, 28360 LA BOURDINIERE-ST-LOUP
☎ 02 37 26 61 90 📠 02 37 26 61 90
www.francebonjour.com/guiard/
Marcel and Marguerite welcome guests to their farmhouse where they have five grade 2 and 3 ground floor guest rooms. Each room has its own entrance, private shower room and wc. Kitchen and TV for guests' exclusive use. Washing machine. Enclosed private parking. Corner garden, outdoor furniture, swings. 4 km from A11. 300m to nearest brasserie and restaurant close by. Open all year.
PRICES: s €30; d €38; t €47; extra person €10 **ON SITE:** Children's play area **NEARBY:** Canoeing (12km) Horse riding (12km) Swimming pool (15km) Tennis (12km) Bicycle hire (15km) Railway station (15km) Shops (6km) **NOTES:** Pets admitted

See advert on opposite page

LES CHATELETS

¶¶¶ ⓘ◎ Genesteux Claude MAILLOT
Genesteux, Les Chatelets, 28270 BREZOLLES
☎ 02 37 48 40 29
An old converted barn offers guests the charm of bygone days with the comforts of today. Claude offers three separate fully furnished bedrooms, each looking over a patio, and with a private shower room, wc and TV. Dining room, living room, library. Special rates for families and long stays. Open 1 April to 30 September.
PRICES: s €49; d €53; t €24 **NEARBY:** Horse riding (15km) Fishing (9km) Swimming pool (12km) Tennis (4km) Railway station (12km) Shops (4km) Restaurant nearby **NOTES:** Pets admitted

NOGENT-LE-PHAYE

¶¶¶ Chambre d'hôtes André LEBOUCQ
1, rue de la Boissière, 28630 NOGENT-LE-PHAYE
☎ 06 09 39 54 60
André and his wife offer five guest rooms on the first floor of their contemporary house, nestled in a peaceful grassy enclosure full of flowers, close to Chartres. One twin room with the beds pushed together, another twin room, two double rooms and another double room also containing a single bed. Each has a private shower or bathroom, wc and TV. Dining room and corner living room available to guests. Open all year.
PRICES: s €43; d €49–€53; t €76 **ON SITE:** Tennis **NEARBY:** Canoeing (7km) Horse riding (3km) Fishing (7km) Swimming pool (7km) Sailing (18km) Railway station (8km) **NOTES:** No pets

NOGENT-LE-ROI

¶¶¶ Moulin du Roi Claude-Jeanne FAURE
Rue du Pont de Demoiselle, 28210 NOGENT-LE-ROI
☎ 02 37 51 32 39 ▤ 02 37 51 22 83
e-mail: cdrhum@hotmail.com http://www.cdrhum.com
Maintenon 8 km. At the edge of the River Eure in a mill surrounded by greenery, guests will be enchanted by the calmness of the surroundings here. There is an enclosed garden full of trees and flowers. Two large bedrooms face the garden, each with a bathroom and wc. On the first floor there are two adjoining rooms with a bathroom and wc. Living room available for country breakfasts or evenings in front of an open fire. Fishing on site. Walking distance from restaurants and the market town. Parking. One hour from Paris and 20 minutes from Chartres Cathedral. Closed Saturday nights except for guests arriving Friday night or Sunday night. Open February to November.
PRICES: s €34–€44; d €44–€54; t €64 **ON SITE:** Fishing Swimming pool **NEARBY:** Canoeing (8km) Horse riding (3km) Tennis (1km) Sailing (8km) Shops (1km) **NOTES:** No pets English spoken

OINVILLE-ST-LIPHARD

¶¶¶ ⓘ◎ Chambre d'hôtes Annette MAILLAUX
1 et 3, rue du Moulin, Détour Beauceron,
28310 OINVILLE-ST-LIPHARD
☎ 02 37 90 28 76
e-mail: detour.beauceron@wanadoo.fr
Between Paris and Orléans, this house offers non-smoking rooms with their own entrance, TV and private shower room. On the ground floor is a double 'yellow' room. On the first floor there is a double 'blue' room also containing a single bed. The 'green' room consists of two adjoining rooms, one double room with additional single bed and one twin room. Cot available. The grounds are full of trees. Restaurants 4 km. Discounts for stays longer than three nights. Reservations possible for evening meals. Parking. Entrance is the grey gate behind the bus stop. Open all year.
PRICES: s €28; d €40; t €52; extra person €12; dinner €10–€20
ON SITE: Children's play area Bicycle hire Hiking **NEARBY:** Swimming pool (4km) Tennis (4km) Railway station (4km) Shops (4km)
NOTES: No pets English spoken

Le Temple
Chambres D'Hôtes
3 route Nationale 10
28360 La Bourdinière St Loup

The proprietors Marguerite and Marcel welcome you to their farm. Each of the five bedrooms are situated on the ground floor in a separate building with their own private entrance, all have en-suite facilities, electric heater and TV. Guests have use of the kitchen, including a washing machine, fridge, cooker and microwave also the garden with garden furniture and swings. Private parking. Open all year. Restaurant 300m. Chartres 15kms south.

Tel & fax: 02 37 26 61 90
Web: www.france-bonjour.com/guiard/

PRE-ST-MARTIN

¶¶¶ 🐓 Le Carcotage Beauceron Jean-Baptiste VIOLETTE
8, rue St-Martin, 28800 PRE-ST-MARTIN
☎ 02 37 47 27 21 & 02 37 47 38 09
e-mail: carcotage.beauceron@wanadoo.fr www.carcotage.com
Chartres 27 km. Comfort is guaranteed at this peaceful setting between Paris and the châteaux of the Loire. There are four tasteful, spacious and comfortable bedrooms on the first floor of this welcoming farm dating from the 18th and early 20th centuries: one double room, one room for three people and two rooms for four people, furnished with family heirlooms. Each has a separate shower room and wc. Living room with TV, open fire and library. Central heating. Pretty garden and lawn bordered by hedges, courtyard, swimming pool for children. Prices for four people: 64 euros; dogs: 6 euros. Kitchen available. Tenth night free of charge. Flights in ultra-light planes 1 km. Off-road cycle track. All reservations not confirmed by 5pm on the same day will not be retained. Open all year.
PRICES: s €38; d €41; t €52; extra person €11 **ON SITE:** Children's play area Bicycle hire **NEARBY:** Canoeing (8km) Horse riding (7km) Fishing (8km) Swimming pool (8km) Tennis (4km) Sailing (25km) Railway station (8km) **NOTES:** Pets admitted English spoken

🐓 Places with this symbol are farmhouses

ⓘ◎
Places with this symbol serve table d'hôtes evening meals - remember to book in advance

CENTRAL FRANCE

SANTILLY

♦♦♦ ❧ ¡○¡ Château Gaillard
Florence et Bruno VILLETTE
12, rue C. Péguy, 28310 SANTILLY
☎ 02 37 90 01 52 & 02 37 90 24 98 ▤ 02 37 90 24 98
Three bedrooms in a comfortable, restored farm in Beauce. The first floor has two twin bedrooms with TV, shower room and wc. The double room has a spa bath in the bathroom. Living room available to guests. Garden contains furniture, a swing and garage. Reservations for evening meals possible. The farm is within easy access of the RN20 but isolated enough to be peaceful. Open all year.
PRICES: s €31-€38; d €39-€45; extra person €12; dinner €13
ON SITE: Children's play area Bicycle hire **NEARBY:** Canoeing (28km) Horse riding (20km) Fishing (20km) Swimming pool (6km) Tennis (6km) Railway station (1km) Shops (6km) **NOTES:** No pets

ST-ELIPH

♦♦♦ ❧ L'Auberdière Jean-Pierre BOUDET
28240 ST-ELIPH
☎ 02 37 81 10 46
Three furnished bedrooms on the first floor of a farm in the Perche region. Each room is a double room (one contains an extra single bed) and has its own shower or bathroom. Communal wc for the three bedrooms. The bedrooms offer a peaceful environment. Corner living room with TV, ideal for reading. Reception on the ground floor. Restricted telephone service. Outdoor furniture and barbecue. Local shops 5 km. Open all year.
PRICES: s €27; d €30; t €37 **NEARBY:** Fishing (1km) Swimming pool (2km) Tennis (1km) Sailing (6km) Bicycle hire (2km) Railway station (2km) Shops (2km) **NOTES:** No pets English spoken

ST-LAURENT-LA-GATINE

♦♦♦ Chambre d'hôtes Francis & Bernadette JAMES
Clos St-Laurent, 28210 ST-LAURENT-LA-GATINE
☎ 02 37 38 24 02
Versailles 55 km. Paris 65 km. This 19th-century house offers three half-timbered bedrooms on the first floor. One twin room, one double room, and one double room containing a child's bed. Each has a private shower room and wc. The ground floor has a living room with open fire, with a furnished patio. Peaceful location. Golf course 15 km away. Open all year.
PRICES: s €49; d €58 **NEARBY:** Canoeing (20km) Horse riding (6km) Fishing (7km) Swimming pool (6km) Tennis (4km) Sailing (10km) Bicycle hire (5km) Railway station (15km) Shops (6km) **NOTES:** No pets

ST-LUPERCE

♦♦♦ ❧ Mousseau Marie-Laure & Gilles PERRIN
28190 ST-LUPERCE
☎ 02 37 26 85 01 ▤ 02 37 26 78 29
e-mail: gillesperrin1@aol.com
Chartres 12 km. Paris 90 km. Between Beauce and Perche, near the River Eure, in a calm and peaceful environment, Marie-Laure and Gilles offer three guest rooms in an outbuilding above an old stable on their farm. Each room has a private bathroom and wc. There are two double rooms 'Bouton d'Or' (also contains a single bed) and 'Myosotis' and a twin room 'Tournesol'. Open all year.
PRICES: s €34; d €49; t €64; extra person €15 **ON SITE:** Fishing **NEARBY:** Horse riding (9km) Swimming pool (9km) Tennis (2km) Sailing (9km) Railway station (9km) Shops (2km) **NOTES:** No pets

ST-MAIXME-HAUTERIVE

♦♦♦ ❧ ¡○¡ La Rondellière Catherine et J-Paul LANGLOIS
11, rue de la Mairie, 28170 ST-MAIXME-HAUTERIVE
☎ 02 37 51 68 26 ▤ 02 37 51 08 53

The owners welcome guests to their farm in a small village. The ground floor has a reception with a living room, open fire and TV. There is a kitchen for family gatherings. There are four bedrooms on the first floor: two twin rooms and two double rooms (one also with a sofa bed). Each has a private bathroom and wc. There are extra beds and a cot available. Evening meals may be booked in advance. Archery and golf 2 km, tennis court and bikes available to guests on site. Open all year.
PRICES: s €30; d €37; extra person €9; dinner €12 **ON SITE:** Tennis Bicycle hire **NEARBY:** Horse riding (2km) Fishing (20km) Swimming pool (5km) Sailing (25km) Railway station (20km) Shops (5km) **NOTES:** No pets English spoken

VER-LES-CHARTRES

♦♦♦ La Varenne Cécile et Guillaume PICAULT
20, rue de Tachainville, 28630 VER-LES-CHARTRES
☎ 02 37 26 45 32
e-mail: lavarenne28@free.fr
Chartres 7km. In the Eure Valley, on the ground floor of a detached and peaceful pavilion there are two double rooms and two adjoining rooms that contain a double bed, a single bed and the possibility of a second single bed. Bathroom or shower room with wc. Kitchenette available. Covered pool heated between 1 April and 31 October. Large garden, private parking. Open all year.
PRICES: s €40-€46; d €45-€53; t €55-€68; extra person €15
ON SITE: Swimming pool **NEARBY:** Canoeing (2km) Horse riding (2km) Fishing (3km) Tennis (2km) Railway station (7km) Shops (3km) **NOTES:** No pets English spoken

VILLIERS-LE-MORHIER

♦♦♦ ❧ Chandelles Catherine et J-Marc SIMON
19, rue des Sablons, 28130 VILLIERS-LE-MORHIER
☎ 02 37 82 71 59 ▤ 02 37 82 71 59
e-mail: info@chandelles-golf.com www.chandelles-golf.com
In the peaceful and grassy grounds of a restored farm, Catherine, who is passionate about horses and Jean-Marc, who is a golf teacher, welcome visitors to their comfortable guest rooms, each with bathroom, wc and TV. Each room has its own entrance and enclosed parking. Golf lessons available and horses welcome.
PRICES: d €58 **ON SITE:** Fishing Bicycle hire **NEARBY:** Horse riding (3km) Swimming pool (3km) Tennis (2km) Railway station (3km) Shops (3km) **NOTES:** No pets CC

INDRE

AIGURANDE

¶¶¶ ⦿ la Crouzette Elise LE JEANNE
route de Chateauroux, 36140 AIGURANDE
☎ 02 54 06 32 61 & 02 54 06 45 81
George Sand Museum at la Châtre 25km. Nohant 30km. This large new house is surrounded by a shaded garden, 200m from the town centre. Two neighbouring double rooms on the ground floor for a family, with bathroom and wc. The first floor has two bedrooms (two double beds and one single) for a family, with a bathroom and wc. Living room (TV) at guests' disposal. Patio with garden furniture. Vallée Noire region nearby. Four people: €61. Open all year.
PRICES: s €30; d €34; t €46; extra person €8; dinner €11
NEARBY: Bathing (20km) Canoeing (20km) Horse riding (10km) Golf (30km) Fishing (1km) Swimming pool (25km) Water sports (20km) Tennis (1km) Railway station (50km) AIGURANDE **NOTES:** Pets admitted

CHALAIS

¶¶¶ ⦿ Le Grand Ajoux Aude DE LA JONQUIERE-AYME
36370 CHALAIS
☎ 02 54 37 72 92 ▤ 02 54 37 56 60
e-mail: grandajoux@AOL.com
http://membersAOL.com/grandajoux
Eighteenth-century manor surrounded by greenery in the Parc de la Brenne. Peace and quiet can be found in a flower garden and deer and boars may be seen at night. Black Du Berry donkeys are bred here. Two bedrooms with suites for four people, plus shower room and wc. Dining room with open fire. Swimming pool. Garden furniture, off-road cycling and table tennis. Private lakes (one and two hectares). Bridle paths for long walks. Fishing. Accompanied outings on off-road bikes. Open from May to September (other times by reservation).
PRICES: s €44; d €49; suite €88 **ON SITE:** Horse riding Fishing Swimming pool **NEARBY:** Bathing (20km) Canoeing (5km) Golf (15km) Aerial sports (20km) Water sports (20km) Tennis (5km) Railway station (35km) Shops (5km) LE BLANC (18km) **NOTES:** No pets CC English spoken

CHEZELLES

¶¶¶ ⦿ Le Priouze Michelle et Georges BABLIN
4 rue du Priouze, 36500 CHEZELLES
☎ 02 54 36 66 28 & 02 54 26 98 08 ▤ 02 54 36 66 28
Château de Bouges 25km and de Valençay 30km. A lovely 18th-century house in a shaded park by a river. First floor has three guest rooms containing two large double beds and two smaller double beds, with bathrooms. TV and telephone in each room. Dining room, living room with open fire (TV, games, library, hi-fi). Kitchen for longer stays. Patio (garden furniture, barbecue, table tennis, outdoor games, and picnic area). Fishery. Price for a week's stay: 245 euros. Reduced price for longer stays. Rural gîte on the property. Brenne natural park nearby. Open all year.
PRICES: s €34; d €43-€49; extra person €15; dinner €16
ON SITE: Fishing Tennis **NEARBY:** Bathing (14km) Canoeing (14km) Horse riding (15km) Golf (6km) Swimming pool (14km) Water sports (14km) Railway station (15km) Shops (6km) CHATEAUROUX (14km)
NOTES: No pets

COINGS

¶¶¶ ♥ Domaine de Villecourte
Claudine DAGUET-RAULT
Route de la Champenoise, 36130 COINGS
☎ 02 54 22 12 56 ▤ 02 54 22 12 56
Estate with character surrounded by greenery, 7 km from Déols

and Châteauroux. Nature lovers will be delighted to see hares, pheasants and roe deer. Four double bedrooms with private shower room. Kitchen available. Living room (telephone, TV, sofa-bed). In the converted outbuildings, two bedrooms with bathrooms and equipped kitchen, TV and telephone. Non-enclosed grounds with view of the water in the distance and the river's edge. Many restaurants only 5 km from Villecourte. Open all year.
PRICES: s €38; d €49; extra person €15; dinner €17 **NEARBY:** Bathing (10km) Canoeing (10km) Horse riding (15km) Golf (17km) Fishing (5km) Swimming pool (10km) Aerial sports (10km) Water sports (10km) Tennis (10km) Railway station (10km) Shops (7km) CHATEAUROUX (10km)
NOTES: No pets English spoken

EGUZON-CHANTOME

¶¶¶ ⦿ La Bergerie à Bousset Philippe et Josy HENRY
36270 EGUZON-CHANTOME
☎ 02 54 47 37 91 ▤ 02 54 47 37 91
Lac d'Eguzon 1km. Close to the market town, this magnificent old and restored residence, has quality furniture. Quiet area. Three guest rooms on the first floor (three double beds and one single) each with a private shower room and wc. Living room with open fireplace (TV). Landscaped, shady park with private swimming pool, garden furniture and parking. Long walks nearby. Open 1 February to 15 November.
PRICES: s €40; d €44; extra person €16; dinner €18 **NEARBY:** Bathing (1km) Canoeing (1km) Horse riding (15km) Fishing (1km) Aerial sports (22km) Water sports (1km) Tennis (1km) Shops (1km) EGUZON-CHANTOME (1km) **NOTES:** No pets English spoken

ETRECHET

¶¶¶ ⦿ Les Menas Nicole LYSTER
36120 ETRECHET
☎ 02 54 22 63 85 ▤ 02 54 22 63 85

Four furnished bedrooms in an 18th-century house, surrounded by a large shaded park. The ground floor consists of two double bedrooms (easy access for guests with disabilities), while on the first floor there are two double bedrooms, one with a fireplace. All rooms have a bathroom and wc. Private living room (TV, library and office). Dining room. Outdoor furniture and swing. Châteauroux 2 km (fishing, swimming, sailing and canoeing on the Belle-Isle lake, walks). Old town and Bertrand Museum close by. Châteauroux Forest (running course, long walks, off-road cycling). Open all year.
PRICES: s €36; d €43-€46; extra person €12; dinner €15
ON SITE: Fishing **NEARBY:** Bathing (1km) Canoeing (1km) Horse riding (6km) Golf (15km) Swimming pool (2km) Aerial sports (1km) Water sports (1km) Tennis (2km) Railway station (1km) Shops (2km) CHATEAUROUX (2km) **NOTES:** Pets admitted English spoken

Use the atlas at the back of the guide to locate your chambre d'hôtes

continued

FLERE-LA-RIVIERE

⌘ ◯ Le Moulin du Bourg Danielle AUMERCIER
36700 FLERE-LA-RIVIERE
☎ 02 54 39 34 41   🖷 02 54 39 34 93
e-mail: lemoulindeflere@wanadoo.fr
Next to a river, in a market town, this old mill offers three guest rooms. The ground floor has a dining room/living room (the old cog room) with TV and hi-fi, and a double room with shower room, wc and access onto the patio. The first floor comprises a double room with additional single bed, and a family suite of one double and one twin room, with adjoining shower room and wc. Library. Parking. Barbecue, table tennis, off-road cycling. Special rates for longer stays except holiday weekends and July/August. Medieval town of Loches 16 km. Footpath GR 46 is very close to the house. Lake opposite mill. Open 1 May to 15 October.
PRICES: s €35; d €40; extra person €7-13; dinner €19 **ON SITE:** Fishing **NEARBY:** Bathing (8km) Horse riding (3km) Golf (30km) Swimming pool (5km) Water sports (30km) Tennis (5km) Railway station (16km) CHATILLON-SUR-INDRE (5km) **NOTES:** No pets

⌘ Le Clos Vincents Claude RENOULT
2, les Vincents, 36700 FLERE-LA-RIVIERE
☎ 02 54 39 30 98   🖷 02 54 39 30 98
A stopover full of charm! Beautiful house situated in a large park full of flowers and trees. Two guest rooms, each with a shower room. One double bedroom 'Les Muriers' and one twin room 'Les Tilleuls'. Living room with open fire (TV). One suite consisting of two rooms (one double bed, two twin beds and a child's bed) with private bathroom and wc. Patio, outdoor furniture and parking. Loches Château 16 km. Footpath GR 46 close by. Open 15 June to 15 September (weekends by reservation).
PRICES: s €43; d €55; extra person €15 **NEARBY:** Bathing (8km) Horse riding (3km) Golf (30km) Fishing (1km) Swimming pool (6km) Water sports (30km) Tennis (6km) Railway station (15km) Shops (1km) CHATILLON-SUR-INDRE (6km) **NOTES:** No pets English spoken

GEHEE

⌘ ◯ Château de Touchenoire Jacques DE CLERCK
36240 GEHEE
☎ 02 54 40 87 34   🖷 02 54 40 87 34
Banish bad moods and tiredness in this beautiful, calm spot, a château set in a large wooded park. There are two first-floor bedrooms (two double beds and two singles) with adjoining shower rooms and wc, and a suite for three people (two single beds and one small double bed) with two shower rooms and two wcs. The second floor has two double rooms with shower rooms and wcs, and one twin room with shower room and a wc on the landing. Dining room, living room with fireplace. Patio, large games room (table tennis, outdoor furniture). Parking available. Private swimming pool. Open 1 May to 30 September.
PRICES: s €46; d €61-76; t €84; dinner €15 **ON SITE:** Fishing **NEARBY:** Horse riding (20km) Golf (30km) Swimming pool (11km) Tennis (11km) Railway station (30km) Shops (3km) VALENCAY (11km) **NOTES:** No pets English spoken

INGRANDES

⌘ ◯ Chateau d'Ingrandes Jacqueline DROUART
place de l'Eglise, 36300 INGRANDES
☎ 02 54 37 46 01   🖷 02 54 28 64 55
e-mail: jdrouart@AOL.com
Renovated 11th-15th-century château at the edge of a river. The ground floor has a 15th-century dining room with a large fireplace. The first floor offers a large living room/library, with fireplace, TV and a cardphone. The four guest rooms comprise one double room, one large attic room for five people (one double bed and three singles), one room in the castle keep with a canopied bed,

and one suite of a double room and a twin room. All rooms have a private bath/shower room and wc. Outdoor furniture, barbecue and parking. The château is open to the public. Open 1 April to 15 June upon reservation and 16 June to 15 October.

PRICES: s €46; d €53-€61; extra person €8; dinner €18 **ON SITE:** Fishing **NEARBY:** Bathing (11km) Canoeing (11km) Horse riding (17km) Golf (16km) Swimming pool (9km) Aerial sports (9km) Tennis (9km) Railway station (48km) Shops (9km) LE BLANC (9km) **NOTES:** Pets admitted English spoken

LE POINCONNET

⌘ ◯ Les Divers Lionel DROUIN
allée Paul Rue, 36330 LE POINCONNET
☎ 02 54 35 40 23   🖷 02 54 35 40 23
Châteauroux 6km. In an 18th-century landlord's house, surrounded by a 15-hectare park, there are two suites for two to five people with a living room, bathroom and adjoining wcs. One double bedroom with private shower room. Living room and TV room. Outdoor furniture, and stables in the grounds. Opportunity for shooting weekends, large spit-roast lamb for 18 people, a nine-hole golf course (clubs provided). National forest nearby. Open all year.
PRICES: s €34-€38; d €40-€43; suite €76; extra person €15
NEARBY: Bathing (5km) Canoeing (6km) Horse riding (2km) Golf (20km) Fishing (4km) Swimming pool (6km) Water sports (6km) Tennis (6km) Railway station (6km) CHATEAUROUX (6km) **NOTES:** No pets

MERS-SUR-INDRE

⌘ Le Lac Françoise GATESOUPE
36230 MERS-SUR-INDRE
☎ 02 54 36 29 49
Nohant 8km, St-Chartier 10km. Five double guest rooms with adjoining shower rooms and wc, situated in a separate house next to the owner's house in a forest. Large communal dining room with a fireplace. Corner living room and small corner kitchen. Large 30 hectare wooded park for long walks and off-road cycling. Outdoor furniture, parking and picnic table. Free fishing in the lake. Open all year.
PRICES: s €25; d €35; t €45; extra person €10 **ON SITE:** Fishing **NEARBY:** Bathing (20km) Canoeing (20km) Horse riding (16km) Golf (20km) Swimming pool (6km) Water sports (20km) Tennis (5km) Railway station (20km) Shops (5km) LA CHATRE (12km) **NOTES:** No pets

NOHANT-VIC

⌘ ◯ Ripoton Martine COLOMB
36400 NOHANT-VIC
☎ 02 54 31 06 10
e-mail: martine.colomb@tak.fr
Nohant 2km, la Châtre 7km. In George Sand's village, in the heart of the Vallée Noire, Martine welcomes guests to her old restored

continued   continued

family farm, next to the River Indre. The first floor has four guest rooms, each with a shower room and wc. (Three double beds, one small double bed and three single beds.) Large communal room with a fireplace, library, tourist information and walk itineraries. Outdoor furniture, parking and cover for cars. Open 1 March to 31 October.
PRICES: s €25; d €35; t €45; dinner €14 **ON SITE:** Bathing Fishing **NEARBY:** Horse riding (12km) Golf (18km) Swimming pool (7km) Water sports (25km) Tennis (7km) Railway station (30km) Shops (2km) LA CHATRE (7km) **NOTES:** Pets admitted English spoken

POULIGNY-NOTRE-DAME

††† 🐓 Le Gachet Monique et Jacques DELACHATRE
36160 POULIGNY-NOTRE-DAME
☎ 02 54 30 20 52 & 02 54 30 11 12
Nohant 15km, St-Chartier 20km, Ste-Sevère 6km. This farm, restored in a style typical of the region, offers rustic, warm surroundings. The first floor has two double rooms with independent entrances. The first room has a corner living room, bathroom and wc. The second room has a shower room and wc. Another bedroom has a double bed and a single bed, equipped kitchen and living room with a sofa and a shower room and wc. Large living/dining room/bar, TV lounge. Outdoor furniture and parking. There is another bedroom for three people. 260 euros/week. Golf and spa treatments 500m away. Open all year.
PRICES: s €34-€43; d €42-€49 **ON SITE:** Golf Fishing Swimming pool Tennis **NEARBY:** Bathing (10km) Canoeing (8km) Horse riding (15km) Water sports (10km) Railway station (45km) Restaurant nearby LA CHATRE (10km) **NOTES:** Pets admitted

PRUNIERS

††† 🍽️ ♿ Le Moulin de Palbas
Joke GEURTSEN-TEN HAAFT
36120 PRUNIERS
☎ 02 54 49 13 01   📠 02 54 49 13 01
e-mail: lemoulindepalbas@yahoo.com www.palbas.com.
Nohant 18km, St-Chartier 15km, Forêt de Bommiers 5km. A magnificent 16th-century residence offers a warm welcome with 33 hectares of heathland, forest and water, and caters for the young and old alike. Private swimming pool, patio, games area, living room with TV, library and fireplace as well as board games. Themed bedrooms with views of the lake include a family room (6 people) with corner living room and a suite for four people with a mezzanine. Simple breakfasts feature fresh bread, homemade jam, eggs and fresh milk. Off-road cycling, fishing and horse-riding. Musical activities in May at the Prée Abbey (20 km). Open all year upon reservation.
PRICES: s €50; d €50; t €80; extra person €15; dinner €15
ON SITE: Fishing Swimming pool **NEARBY:** Bathing (15km) Canoeing (15km) Horse riding (5km) Golf (15km) Aerial sports (15km) Water sports (15km) Tennis (5km) Railway station (20km) Shops (5km) ISSOUDUN (20km) **NOTES:** Pets admitted CC English spoken

REBOURSIN

††† Le Moulin Gerard CHENEAU
36150 REBOURSIN
☎ 02 54 49 72 05
Château de Valençay: 10km. Eighteenth-century house full of character offers a suite for four people. One double bedroom with bathroom and adjoining wc also with two single beds. A mezzanine has two double beds. There is a living room at guests' disposal. Large shaded park with outdoor furniture and there is also covered parking. There is a sports complex 20 km away at Issoudun. Fishing on the Lake Reboursin (2 km). Open 1 July to 15 August.

PRICES: s €38; d €49 **NEARBY:** Horse riding (12km) Golf (20km) Fishing (3km) Swimming pool (3km) Aerial sports (18km) Tennis (3km) Railway station (20km) Shops (3km) VALENCAY (28km) **NOTES:** No pets English spoken

SAINT-BENOIT-DU-SAULT

††† Le Portail Marie-France BOYER
cité Médievale, 36170 ST-BENOIT-DU-SAULT
☎ 02 54 47 57 20   📠 02 54 47 57 20

14th-15th-century house full of character, which acts as a fortified gateway to the city. One double room with shower room and wc. A second double room also contains two single beds, a corner living room and colour TV with shower room and wc. There is another bedroom with a small double bed and a single bed, shower room, corner living room and colour TV. Equipped kitchen on the ground floor. Small terrace and parking. Mme Boyer has an artist's studio. Open all year.
PRICES: s €30-€38; d €38-€50; extra person €15 **NEARBY:** Bathing (10km) Horse riding (10km) Golf (30km) Fishing (1km) Swimming pool (18km) Water sports (18km) Tennis (1km) Railway station (18km) SAINT-BENOIT-DU-SAULT **NOTES:** No pets

SARZAY

††† 🍽️ Château de Sarzay Richard HURBAIN
36230 SARZAY ☎ 02 54 31 32 25

Four fully-furnished guest rooms in a 14th-century château open to the public (guided visits available). Large interior court (with various displays), large meeting hall for weddings and family celebrations. The ground floor offers a large living room with a fireplace, piano and corner kitchen, and a double bedroom with adjoining shower room and wc. The first floor has a comfy corner (sofa, TV and video) and three bedrooms (two double beds and two single beds) each with a shower room and wc. Children €5. Open all year.
PRICES: s €41; d €46; dinner €9 **NEARBY:** Bathing (25km) Canoeing (25km) Horse riding (20km) Golf (22km) Fishing (6km) Swimming pool (7km) Water sports (25km) Tennis (7km) Railway station (7km) Shops (7km) LA CHATRE (7km) **NOTES:** Pets admitted English spoken

continued

♦♦♦ ⚫ Montgarni Michel LABAURIE
36230 SARZAY
☎ 02 54 31 31 05 📠 02 54 31 30 10

*Château de Sarzay, Nohant: 8km, G.Sand circuit, St-Chartier
14km.* Nineteenth-century family mansion surrounded by a shaded
park. Three guest rooms on the first floor (two double beds and
two single beds) with bathroom and adjoining wc for each room.
Large communal room divided into living room (with fireplace), TV
corner, lounge/library, music corner, dining room and all at guests'
disposal. Patio overlooking the park. Private swimming pool,
parking and farm produce available. Formula 3 circuit at La Châtre.
Open all year.
PRICES: s €30; d €38; extra person €9; dinner €9-€14
ON SITE: Swimming pool **NEARBY:** Bathing (25km) Canoeing (25km)
Horse riding (20km) Golf (20km) Fishing (1km) Water sports (25km)
Tennis (7km) Railway station (7km) Shops (7km) LA CHATRE (7km)
NOTES: No pets English spoken

SAULNAY

♦♦♦ 🐓 La Marchandière Alain et Jocelyne RENONCET
36290 SAULNAY
☎ 02 54 38 42 94
Situated in the Mille Etangs region, Alain and Jocelyne welcome
guests to their farm. Guaranteed peaceful location with footpaths
and a river nearby. Two double rooms on the ground floor and
one family room for five people on the first floor (one double bed
and three singles); each has a shower room and wc. Dining room
with TV and fireplace, living room with video recorder. A barn has
been converted into a games room with table tennis, bar billiards
and a fitted kitchen for longer stays. There is a patio, outdoor
furniture, barbecue, off-road cycling and a porch. Open all year
upon reservation.
PRICES: s €30; d €38; extra person €12 **ON SITE:** Fishing
NEARBY: Bathing (11km) Canoeing (11km) Horse riding (12km)
Swimming pool (16km) Aerial sports (10km) Water sports (11km) Tennis
(8km) Railway station (45km) Shops (3km) MEZIERES-EN-BRENNE
(10km) **NOTES:** Pets admitted

TOURNON-SAINT-MARTIN

♦♦♦ Chambre d'hôtes Christiane et André SIMONNET
24 bis, route de le Blanc, 36220 TOURNON-SAINT-MARTIN
☎ 02 54 28 77 34 📠 02 54 28 77 34
*Roche Posay 12km, Abbaye de Fontgombault 8km, Futurosope, Le
Blanc 15km.* In Mille Etangs country, near Creuse, there are three
double guest rooms each with a bathroom, wc and private patio.
All situated in a contemporary setting, surrounded by a
landscaped garden together with a swimming pool and outdoor
furniture. Open all year (must book in advance).
PRICES: s €46; d €53 **ON SITE:** Bathing Canoeing Fishing Swimming
pool Tennis **NEARBY:** Horse riding (12km) Golf (8km) Aerial sports
(15km) Railway station (35km) LE BLANC (15km) **NOTES:** No pets

VICQ-SUR-NAHON

♦♦♦ 🐓 ⚫ l'Echalier Helmut et Banyen MOSZKOWICZ
36600 VICQ-SUR-NAHON
☎ 02 54 40 35 98 📠 02 54 40 36 00
e-mail: hmoszko@wanadoo.fr
A farm in the middle of 34 hectares of fields and woods. The
atmosphere is one of calm and rural charm. Rest and relaxation
guaranteed. Two double guest rooms and one quadruple room,
each with private shower room. Outdoor furniture. Separate room
with a bar, bar billiards and off-road cycling. There is a fish pond
and the owner can take visitors on flights in a light aircraft above
the Valencay Château. There are footpaths nearby. Open all year.
PRICES: s €35; d €40; t €52; extra person €11; dinner €11-€23
ON SITE: Aerial sports **NEARBY:** Bathing (20km) Canoeing (20km)
Horse riding (20km) Golf (30km) Fishing (3km) Swimming pool (7km)
Water sports (25km) Tennis (3km) Railway station (20km) Shops (3km)
VALENCAY (7km) **NOTES:** Pets admitted English spoken

INDRE-ET-LOIRE

ATHEE-SUR-CHER

♦♦♦ Vallet Augustin CHAUDIERE
37270 ATHEE-SUR-CHER
☎ 02 47 50 67 83 📠 02 47 50 68 31
e-mail: pavillon.vallet@wanadoo.fr
In a distinctive 18th-century house on the edge of Cher, one
ground floor room and two upstairs rooms, all equipped with
bathroom and wc. Two of the rooms sleep three (one double and
one single bed). The third room is a double. Terrace, lovely park,
parking.
PRICES: d €46-€61; extra person €15 **ON SITE:** Canoeing Fishing
Hiking **NEARBY:** Horse riding (5km) Swimming pool (5km) Tennis
(5km) Sailing (5km) Railway station (22km) Shops (2km) BLERE (5km)
NOTES: Pets admitted English spoken

AZAY-LE-RIDEAU

♦♦♦ La Petite Loge Christine BANTAS
15, route de Tours, 37190 AZAY-LE-RIDEAU
☎ 02 47 45 26 05 & 06 61 81 94 07
e-mail: lapetiteloge@free.fr
Five guest rooms with the advantage of separate access in a small
old farmhouse on a partly wooded grounds of one hectare, 1 km
from the centre of Azay-le-Rideau. One room with two double
beds; one room with twin single beds; and three rooms each with
a double bed. All have shower and wc. Corner-kitchen available
for use. Parking, garden furniture, metal detector.
PRICES: d €43-€54; t €58-€69 **ON SITE:** Children's play area
NEARBY: Horse riding (8km) Golf (14km) Fishing (1km) Swimming
pool (1km) Tennis (1km) Railway station (3km) Shops (3km) AZAY-LE-
RIDEAU (2km) **NOTES:** No pets English spoken

AZAY-SUR-CHER

♦♦♦♦ Château du Côteau TASSI
37270 AZAY-SUR-CHER
☎ 02 47 50 47 47 & SR : 02 47 27 56 10
🖷 02 47 50 49 60
Six upstairs rooms in the clockhouse of a romantic 19th-century property, in a 12ha park (with animals) on the edge of Cher. All rooms have bath or shower, wc and television. Four rooms with two single beds (which can be combined to make a double); one double room with 160cm bed; one flat with sitting room, cooking area, one bedroom with a double bed and one bedroom with three singles. Living room for guests' use with piano. Tariff: €119 for the flat for two people. Hot-air ballooning.
PRICES: s €74-€91; d €74-€119; t €121-€150; extra person €30
ON SITE: Horse riding Fishing Hiking **NEARBY:** Golf (15km) Swimming pool (5km) Tennis (5km) Railway station (17km) Shops (2km) BLERE (12km) **NOTES:** No pets English spoken

---

AZAY-SUR-INDRE

♦♦♦ La Bihourderie Marie-Agnès BOUIN
37310 AZAY-SUR-INDRE
☎ 02 47 92 58 58 🖷 02 47 92 22 19
e-mail: mignes.bouin2@freesbee.fr
The house, typical of Lochois, is first-prize winner for 'gîtes in bloom'. Each of the four ground-floor rooms has shower or bath and wc. One twin room, one double and two triples. Cot available. Living room for guests (kitchen, television, video). Garden (table tennis, bikes, pétanque). Midday picnic lunch can be arranged. Space and calm guaranteed. The inn in the village (2 km) offers a special price of €14.49 to guests, wine and coffee included.
PRICES: s €37; d €40-€43; extra person €14 **ON SITE:** Children's play area **NEARBY:** Canoeing (20km) Horse riding (6km) Golf (60km) Fishing (3km) Swimming pool (10km) Hiking (1km) Tennis (6km) Sailing (18km) Railway station (4km) Shops (5km) LOCHES (10km) **NOTES:** No pets English spoken

♦♦♦ Moulin de la Follaine Danie LIGNELET
37310 AZAY-SUR-INDRE
☎ 02 47 92 57 91 🖷 02 47 92 57 91
e-mail: moulindelafollaine@wanadoo.fr
www.multimania.com/moulindefollaine

Four rooms (two of them suites) in a working mill. La Follaine is the ancient hunting estate of the Marquis de La Fayette, situated between the Val de Loire and south Touraine. Guests will enjoy the tranquillity of the two-hectare water park. Each room has bathroom and wc. One double room at garden level. Upstairs: one suite with three single beds; one suite with double bed, medium bed and single bed. Living room with television and open fire. Television if requested in bedrooms. Park with garden furniture. Fishing possible. Many châteaux nearby (10-25 km).

PRICES: s €46-€52; d €52-€59; t €67-€75; extra person €15
ON SITE: Fishing Hiking **NEARBY:** Canoeing (1km) Horse riding (6km) Golf (20km) Swimming pool (10km) Tennis (3km) Sailing (10km) Railway station (10km) Shops (3km) LOCHES (10km) **NOTES:** No pets English spoken

---

BALLAN-MIRE

♦♦♦♦ Château de Bois Renault François DUHOUX
37510 BALLAN-MIRE
☎ 02 47 67 89 38 🖷 02 47 67 10 92
e-mail: boisrenault@free.fr www.chateauxcountry.com

Five luxury rooms upstairs in an 18th-century castle (modified in the 19th) in a walled 22ha wooded park, just ten minutes from Tours. Every room has a large bathroom with wc, and has either two single beds, or one large double bed (160 or 180cm). One of the rooms opens onto a terrace overlooking the park. All rooms have telephones, and two are air-conditioned. Living room. Television room.
PRICES: s €85; d €95-€115; extra person €25 **ON SITE:** Hiking **NEARBY:** Horse riding (1km) Golf (2km) Fishing (2km) Swimming pool (5km) Tennis (4km) Railway station (14km) Shops (3km) BALLAN-MIRE (3km) **NOTES:** No pets English spoken

♦♦♦ |O| Château du Vau Bruno CLEMENT
37510 BALLAN-MIRE
☎ 02 47 67 84 04 🖷 02 47 67 55 77
e-mail: chateauduvau@chez.com www.chez.com/chateauduvau
Five upstairs rooms in a castle built towards the end of the 18th-century, situated in 110 hectares of forest and park. Near a farm producing foie gras, with poultry, sheep and horses. Half way between Tours and Azay-le-Rideau. One room for three (double bed and single); one twin room; and three double rooms. Each has private bathroom and wc. Two day rooms for guests' exclusive use. 18-hole golf only 300m.
PRICES: s €78-€84; d €85-€92; t €114; extra person €18; dinner €29
ON SITE: Golf **NEARBY:** Horse riding (2km) Swimming pool (9km) Tennis (2km) Railway station (13km) Shops (2km) BALLAN-MIRE (2km) **NOTES:** No pets English spoken

---

BEAUMONT-EN-VERON

♦♦♦ Chambre d'hôtes Micheline BACH
Grezille, 37420 BEAUMONT-EN-VERON
☎ 02 47 58 43 53 & 06 08 30 61 00 🖷 02 47 58 43 63
e-mail: grezille.bach@wanadoo.fr
Three upstairs rooms in an 18th-century rural property in the heart of Chinon. Separate access, large lounge, living room with cooking area. One twin room with bathroom and wc; two double rooms with shower and wc. Shaded garden with outdoor furniture. View over the vineyards.
PRICES: d €48 **NEARBY:** Horse riding (3km) Golf (12km) Fishing (1km) Swimming pool (2km) Hiking (1km) Tennis (2km) Railway station (6km) Shops (4km) CHINON (6km) **NOTES:** No pets

continued

CENTRAL FRANCE

¶¶¶ La Balastière Antoinette DEGREMONT
Grezille, 37420 BEAUMONT-EN-VERON
☎ 02 47 58 87 93 & 06 81 69 35 06 ▤ 02 47 58 82 41
e-mail: balastiere@infonie.fr perso.infonie.fr/balastiere
Four rooms with separate access in a 15th-century farmhouse
restored in the 19th century and halfway between Chinon and
Bourgueil. Large shady garden surrounded by vineyards. On the
ground floor: two rooms sleeping two (either double or twin bed),
each with bath or shower. Small kitchen. Upstairs: one double
room with shower and wc; one large room with one double and
two single beds, bath, wc, cooking area. Sitting room and kitchen.
Open all year except January.
PRICES: d €38-€50; t €60 **ON SITE:** Hiking **NEARBY:** Horse riding
(4km) Fishing (2km) Swimming pool (4km) Tennis (4km) Sailing (5km)
Railway station (5km) Shops (4km) CHINON (5km) **NOTES:** No pets
English spoken

BEAUMONT-LA-RONCE

¶¶¶ 🐓 La Louisière Michel CAMPION
37360 BEAUMONT-LA-RONCE ☎ 02 47 24 42 24
Three guest rooms on a working farm opposite the park of the
Château de Beaumont, on the edge of the forest. The rooms are
on the first floor and all have private shower or bathroom and wc.
The rooms contain in turn: two single beds; one double and one
single; one double and three single. Cot available. Television in
every bedroom. Lounge with open fire and television. Garden.
Parking. Bikes. Restaurant 300m. Open all year.
PRICES: s €32; d €40; t €51; extra person €11 **ON SITE:** Children's play
area Hiking Tennis **NEARBY:** Horse riding (5km) Golf (10km) Fishing
(1km) Swimming pool (20km) Railway station (20km) NEUILLE-PONT-
PIERRE (9km) **NOTES:** No pets English spoken

BERTHENAY

¶¶¶ La Grange aux Moines Janine MILLET
37510 BERTHENAY ☎ 02 47 50 06 91 ▤ 02 47 50 06 91
Tours 12 km. Villandry 6 km. Five rooms in a restored 17th-century
farmhouse in a hamlet on the banks of the Loire. All rooms
have separate access, shower and wc. One ground floor room with
a double bed and two singles. Upstairs: one suite sleeping four; two
double rooms; one twin room. Shady park. Locked garage. Cycle
hire. Private swimming pool.
PRICES: s €44; d €52-€59; t €73-€96 **ON SITE:** Swimming pool
NEARBY: Canoeing (5km) Horse riding (7km) Golf (9km) Fishing (1km)
Hiking (1km) Tennis (5km) Sailing (12km) Railway station (14km) Shops
(3km) JOUE-LES-TOURS (5km) **NOTES:** No pets English spoken

BLERE

¶¶¶ 🍽 Moulin du Fief Gentil Ann MASON
37150 BLERE ☎ 02 47 30 32 51 ▤ 02 47 30 22 38
e-mail: fiefgentil@wanadoo.fr perso.wanadoo.fr/fiefgentil

Four guest rooms in a mill (16th and 19th centuries) on the road
out of Bléré, in grounds of 2.3ha. A large pond feeds the millrace

which passes under the living room where meals are served. Two
rooms have 160cm beds and bathroom and wc. The other rooms
have twin beds, wc and either shower or bath. 10% reduction for
three nights or more. Meals may be booked.
PRICES: s €60-€84; d €70-€90; extra person €15; dinner €27
ON SITE: Fishing Hiking **NEARBY:** Horse riding (10km) Golf (30km)
Swimming pool (1km) Tennis (1km) Sailing (1km) Railway station (20km)
Shops (1km) BLERE (1km) **NOTES:** No pets English spoken

BOSSAY-SUR-CLAISE

¶¶¶ 🍽 La Fertauderie Famille GLENN
37290 BOSSAY-SUR-CLAISE
☎ 06 87 45 61 87 & 02 47 94 43 74 ▤ 02 47 94 44 63
e-mail: glennhome@free.fr
Four rooms in an outbuilding on a small, quiet 16th-century farm
in the open countryside. Near the valleys of the Claise and the
Creuse, and the hot springs of Roche-Posay. On the ground floor:
one room for four, with bath and wc. Upstairs: two double rooms
with shower and wc; a suite with one double bed, shower, wc,
living room/kitchen and two folding single beds. Kitchen and
music room (with instruments!) available. Lounge with open fire
and television. Dinner (must be booked) Friday, Saturday, Sunday.
Private swimming pool.
PRICES: s €33; d €38-€42; extra person €10; dinner €12
ON SITE: Swimming pool **NEARBY:** Horse riding (3km) Golf (15km)
Fishing (3km) Tennis (6km) Railway station (25km) Shops (3km)
PREUILLY-SUR-CLAISE (6km) **NOTES:** Pets admitted

BOURGUEIL

¶¶¶ 🍽 Le Moulin de Touvois Myriam MARCHAND
37140 BOURGUEIL
☎ 02 47 97 87 70 ▤ 02 47 97 87 70
e-mail: moulindetouvois@wanadoo.fr
www.moulindetouvois.com

This 18th-century mill, 5 km from Bourgueil (and just 100 m from
a gastronomic restaurant) houses five bedrooms, one downstairs
and four upstairs. Four rooms have double bed, or twin beds
which can be joined, plus bath and wc. The last room has two
single beds, shower and wc. On site, for guests' use, a private
swimming pool in a large lawn reached by a wooden bridge over
a stream. Walking trails from the doorway of the mill. Meals
available, if booked.
PRICES: s €41-€48; d €46-€53; t €56-€64; extra person €11; dinner €16
ON SITE: Fishing Swimming pool Hiking **NEARBY:** Horse riding
(12km) Golf (22km) Tennis (5km) Sailing (15km) Railway station (10km)
Shops (5km) BOURGUEIL (5km) **NOTES:** No pets English spoken

For further information on these and
other chambres d'hôtes, consult
the Gîtes de France website
www.gites-de-france.fr

continued

BRAYE-SUR-MAULNE

Domaine de la Bergerie Colette DEFOND
37330 BRAYE-SUR-MAULNE
☎ 02 47 24 90 88 📠 02 47 24 90 88
e-mail: clairedefond@gmx.net

A château on a romantic estate dating from 1850 in 12ha of parkland. This site, endowed with a huge ornamental lake, is a haven of quiet in a verdant setting. The rooms, all on the second floor, have air conditioning, large double beds (160 x 200cm), bathrooms and wcs. A suite offers an additional two single beds. Private lounge for guests. Meals may be booked. Three self-catering gîtes also available.
PRICES: d €65; t €100; dinner €20 **ON SITE:** Fishing Hiking
NEARBY: Horse riding (4km) Golf (8km) Swimming pool (12km) Tennis (3km) Railway station (12km) Shops (3km) CHATEAU-LA-VALLIERE (3km) **NOTES:** Pets admitted English spoken

CANDES-SAINT-MARTIN

Les Sarments André LHERBETTE
15, rue Trochet, 37500 CANDES-SAINT-MARTIN
☎ 02 47 95 93 40 & SR : 02 47 27 56 10 📠 02 47 95 93 40
Late 19th-century farmhouse high in the village of Candes, which has panoramic views of the confluence of the Vienne and the Loire. Three rooms (one a suite), each with private facilities. One double room; one sleeping four (double bed and two singles); suite (two double beds and one single). Television if requested in bedrooms. Large garden with terrace and views over Montsoreau and the vineyards. Meals by arrangement.
PRICES: s €40; d €44; t €56; dinner €15 **ON SITE:** Hiking
NEARBY: Canoeing (12km) Horse riding (10km) Golf (7km) Fishing (1km) Swimming pool (8km) Tennis (1km) Railway station (12km) Shops (1km) CHINON (12km) **NOTES:** Pets admitted

CHAMBOURG-SUR-INDRE

Le Petit Marray Serge PLANTIN
37310 CHAMBOURG-SUR-INDRE
☎ 02 47 92 50 67 📠 02 47 92 50 67
e-mail: splantin@opencom.fr

The farmhouse dates from 1830 and offers four large rooms with separate access. On the ground floor is a two-roomed suite (one double bed, two singles) with shower and wc. Upstairs: a suite (salon with pull-out bed, room with double bed, bath and wc); double room with shower and wc. In separate accommodation, a large room is accessible to guests with disabilities, and has a double bed and two spare single beds, bath and wc. Television in all rooms. Three rooms have microwave and fridges. Library, games. Large garden. Meals must be booked. Children under 12: €11.
PRICES: s €45-€52; d €50-€60; t €60-€70; dinner €21 **NEARBY:** Horse riding (4km) Fishing (2km) Swimming pool (4km) Hiking (1km) Tennis (2km) Sailing (15km) Railway station (4km) Shops (4km) LOCHES (4km)
NOTES: Pets admitted English spoken

CHANCAY

Ferme de Launay Jean-Pierre SCHWEIZER
37210 CHANCAY
☎ 02 47 52 28 21 📠 02 47 52 28 21
Old farmhouse dating from 14th-18th centuries, in a Vouvray vineyard of 1.6 hectares. Three guest rooms: one double room on the ground floor with wc and bath; and one double and one twin room upstairs each with shower and wc. Lounge with open fireplace. A non-smoking establishment.
PRICES: s €54-€70; d €62-€78; extra person €8 **NEARBY:** Fishing (1km) Swimming pool (6km) Hiking (1km) Tennis (2km) Railway station (15km) Shops (2km) VOUVRAY (7km) **NOTES:** No pets English spoken

Le Moulin de Bacchus Françoise SURIN
37210 CHANCAY
☎ 02 47 52 27 90 📠 02 47 52 26 03
e-mail: didier-surin@wanadoo.fr
www.moulin-de-bacchus.com
In the heart of Vouvrillon, this large mill (17th/19th centuries) on the Brenne between Chançay and Vernou, offers four upstairs non-smoking guest rooms and a suite, all with bathroom or shower and wc. On the second floor, there is a suite with one double and two single beds; one double room with 160cm bed; and one twin room. On the third floor: two air-conditioned rooms sleep four in a double and two singles. Reading/sitting room with television. Four-hectare estate with 300m of river. Heated swimming pool, solarium, sunbeds, summer kitchen, barbecue and table tennis.
PRICES: s €59-€68; d €65-€74; extra person €18 **ON SITE:** Fishing Swimming pool Hiking **NEARBY:** Tennis (2km) Railway station (15km) Shops (6km) VOUVRAY (6km) **NOTES:** No pets

CHARNIZAY

Les Bénestières Martine ROBERT
37290 CHARNIZAY
☎ 02 47 94 56 78 📠 02 47 94 41 70
e-mail: henri-martine.robert@wanadoo.fr
A working farm (cereals and beef) in open countryside near the Valleys of the Creuse and Brenne. Four guest rooms each with shower and wc. On the ground floor: a double room with access for guests with disabilities, and a room sleeping four (double and two single beds). Upstairs: two rooms sleeping three. Kitchen area. Lounge. Garden with lawn. Guests can visit the farm and the nearby archaeological sites, and wander the forests. Meals must be booked. One hour to Futuroscope. Dogs accepted with the prior agreement of the owners (€3 supplement). Tariff: half board €32/person in a double room, for stays of two days or more.
PRICES: s €34; d €38; extra person €15; dinner €15 **ON SITE:** Hiking
NEARBY: Canoeing (25km) Horse riding (12km) Golf (16km) Fishing (5km) Swimming pool (5km) Tennis (5km) Railway station (30km) Shops (5km) PREUILLY-SUR-CLAISE (5km) **NOTES:** Pets admitted English spoken

continued

CHATEAU-LA-VALLIERE

♛♛♛ ♞ |◎| Vaujours RIBERT
37330 CHATEAU-LA-VALLIERE
☎ 02 47 24 08 55 📠 02 47 24 19 20
e-mail: rib007@aol.com

Three separate rooms on the ground floor of a farmhouse (on a goat farm), each with shower and wc. Colour television. One twin room and two doubles. Spare bed and cot also available. Parking. Garden with outdoor furniture and barbecue. Restaurant 400m. Meals may be booked. Private swimming pool.

PRICES: s €33; d €39; extra person €13; dinner €13 **ON SITE:** Fishing Swimming pool **NEARBY:** Horse riding (7km) Golf (5km) Hiking (1km) Tennis (3km) Sailing (12km) Railway station (3km) Shops (3km) CHATEAU-LA-VALLIERE (3km) **NOTES:** No pets English spoken

CHAVEIGNES

♛♛♛♛ La Varenne DRU-SAUER
37120 CHAVEIGNES
☎ 02 47 58 26 31 📠 02 47 58 27 47
e-mail: dru-sauer@la-varenne.com www.la-varenne.com

In the open countryside 4 km from Richelieu, this is a lovely house in a unique architectural style on an estate dedicated to the production of nuts and honey. Exceedingly large and quiet, the three guest rooms have bath and wc, and either a 160cm double bed or two singles. Cosy sitting room with piano and open fireplace. Generous breakfasts. In the grounds: heated swimming pool, table tennis, 5ha of woods, footpaths, bikes and solex (motorised bike) for hire. Futuroscope 40 km.

PRICES: s €67-€93; d €74-€100; extra person €25
ON SITE: Swimming pool Hiking **NEARBY:** Horse riding (15km) Fishing (4km) Tennis (3km) Railway station (28km) Shops (4km) RICHELIEU (4km) **NOTES:** No pets English spoken

CHEILLE

♛♛♛ Le Vaujoint JOLIT
Cheille, 37190 AZAY-LE-RIDEAU
☎ 02 47 45 48 89 📠 02 47 58 68 11

Three guest rooms of character in an outbuilding of a 19th-century family property, in a hamlet 4 km from Azay-le-Rideau. Sitting room reserved for guests (television, open fire, antique furniture). Two double rooms and one twin, with private shower and wc. Large shaded garden with outdoor furniture and barbecue. Private parking. GR3 500m. Forest 800m. A dozen châteaux in a 20 km radius.

PRICES: s €41; d €45; extra person €15 **NEARBY:** Canoeing (4km) Horse riding (10km) Golf (16km) Fishing (1km) Swimming pool (5km) Hiking (1km) Tennis (5km) Sailing (18km) Railway station (4km) Shops (4km) AZAY-LE-RIDEAU (4km) **NOTES:** Pets admitted English spoken

> Ask the proprietor for directions
> when booking

CHENONCEAUX

♛♛♛ Le Clos Mony Betty LE CLAINCHE
6, rue des Bleuets, 37150 CHENONCEAUX
☎ 02 47 23 82 68 📠 02 47 23 82 68
e-mail: clos.mony@wanadoo.fr
www.france-bonjour.com/clos-mony/

Three upstairs rooms in a late 19th-century house in a quiet area in the centre of Chenonceaux; 500m from the entrance to its famous château. Each room has a shower and wc. There are two double rooms and one twin room. Large garden and lovely ornamental pond with restricted access.

PRICES: s €44; d €49; extra person €15 **ON SITE:** Hiking **NEARBY:** Canoeing (2km) Fishing (1km) Swimming pool (6km) Tennis (1km) Sailing (6km) BLERE (6km) **NOTES:** No pets English spoken

♛♛♛ La Baiserie Claude GUYOMARD
37150 CHENONCEAUX
☎ 02 47 23 90 26 📠 02 47 23 81 26
e-mail: info@labaiserie.com www.labaiserie.com

Three guest rooms in a 15th-century farmhouse, restored last century, in a quiet and flower-bedecked environment, near the château and village. Separate ground floor entrance to a double room with shower, wc and television. Upstairs, two rooms, one sleeping three and the other four, each with bathroom and wc. Dining/sitting room, with television, reserved for guests. One hectare park with farm animals. Terrace, garden furniture. Mountain bikes available. Secure parking. Open all year.

PRICES: ; d €46-€64; t €73-€76; extra person €12 **NEARBY:** Fishing (1km) Swimming pool (6km) Hiking (1km) Tennis (1km) Sailing (8km) Railway station (1km) Shops (1km) BLERE (6km) **NOTES:** No pets

CHISSEAUX

♛♛♛ |◎| Chambre d'hôtes Mireille ANSAR
5, rue du Perpasse, 37150 CHISSEAUX
☎ 02 47 23 81 20
e-mail: lestilleulsduperpasse@wanadoo.fr
Chenonceau 2km. Ground floor rooms on a 19th-century vineyard, in the village. The owners serve dinner (booking required) in the basement dining room or on the terrace. One double and one twin room with shower and wc. One triple room with bath and wc. One family room sleeping five, with shower and wc. Child's meal (under 12): €11. Pleasant garden and organic kitchen garden.

PRICES: s €41; d €46-€53; t €66; extra person €10-€13; dinner €18 **ON SITE:** Hiking **NEARBY:** Golf (15km) Fishing (1km) Swimming pool (7km) Tennis (1km) Railway station (2km) Shops (2km) BLERE (9km) **NOTES:** No pets English spoken

CINQ-MARS-LA-PILE

♛♛♛ La Meulière Patrick VOISIN
rue du Breuil, 37130 CINQ-MARS-LA-PILE
☎ 02 47 96 53 63

Three upstairs rooms in a bourgeois house near the station. Two double rooms with shower and wc. One family room with two double beds, bath and wc. Television lounge.

PRICES: s €34; d €40; t €51 **NEARBY:** Golf (8km) Fishing (1km) Swimming pool (4km) Hiking (1km) Tennis (1km) Sailing (4km) Railway station (1km) Shops (1km) LANGEAIS (4km) **NOTES:** No pets English spoken

CIVRAY-DE-TOURAINE

♛♛♛ |◎| Chambre d'hôtes Marie BOBLET
22, vallée de Mesvres, 37150 CIVRAY-DE-TOURAINE
☎ 02 47 23 51 04 & 06 88 83 82 48
e-mail: marmittiere@libertysurf.fr perso.libertysurf/marmittiere/
Château de Chenonceau 4 km. Two rooms and one suite in a

continued

separate early 20th-century building beside a 17th-century mansion, which also offers a country gîte. One ground floor double room (160cm bed, bathroom, wc, fireplace); one upstairs room (double bed, shower, wc); ground floor suite (two rooms, 160cm double bed, two single beds, shower, wc, room with kitchen, dining area, sitting room, television). Partly wooded 3ha park with donkeys and chickens. Table tennis. Meals prepared using organic produce - must be booked. Garden platter in summer (€11). 10% reduction on stays of more than three nights. **PRICES:** s €46; d €53; t €76; extra person €15; dinner €19 **ON SITE:** Hiking **NEARBY:** Horse riding (10km) Fishing (3km) Swimming pool (3km) Tennis (2km) Sailing (3km) Railway station (10km) Shops (3km) BLERE (3km) **NOTES:** No pets English spoken

CORMERY

♦♦♦ ⦿ Chambre d'hôtes Susanna MCGRATH
3, rue Alcuin, 37320 CORMERY
☎ 02 47 43 08 23
e-mail: sacriste@creaweb.fr
Azay-le-Rideau & Villandry 30 km. Chenonceau & Loches 20 km.
Three guest rooms in a house of character from the 15th and 19th centuries, attached to the ancient Carolingian abbey in the historic centre of Cormery. The rooms are on the ground floor and second floor, all with private bath or shower and wc. One room sleeping three, one double room, and one twin room. Lounge with open fire. Indoor parking. Garden with 12th-century Roman gate. Bikes available. Meals may be booked, not on Saturday.
PRICES: s €59-€68; d €65-€74; t €94; dinner €26 **ON SITE:** Fishing Hiking **NEARBY:** Horse riding (11km) Golf (18km) Swimming pool (6km) Tennis (1km) Railway station (20km) CHAMBRAY-LES-TOURS (13km) **NOTES:** No pets English spoken

CRAVANT-LES-COTEAUX

♦♦♦ Pallus Bernard et Barbara CHAUVEAU
37500 CRAVANT-LES-COTEAUX
☎ 02 47 93 08 94 ⊟ 02 47 98 43 00
e-mail: bcpallus@club-internet.fr
An old house of some character in a winegrowing hamlet. Three guest rooms on the first floor with double bed, bathroom and wc. One is a suite with additional twin beds. Sitting room for guests. Quality furnishings. Private swimming pool in garden.
PRICES: ; d €80-€88; extra person €23 **ON SITE:** Swimming pool **NEARBY:** Canoeing (10km) Horse riding (10km) Fishing (2km) Hiking (1km) Tennis (2km) Railway station (11km) Shops (2km) L'ILE-BOUCHARD (11km) **NOTES:** No pets English spoken

CROUZILLES

♦♦♦ ⦿ Château de Pavier Bernard DE NOUEL
37220 CROUZILLES
☎ 02 47 58 55 14 ⊟ 02 47 58 55 14
e-mail: bernard.de-nouel@wanadoo.fr
Chinon & Azay-le-Rideau 15 km. Three guest rooms with separate access in a wing of the Château de Pavier, a 15th-century home restored in the 19th. Surrounded by dry moats. Each room has private bathroom or shower and wc. Two ground floor double rooms and one suite on the first floor with a 160cm double bed and two singles. Stroll in the 25ha park. Private swimming pool in grounds. Meals may be booked.
PRICES: s €65; d €75; t €90; extra person €15; dinner €25 **ON SITE:** Swimming pool Hiking **NEARBY:** Horse riding (7km) Golf (30km) Fishing (1km) Tennis (5km) Railway station (10km) Shops (5km) ILE-BOUCHARD (5km) **NOTES:** No pets

EPEIGNE-LES-BOIS

♦♦♦ ⦿ Les Doumées Vasco et Martine COSTA
2, route d'Echedan, 37150 EPEIGNE-LES-BOIS
☎ 02 47 23 84 21 & 06 71 52 81 60 ⊟ 02 47 23 84 21
e-mail: quima@wanadoo.fr
Three upstairs rooms in a restored Tourangel house in a hamlet near Chenonceaux and Montrichard (10 km). The rooms each have private wc and either shower or bathroom. One double room and two rooms sleeping three. Lounge for use of guests with open fire and television. Shaded enclose garden. Meals - booking required.
PRICES: s €41; d €47; t €58; extra person €13; dinner €18 **ON SITE:** Hiking **NEARBY:** Canoeing (20km) Horse riding (15km) Fishing (3km) Swimming pool (10km) Tennis (10km) Sailing (15km) Railway station (10km) Shops (10km) BLERE (10km) **NOTES:** Pets admitted English spoken

EPEIGNE-SUR-DEME

♦♦♦♦ Château de Girardet
Jacques et Maryse CHESNAUX
37370 EPEIGNE-SUR-DEME
☎ 02 47 52 36 19 ⊟ 02 47 52 36 90
Five rooms (one a suite) on the first and second floors of a château built and restored over the 15th, 16th and 19th centuries, looking out over a 5ha park with wild boar and roe deer. Two double rooms, two triple rooms (one being the suite), and one room sleeping four. Four rooms have bathroom and wc, and the other has shower and wc. Day room with open fire. Lounge with open fireplace. Two sitting rooms for guests. Table tennis. Cycle hire on site.
PRICES: s €55-€93; d €61-€104; t €117-€127 **ON SITE:** Fishing Hiking **NEARBY:** Canoeing (6km) Horse riding (6km) Golf (15km) Swimming pool (7km) Tennis (2km) Sailing (15km) Railway station (20km) Shops (2km) NEUVY-LE-ROI (8km) **NOTES:** Pets admitted English spoken

ESVRES-SUR-INDRE

♦♦♦ ⦿ Les Moulins de Vontes Odile DEGAIL
37320 ESVRES-SUR-INDRE
☎ 02 47 26 45 72 ⊟ 02 47 26 45 35
e-mail: odile.degail@worldonline.fr www.moulinsdevontes.com
On the banks of the Indre, 2.5 km from the village of Esvres, stands one of the Mills of Vontes which were reconstructed at the end of the 18th century. The spot is a gem of greenery and water. Spread over three floors are three rooms, each with shower and wc. Two double rooms (160cm bed) and one twin room. They are separate from the main mill, where guests will find a sitting room with television for their use. 10% reduction on three nights or more. Meals may be booked.
PRICES: s €68-€83; d €76-€90; extra person €23; dinner €23 **ON SITE:** Fishing **NEARBY:** Canoeing (7km) Horse riding (5km) Golf (20km) Swimming pool (3km) Tennis (3km) Sailing (15km) Railway station (3km) Shops (3km) MONTBAZON (8km) **NOTES:** No pets English spoken

FERRIERE-LARCON

♦♦♦ ♥ ⦿ Châtre François GUILLARD
37350 FERRIERE-LARCON
☎ 02 47 59 67 47 ⊟ 02 47 59 67 47
South-west of Loches, between the D50 and the D59, stands a farmhouse of character. Three guest rooms at ground level with separate access, each with private shower and wc. Kitchenette for guests. Shaded lawn, garden furniture, basketball, metal detectors. 10% reduction for stays over three nights. Meals - at the proprietors' table - may be booked in advance. Children's menu €8. Futuroscope 45 minutes.

continued

PRICES: s €32; d €38; t €53; extra person €15; dinner €15
NEARBY: Fishing (1km) Swimming pool (6km) Hiking (1km) Tennis (6km) Sailing (11km) Railway station (18km) Shops (6km) LE GRAND-PRESSIGNY (5km) **NOTES:** No pets

FRANCUEIL

♦♦♦♦ ΙΟΙ Le Moulin Solange NAESS
28, rue du Moulin Neuf, 37150 FRANCUEIL
☎ 02 47 23 93 44 📠 02 47 23 94 67
e-mail: le-moulin.naess@wanadoo.fr
www.france-bonjour.com/le-moulin/

Five rooms in a 19th-century mill, each with private bathroom and wc. Parkland with rivers, waterfall, pond and ducks. Breakfast served by the water. Winter garden and large lounge for guests to enjoy. Private heated swimming pool. Outdoor furniture. Midday picnic hamper available. Wine tasting. Enclosed parking. 15% reduction from October to March inclusive.
PRICES: s €50-€122; d €58-€130; t €81-€93; dinner €22
ON SITE: Fishing Swimming pool **NEARBY:** Canoeing (6km) Horse riding (20km) Golf (20km) Hiking (1km) Tennis (6km) Sailing (6km) Railway station (3km) Shops (1km) BLERE (7km)
NOTES: Pets admitted English spoken

GENILLE

♦♦♦ La Frillère Bernard VALLETTE
37460 GENILLE
☎ 02 47 59 51 01
Four upstairs rooms in a home of character in a forest park. Very quiet. On the second floor: a suite with two double beds and a medium bed, bath and wc; one double room with shower and wc. On the third floor: one suite with four single beds, shower and wc; one room with double bed and two singles, shower and wc. Lake with chalet for fishing and picnics. Open 15 April to 1 October, and out of season by reservation.
PRICES: s €27-€35; d €34-€41; t €46 **NEARBY:** Fishing (1km) Swimming pool (5km) Hiking (1km) Tennis (5km) Sailing (5km) Railway station (10km) Shops (5km) MONTRESOR (10km)
NOTES: Pets admitted

♦♦♦ Le Moulin de la Roche Josette et Clive MIEVILLE
37460 GENILLE
☎ 02 47 59 56 58 📠 02 47 59 59 62
e-mail: clive.mieville@wanadoo.fr www.moulin-de-la-roche.com
Four guest rooms in a mill dating from the 15th, 17th and 19th centuries on the Indre, near Loches and the Cher Valley. On the ground floor: one double room with shower and wc. Upstairs: two rooms with either a 150cm double or two single beds; and one room for three (double and single bed) All have shower and wc. Lounge with open fire. Shaded garden enclosed by the river and millstream. Private parking. The hosts are Franco-British. Table tennis. Restaurant nearby.

PRICES: d €55-€58; t €69-€72; extra person €14 **ON SITE:** Fishing Hiking **NEARBY:** Horse riding (8km) Swimming pool (1km) Tennis (1km) Sailing (8km) Railway station (11km) Shops (1km) MONTRESOR (10km) **NOTES:** No pets English spoken

HOMMES

♦♦♦♦ ΙΟΙ Le Vieux Château Albine HARDY
Relais du Vieux Château, 37340 HOMMES
☎ 02 47 24 95 13 & SR : 02 47 27 56 10
📠 02 47 24 68 67
e-mail: levieuxchateaudehommes@wanadoo.fr

Five guest rooms in a 15th-century tithe barn. Large living room for use of guests, with open fire, television and telephone. One ground floor room with disabled access (two double beds). Four upstairs rooms with either double bed or twin beds. Each has private bathroom and wc. Park and courtyard. Private swimming pool, mountain bike hire. Meals can be booked. Tariff: half board €75/day/person.
PRICES: s €78; d €94-€106; t €121; extra person €23; dinner €28
ON SITE: Children's play area Fishing Swimming pool Hiking
NEARBY: Canoeing (2km) Horse riding (3km) Golf (7km) Tennis (4km) Sailing (2km) Railway station (12km) Shops (3km) CHATEAU-LA-VALLIERE (13km) **NOTES:** No pets English spoken

HUISMES

♦♦♦♦ Château de la Poitevinière
Marie-Christine PESQUET, 37420 HUISMES
☎ 02 47 95 58 40 📠 02 47 95 43 43
e-mail: chris@chateauloire.com www.chateauloire.com
Chinon 4km. Five spacious upstairs guest rooms in a beautiful 18th-century home opening on to a 5ha park. All rooms have private bathroom and wc. One room has a queen-size double bed (160cm x 200cm); three others have king-size doubles (200cm x 200cm); the last has twin beds. Living room for guests, with satellite television. A non-smoking establishment.
PRICES: s €100-€115; d €110-€125; t €140 **ON SITE:** Hiking
NEARBY: Horse riding (1km) Golf (19km) Fishing (4km) Swimming pool (6km) Tennis (2km) Railway station (4km) Shops (3km) CHINON (4km) **NOTES:** No pets English spoken

continued

♦♦♦ La Chaussée Marie-José BRINCKMAN
37420 HUISMES
☎ 02 47 95 45 79 ▯ 02 47 95 45 79
e-mail: ariasse@yahoo.fr   www.lachaussee.fr.st
Three rooms in a beautiful 19th-century house with a romantic setting in a 1.5ha park with lots of woodland and a little river. Two rooms with double bed, shower and wc. One room with double bed, medium bed, large bathroom with tub, shower and wc. Private swimming pool in grounds.
PRICES: s €50-€70; d €59-€83; extra person €23 **ON SITE:** Swimming pool Hiking **NEARBY:** Horse riding (2km) Tennis (1km) Railway station (6km) Shops (3km) CHINON (6km) **NOTES:** No pets English spoken

♦♦♦ La Pilleterie Marie-Claire PRUNIER
37420 HUISMES
☎ 02 47 95 58 07
e-mail: mcguilletat.prunier@wanadoo.fr
Three rooms of character in an outbuilding of a restored old farm. A really rustic spot, where peace is guaranteed. One twin room (shower and wc); one double room (bath and wc); one suite (one double and two single beds with bath and wc). Sitting room created for visitors, open fire and colour television. Garden furniture. Parking. Bookings may be taken by the week.
PRICES: d €44-€54; t €76; extra person €15 **ON SITE:** Children's play area **NEARBY:** Horse riding (4km) Fishing (3km) Swimming pool (6km) Hiking (1km) Tennis (2km) Railway station (6km) Shops (2km) CHINON (6km) **NOTES:** No pets

♦♦♦ ◯ Le Clos Saint André Michèle PINCON
37140 INGRANDES-DE-TOURAINE
☎ 02 47 96 90 81 & 06 73 19 96 12 ▯ 02 47 96 90 81
e-mail: mmpincon@club-internet.fr

Six guest rooms (each with private bathroom and wc) on a winegrowing estate (16th and 18th centuries). On the ground floor: one room with a double bed and two singles. First floor: two double rooms and a triple room. Second floor: one triple room and a twin room with an extra child's bed. Living room with open fireplace. Parking, shady garden terrace for guests; pétanque. Estate wines (Bourgueil). Generous dinners by reservation - not Saturdays, with half bottle of Bourgueil AOC included. Open 1 April to 15 October - other dates may be possible.
PRICES: s €40; d €45-€52; t €64; extra person €12; dinner €24 **NEARBY:** Canoeing (20km) Horse riding (13km) Golf (28km) Fishing (3km) Swimming pool (12km) Hiking (1km) Tennis (1km) Sailing (12km) Railway station (3km) Shops (8km) LANGEAIS (12km) **NOTES:** Pets admitted English spoken

LA CELLE-SAINT-AVANT

♦♦♦ Le Grignon Claude CHUIT
3, allée du Grignon, 37160 LA CELLE-SAINT-AVANT
☎ 02 47 65 13 61 & 06 86 50 61 92
e-mail: nicoleclaudechuit@minitel.net
Two rooms and one suite upstairs in a restored small farmhouse in a hamlet between Celle-Saint-Avant and Descartes (the birthplace of the philosopher), and just 35 minutes from Futuroscope. Two double rooms with shower and wc. Suite with 120cm bed, two singles, child's bed, bathroom and wc. Living room with television and open fireplace. Extra children's beds available. Lawned garden. Parking. Golf 35 minutes.
PRICES: s €31-€34; d €37-€40; t €49-€52 **ON SITE:** Hiking **NEARBY:** Canoeing (6km) Horse riding (7km) Golf (30km) Fishing (2km) Swimming pool (6km) Tennis (6km) Sailing (25km) Railway station (12km) Shops (6km) DESCARTES (6km) **NOTES:** No pets

LANGEAIS

♦♦♦ ◯ Domaine de Châteaufort GROSOS
37130 LANGEAIS
☎ 02 47 96 85 75 ▯ 02 47 96 86 03
e-mail: resa@i-a-s.fr
Just off the road near the centre of Langeais (800m from the château), this house is in the middle of a wooded 9ha park with a private heated swimming pool. Six guest rooms on the first and second floors, all equipped with bathroom or shower room and wc. Two large rooms for the use of guests. Dinner only if reserved.
PRICES: s €66-€81; d €73-€88; t €91-€107; dinner €23 **ON SITE:** Children's play area Horse riding Swimming pool Hiking **NEARBY:** Golf (15km) Fishing (1km) Tennis (1km) Railway station (2km) Shops (1km) LANGEAIS (2km) **NOTES:** No pets English spoken

♦♦♦ 🐓 ◯ L'Epeigné Martine HALOPE
37130 LANGEAIS
☎ 02 47 96 54 23 & 02 47 96 84 06 ▯ 02 47 96 54 23
Three upstairs rooms in a beautiful restored farmhouse on a working farm, raising Limousin cattle. Two double rooms and a suite for four people, each with shower and wc. Kitchen and living room exclusively for guests. Rooms can be reserved by groups. Lovely garden, woods, stables for horses. Meals available (farm produce, poultry and beef). Tariff: half board for more than three nights: €72/two people.
PRICES: s €40; d €46; t €58; extra person €12; dinner €17 **NEARBY:** Horse riding (1km) Golf (15km) Fishing (1km) Swimming pool (2km) Hiking (1km) Tennis (2km) Sailing (7km) Railway station (2km) Shops (2km) LANGEAIS (2km) **NOTES:** Pets admitted English spoken

LERNE

♦♦♦ 🐓 La Grande Cheminée Suzanne BLANCHARD
37500 LERNE
☎ 02 47 95 94 46 & 06 73 05 82 74 ▯ 02 47 95 86 20
On a 17th-century poultry farm on the borders of Poitou, Touraine and Anjou. Three upstairs rooms with separate access. One twin room with separate shower and wc. One double room and one suite (double and two single beds), each with shower and wc. Small sitting room for guests. Large shady garden. Extra beds available, and baby equipment. Kitchen area available. Farm produce and wine.
PRICES: s €31; d €37-€40; t €54; extra person €15 **ON SITE:** Children's play area **NEARBY:** Golf (4km) Fishing (6km) Swimming pool (15km) Hiking (1km) Tennis (3km) Railway station (15km) Shops (4km) CHINON (15km) **NOTES:** Pets admitted

CENTRAL FRANCE

LIGRE

♦♦♦♦ ✌ Le Clos de Ligre Martine DESCAMPS
22, rue du Rouilly, 37500 LIGRE
☎ 02 47 93 95 59 ▤ 02 47 93 06 31
e-mail: martinedescamps@hotmail.com
Three bedrooms on the ground and first floors of a lovely
bourgeois house dating from 1850 with a delightful one-hectare
garden. All rooms have private bathroom and wc. One double
room is in an old winepress. Another is in an old fruit store (two
single beds plus another single in an adjoining room). The third
room is in the main house (one double bed and one single bed).
Music and reading room. Private swimming pool. Covered terrace
with garden furniture. 10% reduction from October to April for
three nights and longer. Meals may be booked.
PRICES: s €60; d €80; extra person €26; dinner €25
ON SITE: Swimming pool Hiking **NEARBY:** Canoeing (7km) Horse
riding (15km) Golf (25km) Fishing (5km) Tennis (7km) Railway station
(7km) Shops (7km) CHINON (12km) **NOTES:** No pets English spoken

♦♦♦♦ La Milaudière Michelle et Laurent MAROLLEAU
5, rue Saint-Martin, 37500 LIGRE
☎ 02 47 98 37 53 ▤ 02 47 93 36 74
e-mail: milaudiere@club-internet.fr
perso.club-internet.fr/mbforma
Four guest rooms in a 16th-century group of buildings in the
centre of Ligré. A haven of peace between Touraine and Poitou,
near Chinon. All bedrooms have bath or shower and wc. One
double room, one twin room and a room sleeping four. Lounge
with television and open fire. Courtyard and country garden. Yoga
classes available with Michelle who teaches viniyoga. Walking
trails. Table tennis. Picnic area. Cooking area available (€3/day).
PRICES: s €34-€40; d €39-€44; t €57; extra person €13 **ON SITE:** Hiking
NEARBY: Canoeing (7km) Horse riding (7km) Golf (20km) Fishing
(4km) Swimming pool (7km) Tennis (7km) Railway station (7km) Shops
(7km) CHINON (15km) **NOTES:** Pets admitted English spoken

LIMERAY

♦♦♦ ❧ Auberge les Grillons Famille GUICHARD
Limeray, 37530 AMBOISE ☎ 02 47 30 11 76
Four guest rooms on a poultry farm. Nearby inn with regional
specialities. Two double rooms and two triples, all with private
bathrooms and wc. Grounds with garden furniture.
PRICES: s €38; d €43-€49; t €55 **NEARBY:** Canoeing (2km) Horse
riding (6km) Fishing (1km) Swimming pool (8km) Hiking (1km) Tennis
(3km) Railway station (1km) Shops (1km) Restaurant nearby AMBOISE
(8km) **NOTES:** No pets English spoken

LOCHE-SUR-INDROIS

♦♦♦ ✌ La Gironnerie Françoise SEDJAL
37460 LOCHE-SUR-INDROIS
☎ 02 47 92 63 36 e-mail: lagiron@club-internet.fr

Three rooms in a bourgeois 1840 house in the open countryside

near Loches and Montrésor. In a park on a 7ha estate with
ornamental lake. One ground floor double room with bath and wc.
Upstairs: one room sleeping three (one double and one single
bed), shower and wc. One two-roomed family suite with two
double beds, one 120cm bed, one single bed, library, shower
room and wc. Lounge with television and open fire. Indoor
parking.
PRICES: s €38; d €44; t €60-€79; extra person €14; dinner €18
ON SITE: Fishing Hiking **NEARBY:** Horse riding (5km) Golf (10km)
Swimming pool (10km) Tennis (3km) Sailing (10km) Railway station
(18km) Shops (3km) MONTRESOR (10km) **NOTES:** Pets admitted
English spoken

MONTHODON

♦♦♦♦ ✌ La Maréchalerie Patricia et Danny NIEDBALSKI
Le Sentier, 6, rue des Rosiers, 37110 MONTHODON
☎ 02 47 29 61 66
e-mail: lamarechalerie@aol.com
http://members.aol.com/lamarechalerie

In a 19th-century, half-timbered blacksmith's between the Loir and
the Loire, near Amboise and its principal châteaux, six rooms
sleeping two up to five people. All have shower and wc. A
distinguished house, separate from the owners', perched above a
pretty valley, in a green and quiet spot. Sitting/dining room for
guests in the old forge, with open fireplace. Country garden
extending to one hectare, with terraces, furniture and leisure area.
Stream, donkeys, bikes for loan, and children's games.
PRICES: s €30; d €34; t €42; extra person €8; dinner €13
ON SITE: Children's play area Hiking **NEARBY:** Canoeing (30km)
Horse riding (1km) Golf (20km) Fishing (2km) Swimming pool (9km)
Tennis (9km) Sailing (30km) Railway station (9km) Shops (4km)
CHATEAU-RENAULT (9km) **NOTES:** Pets admitted English spoken

MONTRESOR

♦♦♦♦ Le Moulin Alain et Sophie WILLEMS
37460 MONTRESOR
☎ 02 47 92 68 20 & SR : 02 47 27 56 10 ▤ 02 47 92 74 65
e-mail: alain.willems@wanadoo.fr
Four rooms in a 19th-century mill built on the Indre, situated on
the road leaving Montrésor village, in a hectare of grounds. One
room has a double and two single beds; one has a double bed.
These have shower and wc. The next room has four single beds;
the last has two single beds, each with bath and wc. Large
lounge/sitting room with abundant character, with a view of the
millstream. Several restaurants near. Private swimming pool.
PRICES: s €45-€50; d €50-€55; extra person €13 **ON SITE:** Fishing
Swimming pool **NEARBY:** Horse riding (12km) Tennis (1km) Sailing
(2km) Railway station (17km) Shops (1km) MONTRESOR **NOTES:** Pets
admitted English spoken

continued

MONTS

⊪ Château de la Roche Diane DE CHAMBURE
37260 MONTS
☎ 02 47 26 70 08 & SR : 02 47 27 56 10
📠 02 47 26 63 94
Three guest bedrooms on the first and second floors of a 19th-century château on the banks of the Indre. In an outstanding location of park and forest near Tours and Azay-le-Rideau. One double room and one twin room, each with shower and wc. One double room with bath and wc. Child's bed available (supplementary charge). Television and telephone in each bedroom.
PRICES: d €107 **NEARBY:** Fishing (3km) Tennis (3km) Railway station (12km) Shops (3km) MONTBAZON (10km) **NOTES:** No pets

MOSNES

⊪ Le Buisson Marie-France BAQUET
37530 MOSNES
☎ 02 47 57 31 09 📠 02 47 57 61 43
e-mail: lebuisson@libertysurf.fr
Three bedrooms on the first floor in an old farmhouse in an elevated position 3 km from the Loire and 12 km from Amboise. Every bedroom has private shower room and wc. One double room and two rooms sleeping three. Available for guests - lounge/sitting room with open fire and television. Situated half way between Blois and Tours (30 km), an ideal base for exploring the heritage of the Touraine. In the grounds: farmyard, lakes, organic kitchen garden, terrace, parking.
PRICES: s €34; d €38-€46; t €54; extra person €11 **ON SITE:** Hiking **NEARBY:** Fishing (3km) Horse riding (3km) Swimming pool (12km) Tennis (2km) Railway station (12km) Shops (3km) AMBOISE (12km) **NOTES:** No pets

NAZELLES-NEGRON

⊪ iOi Château de Nazelles Véronique FRUCTUS
16, rue Tue la Soif, 37530 NAZELLES-NEGRON
☎ 02 47 30 53 79 📠 02 47 30 53 79
e-mail: info@chateau-nazelles.com
www.chateau-nazelles.com

Three guest rooms in an authentic 16th-century home which is a classified historic monument, constructed by Thomas Bohier (builder of the Château de Chenonceau). The house looks over the Loire Valley to the south and the Château d'Amboise. One double room in a house. Two double rooms upstairs in the château (one with two single beds). All rooms have adjoining bathroom and wc. Large lounge. The park has a succession of terraces, cave dwellings and a private swimming pool tucked away among the rocks.
PRICES: ; d €85-€90; extra person €16; dinner €23
ON SITE: Swimming pool Hiking **NEARBY:** Horse riding (4km) Golf (9km) Fishing (1km) Railway station (2km) AMBOISE (5km) **NOTES:** No pets English spoken

⊪ Le Château des Ormeaux Emmanuel GUENOT
Nazelles-Négron, 37530 AMBOISE
☎ 02 47 23 26 51 📠 02 47 23 19 31
e-mail: chateaudesormeaux@wanadoo.fr
www.chateaudesormeaux.com
Six upstairs rooms in a romantic château looking south down the Loire Valley, near Amboise and the vineyard of Vouvray. Three double rooms and three twin rooms, all with a view of the valley, period furniture, direct telephone, shower or bathroom and wc. Living room with open fireplace. 25ha park with private swimming pool. Small animals accepted with conditions.
PRICES: s €99-€107; d €107-€115; extra person €30
ON SITE: Fishing Swimming pool Hiking **NEARBY:** Horse riding (3km) Tennis (2km) Railway station (4km) Shops (2km) AMBOISE (4km) **NOTES:** Pets admitted English spoken

NEUILLE-LE-LIERRE

⊪ La Roche RAMEAU
37380 NEUILLE-LE-LIERRE
☎ 02 47 52 98 10 & 06 71 15 55 58
Four upstairs rooms in a wing of a 14th-century *seigneurie* in an 8-hectare park with 4 hectares of woods, beside a river. Separate access to rooms. Two double rooms; one twin room; each with bath and wc. One triple room with shower and wc. Lounge with cooking area set aside for guests. Parking. A minute from the Amboise exit from the A10. Travellers' cheques accepted.
PRICES: s €38; d €49; t €64; extra person €15 **NEARBY:** Horse riding (5km) Golf (20km) Fishing (1km) Swimming pool (12km) Hiking (1km) Tennis (4km) Sailing (12km) Railway station (10km) Shops (1km) VOUVRAY (10km) **NOTES:** No pets

NEUIL-SACHE

⊪ ✿ iOi Les Hautes Mougonnières
Soline MESTIVIER
37190 NEUIL
☎ 02 47 26 87 71 📠 02 47 26 82 29
e-mail: jp.mestivier@voila.fr

Saché 5km. Azay-le-Rideau 12km. This working farm (foie gras, strawberries, poultry) offers five upstairs guest rooms, each with private shower and wc. One suite sleeping four; two rooms for three (one of which has separate access and a cooking area); one double room; one single room. Upstairs: lounge area with library. On the ground floor: living room for visitors, with antique furniture. Parking. Garden. Lawn. Regional produce on sale. Futuroscope 1 hour. Cooking facilities. Veranda. Tariff: half board for three nights: €36/person/night (double room): suite €74.
PRICES: s €40; d €40; t €54-€74; dinner €18 **ON SITE:** Children's play area **NEARBY:** Golf (15km) Fishing (5km) Swimming pool (10km) Hiking (1km) Tennis (2km) Railway station (10km) Shops (2km) SAINTE-MAURE-DE-TOURAINE (10km) **NOTES:** No pets English spoken

CENTRAL FRANCE

NEUVY-LE-ROI

⦅⦆ 🐓 🍴 Le Château du Bois Marie CORMERY
37370 NEUVY-LE-ROI
☎ 02 47 24 44 76 · 📠 02 47 24 86 58
Four rooms on the first floor of a working farm dating from the 19th-century. Beautiful 16th-century barn in grounds. Close to the market town on the D2. Two double rooms and two rooms sleeping four, each with bathroom and wc. Television lounge for guests. Garden with furniture.
PRICES: d €31-€48; dinner €11 **NEARBY:** Horse riding (7km) Golf (13km) Fishing (1km) Swimming pool (9km) Hiking (1km) Tennis (1km) Sailing (15km) Railway station (11km) Shops (2km) NEUVY-LE-ROI (8km)
NOTES: Pets admitted English spoken

ORBIGNY

⦅⦆ 🍴 La Canterie Gérard PERRAUD
37460 ORBIGNY ☎ 02 47 92 61 44
e-mail: perraud-valy@worldonline.fr
http://perso.worldonline.fr/la-canterie
Three rooms in an outbuilding of an ancient small-holding right out in the country between Touraine and Berry. Two rooms, a double and a twin, with bath or shower and wc. A second twin room has bathroom and wc. Lounge reserved for guests; sitting room with television. Large garden with outdoor furniture. Mountain bikes. Forest 500m. Leisure centre and baths 12 km.
PRICES: s €37; d €41; t €55; extra person €10; dinner €16
ON SITE: Hiking **NEARBY:** Horse riding (15km) Fishing (5km) Swimming pool (5km) Tennis (5km) Sailing (12km) Railway station (15km) Shops (5km) MONTRESOR (8km) **NOTES:** No pets English spoken

RAZINES

⦅⦆ Château de Chargé
Claude & Marie-Louise D'ASFELD
37120 RAZINES
☎ 02 47 95 60 57 · 📠 02 47 95 67 25
e-mail: charge@chateauxcountry.com
www.chateauxcountry.com
Futuroscope 35 km. The Château de Chargé (14th/17th centuries), the ancient seat of the governors of Chinon and Richelieu, offers four guest rooms on the first floor. The 14th-century room has a 180cm double and two 90cm single beds; the 17th-century room has a 160cm double. Each has bath and wc. The 18th-century room and the Ladies' Room each have a double bed plus shower room and wc. Salon for use of guests. Park with private swimming pool. Reduction for stays over three nights.
PRICES: s €69-€100; d €77-€107; extra person €24
ON SITE: Swimming pool Hiking **NEARBY:** Horse riding (14km) Fishing (10km) Tennis (5km) Railway station (17km) Shops (7km) RICHELIEU (7km) **NOTES:** Pets admitted English spoken

⦅⦆ 🍴 La Prunelière MENANTEAU-BERTON
37120 RAZINES ☎ 02 47 95 67 38
Three guest rooms (one a suite) with separate access, upstairs in an old restored farmhouse on a 16th and 17th-century rural estate typical of the region. All rooms have television, shower and wc. One double room; one single room; and a two-roomed suite with double bed and two singles, cot, fridge, microwave. Large lounge with ancient winepress. The 1.5-hectare grounds offer terraces, country gardens, kitchen garden. Lavish catering. Bikes, piano, boules. 'Swin-golf' 4km.
PRICES: s €35-€42; d €40-€46; t €58; extra person €8; dinner €16
ON SITE: Hiking **NEARBY:** Horse riding (5km) Fishing (4km) Swimming pool (8km) Tennis (4km) Railway station (20km) Shops (8km) RICHELIEU (8km) **NOTES:** No pets

RESTIGNE

⦅⦆ 🐓 🍴 Chambre d'hôtes Annette GALBRUN
15, rue Croix des Pierres, 37140 RESTIGNE
☎ 02 47 97 33 49 · 📠 02 47 97 46 56

Three rooms upstairs in a Tourangel house on a wine estate, each with shower and wc. One double room, one single room and a room sleeping four, each with separate access. Kitchen (€13/day, also weekly price); parking; garden. Meals may be booked. Restaurant 1 km. Farm activities; initiation to the game of Boule de Fort; wine tasting in a picturesque cellar (Vin de Bourgueil from the estate); visit to cellars.
PRICES: d €42-€44; t €54; extra person €15; dinner €15
NEARBY: Horse riding (8km) Golf (20km) Fishing (3km) Swimming pool (8km) Hiking (1km) Tennis (4km) Railway station (5km) Shops (1km) BOURGUEIL (4km) **NOTES:** No pets

RICHELIEU

⦅⦆ Chambre d'hôtes Marie-Josephe LEPLATRE
1, rue Jarry, 37120 RICHELIEU
☎ 02 47 58 10 42 & SR : 02 47 27 56 10

Four stylish guest rooms (for two or three people) in a house of character in the middle of Richelieu. Private showers and wcs. Quality furniture. Winter garden exclusively for guests. French gardens. Nearby restaurants. Pony-trekking 6 km. 'Swin-golf' 9km.
PRICES: s €43; d €58; t €76; extra person €9 **NEARBY:** Fishing (1km) Swimming pool (1km) Hiking (1km) Tennis (1km) Sailing (1km) Railway station (25km) Shops (1km) RICHELIEU (1km) **NOTES:** No pets

🐓Places with this symbol are farmhouses

For further information on these and other chambres d'hôtes, consult the Gîtes de France website
www.gites-de-france.fr

♦♦♦♦ Chambre d'hôtes
Michèle COUVRAT-DESVERGNES
6, rue Henri Proust, 37120 RICHELIEU
☎ 02 47 58 29 40 🖷 02 47 58 29 40
e-mail: lamaisondemichele@yahoo.com

Four upstairs guest rooms in a beautiful bourgeois home dating from the early 19th century situated in a group of 17th-century buildings in Richelieu. Opening onto a quiet enclosed 0.2 hectare park. All rooms have private bathroom and wc. Two rooms have large twin beds; the other two rooms have 170 x 200cm double beds. Large living room with open fire, pay-telephone and television. Indoor parking and garage. Animals accepted under certain conditions.
PRICES: s €70; d €80; extra person €15 **NEARBY:** Horse riding (7km) Fishing (1km) Swimming pool (1km) Tennis (1km) Railway station (25km) RICHELIEU **NOTES:** Pets admitted English spoken

RIGNY-USSE

♦♦♦♦ Le Pin Jany BROUSSET
37420 RIGNY-USSE
☎ 02 47 95 52 99 🖷 02 47 95 43 21
Four bedrooms in an old restored farmhouse at the edge of a forest. All rooms have private bathrooms and wcs. One twin room; two double rooms; one duplex with double bed and cooking area. Living room with open fire and exposed beams, billiards and television. Sauna and private swimming pool. Parking. Table tennis. Situated in the grounds of 'Sleeping Beauty's castle'. A dozen more châteaux in a radius of 20 km.
PRICES: s €39-€61; d €39-€61; t €77 **ON SITE:** Children's play area Swimming pool **NEARBY:** Horse riding (9km) Fishing (2km) Hiking (1km) Railway station (14km) Shops (2km) AZAY-LE-RIDEAU (14km) **NOTES:** No pets English spoken

SACHE

♦♦♦♦ Le Moulin Vert de la Chevrière
Gérard LETOURNEAU
12, route Basse Chevrière, 37190 SACHE
☎ 02 47 26 83 95 🖷 02 47 26 83 95
e-mail: gs.letourneau@wanadoo.fr
Four rooms on the first and second floors of a mill dating from the 15th century on the Indre, 1 km from Saché, and 7 km from Azay-le-Rideau.. All rooms have private bathroom and wc. Three double rooms (two with 160cm beds) and a twin room. On the third floor is a large sitting room with large screen satellite television and video, library and billiards. Terrace on a spur on the river. River walks in a four-hectare estate. A non-smoking establishment.
PRICES: s €75; d €83 **ON SITE:** Fishing Hiking **NEARBY:** Horse riding (3km) Swimming pool (7km) Tennis (2km) Railway station (7km) Shops (2km) AZAY-LE-RIDEAU (7km) **NOTES:** Pets admitted

♦♦♦ Les Tilleuls - La Sablonnière Michelle PILLER
37190 SACHE, ☎ 02 47 26 81 45 🖷 02 47 26 84 00
One room and a suite on the first floor of a late 19th-century house, plus two rooms in a separate building in a hamlet dominating the valley of the Indre, 1.5 km from the lovely village of Saché. All rooms have private shower and wc. Three double rooms, and one room with three single beds. TV lounge. Garden.
PRICES: s €46; d €61; t €77; extra person €15 **NEARBY:** Fishing (1km) Swimming pool (6km) Hiking (1km) Tennis (6km) Sailing (5km) Railway station (19km) Shops (2km) AZAY-LE-RIDEAU (6km) **NOTES:** Pets admitted English spoken

SAVIGNY-EN-VERON

♦♦♦♦ ⍥ Chevire Marie-Françoise CHAUVELIN
11, rue Basse, 37420 SAVIGNY-EN-VERON
☎ 02 47 58 42 49 🖷 02 47 58 42 49
Three no-smoking rooms in a 19th-century barn attached to the owners' beautiful home, in a winegrowing village in the Regional Natural Park. One double room with two extra folding beds, bathroom and wc; one double room with shower room and wc (not adjoining); one room sleeping three with bath and wc. Large living room with kitchen area. Cot available. Courtyard and garden. Garage. Meadow with picnic area. Dinner available, except Sunday and Monday. Closed 15 December to 15 January.
PRICES: s €29-€36; d €36-€43; extra person €11; dinner €16 **ON SITE:** Wine tasting Hiking **NEARBY:** Canoeing (10km) Horse riding (6km) Golf (15km) Fishing (2km) Swimming pool (4km) Tennis (1km) Railway station (10km) Shops (1km) CHINON (10km) **NOTES:** No pets English spoken

SEPMES

♦♦♦ 🐓 ⍥ La Ferme des Berthiers
Anne-Marie VERGNAUD, 37800 SEPMES
☎ 02 47 65 50 61 🖷 02 47 65 50 61
e-mail: lesberthiers@libertysurf.fr
Six rooms in a family mansion (1856) on a Tourangel farm. Three rooms on the first floor: two triple rooms and one double. One two-roomed ground-floor suite with a 150cm bed and a 120cm bed. Two rooms in a separate building: one sleeping two and one sleeping four. All rooms have private facilities. Living room, sitting room, courtyard, shady garden. Cot and children's beds available.
PRICES: s €34; d €41-€46; t €49-€58; dinner €18 **ON SITE:** Children's play area Hiking **NEARBY:** Fishing (3km) Swimming pool (7km) Tennis (1km) Railway station (7km) Shops (1km) DESCARTES (7km) **NOTES:** Pets admitted English spoken

SOUVIGNE

♦♦♦♦ La Mésange Potière Liliane et Patrick BRUNET
10, rue Juliette Aveline, 37330 SOUVIGNE
☎ 02 47 24 54 36 🖷 02 47 24 54 36
e-mail: mesangep@club-internet.fr
http://perso.club-internet.fr/mesangep

continued

Four guest rooms (two of them suites) on the ground floor of outbuildings of a beautiful 18th-century building on the edge of the village. The rooms look out onto lovely grounds within ancient walls. Duplex suite (double and two single beds and television); double room with television; twin room; all with shower and wc. Suite with 160cm double bed, single sofa bed and 150cm folding bed. Living room with open fireplace and television. Cot available. Washing and drying facilities available. Telephone. Reduction for stays over three nights. Terrace. Pottery workshop. Small river alongside garden. Outdoor furniture.
PRICES: s €31-€34; d €35-€43; t €56; extra person €10-€16
ON SITE: Fishing **NEARBY:** Horse riding (10km) Golf (5km) Swimming pool (11km) Hiking (1km) Tennis (5km) Sailing (20km) Railway station (30km) Shops (7km) CHATEAU-LA-VALLIERE (7km) **NOTES:** Pets admitted English spoken

ST-BAULD

Le Moulin du Coudray Sylvie PERIA
37310 ST-BAULD
☎ 02 47 92 82 64 & 06 67 20 02 17 02 47 92 82 64
Three upstairs rooms in a 16th-century mill restored in the 20th century. Situated on 3ha of parkland with a 1ha pond (fishing possible). All rooms have luxury bathrooms and sleep two, either in double beds or two singles. Dayroom reserved for guests and sitting room with open fire. Shaded paved terrace overlooking the park. Mountain bikes. Gym available. Dinners (must be pre-booked) except Wednesday. Open all year.
PRICES: s €43; d €52; extra person €15; dinner €20 **ON SITE:** Fishing **NEARBY:** Canoeing (15km) Horse riding (3km) Golf (20km) Swimming pool (8km) Tennis (5km) Railway station (15km) Shops (4km) LOCHES (15km) **NOTES:** Pets admitted English spoken

ST-BRANCHS

La Paqueraie Monique BINET
37320 ST-BRANCHS/CORMERY
☎ 02 47 26 31 51 02 47 26 39 15
e-mail: monique.binet@wanadoo.fr
http://perso.wanadoo.fr/lapaqueraie/
Four rooms in a very beautiful restored house overlooking a lawn. Two double rooms and two twin rooms, all with shower or bathroom and wc. Lounge with open fireplace. 1ha park with parking and garage. Lovely lawn. Private swimming pool.
PRICES: d €59-€69; extra person €19; dinner €23 **ON SITE:** Swimming pool **NEARBY:** Horse riding (3km) Fishing (2km) Tennis (4km) Railway station (22km) Shops (4km) MONTBAZON (18km) **NOTES:** Pets admitted English spoken *See advert on opposite page*

ST-EPAIN

La Maison Rouge Josseline ROSSI
37800 ST-EPAIN
☎ 02 47 73 59 76
e-mail: chambredhote@aol.com
An outbuilding dating from the late 17th century in a range of rustic buildings above the Valley of the Manse, 800m from Crissay-sur-Manse, which is classified as one of the most beautiful villages of France. Three large rooms for four people, all with shower and wc. One ground floor room with 160cm double and two fold-out beds; a ground floor room with a 160cm double on a mezzanine plus two fold-out beds; and a first floor room with a double bed and two fold-out singles.
PRICES: s €39-€43; d €43-€46; t €55-€58; extra person €10; dinner €18
ON SITE: Canoeing Horse riding Fishing Hiking Sailing **NEARBY:** Golf (10km) Swimming pool (10km) Tennis (2km) Railway station (16km) Shops (2km) SAINTE-MAURE-DE-TOURAINE (16km) **NOTES:** Pets admitted English spoken

ST-ETIENNE-DE-CHIGNY

Le Portail DE CLERVAL
Vieux Bourg, 37230 ST-ETIENNE-DE-CHIGNY
☎ 02 47 55 66 12
e-mail: declerval@hotmail.com www.multimania.com/leportail/
Calm, rest and simplicity on the ground floor of an outbuilding of a 17th and 19th-century property overlooking the old town of Saint-Etienne, a village of character near Luynes. Three charming guest rooms with separate access, each with double bed and sofa bed, bathroom and wc. Large private swimming pool. Terrace in a huge wooded garden.
PRICES: s €45; d €50; t €65; extra person €15 **ON SITE:** Swimming pool Hiking **NEARBY:** Horse riding (5km) Golf (17km) Fishing (2km) Tennis (3km) Railway station (12km) Shops (3km) SAINT-CYR-SUR-LOIRE (13km) **NOTES:** Pets admitted English spoken

ST-HIPPOLYTE

Le Vallon de Vitray Robert et Michelle DESNOS
37600 ST-HIPPOLYTE
☎ 02 47 94 75 73 02 47 94 75 73
e-mail: miro@micro-video.fr
Four guest rooms in an outbuilding of a restored 18th-century farmhouse between Touraine and Berry in a small, quiet and green valley. One twin room on the ground floor is accessible to guests with disabilities, and there are three upstairs rooms, all with shower and wc. Upstairs are two doubles and a room sleeping four. Televisions in bedrooms. Dining room with fireplace. Separate access. Large country garden with outdoor furniture and table tennis. Terrace looks over the valley. Mountain bike hire.
PRICES: s €36; d €41; t €53; extra person €11; dinner €16
ON SITE: Fishing Hiking **NEARBY:** Horse riding (3km) Golf (10km) Swimming pool (12km) Tennis (12km) Sailing (20km) Railway station (12km) Shops (12km) LOCHES (12km) **NOTES:** No pets English spoken

ST-MARTIN-LE-BEAU

Domaine de Beaufort MOYER
Rue des Caves Cange, 37270 ST-MARTIN-LE-BEAU
☎ 02 47 50 61 51 02 47 50 27 56
e-mail: aurore.de.beaufort@wanadoo.fr
Tours 16 km. Amboise 8 km. Five ground floor rooms on a 19th-century wine estate, in the heart of Montlouis wine country. Separate access to rooms that each have shower, wc and television. The rooms are: one double; two sleeping five in single beds (three on mezzanine); one double with extra convertible double; one twin. Large lounge with telephone, library and fireplace. Kitchenette. Garden with furniture. Parking. Restaurant 2 km. TGV station 12 km. Wine sampling. Open all year.
PRICES: s €34; d €44; t €56; extra person €12 **ON SITE:** Wine tasting Hiking **NEARBY:** Horse riding (4km) Golf (30km) Fishing (2km) Swimming pool (8km) Tennis (2km) Sailing (2km) Railway station (2km) Shops (2km) BLERE (8km) **NOTES:** Pets admitted English spoken

ST-OUEN-LES-VIGNES

Le Bois de la Chainée Michèle PASSEMARD
37530 ST-OUEN-LES-VIGNES
☎ 02 47 30 13 17 02 47 30 10 75
e-mail: gpassemard@aol.com
Three upstairs guest rooms in a restored 19th-century farmhouse situated in a wooded hamlet 1 km from town, near Amboise and the Loire Valley. Separate entrances. Indoor parking. One two-roomed suite with corner kitchen (two single beds, very comfortable convertible double bed, second double bed, plus single). A second two-roomed suite sleeping five. All have shower

continued

and wc. Weekly prices available. Garden with lawn and woods of 1ha. Outdoor furniture.
PRICES: s €34; d €40-€47; extra person €14 **ON SITE:** Hiking
NEARBY: Horse riding (2km) Golf (25km) Fishing (2km) Swimming pool (6km) Tennis (6km) Railway station (6km) Shops (1km) AMBOISE (6km) **NOTES:** No pets English spoken

TAUXIGNY

🎏 La Maison des Sources
Christophe MARZAIS-KERBRIAND
2 ruelle des Sources, 37310 TAUXIGNY
☎ 02 47 92 13 91 📠 02 47 61 28 48
In the middle of the village of Tauxigny, half way between Tours and Loches, this 17th-century bourgeois house has lots of character. Three en suite rooms opening onto a courtyard with a spring; two have separate entrances. One room sleeping three on the ground floor; one first floor room sleeping four; one first floor twin room. Kitchen corner for guests. Raised leisure garden with outdoor furniture. Bike hire possible, route planning available.
PRICES: d €41-€49; extra person €12 **ON SITE:** Fishing
NEARBY: Swimming pool (8km) Hiking (1km) Tennis (1km) Sailing (12km) Railway station (18km) Shops (8km) LOCHES (18km)
NOTES: No pets English spoken

TRUYES

🎏 🍽 Manoir de Chaix Dominique CASAROMANI
Chaix, 37320 TRUYES
☎ 02 47 43 42 73 📠 02 47 43 05 87
e-mail: pascal.casaromani@free.fr www.manoir-de-chaix.com
A 16th-century manor 3 km from the village of Truyes. Six bedrooms on ground, first and second floors. Roomy and quiet, all have bathroom or shower and wc. On the ground floor: one double room. First floor: two rooms for two, three or four people. Second floor: two double rooms and a triple room. Lounge for use of guests. Private swimming pool and tennis courts. Meals must be booked.
PRICES: s €36-€42; d €46-€53; t €63-€69; dinner €17
ON SITE: Swimming pool Tennis **NEARBY:** Horse riding (8km) Fishing (2km) Hiking (1km) Railway station (20km) Shops (3km) MONTBAZON (20km) **NOTES:** Pets admitted English spoken

VERNOU-SUR-BRENNE

🎏 🍽 Château de Jallanges FERRY-BALIN
Vernou-sur-Brenne, 37210 VOUVRAY
☎ 02 47 52 06 66 📠 02 47 52 11 18
e-mail: info@chateaudejallanges.fr
www.chateaudejallanges.fr
In Vouvray wine country between Tours and Amboise, right in the middle of the Loire Valley and the most beautiful châteaux. Two suites for two to five people and four rooms in a château built by Louis XI in 1460. The rooms have period furnishings and open fires, and look out over a 25ha park. Private bathrooms and wcs. Minibar. Lounge for use of guests. Changing exhibitions, billiards, park, French Renaissance garden. In the grounds: swimming pool, winetasting, sales of wine, rides in horse-drawn carriages, hot-air ballooning, croquet, cycles. Airport 9 km.
PRICES: s €110-€175; d €110-€175; t €150-€215; extra person €40; dinner €45 **ON SITE:** Children's play area Swimming pool
NEARBY: Horse riding (10km) Golf (12km) Fishing (2km) Hiking (1km) Tennis (2km) Railway station (6km) Shops (2km) VOUVRAY (16km) **NOTES:** Pets admitted CC English spoken

La Paqueraie
37230 Saint Branchs/Cormery
Tel: 02 47 26 31 51   Fax: 02 47 26 39 15
Email: monique.binet@wanadoo.fr
Web site: http://perso.wanadoo.fr/lapaqueraie/

This lovely house designed by your hosts Monique and François Binet features old-fashioned tiling and is situated in its own grounds of trees and flowers. Inside Monique Binet's refined decoration and elegance has created four individual en-suite bedrooms. Before dinner, enjoy an aperitif by the fireplace in winter or on the patio beside the swimming pool in warmer months. Table decoration, haute cuisine and wine knowledge are further talents of your hosts. During your stay attend cookery classes run by your host, Monique or visit and learn about wine at local winegrowers.

🎏 Ferme des Landes Geneviève BELLANGER
Vallée de Cousse, 37210 VERNOU-SUR-BRENNE
☎ 02 47 52 10 93 📠 02 47 52 08 88
In a 15th-century farmhouse, with antique furniture, four independent ground floor rooms and two first floor rooms with private bathrooms and wcs. Three double rooms, two twin rooms and a room for four.
PRICES: s €41; d €50-€67 **NEARBY:** Fishing (7km) Swimming pool (7km) Hiking (1km) Tennis (7km) Railway station (15km) Shops (3km) VOUVRAY (15km) **NOTES:** Pets admitted

VOUVRAY

🎏 Domaine des Bidaudières
Pascal et Sylvie SUZANNE
Rue du Peu Morier, 37210 VOUVRAY
☎ 02 47 52 66 85 📠 02 47 52 62 17
e-mail: infohote@bidaudieres.com www.bidaudieres.com
Six luxury air-conditioned rooms on the second floor (with lift) of an 18th-century castle on a 12-hectare estate, an old vineyard on the open hillside south of Vouvray. Four double rooms, one triple room and one twin, all with bathroom and wc. Television lounge for guests. Large underground room for weddings and receptions. Park with large private swimming pool and terraces.
PRICES: s €75; d €105-€120; t €120; extra person €15
ON SITE: Swimming pool **NEARBY:** Horse riding (3km) Fishing (2km) Tennis (2km) Railway station (12km) Shops (2km) VOUVRAY (2km) **NOTES:** No pets English spoken

LOIRET

BRAY-EN-VAL

††† Les Saules Monique et Jacques BEZIN
18,rue des jardins du Coulouis, 45460 BRAY-EN-VAL
☎ 02 38 29 08 90
Between Loire and the Forest of Orléans, this old restored
property offers three elegant guest rooms with private bath or
shower room. There are two doubles on the ground floor, and
one large room on the first floor has a double and two single
beds. A cot or an extra single bed can be installed. Lounge and
billiard room, terraces with garden furniture, walks in the wooded
and landscaped park (3 hectares) crossed by a river. Picnics
possible, central heating, locked car park. Open all year.
PRICES: s €37-€46; d €44-€54; extra person €14 **ON SITE:** Fishing
Stretch of water Hiking **NEARBY:** Horse riding (2km) Forest (1km) Golf
(12km) Swimming pool (8km) Place of interest (4km) Railway station
(35km) SULLY-SUR-LOIRE (7km) **NOTES:** Pets admitted

BRETEAU

††† ♥ ⏀ la Chenauderie Brigitte ROBILLIART
45250 BRETEAU
☎ 02 38 31 97 88 📠 02 38 29 69 38
On a working farm, this converted barn offers five spacious guest
rooms, close to the Puisaye lakes (fishing). There is a large dining
room and lounge on the ground floor, plus a bedroom equipped
for guests with disabilities, with private shower room and wc. On
the first floor, there is a room with a double and two single beds,
bathroom and wc, plus three bedrooms with four singles and two
double beds; each has its own shower room and wc. Garden
furniture. Table d'hôte meals available on reservation.
PRICES: s €35; d €43; t €52; extra person €9; dinner €16
ON SITE: Fishing Hiking **NEARBY:** Horse riding (5km) Swimming pool
(3km) Place of interest (25km) Railway station (25km) Shops (3km)
BRIARE (15km) **NOTES:** Pets admitted English spoken

BRIARE

††† Domaine de la Thiau
Benedicte FRANCOIS-DUCLUZEAU
la Thiau, 45250 BRIARE
☎ 02 38 38 20 92 📠 02 38 67 40 50
e-mail: lathiau@club-internet.fr perso.club-internet.fr/lathiau

Between Gien and Briare, this 18th-century, Mansart-style house,
close to the owners' home, is set in a three-hectare landscaped
park, 300m from the Loire, accessed by a private lane. Ground
floor: large room with kitchen, private bathroom and wc, one
double bed, one single bed (an extra single bed can be installed)
and a fireplace. First floor: three rooms with a double and a single
bed, private bathroom and wc. Lounge (TV, books and games),
washing machine, tennis, table tennis, children's play area. Two
mountain bikes available for hire. Pets 5 euros/day. 10% reduction
for stays of three nights or more.

PRICES: s €40-€53; d €44-€57; t €57-€73; extra person €13
ON SITE: Children's play area Forest Fishing Hiking **NEARBY:** Horse
riding (6km) Golf (25km) Swimming pool (4km) Stretch of water (20km)
Place of interest (4km) Railway station (4km) Shops (4km) BRIARE (4km)
NOTES: Pets admitted English spoken

CHAILLY-EN-GATINAIS

††† ♥ Ferme du Grand Chesnoy
Benoist et Marie CHEVALIER
45260 CHAILLY-EN-GATINAIS
☎ 02 38 96 27 67 & 06 72 14 68 78 📠 02 38 96 27 67

This house is set in wooded grounds bordering the Orléans canal
(fishing possible), and is linked to the forest by footpaths. On the
first floor, a double room has a large bathroom with a view and a
wc. There is also a suite containing a double bed and a lounge
with a 100cm bed, shower room and wc. On the second floor, a
bedroom with a large double bed benefits from a dual aspect
south and west, a large bathroom with a view and a wc. There is a
further room with twin beds and a dual aspect north and west,
large bathroom with a view and a wc. Lounge/dining room,
billiards room. Table d'hôtes meals possible, sometimes served in
the garden. Open all year (from 1 November to 31 March by
reservation).
PRICES: s €46; d €53; t €69 **ON SITE:** Forest Fishing Hiking
NEARBY: Horse riding (6km) Golf (25km) Swimming pool (7km)
Stretch of water (6km) Place of interest (24km) Railway station (20km)
Shops (6km) LORRIS (6km) **NOTES:** No pets English spoken

CHATILLON-SUR-LOIRE

††† Les Brulis Robert et Micheline EDMET
45360 CHATILLON SUR LOIRE
☎ 02 38 31 42 33
Three guest rooms are offered at this renovated rural property,
peacefully set close to the banks of the Loire, Gien and the
Sancerrois. Ground floor: twin room with private separate shower
and wc. First floor: two double rooms with private shower and wc.
Guests have use of a lounge/dining room, kitchenette, TV and
telephone. Garden furniture. Use of owners' swimming pool.
PRICES: s €35; d €44 **ON SITE:** Swimming pool Hiking
NEARBY: Horse riding (6km) Forest (12km) Golf (6km) Fishing (6km)
Place of interest (30km) Railway station (12km) Shops (6km) CHATILLON-
SUR-LOIRE (6km) **NOTES:** Pets admitted

CHAUSSY

††† ⏀ Château de Chaussy
Yan et Genevieve HAENTJENS
2, place du Chateau, 45480 CHAUSSY
☎ 02 38 39 36 98 & 06 12 63 74 26 📠 02 38 39 36 98
e-mail: genevieve-haentjens @ free.fr
This 17th-century residence is situated on the Châteaudun-
Pithiviers road, 5km from Toury in Eure-et-Loir. On the first floor,
there is a two-room suite with a double and a single bed, private

continued

continued

bathroom and wc. There are four further rooms (two of which are awaiting classification) in converted outbuildings with private wc and bath or shower room. Private pool, table d'hôte meals on reservation. Dogs 4.5 euros. Open all year.
PRICES: s €43; d €56-€59; t €64-€69; dinner €18 **ON SITE:** Forest Hiking **NEARBY:** Horse riding (15km) Railway station (5km) Shops (7km) OUTARVILLE (7km) **NOTES:** Pets admitted English spoken

CHECY

🏙 Les Courtils Annie MEUNIER
rue de l'Avé, 45430 CHECY
☎ 02 38 91 32 02 📠 02 38 91 48 20
e-mail: les.courtils@wanadoo.fr
In the church square of a little village, this old renovated barn offers three guest rooms, one of which is on the ground floor. This room offers a double bed, seating, bathroom and wc. There are two rooms on the first floor, one with twin beds (two additional beds can be installed), bathroom and wc, and one with a double bed, bathroom and wc. An extra double room with a bathroom and wc is also available. Reception room with fireplace. Terrace, enclosed, wooded garden, views of the canal and the Loire. Restaurants nearby.
PRICES: s €38; d €49; t €64; extra person €15 **ON SITE:** Fishing Stretch of water Hiking **NEARBY:** Horse riding (5km) Forest (6km) Golf (6km) Swimming pool (5km) Place of interest (10km) Railway station (10km) ORLEANS (10km) **NOTES:** No pets English spoken

CHEVANNES

🏙 🍽 Le Village Olivier TANT
45210 CHEVANNES
☎ 02 38 90 92 23 & 06 11 84 99 20
Mireille and Olivier welcome guests to their old renovated farmhouse in a small Gâtinais village, just one hour from Paris. There are three guest rooms in this detached house: one on the ground floor with a double and a single bed, and on the first floor, one room with a double and a single bed, plus a single bed on a mezzanine level, and one room with a double and a single bed. Each room has a private shower room and wc. Child's bed by request. Communal lounge with fireplace. Table d'hôte meals on reservation. Garden furniture. Open all year.
PRICES: s €28; d €35; t €45; extra person €10; dinner €14 **ON SITE:** Forest Fishing Hiking **NEARBY:** Horse riding (12km) Swimming pool (5km) Place of interest (5km) Railway station (5km) Shops (3km) FERRIERES EN GATINAIS (8km) **NOTES:** Pets admitted English spoken

COULLONS

🏙 Gault Jean-Luc RAFFIN
45720 COULLONS
☎ 02 38 67 59 77
Set in three hectares, this ancient farm dates back to the Second Empire. On the ground floor: three double rooms (grade 2) with private bathroom and shared wc. On the first floor: one large, very comfortable room for four people (grade 3) with private bathroom and wc. Dining room and lounge area, TV. Picnic area, garden furniture. Private lake - fishing possible. Open all year.
PRICES: s €29; d €37-€52; t €58 **ON SITE:** Fishing Hiking **NEARBY:** Horse riding (6km) Forest (10km) Place of interest (10km) Railway station (10km) Shops (5km) GIEN (10km) **NOTES:** Pets admitted

DONNERY

🏙 Cornella Jacques AVRIL
27 rue de Vennecy, 45450 DONNERY
☎ 02 38 59 26 74 📠 02 38 59 29 69

Just 700m from the village, this ancient renovated farm has a stylish, rustic atmosphere. Ground floor: double room with private shower room and wc. First floor: twin room with child's bed, private bathroom and wc. Garden. Open all year.
PRICES: s €37; d €44; extra person €16 **ON SITE:** Forest Hiking **NEARBY:** Horse riding (3km) Fishing (1km) Place of interest (10km) Railway station (16km) Shops (1km) ORLEANS (17km) **NOTES:** No pets

🏙 🌿 🍽 La Poterie Dominique CHARLES
45450 DONNERY
☎ 02 38 59 20 03 📠 02 38 57 04 47
e-mail: lapoteriecharles@wanadoo.fr
Close to the Orléans forest and canal, this working farm is on the D709 between Donnery and Fay-aux-Loges. It offers two doubles and one triple room, each with private shower room and wc. A living room with kitchenette is available, as are table d'hôte meals on reservation. Reduction for more than four nights. Open all year.
PRICES: s €31; d €40; t €49; extra person €9; dinner €15 **ON SITE:** Golf Fishing Hiking **NEARBY:** Horse riding (3km) Forest (10km) Stretch of water (12km) Place of interest (10km) Railway station (20km) Shops (1km) ORLEANS (18km) **NOTES:** No pets English spoken

FAY-AUX-LOGES

🏙 Herbault Dominique SONNEVILLE
route de Vitry-aux-Loges, 45450 FAY-AUX-LOGES
☎ 02 38 59 21 18
Four guest rooms in an ancient building at the end of the village, in a rural, peaceful setting. Herbault is close to the Forest of Orléans and a few kilometres from the Loire (Vitry road). On the ground floor there is a large breakfast room with lounge area. On the first floor: one double room, one twin room and two rooms with a double and a single bed. Each has its own shower room and wc. Picnics possible; restaurant in the village. Open all year.
PRICES: s €38; d €46; t €53 **ON SITE:** Horse riding Forest Hiking **NEARBY:** Golf (1km) Fishing (1km) Swimming pool (1km) Stretch of water (5km) Place of interest (20km) Railway station (20km) Shops (1km) ORLEANS (23km) **NOTES:** No pets English spoken

FEROLLES

🏙 🍽 Chambre d'hôtes Susan DE SMET
8, route du Martroi, la Breteche, 45150 FEROLLES
☎ 02 38 59 79 53
Newly built house in a very tranquil village. On the first floor there is a double room in which an additional double bed can be installed, and on the ground floor, there is a twin room and a separate room with a double bed (extra bed possible). Each room has a private shower room and wc. Large, enclosed, tree-lined garden. Table d'hôte meals on reservation (13 euros per person). Open all year.
PRICES: s €28; d €40; t €50; extra person €11; dinner €13 **NEARBY:** Horse riding (5km) Forest (10km) Golf (6km) Fishing (10km) Swimming pool (10km) Hiking (3km) Place of interest (15km) Railway station (20km) Shops (4km) ORLEANS (16km) **NOTES:** No pets English spoken

GERMIGNY-DES-PRES

🏙 🍽 Chambre d'hôtes Marie et Laurent KOPP
28, route de Chateauneuf, 45110 GERMIGNY-DES-PRES
☎ 02 38 58 21 15 📠 02 38 58 21 15
e-mail: marie.kopp@free.fr www.kopp.fr
In a small Ligérien village, famous for its Carolingian Oratory, five very peaceful bedrooms for 2-4 people, with single and/or double beds. Extra beds can be arranged, and each room has a private bathroom and wc. Situated in an adjoining building, the rooms open onto a large landscaped garden (French windows on the

continued

continued

ground floor). Guests may use the barbecue, the garden furniture, children's games and the equipped kitchen. In the lounge: books, games and TV. There is an exhibition of local artists on site. Private parking. Excellent restaurant 200m away. Table d'hôte meals from October to March on reservation. Open all year.

PRICES: s €34; d €43; t €50; extra person €8; dinner €13
ON SITE: Children's play area Fishing Hiking Place of interest
NEARBY: Horse riding (4km) Forest (2km) Golf (15km) Swimming pool (4km) Stretch of water (15km) Railway station (30km) Shops (1km) CHATEAUNEUF-SUR-LOIRE (5km) **NOTES:** No pets English spoken

LA BUSSIERE

¶¶¶ La Chesnaye Madeleine & Marcel MARTIN-DENIS
45230 LA BUSSIERE
☎ 02 38 35 99 39
Four spacious rooms, including two suites, are available at the little Château de la Chesnaye, a 19th-century building. First floor: two double rooms, two bathrooms, one of which has a spa bath, and private wc in each room. Second floor: two suites, each with two double beds, bathroom and wc. There is also one grade 2 room with private bathroom and wc on the landing.
PRICES: d €61; t €53; extra person €23 **NEARBY:** Horse riding (10km) Forest (10km) Golf (15km) Fishing (1km) Stretch of water (10km) Hiking (10km) Place of interest (1km) Railway station (10km) Shops (1km) GIEN (12km) **NOTES:** Pets admitted

LA FERTE SAINT-AUBIN

¶¶¶ La Vieille Forêt Marie-Françoise RAVENEL
route de Jouy le Potier, 45240 LA FERTE-SAINT-AUBIN
☎ 02 38 76 57 20 📠 02 38 64 82 80
Peace and comfort await guests in this old renovated farmhouse in the heart of the countryside. Ideal base from which to visit the châteaux of the Loire and to discover the delights of the Sologne. There are two bedrooms and two family bedrooms in the converted outbuildings, each with independent access, private bathroom and wc. Kitchen and communal room available. Cot on request. Garden with furniture. Walks and fishing on site. Open all year.
PRICES: s €34; d €42; t €50; extra person €11 **ON SITE:** Forest Fishing Stretch of water Hiking **NEARBY:** Horse riding (5km) Golf (1km) Swimming pool (5km) Place of interest (5km) Railway station (5km) Shops (5km) ORLEANS (20km) **NOTES:** No pets English spoken

¶¶¶¶ Le Château Catherine GUYOT
45240 LA FERTE SAINT-AUBIN
☎ 02 38 76 52 72 📠 02 38 64 67 43
Period-furnished bedrooms on the first floor of a 17th-century château. The 18th-century bedroom-suite has views of the park, private bathroom and wc. The 17th-century room has a four-poster bed, views of the gardens and courtyard, private bathroom and wc. Another room shares these views and has a bed which dates back to the 19th century. This historic private château and 40-hectare park is open to the public between 10am and 7pm. Chambres d'hotes open 1 May to 30 September.
PRICES: d €91-€170; t €230 **ON SITE:** Fishing Place of interest **NEARBY:** Horse riding (10km) Forest (1km) Golf (2km) Swimming pool (5km) Hiking (1km) Railway station (1km) Shops (1km) LA FERTE SAINT-AUBIN (1km) **NOTES:** Pets admitted

---

🍽
Places with this symbol serve table d'hôtes evening meals - remember to book in advance

---

LORCY

¶¶¶ La Petite Cour Danielle DE MERSAN
15, rue de la Mairie, 45490 LORCY
☎ 02 38 92 20 76 📠 02 38 92 91 97
e-mail: la_petite_cour@yahoo.fr www.la-petite-cour.com
At the centre of a little village between the Forest of Orléans and Montargis, this 18th-century, typically Gâtinais house adjoins a 'maison bourgeoise'. The three elegant bedrooms comprise one first-floor room with a large double and a single bed, bathroom and wc, and two ground-floor double rooms, one of which also has a single bed on a mezzanine floor. Each room has a private bath or shower room and wc. Dining room, lounge and TV available. Bikes can be borrowed. Private parking. Garden furniture.
PRICES: s €48-€58; d €55-€66; t €68-€79; extra person €13
ON SITE: Hiking **NEARBY:** Horse riding (10km) Forest (15km) Golf (29km) Fishing (8km) Swimming pool (12km) Stretch of water (20km) Place of interest (12km) Railway station (25km) BEAUNE-LA-ROLANDE (10km) **NOTES:** Pets admitted English spoken

MARIGNY-LES-USAGES

¶¶¶ Les Usses Kris et Jean-Claude MARIN
145, rue du Courtasaule, 45760 MARIGNY-LES-USAGES
☎ 02 38 75 14 77 📠 02 38 75 90 65
e-mail: Kris.marin@wanadoo.fr
In a building adjoining the owners' home, this chambre d'hôtes offers three spacious double rooms on the first floor, each with private bathroom and wc and direct-dial telephones. Two additional single beds can be installed in the library. On the ground floor there is a large dining room with kitchenette. Baby equipment can be supplied on request.
PRICES: s €45; d €50; t €59; extra person €9 **ON SITE:** Hiking **NEARBY:** Horse riding (1km) Forest (8km) Golf (8km) Fishing (4km) Swimming pool (8km) Stretch of water (12km) Place of interest (12km) Railway station (12km) Shops (1km) ORLEANS (12km) **NOTES:** No pets

MENESTREAU-EN-VILLETTE

¶¶¶¶ La Ferme des Foucault Rosemary BEAU
les Foucault, 45240 MENESTREAU-EN-VILLETTE
☎ 02 38 76 94 41 📠 02 38 76 94 41
Very comfortable accommodation in the heart of the Sologne forest, in a beautiful and peaceful setting. There is a ground-floor suite with two double beds, lounge and fireplace, TV and independent access, private bathroom and wc. On the first floor, there are two very large double bedrooms (extra bed possible), one of which has a private terrace, with TV, private bathroom and wc. Large, verdant grounds with many walks nearby. Garden furniture. Animals accepted with prior agreement. Open all year.
PRICES: s €54-€63; d €60-€69; extra person €16 **ON SITE:** Forest Fishing Hiking **NEARBY:** Horse riding (10km) Golf (8km) Swimming pool (7km) Stretch of water (8km) Place of interest (15km) Railway station (15km) Shops (7km) LA FERTE SAINT-AUBIN (15km) **NOTES:** Pets admitted English spoken

MEUNG-SUR-LOIRE

¶¶¶ Chambre d'hôtes Raymonde BECHU
30 rue de la Batissière, hameau de la Nivelle,
45130 MEUNG SUR LOIRE
☎ 02 38 44 34 38 📠 02 38 44 34 38
In a very peaceful hamlet, this house is surrounded by a tree and flower-lined garden. On the ground floor, there is a twin room with private facilities, while the first floor offers a double room with an adjoining children's room (twin beds), both sharing a bathroom and wc. TV aerial in each room. Large terrace, garden

continued

with furniture, bicycle hire. Discounted tariff after two nights. Open all year.
PRICES: s €30; d €40 **ON SITE:** Fishing Hiking **NEARBY:** Horse riding (3km) Golf (10km) Swimming pool (3km) Stretch of water (10km) Place of interest (3km) Railway station (3km) Shops (3km) ORLEANS (17km) **NOTES:** Pets admitted

MONTLIARD

♦♦♦♦ ⃝ Château de Montliard
Annick et François GALIZIA
5, route de Nesploy, 45340 MONTLIARD
☎ 02 38 33 71 40 ⃞ 02 38 33 86 41
e-mail: a.galizia@infonie.fr
www.France-bonjour.com/montliard/

Surrounded by moats and a 14-hectare park, at the edge of the Forest of Orléans and 100 km from Paris, this château has belonged to the same family since 1384. The four very comfortable and spacious guest rooms are on the first floor; each room has stacks of character, elegant décor, private shower or bathroom and wc, plus baby things if required. Prepare to be enchanted by the charm, peace and authenticity of this place - a great place to relax and unwind. Park, bicycles, table tennis, games, TV, etc. Stables and kennels. Babies free. Close to several châteaux. Open all year (winter on reservation).
PRICES: s €46-€61; d €59-€84; t €69-€99; extra person €15; dinner €18-€26 **ON SITE:** Fishing Stretch of water Hiking **NEARBY:** Horse riding (3km) Forest (1km) Golf (25km) Swimming pool (5km) Place of interest (15km) Railway station (25km) Shops (2km) BELLEGARDE (5km) **NOTES:** Pets admitted Minimum 2 night stay English spoken

NEVOY

♦♦♦ ⃝ Sainte-Barbe Annie LE LAY
45500 NEVOY
☎ 02 38 67 59 53 ⃞ 02 38 67 28 96
e-mail: annielelay@aol.com
www.france-bonjour.com/sainte-barbe/
Overlooking the garden, this 19th-century rural property has lots of character. The first-floor guest rooms comprise one large double room (extra single bed possible) with private bathroom and wc, one double room with private bathroom and wc, and one single room with private shower room and wc. Independent entrance. On the ground floor there is a reception room and a lounge with TV. Tennis courts on site.
PRICES: s €34-€42; d €58; t €70; extra person €12; dinner €23-€30 **ON SITE:** Forest Fishing Swimming pool Hiking **NEARBY:** Horse riding (9km) Place of interest (3km) Railway station (3km) Shops (3km) GIEN (3km) **NOTES:** No pets English spoken

> Ask the proprietor for directions
> when booking

PAUCOURT

♦♦♦ ⃝ Bel Ebat A et E DE JESSE CHARLEVAL
191, allée de Bel Ebat, 45200 PAUCOURT
☎ 02 38 98 38 47 ⃞ 02 38 85 66 43
This property offers three guest rooms and a suite, all with private bathrooms. Breakfast includes fresh fruit juice, pastries and home-made jams, and table d'hôte meals feature *cuisine bourgeoise* (terrines, soufflés, etc.). TV, telephone, games room. Golf, swimming pool, tennis, mountain bikes, forest, horses, fishing, hunting. Three-hectare park. Discover the Sologne and the châteaux of the Loire, as well as historic monuments and the Sancerre and Chablis vineyards. Open all year.
PRICES: s €95; d €115; t €125; dinner €35 **ON SITE:** Horse riding **NEARBY:** Forest (5km) Golf (5km) Fishing (10km) Swimming pool (5km) Hiking (5km) Place of interest (6km) Railway station (4km) Shops (7km) MONTARGIS (5km) **NOTES:** No pets English spoken

ST-BENOIT-SUR-LOIRE

♦♦♦ ⤙ ⃝ Chambre d'hôtes Dom. et Mireille BOUIN
6 chemin de la Borde, 45730 ST BENOIT SUR LOIRE
☎ 02 38 35 70 53 ⃞ 02 38 35 10 06
e-mail: Mireille-Dominique.BOUIN@wanadoo.fr
http://www.france-bonjour.com/la-borde/

This chambre d'hôtes is located on a cereal farm between Sully-sur-Loire and Saint-Benoît. On the ground floor there are two twin rooms with private shower room and wc. On the first floor, there is a room with three single beds and a room with twin beds, also with private shower room and wc. In a separate house in the garden there is level access to a suite with four single beds, private bathroom and wc, and a twin room equipped for guests with disabilities, with shower room and wc. Reception room and equipped kitchen available. Pleasant tree-lined garden with vegetable patch and garden furniture. Bikes may be hired or borrowed free-of-charge if staying for a weekend or longer. Open all year.
PRICES: s €37-€40; d €43-€46; t €61-€76; extra person €16; dinner €16 **ON SITE:** Hiking **NEARBY:** Horse riding (6km) Forest (10km)⁺ Golf (12km) Fishing (2km) Swimming pool (7km) Stretch of water (20km) Place of interest (2km) Railway station (25km) Shops (2km) SULLY-SUR-LOIRE (6km) **NOTES:** Pets admitted

TAVERS

♦♦♦ ⃝ Le Clos de Pontpierre Patricia FOURNIER
115, rue des Eaux Bleues, 45190 TAVERS
☎ 02 38 44 56 85 ⃞ 02 38 44 58 94
e-mail: le.clos.de.pontpierre@wanadoo.fr
www.france-bonjour.com/clos-de-pontpierre/
Peacefully set in the Loire Valley, this renovated 18th-century farm offers four pleasant, restful guest rooms with independent access and views over the park. Ground floor: one twin room and one room with a double and a single bed. First floor: one double room and one room with a double and two single beds plus lounge

continued

CENTRAL FRANCE *(side margin)*

area. Each room has a TV, and private shower room and wc. Lounge with antique furnishings. Shady, flower-filled park. Use of bicycles and owners' swimming pool. Table tennis, garden furniture. Meals on reservation (except Sunday) prepared by Pierre, a professional chef. Locked parking. Open all year.

PRICES: s €40-€46; d €53; t €66; extra person €12; dinner €18 **ON SITE:** Forest Swimming pool Hiking **NEARBY:** Horse riding (10km) Golf (10km) Fishing (2km) Stretch of water (2km) Place of interest (2km) Railway station (2km) BEAUGENCY (2km) **NOTES:** No pets English spoken   *See advert on opposite page*

VANNES-SUR-COSSON

▦ ΙΟΙ **Chambre d'hôtes** Aleth NICOURT
6, rue de la Croix Madeleine, 45510 VANNES-SUR-COSSON
☎ 02 38 58 15 43
This house, typical of the Sologne, offers one double room with bathroom and wc, one room with a double and a single bed, shower room and wc, and one twin room with shower and wc. Communal lounge with fireplace. Garden and terrace. Table d'hôte meals on request. Open all year.

PRICES: s €35; d €40; t €49; dinner €11-€15 **ON SITE:** Forest Fishing Hiking Place of interest **NEARBY:** Horse riding (25km) Golf (10km) Swimming pool (15km) Stretch of water (15km) Railway station (34km) SULLY-SUR-LOIRE (15km) **NOTES:** Pets admitted

LOIR-ET-CHER

AZE

▦ ❦ ΙΟΙ **Ferme de Crislaine** Christian GUELLIER
41100 AZE
☎ 02 54 72 14 09 & SR : 02 54 58 81 64   02 54 72 18 03
Five rooms on the farm with independent access (10 minutes from TGV station). On the ground floor: 1 family room; three double rooms; one twin. Possible extra bed for each room. All have wc, shower and washbasin. Mezzanine with television, opening on to communal room with cooking area. For families with young children there are nursery facilities. In the orchard there is an open swimming pool. Pétanque, outdoor furniture, bikes, mountain bikes, taxis, farming activities (dairy and organic farming). Meals if booked, €16 (not Sunday). Family room (two to four people) €53/four people.

PRICES: s €29; d €36-€37; t €44; extra person €5; dinner €16 **ON SITE:** Children's play area Swimming pool Hiking Bicycle hire **NEARBY:** Horse riding (3km) Forest (1km) Golf (20km) Fishing (3km) Water sports (7km) Tennis (3km) Railway station (6km) Shops (3km) VENDOME (9km) **NOTES:** Pets admitted

▦ ❦ ΙΟΙ **La Ferme des Gourmets**
Michel et Nadège BOULAI
Gorgeat, 41100 AZE
☎ 02 54 72 04 16 & SR : 02 54 58 81 64   02 54 72 04 94
e-mail: michel.boulai@wanadoo.fr
http://perso.wanadoo.fr/gorgeat
This organic farm with pigs, chickens & cereals is located on the edge of the forest, 3km from the TGV station (owner can organise lifts). Organic produce on sale. Three double rooms (140cm beds) and two family rooms, all with shower and wc. One room with balneotherapy bath. Living room with cooking area for guests. Possible spa break, with organic food. Meals if booked. Animals by prior arrangement. Tariff: four guests €53. 10% reduction for stays longer than a week. Open all year.

PRICES: s €29-€31; d €36-€46; t €44; extra person €8; dinner €15 **ON SITE:** Forest Fishing Hiking Tennis Bicycle hire **NEARBY:** Horse riding (1km) Golf (20km) Swimming pool (5km) Water sports (4km) Railway station (3km) Shops (2km) VENDOME (9km) **NOTES:** Pets admitted English spoken

BOURRE

▦ **Manoir de la Salle** Patricia BOUSSARD
69 route de Vierzon, Domaine de la Salle du Roc,
41400 BOURRE
☎ 02 54 32 73 54 & SR : 02 54 58 81 64   02 54 32 47 09
In the heart of the Cher Valley, four rooms in an 18th-century manor house. Upstairs: two rooms (140cm beds) with private bathroom facilities; one large room with bathroom, dressing room, wc. On the ground floor: a suite of two double rooms with private facilities. Open all year.

PRICES: s €60; d €70-€110 **ON SITE:** Fishing Tennis **NEARBY:** Horse riding (10km) Swimming pool (4km) Water sports (10km) Bicycle hire (4km) Railway station (3km) Shops (4km) MONTRICHARD (5km) **NOTES:** No pets English spoken

CANDE-SUR-BEUVRON

▦ ❦ **Le Court au Jay** MARSEAULT
41120 CANDE-SUR-BEUVRON
☎ 02 54 44 03 13   02 54 44 03 13
In a farmhouse, one room for three (double and single bed) shower and wc. Upstairs: one double room with bath and wc; one twin room with shower and wc. Possible extra bed for each room (€8). Central heating; dried flower workshop. 10% discount on stays longer than seven days, 20% discount for one month. Tariff: €58/four guests. Open all year.

PRICES: s €32-€35; d €35-€38; t €43-€50; extra person €8 **ON SITE:** Forest Fishing Bicycle hire **NEARBY:** Horse riding (1km) Fishing (1km) Swimming pool (16km) Water sports (16km) Tennis (1km) Railway station (10km) Shops (1km) BLOIS (16km) **NOTES:** No pets

CHATEAUVIEUX

▦ **La Pouarderie** VENISSE
41110 CHATEAUVIEUX
☎ 02 54 75 32 23   02 54 75 06 53
e-mail: yves.venisse@wanadoo.fr
http://www.geocities.com/avenisse/
Amidst the pines in an old restored farmhouse, three guest rooms with separate access, one for persons with reduced mobility (double bed). Two rooms for three or four (double and twin beds) with shower and wc. Cot, high chair and baby bath available. Large living room with cooking corner. Open fire and barbecue. Extensive green space. Beauval Zoo 1km. Tariff: €59/four guests. Open all year.

PRICES: s €35; d €40; t €49; extra person €10 **ON SITE:** Hiking **NEARBY:** Horse riding (4km) Forest (2km) Golf (30km) Fishing (3km) Swimming pool (4km) Water sports (5km) Tennis (4km) Bicycle hire (4km) Railway station (5km) Shops (4km) SAINT AIGNAN SUR CHER (4km) **NOTES:** No pets English spoken

CHAUMONT-SUR-LOIRE

▦ **Les Hauts de Chaumont** Daniel GOMBART
2 rue des Argillons, 41150 CHAUMONT-SUR-LOIRE
☎ 02 54 33 91 45 & SR : 02 54 58 81 64   02 54 33 91 45
e-mail: gombart@free.fr
http://www.france-bonjour.com/hauts-de-chaumont/
100m from the Château de Chaumont, Loire and the International Garden Festival. Three upstairs rooms with shower and wc, two doubles and one twin. On the ground floor: living room for guests with breakfast tables, kitchenette, television/video recorder, open fire, piano, board games. Swimming pool. Terraces. Table tennis. Private parking. Cycle hire. Special price for one or two people out of season (November to March). €43 for two people for stays greater than 3 nights. Open all year.

PRICES: s €47; d €47; extra person €12 **ON SITE:** Swimming pool Hiking Tennis Bicycle hire **NEARBY:** Horse riding (1km) Forest (15km) Golf (5km) Fishing (1km) Railway station (4km) BLOIS (20km) **NOTES:** No pets

CHAUMONT-SUR-THARONNE

La Farge DE GRANGENEUVE
41600 CHAUMONT-SUR-THARONNE
☎ 02 54 88 52 06 🖷 02 54 88 51 36
e-mail: SylvieLansier@wanadoo.fr
http://www.france-bonjour.com/la-farge/
A house of character in a 40ha wooded park. On the ground floor: one double room with bath and wc; one suite of two rooms (one double bed, two singles) with bath, shower and wc; one three-person flat (double bed and sofabed) with living room with open fire, kitchen and television. Possible evening meal. Swimming pool. Horseriding. Animals accepted with prior booking. Tariff: flat €69/76. €76/four persons. Open all year.
PRICES: d €53-€69; t €76; extra person €12 **ON SITE:** Horse riding Forest Swimming pool Hiking **NEARBY:** Golf (5km) Fishing (5km) Tennis (5km) Bicycle hire (5km) Railway station (10km) Shops (5km) LAMOTTE BEUVRON **NOTES:** Pets admitted English spoken

CHEVERNY

Ferme des Saules Didier MERLIN
41700 CHEVERNY
☎ 02 54 79 26 95 🖷 02 54 79 97 54
e-mail: merlin.cheverny@infonie.fr
2km from the Château at Cheverny, in an area of forest and open countryside. Six guest rooms with bath and wc. Four double bedrooms (two with 160cm beds), and two twin rooms. Extra child's bed available. Dinner, booking required, Friday, Saturday and Monday, with local produce prepared by the owner who is a chef. Restaurants 1.8km. Swimming pool. Tariff: €89/four persons. Open all year.
PRICES: d €55-€75; t €78; dinner €22 **ON SITE:** Forest Golf Fishing Swimming pool Hiking **NEARBY:** Horse riding (5km) Water sports (10km) Tennis (5km) Bicycle hire (5km) Railway station (20km) Shops (2km) BLOIS **NOTES:** No pets English spoken

CHITENAY

Le Clos Dussons Roland BRAVO
Le Clos Bigot, 41120 CHITENAY
☎ 02 54 44 21 28 & 06 02 12 97 32 🖷 02 54 44 38 65
e-mail: clos.bigot@wanadoo.fr
http://www.multimania.com/closbigot
Surrounded by the Châteaux of the Loire, 6 km from Cheverny, a 17th-century property of considerable character, in a peaceful location. Three guest rooms with shower and wc. One double room, one suite for two or four people, and a flat for two to four in a 16th-century pigeon-loft. Lavish breakfasts. Many of restaurants nearby. Garden furniture. Monsieur Bravo, an architecture afficianado, will advise guests on visiting the châteaux in the area. Tariff: €96-117/four guests.
PRICES: ; d €44-€85; t €60-€101; extra person €16 **ON SITE:** Hiking **NEARBY:** Horse riding (1km) Forest (1km) Golf (6km) Fishing (5km) Swimming pool (15km) Water sports (15km) Tennis (2km) Bicycle hire (6km) Railway station (15km) Shops (2km) BLOIS (15km) **NOTES:** No pets English spoken

Le Clos de Pont-pierre
115 rue des Eaux Bleues
45190 Tavers

An ancient farm situated in the heart of the Loire valley renovated in the 18th C. Four spacious bedrooms with TV, heating and views of the park. The bedrooms are non-smoking and have separate entrances. The proprietor Pierre Fournier is a professional chef and prepares traditional cooking of the area. Breakfast and dinner can be taken on the terrace beside the swimming pool weather permitting. Open all year.

Tel: 02 38 44 56 85   Fax: 02 38 44 58 94
Email: le.closde.pontpierre@wanadoo.fr
Web: www.france-bonjour.com/clos-de-pontpierre/
www.coeur-de-France.com/hebergement-fournier.html

CONTRES

La Rabouillère Martine THIMONNIER
Chemin de Marcon, 41700 CONTRES
☎ 02 54 79 05 14 & SR : 02 54 58 81 64 🖷 02 54 79 59 39
e-mail: rabouillere@wanadoo.fr
http://rabouillere.ifrance.com/
In Châteaux country, near Cheverny this is a typical house of the area, situated within a park. Four rooms (two doubles and two twins) with their own bath and wc. One suite in annexe for two people with 180cm bed, bathroom, wc, and living room with open fire. Sitting room. Communal kitchen shared between two rooms. Restaurant 3km. Tariff: €122/four guests. Open all year.
PRICES: s €46; d €55-€107; t €99-€122; extra person €15
ON SITE: Bicycle hire **NEARBY:** Horse riding (20km) Forest (1km) Golf (6km) Fishing (10km) Swimming pool (3km) Hiking (1km) Water sports (20km) Tennis (3km) Railway station (25km) Shops (3km) BLOIS (20km) **NOTES:** No pets English spoken

COULOMMIERS-LA-TOUR

Chambre d'hôtes Patricia BLUET
15 rue Vendomoise, 41100 COULOMMIERS-LA-TOUR
☎ 02 54 77 00 33 🖷 02 54 77 00 33
Restored tower house 6km south-east of Vendome. Three upstairs rooms: one twin, one double, and one family room (one double and three single beds). Shower, washbasin and wc in each room. For the guests' use: a dining room, lounge with television and garden furniture. Indoor and outdoor games, table tennis, children's pedal go-karts. Baby facilities to hand. Cot: €5. Open all year.
PRICES: s €30; d €40; extra person €12 **ON SITE:** Children's play area Fishing Hiking **NEARBY:** Horse riding (6km) Forest (2km) Golf (10km) Swimming pool (6km) Fishing (6km) Tennis (1km) Railway station (7km) Shops (6km) VENDOME (6km) **NOTES:** No pets English spoken

COUR-CHEVERNY

¶¶¶ Le Beguinage Brice et Patricia DELOISON
41700 COUR-CHEVERNY
☎ 02 54 79 29 92 & SR : 02 54 58 81 64 🖷 02 54 79 94 59
e-mail: le.beguinage@wanadoo.fr
http://www.multimania.com/beguinage/
Close to the Château de Cheverny, in a house of character, six
guest rooms. One twin with cot; two rooms sleeping four (one
double bed plus two singles); three doubles. All have shower or
bath and wc. Large country park. Private parking. Fishing available
- the river is at the foot of the garden. Hot air ballooning from the grounds or locally, depending on
weather. Tariff: €77/84/four persons. Open all year.
PRICES: s €42-€49; d €45-€60; t €65-€69; extra person €16
ON SITE: Fishing Hiking Tennis Bicycle hire **NEARBY:** Horse riding
(5km) Forest (1km) Golf (3km) Swimming pool (2km) Water sports
(15km) Railway station (15km) BLOIS (15km) **NOTES:** Pets admitted
English spoken

CROUY-SUR-COSSON

¶¶¶ ꙮ Le Moulin de Crouy Nathalie HARRAULT
3 route de la Cordellerie, 41220 CROUY-SUR-COSSON
☎ 02 54 87 56 19 & SR : 02 54 58 81 64 🖷 02 54 87 51 61
e-mail: lemoulindecrouy@wanadoo.fr
Parc de Chamborg 10km. Ninety minutes from Paris, in a quiet
spot, four upstairs rooms in a mill, personally designed by the
owners who are interior decorators. A double with 160cm bed;
and two doubles with 140cm beds. All have shower or bath and
wc. Also a family suite on the second floor (one double bed, four
singles and a canopied bed). Very large living room with fireplace
and TV, opening onto a terrace. The 14ha park has a tennis court.
Meals may be booked. Tariff: €90/four persons. Open all year.
PRICES: s €45-€50; d €50-€55; extra person €13; dinner €18
ON SITE: Forest Fishing Hiking Tennis **NEARBY:** Horse riding (4km)
Swimming pool (8km) Railway station (20km) Shops (6km) BLOIS
(25km) **NOTES:** No pets

DANZE

¶¶¶ La Borde KAMETTE, La Borde, 41160 DANZE
☎ 02 54 80 68 42 🖷 02 54 80 63 68
e-mail: michelkamette@minitel.net http://www.la-borde.com

This house of much character is situated between Danzé and la Ville
aux Clercs, on a wooded estate of 10 hectares. Five very comfortable,
upstairs rooms each have a private shower and wc, and an extra bed
if required. Television lounge for guests. Garden furniture. Price
reduction over two nights. Tariff: €72/78/four persons. Open all year
PRICES: s €28-€39; d €37-€68; t €62-€68; extra person €10
ON SITE: Fishing Swimming pool **NEARBY:** Horse riding (7km) Forest
(3km) Golf (15km) Hiking (3km) Water sports (20km) Tennis (2km)
Bicycle hire (15km) Railway station (15km) Shops (2km) VENDOME
(15km) **NOTES:** No pets English spoken

ECOMAN

¶¶¶ ꙮ Château d'Ecoman Richard BIGOT/FONTAINE
11 - 13 rue de Châteaudun, 41290 ECOMAN
☎ 02 54 82 68 93 & SR : 02 54 58 81 64 🖷 02 54 82 00 66
e-mail: bigot-ecoman@club-internet.fr
http://www.chateau-decoman.fr
At the crossroads of Perche, la Beauce and la Sologne, a warm
welcome awaits at the Château d'Ecoman, a recently restored
19th-century house. Upstairs are four guest rooms: one suite with
two 140cm beds; one double for parents with children (two 140cm
beds) and two other double rooms. All have shower and wc. Extra
bed and cot available. Meals may be booked. Private parking.
Lounge area with television reserved for guests. The house is
surrounded by a 10ha park. Tariff: €99/four persons per night.
Open all year.
PRICES: s €49; d €53-€69; t €84; extra person €15; dinner €18
ON SITE: Forest Fishing Hiking Bicycle hire **NEARBY:** Horse riding
(25km) Golf (4km) Swimming pool (8km) Water sports (6km) Tennis
(3km) Railway station (27km) Shops (6km) VIEVY LE RAYE (4km)
NOTES: No pets

FAVEROLLES-SUR-CHER

¶¶¶ Chambre d'hôtes Christiane CORDIER
27 rue de la Clémencerie, 41400 FAVEROLLES-SUR-CHER
☎ 02 54 32 26 96 & SR : 02 54 58 81 64
e-mail: Christiane.CORDIER@wanadoo.fr
http://site.voila.fr/clemencerie
On the Wine Route, close to the Chenonceaux, Amboise and
Chaumont sur Loire, Christiane will be delighted to greet you.
Choose from a suite of two large rooms (double and a twin) with
antique furniture; one twin room and two double rooms. All have
bath or shower and wc. Living room and kitchenette for guests.
Parking. Garden furniture. Reduction for stays over three nights.
Tariff: €73/four persons. Open all year.
PRICES: s €32; d €39-€50; t €61; extra person €13 **ON SITE:** Children's
play area **NEARBY:** Horse riding (19km) Forest (6km) Golf (30km)
Fishing (2km) Swimming pool (4km) Hiking (1km) Water sports (4km)
Tennis (4km) Bicycle hire (5km) Railway station (5km) Shops (3km)
MONTRICHARD (3km) **NOTES:** No pets CC

FEINGS

¶¶¶ Le Petit Bois Martin PAPINEAU
Favras, 41120 FEINGS
☎ 02 54 20 27 31 & SR : 02 54 58 81 64 🖷 02 54 33 20 98
Only 15km from Blois - come and discover the Loire Valley, its
museums, its châteaux, its abbeys. An 18th-century house of
character offering one suite (double room and twin room, bath,
wc, television); one suite as before with shower; one double room
(shower, wc, television). Games room, kitchen area. Relish the
lavish breakfast with home-made preserves. Shady park. Cultural
events in summer (classical music concerts, historical re-
enactments, son et lumières). Tariff €70/four persons. Reduced
prices for more than three nights. Open 1 March to 15 November.
PRICES: s €38; d €43-€50; t €60; extra person €12 **ON SITE:** Fishing
NEARBY: Horse riding (7km) Forest (15km) Golf (8km) Swimming pool
(5km) Water sports (15km) Tennis (5km) Bicycle hire (7km) Railway
station (15km) Shops (5km) BLOIS (20km) **NOTES:** No pets

¶¶¶ Les Roseaux Jean et Gisèle LIONDOR
Favras, 41120 FEINGS
☎ 02 54 20 27 70 & SR : 02 54 58 81 64
On the Châteaux of the Loire route, 20km from Blois, on an old
wine estate. Two upstairs guest rooms in the main house, with
independent access. 'Les Pensées' (one double and one single
bed); 'Les Anémones' (one double bed). On the ground floor of a
separate house, 'Les Lauriers' (160cm double bed) with a salon

continued

containing a 140cm canopied bed. All the rooms have shower, wc and television. Breakfast served in the family dining room. Separate kitchen with fireplace and individual fridges for the use of guests. Wooded park with private pond. Open 1st March to 15th November.
PRICES: s €40; d €50; t €60 **ON SITE:** Fishing Hiking Bicycle hire
NEARBY: Horse riding (5km) Forest (1km) Golf (7km) Swimming pool (6km) Water sports (15km) Tennis (3km) Railway station (20km) Shops (3km) BLOIS (20km) **NOTES:** No pets

GIEVRES

♦♦♦ La Pierre Isabelle VATIN
41130 GIEVRES
☎ 02 54 98 66 93 & 06 63 74 49 89 📠 02 54 98 66 93
e-mail: vat-isa@clubinternet.fr http://www.lechampdupre.com
A hundred metres off the Tours/Vierzon road on a cereal farm. Three rooms with separate access. On the ground floor two rooms for four (one double and two single beds), each with shower and wc. Sitting room upstairs and one room for four (one 160cm bed and two singles) with bath and wc. Lounge with fireplace and kitchen area reserved for guests. Possible extra bed. Pond. Covered car area. Garden furniture. Children's games. Animals with prior notice. Tariff: €56/four guests. Open all year except February holidays.
PRICES: s €32; d €38-€43; t €49; extra person €8 **ON SITE:** Children's play area Forest Fishing Hiking **NEARBY:** Horse riding (5km) Golf (40km) Swimming pool (5km) Water sports (10km) Tennis (3km) Bicycle hire (10km) Railway station (30km) Shops (3km) ROMORANTIN (10km)
NOTES: Pets admitted

LANGON

♦♦♦ Nocfond Thierry COUTON-PROD'HOMME
41320 LANGON
☎ 02 54 98 16 21 & SR : 02 54 58 81 64

An old restored farmhouse in a large flower-filled and shady park in the open Sologne countryside. The named rooms are 'Bagatelle' (twin beds with bath and wc); 'Berthe St James' (double bed with bath and wc); 'La Varende' (double bed with shower and wc); 'Les Guernazelles' (double bed with shower and wc). Private parking. Dogs accepted. Open all year.
PRICES: d €43-€50; extra person €11 **ON SITE:** Forest Hiking Bicycle hire **NEARBY:** Horse riding (3km) Golf (20km) Fishing (3km) Swimming pool (6km) Tennis (7km) Railway station (17km) Shops (6km) ROMORANTIN (12km) **NOTES:** Pets admitted

LESTIOU

♦♦♦ ïOï Chambre d'hôtes Marie-Jeanne FAUCONNET
56 Grande Rue, 41500 LESTIOU
☎ 02 54 81 22 36 & SR : 02 54 58 81 64 📠 02 54 81 22 36
Amidst the Châteaux of the Loire, and 90 minutes from Paris is this authentically restored 17th-century house. Three distinctive guest rooms with exposed timbers. One double room; one room

sleeping four; and one room with a double bed and a convertible bed. Each has bath and wc. From upstairs there is a superb view of the Loire, the countryside and the garden. Meals (booking required) are served in the dining room with open fireplace and view over the garden. Closed parking. Tariff: €88/four persons per night. Open Easter to December.
PRICES: s €50-€55; d €54-€58; t €73; extra person €15; dinner €21
ON SITE: Fishing Hiking Tennis **NEARBY:** Horse riding (24km) Forest (12km) Golf (10km) Swimming pool (7km) Water sports (7km) Bicycle hire (7km) Railway station (7km) Shops (2km) MER (9km) **NOTES:** No pets

MAREUIL-SUR-CHER

♦♦♦ ïOï Les Aulnaies Bernard BODIC
2 rue des Aulnaies, 41110 MAREUIL-SUR-CHER
☎ 02 54 75 43 89 📠 02 54 75 43 89
e-mail: lesaulnaies@aol.com http://www.lesaulnaies.com

Old sheep farm among the vineyards and the forest. Five rooms all with bathroom and wc (three double rooms and two sleeping four). Television with European channels. Private swimming pool, pond, fishing, cycles available, volleyball court. Three hectare park. Beauval Zoo 2km. Tariff: €100/four guests. Open 15 February to 31 December.
PRICES: s €50; d €60; t €80; extra person €20; dinner €22
ON SITE: Fishing Swimming pool Hiking **NEARBY:** Horse riding (4km) Golf (30km) Water sports (4km) Tennis (3km) Railway station (5km) Shops (4km) SAINT AIGNAN SUR CHER (5km) **NOTES:** Pets admitted

MER

♦♦♦ Chambre d'hôtes Claude et Joëlle MORMICHE
9 rue Jean et Guy Dutems, Le Clos, 41500 MER
☎ 02 54 81 17 36 & SR : 02 54 58 81 64 📠 02 54 81 70 19
http://www.France-bonjour.com/mormiche/

Five guest rooms in a house of some character; two triples (double bed and single); one double with possible spare bed; one double (two joining twin beds); one two-roomed suite with four single beds. All have private facilities. Guests have a kitchenette and sitting room at their disposal. Billiards. Display and sale of paintings. Leisure area. Garden with enclosed parking. Two

continued

continued

country gîtes nearby. Tariff: €65/90/four persons. Open all year.
PRICES: s €40; d €45-€55; t €58-€80; extra person €12 **ON SITE:** Hiking
Bicycle hire **NEARBY:** Horse riding (10km) Forest (5km) Golf (12km)
Fishing (2km) Swimming pool (1km) Water sports (15km) Tennis (1km)
BLOIS (15km) **NOTES:** No pets

MEUSNES

₸₸₸ La Saulaie Patrick et Dominique LEGRAS
210 rue Jean Jaurès, 41130 MEUSNES
☎ 02 54 32 59 66 & SR : 02 54 58 81 64
e-mail: plegras@infonie.fr
http://www.chez.com/closeriedemeusnes/
A charming and tranquil girls' school dating from the end of the
18th-century. Four bedrooms opening into a walled garden. One
suite with a 140cm double bed, a small day bed, shower, bath, wc.
Large room with double and single bed, bath and wc. Double
room with shower and wc. Large double room (with possible extra
double bed). Covered swimming pool. Garden furniture. Picnic in
the park. Tariff: €61-77. Open all year.
PRICES: s €39-€48; d €45-€54; t €58-€63 **ON SITE:** Swimming pool
Hiking **NEARBY:** Horse riding (12km) Forest (1km) Golf (30km) Fishing
(1km) Water sports (12km) Tennis (1km) Railway station (6km) SELLES
SUR CHER (8km) **NOTES:** Pets admitted

MONTEAUX

₸₸₸ Les Cèdres Michel LECOMTE
20 rue de la Briderie, 41150 MONTEAUX
☎ 02 54 70 20 09 & SR : 02 54 58 81 64 📠 02 54 70 20 09
e-mail: michel.lecomte2@freesbee.fr
http://www.chambres-les-cedres.com

Just 200m from the centre of the village, on the Vineyard Trail.
Three guest rooms - one suite for two to four people with two
double beds (one with canopy), shower, wc and kitchenette.
Upstairs in the owners' house, with separate access, two double
rooms with bath and wc. Extra bed available (€9). Enclosed garden
with garden furniture. Private parking. Baby equipment available.
Tariff: €62/four persons. Open all year.
PRICES: s €34-€43; d €43-€53; t €60; extra person €10 **ON SITE:** Hiking
NEARBY: Horse riding (15km) Forest (10km) Golf (13km) Fishing (2km)
Swimming pool (11km) Water sports (40km) Tennis (5km) Bicycle hire
(5km) Railway station (2km) BLOIS (20km) **NOTES:** Pets admitted

MONTHOU-SUR-BIEVRE

₸₸₸ Le Chêne Vert Marie-France TOHIER
41120 MONTHOU-SUR-BIEVRE
☎ 02 54 44 07 28 📠 02 54 44 17 94
A 16th-century farmhouse in the middle of parkland, near the
Châteaux of the Loire. Two rooms for two or three people, one on
the ground floor of a separate building, with shower and wc. A
suite for up to eight people, with two showers, two wcs, lounge
with open fire and television. If staying for more than two nights,
cooking facilities are available. Tariff: €130/four persons.

PRICES: s €53; d €64-€84; t €84; extra person €15 **ON SITE:** Hiking
NEARBY: Horse riding (3km) Fishing (3km) Water sports (16km) Tennis
(3km) Railway station (12km) Shops (3km) BLOIS (16km) **NOTES:** No
pets English spoken

MONTLIVAULT

₸₸₸ ⎰◯⎱ Chambre d'hôtes Jean-Claude PARZY
1 rue de St-Dye, 41350 MONTLIVAULT
☎ 02 54 20 69 55 & SR : 02 54 58 81 64 📠 02 54 20 69 55
e-mail: salamandres@ifrance.com http://salamandres.fr.fm

Between Loire and Chambord, at the gateway to the Sologne. Lots
of tourist and sporting activities - cycling, tennis, rambling. Five
guest rooms on an ancient wine-growing farm, all at ground level
with separate access. Family suite (one double bed and two
singles); one room with three single beds; three double rooms. All
have bath or shower and wc. Closed private parking. Garden.
Traditional meals with the owners - booking required. Tariff:
€75/four guests. 4km from Chambord and 10km from Blois. Open
all year.
PRICES: s €42-€75; d €42-€75; t €60-€75; extra person €13; dinner €20
ON SITE: Tennis Bicycle hire **NEARBY:** Horse riding (2km) Forest
(4km) Fishing (1km) Swimming pool (8km) Hiking (4km) Water sports
(4km) Railway station (12km) BLOIS (12km) **NOTES:** No pets English
spoken

MONT-PRES-CHAMBORD

₸₸₸₸ Manoir de Clénord Christiane RENAULD
998 route de Clenord, 41250 MONT-PRES-CHAMBORD
☎ 02 54 70 41 62 & SR : 02 54 58 81 64
📠 02 54 70 33 99
e-mail: info@clenord.com http://www.clenord.com
A 17th-century manor house offering two suites sleeping three
or four and a double room in the main house. In an annexe
are two double rooms and one twin. All have private facilities.
Cot available free. Supplement for extra child's bed: €9. Tariff
€160-181/four people. Open 1 February to 15 December and
out of season on request.
PRICES: s €49-€120; d €56-€146; t €151-€164; extra person €15
ON SITE: Forest Fishing Swimming pool Hiking Tennis
NEARBY: Horse riding (6km) Golf (5km) Water sports (9km)
Bicycle hire (5km) Railway station (10km) Shops (3km) BLOIS
(10km) **NOTES:** Pets admitted English spoken

NEUNG-SUR-BEUVRON

₸₸₸ Breffni Patrick CREHAN
16 rue du 11 Novembre, 41210 NEUNG-SUR-BEUVRON
☎ 02 54 83 66 56 & SR : 02 54 58 81 64 📠 02 54 83 66 56
e-mail: breffni65@hotmail.com
In the town, near the Châteaux of the Loire. Three guest rooms,
one in an annexe, containing one double bed plus one single bed
and a canopied double on a mezzanine, shower, wc, lounge,
cooking area. Upstairs two double rooms with private facilities,

continued

continued

possible extra bed and cot. Large garden, bikes boules area, indoor parking. Restaurant 400m. Tariff: €46/four guests. Open all year.
PRICES: s €30-€46; d €43-€46; t €46-€53; extra person €11
ON SITE: Forest Fishing Hiking Bicycle hire **NEARBY:** Horse riding (17km) Golf (10km) Swimming pool (17km) Water sports (30km) Tennis (1km) Railway station (22km) ROMORANTIN (22km) **NOTES:** No pets English spoken

NOUAN-SUR-LOIRE

♥♥♥ ❧ Bois Renard Michel DE WARREN
6 rue Edouard Fournier, 75116 PARIS
☎ 01 40 72 82 78/02 54 87 00 26 & SR : 02 54 58 81 64
19th-century château with a gîte, in a park surrounded by woods, by the Parc du Chambord. Upstairs: two twin rooms with bath and wc; one room with double and single bed; one family suite of three rooms with six single beds, bath and wc. Living room for guests. Tariff: €91/four persons; €137/five-six persons. Open July and August.
PRICES: s €61-€76; d €61-€76; t €91-€101; extra person €15
ON SITE: Forest Fishing **NEARBY:** Horse riding (7km) Golf (5km) Fishing (2km) Swimming pool (5km) Water sports (20km) Tennis (2km) Railway station (7km) Shops (2km) BLOIS (25km) **NOTES:** No pets English spoken

OISLY

♥♥♥ ❧ Chambre d'hôtes François BONNET
Rue du Stade, Le Bourg, 41700 OISLY
☎ 02 54 79 52 78
Three guest rooms on the ground floor of a farmhouse in the village. One room with a kitchen (single bed and double bed, television) on ground floor. Upstairs: a room sleeping three, with kitchenette and television; one twin room. Showers and wcs in each room, electric heating and central heating. Garage. Games room. Fishing area. Restaurants in the village. Open all year.
PRICES: s €25; d €31-€34; t €45; extra person €10 **ON SITE:** Fishing Hiking **NEARBY:** Horse riding (10km) Forest (12km) Swimming pool (5km) Tennis (5km) Bicycle hire (5km) Shops (5km) MONTRICHARD (18km) **NOTES:** No pets

---

Prices are given in Euros €1 = £0.62
at the time of going to press

PONTLEVOY

♥♥♥ ❧ Les Bordes Josiane GALLOUX
Route de Chaumont-sur-Loire, 41400 PONTLEVOY
☎ 02 54 32 51 08 ▤ 02 54 32 64 43
Among the Châteaux of the Loire, 3km from Pontlevoy on the D114 to Chaumont sur Loire, a farmhouse with six guest rooms, separate from the main residence. One ground floor room (one double and two single beds); five upstairs rooms, one twin room, three double rooms and one sleeping three. All have bath and wc. Electric heating. Park and games. Reception room. 10% reduction for stays of a week. Tariff: €57/four persons. Open all year.
PRICES: s €32; d €37-€42; t €49; extra person €11 **ON SITE:** Hiking **NEARBY:** Horse riding (3km) Forest (6km) Golf (20km) Fishing (9km) Swimming pool (7km) Water sports (7km) Tennis (3km) Bicycle hire (7km) Railway station (8km) Shops (3km) MONTRICHARD (9km) **NOTES:** No pets

ROCE

♥♥♥ ❧ La Touche Jean-Louis NOUVELLON
41100 ROCE
☎ 02 54 77 19 52 & SR : 02 54 58 81 64 ▤ 02 54 77 06 45
e-mail: jl-nouvellon@yahoo.fr

Five kilometres east of Vendôme, in a green and relaxing spot. One twin room with washbasin, shower and wc; two rooms sleeping three with sitting area; one family room on two levels for four to five people, with washbasin, shower, wc, small kitchen. Volleyball, archery, table tennis, cycles and mountain bikes. Tariff: €60/four guests. Open May to September.
PRICES: s €30; d €40; t €50; extra person €10 **ON SITE:** Forest Fishing Hiking Bicycle hire **NEARBY:** Horse riding (7km) Golf (15km) Swimming pool (6km) Water sports (14km) Tennis (3km) Railway station (14km) Shops (6km) VENDOME (5km) **NOTES:** Pets admitted English spoken

SAMBIN

♥♥♥ ⍾◯⍾ Le Prieuré Sophie GELINIER
23 rue Fontaine-St-Urbain, 41120 SAMBIN
☎ 02 54 20 24 95 & SR : 02 54 58 81 64
e-mail: sophie.gelinier@libertysurf.fr
Between Chambord, Amboise and Chenonceau, in old, now restored, farm buildings in a large peaceful garden, there are five guest rooms on offer. Enormous living room, terrace and veranda. Three single rooms and two doubles. Two rooms can form a family suite. Each has private facilities. Parking in the grounds. Swings and children's games. Meals may be booked - 80% organic produce. Open February to October.
PRICES: s €35-€39; d €41-€45; extra person €11; dinner €16
ON SITE: Children's play area Hiking Tennis **NEARBY:** Horse riding (6km) Forest (12km) Golf (15km) Fishing (8km) Swimming pool (11km) Water sports (20km) Railway station (20km) BLOIS (20km) **NOTES:** Pets admitted

SANTENAY

¶¶¶ 🐓 ⦿¶ Le Bas Beau Pays Jean et Monique DEUTINE
41190 SANTENAY
☎ 02 54 46 12 33 & 06 71 72 18 96 📠 02 54 46 12 33
On an agricultural estate in the Loire Valley, near the Châteaux, are four guest rooms. On the ground floor a room sleeping three (double bed and single). Upstairs, a room sleeping four, a twin room and a double. Each has shower, wc and separate entry. Central heating, shady garden. Meals may be booked. Tariff: €59/four persons. Open all year.
PRICES: s €28; d €35; t €47; extra person €12; dinner €16
ON SITE: Fishing Hiking **NEARBY:** Horse riding (20km) Forest (10km) Golf (20km) Swimming pool (4km) Water sports (20km) Tennis (4km) Bicycle hire (13km) Railway station (14km) Shops (4km) BLOIS (25km)
NOTES: No pets

SARGE-SUR-BRAYE

¶¶¶ La Vougrerie Claude et Martine ROUSSEAU
41170 SARGE-SUR-BRAYE
☎ 02 54 72 78 24 & SR : 02 54 58 81 64 📠 02 54 72 75 96
e-mail: vougrerie@free.fr
Four kilometres out of town, in a farmhouse in open country with a panoramic view over the Percheron *bocage*. Three rooms with private facilities. Sitting room for guests. Ten-speed bikes and mountain bikes available. Private swimming pool. Fishing in ponds. Silk-painting lessons. Kitchen corner. Animals accepted with prior notice.
PRICES: s €29; d €36; t €44; extra person €9 **ON SITE:** Fishing Swimming pool Hiking Bicycle hire **NEARBY:** Horse riding (4km) Forest (20km) Water sports (18km) Tennis (4km) Railway station (9km) Shops (4km) VENDOME (25km) **NOTES:** Pets admitted

SELLES-ST-DENIS

¶¶¶ Les Atelleries Caroline QUINTIN
41300 SELLES-ST-DENIS
☎ 02 54 96 13 84 📠 02 54 96 13 78
e-mail: caroline.quintin@wanadoo.fr
http://perso.wanadoo.fr/caroline.quintin/

At the heart of Sologne on 65ha, three guest rooms in the outbuildings of a restored farmhouse. Two are in a bakery, restored along with its ovens. On the ground floor, one double room with 160cm bed, bath and wc. Upstairs, a room for three (double and single bed), bath and wc. A room for three in a half-timbered building (three single beds), bath and wc. Kitchen available. Lounge reserved for guests. Dogs accepted in kennels if pre-booked. Fixed-price hunting on the estate. Tariff: €61/four persons. Open all year.
PRICES: s €37; d €46; t €54 **ON SITE:** Forest Fishing Bicycle hire **NEARBY:** Horse riding (14km) Golf (15km) Swimming pool (14km) Hiking (5km) Water sports (13km) Tennis (5km) Railway station (5km) Shops (5km) ROMORANTIN (14km) **NOTES:** Pets admitted English spoken

SERIS

¶¶¶ 🐓 ⦿¶ Chambre d'hôtes
Jean-Yves et Annie PESCHARD
10 Chemin de Paris, 41500 SERIS
☎ 02 54 81 07 83 & SR : 02 54 58 81 64 📠 02 54 81 39 88
e-mail: jypeschard@wanadoo.fr

In the Loire Valley with its famous Châteaux, a working farm with five guest rooms in its 19th-century farmhouse. On the ground floor, each with shower and wc: one double room; one twin room with two extra beds; one double with an extra convertible double bed. Upstairs: one room with double bed, single bed, spare bed and cot; one double (160cm bed) and television, shower and wc. Living room for guests in old cellar. Covered garden area. Outdoor games. Cycling. Possible guided tours. Mountain bikes and road bikes available for hire. Preserve making. Animals allowed if booked. Tariff: €72/four persons. Open all year.
PRICES: s €39-€40; d €43-€49; t €60-€71; dinner €16 **ON SITE:** Bicycle hire **NEARBY:** Horse riding (10km) Forest (10km) Fishing (10km) Swimming pool (7km) Hiking (10km) Water sports (15km) Tennis (5km) Railway station (7km) Shops (5km) BLOIS (25km) **NOTES:** Pets admitted English spoken

ST-AIGNAN-SUR-CHER

¶¶¶ Chambre d'hôtes Geneviève BESSON
66 rue Maurice Berteaux, 41110 ST-AIGNAN-SUR-CHER
☎ 02 54 75 24 35 📠 02 54 75 24 35
Near the Châteaux of the Loire, four charming guest rooms, in a town house. On the first floor: a stylish two-roomed suite with two double beds, bath and wc. On the second floor: a twin room with shower and wc; a stylish room with double bed and large single, bath and wc; one room sleeping four opening on to the garden, with shower and wc. Tariff: €70/four persons. Open all year.
PRICES: ; d €40-€50; t €60; extra person €13 **ON SITE:** Fishing Swimming pool Water sports Tennis **NEARBY:** Horse riding (3km) Forest (2km) Golf (25km) Hiking (2km) Railway station (2km) SAINT AIGNAN SUR CHER **NOTES:** No pets

ST-AMAND-LONGPRE

¶¶¶ Chambre d'hôtes Chantal GATIEN
3 avenue du Président Grellet, 41310 ST-AMAND-LONGPRE
☎ 02 54 82 94 44
In the Loire Valley, 12km from Vendôme, This house of some character has a large garden and private swimming pool. Three guest rooms - one suite sleeping five to six; one room for three; and one double (with spare single bed). All have bath and wc. Television lounge and reception area with open fire. Substantial breakfasts with home-made produce. Tariff: €67-70/four persons. Open all year.
PRICES: s €32-€39; d €40-€46; t €52-€58; extra person €12
ON SITE: Swimming pool Hiking Bicycle hire **NEARBY:** Horse riding (5km) Fishing (1km) Water sports (30km) Tennis (1km) Railway station (10km) Shops (1km) VENDOME (14km) **NOTES:** No pets

ST-DENIS-SUR-LOIRE

♦♦♦♦ La Malouinière Edith DE ST-LEGER
1 rue Bernard Lorjou, 41000 ST-DENIS-SUR-LOIRE
☎ 02 54 74 62 56 & SR : 02 54 58 81 64
🖻 02 54 74 62 56
e-mail: infos@la-malouiniere.com www.la-malouiniere.com
5km from the Château at Blois, the silhouette of the
Malouinière stands out. This is the old house of painter
Bernard Lorjou. The gentle light over its roofs, the park,
swimming pool and old walled garden are an invitation to
pleasant living. The four guest rooms combine charm with
great comfort, as do the sitting room and billiard room. Cosy
dining room with 100-year-old oak beams. Tariff:€152/four
persons. Open all year; booking required.
PRICES: s €76; d €99-€122; t €122-€152; extra person €23
ON SITE: Swimming pool Hiking Bicycle hire **NEARBY:** Horse
riding (3km) Golf (15km) Water sports (3km) Tennis (3km) Railway
station (5km) BLOIS (5km) **NOTES:** No pets

♦♦♦ 🍴 La Villa Medicis Muriel CABIN-ST-MARCEL
Mace, 41000 ST-DENIS-SUR-LOIRE
☎ 02 54 74 46 38 🖻 02 54 78 20 27
3km from Blois, an 18th/19th-century house in parkland on the
banks of the Loire. Six rooms: one double room at ground level;
upstairs two rooms sleeping four and three sleeping two. All have
private facilities. Guests have use of the sitting room and library.
Meals may be booked (€30). Tariff: €86-128/four persons. Open all
year; booking required in winter.
PRICES: s €56-€80; d €66-€96; t €76-€112; extra person €17; dinner €30
ON SITE: Tennis **NEARBY:** Horse riding (2km) Forest (10km) Golf
(15km) Fishing (1km) Swimming pool (4km) Water sports (1km) Bicycle
hire (3km) Railway station (5km) Shops (1km) BLOIS (3km)
NOTES: No pets English spoken

ST-GEORGES-SUR-CHER

♦♦♦ La Chaise Danièle DURET-THERISOLS
Prieure de la Chaise, 8 rue du Prieure,
41400 ST-GEORGES-SUR-CHER
☎ 02 54 32 59 77 & SR : 02 54 58 81 64 🖻 02 54 32 69 49
e-mail: prieuredelachaise@yahoo.fr
Near the Châteaux of the Loire, the Priory de la Chaise (14th-
century, with 12th-century chapel) is an oasis of calm, on a wine
estate. On the ground floor, two double rooms with shower and
wc. On the first floor, a two-roomed apartment with bathroom and
wc (one 140cm double bed, one 160cm, and a two-person pull-out
bed). Tariff: €107/four persons. Open all year.
PRICES: s €60; d €61-€80; t €95; extra person €16 **ON SITE:** Forest
NEARBY: Horse riding (5km) Golf (20km) Fishing (2km) Swimming
pool (5km) Hiking (1km) Tennis (5km) Bicycle hire (2km) Railway station
(5km) Shops (2km) MONTRICHARD (5km) **NOTES:** No pets English
spoken

ST-LAURENT-NOUAN

♦♦♦ Chambre d'hôtes Maurice et Catherine LIBEAUT
26 rue de l'Ormoie, 41220 ST-LAURENT-NOUAN
☎ 02 54 87 24 72 🖻 02 54 87 24 93
e-mail: maurice.catherine.libeaut@wanadoo.fr.
http://www.france-bonjour.com/lormoire/
Close to the Châteaux of the Loire and the footpaths of the
Sologne, and a few minutes from Chambord, Catherine and
Maurice invite guests to share the calm and charm of their 17th-
century home and park. Three lovely bedrooms, each with private
shower room. Two double rooms and a room for three with a
double bed and a single. Lounge/dining room for guests.
Picnicking possible in park. Open all year.
PRICES: d €50; t €60 **ON SITE:** Hiking Tennis Bicycle hire

NEARBY: Horse riding (10km) Forest (1km) Golf (1km) Fishing (1km)
Swimming pool (1km) Water sports (1km) Railway station (8km) Shops
(1km) BLOIS (25km) **NOTES:** No pets

SUEVRES

♦♦♦ Le Moulin de Choiseaux-Diziers
Marie-Françoise SEGUIN
8 rue des Choiseaux, Diziers, 41500 SUEVRES
☎ 02 54 87 85 01 & SR : 02 54 58 81 64 🖻 02 54 87 86 44
e-mail: choiseaux@wanadoo.fr http://choiseaux.ifrance.com
Guests will love the quietness and the wildlife by the water in this
18th-century water mill in the middle of the Loire Valley, between
Chambord and Blois. The hosts will advise on itineraries, visits,
walks, etc. Enormous country garden with private swimming pool.
Restaurant only 1km. Four lovely bedrooms (one double room,
one single, and two sleeping three) with bath and wc, and one
family suite. The suite has a 180cm double bed and two 90cm
singles). Tariff: €105/four persons. Open all year.
PRICES: s €43; d €49-€73; t €76-€89; extra person €16
ON SITE: Fishing Swimming pool Bicycle hire **NEARBY:** Horse riding
(15km) Forest (10km) Golf (15km) Water sports (15km) Tennis (1km)
Railway station (5km) Shops (1km) BLOIS (12km) **NOTES:** English
spoken

THOURY

♦♦♦ La Grange aux Herbes
Claude VERMET & Dominique GOBY
4 rue du Pavillon, 41220 THOURY
☎ 02 54 87 55 79 & SR : 02 54 58 81 64

Near the Sologne with its forests, hunting, hiking and riding, just
300m from the entrance to the Park of Chambord, an old
farmhouse in a shady park with pond. Three double rooms and
two triple, all with shower and wc, plus a family room (double bed
and two singles), with bathroom and wc. Cot available. Private
parking. Kitchen for use of guests. Television lounge with open fire,
for guests. Tariff: €88/four persons. Open all year.
PRICES: s €37-€52; d €49-€64; t €61-€76; extra person €12
ON SITE: Fishing Hiking Bicycle hire **NEARBY:** Horse riding (10km)
Forest (3km) Golf (10km) Swimming pool (10km) Water sports (10km)
Tennis (3km) Railway station (10km) Shops (1km) BLOIS (20km)
NOTES: Pets admitted

🍴

Places with this symbol serve table d'hôte
evening meals - remember to book in advance

continued

CENTRAL FRANCE

VALAIRE

♥♥♥ ❤ La Caillaudière Etienne GALLOU
41120 VALAIRE
☎ 02 54 44 03 04 📠 02 54 44 03 04

Among the Châteaux of the Loire near the Sologne (forests, hunting), and Chaumont sur Loire is this 16th-century farmhouse. Three upstairs rooms, two double rooms and a twin, each with shower and wc. Kitchenette for guests. Living room/lounge area. Open all year.

PRICES: s €30; d €37; t €48; extra person €11 **ON SITE:** Fishing
NEARBY: Horse riding (5km) Forest (2km) Golf (20km) Swimming pool (15km) Hiking (2km) Water sports (20km) Tennis (6km) Bicycle hire (7km) Railway station (12km) Shops (4km) BLOIS (15km) **NOTES:** No pets

VALLIERES-LES-GRANDES

♥♥♥ ℟◯ Ferme de la Quantinière Annie DOYER
41400 VALLIERES-LES-GRANDES
☎ 02 54 20 99 53 📠 02 54 20 99 53
e-mail: fermequantiniere@minitel.net
http://www.france-bonjour.com/la-quantiniere/

Between Loire and Cher, at the heart of the 'Golden Triangle', five rooms in an old restored farm, each equipped with shower or bath and wc. Come and enjoy the quiet, leisure and high quality cuisine at la Quantinière, a magnificent 19th-century farmhouse. Meals may be booked. Tariff: €80/four persons. Open 1 April to 31 December, and out of season on request.

PRICES: s €44; d €50; t €65; extra person €15; dinner €21
ON SITE: Forest Hiking Bicycle hire **NEARBY:** Horse riding (10km) Golf (12km) Fishing (4km) Swimming pool (8km) Water sports (8km) Tennis (3km) Railway station (8km) Shops (3km) MONTRICHARD (8km) **NOTES:** No pets English spoken

VENDOME

♥♥♥ ℟◯ La Bretonnerie Yves et Claudine SALAÜN
32 route du Bois la Barbe, 41100 VENDOME
☎ 02 54 77 46 22 & SR : 02 54 58 81 64 📠 02 54 77 46 22
e-mail: bretonnerie@aol.com

Near Vendome, three guest rooms in a 2ha wooded park. One room has a double bed, a single and a spare bed. A two-roomed suite has a double bed, bunks and a cot. One double room. All have private facilities and television. Lounge. Garden furniture and barbecue. Central heating. Baby equipment to hand. Meals are bookable. Animals accepted with prior notice - to be kept on lead. Tariff: €54/four persons. Open all year.

PRICES: s €32; d €40; t €47; extra person €7; dinner €15
ON SITE: Forest **NEARBY:** Horse riding (3km) Golf (12km) Fishing (1km) Swimming pool (2km) Hiking (3km) Water sports (2km) Tennis (2km) Bicycle hire (2km) Railway station (3km) Shops (2km) VENDOME (2km) **NOTES:** Pets admitted

VILLEBAROU

♥♥♥ Chambre d'hôtes Jacques et Agnès MASQUILIER
8 rte de la Chaussée St-Victor, Le Retour - Francillon, 41000 VILLEBAROU
☎ 02 54 78 40 24 📠 02 54 56 12 36

Only 5km from Blois. Four guest rooms in a distinctive house - three doubles on the ground floor with separate access, shower and wc. One room is accessible for people with reduced mobility. Upstairs a large suite with mezzanine, containing two double beds with bath, shower and wc. Fully equipped large kitchen/dining area. Communal television for guests. Flowery courtyard with closed parking. Table tennis. Shaded park. Metal detectors. Tariff: €69-97/four persons. Open all year; booking essential in winter.

PRICES: s €38; d €45-€73; t €57-€85; extra person €12
ON SITE: Children's play area Bicycle hire **NEARBY:** Horse riding (10km) Golf (10km) Fishing (10km) Swimming pool (4km) Hiking (15km) Water sports (10km) Tennis (1km) Railway station (5km) Shops (2km) BLOIS (4km) **NOTES:** Pets admitted English spoken

VILLENY

♥♥♥ Château de la Giraudière Anne ORSINI
La Giraudière, 41220 VILLENY
☎ 02 54 83 72 38

On the first floor of an 18th-century house, three twin rooms, two with private bath and wc. On the second floor, two twin rooms with bathroom or washbasin, and wc on landing. Private tennis court. 15% reduction for one week's stay. Tariff: €110/four persons. Open 1 April to 11 November.

PRICES: s €60-€65; d €60-€65; t €110; extra person €15
ON SITE: Forest Hiking Tennis **NEARBY:** Horse riding (10km) Golf (20km) Fishing (10km) Swimming pool (25km) Water sports (35km) Bicycle hire (10km) Shops (3km) BLOIS (25km) **NOTES:** No pets

VILLERBON

♥♥♥ Chambre d'hôtes Elisabeth LESOURD
3 route des Grèves, Villejambon - cedex 8520, 41000 VILLERBON
☎ 02 54 46 83 16 📠 02 54 46 83 16

On an old farm near Blois, an old wine store, now restored, with three guest rooms, two double rooms and one twin, each with shower and wc. Guests' lounge and living room with local style furniture. Games. The garden may be available for leisure and picnicking by arrangement. Kitchen for guests. Animals if pre-booked. Open all year (by reservation only November to March).

PRICES: s €39; d €44; extra person €13 **NEARBY:** Horse riding (10km) Forest (10km) Golf (2km) Fishing (4km) Swimming pool (10km) Hiking (10km) Water sports (8km) Tennis (2km) Bicycle hire (10km) Railway station (10km) Shops (8km) BLOIS (10km) **NOTES:** Pets admitted

CHAMPAGNE-ARDENNE

ARDENNES

ACY-ROMANCE

♥ Chambre d'hôtes Alain & Noëlle LEBEGUE
Rue de l'Oseraie, 08300 ACY-ROMANCE
☎ 03 24 38 50 16 & 06 78 58 37 93 📠 03 24 38 50 16
Situated in a pretty town, this turn-of-the-century farm comes with two bedrooms, a suite, and an annexe, and sleeps up to eleven. The rooms come with showers and wcs and a cot is also provided. On the ground floor there is a guests' room with TV. There is plenty to see and do, including, country walks, mountain biking, and visiting local churches and museums. Parking available. Open all year.
PRICES: s €27; d €34; extra person €9 **ON SITE:** Fishing
NEARBY: Bathing (1km) Canoeing (25km) Forest (15km) Golf (20km) Swimming pool (2km) Tennis (1km) Sailing (25km) Railway Station (1km) Shops (1km) RETHEL (1km) **NOTES:** No pets

BOGNY-SUR-MEUSE

🍽 Le Berceau des Legendes
Ghislain & Régine LAUNOIS
6, rue de la Vinaigrerie, 08120 BOGNY-SUR-MEUSE
☎ 03 24 53 07 17 & 06 83 66 21 65 📠 03 24 53 07 17
A stone-clad house bordering a beautiful forest with four bedrooms. On the first floor there are three double rooms, the second floor and attic house a double room and room for a possible two single beds and cot. All rooms have showers and wcs. Two of the rooms have balconies with views of the woods. Gas central heating, charming sitting room, garage parking. Outdoor activities include mountain biking. Table d'hôte meals at lunch and dinner on reservation. A non-smoking establishment. Open all year.
PRICES: s €28-€33; d €34-€38; extra person €13-€15; dinner €13
ON SITE: Children's play area Forest Fishing **NEARBY:** Bathing (15km) Canoeing (5km) Swimming pool (15km) Tennis (1km) Sailing (15km) Railway Station (1km) Shops (1km) CHARLEVILLE-MEZIERES (18km)
NOTES: No pets

BOSSEVAL

🍽 Chambre d'hôtes Jacqueline & J.F. LAMBERTY
4, place de la République, 08350 BOSSEVAL
☎ 03 24 29 48 25 & 06 80 31 76 15 📠 03 24 52 79 60
An 18th-century presbytery of great character and antique furniture, which has accommodation for eight, two doubles and one sleeps four. All have private bathrooms, wcs and TVs. Table d'hôte meals are served in the evenings with 48 hours notice, from 1 September to 15 May. Lawn, barbecues, tennis and mountain bikes. 10% reduction if the stay exceeds four nights. Open all year.
PRICES: s €30; d €38; t €49; extra person €12; HB €46; dinner €15
ON SITE: Children's play area Forest Tennis **NEARBY:** Bathing (10km) Canoeing (10km) Golf (15km) Fishing (3km) Swimming pool (10km) Sailing (10km) Railway Station (10km) Shops (3km) SEDAN (10km)
NOTES: No pets

BRIENNE-SUR-AISNE

♥ Chambre d'hôtes J & Jean-Pier LERICHE
13, route de Poilcourt Sydney, 08190 BRIENNE-SUR-AISNE
☎ 03 24 72 94 25 📠 03 24 72 94 25
Reims (champagne caves) 20 km. Chemin des Dames 25 km. In the calm and relaxed atmosphere of this working farm, four rooms of character accommodate seven. The rooms include colour TVs, showers and private wcs. Centrally heated, there are also cooking facilities for snacks and a living room downstairs. Amusements involve a games room with ping-pong and a private museum nearby. Open all year.
PRICES: s €23-€28; d €28-€38; t €46; extra person €11
ON SITE: Children's play area Forest **NEARBY:** Bathing (25km) Canoeing (7km) Golf (4km) Fishing (1km) Swimming pool (18km) Tennis (18km) Sailing (25km) Railway Station (18km) Shops (1km) RETHEL (30km) **NOTES:** No pets

CHAMPIGNEULLE

♥ Chambre d'hôtes Marie-Ange DECORNE
08250 CHAMPIGNEULLE
☎ 03 24 30 78 66 & 03 24 30 78 31
Within a farm very close to the forest of Argonne, three rooms offer accommodation for nine, one double, a three person and a four person room. All rooms have showers or baths and private wcs. Downstairs there is a sitting room, and parking is not a problem. For food, why not picnic by the river or there is a restaurant nearby. Open all year.
PRICES: s €25; d €33; t €40; extra person €8 **ON SITE:** Forest
NEARBY: Bathing (10km) Fishing (1km) Swimming pool (25km) Tennis (6km) Sailing (20km) Railway Station (55km) Shops (6km) VOUZIERS (25km) **NOTES:** No pets

CHATEL-CHEHERY

🍽 Château de Châtel Jacques & Simone HUET
08250 CHATEL-CHEHERY
☎ 03 24 30 78 54 📠 03 24 30 25 51

Three bedrooms are available in this most exceptional and picturesquely located 18th-century château. The rooms come with showers and wcs and are a mix of doubles and singles sleeping eight in total. Table d'hôte meals are by reservation only and there are snack making facilities in one of the rooms. Apart from the food there is plenty to enjoy, a heated swimming pool (May to September) fishing and sightseeing. Open all year. Discounts for stays of more than four nights.
PRICES: s €53-€57; d €61-€69; extra person €23; dinner €16
ON SITE: Forest Fishing Swimming pool Tennis **NEARBY:** Bathing (30km) Canoeing (30km) Sailing (30km) Railway Station (25km) Shops (12km) VOUZIERS (25km) **NOTES:** No pets

continued

NCHERY

♦♦♦♦ ⦿ Le Sautou
Michèle & Yvon GARDAN
08350 DONCHERY
☎ 03 24 52 70 08 📠 03 24 52 70 08

At the heart of the Ardennes, this superb 14-century château offers four charming and spacious rooms that accommodate nine guests. All rooms have sitting areas, showers or baths and wcs. There is also a guest lounge and sitting room on the ground floor. Table d'hôte meals by reservation. With the woods, stream, tennis courts and swimming pool there is plenty to do. Open all year.

PRICES: s €60; d €75; extra person €16; dinner €19-€22
ON SITE: Forest Swimming pool Tennis **NEARBY:** Bathing (4km) Canoeing (20km) Golf (20km) Fishing (4km) Sailing (30km) Railway Station (8km) Shops (4km) SEDAN (10km) **NOTES:** No pets

FUMAY

♦♦♦ Chambre d'hôtes Liliane & J.Claude LORENT
3, rue du docteur Bourgeois, 08170 FUMAY
☎ 03 24 41 29 66 & 03 24 41 12 12

Three rooms are available in this lovely 18th-century house bordering the Meuse. On the ground floor there is a guest lounge and sitting room with TV. Upstairs are two double rooms and a suite with a double bed and a single, with a possible extra bed. All come with private showers or baths and wcs. The house is centrally heated. Meals may be taken at a nearby restaurant (50% discount for children). Open all year.

PRICES: s €38; d €43; extra person €15 **ON SITE:** Forest Fishing Tennis **NEARBY:** Bathing (15km) Canoeing (2km) Golf (40km) Swimming pool (8km) Sailing (15km) Railway Station (2km) CHARLEVILLE-MEZIERES (40km) **NOTES:** No pets

GRIVY-LOISY

♦♦♦ Auberge du Pied des Monts Maurice CREUWELS
Le Pied des Monts, Grivy, 08400 GRIVY-LOISY
☎ 03 24 71 92 38 📠 03 24 71 96 21
e-mail: auberge-du-pied-des-monts@wanadoo.fr
www.pied-des-monts.com

Close to a lake and situated in a hamlet, this establishment offers five bedrooms that sleep eleven. On the first floor (mezzanine) there are four doubles with a shower and wcs, and a suite with a double and single bed, shower and wc. Each room contains TV, telephone and sitting area. Downstairs there is an auberge serving breakfast and snacks. There are plenty of activities to enjoy including canoeing and mountain biking. Open all year.

PRICES: s €40; d €44; t €59; extra person €12; HB €50; dinner €15-€24 **NEARBY:** Bathing (16km) Canoeing (4km) Forest (15km) Golf (25km) Fishing (15km) Swimming pool (6km) Sailing (16km) Railway Station (26km) Shops (6km) Restaurant nearby VOUZIERS (6km) **NOTES:** No pets

LALOBBE

♦♦♦ ⦿ La Besace Claude CARPENTIER
08460 LALOBBE
☎ 03 24 52 81 94 & 03 24 52 82 15

Signy-l'Abbaye 5 km. Escape to this charming house in the middle of a forest. Four listed bedrooms, a large, beautiful garden and plenty of pastimes are provided for a possible nine guests. Two grade 2 rooms are doubles, one double grade 3, and a grade 3 double suite, also includes a single, all have private showers and wcs. A drinks inclusive table d'hôte menu is on offer by reservation, with game on the menu from October to January. 10% reduction for stays over four nights. Open all year.

PRICES: s €33-€36; d €38-€40; t €49; extra person €8; dinner €14-€23
ON SITE: Forest **NEARBY:** Bathing (35km) Canoeing (35km) Golf (28km) Fishing (3km) Swimming pool (24km) Tennis (5km) Sailing (35km) Railway Station (24km) Shops (5km) RETHEL (24km)
NOTES: No pets English spoken

ROCROI

♦♦♦ ⦿ Chambre d'hôtes Françoise DUMONCEAU
5, rue d'Hersigny, 08230 ROCROI
☎ 03 24 53 86 37 📠 03 24 53 86 37
levdum@aol.com

On the Franco-Belgian border, this is a great stop-off point for pilgrims of St-Jaques de Compostelle. All rooms include colour, satellite TV (grade 2 and 3) doubles and a twin with a possible extra single and double bed. Only one of the rooms has a separate shower and wc, the rest are shared. Also at the guests' disposal are a washing machine, terrace, and sitting room. Table d'hôte meals by reservation only, drinks inclusive. 50% discount for children under twelve. Non-smokers only. Open all year.

PRICES: s €26-€29; d €38-€40; extra person €18; dinner €15-€18
ON SITE: Swimming pool **NEARBY:** Bathing (8km) Canoeing (8km) Forest (2km) Fishing (8km) Tennis (8km) Sailing (8km) Railway Station (12km) CHARLEVILLE-MEZIERES (35km) **NOTES:** No pets

TOULIGNY

♦♦♦ 🌿 ⦿ Ferme de la Basse Touligny
J.Claude & D LEDOUX-FOSTIER
La Basse Touligny, 08430 TOULIGNY
☎ 03 24 35 60 07 📠 03 24 35 51 45

Go fishing in the Vence from this historic country farm. Two bedrooms and a suite sleep eleven. The rooms are equipped with showers or baths and wcs. Downstairs for the guests are a lounge and a sitting room with a TV and fireplace. Evening table d'hôte meals are by reservation only, drinks are inclusive. Open all year. Reductions for groups and long stays.

PRICES: s €30; d €40; t €50; extra person €10; dinner €20
ON SITE: Forest Fishing **NEARBY:** Bathing (18km) Canoeing (18km) Golf (15km) Swimming pool (15km) Tennis (3km) Sailing (18km) Railway Station (15km) Shops (3km) CHARLEVILLE-MEZIERES (15km)
NOTES: Pets admitted English spoken

VIEL-ST-REMY

♦♦♦ ⦿ Margy Thérèse & René TURQUIN
08270 VIEL-ST-REMY
☎ 03 24 38 56 37 📠 03 24 38 56 37

This farm is delightfully rural and there is a stream for fishing. All rooms come with showers and wcs and are decorated with the personal touch of the proprietor. Downstairs there is a sitting room and lounge. Snack-making facilities are available. Table d'hôte meals Sunday and Monday evenings are by reservation, Drinks are included, there is also a restaurant nearby. Garage parking. Open all year.

continued

continued

PRICES: s €29; d €35; t €49; extra person €12; dinner €15
ON SITE: Fishing **NEARBY:** Bathing (30km) Canoeing (18km) Forest (7km) Golf (22km) Swimming pool (18km) Tennis (6km) Sailing (30km) Railway Station (18km) Shops (6km) RETHEL (18km) **NOTES:** No pets

VIEUX-LES-ASFELD

♥♥♥ Auberge D'Ecry

Christiane LAMOTTE et Michel BOUCTON,
08190 VIEUX-LES-ASFELD
☎ 03 24 72 94 65 🖹 03 24 38 39 41
e-mail: ferme.d.ecry@wanadoo.fr
www.multimania.com/fermedecry
Reims 25 km. There is plenty to occupy visitors to this former farm surrounded by flowers; museums, fishing, mountain biking and a 16th-century church for example. There are four bedrooms, sleeping a possible twelve guests. Rooms come with showers, TV and private wc and are centrally heated. For food there is a country auberge in the vicinity. Open all year.
PRICES: s €30; d €38; extra person €13-€16; dinner €12-€24
ON SITE: Children's play area **NEARBY:** Bathing (25km) Canoeing (1km) Forest (1km) Golf (10km) Fishing (1km) Swimming pool (25km) Tennis (5km) Sailing (40km) Railway Station (25km) Shops (2km) Restaurant nearby RETHEL (25km) **NOTES:** No pets

VILLERS-SUR-LE-MONT

♥♥♥ ♥ 🍽 Chambre d'hôtes

M.France & J.Claude COLINET
08430 VILLERS-SUR-LE-MONT
☎ 03 24 32 71 66 🖹 03 24 32 71 66
On an isolated farm in the middle of the countryside four bedrooms accommodate eleven people. Rooms come with baths or showers and private wcs. Table d'hôte menu is available drinks inclusive. Other amenities include courtyard, garden, sitting room with TV, and parking. Open all year.
PRICES: s €28; d €34; t €45; extra person €11; dinner €12
ON SITE: Fishing **NEARBY:** Bathing (25km) Canoeing (25km) Forest (3km) Golf (5km) Swimming pool (14km) Tennis (3km) Sailing (25km) Railway Station (14km) Shops (3km) CHARLEVILLE (14km) **NOTES:** No pets

AUBE

BERNON

♥♥♥ ♥ 🍽 La Fontaine de Bernn

Daniel et Claudine PETIT
2 Rue de la Fontaine, 10130 BERNON
☎ 03 25 70 55 42 & 03 25 70 08 34 🖹 03 25 70 50 90
An old cheese dairy on a snail farm, at the gateway to Burgundy and on the edge of the Chablis region. There is independent access to the two ground-floor rooms, one of which is a double and one of which is a single, both with bathroom facilities and TV. Upstairs there is a double room and a four-person room, both with private facilities. Lounge, telephone and kitchen available. Garden and parking facilities. Tasting is available at the farm on reservation. Local produce for sale.
PRICES: s €32-€35; d €35-€38; dinner €14 **ON SITE:** Wine tasting Forest Hiking **NEARBY:** Bathing (10km) Horse riding (12km) Fishing (1km) Swimming pool (17km) Tennis (12km) Sailing (40km) Railway Station (17km) CHAOURCE (15km) **NOTES:** Pets admitted English spoken

For further information on these and other chambres d'hôtes, consult the Gîtes de France website
www.gites-de-france.fr

BOUILLY

♥♥♥ ♥ 🍽 Chambre d'hôtes

Jean-Paul et Michèle BENOIT
27 Rue du Bois, 10320 BOUILLY
☎ 03 25 40 25 35 & SR : 03 25 73 00 11
Ten minutes from Troyes and 30 minutes from lakes on the edge of the Othe Forest, Michèle and Jean-Paul welcome guests to their farm beside a wood. There are two double bedrooms with an extra bed and private bathroom facilities, and one bedroom with one double bed and two single beds. Lounge with TV and books. Enclosed flower-filled courtyard and shaded park with children's games. Set meals available from 11-15 euros, not including drinks. Reservation is necessary.
PRICES: s €32; d €38; extra person €12; dinner €11-€14 **ON SITE:** Forest Hiking Tennis **NEARBY:** Bathing (13km) Horse riding (8km) Fishing (10km) Swimming pool (13km) Sailing (25km) **NOTES:** Pets admitted

BOURGUIGNONS

♥♥♥ La Capitainerie de St-Vallier

Raymond GRADELET
10110 BOURGUIGNONS
☎ 03 25 29 84 43
An old head lock-keeper's cottage on the Champagne route with bedroom views over the Seine. There is one twin bedroom with a double and two single beds, two double bedrooms and one double bedroom with the possibility of an extra bed for 12 euros. Each room has separate bathroom facilities. There is a lawn with garden furniture. There is also a summer kitchen and a veranda. Breakfast is served on old, brightly coloured porcelain. The bedrooms are non-smoking.
PRICES: s €31; d €41; t €53; extra person €12 **ON SITE:** Fishing Hiking **NEARBY:** Bathing (18km) Horse riding (19km) Forest (3km) Swimming pool (30km) Tennis (2km) Sailing (18km) BAR SUR SEINE (2km) **NOTES:** No pets

BOUY-LUXEMBOURG

♥♥♥ 🍽 Les Epis d'Or E.A.R.L. BOUVRON

10220 BOUY-LUXEMBOURG
☎ 03 25 46 31 67 🖹 03 25 46 31 67
Nicole, Serge and their children welcome you into their working family farm. There are four bedrooms in a separate renovated building, each with its own wc and shower. There are two bedrooms with a double and a single bed, and two double bedrooms, one of which also contains bunk beds. Extra bed possible. Kitchen and large lounge. Visit the 15th/16th century church.
PRICES: s €24; d €32; t €40; extra person €8; dinner €13
ON SITE: Hiking **NEARBY:** Bathing (10km) Horse riding (10km) Forest (10km) Fishing (10km) Swimming pool (15km) Tennis (10km) Sailing (10km) Railway Station (15km) Shops (5km) PINEY (5km) **NOTES:** Pets admitted

BREVONNES

♥♥♥ 🍽 La Bergeotte Gilles ANTOINE

6 Rue de Dienville, 10220 BREVONNES
☎ 03 25 46 31 44
This large quiet house in a big shaded garden is located amongst the large lakes of the Forest of Orient. There are three en suite bedrooms on the ground floor: two doubles and one bedroom with a double and a single bed. Extra beds can be provided. A small kitchen and a barbecue are available for guest use. Children's games are also available. Table d'hôte meals on reservation.
PRICES: s €25; d €35; t €43; extra person €8; dinner €15
ON SITE: Forest Hiking Tennis **NEARBY:** Bathing (10km) Horse riding (10km) Fishing (5km) Swimming pool (20km) Sailing (10km) Railway Station (30km) Shops (5km) PINEY (5km) **NOTES:** No pets

URTERON

⚑ IOI Ferme de la Gloire Dieu
a Gloire Dieu, 10250 COURTERON
☎ 03 25 38 20 67

Situated in part of a large 16th-century fortified farm with an old monastery dating from the 13th century. There are three intimate bedrooms on the same floor with exposed stone and pastel drawings. There is one twin bedroom with a double and a single bed and two double bedrooms. Each bedroom has its own bathroom facilities. There is a restaurant open at weekends. There is a flower-filled garden. A ramblers' path and Champagne tourist route passes through the village. Poultry and foie gras are on sale at the farm.

PRICES: s €29; d €34; t €46; extra person €12; dinner €15
ON SITE: Bathing Hiking **NEARBY:** Horse riding (10km) Forest (1km) Fishing (2km) Swimming pool (20km) Tennis (8km) Sailing (35km) Shops (10km) BAR SUR SEINE (10km) **NOTES:** Pets admitted

EAUX-PUISEAUX

⚑ 🐾 La Ferme des Hauts Frenes
Francis LAMBERT
10130 EAUX-PUISEAUX
☎ 03 25 42 15 04 ▤ 03 25 42 02 95

Marie-Paule and Francis welcome you into their farm, offering three fully equipped bedrooms with bathroom facilities and TV points. There is one double bedroom, one twin bedroom and one bedroom with a double bed a bunk bed and a single bed. Children's games are available. Mountain bike hire is available on site. Cider museum in the village.

PRICES: s €27; d €35; extra person €9 **ON SITE:** Forest Hiking **NEARBY:** Bathing (15km) Horse riding (14km) Fishing (4km) Swimming pool (20km) Tennis (5km) Sailing (35km) Shops (4km) ERVY LE CHATEL (9km) **NOTES:** No pets English spoken

ESTISSAC

⚑ IOI Domaine du Moulin d'Eguebaude
Edouard MESLEY
Moulin d'Eguebaude, 10190 ESTISSAC
☎ 03 25 40 42 18 & 03 25 40 40 92 ▤ 03 25 40 40 92

A superbly restored wooden mill in the heart of a park. There are four double bedrooms and one triple bedroom. There is a sauna and a lounge available for guests' use. There is parking, a phone and a shop selling locally produced gifts. An animal park is also nearby. Set meals are based around local produce and trout and cost 18 euros. Breakfast is served when guests wish.

PRICES: s €49; d €56-€66; t €66-€76; dinner €18 **ON SITE:** Forest Fishing Hiking **NEARBY:** Bathing (6km) Horse riding (3km) Swimming pool (7km) Tennis (1km) Sailing (10km) Railway Station (25km) ESTISSAC **NOTES:** No pets English spoken

⚑ Les Fontaines du Betrot Laurent PHILIPPE
23 Rue J. Hector, 10190 ESTISSAC
☎ 03 25 40 67 01 & 06 80 65 54 93

Laurent and his two daughters welcome guests into their house in a lovely shaded park with a lake and a covered heated swimming pool. There is one double bedroom, one twin bedroom and one bedroom with two double beds. Each bedroom has a bath, shower, wc and TV. A cot can be provided. Plentiful breakfasts are available, including jams, honey and pastries.

PRICES: s €30; d €37; t €43; extra person €6 **ON SITE:** Forest Fishing Hiking **NEARBY:** Bathing (6km) Horse riding (3km) Swimming pool (7km) Tennis (1km) Sailing (10km) ESTISSAC **NOTES:** Pets admitted English spoken

FOUCHERES

⚑ Le Prieure Gilles et Sylvie BERTHELIN
Place de l'église, 10260 FOUCHERES
☎ 03 25 40 98 09

This 11th-century priory is situated on a working farm, just next to the church, in a wooded village crossed by the Seine. There are three bedrooms with fireplaces. On the ground floor there is a room with two double beds and on the first floor there is another room with two double beds and one bedroom with two double beds and one single bed. Each has a shower room and wc. In another restored building there are two further bedrooms with furnishings from the 18th and 19th centuries (one double and one single bed).

PRICES: s €35; d €35-€45; extra person €13 **ON SITE:** Bathing Forest Fishing Swimming pool Hiking **NEARBY:** Horse riding (8km) Tennis (5km) Sailing (18km) Railway Station (22km) Shops (4km) BAR SUR SEINE (8km) **NOTES:** Pets admitted

JEUGNY

⚑ IOI La Louviere Jean CHALONS
22 Rue de Villeneuve, 10320 JEUGNY
☎ 03 25 40 21 93 & SR : 03 25 73 00 11
e-mail: jean.chalons@worldonline.fr www.lalouviere.fr.st

Jean and Danielle welcome guests to this old wooden farmhouse. There are two single bedrooms, one triple bedroom and one bedroom with one double and one single bed. The bedrooms are on the same floor along with the bathroom facilities. There is also a communal room and parking. The undulating countryside with forests, rich with mushrooms and game, is ideal for long walks and cycle rides. Possible excursions: Troyes, the Champagne route and the park at the forest of Orient. The cost of dinner is 15 euros, with an aperitif and wine included.

PRICES: s €29; d €37; t €44; dinner €15 **ON SITE:** Forest Hiking **NEARBY:** Bathing (25km) Horse riding (15km) Fishing (15km) Swimming pool (30km) Sailing (30km) Shops (2km) BOUILLY (10km) **NOTES:** No pets

LA-MOTTE-TILLY

⚑ ♿ Les Bienvenues Marie-Louise RONDEAU
12 Rue du Chîne, 10400 LA-MOTTE-TILLY
☎ 03 25 39 83 85 & SR : 03 25 73 00 11

This separate house in a farm courtyard is situated in the Seine Valley, close to the castle of Motte Tilly. Each bedroom has bathroom facilities and a TV point. On the ground floor there is one twin bedroom, suitable for the less mobile guest. On the first floor there are four double bedrooms. A kitchen is available for guests. Plentiful breakfasts include pastries and home-made jams.

PRICES: s €28; d €38 **ON SITE:** Forest Fishing Hiking **NEARBY:** Bathing (4km) Horse riding (10km) Swimming pool (6km) Tennis (6km) Sailing (4km) Shops (4km) NOGENT SUR SEINE (6km) **NOTES:** No pets

LAUBRESSEL

♦♦♦ Au Colombage Champenois Joëlle JEANNE
33 rue du Haut, 10270 LAUBRESSEL
☎ 03 25 80 27 37 📠 03 25 80 80 67
On the tourist route of the Parc Naturel de la Forêt d'Orient, amidst wooded, flower-filled grounds, there are six bedrooms with separate bathroom facilities in an old barn and pigeonry built in the local stone. One double bedroom, two bedrooms with one double and two single beds, one bedroom with four single beds and two bedrooms with two double beds. Two of the rooms have a corner kitchen and one has a fireplace. Washing facilities, a garden and barbecue are available. Plentiful breakfasts include milk, homemade yoghurt, pastries and homemade jams. Private parking.
PRICES: s €25; d €37; t €44; extra person €6 **ON SITE:** Forest Swimming pool Hiking **NEARBY:** Bathing (10km) Horse riding (7km) Fishing (4km) Tennis (8km) Sailing (10km) Shops (8km) LUSIGNY SUR BARSE (10km) **NOTES:** Pets admitted

♦♦♦ La Coraline Nelly NOAILLY
2, Rue Paty, 10270 LAUBRESSEL ☎ 03 25 80 61 77
Nelly welcomes guests to la Corline, a wood-sided house typical of the Champagne region. The house is situated between the lakes of the forest of Orient and Troyes. There are two twin bedrooms and one bedroom for three or five people. There are private bathroom facilities. There is a lounge on the ground floor. Plentiful breakfasts are served. The house has a wooded garden.
PRICES: s €26; d €37; t €43; extra person €9 **ON SITE:** Forest Hiking **NEARBY:** Bathing (10km) Horse riding (7km) Fishing (4km) Swimming pool (10km) Tennis (8km) Sailing (10km) Shops (8km) LUSIGNY SUR BARSE (10km) **NOTES:** No pets

LES CROUTES

♦♦♦♦ ♥ |○| Les Bruyères
Marie-Anne ALBERT-BRUNET
10130 LES CROUTES ☎ 03 25 70 60 90
This contemporary house, full of character, in a wooded park is situated between Champagne and Burgundy on the edge of the Chablis region. There are two double bedrooms and one triple bedroom with a double and two single beds. Each bedroom has its own bathroom facilities. There is a relaxing area around a large fireplace, with a TV and video. A lounge, books and garden are available for guests use. Quality set meals are served. Breakfast features pastries and homemade jams.
PRICES: s €30-€35; d €35-€43; t €50; extra person €9; dinner €17 **ON SITE:** Forest Fishing Hiking **NEARBY:** Bathing (3km) Horse riding (15km) Swimming pool (25km) Railway Station (12km) Shops (5km) ERVY LE CHATEL (8km) **NOTES:** Pets admitted

LONGCHAMP-SUR-AUJON

♦♦♦ Les Tremières Robert BRESSON
Hameau d'Outre Aube, 10310 LONGCHAMP-SUR-AUJON
☎ 03 25 27 80 17 📠 03 25 27 87 69
e-mail: GILBERTE.BRESSON @wanadoo.fr
The proprietor welcomes guests as friends to his traditional house at the foot of the Abbey of Clairvaux, in the Aube Valley. On the first floor there is a triple bedroom with a double and a single bed. On the second floor there is one double bedroom and one triple bedroom with a double and a single bed. Each has bathroom facilities. There is also a communal wc on each floor. The reception room has a large fireplace. Breakfast includes farm milk and homemade breads and jams. There is a veranda, garage and garden. Visits to the Abbey are available every Saturday afternoon.
PRICES: d €34; t €42; extra person €8 **ON SITE:** Forest Fishing Hiking Tennis **NEARBY:** Bathing (13km) Horse riding (3km) Swimming pool (13km) Sailing (40km) BAR SUR AUBE (14km) **NOTES:** No pets

LUSIGNY-SUR-BARSE

♦♦♦ ♥ |○| La Rose des Vents Philippe HUOT
Ferme de la porcherie, 10270 LUSIGNY-SUR-BARSE
☎ 03 25 41 54 20 & SR : 03 25 73 00 11 📠 03 25 41 54 77
e-mail: pat.phi.huot@wanadoo.fr
http://Perso.wanadoo.fr/rosedesvents/
This tastefully restored house in an annexe of the farm offers six bedrooms in a private garden. There are two double en suite bedrooms. On the first floor there are two double bedrooms with a shower and a wc, in a separate wing at garden level one single bedroom with a shower and wc and one triple room with a shower. Each bedroom has a television. There is also a communal room, books, sauna, table tennis and a basement meeting room.
PRICES: s €28-€35; d €40-€43; t €50; dinner €17 **ON SITE:** Horse riding Forest Hiking **NEARBY:** Bathing (4km) Fishing (4km) Swimming pool (20km) Tennis (4km) Sailing (4km) Railway Station (15km) Shops (3km) Restaurant nearby LUSIGNY SUR BARSE **NOTES:** No pets

MESSON

♦♦♦ La Cray 'Othe S.A.R.L. DEBROUWER
10190 MESSON ☎ 03 25 70 31 12 📠 03 25 70 37 03
Five bedrooms in a house full of character, located in a small village in the Pays d'Othe region. There is one twin bedroom, two bedrooms with one double and one single bed, one triple bedroom and one bedroom with one double and two single beds. The surrounding forest is ideal for walks. An adjoining self-catering gîte means a total of 19 people can be accommodated at this property. Ferme-auberge opposite.
PRICES: s €29; d €39; t €46; extra person €54 **ON SITE:** Forest **NEARBY:** Bathing (10km) Horse riding (30km) Fishing (15km) Swimming pool (30km) Tennis (8km) Sailing (30km) Railway Station (15km) Shops (8km) Restaurant nearby ESTISSAC (9km) **NOTES:** No pets

NOGENT-SUR-SEINE

♦♦♦ |○| Péniche la Quiètude Anita FARGUES
Rue de l'Ile Olive, 10400 NOGENT-SUR-SEINE
☎ 03 25 39 80 14 & 03 25 40 79 39 📠 03 25 39 80 14
e-mail: http://perso.wanadoo.fr/quietude/
La Quiètude is a restored barge dating from 1931, moored at Nogent with views over the 19th-century mills. Guests will sleep very well, gently lulled by the sound of the Seine. Nautical types will love the five wood-panelled, themed bedrooms. There is a water level view through the copper portholes. Three double bedrooms, one twin bedroom and one bedroom with a double and a single bed, each with private bathroom and wc. Fireplace, piano, books and lounge. Bikes and a canoe are on board for guests' use. Set meals on reservation.
PRICES: s €39-€53; d €46-€61; t €61; dinner €16-€23 **ON SITE:** Bathing Fishing Swimming pool Hiking Tennis Sailing **NEARBY:** Horse riding (30km) **NOTES:** No pets English spoken

POUGY

♦♦♦ Château de Pougy Antoine MORLET
Grande rue, 10240 POUGY
☎ 03 25 37 09 41 📠 03 25 37 87 29
This superb five bedroom 18th-century property is situated near lakes in a park of about a hectare which is full of trees, many of which are more than 100 years old. There are three double bedrooms, with the possibility of an extra bed, one double bedroom and one bedroom with one double and two single beds. Each bedroom has bathroom facilities. On the first floor there is a small relaxing lounge with tourist information. Fishing in the lake.
PRICES: s €35; d €39; extra person €5 **ON SITE:** Bathing Forest Fishing Hiking **NEARBY:** Horse riding (14km) Swimming pool (30km) Tennis (7km) Sailing (20km) Railway Station (30km) Shops (8km) RAMERUPT (11km) **NOTES:** Pets admitted English spoken

SAINT-GERMAIN

♦♦♦ Les Beauchots Marie MEEKEL
412 Route de Lépine, 10120 SAINT-GERMAIN
☎ 03 25 79 51 92 & SR : 03 25 73 00 11
This charming house that offers five guest rooms has a flower-filled park and an orangery and is situated 6km from the centre of Troyes and 3km from factory shops. On the ground floor, there is one double bedroom with a washroom. On the first floor there are four double or twin bedrooms. All bedrooms are non-smoking.
PRICES: s €38; d €44; extra person €12 **ON SITE:** Horse riding Fishing Hiking Tennis **NEARBY:** Bathing (20km) Forest (15km) Swimming pool (5km) Sailing (20km) Railway Station (5km) Shops (2km) SAINT ANDRE LES VERGERS **NOTES:** No pets English spoken

VIREY-SOUS-BAR

♦♦♦ ⚫ La Ferme de la Chapelle Francis GRIS
28 Rue Jean Monnet, 10260 VIREY-SOUS-BAR
☎ 03 25 29 73 19 & SR : 03 25 73 00 11
This old restored farm is at the heart of the Champagne wine region. There are five en suite bedrooms on the same floor, two have a double and one single bed, two are double bedrooms and one is a single bedroom. This property also has a lounge room with a television, fireplace and corner kitchen. There is a garden in a large flower-filled courtyard, with secure parking.
PRICES: s €18-€24; d €35-€40; t €53; extra person €18; dinner €14 **ON SITE:** Forest Fishing Hiking Tennis **NEARBY:** Bathing (20km) Horse riding (3km) Swimming pool (25km) Sailing (20km) Shops (2km) BAR SUR SEINE (5km) **NOTES:** Pets admitted

VULAINES

♦♦♦♦ Le Saule Fleuri Fandard SCHMITE
7 Rue de l'ancienne Gare, 10160 VULAINES
☎ 03 25 40 80 99 📠 03 25 40 80 99
A five bedroom 19th-century house full of character. The rooms are bright and have been carefully decorated. On the ground floor, there are three double bedrooms and three twin bedrooms. Each bedroom has its own bathroom facilities. Guests will enjoy the quiet, flower-filled garden and terrace. There is a restaurant 200 metres away. Plentiful, varied breakfasts are served, including pastries and homemade jams.
PRICES: s €30-€34; d €35-€42; extra person €10 **ON SITE:** Forest Hiking **NEARBY:** Bathing (5km) Horse riding (50km) Fishing (5km) Swimming pool (35km) Tennis (3km) Sailing (5km) Shops (4km) AIX EN OTHE (5km) **NOTES:** No pets

HAUTE-MARNE

BAY-SUR-AUBE

♦♦♦♦ ⚫ La Maison Jaune
Marian JANSEN-GERRETSEN
Rue Principale, 52160 BAY SUR AUBE
☎ 03 25 84 99 42 📠 03 25 87 57 65
e-mail: jwjansen@club-internet.fr
Langres 32km, Dijon 75km. Next to the River Aube, La Maison Jaune is a beautiful four-bedroom house set in large grounds, with authentic paintings and antique furniture. Breakfast and table d'hôte meals use local produce. Picnics are popular and a hamper can be arranged. TV, games and books, private parking and courtyard. Fishing and swimming in the river. Open all year.
PRICES: s €50; d €60; t €70; dinner €25 **ON SITE:** Bathing Forest Fishing **NEARBY:** Horse riding (14km) Swimming pool (14km) Stretch of water (25km) Tennis (14km) Sailing (25km) Railway Station (32km) Shops (4km) **NOTES:** No pets English spoken

CHALINDREY

♦♦♦ ⚫ Gîtes des Archots Serge et Véronique FRANCOIS
Les Archots, 52600 CHALINDREY
☎ 03 25 88 93 64 & 06 78 02 28 94 📠 03 25 88 93 64
Langres 10 km Set in five hectares, bordered by an old Roman road, and at the edge of a large, wild forest, this house has five bedrooms each with a private showers and wc; two rooms sleep five, two are double/twins, and the fifth sleeps four. Games room, children's play area, book selection and living room. Table d'hôte meals by reservation. Open all year.
PRICES: s €26; d €37; t €47; extra person €11; dinner €12 **ON SITE:** Forest Fishing **NEARBY:** Bathing (10km) Horse riding (3km) Swimming pool (10km) Stretch of water (10km) Tennis (3km) Sailing (10km) Railway Station (3km) Shops (3km) **NOTES:** Pets admitted English spoken

CHAMOUILLEY

♦♦♦ Chambre d'hôtes Liliane et Antoine MARSAL
4 route d'Eurville, 52410 CHAMOUILLEY
☎ 03 25 55 02 26
This is a four-bedroom house with plenty of character. Two rooms are double/twins, and two each sleep three; all have a private showers and wc. TV, courtyard, parking, billiards room and cooking facilities. Separate guest entrance. Open all year.
PRICES: s €30; d €35; t €41; extra person €8 **NEARBY:** Bathing (12km) Horse riding (8km) Forest (1km) Fishing (1km) Swimming pool (8km) Stretch of water (12km) Tennis (1km) Sailing (12km) Railway Station (3km) Shops (1km) **NOTES:** Pets admitted English spoken

COLMIER-LE-BAS

♦♦♦ ⚫ Le Chat-Dodu Terence McNAMARA
52160 COLMIER-LE-BAS
☎ 03 25 88 93 43 📠 03 25 88 93 43
e-mail: LeChatDodu@aol.com
http://members.aol.com/lechatdodu/Index.htm

The English owners have renovated this period home, with superb views, to its former glory. There are four good sized, comfortable double bedrooms with tea and coffee-making facilities and private bathrooms with wc. Living room, reading and music room, and library. The classic table d'hôte menu is by reservation only and vegetarians are welcome. Open all year. Non-smokers only.
PRICES: s €34; d €44; t €55; extra person €11; dinner €14 **NEARBY:** Bathing (4km) Horse riding (4km) Forest (1km) Fishing (4km) Swimming pool (35km) Stretch of water (35km) Tennis (4km) Sailing (35km) Railway Station (35km) Shops (10km) **NOTES:** No pets CC English spoken

Use the atlas at the back of the guide to locate your chambre d'hôtes

ESNOMS-AU-VAL

♯♯♯ ℟ Au Gîte du Val Gérard PASCARD
52190 ESNOMS-AU-VAL
☎ 03 25 84 82 02
Langres 25 km, Dijon 45 km. Each of the four bedrooms in this house has a private shower and wc. Lounge and sitting room, TV and fireplace. Outdoor activities include, mountain biking, horse riding and there are 600 hectares of land and an orchard for ramblers and walkers to enjoy. Open all year.
PRICES: s €27; d €38; t €50; extra person €12; dinner €12
ON SITE: Children's play area Tennis **NEARBY:** Bathing (12km) Horse riding (4km) Forest (1km) Fishing (5km) Swimming pool (25km) Stretch of water (12km) Sailing (12km) Railway Station (25km) Shops (8km)
NOTES: Pets admitted

FLAGEY

♯♯♯ ❧ ℟ Chambre d'hôtes Sylvie JAPIOT
52250 FLAGEY ☎ 03 25 84 45 23
Langres 12 km A family house, renovated by its owners, with four bedrooms sleeping twelve comfortably. Three kilometres from a small village and an old farm, it also boasts a prize-winning garden. The amenities offered are private bathrooms with wcs, lounge, sitting room, TV, library, electric heating and a garage. Mountain bikes hire nearby. Open all year.
PRICES: s €30; d €42; t €54; extra person €13; dinner €13
ON SITE: Forest **NEARBY:** Bathing (5km) Horse riding (10km) Fishing (5km) Swimming pool (12km) Stretch of water (5km) Tennis (5km) Sailing (5km) Railway Station (14km) Shops (5km) **NOTES:** No pets

GRANDCHAMP

♯♯♯♯ ℟ La Vallée Verte Tanja et Alie KALSE-KUIK
52600 GRANDCHAMP
☎ 03 25 88 03 45 📄 03 25 88 03 45
e-mail: info@lavalleeverte.nl www.lavalleeverte.nl
Langres 20km. Le Pailly: château 8km A superb 15th-century manor in the heart of the countryside, with period furniture and paintings. There are two bedrooms and three suites with TV, mini-bar, tea and coffee, private baths and wcs. Breakfast and table d'hôte meals use fresh farm produce. Vegetarians and special diets can be catered for. A library, games room, sitting room and art gallery with exhibitions. Horse riding, fishing and cycling. Open all year.
PRICES: s €46; d €76; t €91; dinner €14 **ON SITE:** Horse riding Fishing **NEARBY:** Bathing (8km) Forest (1km) Swimming pool (10km) Stretch of water (8km) Tennis (10km) Sailing (8km) Railway Station (12km) Shops (12km) **NOTES:** Pets admitted English spoken

LONGEVILLE-SUR-LA-LAINES

♯♯♯ ℟ Chambre d'hôtes Philippe & Christine VIEL-CAZAL
Boulancourt, 52220 LONGEVILLE-SUR-LA-LAINES
☎ 03 25 04 60 18

Lac du Der 15 km. This house sits in quiet parkland with a pond and river and offers five double/twin bedrooms with showers and wcs. One bedroom has an adjoining suite for two children. Nearby for visits: churches, a wildlife museum and an old railway line. Table d'hôte meals by reservation. Open all year.
PRICES: s €41-€50; d €44-€53; t €59-€69; extra person €15; dinner €23
ON SITE: Fishing **NEARBY:** Bathing (15km) Horse riding (7km) Forest (2km) Swimming pool (25km) Stretch of water (15km) Tennis (2km) Sailing (15km) Railway Station (40km) Shops (10km) **NOTES:** No pets English spoken

LOUVIERES

♯♯♯ ℟ Au Pré l'Eau d'Anirol Annie SASTRE
rue Pacotte, 52800 LOUVIERES
☎ 03 25 32 16 49
Langres 20km, Chaumont 17km. Pré l'eau d'Anirol is in an area with plenty of outdoor activities including mountain biking, horse riding and donkey walks, along with woodland to explore. This house offers one bedroom and two-room suites, with private showers and wcs. Also a living room, sitting room, TV and library books. Table d'hôte meals are offered along with regional cuisine tasting by reservation. Parking available. Open all year.
PRICES: s €20; d €42; t €50; extra person €8; dinner €15
NEARBY: Bathing (15km) Horse riding (7km) Forest (3km) Fishing (1km) Swimming pool (7km) Stretch of water (15km) Tennis (7km) Sailing (15km) Railway Station (17km) Shops (7km) **NOTES:** Pets admitted

MANDRES-LA-COTE

♯♯♯ ℟ Chambre d'hôtes
Christiane et Robert LESPRIT
6 rue de Normandie, 52800 MANDRES-LA-COTE
☎ 03 25 01 94 03 📄 03 25 01 94 03
Nogent 4 km. Langres 28 km. This old renovated farm offers accommodation for eleven. There are two double/twin rooms, one room sleeps four, and the two room suite sleeps five. There are private showers, wcs and a TV in each room. Other amenities include library, living room and playground. Parking available. Open all year.
PRICES: s €27; d €34; t €43; extra person €9; dinner €11
ON SITE: Tennis **NEARBY:** Bathing (2km) Horse riding (4km) Forest (1km) Fishing (10km) Swimming pool (4km) Stretch of water (25km) Railway Station (17km) Shops (4km) **NOTES:** Pets admitted

PRANGEY

♯♯♯ Chambre d'hôtes
Monique et Patrick TRINQUESSE
L'Orangerie, 52190 PRANGEY
☎ 03 25 87 54 85 📄 03 25 88 01 21
Lake Villegusien 2 km. Langres 15 km. The owners welcome guests to this charming three-bedroom property set in peaceful countryside next to a château. Each bedroom has a private bathroom and wc. There are two doubles and one twin room. Guests' sitting room. Covered parking. Open all year. Reservations necessary out of season.
PRICES: s €37; d €44-€49; extra person €12 **ON SITE:** Forest **NEARBY:** Bathing (2km) Horse riding (18km) Fishing (2km) Swimming pool (10km) Stretch of water (2km) Tennis (2km) Sailing (2km) Railway Station (15km) Shops (2km) **NOTES:** No pets English spoken

---

℟
Places with this symbol serve table d'hôtes evening meals - remember to book in advance

---

continued

RAUTHOY

♦♦♦ ⓘ◎ⓘ Château de Prauthoy Rémy PUGEAUT
22 grand'rue, 52190 PRAUTHOY
☎ 03 25 84 95 70 & 03 25 87 37 19 ▧ 03 25 87 37 19
e-mail: ch.prauthoy@infonie.fr
Langres 20km, Dijon 45km. An elegant 17th-century château steeped in history, extended in the 19th century and well decorated with period furniture. There are two bedrooms and two two-room suites with private baths and wcs. Breakfast and table d'hôte meals are offered. Sitting rooms, library, TV and video and smoking room. Park with a swimming pool, heated from May to September. Open all year. Reservations necessary.
PRICES: s €78; d €85; t €100; dinner €25 **ON SITE:** Swimming pool Tennis **NEARBY:** Bathing (5km) Forest (2km) Fishing (5km) Stretch of water (5km) Sailing (5km) Railway Station (20km) Shops (1km) **NOTES:** Pets admitted CC

PRESSIGNY

♦♦♦ ⓘ◎ⓘ Maison Perrette Evalyne et Michel POOPE
52500 PRESSIGNY
☎ 03 25 88 80 50 ▧ 03 25 88 80 49
e-mail: POOPEMichel@net-up.com
Langres 30km. A 19th-century mansion, in a quiet and friendly town and close to a fishing pond, offers three bedrooms and a suite. Two bedrooms are double/twin with private shower, one room sleeps three with private shower and wc. The suite sleeps three to four. Sitting room, lounge, games room, TV and library, also a garden and parking. Exhibition of watercolours by the owner. The suite costs €46/75 based on three to four sharing. Open all year.
PRICES: s €29-€34; d €34-€39; t €55; extra person €15; dinner €12 **ON SITE:** Forest Fishing Swimming pool Tennis **NEARBY:** Bathing (10km) Horse riding (15km) Stretch of water (10km) Sailing (30km) Railway Station (25km) **NOTES:** No pets English spoken

See advert on opposite page

ST-BROINGT-LES-FOSSES

♦♦♦ Chambre d'hôtes Marie-Bernard PETIT
52190 ST-BROINGT-LES-FOSSES
☎ 03 25 88 40 83 ▧ 03 25 88 95 23
Langres 19 km. A four-bedroom, renovated farmhouse with swing and garden furniture. Two bedrooms sleep three and two are twin/doubles with private wc and showers. The house is centrally heated and has garage parking. Open all year. Cots are available.
PRICES: s €27; d €37; extra person €12 **ON SITE:** Forest **NEARBY:** Bathing (5km) Horse riding (15km) Fishing (5km) Swimming pool (15km) Stretch of water (5km) Tennis (5km) Sailing (5km) Railway Station (20km) Shops (3km) **NOTES:** No pets

THONNANCE-LES-JOINVILLE

♦♦♦ Le Moulin Myriam et J.Pierre GEERAERT
Route de Nancy, 52300 THONNANCE-LES-JOINVILLE
☎ 03 25 94 13 76 & 06 07 82 90 91 ▧ 03 25 94 02 52
Joinville 3 km. This mill bordering a forest offers four rooms with private showers and wcs. Centrally heated throughout there is also a lounge, sitting room, TV, fireplace and games room, plus a selection of books and videos. A free visit to a crayfish breeding farm is offered! Private fishing facilities at the fixed price of €18 per day, and €12 per half day. Open all year.
PRICES: s €35; d €40; t €50; extra person €12 **ON SITE:** Forest **NEARBY:** Bathing (1km) Fishing (1km) Stretch of water (30km) Tennis (3km) Sailing (30km) Railway Station (3km) Shops (1km) **NOTES:** No pets English spoken

VILLIERS-SUR-SUIZE

♦♦♦ ❤ ⓘ◎ⓘ Chambre d'hôtes Roselyne et Eric GRUOT
52210 VILLIERS-SUR-SUIZE
☎ 03 25 31 11 80 & 03 25 31 23 07
Langres 15 km. Chaumont 17 km. For stargazers, this renovated farmhouse is situated close to a private observatory and recommends starlit walks in the local countryside. The house has two rooms sleeping three and one double/twin, private showers and wcs. Extra beds available. Centrally heated. Lounge, garage parking and garden furniture. Restaurant nearby and mountain bike hire. Open all year.
PRICES: s €30; d €41; t €47; extra person €12; dinner €12 **ON SITE:** Forest Fishing **NEARBY:** Bathing (13km) Horse riding (6km) Swimming pool (15km) Stretch of water (13km) Tennis (3km) Sailing (25km) Railway Station (15km) **NOTES:** No pets English spoken

MARNE

AVIZE

♦♦♦ ⓘ◎ⓘ Le Vieux Cèdre
Imogen & Didier PIERSON-WHITAKER
14 route d'Oger, 51190 AVIZE
☎ 03 26 57 77 04 ▧ 03 26 57 97 97
e-mail: champagnepiersonwhitaker@worldnet.fr
A typical family home, built around 1840, includes amongst its many attractions three guest bedrooms (one double, one twin, and a grade 2 double) each with its own bathroom and wc. In the heart of the Côte des Blancs region there are plenty of wine related activities to pursue. Closed during grape harvesting season.
PRICES: d €42; t €54; extra person €13; dinner €22 **ON SITE:** Forest Hiking Tennis Bicycle hire **NEARBY:** Horse riding (1km) Golf (30km) Swimming pool (8km) Railway Station (10km) EPERNAY (12km) **NOTES:** No pets English spoken

BANNAY

♦♦♦ ❤ ⓘ◎ⓘ Chambre d'hôtes J.Pierre et Muguette CURFS
51270 BANNAY ☎ 03 26 52 80 49 ▧ 03 26 59 47 78

In a rustic setting this charming house offers comfort and relaxation. There are three bedrooms, sleeping eight people, a double, and two triples, each with private bathrooms and wcs. In a separate building there is accommodation for a further four people, featuring a kitchenette, shower and wc. Sample the local farm produce, table d'hôte meals are served. Open all year.
PRICES: s €35-€46; d €43-€52; extra person €15-€26; dinner €22-€25 **ON SITE:** Forest Hiking **NEARBY:** Horse riding (8km) Fishing (5km) Swimming pool (15km) Tennis (10km) MONTMORT (12km) **NOTES:** No pets English spoken

BELVAL-SOUS-CHATILLON

♦♦♦ ⓘ◎ⓘ Hameau du Paradis Daniel GRAFTIAUX
51480 BELVAL SOUS CHATILLON
☎ 03 26 58 13 15 ▧ 03 26 58 11 67

continued

Perfectly situated between forests and vineyards, this charming, renovated farmhouse, sleeps six in comfort, in three double rooms each with private showers and wcs. Table d'hôte meals are strictly by reservation each day except Tuesday, when meals are not served. Open all year.
PRICES: s €32; d €46; t €58; extra person €15; dinner €23
ON SITE: Forest Hiking Bicycle hire **NEARBY:** Horse riding (8km) Golf (15km) Fishing (10km) Swimming pool (15km) Water sports (12km) Tennis (10km) Railway Station (15km) Shops (5km) **NOTES:** No pets

BOURSAULT

♦♦♦ Les Impériales Françoise & Dominique CUCHET
2 rue de l'Ascension, 51480 BOURSAULT
☎ 03 26 58 63 71 & 06 62 70 04 85 📠 03 26 57 87 94
Edged by forest, on the hillside of the Marl Valley, this old house comes complete with vineyards. Five rooms are offered with private showers and wcs, along with a lounge with a park view, sitting room with TV, terrace and garden furniture, separate guest entry hall, and numerous walks and sites to explore locally.
PRICES: s €39; d €42-€46; t €55; extra person €13 **ON SITE:** Forest Hiking **NEARBY:** Horse riding (8km) Golf (15km) Fishing (2km) Swimming pool (10km) Stretch of water (30km) Tennis (3km) Railway Station (9km) Shops (3km) EPERNAY **NOTES:** No pets

BROUILLET

♦♦♦ Chambre d'hôtes Remi et Marie ARISTON
4 et 8 Grande Rue, 51170 BROUILLET
☎ 03 26 97 43 46 📠 03 26 97 49 34
e-mail: contact@champagne-aristonfils.com
www.champagne-aristonfils.com
Reims 20km, Paris 130km. A perfect stopover on the Champagne tourist trail, why not stay a few nights in this delightful 18th-century house, in the Vallee de l'Ardre? Three doubles with private showers or bathrooms and wcs, and TV in each room. Visit cellars and try out some of the wines, or just stroll through the countryside. Open all year.
PRICES: d €42-€46 **ON SITE:** Hiking **NEARBY:** Golf (10km) Fishing (8km) Swimming pool (18km) Tennis (10km) Bicycle hire (5km) Railway Station (11km) Shops (3km) **NOTES:** No pets CC English spoken
See advert on this page

CONDE-SUR-MARNE

♦♦♦ 🍽 Chambre d'hôtes Jeanne BARRAULT
7 rue Albert Barre, 51150 CONDE SUR MARNE
☎ 03 26 67 95 49 & 03 26 66 90 61 📠 03 26 66 82 97
A converted farmhouse of great quality and stylishly decorated, situated in a town in the heart of the Champagne vineyard tourist trail. Three bedrooms, a twin and two doubles, sleep six in comfort. Each room provides shower and wc. There is also a kitchen, dining room, sitting room with TV, veranda and lawn all reserved for the guests' sole use. Activities abound including mountain biking. Table d'hôte meals served on reservation. Open all year.
PRICES: s €30; d €38-€43; extra person €15; dinner €16
ON SITE: Fishing Stretch of water Hiking Tennis Bicycle hire
NEARBY: Horse riding (10km) Forest (8km) Swimming pool (15km) Railway Station (15km) Shops (4km) (15km) **NOTES:** No pets

CONGY

♦♦♦ 🍽 Chambre d'hôtes André et M.Therèse TRUFFAUT
20 rue St Remy, 51270 CONGY
☎ 03 26 59 31 23 📠 03 26 59 60 07
Come and explore Champagne from this family-run house of great charm and character. Five rooms, three doubles and two twins, each with well equipped bathrooms and wc, provide

Maison Perrette
24 rue Augustin Massin
52500 Pressigny
Tel: 03 25 88 80 50   Fax: 03 25 88 80 49
Email: POOPEMichel@net-up.com

Maison Perrette is an elegant 19th century house in the old village of Pressigny with the deserving title of 'Welcoming Village'. Private gardens and terraces surround the house; the inside is full of character with many original features and watercolours by the proprietor. The spacious bedrooms are comfortable, charming and have a bathroom with a shower (34€/46€ for 2, including breakfast). The dinner, traditional French cuisine is served created from local produce (12€ per person, including aperitif, wine & coffee). There are lots of lovely places to walk and cycle and bikes are available. There is a large garage for parking. 30km from the fortified village of Langres and 80km from Dijon.

ARISTON FILS
4 & 8 Grande Rue, 51170 Brouillet
Tel: 00 33 03 2697 4346   Fax: 00 33 03 2697 4934
Email: contact@champagne-aristonfils.com
Web: www.champagne-aristonfils.com

Located in the Ardre valley this 18th century house within the family's business of Champagne production has rooms available for bed & breakfast. The three spacious bedrooms have central heating and bath or shower en-suite. Guests can sample and learn about the prestigious sparkling wines and visit the cellars with a collection of ancient wine producing equipment. Produce from a local collective of farmers and artisans is available for purchase. No smoking.

continued

...dation. There is also a lounge, sitting room, and a lawn ..., along with all the local food and wine to sample. Open during harvesting season.
...S: s €43; d €53; t €69; extra person €15; dinner €23–€34
...ITE: Wine tasting Hiking Bicycle hire **NEARBY:** Horse riding ...km) Forest (1km) Fishing (9km) Swimming pool (20km) Stretch of ...ater (12km) Tennis (20km) Railway Station (25km) Shops (1km) ...MONTMORT (11km) **NOTES:** No pets

CRAMANT

⊞ Chambre d'hôtes Valérie et Patrick VOIRIN
555 rue de la Libération, 51530 CRAMANT
☎ 03 26 57 91 19 🖹 03 26 57 56 29
A family-run enterprise in the middle of the Champagne vineyard region. Four bedrooms provide accommodation for nine. Two grade 3 doubles and two grade 2 rooms sleep two and three people. All have private bathrooms and wc except the grade 2 rooms which share a wc. Other amenities include colour TV and parking, along with panoramic views, and plenty of excursions and activities. Open all year except for harvest season, Christmas and New Year.
PRICES: s €27–€30; d €37–€40; t €46 **ON SITE:** Wine tasting Forest Hiking Bicycle hire **NEARBY:** Horse riding (10km) Golf (25km) Fishing (10km) Swimming pool (8km) Stretch of water (6km) Water sports (25km) Tennis (4km) Railway Station (10km) Shops (1km) **NOTES:** No pets

CUMIERES

⊞ Le Chîne Plat Anne et Jean Pol PATE
177 rue de Dizy, 51480 CUMIERES
☎ 03 26 51 66 46 & 06 80 72 37 39
Abbaye d'Hautvillers 1km. Epernay 3km. Three rooms sleeping a total of seven, each with shower and wc, are provided along with a sitting room, TV and garden furniture. Perfectly located among the vineyards and at the foot of the hills. Open all year.
PRICES: s €37; d €43; t €51 **ON SITE:** Hiking Bicycle hire **NEARBY:** Swimming pool (4km) Tennis (4km) Railway Station (4km) EPERNAY (4km) **NOTES:** Pets admitted

IGNY-COMBLIZY

⊞ i○i Château du Ru Jacquier Robert GRANGER
51700 IGNY-COMBLIZY
☎ 03 26 57 10 84 🖹 03 26 57 82 80
A superb 18th-century château in fifteen hectares of parkland. It boasts six bedrooms of character, each with a bathroom and a private wc, as well as a Louis XVI dining room with fireplace, a Louis XV sitting room, a library and TV. For food there is a recommended restaurant nearby or guests can book the table d'hôte meals. Open all year.
PRICES: s €58–€73; d €61–€76; t €76–€91; HB €27–€38; dinner €15
ON SITE: Forest Fishing **NEARBY:** Golf (9km) Swimming pool (7km) Railway Station (7km) Shops (7km) DORMANS (7km) **NOTES:** No pets

ISLES-SUR-SUIPPE

⊞ Chambre d'hôtes Simone DEIBENER
34 rue du Piquelet, le Chignicourt, 51110 ISLES SUR SUIPPE
☎ 03 26 03 82 31
Accommodating up to seven guests, this house sits on the banks of a river, and has a lovely garden. Downstairs there is a sitting room, dining room, TV, and games. Upstairs the rooms consist of a large grade 2 double with an extra bed, bathroom and wc are separate from the room, also two doubles with showers and wcs. Restaurant nearby. Garage parking. Open all year.
PRICES: s €30; d €40; t €57 **ON SITE:** Hiking Tennis **NEARBY:** Golf (18km) Swimming pool (17km) Railway Station (17km) Shops (1km) REIMS (17km) **NOTES:** No pets

LE GAULT-SOIGNY

⊞ i○i Ferme de la Desire Guy et Nicole BOUTOUR
51210 LE GAULT-SOIGNY
☎ 03 26 81 60 09 🖹 03 26 81 67 95
e-mail: domaine_de_desire@yahoo.fr
This farmhouse offers unique accommodation, in rooms of great style. On the first floor, a Scandinavian-style twin, and a grade 2 romantic-style double, both with bathroom and wc. There is also another room in the proprietors' section of the house, an antique-style room sleeping three, also with bathroom and wc. Situated on farmland and close to a beautiful forest. Table d'hôte meals by reservation. Open all year.
PRICES: s €29; d €34; t €43; extra person €12; dinner €16
ON SITE: Forest Hiking **NEARBY:** Horse riding (3km) Fishing (8km) Tennis (10km) Railway Station (30km) Shops (10km) MONTMIRAIL (10km) **NOTES:** No pets English spoken

LES CHARMONTOIS

⊞ ❤ i○i 👌 Chambre d'hôtes
Bernard et Nicole PATIZEL
5 rue St Bernard, 51330 LES CHARMONTOIS
☎ 03 26 60 39 53 🖹 03 26 60 39 53
e-mail: nicole.patizel@wanadoo.fr
In a rural setting this renovated farmhouse provides accommodation for seven. On the ground floor with its own entry is a double and a small sitting room, and a room sleeping three. Upstairs there is another double. Showers and wcs are in each room. The guests also have the use of a garden, lounge and a piano! Open all year.
PRICES: s €29; d €36; extra person €10; dinner €13 **ON SITE:** Horse riding Forest Fishing Hiking **NEARBY:** Swimming pool (18km) Tennis (9km) Railway Station (18km) SAINTE MENEHOULD (18km) **NOTES:** Pets admitted

LES GRANDES-LOGES

⊞ ❤ 👌 Chambre d'hôtes Etienne JANSON
1 rue de Chalons, 51400 LES GRANDES LOGES
☎ 03 26 67 32 38
An old family house, on a farm, sleeps seven in three rooms, one of which has wheelchair access; each has private shower and wc. During the day guests may use the courtyard, swing and garden furniture. In the evening, why not relax by the fire and play games? There are also kitchen facilities and covered parking, as well as tennis and table tennis in the town nearby. Graduated prices for more than three nights.
PRICES: s €30; d €40; t €50 **ON SITE:** Hiking Tennis **NEARBY:** Forest (10km) Golf (25km) Fishing (6km) Swimming pool (13km) Stretch of water (60km) Water sports (60km) Railway Station (18km) Shops (11km) CHALONS (13km) **NOTES:** No pets

MAREUIL-SUR-AY

⊞ i○i Chambre d'hôtes Guy CHARBAUT
SARL Champagne Guy Charbaut, 12 rue du Pont,
51160 MAREUIL SUR AY
☎ 03 26 52 60 59 🖹 03 26 51 91 49
e-mail: champagne.guy.charbaut@wanadoo.fr
www.champagne-guy-charbaut.com
An ideal place for those who greatly enjoy their wine and good French food. Seven kilometres from Epernay, this is an old house where producers of Champagne still live. There are six distinctive rooms, each with showers and wcs and independent access. A sitting room with minibar, and large enclosed garden are at the visitors' disposal. Special table d'hôte meals are served in an old champagne cellar. Small pets are welcome. Open all year.

continued

PRICES: s €53; d €61-€76; t €99-€115; dinner €30-€46 **ON SITE:** Fishing Stretch of water Bicycle hire **NEARBY:** Horse riding (2km) Forest (5km) Golf (10km) Swimming pool (7km) Tennis (1km) Railway Station (3km) EPERNAY (7km) **NOTES:** Pets admitted English spoken

♦♦♦♦ ⚫ |◯| **Chambre d'hôtes** Yves et Martine GIRAUD
11 rue Sadi Carnot, domaine de la Marotière,
51160 MAREUIL SUR AY
☎ 03 26 52 11 00 & 03 26 52 03 13 📠 03 26 52 95 30
e-mail: lamarotiere@wanadoo.fr
This used to be the home of a master winegrower in the 18th century. It is a very comfortable place with activities and amenities to suite almost every taste. There are three bedrooms, two doubles, and a duplex grade 3 double with extra sofa bed. All have private bathrooms and wcs and are well equipped. Kitchen facilities are provided along with a dining room. Table d'hôte meals are available by reservation, but not on Sunday. Open all year except February.
PRICES: s €53-€61; d €58-€69; t €69-€84; dinner €24
ON SITE: Horse riding Fishing Stretch of water Bicycle hire
NEARBY: Forest (3km) Golf (10km) Swimming pool (9km) Hiking (1km) Water sports (1km) Tennis (1km) Railway Station (3km)
EPERNAY (7km) **NOTES:** No pets English spoken

MARGERIE-HANCOURT

♦♦♦ ⚫ |◯| **Ferme de Hancourt**
Michelle et Denis GEOFFROY
51290 MARGERIE HANCOURT
☎ 03 26 72 48 47 📠 03 26 72 48 47

This separate house in amongst farm buildings offers accommodation for nine. Downstairs there is a family room with kitchenette, TV and fireplace. There are also two bedrooms, grade 2 and grade 3 doubles. Upstairs, one grade 2 room sleeps three, and one grade 3 room sleeps two. All rooms have shower and wc. Guests may use the garden, with outdoor furniture and a swing. Reduced rates are offered for stays of more than four nights.
PRICES: s €24; d €30; t €38; extra person €7; dinner €11 **NEARBY:** Horse riding (15km) Forest (2km) Golf (15km) Fishing (2km) Swimming pool (20km) Stretch of water (1km) Water sports (20km) Tennis (8km) Railway Station (20km) Shops (6km) (15km) **NOTES:** Pets admitted

MATOUGUES

♦♦♦ ⚫ |◯| **Chambre d'hôtes** Jacques et Nicole SONGY
chemin de Saint-Pierre, la Grosse Haie, 51510 MATOUGUES
☎ 03 26 70 97 12 📠 03 26 70 12 42
e-mail: songy.chambre@wanadoo.fr

An extremely comfortable house surrounded by lush countryside and with a relaxed atmosphere. A destination for those who enjoy their food and wine, this house offers gourmet meals, raclette and fondue evenings (except Sundays). The house is close to Champagne vineyards. There are three rooms, a grade two double, and two grade three rooms sleeping between two and four people, all with private showers or baths and wcs. Guests will also find plenty of opportunity for outdoor pursuits such as mountain biking and walking.
PRICES: s €31; d €42; t €46; dinner €18-€27 **ON SITE:** Hiking Tennis **NEARBY:** Golf (18km) Fishing (4km) Swimming pool (10km) Stretch of water (60km) Water sports (60km) Railway Station (8km) Shops (5km) CHALONS-SUR-MARNE (8km) **NOTES:** No pets

MONDEMENT-MONTGIVROUX

♦♦♦ ⚫ **Chambre d'hôtes** Laurent CARBONARO
Domaine equestre Montgivroux,
51120 MONDEMENT-MONTGIVROUX
☎ 03 26 42 06 95 & 03 26 42 06 93 📠 03 26 42 06 94
A typical 17th-century farmhouse of the Brie Champenoise area. Completely renovated, six attic bedrooms provide great comfort and all mod cons; bathrooms, wc, TV and telephone. With plenty of land and stables, there shouldn't be a shortage of things to keep guests occupied, even if its just a relaxing weekend they are looking for. Open all year except November-February.
PRICES: s €53; d €61; t €84 **ON SITE:** Horse riding Forest Hiking Bicycle hire **NEARBY:** Swimming pool (10km) Tennis (10km) Railway Station (38km) Shops (10km) SEZANNE (10km) **NOTES:** Pets admitted

OEUILLY

♦♦♦ **Chambre d'hôtes** Jean-Mary TARLANT
51480 OEUILLY
☎ 03 26 58 30 60 📠 03 26 58 37 31
e-mail: Champagne@Tarlant.com www.tarlant.com
On offer here are four double rooms with private showers and wcs in a separate lodge on a wine grower's property. Perfectly situated for sampling and visiting many vineyards and their produce. As well as being near museums and historic churches, this house has splendid views over the Marne Valley. Open from April until November.
PRICES: s €36; d €43; t €55; extra person €15 **ON SITE:** Wine tasting Forest Hiking Tennis **NEARBY:** Horse riding (3km) Golf (10km) Fishing (2km) Swimming pool (12km) Water sports (12km) Bicycle hire (12km) Railway Station (10km) Shops (3km) EPERNAY (12km) **NOTES:** No pets English spoken

PASSY-GRIGNY

¶¶¶ Le Temple Michel et Chantal LE VARLET
51700 PASSY-GRIGNY
☎ 03 26 52 90 01 ▤ 03 26 52 18 86
e-mail: m.levarlet@free.fr

Amongst historic ruins and some great countryside, four bedrooms offer accommodation for nine people over two floors. All rooms have own shower and wc. Separate guests entrance. Relaxing garden. Open all year.
PRICES: s €47; d €49; t €64 **ON SITE:** Hiking **NEARBY:** Horse riding (10km) Golf (2km) Railway Station (10km) DORMANS (1km) **NOTES:** No pets English spoken

PROUILLY

¶¶¶ Chambre d'hôtes Jean Marie GOULARD
13 grande rue, 51140 PROUILLY
☎ 03 26 48 21 60 ▤ 03 26 48 23 67
e-mail: goulard@club-internet.fr http://surf.to/goulard
A wine grower's home offers three twin bedrooms, each with its own shower and wc. Local amenities, shops, restaurants and a station, are close by. A perfect pit-stop on a trip through Champagne. Closed during the grape harvest.
PRICES: s €32; d €43 **ON SITE:** Wine tasting Hiking Bicycle hire **NEARBY:** Horse riding (8km) Forest (1km) Golf (9km) Fishing (8km) Swimming pool (15km) Stretch of water (25km) Water sports (25km) Tennis (2km) Railway Station (2km) Shops (2km) **NOTES:** No pets

RILLY-LA-MONTAGNE

¶¶¶ Au Chérubin Didier JEANGOUT
3 rue Gervais, 51500 RILLY LA MONTAGNE
☎ 03 26 03 41 90 & 06 10 02 80 52 ▤ 03 26 03 49 39
In the home of the wine grower, three bedrooms have room to sleep seven people (two triple rooms and a double); each room has private shower and wc. Kitchen and barbecue facilities are available as well as a guest room. This house is close to all local amenities and restaurants and is free for children of up to three years. Open year round.
PRICES: s €35; d €43-€52; t €53; extra person €9 **ON SITE:** Forest Hiking Tennis Bicycle hire **NEARBY:** Golf (20km) Swimming pool (7km) **NOTES:** No pets CC

STE-EUPHRAISE-ET-CLAIRIZET

¶¶¶ Chambre d'hôtes Guy DELONG
24 rue des Tilleuls, 51390 STE EUPHRAISE ET CLAIRIZET
☎ 03 26 49 20 86 ▤ 03 26 49 24 90
guydelongch@wanadoo.fr
This wine-growing family home has four bedrooms with showers and wcs (three doubles and a twin). Guests have the use of a large reception room for breakfasts as well as courtyard and garden furniture. A selection of local excursions and the lovely countryside are sure to please. Open all year.

PRICES: s €46; d €52 **ON SITE:** Wine tasting Hiking **NEARBY:** Fishing (6km) Swimming pool (12km) Railway Station (13km) Shops (6km) **NOTES:** No pets

ST-GERMAIN-LA-VILLE

¶¶¶ ✿ Les Perrieres Nicole et Denis LESAINT
7 rue de Chalons, 51240 ST GERMAIN LA VILLE
☎ 03 26 67 51 13 & 06 70 35 40 32
e-mail: denis.lesaint@wanadoo.fr
Denis and Nicole welcome visitors to their guest house in the Champagne region, providing a twin and two double rooms with private showers and wcs along with guest sitting room, TV and kitchenette. Open all year.
PRICES: s €28; d €37; t €45 **ON SITE:** Fishing Hiking Bicycle hire **NEARBY:** Horse riding (10km) Forest (35km) Golf (20km) Swimming pool (12km) Stretch of water (50km) Water sports (50km) Tennis (4km) Railway Station (13km) Shops (4km) CHALONS **NOTES:** No pets

ST-MARTIN-D'ABLOIS

¶¶¶ Chambre d'hôtes Christian DAMBRON
route de Vauciennes, Montbayen, 51530 ST MARTIN D'ABLOIS
☎ 03 26 59 95 16 & 06 81 85 74 23 ▤ 03 26 51 67 91
e-mail: christine.dambron@wanadoo.fr
This vintner's house is well situated, with fabulous views, between a forest and the vineyards. The house offers three double rooms and a triple with an attached children's bedroom (€20 1 person, €34 2 persons). Showers and wcs are provided in each room. There is also a kitchenette, sitting room with TV and stereo and a garden and parking area. Naturally the area offers plenty of activities and visits to cellars and tastings. Open all year. Special rates for children and off season.
PRICES: s €35; d €42; t €56; extra person €14 **ON SITE:** Wine tasting **NEARBY:** Horse riding (10km) Forest (1km) Golf (20km) Fishing (2km) Swimming pool (12km) Hiking (1km) Tennis (1km) Railway Station (12km) Shops (1km) EPERNAY (10km) **NOTES:** Pets admitted English spoken *See advert on opposite page*

VAL-DE-VESLE

¶¶¶ ✿ ᵫ Chambre d'hôtes Joy et Laurent LAPIE
1 rue Jeanne d'Arc, 51360 VAL DE VESLE
☎ 03 26 03 92 88 ▤ 03 26 02 76 16

A rather fine family home at the foot of a Champagne vineyard. This property provides five charmingly decorated rooms over two floors, with private showers and wcs. All the rooms have separate access and reserved for the guests are a dining room, kitchen and sitting room with TV. Many local sights, including a 12th-century church and visits to cellars and vineyards, are on the doorstep here. Open all year.
PRICES: s €35; d €44; t €58; extra person €71 **ON SITE:** Children's play area Fishing **NEARBY:** Forest (4km) Golf (25km) Swimming pool (18km) Hiking (5km) Tennis (2km) Bicycle hire (5km) Railway Station (18km) REIMS (18km) **NOTES:** Pets admitted English spoken

continued

VERTUS

♨ Chambre d'hôtes Serge JUMEL
31 avenue de Bammental, 51130 VERTUS
☎ 03 26 52 02 80 📠 03 26 52 06 58
A wine-making couple welcome guests to this peaceful, lush environment at the heart of the Champagne vineyards. Independent access to three tastefully decorated double rooms plus one twin room. Additional bed and cot possible. Shower and wc in each room. Lounge, TV, fireplace. Terrace with garden furniture. Indoor parking. Restaurants and shops close by. Open all year except during the wine harvest (January and February).
PRICES: s €34; d €41; extra person €12 **ON SITE:** Hiking
NEARBY: Forest (1km) Fishing (2km) Swimming pool (1km) Stretch of water (2km) Tennis (1km) Railway Station (20km) Shops (1km)
NOTES: No pets

♨ 🍴 La Madeleine René et Huguette CHARAGEAT
51130 VERTUS
☎ 03 26 52 11 29 📠 03 26 59 22 09
In a peaceful setting at the heart of the Champagne vineyards, close to the forest, this welcoming farmer's home offers two double rooms with mezzanine and balcony. Independent access to a further room for three people. All have private bathroom facilites. Lounge, TV and phone available. Additional bed possible. Cot free of charge. Climbing and sports ground 800m, tourist and walking routes, vineyard visits. Aerial sports 4 km. Table d'hôte meals by reservation (except Sunday). Open all year.
PRICES: s €30; d €42; t €50; extra person €12; dinner €18-€24
ON SITE: Forest Hiking **NEARBY:** Fishing (2km) Swimming pool (2km) Stretch of water (70km) Water sports (70km) Tennis (2km) Railway Station (18km) EPERNAY (18km) **NOTES:** Pets admitted

VILLE-EN-TARDENOIS

♨ 🐓 Chambre d'hôtes Nathalie et Eric LELARGE
Ferme du Grand Clos, rue de Jonquery,
51170 VILLE-EN-TARDENOIS
☎ 03 26 61 83 78 📠 03 26 50 01 32
Reims & Epernay 20 km. Paris 1 hour. Independent access to four guest rooms on an old farm in a farming village: one double with a connecting single suite and TV; two doubles each with an adjoining double suite (one has a TV); and one double bedroom. All have private bathrooms and wcs. Furnished terrace. Sheltered, locked parking. Restaurant in the village. Shops close by. Lovely walks. Open 1 March to 20 December.
PRICES: s €38; d €46; t €58 **NEARBY:** Golf (10km) Fishing (7km) Swimming pool (20km) Railway Station (20km) REIMS (20km)
NOTES: No pets

VILLENEUVE-RENNEVILLE

♨ 🍴 Chambre d'hôtes Jacques COLLARD
Château de Renneville, 51130 VILLENEUVE RENNEVILLE
☎ 03 26 52 12 91 📠 03 26 51 10 49
At the heart of the Côte des Blancs vineyard, on a wine growing estate, three guest rooms in a peaceful setting. Two double rooms with bathroom and wc and one grade 3 double with shower room and wc. No charge for children under two. Reduced rates after the third night. Gastronomic meals on reservation, six people minimum. Jacques Collard Champagne sold on site, visit the cellars, wine press, etc. Open all year.
PRICES: s €43; d €53; t €69; dinner €23-€38 **ON SITE:** Horse riding **NEARBY:** Fishing (4km) Swimming pool (4km) Tennis (4km) Railway Station (20km) Shops (4km) CHALONS SUR MARNE (20km)
NOTES: No pets

VINCELLES

♨ 🍴 Chambre d'hôtes Alain SIMON
3 rue Paul Chapelle, 51700 VINCELLES
☎ 03 26 58 87 94 & 06 84 43 52 32 📠 03 26 58 87 94
e-mail: simonal@minitel.net
In a village of the Marne valley, in the middle of the Champagne vineyards, four guest rooms in a house with lots of character. First floor: two double grade 2 rooms with private bathroom and wc on the landing, one double grade 3 room with bathroom and wc, one suite for three people with bathroom and wc. Lounge with TV available. Terrace, garden furniture, covered shelter for cars. Guided themed visits, mountain bike hire, boat trips with picnic, golf, fishing.
PRICES: d €46-€69; t €58-€81; extra person €12; dinner €24
ON SITE: Fishing Stretch of water Hiking Bicycle hire **NEARBY:** Horse riding (1km) Forest (1km) Golf (2km) Swimming pool (1km) Water sports (1km) Tennis (1km) Railway Station (1km) Shops (1km) DORMANS (1km) **NOTES:** Pets admitted

🍴 Places with this symbol serve table d'hôtes evening meals - remember to book in advance

🐓 Places with this symbol are farmhouses

FRANCHE-COMTÉ

DOUBS

AUBONNE

♥ ✗ ۞ La Ferme du Château

Véronique LOMBARDOT
2 rue du Château, 25520 AUBONNE
☎ 03 81 69 90 56 ◈ 03 81 69 90 56
Close to the popular Loue and Lison valleys, this 18th-century residence offers three first-floor guest rooms, each with private bath or shower room. The first room has a double bed and bunk beds. The second room has a double bed and a double sofabed, while the third room has its own entrance hall, a double bed and bunk beds. There is a private lounge with TV and a library. The house is set in a huge park with garden furniture and table tennis available; there is also a smallholding within the grounds. Meals feature produce from the farm (not available Monday evening).
PRICES: s €32; d €38; t €47; extra person €9; HB €45-€51; dinner €13
ON SITE: Bicycle hire **NEARBY:** Canoeing (14km) Horse riding (23km) Fishing (9km) Swimming pool (16km) Cross-country skiing (6km) Downhill skiing (23km) Tennis (6km) Railway station (15km) Shops (9km)
NOTES: No pets English spoken

BRETONVILLERS

♥ La Joux Patrick DORGET

25380 BRETONVILLERS ☎ 03 81 44 35 78
This old farm building is typical of the Haut-Doubs region and is entered via a covered bridge. It offers four individually named rooms, each with its own bath or shower room and wc. The 'Mont du Frêne' room contains four single beds, while 'Prés du Fol' is a double room. 'Pierre Perthuis' has three single beds and the fourth room, 'La Racine', is a twin-bedded room. Communal lounge with books and TV, garden furniture within the grounds. There are walking trails from the property, and rock climbing is 5 km away. Restaurant in the village.
PRICES: s €27; d €38; t €49; extra person €11 **ON SITE:** Children's play area Bicycle hire **NEARBY:** Horse riding (3km) Fishing (6km) Swimming pool (26km) Cross-country skiing (8km) Tennis (6km) Railway station (30km) Shops (4km) **NOTES:** No pets English spoken

CHARQUEMONT

♥ Chambre d'hôtes Sylvie MARCELPOIX

Le Bois de la Biche, 25140 CHARQUEMONT
☎ 03 81 44 07 01
Two of the guest rooms at this house are situated on the first floor and are accessed by a private exterior staircase. Grillon ('cricket') 1 has a double bed, bathroom and wc. Grillon 2 (a grade 3 room) has a double and a single bed, bathroom and wc. A single folding bed can be installed if required. There are two further rooms on the ground floor of a neighbouring wing, both of which open onto the terrace. Grillon 3 contains three single beds, a separate bathroom and wc, telephone and TV, while Grillon 4 (grade 3) has twin beds, a shower room and wc, phone and TV. Dining room, library, terrace. Restaurant 100m. Open all year.
PRICES: s €32; d €40; t €55; extra person €15 **ON SITE:** Cross-country skiing **NEARBY:** Canoeing (18km) Horse riding (12km) Fishing (15km) Swimming pool (20km) Downhill skiing (3km) Tennis (12km) Railway station (30km) Shops (5km) **NOTES:** No pets English spoken

CROSEY-LE-PETIT

♥ ✗ ۞ La Montnoirotte Joëlle et Alain BOUCHON

Relais equestre Montnoirotte, route de Vellevans,
25340 CROSEY-LE-PETIT
☎ 03 81 86 83 98 & 06 80 66 85 10 ◈ 03 81 86 82 53
Château de Belvoir 7 km This typical Franche-Comté farm is peacefully set in a secluded, verdant location on the Lomont range, between the Cusansin and Doubs valleys. On the ground floor there is a dining room and covered terrace, and a twin room which is suitable for guests with disabilities. A communal room is available on the raised ground floor; this has a kitchenette and a lounge area with books, TV and video. A washing machine, tumble dryer and TV are also available. The remaining bedrooms are situated on the first floor; these include two double rooms, one with a child's bed or cot if required, and one with bunkbeds. A further room contains two sets of bunkbeds, two single beds and a shower room. Each bedroom has a private wc. Within the grounds there is an unsupervised swimming pool, garden furniture and a barbecue. The owners breed horses, and you can go riding or take lessons with a qualified instructor.
PRICES: s €27; d €41; extra person €15; dinner €8-€14 **ON SITE:** Horse riding Swimming pool **NEARBY:** Fishing (10km) Cross-country skiing (20km) Tennis (10km) Railway station (16km) Shops (10km)
NOTES: Pets admitted

GILLEY

۞ Chambre d'hôtes Marie-Laure XAVIER

10 rue Pasteur, 25650 GILLEY
☎ 03 81 43 35 14 ◈ 03 81 43 35 14
Abbaye de Montbenoit 4km. Clock museum 12km (Morteau). A must for chocoholics, La Fée Chocolatine offers chocolate-making demonstrations and/or courses, with plenty of opportunity for tasting. There are three guest rooms: 'Merisier' and 'A l'Aurore' are both doubles with private shower room and wc; 'Musumara' is a family suite with a large double bed and a single corner bed, private shower room and lounge with hifi. Each room is equipped with a power shower and a TV. An extra bed or cot can be provided on request. Guests are welcome to use the proprietor's lounge. High-quality table d'hôtes meals feature chocolate desserts. The house is set within large, enclosed, tree-lined grounds. Private parking. The price for children over the age of 6 is €9; younger children can stay for free. Open all year.
PRICES: s €23; d €43; t €73; dinner €15 **ON SITE:** Children's play area Cross-country skiing Tennis **NEARBY:** Canoeing (12km) Horse riding (5km) Fishing (1km) Swimming pool (20km) Downhill skiing (24km) Railway station (1km) **NOTES:** No pets English spoken

LAVANS-VUILLAFANS

♥ Chambre d'hôtes Bernard BOURDIER

Ferme du Rondeau, 25580 LAVANS-VUILLAFANS
☎ 03 81 59 25 84 & 03 81 59 26 64 ◈ 03 81 59 29 31
This farm-inn offers four comfortable guest rooms in the main building, and one further room in a separate chalet close by. The ground-floor rooms are both doubles; one has a private bathroom and wc, while the other has its own shower room but shares a wc. On the first floor, one room contains a double and twin beds, the other a double and three single beds. Both rooms have their own bathroom and wc. The chalet room sleeps four (one double and two single beds) and has its own shower room, wc and lounge

continued

area. Guests can sit out on the terrace. Drinks not included in the price of meals. Breakfasts are of a high standard, and you can buy farm produce to take home with you. Longer stays are possible - consult the proprietors for details. Open from January to November.

PRICES: s €42-€50; d €45-€52; extra person €20; dinner €14-€25
NEARBY: Canoeing (8km) Horse riding (18km) Fishing (8km) Swimming pool (9km) Cross-country skiing (6km) Tennis (5km) Railway station (9km) Shops (9km) Restaurant nearby **NOTES:** Pets admitted English spoken

LES ECORCES

♦♦♦ Bois Jeunet Paul & Marie-Therèse PERROT
25140 LES ECORCES
☎ 03 81 68 63 18 ▤ 03 81 68 63 18
In a delightful rural setting, this typical Haut-Doubs house offers three first-floor guest rooms next to three other holiday homes. The single room has its own balcony and a washbasin; a private bathroom and wc are available on the ground floor. Another room has a double bed, single bed and a washbasin; there is a private bathroom and wc on the landing. A further room has a double bed and twin beds, private bathroom and wc. A cot can be provided if required and guests can use the laundry room and library. Table d'hôte meals are available by prior reservation only (€23 per meal), and there are restaurants 2 km away if you prefer to eat out. The house is set within a large park with terrace, swimming pool, table tennis, garden furniture and private parking. Pets are admitted at a charge of €5 per day. Reduced price for children, for stays of more than one night. Open all year.

PRICES: s €30; d €40; t €55; extra person €15; dinner €23
ON SITE: Swimming pool Bicycle hire **NEARBY:** Canoeing (15km) Horse riding (8km) Fishing (7km) Cross-country skiing (1km) Downhill skiing (2km) Tennis (2km) Railway station (25km) Shops (2km)
NOTES: Pets admitted English spoken

LOMBARD

♦♦♦ Chambre d'hôtes Jean-Luc et Andrée CARRIERE
16 Grande rue, 25440 LOMBARD
☎ 03 81 63 67 95 & 06 74 97 19 93
e-mail: CARRIEREJL@aol.com perso.ksurf.net/jlcarriere
This very attractive 'maison bourgeoise' offers three spacious first-floor guest rooms. All three rooms are doubles, and two have an additional child's bed. Each room has a private shower room and wc. Guests have use of a lounge with books, TV and internet access. There is a tree-lined garden with furniture. Private parking. Cot and changing mat available. Restaurant in Quingey, 4 km away.

PRICES: s €30; d €40; extra person €11 **ON SITE:** Fishing
NEARBY: Horse riding (14km) Swimming pool (22km) Cross-country skiing (33km) Tennis (4km) Railway station (5km) Shops (4km)
NOTES: No pets English spoken

VAUDRIVILLERS

♦♦♦ ⚹◎⚹ Chez Mizette Marie-Josephe PHILIPPE
3 rue de l'église, Chez Mizette, 25360 VAUDRIVILLERS
☎ 03 81 60 45 70 ▤ 03 81 60 45 70
e-mail: chez-mizette@wanadoo.fr
//perso.wanadoo.fr/guy.pommier/mizette
Situated in a little village on the Lomont plateau, this house offers four double guest rooms on the first and ground floors, each with private shower and wc. A child's bed can be added. There is a guest lounge with colour TV, library and kitchenette. Grounds not enclosed. Open all year.

PRICES: s €30; d €40; t €53; extra person €13; HB €42; dinner €13
ON SITE: Canoeing Bicycle hire **NEARBY:** Horse riding (11km) Fishing (8km) Swimming pool (23km) Cross-country skiing (19km) Tennis (16km) Railway station (15km) Shops (3km) **NOTES:** No pets

CULT

♦♦♦♦ ◎⚹◎ Les Egrignes Fabienne LEGO-DEIBER
Château de Cult - rte d'Hugier, 70150 CULT
☎ 03 84 31 92 06 & 06 84 20 64 91 ▤ 03 84 31 92 06
e-mail: lesegrigues@wanadoo.fr

Marnay 4 km. Vallée de l'Ognon 4 km. A warm welcome awaits in this beautiful country mansion built in 1854. Succumb to the charm of the peaceful surroundings, the elegant decor and the excellent cuisine. The two double suites and the one twin room all have private facilities. Pastries, home made jams and cereals are served for breakfast, whilst terrines, *magret de canard aux griottines* and *croustillant d'escargots* are served at the table d'hôte meals. Lounge, board games, table tennis, large grounds and bicycles.

PRICES: s €46-€53; d €53-€61; extra person €18; dinner €23
NEARBY: Horse riding (20km) Golf (25km) Fishing (5km) Swimming pool (20km) Hiking (5km) Tennis (5km) Railway station (25km) Shops (4km) **NOTES:** Pets by arrangement English spoken

ECROMAGNY

♦♦♦ ◎⚹◎ La Champagne Luzia et Adalbert BORK
70270 ECROMAGNY
☎ 03 84 20 04 72 ▤ 03 84 20 04 72
Luxeuil-les-Bains 17 km. A renovated farmhouse situated in the middle of woods on the outskirts of the village on the Plateau of 1000 Lakes. Two double rooms each with private adjoining shower and wc; a child's bed is available for one of the rooms; one room with double bed and bed for child up to 10 years, a sofa-bed and adjoining private shower and wc; two twin rooms with adjoining private shower and wc; child's bed available. Lounge with private sitting area and a terrace with garden furniture. Table d'hôte meals.

PRICES: s €29; d €38; t €53; extra person €15; dinner €12-€21
ON SITE: Hiking **NEARBY:** Canoeing (8km) Fishing (1km) Swimming pool (7km) Tennis (7km) Railway station (15km) Shops (7km)
NOTES: Pets admitted English spoken

ESMOULIERES

♦♦♦ ⚹� & Es Vouhey Colette DUCHANOIS
70310 ESMOULIERES
☎ 03 84 49 35 59
An old farmhouse, typical of the Vosges Saônoises and situated in the heart of the Ballon des Vosges regional park where one can explore the picturesque Plateau of 1000 Lakes. The detached cottage consists of: a ground-floor self-catering flat with three twin rooms - one adapted for disabled use - and two double rooms, each with a shower and wc. Kitchenette/dining room/lounge, library, terrace and television. Table d'hôte meals available if booked in advance.

PRICES: s €39; d €44 **ON SITE:** Hiking **NEARBY:** Canoeing (38km) Horse riding (20km) Golf (32km) Fishing (5km) Tennis (20km) Sailing (32km) Railway station (50km) Shops (7km) **NOTES:** No pets

FRAHIER

♥♥♥ ♥ ⍥ Les Gros Chênes M-Elisabeth/Philippe PEROZ
70400 FRAHIER
☎ 03 84 27 31 41 🖷 03 84 27 31 41
e-mail: e-peroz@libertysurf.fr www.amiesenfranchecomte.com

Belfort 10 km. This country house is situated in undulating
countryside at the foot of the Ballon d'Alsace and the Ballon de
Servance. One wing with a separate entrance is reserved for
guests. There are two double rooms, one twin and one room with
four single beds. Each room has a shower and wc. Guests can use
the furnished terrace, the attractive grounds and veranda.
€59/4pers, 15% discount for bookings of 4 days or more. Children
under 5 free. Mini-golf 12 km.
PRICES: s €35; d €40; t €51; extra person €8; HB €29; dinner €12
ON SITE: Children's play area Fishing Hiking **NEARBY:** Canoeing
(5km) Horse riding (5km) Swimming pool (10km) Tennis (10km) Sailing
(5km) Railway station (10km) Shops (1km) **NOTES:** Pets admitted
Minimum 2 night stay English spoken

HUGIER

♥♥♥ Chambre d'hôtes Pierre KNAB
route de Sornay, 70150 HUGIER
☎ 03 84 31 58 30 & 03 84 31 53 82
Situated in the lower valley of the River Ognon this house offers
one room on the ground floor with one double and two single
beds and adjoining private shower and wc. On the first floor is a
room with double bed and child's bed, television and bathroom
with wc and one room for two people with television and
adjoining private bathroom with wc. There is a dining room and
guests have the use of a swimming pool (at their own risk), a
covered terrace, garden furniture, barbecue and private parking
PRICES: s €24-€27; d €32-€38; t €43; extra person €11
NEARBY: Canoeing (15km) Horse riding (3km) Golf (42km) Fishing
(6km) Hiking (6km) Tennis (13km) Sailing (6km) Railway station (30km)
Shops (6km) **NOTES:** No pets

MELIN

♥♥♥ A l'Abri du Pin Raymond VIENNOT
70120 MELIN ☎ 03 84 92 12 50
e-mail: abridupin@chez.com www.chez.com/abridupin
A renovated farmhouse next to the owner's house, in large open
grounds. There are three double rooms, each with adjoining
private shower and wc. Children and babies may be
accommodated. Guests have the use of a breakfast room/lounge
and kitchen facilities, a fireplace, television, a covered terrace with
garden furniture, a garage, barbecue, table tennis table and
bicycles. There is a pizzeria and local produce for sale in the
village and a leisure park 9 km away with cycle trails nearby.
PRICES: s €23-€27; d €29-€34; extra person €8-€15 **ON SITE:** Children's
play area **NEARBY:** Horse riding (15km) Fishing (3km) Swimming pool
(15km) Tennis (15km) Railway station (15km) Shops (7km) **NOTES:** No
pets English spoken

SAUVIGNEY-LES-PESMES

♥♥♥ Chambre d'hôtes Claude-Marie BONNEFOY
70140 SAUVIGNEY-LES-PESMES
☎ 03 84 31 21 01 🖷 03 84 31 20 67
Pesmes 1.5 km. The village of Sauvigny-les-Pesmes is in the lower
valley of the River Ognon - where you can fish, kayak and walk.
Each of the six rooms in the owner's house has its own entrance.
One single room, two double rooms, two rooms with one double
bed and a single bed and one room with a double and two single
beds - each has adjacent private shower and wc. Guests have the
use of a lounge, television, a courtyard, garden furniture and a
lock-up garage. Restaurants 1.5 km. Open 1 March to 31 Oct.
PRICES: s €37; d €43-€50; t €56; extra person €14; dinner €14-€18
ON SITE: Hiking **NEARBY:** Canoeing (2km) Horse riding (20km) Golf
(40km) Fishing (2km) Swimming pool (15km) Tennis (2km) Sailing
(17km) Railway station (20km) Shops (2km) **NOTES:** No pets English
spoken

TERNUAY

♥♥♥ Chambre d'hôtes Urs STOCKLI
Route de Melay, 70270 TERNUAY
☎ 03 84 63 88 05
This house is situated in the Ballon des Vosges Regional Park, with
exceptional scenery including the Plateau of 1000 Lakes.
Accommodation is in the owner's house with two twin-bedded
rooms, one double room, a room with two double beds and a
room with one double and one single bed. Each room has an
adjoining private shower and wc. The dining room and lounge are
shared with the owner. Magazines and games, a terrace, stables
and garden furniture are available. €58/4pers.
PRICES: s €30; d €40; t €49; extra person €9 **ON SITE:** Fishing Hiking
NEARBY: Horse riding (16km) Swimming pool (13km) Tennis (5km)
Sailing (27km) Railway station (13km) Shops (7km) **NOTES:** No pets

JURA

ANDELOT-LES-SAINT-AMOUR

♥♥♥♥ Chambre d'hôtes Harry BELIN
Rue de l'Eglise, 39320 ANDELOT-LES-ST-AMOUR
☎ 03 84 85 41 49 🖷 03 84 85 46 74
Set in a ten-hectare park, this magnificent residence dates
back to the 12th and 14th centuries, and was built by the
illustrious de Coligny family, who predominate throughout the
village and the Suran Valley. There are three bedrooms in the
old keep, and guests make use of a reading room and a large
lounge. Outside there is a courtyard and terrace. Activities on
site include tennis, ballooning and archery. Open all year.
PRICES: d €195; extra person €23 **ON SITE:** Fishing Hiking Tennis
NEARBY: Golf (30km) Shops (5km) SAINT AMOUR (10km)
NOTES: No pets English spoken

ARLAY

♥♥♥ ⍥ Le Jardin de Misette M-Claude & Christian PETIT
Rue Honoré Chapuis, 39140 ARLAY
☎ 01 11 63 86 58
This old winegrower's house is set beside a river in an historic
village with a rich cultural heritage. The pretty flower garden offers
plenty of shade, and is a convivial yet tranquil place in which to
relax. One of the bedrooms is located in a little house in the
garden. Guests have use of a music room, a reading room with a
library of books and an open fireplace. Open all year.
PRICES: d €42; t €55; extra person €13; dinner €14 **ON SITE:** Fishing
Hiking Tennis **NEARBY:** Bathing (3km) Horse riding (6km) Golf (18km)
Cross-country skiing (60km) Downhill skiing (70km) Water sports (30km)
Railway station (15km) Shops (5km) Restaurant nearby BLETTERANS
(5km) **NOTES:** Pets admitted English spoken

BAUME-LES-MESSIEURS

▦ ⎢◯⎢ L'Abbaye Ghislain BROULARD
39210 BAUME-LES-MESSIEURS
☎ 03 84 44 64 47 🖷 03 84 44 90 25
An opportunity to stay in the prestigious setting of the Abbaye de Baume les Messieurs, with very pretty views of the listed village and distant landscape. The three guest bedrooms each have their own bathroom, and there is a large lounge with a billiard table. Regional produce can be bought or sampled in the shop and restaurant on site. Open all year.
PRICES: s €59; d €59; extra person €16 **ON SITE:** Fishing Hiking **NEARBY:** Bathing (12km) Horse riding (20km) Golf (15km) Water sports (12km) Tennis (6km) Railway station (12km) Shops (6km) VOITEUR (6km) **NOTES:** Pets admitted English spoken

BONLIEU

▦ 🐦 Chambre d'hôtes Christine & Dominique GRILLET
12 Rue de la Maison Blanche, 39130 BONLIEU
☎ 03 84 25 59 12 e-mail: dominique.grillet@wanadoo.fr
Set in the heart of the lake region, at the gateway to the Haut-Jura, this early 19th-century farm has been completely renovated to provide four comfortable guest rooms with private bathrooms. There is a delightful garden, a large terrace and a courtyard with garden furniture. Open all year.
PRICES: s €30-€34; d €34-€42; t €42-€50; extra person €8
ON SITE: Hiking **NEARBY:** Bathing (2km) Horse riding (1km) Golf (20km) Fishing (3km) Cross-country skiing (13km) Downhill skiing (30km) Water sports (2km) Tennis (5km) Railway station (18km) Shops (10km) Restaurant nearby CLAIRVAUX LES LACS (10km) **NOTES:** No pets English spoken

BONNAISOD

▦ ⎢◯⎢ Jardin de Champs Derrière
Nicole et Maurice JACQMIN
2 Route de Rieland, Bonnaisod, 39190 VINCELLES
☎ 03 84 25 19 17 🖷 03 84 25 17 78
e-mail: champsderriere@worldonline.fr
www.multimania.com/champsderriere/
Tranquilly set at the heart of the Bresse bocage, this renovated farmhouse offers independent access to its first-floor guest rooms, each with private bathroom. The cowshed has been converted into a large lounge with dining room, library and TV area. Large garden with trees and flowers, terraces and garden furniture and panoramic views of the countryside and the Revermont hills. Table d'hôte meals are served (by prior arrangement) featuring home-grown and regional produce. Open all year. Bikes available.
PRICES: s €35; d €40; t €50; dinner €15 **ON SITE:** Hiking **NEARBY:** Bathing (15km) Horse riding (4km) Golf (15km) Fishing (2km) Cross-country skiing (70km) Downhill skiing (80km) Water sports (25km) Tennis (6km) Railway station (12km) Shops (5km) Restaurant nearby BEAUFORT (5km) **NOTES:** Pets admitted English spoken

CERNON

▦ ⎢◯⎢ Sous le château Françoise LAMARCHE
Viremont, 39240 CERNON
☎ 03 84 35 75 17 🖷 03 84 35 75 17
e-mail: af.lamarche@wanadoo.fr
http://site.wanadoo.fr/sous-le-chateau
Set in a region with a rich natural heritage, this peaceful, comfortable property offers wonderful views of the surrounding countryside. The guest rooms are situated in a chalet, each with its own bathroom. Meals feature produce from the garden. Numerous lakes and forests nearby. Open from 1 February to 31 October.
PRICES: s €41; d €46; t €59; extra person €14; HB €34; dinner €14

ON SITE: Hiking Tennis **NEARBY:** Bathing (5km) Horse riding (12km) Golf (25km) Fishing (2km) Water sports (5km) Railway station (30km) Shops (12km) ORGELET (12km) **NOTES:** No pets English spoken

CHAREZIER

▦ ⎢◯⎢ Chambre d'hôtes Jacqueline DEVENAT
Rue du vieux Lavoir, 39130 CHAREZIER
☎ 03 84 48 35 79
Set in the lake region, this property offers three rooms with private bathroom in a little house in the garden and one further room in the proprietor's house. Guests have use of a lounge, TV room and terrace. The surrounding area is characterised by wide pastures, forests, lakes and waterfalls. Open all year.
PRICES: d €32; t €39; extra person €7; HB €24; dinner €9
ON SITE: Hiking **NEARBY:** Bathing (5km) Horse riding (5km) Golf (20km) Fishing (1km) Cross-country skiing (20km) Downhill skiing (30km) Water sports (5km) Tennis (5km) Railway station (22km) Shops (5km) Restaurant nearby CLAIRVAUX (5km) **NOTES:** Pets admitted

CHATENOIS

▦ ⚕ La Thuilerie des Fontaines Françoise & Michel
MEUNIER 2 Rue des fontaines, 39700 CHATENOIS
☎ 03 84 70 51 79 e-mail: michel.meunier2@wanadoo.fr
//perso.wanadoo.fr/hotes-michel.meunier/michel.htm
On the borders of Franche-Comté and Burgundy, between the Serre Massif and the Chaux forest, and close to the lower Doubs Valley, this mid-18th-century residence offers four guest rooms with private wc and bath or shower room. Guests have use of the reading room and library. There is a heated swimming pool and garden furniture in the shady park adjacent. Open all year.
PRICES: s €34; d €41; t €49; extra person €8 **ON SITE:** Bathing Hiking Tennis **NEARBY:** Golf (15km) Fishing (2km) Cross-country skiing (50km) Water sports (2km) Railway station (6km) Shops (6km) Restaurant nearby ROCHEFORT SUR NENON (2km) **NOTES:** No pets English spoken

GERUGE

▦ 🐦 ⎢◯⎢ La Grange Rouge Anne-Marie VERJUS
39570 GERUGE ☎ 03 84 47 00 44 🖷 03 84 47 34 15
This ferme-auberge has lots of character and is situated in beautiful surroundings. Each bedroom has its own bathroom, and there is a living room with TV. The large garden has several shady terraces. Open all year except end August/beginning September.
PRICES: s €32; d €40; t €50; extra person €10; dinner €11
ON SITE: Fishing Hiking **NEARBY:** Bathing (20km) Horse riding (6km) Golf (6km) Water sports (20km) Tennis (5km) Railway station (16km) Shops (10km) LONS LE SAUNIER (10km) **NOTES:** Pets admitted

GEVRY

▦ ⎢◯⎢ Chambre d'hôtes Monique/Jean Gabriel PILLOUD
3 rue du Puits, 39100 GEVRY
☎ 03 84 71 05 93 & 06-89-33-06-17 🖷 03 84 71 08 08
e-mail: gabriel.pilloud@wanadoo.fr

continued

continued

213

Situated in the centre of a small village, this 18th-century farm offers five guest rooms (each sleeping two or three people). Each has its own bathroom and wc. There is a large dining room, a lounge with open fireplace and a large enclosed park with trees and flower borders. Open all year.
PRICES: s €33; d €40; t €47; extra person €8; dinner €16
ON SITE: Hiking Water sports **NEARBY:** Bathing (3km) Golf (4km) Fishing (1km) Tennis (4km) Railway station (6km) Shops (6km) Restaurant nearby DOLE (6km) **NOTES:** Pets admitted

---

LE FRASNOIS

▦ ⦿⃝ ⅄ Chambre d'hôtes
Laurence & Philippe COLOMBATO
66 route des Lacs, 39130 LE FRASNOIS
☎ 03 84 25 51 32 🖷 03 84 25 51 32
e-mail: pcolomba@club-internet.fr http://auberge.5.lacs.free.fr
This old renovated farm, in the heart of the lakes, offers five rooms with private bathroom, one of which is suitable for the less mobile. There is a mezzanine lounge with TV, library and fire; guests can also sit out on the terrace or in the garden. Baby facilities available. No smoking. Open all year.
PRICES: s €34; d €43; t €56; extra person €13; HB €31; dinner €14
ON SITE: Horse riding Hiking Tennis **NEARBY:** Bathing (1km) Fishing (1km) Cross-country skiing (10km) Downhill skiing (20km) Water sports (1km) Railway station (12km) Shops (10km) SAINT LAURENT EN GVX (14km) **NOTES:** No pets English spoken

▦ Chambre d'hôtes Christian MONNERET
39130 LE FRASNOIS
☎ 03 84 25 57 27 & 03 84 25 50 60 🖷 03 84 25 50 38
This large chalet is situated in the middle of a small valley, in the heart of the lakes. The four guest rooms sleep between three and five people. Each room has a private shower room and wc, a seating area and access to a private terrace. Two rooms also have a mezzanine level. There is a large communal lounge and the nearest inn is only 100m away. Botanical garden and exhibition on site. Open 1 February to 11 November and 20 December to 5 January.
PRICES: s €34; d €43-€48; t €53-€57; extra person €10 **ON SITE:** Hiking **NEARBY:** Bathing (1km) Horse riding (1km) Golf (30km) Fishing (1km) Cross-country skiing (6km) Downhill skiing (20km) Water sports (1km) Tennis (2km) Railway station (10km) Shops (3km) Restaurant nearby CLAIRVAUX LES LACS (18km) **NOTES:** No pets English spoken

---

LES-PLANCHES-EN-MONTAGNE

▦ ⦿⃝ A la Montagne Ronde Didier PREVOT
3 chemin de la Montagne Ronde,
39150 LES-PLANCHES-EN-MONTAGNE
☎ 03 84 51 53 98 🖷 03 84 51 49 48
In a very restful countryside location, this huge old Jura farmhouse has been completely renovated to provide charming, tasteful guest rooms. Regional cuisine is served at table d'hôte meals every evening except Friday. The river is just a couple of steps away, and the Gorges de la Langouette are close by. Closed October.
PRICES: s €32; d €40; extra person €15; HB €14; dinner €17
ON SITE: Fishing Hiking **NEARBY:** Bathing (12km) Horse riding (6km) Golf (35km) Cross-country skiing (10km) Downhill skiing (6km) Water sports (12km) Tennis (4km) Railway station (15km) Shops (15km) SAINT LAURENT EN GVX (20km) **NOTES:** No pets English spoken

---

MONTIGNY-SUR-AIN

▦ ⦿⃝ Au Douillet Gourmet
Christelle & Pascal OLIVIER
Rue du Château, 39300 MONTIGNY-SUR-AIN
☎ 03 84 51 27 24 & SR : 03 84 87 08 88 🖷 03 84 51 28 14

This renovated farm offers three very individual guest rooms, each with its own bathroom. Rivers, waterfalls, lakes and forests form the backdrop to the region. Open all year.
PRICES: s €27; d €41; extra person €12; dinner €15 **ON SITE:** Hiking **NEARBY:** Bathing (10km) Horse riding (3km) Golf (25km) Fishing (10km) Cross-country skiing (30km) Downhill skiing (45km) Water sports (10km) Railway station (20km) Shops (4km) Restaurant nearby CHAMPAGNOLE (13km) **NOTES:** No pets English spoken

---

PRESILLY

▦ ⦿⃝ La Barratte Régine CHALET
39270 PRESILLY
☎ 03 84 35 55 18 🖷 03 84 35 56 05
Présilly is a small village on a plateau, close to the Vouglans lake and dominated by an 11th-13th-century castle. This old village farmhouse has been completely renovated to provide 4 guest rooms with private bathrooms and TV. There is a large communal lounge with an open fireplace. Regional dishes await you at the table d'hôtes, the price of which includes wine. Open all year.
PRICES: s €45; d €51; extra person €21; HB €42; dinner €17
NEARBY: Bathing (10km) Horse riding (9km) Golf (18km) Fishing (3km) Hiking (2km) Cross-country skiing (50km) Downhill skiing (65km) Water sports (10km) Tennis (3km) Railway station (15km) Shops (8km) ORGELET (8km) **NOTES:** Pets on request

---

ROTALIER

▦ ⦿⃝ Château Gréa Pierre DE BOISSIEU
39190 ROTALIER
☎ 03 84 25 05 07 🖷 03 84 25 18 87
Situated in the sunny Jura vineyards, Château Gréa is a beautiful 18th century building. The bedrooms - two suites and two double rooms - are magnificently equipped. From the terrace, you can see as far as Burgundy. Table d'hôte on request. Open all year.
PRICES: s €58-€61; d €70-€73; extra person €23; dinner €15
ON SITE: Hiking **NEARBY:** Bathing (12km) Horse riding (6km) Golf (12km) Fishing (4km) Water sports (40km) Tennis (5km) Railway station (12km) Shops (5km) Restaurant nearby BEAUFORT (5km) **NOTES:** No pets

---

SAINT-AMOUR

▦ ⦿⃝ L'Achapt Rita et Hans NAEGELI
6 Avenue de Lyon, 39160 SAINT-AMOUR
☎ 03 84 48 75 70 🖷 03 84 48 70 50
e-mail: lachapt@wanadoo.fr
This beautiful, late 18th-century residence dominates the town of Saint-Amour. The park is planted with old trees, while a large, beautiful rotunda borders the pool and opens onto a flower-filled garden. The five double rooms have private bathrooms, and there is a reading room, TV and sauna. Open April to September.
PRICES: s €50; d €60 **ON SITE:** Hiking Swimming pool
NEARBY: Bathing (10km) Golf (35km) Fishing (1km) Water sports (10km) SAINT AMOUR **NOTES:** No pets English spoken

---

SAMPANS

▦ ⦿⃝ Au champs du Bois Colette LAGE
Route de Dole, 39100 SAMPANS
☎ 03 84 82 25 10 🖷 03 84 82 25 10
This pretty manor house dates from the beginning of the last century, and is situated 4 km from Dole, Pasteur's birthplace. The three stylish bedrooms each have their own wc and bath or shower room. There is a large, enclosed wooded park with parking for boats and trailers. Guests may use the library and TV lounge. Open all year.

continued   continued

PRICES: s €33; d €40; t €47 **ON SITE:** Fishing Hiking
NEARBY: Bathing (4km) Golf (10km) Water sports (4km) Tennis (4km)
Railway station (4km) Restaurant nearby DOLE (4km) **NOTES:** Pets
admitted English spoken

SYAM

¶¶¶¶ Vieux Château Jean-Paul GAY BANTEGNIE
SCI Alesia, Château Bontemps, 39600 ARBOIS
☎ 03 84 66 25 34 & 03 84 66 14 13 ▤ 03 84 66 14 13
At the heart of the lakes and the Haut-Jura, the Domaine de
Syam is a collection of buildings with multicoloured roofs. This
magnificent residence with period furnishings offers bedrooms
with private bathrooms, TV and telephone. Guests have use of
a reception room and a library. There is a river and a fishing
course in the park. Open April to September.
PRICES: s €43; d €58 **ON SITE:** Bathing Fishing Hiking Water
sports **NEARBY:** Horse riding (10km) Cross-country skiing (15km)
Downhill skiing (50km) Tennis (5km) Railway station (8km) Shops
(8km) Restaurant nearby CHAMPAGNOLE (8km) **NOTES:** No pets
English spoken

VILLERS-ROBERT

¶¶¶ ⦶ Le Moulin Jacqueline MONAMY
39120 VILLERS-ROBERT ☎ 03 84 71 52 39
This old restored mill offers bedrooms with private bathrooms.
Guests may use the dining room and lounge with open fireplace.
The tree-lined park borders the river, and private fishing is
possible in the grounds. Open all year.
PRICES: s €41; d €49; t €66; dinner €11; dinner €15
ON SITE: Bathing Fishing Hiking Tennis **NEARBY:** Golf (7km) Water
sports (15km) Railway station (15km) Shops (8km) Restaurant nearby
CHAUSSIN (8km) **NOTES:** Pets admitted English spoken
See advert on this page

VOITEUR

¶¶¶ ⦶ Chambre d'hôtes Colette MONACI
5 route de Menetrux, 39210 VOITEUR ☎ 03 84 85 28 43
This modern house nestles in a verdant riverside setting at the
heart of the Jura vineyards. Bedrooms have their own bathrooms,
and guests are welcome to use the lounge or sit out on the terrace
or in the garden. There is a private pool and bicycles can be
borrowed. Table d'hôte meals served by prior arrangement. Open
all year.
PRICES: s €43; d €49; dinner €14 **ON SITE:** Fishing Hiking
NEARBY: Bathing (10km) Horse riding (10km) Golf (15km) Cross-
country skiing (50km) Downhill skiing (70km) Water sports (20km)
Tennis (10km) Railway station (10km) VOITEUR **NOTES:** No pets
English spoken

Le Moulin
39120 Villers-Robert
Tel: 03 84 71 52 39

An old mill once owned by Marcel Aymé's uncle has
been restored to provide three character bedrooms and
two communicating family rooms. All have en-suite and
TV. Also available is a large en-suite bedroom with its
own entrance and fireplace. Guests have use of lounge
and dining room. There are walks in the extensive
wooded garden or along the adjoining river.
Private fishing is possible and the area is outstanding
for ponds and forests. Nearby is Dole birthplace of
Pasteur. Open all year.

¶¶¶¶ ⦶ Château Saint-Martin
Brigitte et Mickaël KELLER
39210 VOITEUR
☎ 03 84 44 91 87 ▤ 03 84 44 91 87
Most of this huge, beautiful house dates back to the 14th
century, although it was extended in the 17th and 18th
centuries. There are five guest rooms with three double and
three single beds. The large park contains a kitchen garden, a
small vineyard, large terraces and old trees. Open all year.
PRICES: s €91; d €61-€100; extra person €23; dinner €16
ON SITE: Fishing Hiking **NEARBY:** Bathing (10km) Horse riding
(15km) Golf (10km) Water sports (10km) Tennis (10km) Railway
station (10km) VOITEUR **NOTES:** No pets English spoken

TERRITOIRE-DE-BELFORT

LEPUIX-GY

¶¶¶ 🐦 Chambre d'hôtes Michel MOREL
Ballon d'Alsace, 90200 LEPUIX-GY ☎ 03 84 23 97 21
This convivial property is at the heart of the Parc Naturel Régional
des Ballons des Vosges. The four bedrooms sleep two people - one
has twin beds - and each has its own bathroom and wc. In the two
guest lounges there are comfortable sofas, armchairs, tables and
chairs, plus a TV. The panoramic view is quite exceptional.
Activities include paragliding, mountain biking, skiing, and hiking.
Open all year.
PRICES: s €35; d €45; extra person €12; HB €46; FB €67; dinner €14
ON SITE: Hiking Cross-country skiing **NEARBY:** Horse riding (5km)
Golf (25km) Swimming pool (20km) Tennis (10km) Railway station
(30km) Shops (10km) Restaurant nearby **NOTES:** Pets admitted

ILE-DE-FRANCE

ESSONNE

MILLY-LA-FORET

♥ Ferme de la Grange Rouge
Sophie et J-Charles DESFORGES
route de Gironville, 91490 MILLY-LA-FORET
☎ 01 64 98 94 21 ▤ 01 64 98 99 91
Milly-la-Forêt 3 km. Sophie and Jean-Charles welcome you to their 15th-century farm, typical of the region and set amidst fields. There is independent access to each of the five character bedrooms. There are three double rooms and two twin rooms in which an extra bed can be provided. Each room is equipped with a TV point, a shower room and wc.
PRICES: s €33; d €40; extra person €10 **NEARBY:** Horse riding (4km) Forest (5km) Golf (14km) Fishing (6km) Swimming pool (4km) Tennis (4km) Railway station (4km) Shops (3km) MILLY LA FORET (3km)
NOTES: No pets

MOIGNY-SUR-ECOLE

▥ Chambre d'hôtes Frédéric LENOIR
9 rue du Souvenir, Milly-la-Forêt, 91490 MOIGNY-SUR-ECOLE
☎ 01 64 98 47 84 ▤ 01 64 98 05 92
Milly-la-Forêt 3 km. Situated in a pretty village, this character property offers three separate guest rooms. There is one double bedroom on the ground floor and a second double on the first floor, where an extra bed can be installed. There is also a suite on the first floor, containing two single beds (extra bed possible). Each room has a TV and private shower room and wc. Breakfast room with kitchenette, huge lounge. Table d'hôte meals served by prior arrangement; wine not included. Landscaped garden with furniture. The GR11 path is nearby, as is the forest of Fontainebleau. Restaurant 3 km. Open all year. Limited parking.
PRICES: s €32; d €43-€49; t €55; extra person €9; dinner €13
NEARBY: Horse riding (1km) Forest (1km) Golf (7km) Fishing (1km) Swimming pool (3km) Tennis (3km) Railway station (9km) Shops (3km) MILLY LA FORET (3km) **NOTES:** Pets admitted English spoken

SACLAS

♥ Ferme des Prés de la Cure
André et Françoise SOUCHARD
17 rue Jean Moulin, 91690 SACLAS
☎ 01 60 80 92 28
Monsieur and Madame Souchard are your welcoming hosts at this beautiful 15th-century farm, situated in the heart of the village. There is independent access to the three first-floor guest rooms; each one has a double bed, private shower room and wc, a TV point, and lots of character. An additional single bed can be installed on request. A huge breakfast is served in the living room, and guests have access to the terrace and garden. The farm is close to a landscaped garden with a stretch of water and the GR111 walking path. Restaurants close by. Open all year except December to February.
PRICES: s €38; d €46; extra person €11 **ON SITE:** Forest Fishing Tennis **NEARBY:** Horse riding (5km) Golf (12km) Swimming pool (6km) Railway station (8km) MEREVILLE (5km) **NOTES:** No pets

VERT-LE-GRAND

♥ ▥ Chambre d'hôtes Lucette LE MEZO
10 rue des Herses, 91810 VERT-LE-GRAND
☎ 01 64 56 00 28

Arpajon 10 km. Paris 35 km. In a village farm, Madame Le Mezo offers two guest rooms on the first floor of her house. The grade 3 suite comprises two bedrooms (one double and one single bed), private shower room and wc. There are two further bedrooms with two double beds and one single, TV point, private shower room and wc. Grade 2 room also available. Parking in the courtyard. A copious breakfast is served in the lounge beside the open fireplace. Table d'hôte meals are possible; drinks are not included. Fishing lakes and walking paths (GR11C) are nearby, as is the Château de Ballancourt. Restaurants 4 km. Open all year.
PRICES: s €30; d €35-€50; t €60; extra person €11; dinner €14
NEARBY: Horse riding (1km) Forest (1km) Golf (3km) Fishing (3km) Swimming pool (6km) Tennis (1km) Railway station (8km) Shops (1km)
NOTES: No pets

SEINE-ET-MARNE

BREAU

▥ Ferme Relais Du Couvent
Nicole et Jacques LEGRAND, Relais du Couvent, 77720 BREAU
☎ 01 64 38 75 15 ▤ 01 64 38 75 75
e-mail: Ferme.Couvent@wanadoo.fr
www.lafermeducouvent.com
Paris 50 km. Melun 15 km. A very pretty restored farm with six hectares of land, this property offers lots of activities including tennis, mountain biking and hot-air ballooning - the farm speciality. On the ground floor there is a breakfast room, a bedroom with a double and a single bed, and a bedroom with a double and two singles. There is a double bedroom on the first floor. Each has an en suite shower room and wc. Phone and baby-sitting service available.
PRICES: s €38; d €43; extra person €19; dinner €16 **ON SITE:** Forest Tennis **NEARBY:** Bathing (7km) Golf (5km) Theme park (30km) Railway station (7km) Shops (1km) **NOTES:** Pets admitted English spoken

BUSSY-ST-MARTIN

▥ Chambre d'hôtes Judith et Gabor ULVECZKI-KOSA
9 rue du Parc, 77600 BUSSY-ST-MARTIN
☎ 01 64 66 01 23 ▤ 01 64 66 36 66
e-mail: ulgab@wanadoo.fr
Paris 25 km. Disneyland Paris 6 km. Situated in a large, tree-lined garden, in a very beautiful village, this old house is within easy access of many tourist sights. Accommodation is in an independent wing of the house. The first family suite is made up of two bedrooms, each containing a double and single bed, a bathroom and wc. There is another double bedroom with bathroom and wc. The lounge/breakfast room has an open fireplace. On the first floor there is another suite comprising one room with a double and a single bed and another single bedroom, shower room and wc. Kitchenette and dining area, terrace and garden.
PRICES: s €42; d €45; extra person €19 **NEARBY:** Bathing (3km) Forest (3km) Golf (2km) Theme park (6km) Tennis (2km) Railway station (3km) Shops (3km) **NOTES:** Pets admitted on request CC English spoken

CHARTRETTES

▥ Château de Rouillon Peggy MORIZE-THEVENIN
41 avenue Charles De Gaulle, 77590 CHARTRETTES
☎ 01 60 69 64 40 & 06 12 52 79 91 ▤ 01 60 69 64 55
e-mail: chateau.de.rouillon@club-internet.fr
Paris 53 km. Fontainebleau 10 km. The Château de Rouillon is a magnificent 17th-century property, situated in two hectares of

continued   continued

lovely parkland on the banks of the Seine. The grounds include a French garden and terrace. The lounge and dining room are on the ground floor and there is both a book and a video library. On the first floor, there is a large double bedroom and a suite containing a very large double bedroom with views over the Seine and the park, and a lounge area. On the second floor, there is a huge double bedroom, and one small single room. Another suite has a double and a twin room. All rooms have bathroom and wc. **PRICES:** s €54-€61; d €60-€75; extra person €25 **NEARBY:** Bathing (5km) Forest (2km) Golf (2km) Theme park (70km) Tennis (2km) Railway station (3km) Shops (1km) **NOTES:** No pets English spoken

CHATRES

¶¶¶ ¡Ol Le Portail Bleu Dominique et Pierre LAURENT
2 route de Fontenay, 77610 CHATRES
☎ 01 64 25 84 94 📄 01 64 25 84 94
e-mail: leportailbleu@voila.fr
Paris 40 km. Tounan-en-Brie 7 km. Disneyland Paris 20 km.
Le Portail Bleu is a welcoming, renovated old farm. There are two bedrooms with lots of character. The first is on the ground floor and is a comfortable double with a shower room and wc. On the first floor, there is a family room with one double bed and three single beds, shower room and wc. There is an enclosed country garden and table tennis. Picnic baskets prepared on request. Baby-sitting service available. Excellent walks nearby.
PRICES: s €42; d €49; extra person €17; dinner €19 **ON SITE:** Tennis **NEARBY:** Bathing (5km) Forest (1km) Golf (25km) Theme park (20km) Railway station (7km) **NOTES:** No pets English spoken

CHOISY-EN-BRIE

¶¶¶ La Marvallère Catherine et Jean MORRIOT
10 rue Bulot, Champonnois, 77320 CHOISY-EN-BRIE
☎ 01 64 04 46 80 & 06 15 09 15 86 📄 01 64 20 44 96
e-mail: cjmorriot@aol.com http://members.aol.com/cjmorriot/

Paris 80 km. Situated 35 minutes from Disneyland Paris, between Coulommiers and La Ferté-Gaucher in the hamlet of Champonnois, this large house, typical of the Brie region, has been tastefully renovated, and has a large flower garden and terrace. The ideal location for peace and relaxation, you will feel at home in the four bedrooms (for 2 to 4 people), each with private bathroom. A family room is available, and a cot can be provided. The lounge/drawing room has a large fireplace, library and television.
PRICES: s €47; d €53; extra person €18 **NEARBY:** Bathing (10km) Forest (10km) Golf (5km) Theme park (40km) Tennis (6km) Railway station (10km) Shops (3km) **NOTES:** No pets English spoken

COURPALAY

¶¶¶ Ferme de Gratteloup Patrick BERTRAND
77540 COURPALAY
☎ 01 64 25 63 04 & 06 07 79 91 07 📄 01 64 25 63 04

Paris 50 km. Melun 25 km. Disneyland Paris 20 km. Rozay-en-Brie 5 km. This renovated equestrian farm has lots of character and dates back to 1383. Isolated in three hectares of undulating grounds, it is rustic in style. Breakfast is served beside the fire in winter or in the shade of parasols in the summer. On the first floor, there are two double bedrooms, and one bedroom with a double and a single bed. There is also a family room with one double and three single beds. Each room has a shower room and wc. Games are provided for the children and the atmosphere is cosy and warm. For walkers, the GR1 is three kilometres away. Special deals available for horse riders and ramblers.
PRICES: s €38; d €43; extra person €17 **ON SITE:** Children's play area **NEARBY:** Bathing (1km) Forest (4km) Golf (12km) Theme park (20km) Tennis (1km) Railway station (10km) Shops (1km) **NOTES:** Pets admitted on request English spoken

CRECY-LA-CHAPELLE

¶¶¶ ¡Ol La Herissonière
T et S BORDESSOULE-BESSELIEVRE
4 rue du Barrois, 77580 CRECY-LA-CHAPELLE
☎ 01 64 63 00 72 & 06 11 24 16 93 📄 01 64 63 06 07

Paris 45 km. Meaux 15 km. Disneyland Paris 15 km. In the heart of the village, bordered by a branch of the Morin river, La Herissonière provides a warm, friendly atmosphere. Accommodation is in five comfortable, tastefully decorated bedrooms, four with one double and one single bed, and one double bedroom. Each bedroom has either an en suite bathroom or shower room, a wc and a TV. A large terrace and floral pergola make up the charming garden on two sides of the building. There is a lounge and dining room where a set menu can be served on request.
PRICES: s €50; d €60; extra person €20; dinner €20 **ON SITE:** Tennis **NEARBY:** Bathing (15km) Forest (3km) Golf (15km) Theme park (15km) Railway station (1km) **NOTES:** Pets admitted English spoken

CRISENOY

¶¶¶ Chambre d'hôtes Josette et Alain VALERY
6 rue de l'Eglise, 77390 CRISENOY
☎ 01 64 38 83 20
Paris 55 km. Melun 12 km. This very beautiful house is a well maintained and tasteful property, set within a village. Enjoy the enclosed garden and terrace and the warm atmosphere and friendly welcome. The breakfast room is on the ground floor. On the first floor there are two double bedrooms with a cot. There is independent access to the third double bedroom, overlooking the garden. There is also a further double room; all have en suite facilities. The rustic lounge has an open fireplace and a cooking area.
PRICES: s €35; d €40; extra person €16 **NEARBY:** Bathing (12km) Forest (5km) Golf (18km) Theme park (35km) Tennis (1km) Railway station (12km) Shops (6km) **NOTES:** Pets admitted English spoken

continued

ECHOUBOULAINS

♥ Ferme de la Recette Famille DUFOUR
Echou, 77820 ECHOUBOULAINS
☎ 01 64 31 81 09 📠 01 64 31 89 42
www.aubergeetfermeauberge.com
Paris 65 km. Fontainebleau 20 km. Melun 20 km. This large farm has stacks of charm and tasteful décor. The breakfast room is on the ground floor, on the first floor, there are three double bedrooms, each with a shower and wc. This is an ideal spot for rambling and mountain biking. Self-catering gîtes available.
PRICES: s €38; d €43; extra person €17 **NEARBY:** Bathing (10km) Forest (1km) Golf (15km) Tennis (3km) Railway station (10km) Shops (3km) Restaurant nearby **NOTES:** No pets English spoken

GRISY-SUR-SEINE

♥ ⵔ Ferme de Toussacq
Dominique et J.Louis COLAS
Grisy-sur-Seine, 77480 VILLENAUXE-LA-PETITE
☎ 01 64 01 82 90 📠 01 64 01 82 61
e-mail: toussacq@terre-net.fr
Paris 95 km. Just off the D411, on the banks of the Seine and 1 hour 15 minutes from Paris, this welcoming farm is located within the park of a château, complete with a pigeonnier and chapel. Renovated from a former sheep fold, the farm has two bedrooms on the ground floor and three bedrooms on the first floor (sleeping two to three people each). Each room has either a shower or bathroom. On the ground floor, there is a dining room with a guests' kitchen area. There is a conservatory. TV is provided in the sitting room and in the bedrooms on request. Large homemade breakfasts with farm produce are served and other meals, including vegetarian, can be provided on request, except Sunday and Tuesday nights. A calm, relaxing atmosphere is assured. Fishing, walking, boat hire and bathing are all possible.
PRICES: s €38; d €45; extra person €15; dinner €12 **NEARBY:** Bathing (18km) Forest (13km) Golf (35km) Theme park (80km) Tennis (3km) Railway station (15km) Shops (6km) **NOTES:** Pets admitted English spoken

LA CHAPELLE-RABLAIS

Château des Moyeux
Corinne et Stéphane FOURNOL
77370 LA CHAPELLE-RABLAIS
☎ 01 64 08 49 51 & 01 64 08 42 74 📠 01 64 08 49 51
e-mail: ch.d.m@wanadoo.fr site.voila.fr/ch_d_moyeux
Paris 70 km. Fontainebleau 20 km. Provins 20 km. Le Château des Moyeux was rebuilt in the 18th century and is situated in a large, 30-hectare park. Three double guest rooms are available on each floor, each with a bathroom and wc. On the ground floor, there is a lounge with a large fireplace and a small music room and dining room. There is also a library with a fireplace and an orangerie housing a swimming pool. Breakfast in style in this superb setting. Explore the chapel crypt or the beautiful, romantic park. Restaurants nearby. Discounts possible for week-long bookings or long weekends. A cot is available on request.
PRICES: s €76; d €91 **ON SITE:** Bathing Forest **NEARBY:** Golf (5km) Theme park (60km) Tennis (6km) Railway station (6km) Shops (6km) **NOTES:** No pets English spoken

LE CHATELET-EN-BRIE

♥ La Fauconnière Christophe DUMORTIER
77820 LE CHATELET-EN-BRIE
☎ 01 60 69 40 45 & 06 70 63 76 49 📠 01 60 69 40 45
Paris 57 km. Vaux-le-Vicomte 14 km. Fontainebleau 12 km. La Fauconnière is a very pretty, well-maintained farm with a cosy feel. The breakfast room is on the ground floor. On the first floor, there

are two double bedrooms with private bathrooms and wcs. There is also a double bedroom and a twin bedroom, each with shower room and wc.
PRICES: s €35; d €42; extra person €16 **NEARBY:** Bathing (7km) Forest (2km) Golf (7km) Theme park (60km) Tennis (3km) Railway station (7km) Shops (3km) **NOTES:** No pets

LIZINES

♥ ⵔ Chambre d'hôtes
Annick et Jean-Marie DORMION
24 rue du Perre, 77650 LIZINES
☎ 01 60 67 32 47 📠 01 60 67 32 47
Paris 80 km. Provins 12 km. Disneyland Paris 50 km. Adjacent to a pretty 18th-century church, this welcoming farm on the D209 has a friendly, family atmosphere. On the ground floor there is a breakfast room and independent access to a double bedroom with private bathroom and wc. There are two further bedrooms on the first floor, one with a double and a single bed, and one with a double bed, shower room and wc. A kitchen is available, and there is a small garden. Table d'hôte meals are served each evening (except Fridays) by prior arrangement, and you can sample some of the farm's own produce. Animals admitted at the owners' discretion. TV available on request. Reduced rates, depending on length of stay.
PRICES: s €38; d €43; extra person €16; dinner €12 **NEARBY:** Bathing (12km) Forest (15km) Golf (12km) Theme park (50km) Tennis (4km) Railway station (7km) Shops (4km) **NOTES:** Pets admitted English spoken

♥ ⵔ Chambre d'hôtes
Christine & J-Claude DORMION
2 rue des Glycines, 77650 LIZINES
☎ 01 60 67 32 56 📠 01 60 67 32 56
Paris 80 km. Provins 12 km. Thirty-five minutes from Disneyland Paris, on the D209, this pretty house is situated opposite the owners' farm. In this tourist region, you are assured of a warm welcome and a family atmosphere. There are five bedrooms for two to three people, each with bathroom and wc. Television can be provided on request. Enjoy the tranquillity of the verdant, flower-filled garden from the comfort of garden furniture. A kitchen area is available for cooking and the barn has been converted into a summer room with open fireplace, barbecue and bar area. Children's games are available and discounts can be negotiated, depending on the length of the holiday. Farm produce and meals can be provided on Monday, Tuesday and Wednesday evenings. Guests can be met at the station.
PRICES: s €37; d €40; extra person €16; dinner €14 **ON SITE:** Children's play area **NEARBY:** Bathing (12km) Forest (15km) Golf (12km) Theme park (50km) Tennis (4km) Railway station (7km) Shops (4km) **NOTES:** Pets admitted English spoken

MONTIGNY-SUR-LOING

Chambre d'hôtes Pascale et J-Michel GICQUEL
46 rue Montgermont, 77690 MONTIGNY-SUR-LOING
☎ 01 64 45 87 92
Paris 70 km. Fontainebleau 8 km. Moret-sur-Loing 6 km. Located in a village in the lovely Loing Valley, this tastefully renovated house has lots of character and is within easy reach of numerous walks and tourist attractions. The breakfast room is on the ground floor, while the double bedrooms are on the first floor; one room has an extra single bed, and each has a shower room, wc and television. A cot is available and there is a garden and parking.
PRICES: s €37; d €41; extra person €16 **NEARBY:** Bathing (9km) Forest (1km) Golf (10km) Theme park (70km) Tennis (3km) Railway station (1km) **NOTES:** Pets admitted English spoken

continued

ILE-DE-FRANCE

MONTMACHOUX

IIII Chambre d'hôtes Catherine et Jacques ROUSSEAU
7 Grande Rue, 77940 MONTMACHOUX
☎ 01 64 70 21 31 & 06 82 66 28 65 📠 01 64 70 29 68
e-mail: la-marechale@infonie.fr
http://perso.infonie.fr/la-marechale/
Paris 80 km. Fontainebleau 20 km. Moret-sur-Loing 10 km. In a
very beautiful village in the Orvanne Valley, this charming house
with flower-filled garden has been tastefully renovated. On the
ground floor, you will find a breakfast room and a lounge area
with open fireplace. There is also one twin bedroom with shower
room and wc, one double bedroom with shower room and wc and
one double bedroom with an extra single bed, shower room and
wc. Beautifully decorated, with a warm atmosphere, this house is
an ideal base for walking and hiking.
PRICES: s €41; d €45-€55; extra person €17 **ON SITE:** Forest
NEARBY: Bathing (8km) Golf (4km) Theme park (90km) Tennis (4km)
Railway station (8km) Shops (4km) **NOTES:** No pets English spoken

ORMEAUX

IIII ↺I Ferme du Vieux Château Inge MAEGERLEIN
77540 ORMEAUX
☎ 01 64 25 78 30 & 06 85 19 04 39 📠 01 64 07 72 91
e-mail: bandb77@wanadoo.fr www.chambres-table-hotes.com
Paris 50 km. Disneyland 25 km. Typical of the Brie region, La
Ferme du Vieux Château has been lovingly restored. The large
cathedral-style drawing room has an open fireplace. On the first
floor there are four non-smoking bedrooms with lots of charm,
colour TVs and private bathrooms featuring power showers or
hydro-massage baths. Telephone, fax and internet access are all
available. Sophisticated country-style breakfasts are served and
table d'hôte meals are of a very high standard. The terrace leads
out onto a large tree-and-flower-lined garden, for absolute calm.
There is also a contemporary art gallery on site, containing a
collection of tools and popular art. Horse riders welcome; billiards
available. Guests can be met from the station, airport and RER.
Open all year round.
PRICES: s €37-€54; d €44-€60; extra person €15; dinner €13-€44
NEARBY: Bathing (10km) Forest (2km) Golf (15km) Theme park (25km)
Tennis (4km) Railway station (15km) Shops (3km) **NOTES:** Pets
admitted English spoken

See advert on this page

PALEY

IIII ↺I Le Petit Moulin Alain BRULE
1 route du Petit Moulin, 77710 PALEY
☎ 01 60 96 53 18 & 06 80 59 88 78
Paris 90 km. Fontainebleau 22 km. Nemours 12 km. This
magnificent restored 16th-century mill, situated on a reach of the
Lunain, has a vast courtyard and terrace. The five guest rooms are
located in an annexe building. On the ground floor there is a
double bedroom and a family suite comprising a double bedroom
and a twin room. The communal lounge room is also on the
ground floor. On the first floor there is a twin bedroom and two
family suites made up of one double bedroom and one twin room.
Each bedroom has a shower room and wc. Quality meals are
available on request.
PRICES: s €46; d €54; extra person €19; dinner €15-€23
NEARBY: Bathing (9km) Forest (4km) Golf (8km) Theme park (80km)
Tennis (1km) Railway station (12km) Shops (3km) **NOTES:** No pets
English spoken

Ask the proprietor for directions
when booking

La Ferme du Vieux Château

You will receive a warm welcome at this 18th century farmhouse,
which has been renovated and decorated to include antique furniture,
collections of old tools and a small modern art picture gallery.
Situated 35 minutes east of Paris, this is the ideal venue for visiting
Disneyland, the many châteaux of the area and the surrounding Brie
countryside. The accommodation consists of a mini flat, a suite, an
apartment on two floors and an apartment on three floors. To complete
your stay, fine French cuisine can be sampled from the 'Four Seasons'
menu which includes Brie and wines from an outstanding wine cellar
plus the unforgettable 'breakfast campagnard'. Open all year.

77540 Ormeaux
Tel: 01 64 25 78 30 Fax: 01 64 07 72 91
Email: inge@wanadoo.fr
Web site: www.chambres-table-hotes.com

POMMEUSE

IIII ↺I Le Moulin de Pommeuse
Annie et Jacky THOMAS
32 avenue du Général Huerne, 77515 POMMEUSE
☎ 01 64 75 29 45 📠 01 64 75 29 45
e-mail: infos@le-moulin-de-pommeuse.com
www.le-moulin-de-pommeuse.com

Paris 50 km. A warm welcome awaits at this authentic 14th-century
watermill, in a small, typical Brie village in the valley. Convenient
for many cultural and leisure activities, the mill is set in a three-
hectare park beside the river with its easily accessible island. Inside,
the vast, relaxing rooms include a large dining room with open
fireplace, and on the first floor there are five characterful rooms, of
which two are family rooms. Each has a private bathroom and wc
and views over the river or park. Outdoor activities include table
tennis, fishing, mountain biking and rambling.
PRICES: s €45; d €50; extra person €22; dinner €17-€23
ON SITE: Children's play area **NEARBY:** Bathing (7km) Forest (1km)
Golf (4km) Theme park (18km) Tennis (2km) Railway station (2km)
Shops (2km) **NOTES:** No pets English spoken

PROVINS

♦♦♦ ❧ Ferme du Chatel Annie et Claude LEBEL
5 rue de la Chapelle St-Jean,
77160 PROVINS-VILLE-HAUTE
☎ 01 64 00 10 73 ▤ 01 64 00 10 99
e-mail: fermeduchatel@wanadoo.fr www.provins.net
Paris 80 km. Fontainebleau 55 km. Disneyland Paris 50 km. This
farm is located near the ramparts of a listed medieval town, which
offers lots of activities during the summer. On the ground floor
there is a small seminar room for 12-15 people and a breakfast
room with kitchen area and grill. Also on the ground floor are one
double bedroom and one room for three people. On the first floor
there are two bedrooms for four and one bedroom for three. Each
bedroom has a shower room and a wc. Baby sitting and picnics
can be arranged. Horses welcome.
PRICES: s €43; d €45; extra person €19 **NEARBY:** Bathing (1km) Forest
(3km) Golf (24km) Theme park (50km) Tennis (1km) Railway station
(1km) Shops (1km) **NOTES:** No pets English spoken

ST-GERMAIN-SUR-MORIN

♦♦♦ ❂ Les Hauts De Montguillon Chantal LEGENDRE
22 rue de St-Quentin, Montguillon, 77860
☎ 01 60 04 45 53 ▤ 01 60 42 28 59
e-mail: chantal.legendre@wanadoo.fr
http://perso.wanadoo.fr/les-hauts-de-montguillon/
Paris 40 km. Disneyland Paris 7 km. Relaxation is assured at this
tastefully restored, typically Briard house, situated in extensive
grounds in the hamlet of Montguillon, on the banks of the Morin.
Guests have independent access to the accommodation, which
includes a lounge with open fireplace and terrace with garden
furniture. Three carefully decorated en suite guest rooms are
available: one double on the ground floor and two further rooms
on the first floor, each with a double bed and twin beds on a
mezzanine level. The area is ideal for walking and the welcome is
always warm. Meals are available on certain days on request. The
Chessy RER station is within easy reach.
PRICES: s €46; d €54; extra person €19; dinner €21 **NEARBY:** Bathing
(15km) Forest (5km) Golf (5km) Theme park (7km) Tennis (2km)
Railway station (2km) Shops (2km) **NOTES:** No pets English spoken

THOURY-FEROTTES

♦♦♦ La Forteresse Michèle et François CRAPARD
77940 THOURY-FEROTTES
☎ 01 60 96 95 10 & 01 60 96 97 00 ▤ 01 60 96 01 41

Paris 85 km. Fontainebleau 25 km. La Forteresse is a beautiful
fortified farm with lots of character and an 18-hole golf course on
site. On the ground floor, there is a tasteful breakfast room and
independent access to two bedrooms, each with one double and
one single bed, shower room and wc. The family suite comprises a
double room and a twin room, bathroom and wc. Meals are
available. Club House.

PRICES: s €37; d €41-€44; extra person €17 **ON SITE:** Forest Golf
NEARBY: Bathing (10km) Theme park (80km) Tennis (4km) Railway
station (10km) Shops (3km) **NOTES:** Pets admitted English spoken

VANVILLE

♦♦♦ ❂ Ferme Grand'Maison Myriam HALLIER
77370 VANVILLE
☎ 01 64 01 63 18 ▤ 01 64 01 65 36
e-mail: hallier@wanadoo.fr http://www.la-grand-maison.com
Paris 60 km. Provins 14 km. Nangis 7 km. The Ferme
Grand'Maison is situated in the heart of historic Brie. This beautiful
farm is arranged around an interior courtyard. A warm welcome
and relaxation are assured. On the ground floor, there is a big
room with a lounge and tea-making area. On the first floor, there
is a family suite with one double and four single beds, a shower
room and wc. Also on this floor is a double bedroom and a twin
bedroom, both with shower room and wc. The ground-floor room
has a double and a single bed, shower room and wc, and is
suitable for guests with disabilities. A reception room is available
for hire. Loose-boxes available for horses.
PRICES: s €50; d €55; extra person €22; dinner €28 **NEARBY:** Bathing
(7km) Forest (5km) Golf (10km) Theme park (45km) Tennis (1km)
Railway station (7km) Shops (7km) PROVINS (14km) **NOTES:** Pets
admitted English spoken

VILLENEUVE-LE-COMTE

♦♦♦ Chambre d'hôtes Eliane et René TEISSEDRE
55 boulevard de l'Est, 77174 VILLENEUVE-LE-COMTE
☎ 01 60 43 28 27 & SR : 01 60 39 60 39 ▤ 01 60 43 10 42
http://perso.chello.fr/martine.teissedre
Paris 33 km. Lagny 10 km. Disneyland Paris 4 km. This welcoming
house with garden and terrace is set in the grounds of the owners'
property. On the ground floor, there is a lounge/dining room, a
breakfast room and a double bedroom with shower and wc. On
the first floor, there are four bedrooms suitable for four people,
each with twin beds on a mezzanine, a shower room and wc.
Electric heating. Chessy RER station is only 4km away.
PRICES: s €41; d €46; extra person €17 **ON SITE:** Forest Tennis
NEARBY: Bathing (12km) Golf (10km) Theme park (4km) Railway
station (4km) **NOTES:** Pets admitted

CHERENCE

♦♦♦ Le St-Denis Andrée PERNELLE
1 rue des Cabarets, 95510 CHERENCE
☎ 01 34 78 15 02 ▤ 01 30 29 30 86
La Roche-Guyon 4 km. Cergy 40 km. Paris 70 km. This rural
character house is peacefully set within a delightful, flower-filled
garden in the heart of the village, on the border of the Parc
Régional du Vexin Français. The five bedrooms are situated on the
first floor, and each has a private bath or shower room and wc. On
the ground floor, there is a dining room, open fireplace, TV and
lounge. The house benefits from central heating. A charming rural
atmosphere prevails. Guests can use the terrace and garden
furniture, and private parking is available. The numerous local
attractions include the Château and Valley of the Seine, gliding,
hot-air ballooning, the Route des Crêtes, the gardens at Giverny,
the American Museum (10 km), Vernon, and the Château de
Villarceaux.
PRICES: d €55 **ON SITE:** Horse riding Tennis **NEARBY:** Bathing
(15km) Forest (1km) Golf (4km) Fishing (2km) Swimming pool (15km)
Railway station (16km) Shops (4km) **NOTES:** Pets admitted English
spoken

continued

ILE-DE-FRANCE

LA ROCHE-GUYON

††† ⏀ Chambre d'hôtes Henri BOUQUET
3 route de Gasny, 95780 LA ROCHE-GUYON
☎ 01 34 79 75 10
Château de La Roche-Guyon. This large 'maison bourgeoise' is situated in the heart of one of France's most beautiful villages, towering above the chalk cliffs of the Seine Valley. There are two double bedrooms and four rooms with a double and a single bed; each has a private bathroom and wc, and each is very comfortably furnished with 1930s pieces. There is a dining room and a lounge with a library and TV. The house has its own orchard and you can try the fruit in season. Meals are served outside during the summer. Discounts available for stays of more than two nights. Open all year.
PRICES: s €35; d €44-€49; t €55; HB €39-€96; dinner €14-€17
ON SITE: Fishing Tennis **NEARBY:** Bathing (15km) Horse riding (4km) Forest (1km) Golf (8km) Swimming pool (15km) Railway station (6km) **NOTES:** No pets English spoken

PARMAIN

††† ♥ Chambre d'hôtes Laurent DELALEU
131 rue du Maréchal Foch, 95620 PARMAIN
☎ 01 34 73 02 92 📠 01 34 08 80 76
Cergy 15 km. L'Isle-Adam 500 m. Auvers-sur-Oise 6 km. This large working farm has an enclosed courtyard complete with tennis court. On the first floor, there are two large double bedrooms and two further rooms on the second floor: one double, and one with two singles and a double bed; all rooms have private bathroom and wc. The kitchen and breakfast room are on the ground floor, and there is a TV room in the vaulted cellar. Indoor parking is available, as is a terrace with garden furniture. Ideally located for guests without their own transport, there is lots to see and do in the immediate vicinity. Price for 4 people: 65.5 euros. Open all year.
PRICES: s €37; d €46; t €57 **NEARBY:** Bathing (1km) Horse riding (2km) Forest (2km) Golf (2km) Fishing (1km) Swimming pool (1km) Tennis (1km) Railway station (1km) Shops (1km) **NOTES:** No pets English spoken

YVELINES

MOISSON

††† Chambre d'hôtes Brigitte LEVI
4, allée du Jamborée, 78840 MOISSON
☎ 01 34 79 37 20 📠 01 34 79 37 58
This 16th-century priory is set in a flower-filled garden in a village on a loop in the Seine. It offers three tasteful bedrooms: on the first floor, one double with private shower room, wc and sauna bath, and a further room with a small double bed and private bathroom and wc. On the second floor there is a double room with private shower room and wc. Further bedrooms are available in an annexe. Video room, heated swimming pool with pool house, barbecue. Generous breakfasts are served, as is brunch on occasion. Vintage car rides can be arranged. Open all year.
PRICES: s €45; d €54; t €61 **ON SITE:** Forest Swimming pool Hiking **NEARBY:** Horse riding (1km) Golf (1km) Fishing (1km) Tennis (1km) Railway station (8km) Shops (1km) **NOTES:** Pets admitted English spoken

NEAUPHLE-LE-CHATEAU

†††† Chambre d'hôtes M/Mme DROUELLE
33, rue Saint-Nicolas, 78640 NEAUPHLE-LE-CHATEAU
☎ 01 34 89 76 10 📠 01 34 89 76 10
Montfort l'Amaury 10 km. Versailles 15 km. Paris 25 km. Set in the middle of a park, in the village of Neauphle-le-Château, this Napoleonic residence offers three very comfortable first-floor guest rooms with independent access from the winter garden. There are two double rooms and one twin, each with

private bathroom facilities. Guests have use of a period lounge with TV. Breakfast is taken on the veranda. Open all year.
PRICES: s €80; d €90; extra person €15 **NEARBY:** Horse riding (3km) Forest (1km) Golf (5km) Swimming pool (3km) Tennis (1km) Railway station (5km) Shops (1km) **NOTES:** Pets admitted English spoken

POIGNY LA FORET

††† Chambre d'hôtes Monsieur LE BRET
2 rue de l'Eglise, 78125 POIGNY LA FORET
☎ 01 34 84 73 42 📠 01 34 84 74 38
e-mail: lechateaudepoigny@wanadoo.fr
Rambouillet 15 km. This beautiful 19th-century residence is surrounded by an immense park, in the heart of the forest of Rambouillet. The six charming guest rooms and lounge have been furnished with period pieces. On the first floor, there are two double bedrooms with private shower room and wc. On the second floor: there are three further double bedrooms with private shower room and wc (one has a TV and mini hifi), and a family room with three single beds. English breakfast is served. Price for 4 people: 108 euros; 5 people: 135 euros. Open all year.
PRICES: d €54-€63; t €81; extra person €16 **ON SITE:** Forest **NEARBY:** Horse riding (1km) Golf (15km) Fishing (10km) Swimming pool (8km) Tennis (1km) Railway station (8km) Shops (8km) **NOTES:** No pets English spoken

PORT-VILLEZ

††† ⏀ Notre Dame de la Mer M/Mme LOGE
10 route du Chêne Monsieur, 78270 PORT-VILLEZ
☎ 01 30 93 12 17
e-mail: www.clanloge@wanadoo.fr
Giverny 8 km. This hunting lodge is situated in a little hamlet amidst the wooded hills of the Seine Valley, and is close to Giverny and the Château de Bizy. On the first floor, there is a double room with private bathroom and wc, and a family suite comprising one twin room and one double room with a shared shower room and wc. On the second floor, there are two double rooms with private bathroom and wc. There are lovely views over the surrounding countryside and peaceful garden. A lounge is available to guests, and table d'hôte meals are served on request. Honeymoon weekends can be arranged. Within easy access of Versailles (50 km) and Paris (72 km), via the A13. Price for 4 people: 99 euros; additional bed: 5 euros. Open from April to October.
PRICES: d €53-€68 **ON SITE:** Forest **NEARBY:** Horse riding (4km) Golf (10km) Fishing (8km) Swimming pool (8km) Tennis (7km) Railway station (4km) Shops (4km) **NOTES:** No pets English spoken

VAUX-SUR-SEINE

††† La Cascade Madame BULOT
30 chemin des Valences, 78740 VAUX-SUR-SEINE
☎ 01 34 74 84 91 & 06 07 04 31 59 📠 01 34 92 02 33
St-Germain-en-Laye 15 km. Versailles 25 km. Situated opposite a forest, on the hillsides of the Seine, this large, typically Ile-de-France residence offers three guest rooms and a heated swimming pool. One bedroom is grade 2. On the first floor, there is a twin room with a balcony, private bathroom and wc, and a double room with a balcony, private shower room and wc. A spiral staircase leads to the second-floor twin-bedded room with additional children's beds, private shower room and wc. A cot can be provided on request (8 euro supplement payable per night). There is a boules pitch and enclosed parking. Price for 4 people: 78/82 euros; additional bed: 16 euros. Open all year.
PRICES: s €35-€40; d €46-€50; t €62-€66 **ON SITE:** Forest Swimming pool **NEARBY:** Horse riding (10km) Golf (12km) Fishing (1km) Tennis (1km) Railway station (1km) Shops (1km) **NOTES:** No pets

continued

ILE-DE-FRANCE

LANGUEDOC-ROUSSILLON

AUDE

ALBIÈRES

Domaine de Boutou Christian LAFARGUE
11330 ALBIÈRES
☎ 04 68 70 04 05
In the heart of Cathar country, five guest rooms are available in this house in the countryside close to a small Corbières village. The five double rooms are on the first floor and have private shower and wc. The centrally heated house has a lounge, a large terrace, well-kept garden and there are hiking trails nearby. Close to the castles of Arques, Termes and Peyrepertuse. Information about the surrounding countryside is available. 10 km from Mouthoumet.
PRICES: s €34; d €38; t €49; extra person €11; dinner €15
NEARBY: Bathing (7km) Canoeing (20km) Sea (65km) Swimming pool (15km) Tennis (7km) Sailing (7km) Railway station (32km) Shops (10km) LIMOUX (32km) **NOTES:** Pets admitted

ARAGON

Le Château d'Aragon Aimé OURLIAC
GITES DE FRANCE-SERVICE RESERVATION, 5 allée Sully, 29322 QUIMPER Cedex
☎ 04 68 11 40 70 & PROP: 04 68 77 19 62
📠 04 68 11 40 72
e-mail: GITESDEFRANCE.AUDE@wanadoo.fr
www.itea.fr/GDF/11
Passionate wine-makers Laetitia and Rodolphe welcome guests to the château of Aragon, whose two towers have looked over this small, peaceful village since the 12th century. Five distinctive, very comfortable rooms, three of which have access to the large balcony with its superb views. You will discover the products of their vineyards whilst admiring the architecture of the lounge and courtyard. 12 km from Carcassonne.
PRICES: d €46-€53; extra person €15 **ON SITE:** Tennis
NEARBY: Bathing (10km) Sea (90km) Swimming pool (10km) Sailing (25km) Railway station (12km) Shops (5km) CARCASSONNE (12km) **NOTES:** No pets CC English spoken

AZILLE

Chambre d'hôtes Pierre TENENBAUM
GITES DE FRANCE-SERVICE RESERVATION, 5 allée Sully, 29322 QUIMPER Cedex
☎ 04 68 11 40 70 & PROP: 04 68 91 56 90 📠 04 68 11 40 72
e-mail: GITESDEFRANCE.AUDE@wanadoo.fr
www.itea.fr/GDF/11
In the centre of a Minervois village, this house has a private garden with furniture and offers four guest rooms, all with en suite facilities. One double room has a private terrace. Also available are one room with three single beds and sitting room, one double room and one double room with sitting room and fireplace. Central heating, communal room and lounge. Nearby attractions include the region's footpaths, walks along the Canal du Midi, and the Jouarres lake, which offers horse riding and bathing.
PRICES: d €50; extra person €16 **ON SITE:** Tennis **NEARBY:** Bathing (3km) Sea (48km) Swimming pool (3km) Sailing (3km) Railway station (18km) LEZIGNAN CORBIERES (16km) **NOTES:** Pets admitted CC English spoken

BIZANET

Domaine St Jean Didier DELBOURG
GITES DE FRANCE-SERVICE RESERVATION, 5 allée Sully, 29322 QUIMPER Cedex, FRANCE
☎ 04 68 11 40 70 & PROP: 04 68 45 17 31 📠 04 68 11 40 72
e-mail: GITESDEFRANCE.AUDE@wanadoo.fr
www.itea.fr/GDF/11
Deep in the Cathar region, this house in a winemaking area in the heart of Corbières offers four guest rooms in an independent building, including one family room with mezzanine. Private shower and wc facilities. Ground-floor reception with lounge and dining room. Breakfast can be taken on the terrace where guests can enjoy the gardens, complementing the natural surroundings. Also available is one triple room with connecting terrace.
PRICES: d €52-€62; extra person €12 **NEARBY:** Bathing (25km) Canoeing (55km) Sea (25km) Swimming pool (12km) Tennis (3km) Sailing (15km) Railway station (12km) Shops (3km) NARBONNE (12km)
NOTES: No pets CC

BOUISSE

Domaine des Goudis
Michele & Michel DELATTRE
GITES DE FRANCE-SERVICE RESERVATION, 5 allée Sully, 29322 QUIMPER Cedex
☎ 04 68 11 40 70 & PROP: 04 68 70 02 76
📠 04 68 11 40 72
e-mail: GITESDEFRANCE.AUDE@wanadoo.fr
www.itea.fr/GDF/11
Situated on the historic Cathar Way, this fully restored stone house offers six guest rooms with telephones and private bathrooms. Dining room with fireplace, lounge, library, park, lawns and terraced garden with furniture. Evening meals available on Saturdays, Sundays and Mondays. With views of the Pyrenees, there are many outdoor activities available, such as pony-trekking, rambling, and a private heated swimming pool. Visit the sights of the region and take a tour of the stud farm.
PRICES: s €66; d €73; t €93; extra person €20; dinner €21
ON SITE: Swimming pool **NEARBY:** Bathing (15km) Canoeing (25km) Sea (70km) Tennis (6km) Sailing (90km) Railway station (17km) Shops (17km) LIMOUX (27km) **NOTES:** No pets CC English spoken

BOUTENAC

La Bastide des Corbières Jacques CAMEL
GITES DE FRANCE-SERVICE RESERVATION, 5 allée Sully, 29322 QUIMPER Cedex
☎ 04 68 11 40 70 & PROP: 04 68 27 20 61 📠 04 68 11 40 72
e-mail: GITESDEFRANCE.AUDE@wanadoo.fr
www.itea.fr/GDF/11
Five attractive guest rooms are offered in this house, including two rooms with private showers and three with private bathroom and dressing room. Reading area and games room. Ground floor dining room and lounge with fireplace. Leafy grounds with terrace and marquee where breakfast and meals are served from May to October. Car park. Winemaking property in the heart of the Corbières region, close to the Lagrasse and Fontfroide abbeys. Also near to the Cathar fortresses and 35 km from Carcassonne.

continued

PRICES: s €55-€60; d €60-€65; extra person €14; dinner €23
ON SITE: Tennis **NEARBY:** Bathing (6km) Sea (30km) Swimming pool (6km) Sailing (30km) Railway station (6km) LEZIGNAN CORBIERES (6km) **NOTES:** No pets CC

BUGARACH

▮▮▮▮ ▯Ⓞ▯ Le Presbytère Monique JEANNIN
11190 BUGARACH
☎ 04 68 69 82 12

Five rooms are available in the former Burgarach presbytery, a striking building with a tree-lined garden looking onto the Pic du Bugarach (1230 m), one of the more famous of the many walks possible in the area. Double, triple and family rooms available, with en suite facilities. Central heating. Dining room available and evening meals provided on reservation. Guaranteed welcome for walkers off-season. Picnic baskets 6 euros, tourist tax 0.46 euros per adult. 8 km from Rennes-les-Bains, 18 km from Donjon-d'Arques and 10 km from Rennes-le-Château. No smoking.
PRICES: s €30; d €41; extra person €21; HB €34; FB €40; dinner €14
NEARBY: Bathing (10km) Canoeing (25km) Sea (70km) Swimming pool (12km) Tennis (10km) Sailing (10km) Railway station (35km) LIMOUX (35km) **NOTES:** No pets CC

CASCASTEL

▮▮▮▮ Domaine Grand Guilhem
Severine et Gilles CONTREPOIS
GITES DE FRANCE-SERVICE RESERVATION, 5 allée Sully, 29322 QUIMPER Cedex
☎ 04 68 11 40 70 & PROP: 04 68 45 86 67
▤ 04 68 11 40 72
e-mail: GITESDEFRANCE.AUDE@wanadoo.fr
www.itea.fr/GDF/11

Four very comfortable rooms are to be had in this pretty 14th-century wine-maker's house, built from local stone and with wooded grounds. Each room has a lounge area, private bathroom and separate wc. Swimming pool and panoramic views of the village château and the surrounding vineyards. Dining room with fireplace and piano. Breakfast can be taken in the garden. The owners are wine-makers who will help you to discover the vintages of the Haut Fitou. Lounge, electric heating and car park.
PRICES: s €59; d €65; t €76; extra person €11 **ON SITE:** Bathing Swimming pool **NEARBY:** Sea (25km) Tennis (2km) Sailing (25km) Railway station (30km) NARBONNE (30km) **NOTES:** No pets CC English spoken

CAUX ET SAUZENS

▮▮▮▮ Domaine des Castelles Isabelle CLAYETTE
11170 CAUX ET SAUZENS
☎ 04 68 72 03 60   ▤ 04 68 72 03 60

This pretty house was once a wine-maker's but now offers three very large guest rooms. Choose between the 'Sunflower Room', the 'Pink Laurel Room' or the 'Palm-tree' suite, which can accommodate five people and looks on to the park. All rooms have private showers. In summer breakfast is served on the terrace. Central heating. Open all year round.
PRICES: d €50-€58; extra person €14 **NEARBY:** Bathing (10km) Sea (77km) Swimming pool (7km) Tennis (2km) Sailing (10km) Railway station (7km) Shops (2km) CARCASSONNE (7km) **NOTES:** No pets English spoken

> Ask the proprietor for directions
> when booking

FABREZAN

▮▮▮▮ Lou Castelet
Jan et Mieke WOUTERS-MACHIELS
GITES DE FRANCE-SERVICE RESERVATION, 5 allée Sully, 29322 QUIMPER Cedex
☎ 04 68 11 40 70 & PROP: 04 68 43 56 98
▤ 04 68 11 40 72
e-mail: GITESDEFRANCE.AUDE@wanadoo.fr
www.itea.fr/GDF/11

This beautiful restored manor house with shady grounds has four attractive guest rooms, including doubles, triples, and one family suite. All have private shower or bathrooms. Breakfast is served either on the terrace or in the authentic 14th-century dining room. Two lounges with games and televisions are available for guest use. The house, which is in the centre of Charles Cros's native village, boasts a tower that enjoys wonderful views of the region's vineyards. Rooms are rented by the week in July and August. Consult the proprietors for off-season prices.
PRICES: s €65; d €69-€95; t €85-€110; extra person €4
ON SITE: Tennis **NEARBY:** Bathing (10km) Canoeing (40km) Sea (40km) Swimming pool (10km) Sailing (40km) Railway station (10km) LEZIGNAN CORBIERES (10km) **NOTES:** No pets CC

FAJAC EN VAL

▮▮▮ ▯Ⓞ▯ La Mignoterie André MIGNOT
GITES DE FRANCE-SERVICE RESERVATION, 5 allée Sully, 29322 QUIMPER Cedex
☎ 04 68 11 40 70 & PROP: 04 68 79 71 42   ▤ 04 68 11 40 72
e-mail: GITESDEFRANCE.AUDE@wanadoo.fr
www.itea.fr/GDF/11

Visitors should take time to fully explore the pleasures of the Corbières region, and convivial La Mignoterie is a step in the right direction. The legend goes that in the 70s, the singer Charles Trenet composed many of his works here. Four en suite guest rooms are available with different colours as a theme. One of the rooms is a family suite accommodating four people. The music room, garden and terrace are available to guests. Off-season price 45 euros.
PRICES: d €46-€50; extra person €15; dinner €9 **NEARBY:** Bathing (1km) Sea (70km) Swimming pool (18km) Tennis (6km) Sailing (18km) Railway station (18km) Shops (10km) CARCASSONNE (18km) **NOTES:** No pets CC

LABECEDE LAURAGAIS

▮▮▮ ▸ ▯Ⓞ▯ Domaine de Villemagne
Mme Gacquiere SCEA LAFOUCADE
GITES DE FRANCE-SERVICE RESERVATION, 5 allée Sully, 29322 QUIMPER Cedex
☎ 04 68 11 40 70 & PROP: 04 68 60 44 89   ▤ 04 68 11 40 72
e-mail: GITESDEFRANCE.AUDE@wanadoo.fr
www.itea.fr/GDF/11

Set in country surroundings, this family mansion offers one grade 2 room and two grade 3 rooms with access to a pretty terrace and views of the Pyrenees to the south. Each room has a private shower and wc and accommodates two to three people. Private lounge. Central heating. Dining room with fireplace and television. Very close to designated footpaths. The St Ferréol lake is an hour by bicycle. The natural setting and the view of the Pyrenees are unforgettable. Horse riding and river fishing available.
PRICES: d €38-€43; extra person €11; dinner €11 **NEARBY:** Bathing (15km) Swimming pool (15km) Tennis (3km) Sailing (15km) Railway station (15km) Shops (15km) CASTELNAUDARY (15km) **NOTES:** Pets admitted CC English spoken

LAURE MINERVOIS

♦♦♦ ❦ ◯ Domaine du Siestou
Gabrielle DHOMS VIE
GITES DE FRANCE-SERVICE RESERVATION, 5 allée Sully, 29322 QUIMPER Cedex
☎ 04 68 11 40 70 & PROP: 04 68 78 30 81 ▤ 04 68 11 40 72
e-mail: GITESDEFRANCE.AUDE@wanadoo.fr
www.itea.fr/GDF/11
Winemakers Gaby and Roger offer four guest rooms in a building adjoining their main house. They offer tastings of the wines kept in their Lauran Cabaret cellar. The guest rooms, all with en suite shower and wc, consist of two double rooms, one twin room, and one family room (with double bed and bunk-beds). Large dining room with lounge area, shady garden with pine trees and car park. Evening meals are available if reserved, except Tuesdays.
PRICES: s €38; d €45; t €60; extra person €15; dinner €14
ON SITE: Wine tasting **NEARBY:** Bathing (4km) Canoeing (8km) Sea (60km) Swimming pool (5km) Tennis (3km) Sailing (10km) Railway station (20km) Shops (3km) CARCASSONNE (20km) **NOTES:** Pets admitted CC

LEUCATE

♦♦♦ 65, Avenue Jean Jaures Pierre VIGIER
GITES DE FRANCE-SERVICE RESERVATION, 5 allée Sully, 29322 QUIMPER Cedex
☎ 04 68 11 40 70 & PROP: 04 68 40 98 55 ▤ 04 68 11 40 72
e-mail: GITESDEFRANCE.AUDE@wanadoo.fr
www.itea.fr/GDF/11
Three distinctive guest rooms in a family house on the main street of a winemaking village. One family suite with en suite shower and two double rooms with shower room are available. Ground floor dining room and lounge with fireplace and television, courtyard garden and patio. Walks and bike riding are possible around the lakes and cliffs of the area. Visit the oyster-farms, the local windsurfing centre and the Leucate cellar where you can sample the wines. Restaurant. Car park opposite the house.
PRICES: s €35; d €43; t €67; extra person €12 **ON SITE:** Tennis
NEARBY: Bathing (2km) Canoeing (10km) Sea (2km) Swimming pool (1km) Sailing (10km) Railway station (5km) NARBONNE (25km)
NOTES: No pets CC English spoken

MARSEILLETTE

♦♦♦ ❦ La Fargues Martine DE ROULHAC
16 avenue de la Belle Aude, 11800 MARSEILLETTE
☎ 04 68 79 13 88 ▤ 04 68 79 13 88
Situated in a small Minervois village alongside the Canal du Midi and the River Aude, this pretty turn-of-the-century house with shady park offers three rooms, all with private shower and wc. Lounge with library and dining room. Breakfast can be served in the park. Bike riding along the shores of the nearby small lake.
PRICES: d €46; extra person €15 **NEARBY:** Bathing (20km) Sea (60km) Swimming pool (5km) Tennis (5km) Sailing (20km) Railway station (20km) Shops (5km) CARCASSONNE (20km) **NOTES:** Pets admitted English spoken

MIREPEISSET

♦♦♦ Beau Rivage Claire LEFEVRE DURAND
11120 MIREPEISSET
☎ 04 68 46 25 07
Near to the sights of Minerve, and the Cistercian barn near Ouveillan, this villa offers three double guest rooms with en suite facilities. Surrounding grounds with car park, covered terrace and communal room. Swimming and other attractions in the village. The area offers walks along the shady edge of the Canal du Midi, a horse farm and museums.

PRICES: s €37; d €42-€45; extra person €16 **ON SITE:** Canoeing
NEARBY: Bathing (1km) Sea (25km) Swimming pool (15km) Tennis (2km) Sailing (20km) Railway station (15km) Shops (1km) NARBONNE (15km) **NOTES:** Pets admitted English spoken

MOUX

♦♦♦ ❦ ◯ Relais de L'Alaric Jean Pierre SARDA
GITES DE FRANCE-SERVICE RESERVATION, 5 allée Sully, 29322 QUIMPER Cedex
☎ 04 68 11 40 70 & PROP: 04 68 43 97 68 ▤ 04 68 11 40 72
e-mail: GITESDEFRANCE.AUDE@wanadoo.fr
www.itea.fr/GDF/11
This family house on the outskirts of a village offers four guest rooms with en suite shower and wc and one room with en suite bathroom. Dining room with TV, library and large fireplace. Visit the owners' winemaking facilities and taste the Corbières produced. Introduction to flying and short recreational flights offered. Mountain bikes available. The nearby railway (100 m) can be noisy.
PRICES: s €34; d €43; t €58; extra person €15; dinner €14
NEARBY: Bathing (20km) Sea (42km) Swimming pool (5km) Tennis (12km) Sailing (20km) Railway station (12km) Shops (1km) LEZIGNAN CORBIERES (12km) **NOTES:** Pets admitted CC English spoken

NARBONNE

♦♦♦ ◯ Chemin du Bas Razimbaud
Jerome BALESTA, 11100 NARBONNE
☎ 04 68 32 52 06
Two grade 2 rooms with private shower room and shared wc and three grade 3 rooms with en suite facilities are offered in this modern detached house. Close to Narbonne, this family home could serve as a starting point for interesting cultural and historical trips or for relaxing days spent by the seaside.
PRICES: d €38; extra person €11; dinner €14 **NEARBY:** Bathing (15km) Sea (15km) Swimming pool (5km) Tennis (2km) Sailing (15km) Railway station (2km) Shops (2km) NARBONNE (2km) **NOTES:** Pets admitted

♦♦♦ Domaine de Jonquières
GITES DE FRANCE-SERVICE RESERVATION, 5 allée Sully, 29322 QUIMPER Cedex
☎ 04 68 11 40 70 & PROP: 04 68 42 85 00
▤ 04 68 11 40 72
e-mail: GITESDEFRANCE.AUDE@wanadoo.fr
www.itea.fr/GDF/11
Part of a winemaking estate, this typical Languedoc house has four very comfortable guest rooms with private bathroom and wc. The house has a communal lounge with fireplace, books and television, tennis courts and a sauna. Close to Narbonne and 20 km from the beach.
PRICES: d €60; extra person €15 **ON SITE:** Tennis
NEARBY: Bathing (5km) Canoeing (5km) Sea (20km) Swimming pool (5km) Sailing (5km) Railway station (10km) Shops (5km) NARBONNE (4km) **NOTES:** No pets CC

OUVEILLAN

♦♦♦ ◯ Grangette Haute Mireille RENOUX-MEYER
GITES DE FRANCE-SERVICE RESERVATION, 5 allée Sully, 29322 QUIMPER Cedex
☎ 04 68 11 40 70 & PROP: 04 68 46 86 24 ▤ 04 68 11 40 72
e-mail: GITESDEFRANCE.AUDE@wanadoo.fr
www.itea.fr/GDF/11
This fully restored house, in a rural setting 2 km from the nearest village, is close to the Canal du Midi, Minerve and the seaside. Guests can enjoy the park with its pine trees, parasols and great views. The house offers four guest rooms with private shower or bathroom, and has a lounge and library. Evening meals can be

reserved and there is a reduced tariff for longer stays.
PRICES: s €43; d €52-€58; t €73; extra person €15; dinner €18
NEARBY: Bathing (20km) Sea (30km) Swimming pool (20km) Tennis (2km) Sailing (30km) Railway station (20km) Shops (2km) NARBONNE (20km) **NOTES:** Pets admitted English spoken

PALAIRAC

🏵 🍽 **Les Ginestous** A et V LACAZE-HOLLIGER
GITES DE FRANCE-SERVICE RESERVATION, 5 allée Sully, 29322 QUIMPER Cedex
☎ 04 68 11 40 70 & PROP: 04 68 45 01 24 🖹 04 68 11 40 72
e-mail: GITESDEFRANCE.AUDE@wanadoo.fr
www.itea.fr/GDF/11
This guest house, next to the village fountain, has bags of character, is extremely quiet and yet only half an hour away from the Cathar castles. The surrounding area also has many attractive walks and the Mediterranean coast is only an hour away by car. One four-person suite and two double rooms with en suite shower and wc. The large and sunny second-floor terrace has a lounge area where breakfast is served. Library available for guest use.
PRICES: s €34; d €44; extra person €19; dinner €15 **NEARBY:** Bathing (12km) Sea (55km) Swimming pool (12km) Tennis (12km) Sailing (55km) Railway station (45km) Shops (12km) TUCHAN (25km)
NOTES: No pets CC English spoken

PENNAUTIER

🏵 **Château de Liet** Claude MEYNIER
Sarl le Liet, 11610 PENNAUTIER
☎ 04 68 11 19 19 🖹 04 68 47 05 22
Six guest rooms are available in this 19th-century château set in a wooded 7-hectare park, consisting of three family suites accommodating three to four people and three double rooms. Two of the rooms and two of the suites enjoy a wonderful view of the park and swimming pool. One suite and one room have access to a private terrace. All rooms have mini-bars. Breakfast is served in the period dining room and the park and pool are strictly reserved for guests. Table tennis also available. Carcassonne 5 km.
PRICES: d €46-€61; t €84-€91; extra person €15 **ON SITE:** Bathing Swimming pool **NEARBY:** Canoeing (80km) Sea (80km) Tennis (2km) Sailing (20km) Railway station (5km) Shops (1km) CARCASSONNE (5km) **NOTES:** No pets English spoken

PEYREFITTE DU RAZES

🏵 🍽 **Domaine de Couchet** Jean Pierre ROPERS
11230 PEYREFITTE DU RAZES
☎ 04 68 69 55 06 🖹 04 68 69 55 06
e-mail: jeanpierre.ropers@fnac.net
Close to the Montbel lake, where guests can swim and practise their fishing skills, and to the old town of Mirepoix, this beautiful 18th-century family house offers four guest rooms with en suite shower rooms. Set in well-tended and attractive gardens, the house has a lounge and library for guest use. Many walks nearby.

continued

10% reduction for stays exceeding three nights. Off-season stays (three days minimum) possible on reservation.
PRICES: s €46; d €27-€53; t €61; extra person €15; dinner €20
NEARBY: Bathing (15km) Canoeing (25km) Sea (90km) Swimming pool (14km) Tennis (19km) Sailing (15km) Railway station (19km) Shops (10km) LIMOUX (19km) **NOTES:** Pets admitted English spoken

PEYRIAC DE MER

🏵 🍽 **L'Oustal Nau** Gerard et Florence BARBOUTEAU
GITES DE FRANCE-SERVICE RESERVATION, 5 allée Sully, 29322 QUIMPER Cedex
☎ 04 68 11 40 70 & PROP: 04 68 41 69 76 🖹 04 68 11 40 72
e-mail: GITESDEFRANCE.AUDE@wanadoo.fr
www.itea.fr/GDF/11
Owned by a family of fishermen, this house is in the heart of the Rocbère wine country. There are three en suite guest rooms, all with access to a covered patio. Lounge reserved for guest use and bicycles are available for those who wish to explore the flora and fauna of this future National Park. Gérard offers you the chance to watch him reel in his nets, and the catch will then be served up by Florence. Off-season tariff is 42 euros for two people.
PRICES: d €49-€69; t €59; extra person €9; dinner €14
NEARBY: Bathing (4km) Canoeing (3km) Sea (16km) Swimming pool (13km) Tennis (4km) Sailing (3km) Railway station (15km) Shops (3km) NARBONNE (15km) **NOTES:** Pets admitted

POUZOLS MINERVOIS

🏵 🍽 **1, Ch de Ste Valiere**
Anne CHARDONNET-TORRES
GITES DE FRANCE-SERVICE RESERVATION, 5 allée Sully, 29322 QUIMPER Cedex
☎ 04 68 11 40 70 & PROP: 04 68 46 38 69 🖹 04 68 11 40 72
e-mail: GITESDEFRANCE.AUDE@wanadoo.fr
www.itea.fr/GDF/11
Four charming en suite double rooms are offered in this centrally heated family house. There is a lounge and library, and breakfast can be served in the garden, weather permitting. The hostess, winemaker Anne, is ready to share her twin passions - vines and wines - with you. There are foot-trails and bike paths nearby and the house is only 300 m from the pretty village of Pouzols.
PRICES: s €41-€43; d €44-€46; extra person €13; dinner €14
ON SITE: Tennis **NEARBY:** Bathing (2km) Sea (35km) Swimming pool (2km) Sailing (35km) Railway station (15km) LEZIGNAN CORBIERES (15km) **NOTES:** Pets admitted CC English spoken

ROQUETAILLADE

🏵 🍽 **Maison de Leoncie** Eric BLONDEL
GITES DE FRANCE-SERVICE RESERVATION, 5 allée Sully, 29322 QUIMPER Cedex
☎ 04 68 11 40 70 & PROP: 04 68 31 58 54 🖹 04 68 11 40 72
e-mail: GITESDEFRANCE.AUDE@wanadoo.fr
www.itea.fr/GDF/11
Set in the heart of a village whose inhabitants cut stone and vines with equal skill, this house has four double or triple rooms, two of which have en suite shower and wc, and two of which have en suite shower and private separate wc. Electric heating. Dining room, lounge area with bread oven, fireplace and library with specialist works and documents about the Cathar region. The village and its 11th-century château overlook the region's vineyards and there are many spectacular views. Evening meal available on reservation.
PRICES: s €30; d €43-€46; extra person €7; dinner €15
NEARBY: Bathing (20km) Canoeing (15km) Sea (60km) Swimming pool (10km) Tennis (10km) Sailing (20km) Railway station (10km) Shops (10km) LIMOUX (10km) **NOTES:** No pets CC English spoken

SAINT FRICHOUX

La Belle Minervoise Dominique JARRY
GITES DE FRANCE-SERVICE RESERVATION, 5 allée Sully, 29322 QUIMPER Cedex
☎ 04 68 11 40 70 & PROP: 04 68 78 23 65 🖷 04 68 11 40 72
e-mail: GITESDEFRANCE.AUDE@wanadoo.fr
www.itea.fr/GDF/11

This 19th-century family house offers five double or triple rooms and serves generous and varied breakfasts, featuring home-made jam, which can be taken on the terrace. Four of the five rooms look onto vineyards and the house boasts two terraces, one facing north and the other south. 200 metres form a small, shady park. The house can be used as a base for local walking and guests can book tasting sessions with the village winemaker. Evening meals available on reservations, except Tuesdays in July and August.

PRICES: d €43; extra person €12-€13; dinner €15 **NEARBY:** Bathing (4km) Canoeing (8km) Sea (50km) Swimming pool (8km) Tennis (3km) Sailing (15km) Railway station (20km) CARCASSONNE (20km)
NOTES: No pets CC English spoken

SAINT HILAIRE

3 Avenue de Limoux P et J HOYOS ET THEVENOT
GITES DE FRANCE-SERVICE RESERVATION, 5 allée Sully, 29322 QUIMPER Cedex
☎ 04 68 11 40 70 & PROP: 04 68 69 41 21 🖷 04 68 11 40 72
e-mail: GITESDEFRANCE.AUDE@wanadoo.fr
www.itea.fr/GDF/11

This guest house is situated in the heart of one of the world's oldest vineyards and has five guest rooms, three with en suite shower and wc and two with private bathroom. Breakfast can either be served in the dining room or in the small garden with patio. Visit the village's two abbeys and refresh yourselves with a dip in the Lauquet river.

PRICES: s €38; d €38-€44; t €58 **ON SITE:** Tennis **NEARBY:** Bathing (5km) Canoeing (20km) Sea (80km) Swimming pool (15km) Sailing (17km) Railway station (15km) CARCASSONNE (15km) **NOTES:** Pets admitted CC English spoken

SAINT MARTIN LALANDE

Domaine Escourrou Gustave DELCROIX
GITES DE FRANCE-SERVICE RESERVATION, 5 allée Sully, 29322 QUIMPER Cedex
☎ 04 68 11 40 70 & PROP: 04 68 94 98 41 🖷 04 68 11 40 72
e-mail: GITESDEFRANCE.AUDE@wanadoo.fr
www.itea.fr/GDF/11

This fully restored 18th-century farmhouse, near to the Canal du Midi and hiking routes, is set in wonderful grounds with flower-beds, swimming pool, garden furniture, barbecue and children's play area. The house has three guest rooms, which consist of one large room with TV and en suite bathroom with spa bath, one double or triple room with TV and private bathroom, and one room with private separate bathroom. The ground floor dining room with fireplace opens onto the park. Meals can be provided if reserved. Close to main road RN 113.

PRICES: s €33-€45; d €40-€53; t €50-€65; dinner €23
ON SITE: Children's play area Bathing Swimming pool
NEARBY: Canoeing (50km) Tennis (6km) Sailing (20km) Railway station (5km) Shops (5km) CASTELNAUDARY (5km) **NOTES:** Pets admitted CC English spoken

For further information on these and other chambres d'hôtes, consult the Gîtes de France website *www.gites-de-france.fr*

La Capelle Jacques SABATTE
11400 ST MARTIN LALANDE
☎ 04 68 94 91 90

Three grade 3 rooms are available in this farmhouse, set in leafy surroundings close to the Canal du Midi (3 km) and the 'cassoulet town' of Castelnaudary (4 km). Electric heating and shower rooms with separate wc. Lounge with cooking area. Also near to the Abbey of St Papoul which boasts panoramic views of the Pyrenees.

PRICES: d €38-€46; t €53; extra person €7; dinner €20
NEARBY: Bathing (5km) Canoeing (70km) Sea (90km) Swimming pool (5km) Tennis (2km) Sailing (20km) Railway station (6km) Shops (2km) CASTELNAUDARY (4km) **NOTES:** No pets

See advert on opposite page

SAINT MARTIN LE VIEIL

Abbaye de Villelongue Jean ELOFFE
GITES DE FRANCE-SERVICE RESERVATION, 5 allée Sully, 29322 QUIMPER Cedex
☎ 04 68 11 40 70 & PROP: 04 68 76 92 58 🖷 04 68 11 40 72
e-mail: GITESDEFRANCE.AUDE@wanadoo.fr
www.itea.fr/GDF/11

This tastefully converted former abbey dates from the 12th century. Its romantic atmosphere and melancholic charm make it a wonderful place to stay. The four guest rooms are part of the old monks' dormitories and are equipped with en suite bathrooms. Breakfast is served either in the former cloisters or in the "Monks' Room".

PRICES: d €50-€54 **NEARBY:** Bathing (8km) Sea (85km) Swimming pool (8km) Tennis (5km) Sailing (20km) Railway station (10km) Shops (8km) CARCASSONNE (25km) **NOTES:** No pets English spoken

SAISSAC

Le Lampy Neuf Claude BOUDET
11310 SAISSAC
☎ 04 68 24 46 07

Close to the Canal du Midi and the in the heart of the Lampy arboretum, this 19th-century house offers four guest rooms, one of which is a double. The rooms all have en suite bathrooms. Breakfast and evening meals served in the large dining room. The house has a lounge and library. Lake nearby. If you want to find out more about La Fontaine, France's answer to Aesop, ask for one of the fable-themed evenings, which your hosts sometimes hold.

PRICES: d €30-€53; extra person €15; dinner €18 **ON SITE:** Bathing Sailing **NEARBY:** Canoeing (50km) Sea (110km) Swimming pool (10km) Tennis (5km) Railway station (25km) Shops (5km) CARCASSONNE (30km) **NOTES:** Pets admitted English spoken

SALSIGNE

Domaine de Combestremieres
Andre LAFAGE, 11600 SALSIGNE
☎ 04 68 77 06 97 🖷 04 68 77 56 39

Four double rooms and one triple room, all with private bathroom facilities, are available in this family house, part of a farming property located between Salsigne and Villardonnel. The magnificent restored farmhouse is surrounded by woods, near to the Cathar fortress of Lastours and the many hiking trails which run along the Cabardès. Evening meals (16 euros) include the farm's own produce, and are served in the attractive dining room with fireplace. Picnics can be provided and mountain bikes are available for hire.

PRICES: d €34; t €41; HB €32; dinner €16 **NEARBY:** Bathing (25km) Sea (85km) Swimming pool (12km) Tennis (12km) Sailing (25km) Railway station (25km) Shops (4km) CARCASSONNE (25km)
NOTES: Pets admitted

SOULATGE

¶¶¶ ¡O¡ La Giraudasse A et K SOMOZA TIBERGHIEN
11330 SOULATGE
☎ 04 68 45 00 16 📠 04 68 45 05 40
e-mail: giraudasse@hotmail.com
Katia and Anibal offer five guest rooms in their 17th-century family mansion. Set halfway between the Cathar strongholds of Quéribus and Peyrepertuse and the Galamus gorge, this non-smoking house has large rooms with private bathrooms. Centrally heated. Large garden with fruit trees where breakfast is served under the bower in summer. In winter, relax by the fire in the lounge with its reading corner. Try the cassoulet, rabbit and lamb on offer at dinner.
PRICES: s €40; d €48; t €58; HB €88; dinner €20 **NEARBY:** Bathing (10km) Canoeing (40km) Sea (55km) Swimming pool (14km) Tennis (14km) Sailing (55km) Railway station (50km) Shops (8km) LIMOUX (50km) **NOTES:** No pets English spoken

VILLARDONNEL

¶¶¶ ♥ ¡O¡ Abbaye de Capservy Daniel MEILHAC
GITES DE FRANCE-SERVICE RESERVATION, 5 allée Sully, 29322 QUIMPER Cedex
☎ 04 68 11 40 70 & PROP: 04 68 26 61 40 📠 04 68 11 40 72
e-mail: GITESDEFRANCE.AUDE@wanadoo.fr
www.itea.fr/GDF/11
Dating from the 11th century, this former abbey is set in stunning rural surroundings and boasts three distinctive guest rooms. Two have mezzanines and en suite shower rooms and can accommodate up to five people. There is also a double room with private bathroom. At dinner, Denise and Daniel will introduce you to local delicacies. The dining room has a fireplace, and there is a reading room and garden with furniture. Small lake and swimming pool. Evening meals are available on reservation, except Sunday and Tuesday.
PRICES: s €34; d €45-€52; t €56-€63; dinner €20 **ON SITE:** Bathing Swimming pool **NEARBY:** Sea (80km) Tennis (5km) Sailing (15km) Railway station (17km) Shops (2km) CARCASSONNE (17km)
NOTES: Pets admitted CC English spoken

¶¶¶ ♥ ¡O¡ Domaine de La Calm
Eric et Marie Noelle MARTIN
11600 VILLARDONNEL
☎ 04 68 26 52 13 & SR : 04 68 11 40 70 📠 04 68 26 58 30
e-mail: lacalm@free.fr
Set on the Carcassonne plain, in Cathar country, 'La Calm' farm is refreshed by the morning mist. Sheep rearers Marie and Eric offer the choice of four attractive guest rooms with private bathrooms and will provide evening meals (on reservation) featuring the farm's own produce. Food is served in the dining room which has a traditional fireplace made of local stone. Breakfast can be taken on the terrace, and homemade jam is guaranteed. Archery sessions possible.
PRICES: s €30; d €40; extra person €15; dinner €12 **NEARBY:** Bathing (5km) Sea (85km) Swimming pool (5km) Tennis (5km) Sailing (10km) Railway station (25km) Shops (4km) CARCASSONNE (25km)
NOTES: No pets CC English spoken

VILLESEQUE DES CORBIERES

¶¶¶ Château du Haut Gleon Leon Nicolas DUHAMEL
11360 VILLESEQUE DES CORBIERES
☎ 04 68 48 85 95 📠 04 68 48 46 20
Six charming guest rooms are available at this winemaking château set in a Corbières valley 25 km from the Mediterranean coast. Guest rooms are either situated in the former shepherd's quarters or in those of the grape-pickers. There are two grade 2 rooms with separate bathroom and four grade 3 rooms with en

La Capelle
11400 Saint Martin Lalande
Tel: 04 68 94 91 90

Bed and breakfast accommodation in an ancient house situated 2km from the village and 3km to the Midi canal, in a green agricultural area. The house has six bedrooms on the ground or first floors with bathroom and WC and electric heating.
Use of washing and drying machine.
Enclosed garden area with terrace, garden furniture and barbecue.

suite facilities. Dining room with lounge area and fireplace. Communal courtyard, car park and shady grounds are accessible to all.
PRICES: d €53-€69 **NEARBY:** Bathing (7km) Sea (25km) Swimming pool (7km) Tennis (2km) Sailing (25km) Railway station (20km) Shops (7km) NARBONNE (20km) **NOTES:** Pets admitted

GARD

AIGREMONT

¶¶¶ ¡O¡ Les Romarins
Ronald & Marie-Claude EDWARDES
Route de Sauve, 30350 AIGREMONT
☎ 04 66 60 47 98 & SR : 04 66 27 94 94
Three spacious bed and breakfast rooms in an ancient barn, renovated with air conditioning. Private bathrooms and large dining room (dinner if required). Large quiet garden with private parking. Reading/television room. A warm welcome in a pleasant village with its 14th-century castle. Convenient for tourists, between the Roman towns of Nîmes and Arles, Le Pont du Gard, Avignon, Anduze and the steam train through the Cévennes. The sea is 45 minutes away, and the Massif Cévenol just 15 minutes away. Open all year.
PRICES: s €42; d €46; t €60; dinner €15 **NEARBY:** Bathing (15km) Canoeing (15km) Horse riding (4km) Forest (20km) Sea (60km) Fishing (5km) Swimming pool (9km) Tennis (9km) Railway station (9km) Shops (4km) **NOTES:** Pets admitted English spoken

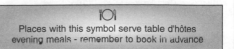

¡O¡
Places with this symbol serve table d'hôtes evening meals - remember to book in advance

continued

AIGUEZE

♦♦♦ Chambre d'hôtes Michel CHENIVESSE
les jardins du Barry, entrée du Village, 30760 AIGUEZE
☎ 04 66 82 15 75 📠 04 66 82 35 85
Gorges de l'Ardèche 2 km. In the peace of a charming village, a noted site overlooking the mouth of the gorges with their waterfalls, this Provençal house is set in a flower garden with olive trees. Each bedroom is individually decorated and self-contained, with a terrace to the garden, private bathroom and fridge. Kitchen/sitting room. A generous breakfast featuring home-made preserves is served on the terrace. At the foot of the garden there is a private 5 x 10m swimming pool (covered out of season) with sunbeds. Locked, private parking. Washing machine. There is a restaurant and grill in the village and access to the Ardèche via mountain paths. Open from Palm Sunday to mid-October.
PRICES: d €54-€58; extra person €70 **ON SITE:** Bathing Canoeing Fishing Swimming pool **NEARBY:** Horse riding (20km) Forest (1km) Sea (110km) Tennis (1km) **NOTES:** Pets admitted by arrangement

AIMARGUES

♦♦♦ Mas des Cabanes Adeline PASQUALINI
30470 AIMARGUES
☎ 04 66 88 03 43 & 06 89 83 90 04 📠 04 66 88 03 43
Five ground-floor rooms, each containing a cooking area, bathroom and wc. Terrace, garden, play area and private parking. Private tennis. In the heart of the Camargue, near Nîmes, Arles and Montpellier. Open all year.
PRICES: s €39; d €46; t €54; extra person €8 **ON SITE:** Children's play area Swimming pool Tennis **NEARBY:** Bathing (5km) Horse riding (10km) Sea (15km) Fishing (5km) Railway station (20km) Shops (2km) **NOTES:** Pets admitted English spoken

ANDUZE

♦♦♦ 🐓 ⏀ Le Cornadel Karine ANFOSSO
30140 ANDUZE
☎ 04 66 61 79 44 📠 04 66 61 80 46
e-mail: anfosso@cornadel.fr www.cornadel.fr

Old restored farm comprising one large room for two or three guests, two rooms for two guests, and two suites for two or four people. Each room has a fridge, TV, video recorder and air conditioning. With its fireplace, the dining room is a lovely setting. Local specialities include ceps, truffles, pork, trout and *aioli de morue*. Open all year except from 12 November to 7 December and from 14 January to 2 February.
PRICES: s €62-€77; d €76-€92; t €100-€115 **ON SITE:** Wine tasting Bathing Fishing Swimming pool **NEARBY:** Canoeing (80km) Horse riding (1km) Forest (50km) Sea (80km) Tennis (1km) Railway station (15km) Shops (2km) Restaurant nearby **NOTES:** No pets CC

🐓 Places with this symbol are farmhouses

ARGILLIERS

♦♦♦♦ La Bastide de Boisset P DE CORNEILLAN
Le Village, 30210 ARGILLIERS
☎ 04 66 22 91 13
e-mail: http://bastidedeboisset.free.fr
Pont du Gard 4 km. Uzès 9 km. Nîmes and Avignon 30 km. Orange 40 km. Beautiful restored old stone house with antique furniture and meticulous décor. Bedrooms comprise one twin with bath, shower and wc; one double, with shower and separate wc; two suites with bath and wc. Library with fireplace. Private swimming pool, terrace and garden. Private parking. The house, set in a small village, is very comfortable; peace and quiet assured. Evening meals can be arranged. A suite for 4 guests costs 99 euros. Open from 6 January to 19 December.
PRICES: d €57-€61; extra person €15 **ON SITE:** Swimming pool **NEARBY:** Bathing (4km) Horse riding (3km) Forest (3km) Sea (80km) Tennis (3km) Railway station (30km) Shops (3km) **NOTES:** No pets English spoken

ARPAILLARGUES-ET-AUREILHAC

♦♦♦♦ Mas de Luna Danielle DUPRAT
place du Pouzet, 30700 ARPAILLARGUES
☎ 04 66 03 30 67 & SR : 04 66 27 94 94
📠 04 66 03 30 67 e-mail: masdeluna@wanadoo.fr
Pont du Gard 15 km. Nîmes 25 km. Arles 45 km. Avignon 45 km. A warm welcome awaits at this totally restored and elegant 18th-century house in a picturesque village 7 km from Uzès. One ground-floor double room, and on the first floor, one small two-roomed suite (one double, two single beds) and one room (one double, one single bed). All rooms have a bathroom and private wc. Communal living room, terrace and balcony. Evening meals featuring traditional cuisine can be arranged. Open all year.
PRICES: s €60; d €70; t €85; extra person €15 **NEARBY:** Bathing (5km) Canoeing (10km) Horse riding (5km) Forest (1km) Sea (70km) Fishing (5km) Swimming pool (6km) Tennis (6km) Railway station (25km) Shops (1km) **NOTES:** Pets admitted English spoken

BARJAC

♦♦♦ La Sérénité C et Y L'HELGOUALCH
place de la Mairie, 30430 BARJAC
☎ 04 66 24 54 63 📠 04 66 24 54 63
A beautiful 18th-century house in the village square, with a superb view of the Cévennes. One suite (one double, one single bed) with large sitting room, bath, separate shower, two washbasins; one family suite with two bedrooms (one double, one twin, bath, basins, wc) and one room with double bed. Substantial wooded garden with enormous terrace for breakfast and relaxing. The bedrooms are vast and comfortable with antique furniture and fittings (the owner is an antique dealer). Sitting room and library at guests' disposal. Great charm, and many treasures to see in the area. Open all year by prior reservation.
PRICES: d €60-€105; t €120 **NEARBY:** Bathing (6km) Canoeing (12km) Horse riding (3km) Sea (110km) Fishing (6km) Swimming pool (7km) Tennis (1km) Railway station (30km) **NOTES:** No pets

BEAUCAIRE

♦♦♦ Domaine des Clos David et Sandrine AUSSET
route de Bellegarde, 30300 BEAUCAIRE
☎ 04 66 01 14 61 & 06 11 81 62 78 📠 04 66 01 00 47
e-mail: aussetd@aol.com www.domaine-des-clos.com
Arles 15 km. Tarascon 7 km. Avignon 25 km. St-Rémy-de-Provence 20 km. This 18th-century Provençal house is set in the middle of the countryside where the décor mixes tiles, enormous stones and colonnades. On the first floor choose from the Yellow, Red, Green,

continued

Pink or Blue Rooms, each with double bed, shower, washbasin and wc. Dining room and communal kitchen for guests. Covered barbecue and swimming pool in large garden. The dovecote, wine cellar, fountain and stables all add to the character. Enjoy golf, cycling, water sports and rambling. Open all year.
PRICES: d €47-€70 **ON SITE:** Swimming pool **NEARBY:** Horse riding (3km) Forest (30km) Sea (45km) Fishing (3km) Railway station (7km) Shops (6km) **NOTES:** No pets English spoken

BEZ-ET-ESPARON

♦♦♦ ⧉ **Château Massal** Françoise DU LUC
30120 BEZ-ET-ESPARON
☎ 04 67 81 07 60 & 06 14 35 45 04 📠 04 67 81 07 60
A 19th-century castle, in the heart of the Cévennes, in an exceptional setting of oak and chestnut forests with views over the Arre Valley. Three double rooms, each with separate bathroom and wc and own entrance. Guests can dine and relax in the wooded and flower-bedecked garden. Large lounge. Meals can be booked in advance. Visit the forests of l'Aigoual, the huge Causses, the Cirques de Navacelle, caves (the Demoiselles), gorges (Tarn, Jonte). Ten euro supplement for a child's bed. Open all year.
PRICES: s €51; d €58-€74; extra person €10; dinner €22
NEARBY: Bathing (7km) Canoeing (20km) Horse riding (7km) Forest (20km) Sea (70km) Fishing (1km) Swimming pool (7km) Tennis (1km) Railway station (75km) Shops (5km) **NOTES:** No pets English spoken

CALVISSON

♦♦♦ ⧉ **Chambre d'hôtes** R et C BURCKEL DE TELL
Pays de Nîmes, Grande Rue 48, 30420 CALVISSON
☎ 04 66 01 23 91 📠 04 66 01 42 19
e-mail: corinne.burckeldetel@free.fr www.bed-and-art.com

Near the village, this 16th-century style, totally restored property stands on its own. There are three bedrooms on the first floor, overlooking an enclosed patio, with individual bathrooms and wcs. Sitting room with fireplace, and terraces. There are guided tours of Arles, Nîmes, Montpellier and Avignon. Painting exhibition on the premises. Garage parking 4 euros. Open beginning February-end November.
PRICES: s €38; d €46-€49; t €58; extra person €8; dinner €15
ON SITE: Swimming pool Tennis **NEARBY:** Bathing (8km) Canoeing (18km) Horse riding (5km) Forest (25km) Sea (20km) Fishing (8km) Railway station (8km) **NOTES:** Pets admitted English spoken

CAMPESTRE-ET-LUC

♦♦♦ ⧉ **Le Luc** Jean-Michel MOHA
Domaine du Luc, Au Pays des Templiers,
30770 CAMPESTRE-ET-LUC
☎ 04 67 82 01 01 📠 04 67 82 01 01
Cirque de Navacelle 25 km. Saint-Guilhem-le-Désert 45 km. A warm welcome awaits at this 1850s home with a relaxed ambience - perfect for recharging your batteries. It offers six rooms each with a separate bath and wc, and a garden with terrace. Meals using

regional produce may be enjoyed at the inn. Parking and locked garage. La Couvertoirade is 20 km. The estate (on a marked GR walking route) is surrounded by 15 tourist sites including some of the best of the region - Lac du Salagou, Cirque de Mourèze, Grottes de Labeil et de Clamouse. Open all year.
PRICES: s €37; d €45; extra person €9; dinner €16 **ON SITE:** Children's play area Horse riding **NEARBY:** Bathing (40km) Canoeing (40km) Forest (20km) Sea (115km) Fishing (15km) Swimming pool (22km) Tennis (15km) Railway station (30km) Shops (15km) Restaurant nearby
NOTES: Pets admitted CC English spoken

CASTELNAU-VALENCE

♦♦♦ ⧉ **La Maison d'Alcalure** André BARTHELEMY
rue du Camp, 30190 CASTELNAU-VALENCE
☎ 04 66 60 13 26 & SR : 04 66 27 94 94 📠 04 66 60 13 26
Uzès 15 km. Nîmes 25 km. This stone-built village house is quiet and comfortable. Spacious bedrooms - on the first floor one room for three guests; on the second one double room, and one for two to five guests. All rooms have full facilities. Dining room and lounge. Terrace and communal swimming pool. Secure parking. Table d'hôte meals featuring Provençal cooking are available on request. Children under seven: 12.50 euros. Open February-end November.
PRICES: s €46; d €54; extra person €16; dinner €15
ON SITE: Swimming pool **NEARBY:** Canoeing (15km) Horse riding (5km) Forest (25km) Sea (60km) Fishing (10km) Tennis (5km) Railway station (6km) Shops (10km) **NOTES:** No pets

CASTILLON DU GARD

♦♦♦ **La Maison d'Elie** Mireille DAUTEUIL
rue Turion Sabatier, 30210 CASTILLON DU GARD
☎ 04 66 37 24 70 & 06 20 46 02 44 📠 04 66 37 24 70
This house is in the heart of a medieval village between Nîmes and Avignon, 3 km from the Pont du Gard. The rooms are vaulted, with Provençal décor, antique furniture, and the sound of cicadas. Three rooms have a hydrotherapy bath and wc, and one room has a hydromassage shower and wc. Satellite TV and minibar. Covered heated swimming pool and rooftop terrace. Sitting room with open fire in winter. There are restaurants in the village that serve typically regional cuisine. Open 15 February-31 December.
PRICES: s €55; d €95; t €110 **ON SITE:** Swimming pool
NEARBY: Bathing (3km) Canoeing (5km) Horse riding (5km) Golf (15km) Sea (80km) Fishing (5km) Railway station (25km) **NOTES:** Pets admitted

♦♦♦ **Mas de Raffin** Michel VIC
30120 CASTILLON-DU-GARD
☎ 04 66 37 13 28 📠 04 66 37 62 55
In the heart of the vineyards and open countryside, this is an old house now completely restored, where rest and relaxation are guaranteed. On the ground floor, there are two vaulted rooms (2-3 people) and one beamed room for two or three. On the first floor, one room with a kitchen bar sleeps two to four people, and another room sleeps two or three. Each room has a separate bath, shower and wc. TV, closed courtyard and parking. The cellar specialises in Côte du Rhône (red and rosé). Only five minutes from the Pont du Gard, and ten minutes from Uzès, the 'First Duchy of France'. Open all year.
PRICES: s €51; d €65-€84; t €88-€100 **ON SITE:** Forest Swimming pool
NEARBY: Bathing (4km) Canoeing (3km) Horse riding (4km) Sea (100km) Fishing (4km) Tennis (2km) Railway station (24km)
NOTES: Pets admitted English spoken

⧉ Places with this symbol serve table d'hôtes evening meals - remember to book in advance

continued

CHAMBORIGAUD

♥ ⭐ ⚫ Le Mas du Seigneur
Louis et Danièle BERTRAND
Altayrac, 30530 CHAMBORIGAUD
☎ 04 66 61 41 52   🖷 04 66 61 41 52
www.i-france.com/seigneur

This 16th-century Cévennes house is set amid 15 hectares of pines and 100-year-old chestnuts. There are five renovated and carefully decorated double rooms, with separate access, all en suite. An extra bed may be added. Library, swimming pool, bowling alley, private parking. Half board: minimum stay one week. Take advantage of the natural environment, the peacefulness, the beauty of the site and of activities such as walking, flower- and fruit-picking, and swimming. Open 1 February-30 November.
PRICES: s €43; d €58; t €74; extra person €16; HB €45; dinner €17
ON SITE: Wine tasting Children's play area Forest Swimming pool
NEARBY: Bathing (2km) Canoeing (15km) Horse riding (10km) Sea (90km) Fishing (1km) Tennis (4km) Railway station (5km) Shops (4km)
NOTES: Pets admitted CC English spoken

COLLORGUES

♥ Mas du Platane Dominique DANZEISEN-LEIJENAAR
30190 COLLORGUES
☎ 04 66 81 29 04

Three separate guest rooms in an old detached house at the edge of the village. One twin, two double, each with separate wc, shower and washbasin. Two rooms are on the ground floor, one on the first floor. Mediterranean garden with individual terraces. Private swimming pool. Locked parking. 11 km from golf course. Open from Easter to 1 November..
PRICES: s €50-€53; d €57-€60 **ON SITE:** Swimming pool
NEARBY: Canoeing (15km) Horse riding (11km) Sea (60km) Fishing (5km) Tennis (11km) **NOTES:** Pets admitted English spoken

COURRY

♥ ⚫ Croix-Parens Catherine MALET
La Picholine, Courry, 30500 ST-AMBROIX
☎ 04 66 24 13 30   🖷 04 66 24 09 63
e-mail: picholine@wanadoo.fr http://www.lapicholine.fr.st
Barjac 20 km. Uzès 50 km. Nîmes 65 km. Guests can be sure of quiet, comfort and a warm welcome at this old restored house, with its 100-year-old vaults and antique furnishings. Three guest rooms on the first floor, each with private bath and wc. Dining room and two sitting rooms with TV. Terrace, garden, pool and private parking. Evening meals are available if pre-booked. Enjoy tennis in the village, mountain-biking, walking, table tennis, boules. Visit the Cévennes National Park, the Bambouseraie, the Ardèche Gorges, the Cèze Valley and the Pont du Gard. Pets 2.50 euros. Open from March to 1 November (by reservation out of season).
PRICES: s €49; d €55-€61; t €73; extra person €16; dinner €19
ON SITE: Children's play area Swimming pool Tennis
NEARBY: Bathing (7km) Canoeing (1km) Horse riding (6km) Forest (5km) Sea (110km) Fishing (7km) Railway station (7km) **NOTES:** Pets admitted English spoken

ISSIRAC

♥ ⚫ Chez Dame Tartine Pascale CHAVE
rue de la Fontaine, 30760 ISSIRAC
☎ 04 66 82 17 06
e-mail: dame.tartine@9online.fr
web-accueil.net/chez-dame-tartine.htm
In a landscape of lavender and cherries sits the small, pretty and quiet village of Issirac, with its alleys and typical bell tower overlooking the Gorges de l'Ardèche and the Cèze Valley. At the foot of the village, this stone-built house of genuine charm offers

three guest rooms with shower, wc and balcony. The large garden has a lovely view. From the house, footpaths and mountain bike tracks lead into beautiful countryside. Open all year.
PRICES: s €41; d €47; t €54; dinner €13 **NEARBY:** Bathing (6km) Canoeing (12km) Horse riding (10km) Forest (1km) Sea (90km) Fishing (6km) Swimming pool (2km) Tennis (6km) **NOTES:** Pets admitted

LA BRUGUIERE

♥ ⭐ ⚫ Le Mas des Santolines
Marie-Claude PARMENTIER
30580 LA BRUGUIERE
☎ 04 66 72 85 04 & SR : 04 66 27 94 94
🖷 04 66 72 87 38
www.mas-santolines.com

Uzès 12 km. Nîmes 30 km. Avignon 35 km. Arles, Camargue 45 km. Early 19th-century house completely renovated, with four rooms and one suite, all of which are very comfortable and prettily decorated. Beds vary in size; bathrooms are convenient and carefully thought-out. The communal rooms, the lounge, kitchen and dining room, are large, light and welcoming. The huge garden is a delight with its Mediterranean plants and private swimming pool. Lavish meals are served under the 100-year-old fig tree. Dogs are allowed. Transport to the station or airport can be arranged. Tucked away in the Gard, Le Mas des Santolines is close to many remarkable sites, and near the Camargue and the Mediterranean. Open all year.
PRICES: s €84; d €84; t €92; HB €60; FB €60; dinner €23
ON SITE: Wine tasting Swimming pool **NEARBY:** Bathing (10km) Canoeing (10km) Horse riding (10km) Forest (2km) Sea (45km) Fishing (10km) Tennis (2km) Railway station (25km) Shops (3km)
NOTES: Pets admitted CC English spoken

LA ROQUE-SUR-CEZE

♥ Chambre d'hôtes Pierre et Yolande RIGAUD
La Roque sur Cèze, 30200 BAGNOLS-SUR-CEZE
☎ 04 66 82 79 37   🖷 04 66 82 79 37
A typical stone house in the centre of the village, a listed site with a historic bridge over the Cèze which flows to the waterfalls at Sautadet. Two rooms on the first floor, and four more on the second. Four are doubles or twins; one room accommodates three, all with shower, washbasin and wc. Garden, barbecue and pool for guests' enjoyment. €76/4 guests, surcharge of €0.46/guest in July and August.
PRICES: s €45; d €54; t €70; extra person €15 **NEARBY:** Bathing (1km) Canoeing (10km) Horse riding (1km) Forest (4km) Sea (100km) Fishing (1km) Tennis (6km) **NOTES:** No pets

> Ask the proprietor for directions
> when booking

continued

LASALLE

♦♦♦ Domaine de Soulages Guillaume GOURGAS
Saint-Louis de Soulages, 30460 LASALLE
☎ 04 66 85 41 83 & 04 67 64 49 13
Uzès, Nîmes, Montpellier 50 km. Bambouseraie, caves, gorges 20 km. As it is situated on a 38-hectare estate this property, with beautiful views, is suitable for either a boisterous party or for enjoying the peace and solitude! The estate was extensively altered when magnificent granite-walled terraces and dams were built. The guest rooms and a suite are large and pleasant, each with bath and wc. The furniture and ornaments are in period style. Open all year by prior reservation.
PRICES: s €74; d €77; t €104; extra person €15 **ON SITE:** Bathing Forest Swimming pool **NEARBY:** Canoeing (20km) Horse riding (2km) Sea (50km) Fishing (10km) Tennis (2km) **NOTES:** No pets

LAUDUN

♦♦♦ Château de Lascours Jean-Louis BASTOUIL
30290 LAUDUN
☎ 04 66 50 39 61 🖹 04 66 50 30 08
e-mail: CHATEAU.DE.LASCOURS@wanadoo.fr

Airports Avignon 25 km and Nîmes 40 km. Uzès 17 km. This castle (12th and 17th centuries) with its moats is classed as a historic monument; it houses four guest rooms and one suite, each with bathroom and wc. Reception room, generous breakfast, parking. Tranquillity is guaranteed. Swimming pool in the park. Around the castle: Laudun - Caesar's camp (archaeological site); listed vineyards; Bagnols-sur-Cèze, museum of painting. 114 euros/4 guests; children under seven: 15 euros. Open all year.
PRICES: s €75; d €84; t €99; extra person €14 **ON SITE:** Bathing Forest Fishing Swimming pool Tennis **NEARBY:** Canoeing (30km) Horse riding (1km) Sea (80km) Railway station (25km) **NOTES:** Pets admitted English spoken

LAVAL PRADEL

♦♦♦♦ ⏐◯⏐ Le Mas de la Cadenede Maxime TURC
Le Mas de Dieu, 30110 LAVAL PRADEL
☎ 04 66 30 78 14 & SR : 04 66 27 94 94 🖹 04 66 30 78 88
e-mail: masdelacadenede@free.fr
www.masdelacadenede.free.fr
A place for gentle living, organised to make your stay in the Cévennes memorable. On the ground floor, rooms with bath, shower and wc, TV, hairdryer and private terrace. Billiard room, games room, library, communal swimming pool and a day room under stone vaults. Private parking. Midday and evening meals can be arranged. The rooms, one with a mezzanine, are equipped with every comfort for guest well-being. Open all year.
PRICES: s €49; d €59; t €69; extra person €10; HB €93-€127; dinner €17 **ON SITE:** Forest Swimming pool **NEARBY:** Bathing (10km) Canoeing (10km) Horse riding (8km) Sea (60km) Fishing (10km) Tennis (3km) Railway station (6km) Shops (3km) Restaurant nearby **NOTES:** Pets admitted CC English spoken

LAVAL-SAINT-ROMAN

♦♦♦ Le Mas de la Chapelle Anne LAMY
Le Village, 30760 LAVAL-SAINT-ROMAN
☎ 04 66 82 36 22 🖹 04 66 82 36 22
A warm welcome can be expected at this house of character which stands alone at the edge of the village, between the Valley of la Cèze and the Gorges of the Ardèche, between Orange and Montelimar, with many sites worth visiting. Ground floor: one room with double and single bed, shower, wc and private terrace; one with a double and two single beds on a mezzanine, with shower and wc. First floor: one double with bath, etc. Heating, fans, mosquito screens. Barbecues in the charming garden, communal kitchen and a fridge at guests' disposal. Sitting room with open fire and a games room. Enclosed parking. 6m x 12m swimming pool. 65 euros/4 people. Open all year.
PRICES: s €47; d €53; t €59 **NEARBY:** Bathing (5km) Canoeing (5km) Horse riding (7km) Forest (5km) Sea (130km) Fishing (5km) Tennis (5km) Railway station (30km) Shops (5km) **NOTES:** Pets admitted English spoken

LE CHAMBON

♦♦♦ Chambre d'hôtes Dominique PASSIEU
place Louis Badourle, 30450 LE CHAMBON
☎ 04 66 61 49 25 🖹 04 66 61 50 36

Alès 32 km. Besseges 12 km. Four bedrooms. Open all year.
PRICES: s €38; d €53 **ON SITE:** Bathing Forest Fishing Tennis **NEARBY:** Canoeing (20km) Horse riding (20km) Sea (100km) Railway station (4km) **NOTES:** No pets

LIOUC

♦♦♦ ✿ ⏐◯⏐ ♿ Clos du Martinou Silvy et Jack RATIER
30260 LIOUC
☎ 04 66 77 41 42 🖹 04 66 77 31 68
Situated in a village of only 80 inhabitants on the River Vidourle, on the edge of the vineyard of Salavès. The village has an 11th-century church, and nearby are old oak forests and opportunities for climbing 10 km away. Five rooms each with separate washing and wc facilities. First floor: two rooms for two adults and three children in bunks, balcony; one double with terrace. Ground floor: two twins. One room is accessible to less mobile guests. Communal dining room. Private swimming pool, mountain-biking, GR and PR footpaths. Forty minutes from the sea and the Cévennes. Open all year.
PRICES: s €37; d €44; t €54; extra person €10; HB €53-€126; dinner €18 **ON SITE:** Swimming pool **NEARBY:** Bathing (1km) Canoeing (60km) Horse riding (2km) Forest (10km) Sea (40km) Fishing (1km) Tennis (1km) Railway station (40km) Shops (1km) **NOTES:** No pets CC English spoken

Prices are given in Euros €1 – £0.62
at the time of going to press

LUSSAN

✦✦✦ ❦ ⅠΟⅠ Mas des Garrigues Sylvia DOLLFUS

La Leque, 30580 LUSSAN

☎ 04 66 72 91 18 🖷 04 66 72 97 91

Four comfortable rooms with separate bathroom and wc, arranged with style in this attractive house in a very picturesque hamlet. Large common room with open fire and billiards. Heating. Provençal-style evening meals are available if pre-booked. Private swimming pool. Walks along the Cèze River. Riding and stables. Open February-2 January.

PRICES: s €49; d €55; t €67; dinner €13 **ON SITE:** Horse riding Swimming pool Tennis **NEARBY:** Bathing (12km) Canoeing (12km) Sea (150km) Fishing (12km) Railway station (50km) Shops (4km) Restaurant nearby **NOTES:** No pets

MONOBLET

✦✦✦ Le Mas de l'Aubret Robert COYNEL

La Pause, 30170 MONOBLET

☎ 04 66 85 42 19 🖷 04 66 85 40 65

e-mail: nr.coynel@laubret.com http://www.laubret.com

Anduze 13 km. Nîmes 50 km. Parc National des Cévennes 15 km. Near the village, this large house has six guest rooms, each for two or three people, with bath and wc. There is a terrace and a large leisure room with open fire, library, summer kitchen, dining area in the shade of the laurels. Between Anduze and St-Hippolyte-du-Fort, Monoblet is a typical village nestling in the Cévennes foothills among vineyards and chestnuts, on walking routes GR6 and GR63. National Meadow Park. Child supplement 11 euros. Open all year.

PRICES: s €30; d €40; t €50; extra person €11 **NEARBY:** Bathing (12km) Canoeing (15km) Horse riding (10km) Forest (2km) Sea (60km) Fishing (12km) Swimming pool (7km) Tennis (7km) Railway station (50km) **NOTES:** Pets admitted English spoken

MONTAREN-SAINT-MEDIERS

✦✦✦ ❦ ⅠΟⅠ Chambre d'hôtes Diane STENGEL

La Bergerie, Montée de Larnac, route de Saint-Ambroix, 30700 MONTAREN-SAINT-MEDIERS

☎ 04 66 03 32 02 & 06 87 45 76 07 🖷 04 66 03 32 02

Nîmes 30 km. Avignon 40 km. Peace and relaxation are assured at this establishment. The bedrooms have individual shower rooms; two rooms sleep four guests and one sleeps two. Panoramic views over the swimming pool and Uzès beyond. Central heating, private pool and games area. Price (half board): 63 euros/person; 80 euros/2 persons; 103 euros/3 persons; 128 euros/4 persons. Child under ten: 10 euros. Open all year.

PRICES: s €48; d €50; t €58; extra person €68 **ON SITE:** Children's play area Swimming pool **NEARBY:** Bathing (15km) Canoeing (15km) Horse riding (15km) Forest (5km) Sea (80km) Fishing (15km) Tennis (6km) Railway station (30km) Shops (6km) **NOTES:** Pets admitted

✦✦✦ ❦ ⅠΟⅠ Chambre d'hôtes

Thérèse STENGEL-DELBOS

Cruviers Larnac, 30700 MONTAREN-SAINT-MEDIERS

☎ 04 66 22 10 89 🖷 04 66 22 06 76

Four upstairs rooms in a house of real character in open countryside, where a restful stay is assured. En suite shower room and wc. Evening meals using farm produce, are available by prior arrangement, and feature preserves, duck, chicken, fruit and asparagus. Heating. Terrace with a commanding view over Uzès. Private swimming pool. 73 euros/ 4 guests. Half board for two guests: 94 euros. Open all year.

PRICES: s €50; d €54; t €63; dinner €20 **NEARBY:** Bathing (8km) Canoeing (10km) Sea (80km) Fishing (10km) Swimming pool (5km) Tennis (5km) **NOTES:** Pets admitted

NAVACELLES

✦✦✦ Hameau de Cal Mireille et Gérard CARRIERE

les Hauts de Séguissous, 30580 NAVACELLES

☎ 04 66 24 87 45 & SR : 04 66 27 94 94

e-mail: mireille.carriere@wanadoo.fr

Two rooms for four people and three twin rooms, all with en suite facilities. Hairdryer, balcony, kitchen and day room with open fireplace where meals may be prepared. The house stands on a rocky outcrop in the Valley of the Cèze, in a hamlet 500 m from the Thermales des Fumades. Many paths to explore. Open all year.

PRICES: s €38-€43; d €43-€49; t €49-€58; extra person €53-€61 **ON SITE:** Forest **NEARBY:** Bathing (6km) Canoeing (6km) Horse riding (1km) Sea (80km) Fishing (5km) Swimming pool (5km) Tennis (5km) Railway station (14km) Shops (4km) **NOTES:** No pets CC English spoken

NIMES

✦✦✦ ⅠΟⅠ Le Garric Michel et Eliane MARTIN

631 chemin d'Engance, 30000 NIMES

☎ 04 66 26 84 77 🖷 04 66 26 84 77

This is a new house, surrounded by dry-stone walls in the heart of a protected scrubland area. In this magnificent landscape many squirrels and birds can be seen. Peace and quiet are guaranteed. Five double rooms with separate bathroom and wc, and a terrace or balcony. Colour TV, telephone. Shaded park, boules, table tennis, billiards. A communal room beside the pool is where breakfast and evening meals are taken. Open 1 March-31 October.

PRICES: s €74; d €81; t €114; extra person €23; HB €53-€69; dinner €24-€25 **ON SITE:** Forest Swimming pool **NEARBY:** Bathing (15km) Canoeing (15km) Horse riding (5km) Golf (7km) Sea (45km) Fishing (15km) Tennis (3km) Railway station (5km) Shops (2km) **NOTES:** No pets Minimum 2 night stay

REMOULINS

✦✦✦✦ La Terre des Lauriers Gérard CRISTINI

Pont du Gard/Rive Droite, 30210 REMOULINS

☎ 04 66 37 19 45 & 06 12 10 61 92 🖷 04 66 37 19 45

www.laterredeslauriers.com

Nimes and Avignon 20 km. Uzès 10 km. Arles 35 km. This grand building houses five spacious double rooms with bath or shower and wc. Each room has a different style, air conditioning and TV. Sitting room with piano. The terrace overlooks the park and there is table tennis, a swimming pool, access to the river and six hectares of woods. Only 900 m from the Pont du Gard, a world heritage site. Lavish breakfast and brunches are served. Locked parking. Extra child's bed 12 euros. Children under two are free. Open March-October.

PRICES: s €70; d €80; t €105 **ON SITE:** Bathing Forest Fishing Swimming pool **NEARBY:** Canoeing (1km) Horse riding (8km) Golf (8km) Sea (50km) Tennis (1km) Railway station (20km) Shops (1km) **NOTES:** No pets English spoken

See advert on opposite page

REVENS

⑪⑪⑪ ⑩ Chambre d'hôtes Madeleine MACQ

Hermitage Saint-Pierre, Saint-Pierre de Revens, 12230 NANT
☎ 05 65 62 27 99

A restored Roman priory dating from the 10th, 11th and 15th-centuries situated in the wild beauty of the Valley of the Dourbies, between Saint-Véran and Cantobre. The five rooms (each with bath and wc - and one with kitchenette) are furnished in antique rustic style, and four have canopied four-poster beds. Evening meals are possible out of season. Open all year.

PRICES: s €46; d €53-€69; extra person €11; dinner €17

ON SITE: Bathing **NEARBY:** Horse riding (14km) Sea (100km) Fishing (2km) Tennis (6km) Railway station (20km) Shops (7km)

NOTES: No pets

RIBAUTE-LES-TAVERNES

⑪⑪⑪ ⑩ Mas de l'Amandier

S LASBLEIZ et B DOMINIQUE
Camp Galhan, 30720 RIBAUTE-LES-TAVERNES
☎ 04 66 83 87 06 ▯ 04 66 83 87 69

Old manor house in open countryside with a view over the Cévennes. Four guest rooms, one a suite, all with private entrances. Three rooms with large double bed and a single; one suite with large double and four single beds. All have individual bathrooms and wc. Fixed price meals, with wine included, are available if pre-booked. Open all year.

PRICES: s €57; d €63; t €69; dinner €20 **NEARBY:** Bathing (10km) Horse riding (2km) Forest (15km) Sea (60km) Fishing (10km) Tennis (2km) Railway station (35km) Shops (2km) **NOTES:** Pets admitted English spoken

ROGUES

⑪⑪⑪ La Jurade Isabelle et Luc BERNIER

Auberge de la Jurade, 30120 ROGUES
☎ 04 67 81 53 17

This typical regional house in open country on the Causse, near the Cirque de Navacelles, La Jurade offers peace and the chance to discover the region's natural and historic heritage. There are four separate rooms (two, three or four guests) and a suite for four, all with wc and shower. One ground-floor room is accessible to less mobile guests. Terrace, garden room, children's games. Restaurant in a separate building. Groups, seminaries, family or friends' reunions - all welcome. Children (half-board): 16 euros; (full board) 22 euros. 54 euros/four guests. Open all year except January and February.

PRICES: s €28; d €36; t €45; HB €16-€28; FB €22-€37

ON SITE: Children's play area **NEARBY:** Canoeing (20km) Horse riding (5km) Forest (2km) Sea (80km) Fishing (10km) Swimming pool (10km) Tennis (2km) Restaurant nearby **NOTES:** Pets admitted CC English spoken

SAUVE

⑪⑪⑪ Chambre d'hôtes Stéphane MEILHAC

La Pousaranque, 30610 SAUVE
☎ 04 66 77 51 97 & 04 66 77 00 97

Guest rooms with mezzanine in a farm building, near the river, situated among the vines, with a well and wheel - a typical curiosity of the region. Two rooms sleep four, the others sleep two. Private baths and wcs. Half board is possible. Private swimming pool. Open all year.

PRICES: s €36; d €40; t €48; extra person €55; dinner €15

ON SITE: Fishing Swimming pool Tennis **NEARBY:** Bathing (2km) Horse riding (3km) Sea (60km) Railway station (40km) Shops (2km) Restaurant nearby **NOTES:** Pets admitted

La Terre Des Lauriers
30210 Remoulins
Tel and fax: 04 66 37 19 45
www.laterredeslauriers.com

Situated in 13 acres of parkland this house, typical of the region, offers bed and breakfast. A homelike atmosphere reflects the warmth and personality of the proprietor who has a passion for many things including fishing. Paintings and souvenirs from travelling are displayed throughout the house. The five air conditioned, en-suite bedrooms have TV and a small balcony, which overlooks the swimming pool and the surrounding countryside. A separate lounge is available solely for the use of the guests. The Pont du Gard is within walking distance. Nearby tennis 1km, cycling 1km, climbing, canoeing and horse riding 6kms. Avignon, Nîmes, les Baux-de-Provence, the Cévennes and Uzès all less than 20km away.

⑪⑪⑪ La Renaudière Annie RENAULT

Perdiguier-Bas, 30610 SAUVE
☎ 04 66 77 36 22 & 06 03 22 46 14

Anduze 12 km. Nîmes 40 km. Montpellier 45 km. Country house on enormous plot of land, among vines, on the banks of the Crieulon. Enjoy peace and relaxation by the pool or in the shade of the trees, with chances for rambling and mountain-biking nearby. Walking routes 5 km. Rooms are on the first floor, with shower and wc in each. Breakfast in the dining room. Terrace, swimming pool and communal parking. Open all year.

PRICES: s €40; d €43 **ON SITE:** Swimming pool **NEARBY:** Bathing (5km) Canoeing (35km) Horse riding (3km) Sea (60km) Shops (5km) **NOTES:** No pets

SAUVETERRE

⑪⑪⑪ ☙ ⑩ l'Hoste Christiane SOULIER

chemin de Saint-Marc, 136, chemin de l'Hoste,
30150 SAUVETERRE
☎ 04 66 82 55 91

L'Hoste has been renovated in period style, with exposed stones and Provençal décor. The three guest rooms each sleep four (one double and two single beds, or four singles), and each have shower room, wc and central heating. Shared sitting room. Terrace, and locked parking. Situated in open countryside with a meadow lawn and an orchard, this is quiet location near the Avignon Pool House. Take advantage of private swimming pool, pétanque, table tennis. Visit the Choregies d'Orange, the Avignon Festival, the Tavel and Châteauneuf-du-Pape vineyards. Open all year.

PRICES: s €53; d €58; t €73; extra person €15; dinner €23

ON SITE: Bathing Swimming pool **NEARBY:** Canoeing (30km) Horse riding (5km) Sea (80km) Fishing (2km) Tennis (2km) Railway station (14km) Shops (2km) **NOTES:** Pets admitted English spoken

SERVAS

♥♥♥ Mas des Commandeurs Myriam SORDI
30340 SERVAS
☎ 04 66 85 67 90
Les Fumades (thermal springs) 3.5 km. In a country location, four double rooms with shower room and wc each, sitting room and common room. Peace guaranteed. Private swimming pool, courtyard with barbecue. Plenty to visit in the neighbourhood - the Falls of Sautadet, Pont du Gard, the Arena at Nîmes. Child €9. €64/4 guests. Open all year.
PRICES: s €43; d €46; t €55 **ON SITE:** Bathing Fishing Swimming pool **NEARBY:** Canoeing (25km) Horse riding (2km) Sea (80km) Tennis (5km) Railway station (5km) Shops (5km) **NOTES:** Pets admitted

SOMMIERES

♥♥♥ Chambre d'hôtes Colette LABBE
8 avenue Emile Jamais, 30250 SOMMIERES
☎ 04 66 77 78 69 📠 04 66 77 78 69
Situated in a peaceful medieval village between the sea and the Cévennes. Three upstairs rooms - two doubles with bathrooms and wc, and one room for four (one double, two singles) with shower room. Separate terrace, garden, private pool and restaurant serving regional cuisine on site. Tennis courts in the village. Open all year.
PRICES: s €51; d €54; t €67; extra person €16 **ON SITE:** Fishing Swimming pool Tennis **NEARBY:** Bathing (24km) Canoeing (40km) Horse riding (1km) Sea (24km) Railway station (12km) **NOTES:** No pets English spoken

ST-AMBROIX

♥♥♥ Chambre d'hôtes Guy et Elisabeth JULHAN
880 Saint-Germain, rte de St-Julien de Cassagnas,
30500 ST-AMBROIX
☎ 04 66 24 31 87 & 06 12 79 43 00 📠 04 66 24 31 87
e-mail: ge.julhan@free.fr www.djourdan.com/stgermain
Uzès and Anduze 35 km. Nîmes 60 km. Vallon Pont d'Arc 20 km. This spacious country house has a magnificent panoramic view. The bedrooms have new furnishings, beautiful bedding, large cupboards and wardrobes, TV and shower rooms with wc. Ample breakfasts. Living room. Near Saint-Ambroix and the thermal springs at Les Fumades. Children under seven 8 euros. Open all year.
PRICES: s €36; d €42; t €62; extra person €10 **ON SITE:** Children's play area **NEARBY:** Bathing (3km) Canoeing (3km) Horse riding (4km) Forest (6km) Sea (90km) Fishing (3km) Swimming pool (5km) Tennis (5km) Railway station (5km) Shops (4km) **NOTES:** Pets admitted

ST-CHRISTOL-LES-ALES

♥♥♥ ﻌ︎◯︎ Boujac Clotilde SALLIERES
Les Micocouliers, 128 chemin des Brusques,
30380 ST-CHRISTOL-LES-ALES
☎ 04 66 60 71 94 & 06 11 99 77 30
This is a large restored Provençal house in the heart of the country, where quiet and relaxation are a certainty. Two rooms and one family suite, with showers and wc, and two rooms with bath and wc. Separate country cottage with its own entrance. Central heating. Large day room with open fire. Provençal cuisine, using seasonal produce. Nearby sports - tennis, horse-riding. Phone for winter reservations. Children under seven, €7.62. Open all year.
PRICES: s €39; d €46; t €61-€62; dinner €19 **ON SITE:** Swimming pool **NEARBY:** Bathing (9km) Horse riding (2km) Sea (70km) Fishing (9km) Tennis (1km) Railway station (5km) Shops (3km) **NOTES:** Pets admitted

ﻌ︎Places with this symbol are farmhouses

ST-GILLES

♥♥♥ Mas Plisset Claude DUPLISSY
route de Nîmes, 30800 ST-GILLES
☎ 04 66 87 18 91
Four guest rooms for one to four people, each with shower room and wc, in a new building. Rooms overlook an enclosed garden. Shady enclosed parking. 53 euros/4 guests. Open all year.
PRICES: s €35; d €40; t €48 **ON SITE:** Swimming pool **NEARBY:** Bathing (30km) Canoeing (30km) Horse riding (5km) Forest (5km) Golf (8km) Sea (35km) Fishing (4km) Tennis (3km) Railway station (17km) Shops (2km) **NOTES:** No pets English spoken

ST-HIPPOLYTE-DU-FORT

♥♥♥ Chambre d'hôtes Arlette NAINTRE-COLLIN
14 rue Blanquerie, 30170 ST-HIPPOLYTE-DU-FORT
☎ 04 66 77 94 10 📠 04 66 77 94 10
e-mail: naintre_collin@libertysurf.fr
http://shf14rb.multimania.com

Charming 18th-century house with character, right in the Cévennes, with a large and peaceful garden. One double room, and four others with twin beds (plus extra if required). Private bathrooms with wc. Terrace and garden for guests to use.
PRICES: s €38; d €50; t €59 **ON SITE:** Swimming pool Tennis **NEARBY:** Canoeing (7km) Horse riding (4km) Forest (7km) Sea (49km) Fishing (7km) Railway station (30km) **NOTES:** Pets admitted English spoken

ST-JULIEN-DE-LA-NEF

♥♥♥ ﻌ︎ Château d'Isis M. ROUDIER et Mme VILLARD
Rive Droite de l'Hérault, 30440 ST-JULIEN-DE-LA-NEF
☎ 04 67 73 56 22 📠 04 67 73 56 22
A peaceful 14th-century castle in grounds with streams, waterfalls, woods and meadows. Three guest rooms: the Pink Room (twin with bathroom) with a French-style ceiling and ancient floor; the Blue Room (double) overlooking the park; the Green Room for four in two four-posters; plus another twin room with two towers, one with wc and basin, the other with mini-bath and basin. Lounge with open fire. Local cuisine: spit-roast leg of lamb, game birds, crayfish, foie gras, vegetarian menu.
PRICES: s €36-€50; d €50-€65; t €65-€80; extra person €16; HB €49; FB €62; dinner €13-€15 **ON SITE:** Forest **NEARBY:** Bathing (1km) Canoeing (1km) Horse riding (3km) Sea (80km) Fishing (1km) Swimming pool (1km) Tennis (5km) Railway station (70km) Shops (6km) Restaurant nearby **NOTES:** Pets admitted English spoken

ST-MAMERT

♥♥♥ ﻌ︎◯︎ Chambre d'hôtes Eliette COUSTON
12 rue de la Mazade, 30730 ST-MAMERT
☎ 04 66 81 17 56 📠 04 66 81 17 56
Nineteenth-century building now restored, offering two double rooms, and one with double and twin beds, all upstairs. Each has en suite bathroom and wc, and overlooks the courtyard and garden. Heating. Open all year.   *continued*

PRICES: s €38; d €46; extra person €15; dinner €15 **ON SITE:** Tennis **NEARBY:** Bathing (20km) Canoeing (20km) Horse riding (6km) Sea (40km) Fishing (15km) Swimming pool (11km) Railway station (15km) **NOTES:** No pets

ST-PAULET-DE-CAISSON

Mas Canet Bernard PELLOUX
30130 ST-PAULET-DE-CAISSON
☎ 04 66 39 25 96 🖹 04 66 89 19 56 www.mascanet.com

Vallée de la Cèze 9 km. Pont-St-Esprit 7 km. Gorges de l'Ardèche 9 km. At the gateway to Provence and the Languedoc, in a lovely national forest, stands this beautiful farmhouse of exposed stone, built by monks in the 16th century. Three doubles with shower rooms and wc, and three doubles with bathrooms and wc. All have large beds and TV points - TV hire may be possible. Swimming pool shared with owners. Pont-Saint-Esprit has a very good market on Saturday morning. 3 km from Chartreuse-de-Valbonne. Open all year.
PRICES: d €47-€50 **ON SITE:** Forest Swimming pool **NEARBY:** Bathing (9km) Canoeing (9km) Horse riding (8km) Sea (100km) Fishing (9km) Tennis (3km) Railway station (10km) Shops (4km) **NOTES:** Pets admitted

ST-QUENTIN-LA-POTERIE

Les Pins de Jols Michèle CLAMENS-DELCOR
30700 ST-QUENTIN-LA-POTERIE
☎ 04 66 03 16 84 🖹 04 66 03 16 84

Uzès 4 km. The Pont du Gard 15 km. Nîmes 30 km. Avignon 35 km. Four rooms for two or three guests, each with private shower and wc; and two rooms with kitchenette, in a charming house standing in a park with a pool. Quiet, comfort and good company, surrounded by pines, only minutes from Uzès and the Pont du Gard, and 45 minutes to the Cévennes and the gorges of the Ardèche. St-Quentin-la-Poterie is the place to see many potters and their art. Open all year.
PRICES: s €46-€50; d €56-€60; t €71-€75; extra person €15 **ON SITE:** Swimming pool **NEARBY:** Bathing (15km) Horse riding (2km) Forest (1km) Sea (75km) Fishing (15km) Tennis (2km) Railway station (30km) Shops (2km) **NOTES:** No pets English spoken

ST-SEBASTIEN-D'AIGREFEUILLE

Le Mas des Sources Sandra NABZDYJAK
Anduze, 30140 ST-SEBASTIEN-D'AIGREFEUILLE
☎ 04 66 60 56 30 🖹 04 66 60 56 30

Anduze 4 km. Bambouseraie 3 km. At the foot of the Cévennes, in a 17th-century silkworm house, five spacious room, with bath, wc, and television. Large living room, kitchen and laundry. Breakfast and other meals served on the terrace or on the patio. This home in its 8-hectare park gives room to relax around the water basin and the arbour, perfect places for lazing and picnics. Reduced tariff for children. Open all year.
PRICES: s €51; d €57; t €71; extra person €16; dinner €19 **ON SITE:** Forest **NEARBY:** Bathing (2km) Canoeing (20km) Horse riding (5km) Golf (6km) Sea (60km) Fishing (2km) Swimming pool (5km) Tennis (4km) Railway station (10km) Shops (4km) **NOTES:** Pets admitted English spoken

THOIRAS

Hameau de Prades Sophie AUVRAY
Mas de Prades, Thoiras, 30140 ANDUZE
☎ 04 66 85 09 00 & 06 80 28 51 46 🖹 04 66 85 09 00

Anduze, Bambouseraie, the Cévennes, mt Aigoual." A 17th-century house with a view over the hills. The enormous bedrooms are decorated with taste, and look out over a flowery patio. Five bedrooms, with all facilities. On the first floor: one room for three with terrace (bath/wc); one double with terrace (shower/wc); one room for three (shower/wc). On the ground floor: one double (bath/wc); one double (shower/wc) with terrace. Television/video room; patio; park; pool. The surroundings will enhance your stay. Open 25 March-1 November.
PRICES: s €54; d €60-€75; extra person €16; dinner €20 **ON SITE:** Swimming pool **NEARBY:** Bathing (1km) Canoeing (1km) Horse riding (3km) Forest (1km) Sea (50km) Fishing (1km) Tennis (1km) Railway station (20km) Shops (2km) **NOTES:** No pets English spoken

TORNAC

♦♦♦♦ ⊙ Chambre d'hôtes Pierre DELJEHIER
Hameau de Bouzène, 30140 TORNAC
☎ 04 66 60 78 40 & 06 13 23 10 17 ▤ 04 66 60 78 40
e-mail: djr2@wanadoo.fr
A beautiful building surrounded by vineyards, bathed in the scent of lavender and rosemary. Each room has its own shower/bath and wc. Two rooms with television. First floor - suite for four; one double; second floor - two doubles, each with additional bed. Each room is decorated in a different style with fine antiques and brightly coloured curtains. Lovely bathrooms. In fine weather meals are served on the shady terrace in the pretty flower garden. Open Easter-end October.
PRICES: s €42; d €53; t €67; extra person €13; dinner €17
NEARBY: Bathing (3km) Horse riding (7km) Forest (3km) Sea (60km) Fishing (2km) Tennis (3km) Railway station (20km) Shops (5km) **NOTES:** No pets English spoken

UZES

♦♦♦ Domaine de Malaric René et Michèle STRAUB
Pont des Charrettes, 30700 UZES
☎ 04 66 22 15 24 ▤ 04 66 03 00 69
Booking advised to stay on this 17th-century farming estate in the heart of the countryside. Very quiet. Four large upstairs rooms, each with double and fold-up bed, shower and wc. One downstairs twin room with private washing facilities and terrace. Day room; sitting room; library with television; refrigerator for guests; heating; courtyard; enclosed parking. Reduced rates over three days. Tax €0.46/person/day. Open March-1 November.
PRICES: s €42; d €52; t €60 **NEARBY:** Bathing (8km) Canoeing (8km) Horse riding (3km) Forest (2km) Golf (1km) Sea (70km) Fishing (1km) Swimming pool (3km) Tennis (3km) Railway station (23km) Shops (1km) **NOTES:** No pets

VERS-PONT-DU-GARD

♦♦♦ ⊙ La Begude Pierre Jean TURION
La Begude de vers Pont du Gard, 30210 REMOULINS
☎ 04 66 37 16 25 & 06 86 90 44 84
Four upstairs guest rooms in an old family house, 1 km from the Pont du Gard. Each room has a mezzanine, shower room and wc. Sitting room with open fireplace and television; rest room; patio; painting exhibition. A minute to the garrigue countryside; mountain bike hire; Circuit F1 6 km; monuments 1 km; historic sites 20 km. €66/4 persons. Open Easter-October.
PRICES: s €38; d €47; t €56; dinner €12 **ON SITE:** Bathing Fishing **NEARBY:** Canoeing (5km) Horse riding (4km) Forest (80km) Sea (50km) Swimming pool (13km) Tennis (1km) Railway station (25km) Shops (3km) **NOTES:** Pets admitted

VILLENEUVE-LES-AVIGNON

♦♦♦ Les Jardins de la Livrée Irène GRANGEON
4 bis rue Camp de Bataille,
30400 VILLENEUVE-LES-AVIGNON
☎ 04 90 26 05 05
Avignon 3 km. In the old centre of historic Villeneuve-les-Avignon, (papal city and art centre), this house commands an enormous lush and peaceful garden. Four upstairs rooms, each with shower and wc, Terrace, private pool and locked parking. If you wish, end the day at the dinner table, enjoying regional cuisine. Good base for exploring Provence and Languedoc. Open all year.
PRICES: s €55-€70; d €60-€93; t €80-€113; dinner €19-€23
ON SITE: Bathing Swimming pool **NEARBY:** Canoeing (60km) Horse riding (1km) Sea (80km) Fishing (1km) Tennis (1km) Railway station (5km) Restaurant nearby **NOTES:** No pets English spoken

ADISSAN

♦♦♦ ⊙ Villa des Roses Siti et Laurent FILLON
15, avenue de Pezenas, 34230 ADISSAN
☎ 04 67 25 01 24 & SR : 04 67 67 71 62
e-mail: villadesroses@club-internet.fr
Family mansion in the heart of the village. On the ground floor - salon, kitchen, lounge. First floor - two rooms for four guests and two doubles, all with bath and wc, and TV. Summer kitchen, terrace, shaded park, table tennis, bikes, parking. Meals, using regional produce, by prior arrangement, and Indonesian food once a week. Low out of season tariff; open all year.
PRICES: s €36; d €43; t €55; extra person €13; dinner €14
ON SITE: Swimming pool **NEARBY:** Bathing (4km) Canoeing (13km) Horse riding (11km) Sea (30km) Fishing (4km) Tennis (3km) Sailing (13km) PEZENAS **NOTES:** No pets English spoken

AVENE

♦♦♦ SICA d'Avene Serge CASTAN
Truscas, 34260 AVENE
☎ 04 67 23 40 99
Five rooms (three doubles, two twins) on two floors, with private baths and wcs. Electric heaters, common room. Separate courtyard opposite the house, with a garden room. Only 3km from the thermal spa of Avène-les-Bains, in the centre of the village.
PRICES: s €30; d €37; t €46 **NEARBY:** Bathing (3km) Horse riding (3km) Golf (30km) Fishing (3km) Swimming pool (3km) Tennis (3km) Sailing (10km) Railway station (25km) Shops (5km) BEDARIEUX **NOTES:** Pets admitted

BESSAN

♦♦♦ ⊙ Chambre d'hôtes Lucien PAUL
30, avenue de la Victoire, 34550 BESSAN
☎ 04 67 77 40 07 ▤ 04 67 77 40 07
Four rooms in a family mansion in a village near the main road. One three-bedded room on the ground floor; two rooms (for two and three) on the first floor; a suite for four on the second floor, each with private facilities and electric heating. Day room exclusively for visitors. TV, fridge/freezer, use of washing machine, table tennis, 3 hectare enclosed garden, locked parking. Exit Autoroute A9 2km from Agde-Pézénas toll. Open all year.
PRICES: s €32; d €40; t €50; extra person €12; dinner €15
ON SITE: Tennis **NEARBY:** Bathing (1km) Horse riding (10km) Golf (10km) Sea (10km) Fishing (1km) Swimming pool (6km) Sailing (10km) Railway station (6km) PEZENAS **NOTES:** No pets

CAPESTANG

♦♦♦ ⊙ La Bastide Vielle Bernard FOUISSAC
34310 CAPESTANG
☎ 04 67 93 46 23 & 06 13 93 93 44
Just 3 km from the Canal du Midi and the village, in the heart of the country. Two double rooms at street level; one room for three. Private baths or showers and wc. Electric heating, day room, sitting room with open fire, telephone, terrace, garden room. Open 1 March to 31 October.
PRICES: d €40; t €54; extra person €13; dinner €15 **NEARBY:** Bathing (25km) Canoeing (25km) Golf (25km) Sea (25km) Fishing (12km) Swimming pool (6km) Tennis (5km) Sailing (25km) Railway station (15km) Shops (3km) BEZIERS **NOTES:** No pets

CAYLAR-EN-LARZAC

♦♦♦ ⊙ Chambre d'hôtes Bernard CLARISSAC
faubourg Saint-Martin, 34520 LE CAYLAR
☎ 04 67 44 50 19 ▤ 04 67 44 52 36

Guest rooms in a house typical of the Causses du Larzac area. Two rooms for two, two rooms for three, and one room for four. Private shower rooms and wcs. Day room, central heating; open fire, terrace, parking. Open all year. 71 euros for four guests.
PRICES: s €36; d €46; t €54; HB €39; dinner €17　**NEARBY:** Bathing (30km) Canoeing (30km) Horse riding (5km) Sea (70km) Fishing (5km) Swimming pool (1km) Tennis (30km) Sailing (30km) Railway station (50km) CLERMONT-L'HERAULT　**NOTES:** Pets admitted

CAZOULS-LES-BEZIERS

🍴 ⵏ◯ⵏ La Noria Marcel RAMOS
domaine de la Plaine, 34370 CAZOULS-LES-BEZIERS
☎ 04 67 93 58 27　🖹 04 67 93 34 97
Authentic 19th-century Languedoc house on an established wine estate, 7km from the Canal du Midi. One suite for four people on the ground floor. Two rooms for three, and one double on the first floor, each with private facilities. TV points, lounge, sitting room, electric heating, telephone. Outside, enjoy the terrace, garden room, barbecue, play area, pergola, bowling alley, summer kitchen with fridge. Laundry, parking and garage. Suite: 60 euros for four people.
PRICES: s €29; d €37; t €48; dinner €13　**NEARBY:** Bathing (4km) Canoeing (4km) Horse riding (8km) Sea (24km) Fishing (4km) Swimming pool (8km) Tennis (5km) Sailing (24km) Railway station (8km) Shops (1km) BEZIERS　**NOTES:** Pets admitted

CELLES

🍴 ⵏ◯ⵏ La Maison du Lac Antoine BERNARD
les Vailhes, Celles, 34700 LODEVE
☎ 04 67 44 16 33　🖹 04 67 44 46 02
Fishing at Lac du Salagou. Old sheep farmhouse now restored and enlarged in traditional style on the edge of the Lac du Salagou. Four double rooms, and one for three (extra bed available). Private shower rooms and wcs. Central heating, washing machine, day room/sitting area, open fire. The terrace has views over the lake. Open all year.
PRICES: s €42; d €48; extra person €20; dinner €16　**ON SITE:** Bathing Canoeing Horse riding Fishing Sailing　**NEARBY:** Golf (35km) Sea (55km) Tennis (7km) Railway station (50km) Shops (9km) CLERMONT-L'HERAULT　**NOTES:** Pets admitted English spoken

CLERMONT-L'HERAULT

🍴 ⵏ◯ⵏ Les Bories Pascal et Martine MOREAU
le Mas Font Chaude, 34800 CLERMONT-L'HERAULT
☎ 04 67 96 19 77　🖹 04 67 96 19 77
e-mail: martine.moreau34@wanadoo.fr
Lac du Salagou fishing. On an estate that is a bird sanctuary, right in the Languedoc hinterland, five minutes from the Lac du Salagou. Three twin rooms at street level (90cm beds, private facilities, TV and telephone). Garden, day room, terrace, parking. Ideal for fishing, mountain biking and windsurfing. Open all year; booking necessary in winter. Minimum stay three days. Sliding scale of charges.
PRICES: s €39; d €46; dinner €14　**NEARBY:** Bathing (2km) Canoeing (3km) Horse riding (1km) Golf (30km) Sea (40km) Fishing (2km) Swimming pool (4km) Tennis (3km) Sailing (2km) Railway station (40km) Shops (3km) CLERMONT-L'HERAULT　**NOTES:** No pets

DIO-ET-VALQUIERES

🍴 ⵏ◯ⵏ Vernazoubres Mme Lauffenberger
34650 DIO-ET-VALQUIERES
☎ 04 67 23 00 65　🖹 04 67 23 00 65
A comfortable house where guests can enjoy a peaceful stay, with five rooms for two or three guests (each with private bath or shower and wc). Day room with open fire, lounge, TV, telephone,

board games, swimming pool. Cuisine includes regional specialities. Hiking and horse-riding tracks in the countryside around Vernazoubres, a tiny hamlet 15 minutes from the Lac du Salagou and near the thermal spas at Avène and Lamalou-les-Bains. Open 30 March to 20 December.
PRICES: s €35; d €48; t €67; extra person €20; HB €38; dinner €15　**ON SITE:** Wine tasting Horse riding Fishing Swimming pool　**NEARBY:** Bathing (11km) Canoeing (8km) Golf (17km) Sea (45km) Tennis (17km) Sailing (11km) Railway station (12km) Shops (12km) BEDARIEUX　**NOTES:** Pets admitted English spoken

GIGNAC

🍴 ♥ Mas de Pelican B et I THILLAYE DE BOULLAY
34150 GIGNAC
☎ 04 67 57 68 92　🖹 04 67 57 68 92
A large Languedoc house looking over the valley, surrounded by vines and the typical garrigue (scrubland). The first floor has three rooms for four with mezzanine, sitting area and private facilities; one double room with private bath and wc. Central heating, washing machine, balcony. Parking in open courtyard. Open from November to end September.
PRICES: s €44; d €52; extra person €11; dinner €19　**ON SITE:** Swimming pool　**NEARBY:** Bathing (15km) Canoeing (10km) Horse riding (10km) Golf (25km) Sea (30km) Fishing (4km) Tennis (1km) Sailing (15km) Railway station (30km) Shops (4km) Restaurant nearby CLERMONT-L'HERAULT　**NOTES:** No pets English spoken

GRABELS

🍴 ⴷ Le Mazet Philippe et Suzanne ROBARDET
253, chemin du Mas de Matou, 34790 GRABELS
☎ 04 67 03 36 57
Accessible with help. Just 4km from Montpellier, on the way to the Hérault hinterland, Le Mazet , a typical Languedoc house, offers three rooms: La Provençale (double) and l'Exotique (twin or double) each with mezzanine and extra single bed, shower and wc. La Méditerranéenne accommodates two guests (shower and wc), with TV lounge. Swimming pool 10am-noon/4-6pm. Enclosed, shaded parking. Breakfast served in rooms. Nearby restaurants. Twin beds supplement: 3 euros. Children under three: 5 euros. Dogs: 1.50 euros per day.
PRICES: s €31; d €40; t €55; extra person €15　**ON SITE:** Swimming pool　**NEARBY:** Bathing (25km) Canoeing (25km) Horse riding (4km) Golf (8km) Sea (16km) Fishing (1km) Tennis (1km) Sailing (16km) Railway station (8km) MONTPELLIER　**NOTES:** Pets admitted English spoken

LA TOUR-SUR-ORB

🍴 ⵏ◯ⵏ Chambre d'hôtes Françoise CHEVALIER-PERIER
34260 LA TOUR-SUR-ORB
☎ 04 67 95 02 99
A 19th-century family mansion offering four rooms sleeping two, and two rooms sleeping three, all with private bath and wc. Heating, lounge, open fire, TV, washing machine. Shady garden and park, terrace, private parking, and patio. Musical, literary and conference events welcomed.
PRICES: s €36; d €42; t €51; extra person €11; dinner €17　**ON SITE:** Bathing Fishing Tennis　**NEARBY:** Canoeing (10km) Horse riding (5km) Golf (12km) Sea (50km) Swimming pool (6km) Sailing (25km) BEDARIEUX　**NOTES:** Pets admitted English spoken

LUNEL

🍴 Le Relais d'Agathe Marie-Ange DOMENECH
35, rue des Cepes, 34400 LUNEL
☎ 04 67 71 29 02　e-mail: Marie-Ange@relaisdagathe.com
Marie-Ange invites guests into her stone-built house at the edge of

continued

continued

the built-up area, near to the Dolmitian Way. Three rooms at street level with private facilities. Two upstairs rooms, with private terrace, shower, wc. Lounge and sitting room, heating, air conditioning, TV. Lovely interior courtyard and swimming pool. Enclosed parking. Bikes for hire. Prices for stays out of season and for groups. Open all year.
PRICES: s €77-€92; d €77-€92 **ON SITE:** Horse riding Fishing Swimming pool **NEARBY:** Canoeing (6km) Golf (10km) Sea (12km) Tennis (3km) Sailing (12km) Railway station (1km) MONTPELLIER
NOTES: No pets CC English spoken

♯♯♯ Ĩ◯Ĩ Mas Saint-Ange Jacques BORDES
629 chemin des Saintes-Maries, 34400 LUNEL
☎ 04 67 83 97 50 & SR : 04 67 67 71 62 🖹 04 67 83 97 50
The Camargue, les Stes-Maries-de-la-mer, Aigues-Mortes. Sylvie and Jacques welcome guests to their house near the Camargue. Four double rooms (one on ground floor) and one for three guests, each with shower and wc. Dining/sitting room, TV, telephone, fireplace, electric heating, terrace, enclosed grounds; swimming pool, summer house, mountain bikes. Meals available if pre-booked.
PRICES: s €46; d €46; t €58; extra person €13; dinner €14
ON SITE: Swimming pool Tennis **NEARBY:** Bathing (12km) Canoeing (50km) Horse riding (1km) Golf (10km) Sea (12km) Fishing (12km) Sailing (12km) Railway station (3km) Shops (2km) LUNEL
NOTES: No pets CC English spoken

MAUREILHAN

♯♯♯ Ĩ◯Ĩ Les Arbousiers B et J FABRE-BARTHEZ
34370 MAUREILHAN
☎ 04 67 90 52 49 & 06 84 20 04 28 🖹 04 67 90 50 50
e-mail: ch.d.hotes.les.arbousiers@wanadoo.fr

In the village centre and five kilometres from the Canal du Midi, the wine-growing owner has six rooms to let. Four air-conditioned rooms for two or three guests with private shower or bath and wc. Two ground floor rooms for two to four people, with shower and wc. Guests' living room, reading room, TV, telephone, fireplace. Garden, games area, shady terrace, enclosed parking. Exit Autoroute 36. Open all year..
PRICES: s €34; d €40; t €52; extra person €12; dinner €15
ON SITE: Tennis **NEARBY:** Bathing (4km) Canoeing (15km) Golf (15km) Sea (20km) Fishing (4km) Swimming pool (9km) Sailing (20km) Railway station (9km) BEZIERS **NOTES:** Pets admitted English spoken

MIREVAL

♯♯♯ L'Enclos Anne-Marie CONTE-PRIVAT
15 avenue de Verdun, 34110 MIREVAL
☎ 04 67 78 39 70 & SR : 04 67 67 71 62 🖹 04 67 78 39 70
e-mail: conte-privat@wanadoo.fr
A comfortable house full of character, with its own park, in the centre of this Languedoc village. Three double rooms (can accommodate a third person) with shower or bath and wc. Electric

heating, TV, video, library, large lounge with fireplace, home cinema, garden furniture, Garage parking. Organised holidays. 4 km to beach, 12 km to Montpellier and the Sète l'Enclos area. Open all year.
PRICES: s €44; d €48; extra person €15 **NEARBY:** Bathing (4km) Canoeing (50km) Horse riding (1km) Golf (25km) Sea (4km) Fishing (4km) Swimming pool (6km) Tennis (1km) Sailing (4km) Railway station (2km) MONTPELLIER **NOTES:** No pets

MONTAGNAC

♯♯♯ Chambre d'hôtes Daniel GENER
34, avenue Pierre Sirven, 34530 MONTAGNAC
☎ 04 67 24 03 21 🖹 04 67 24 03 21
On an established wine estate by the N113. Three separate double rooms, and one for three or four, each with private shower and wc. Electric heating, lounge, dining room, kitchen, laundry. Shady walled garden with terrace and furniture. Enclosed parking. Open all year.
PRICES: s €38; d €42; t €50; extra person €7 **ON SITE:** Tennis **NEARBY:** Canoeing (4km) Horse riding (3km) Golf (20km) Sea (22km) Fishing (4km) Swimming pool (5km) Sailing (22km) Railway station (22km) PEZENAS **NOTES:** Pets admitted English spoken

MURVIEL-LES-BEZIERS

♯♯♯ Château de Murviel Marie-Laure BERNARD
1, place Clemenceau, 34490 MURVIEL-LES-BEZIERS
☎ 04 67 32 35 45 & 06 08 24 57 28 🖹 04 67 32 35 25
e-mail: chateau-de-murviel@wanadoo.fr
Three guest rooms in a medieval castle above the village. One double with four-poster bed, shower room and wc; one room with three singles; a suite with double canopied bed, shower room and wc. TV, electric heating, lounge, dishwasher, possible use of washing machine. Interior courtyard. Closed parking. Open all year except February, and the week between Xmas & New Year. Children under two are free.
PRICES: s €65; d €70; t €85; extra person €15 **NEARBY:** Bathing (3km) Canoeing (5km) Horse riding (10km) Golf (25km) Sea (25km) Fishing (3km) Swimming pool (15km) Tennis (1km) Sailing (25km) Railway station (15km) Shops (1km) BEZIERS **NOTES:** No pets English spoken

♯♯♯ Ĩ◯Ĩ L'Hacienda des Roucans
P et L BLANPAIN-VANDERMOSTEN
route de Reals, 34490 MURVIEL-LES-BEZIERS
☎ 04 67 32 90 10 🖹 04 67 32 90 81

A haven of peace in nearly a hectare of land beside the river, where a warm welcome awaits. One twin room with lounge, three double rooms, one room with canopied twin beds, one room and sitting room with canopied double bed. Each has bathroom and wc, TV, fridge, and access to the garden and pool. Library and sauna. Private parking, garage, barbecue, table tennis, table football, bikes, mountain bikes. Open all year.
PRICES: d €62-€89; extra person €15; dinner €21 **ON SITE:** Bathing

continued   continued

Canoeing Fishing Swimming pool **NEARBY:** Horse riding (5km) Golf (25km) Sea (20km) Tennis (2km) Sailing (20km) Railway station (15km) Shops (2km) BEZIERS **NOTES:** No pets English spoken

NOTRE-DAME-DE-LONDRES

♦♦♦ Le Pous Elisabeth NOUALHAC
34380 NOTRE-DAME-DE-LONDRES
☎ 04 67 55 01 36

A beautiful 18th-century house in extensive grounds surrounded by woods and scrubland. Six double rooms with private shower or bath and wc. Heating, lounge, telephone. Open all year.
PRICES: s €43; d €46-€54; t €54; extra person €8 **NEARBY:** Bathing (10km) Canoeing (10km) Horse riding (2km) Sea (40km) Fishing (12km) Tennis (2km) Sailing (40km) Railway station (35km) Shops (9km) GANGES **NOTES:** No pets

PEZENES-LES-MINES

♦♦♦ ▮◉▮ Les Vignals Roland VERDIER
34600 PEZENES-LES-MINES
☎ 04 67 95 12 42 📠 04 67 95 12 42
e-mail: VERDIERR@aol.com
Situated only 10km from town yet guests will feel far away from it all in this wild landscape. Bedrooms include one room for four, with shower and wc. Electric heating, lounge with open fireplace, terrace, barbecue, boules, private parking. Meals are made using garden produce. Half board available. Open all year.
PRICES: s €30; d €40; t €50; dinner €14 **NEARBY:** Bathing (10km) Canoeing (10km) Horse riding (10km) Golf (15km) Sea (45km) Fishing (9km) Swimming pool (9km) Tennis (9km) Sailing (10km) Railway station (9km) Shops (9km) BEDARIEUX **NOTES:** Pets admitted English spoken

POMEROLS

♦♦♦ ▮◉▮ Domaine Fon de Rey
Monique & Jean-Pierre BECK & Jeanette & Alain DELUARD
route de Pezenas, 34810 POMEROLS
☎ 04 67 77 08 56 📠 04 67 77 21 09
Only 10km from the Mediterranean in a park of pine trees, among vineyards, stands this 17th-century country house, with apartments to let in an annexe. First floor: two family rooms for four (one with terrace). Second floor: two doubles with shower or bath and wc. Central heating, lounge with French billiards and TV. Covered swimming pool, garden furniture, table tennis. Out of season groups if booked. Open March to November. Dinner price does not include wine.
PRICES: s €40-€87; d €45-€92; extra person €16; dinner €17
ON SITE: Wine tasting Swimming pool **NEARBY:** Bathing (10km) Canoeing (10km) Horse riding (5km) Golf (10km) Sea (10km) Fishing (3km) Tennis (1km) Sailing (10km) Railway station (10km) Shops (1km) Restaurant nearby SETE **NOTES:** No pets English spoken

POUSSAN

♦♦♦ ▮◉▮ ♿ Chemin des Cresses Pierre BARBE
65, bis rue des Horts, 34560 POUSSAN
☎ 04 67 78 29 39 & SR : 04 67 67 71 62
e-mail: bbe2000@aol.com
Near the A9 and the Bassin de Thau, at the foot of La Moure hill and the Massif de la Gardiole, this is a new building offering five rooms. At ground level, accessible to people with limited mobility, three twin rooms with private shower and wc. On the first floor, two double rooms with private bath and wc. Geothermal heating and air conditioning, lounge/sitting room, mezzanine library, fireplace. Enclosed grounds with swimming pool, garden furniture, covered parking and table tennis. Meals available if booked. Reduced tariff for stays over seven days. Open all year.
PRICES: s €50-€60; d €60; t €75; extra person €15; dinner €20
ON SITE: Swimming pool Tennis **NEARBY:** Bathing (4km) Canoeing (30km) Horse riding (1km) Golf (20km) Sea (12km) Fishing (4km) Sailing (4km) Railway station (8km) Shops (1km) MONTPELLIER
NOTES: No pets CC English spoken

POUZOLLES

♦♦♦ ▮◉▮ Domaine de l'Eskillou Brigitte GELLY
4, rue de la Distillerie, 34480 POUZOLLES
☎ 04 67 24 60 50 📠 04 67 24 60 50
e-mail: brigitte.gelly@wanadoo.fr
Air-conditioned rooms in a house adjacent to the wine-growing proprietors'. On the ground floor is a living room/sitting room. On the first floor, five rooms for two to four people, with shower or bath and wc. Electric heating, open fire, TV, telephone, fridge. Swimming pool open 8am-8pm. Enclosed parking. Evening meal with wine included. Garden, shady terrace, bike garage. Motorbikes, swings, board games and table tennis in games room. Open 1 April to 22 September. Child's meal (from age six): 10 euros. 7 nights low season: 250 euros per person (half board).
PRICES: s €43; d €49; t €65; extra person €16; HB €41; dinner €16
ON SITE: Wine tasting Swimming pool Tennis **NEARBY:** Bathing (10km) Canoeing (20km) Horse riding (8km) Golf (8km) Sea (31km) Fishing (10km) Sailing (25km) Railway station (6km) PEZENAS
NOTES: Pets admitted

QUARANTE

♦♦♦ ▮◉▮ Chambre d'hôtes Helge WOLFF
24, grande Rue, 34310 QUARANTE
☎ 04 67 89 34 72 📠 04 67 89 30 64
e-mail: wolffhelge@hotmail.com
Located between the sea and the mountains this undulating country is ideal for rambling. The 19th-century family mansion is 4km from the Canal du Midi in a 3.5 hectare, shady park. Four large rooms each sleep 3-4 people and have a private bathroom and wc. Sitting room with TV and open fire. Enclosed parking, swimming pool, pétanque, cycling. Meals available if booked. Restaurants nearby. Béziers and Narbonne 25 km.
PRICES: d €43-€50; t €57-€64; extra person €15; dinner €19
ON SITE: Swimming pool Tennis **NEARBY:** Canoeing (19km) Horse riding (2km) Golf (21km) Sea (35km) Fishing (1km) Sailing (35km) Railway station (25km) BEZIERS **NOTES:** Pets admitted English spoken

RIOLS

♦♦♦ ▮◉▮ La Cerisaie Honorah et Albert KARSTEN
1, route de Bedarieux, 34220 RIOLS
☎ 04 67 97 03 87 📠 04-67-97-03-88
e-mail: CERISERAIE@wanadoo.fr
La Cerisaie is a very beautiful 19th-century house with a splendid shady park. Five rooms on two levels. Ground floor: dining room, library, lounge. First floor: two double rooms. Second floor: three

continued

doubles. Private showers/wcs. Open fire, TV, telephone, electric heating. Outside: terrace, garden room, pool, table tennis, parking. Meals available if booked. Nearby sites: the Gorges of Héric, Massif du Caroux, Lac de la Raviège, Grottes de la Devèze. Open 1 February to 1 December. 10% reduction for 7 days.

PRICES: s €55; d €60-€75; extra person €19; dinner €20
ON SITE: Fishing Swimming pool Tennis **NEARBY:** Bathing (25km) Canoeing (15km) Horse riding (20km) Golf (35km) Sea (60km) Sailing (60km) Railway station (50km) Shops (4km) SAINT-PONS-DE-THOMIERES **NOTES:** Pets admitted English spoken

ROQUEBRUN

¶¶¶ ⃝⃞ Les Mimosas Denis et Sarah LA TOUCHE
avenue des Orangers, 34460 ROQUEBRUN
☎ 04 67 89 61 36 📠 04 67 89 61 36
e-mail: la-touche.les-mimosas@wanadoo.fr

In a beautiful village on the edge of the Orb, and at the entrance to the Haut-Languedoc Park, a lovely 19th-century mansion. Ground floor: sitting room, library, one double room. First floor: one double room; a suite for four. Second floor: one double room, with seating area. All have shower and wc. TV. Terrace, garage. This is a no-smoking house.

PRICES: s €61-€69; d €65-€73; extra person €10-€16; dinner €27
ON SITE: Bathing Canoeing Fishing Tennis **NEARBY:** Horse riding (25km) Golf (25km) Sea (45km) Swimming pool (15km) Sailing (45km) Railway station (30km) BEZIERS **NOTES:** No pets CC English spoken

SAINT-ANDRE-DE-BUEGES

¶¶¶ ⃝⃞ Bombequiols Anne-Marie BOUEC
route de Brissac, 34190 ST-ANDRE-DE-BUEGES
☎ 04 67 73 72 67 📠 04 67 73 72 67
Medieval country house, in a wild and preserved spot. Dine under the arches of the terrace or in front of the fire. Two rooms, one duplex and three suites (with open fires), each with their own access, set around the closed courtyard. Private baths and wcs. Swimming pool, 50 hectare park, and a lake among the hills. Peace and unbroken silence. Dine on local produce and wine. Explore St-Guilhem-le-Désert, La Couvertoirade, the Roman churches, Grotté des Demoiselles, the Bambouseraie. Price: suite: 110 euros.

PRICES: d €80-€110; extra person €25; dinner €25 **ON SITE:** Wine tasting Bathing Fishing Swimming pool **NEARBY:** Canoeing (2km) Horse riding (6km) Tennis (12km) Shops (12km) GANGES **NOTES:** No pets

SAINT-CLEMENT-DE-RIVIERE

¶¶¶ Chambre d'hôtes Calista BERNABE
domaine de Saint-Clement, 34980 ST-CLEMENT-DE-RIVIERE
☎ 04 67 66 70 89 📠 04 67 84 07 96
e-mail: calista.bernabé@wanadoo.fr
A haven of peace and quiet awaits in this 18th-century mansion in the middle of parkland. Four rooms. Ground floor: one room for

three. Upstairs: one double, one twin, one family (double room plus single room with additional child's bed). Dining room, sitting room with fire. Television, swimming pool. Nearby attractions: Montpellier, Nîmes, water and mountain sports, Roman art and history, the Camargue, Haut Languedoc Park.

PRICES: s €65-€80; d €80-€90; t €110 **ON SITE:** Bathing Fishing Swimming pool **NEARBY:** Horse riding (8km) Golf (5km) Sea (15km) Tennis (1km) Sailing (15km) Railway station (7km) Shops (1km) MONTPELLIER **NOTES:** Pets admitted English spoken

SAINTE-CROIX-DE-QUINTILLARGUES

¶¶¶ L'Euziere Michele et Bernard GUEUGNEAU
chemin des Clausses,
34270 STE-CROIX-DE-QUINTILLARGUES
☎ 04 67 59 52 68 & SR : 04 67 67 71 62

A peaceful location between the Cévennes, the Camargue and Montpellier, for a house of character in a typical Languedoc village. One room for three and three double rooms on the ground floor, with separate entrances, one with access for the less mobile guest. Each has private shower, wc, mini bar. Dining room, sitting room, TV, central heating, kitchen if desired. Covered terrace, large wooded grounds, summer house. Covered parking. Choice of cultural, sporting and artistic activities. Climbing 5km. 43 euros for stays exceeding 5 nights. Open all year.

PRICES: s €42; d €45; t €60; extra person €16 **NEARBY:** Bathing (20km) Canoeing (20km) Horse riding (5km) Golf (15km) Sea (25km) Fishing (8km) Swimming pool (5km) Tennis (5km) Sailing (25km) Railway station (30km) Shops (5km) MONTPELLIER **NOTES:** Pets admitted English spoken

SAINT-FELIX-DE-L'HERAS

¶¶¶ ♿ Madieres-le-Haut Guilhem TEISSERENC
34520 ST-FELIX-DE-L'HERAS
☎ 04 67 44 50 41 📠 04 67 44 50 41
Four ground-floor rooms in a building attached to a farm in Larzac, with a great view over the countryside. Each sleeps three, with private shower and wc. Guests' common room, TV, payphone, electric heating. Outside: terraces, summer houses, and an inn on the site. Open 1 April to 15 November.

PRICES: s €46; d €61; t €77; extra person €8 **NEARBY:** Bathing (20km) Horse riding (12km) Golf (50km) Sea (70km) Fishing (2km) Swimming pool (10km) Tennis (4km) Sailing (20km) Railway station (45km) Shops (2km) Restaurant nearby CLERMONT-L'HERAULT **NOTES:** Pets admitted CC English spoken

SAINT-SERIES

¶¶¶ Mas de Fontbonne Luc LIGNON
34400 St-SERIES
☎ 04 67 86 00 30 & 04 67 86 08 74 📠 04 67 86 00 30
e-mail: fontbonne@wanadoo.fr
A country house among the vines. Five ground-floor rooms, each sleeping two, with shower room and wc. Electric heating, mini bar,

continued

continued

lounge area (TV in low season). Grounds, terrace, summer house, barbecue, covered parking, covered swimming pool (April to October), table tennis, football, volleyball, archery, children's games. Restaurant 1.5km. Autoroute exit 5km. Gîtes in the grounds. Open all year.
PRICES: s €36; d €47; t €53; extra person €7 **ON SITE:** Children's play area Swimming pool **NEARBY:** Bathing (2km) Canoeing (2km) Horse riding (6km) Golf (13km) Sea (20km) Fishing (2km) Tennis (2km) Sailing (20km) Railway station (7km) Shops (2km) MONTPELLIER **NOTES:** Pets admitted English spoken

SAUSSAN

Chambre d'hôtes Ariane GINE
6, rue des Penitents, 34570 SAUSSAN
☎ 04 67 47 81 01
A warm welcome awaits at this old, exposed stone, vineyard house in the village centre. Four rooms with separate access. Ground floor: large lounge, sitting room, two double rooms with shower and wc. First floor: two doubles, with shower and wc. Central heating. Shady terrace and large wooded garden. Parking.
PRICES: s €31; d €39 **ON SITE:** Tennis **NEARBY:** Horse riding (4km) Golf (10km) Sea (10km) Swimming pool (3km) Sailing (10km) Railway station (10km) MONTPELLIER **NOTES:** No pets

VILLETELLE

Les Bougainvillées Daniel BARLAGUET
343 chemin des Combes Noires, 34400 VILLETELLE
☎ 04 67 86 87 00 📠 04 67 86 87 00
Beautiful character house with rooms on ground floor level, each with its own entrance, terrace and garden room. Four double rooms with sitting area (extra settee) and bath or shower and wc. One suite for four guests. Electric heating, washing machine, cooking area, TV. Covered heated swimming pool, sauna, Turkish bath, tennis, two hectares of enclosed grounds, covered parking, various games. Open all year. Evening meals sometimes possible.
PRICES: s €54; d €57; t €72; extra person €16 **ON SITE:** Swimming pool Tennis **NEARBY:** Canoeing (1km) Horse riding (1km) Golf (20km) Sea (20km) Fishing (1km) Sailing (20km) Railway station (6km) Shops (1km) MONTPELLIER **NOTES:** No pets English spoken

Villa l'Amairadou Paul SCALESSE
320, chemin de Montpellier, 34400 VILLETELLE
☎ 04 67 86 80 65 & 06 81 84 75 00
A house with beautiful rooms in wooded grounds near the Camargue and the Mediterranean. Ground floor: a suite for three and a double room. Upstairs: one double with terrace. Separate ground floor suite at ground level for four people (one canopied bed and one 160cm bed). All have shower or bath and wc. TV, telephone, lounge, sitting room, summer kitchen, fitness room (sauna, balneotherapy). Garden with enclosed parking, terrace, open air swimming pool. Open all year.
PRICES: d €64-€74; extra person €16; dinner €20
ON SITE: Swimming pool Tennis **NEARBY:** Canoeing (1km) Horse riding (1km) Golf (20km) Sea (20km) Fishing (1km) Sailing (20km) Railway station (7km) Shops (1km) MONTPELLIER **NOTES:** No pets English spoken

> For further information on these and other chambres d'hôtes, consult the Gîtes de France website
> *www.gites-de-france.fr*

LOZÈRE

BARRE DES CEVENNES

Chambre d'hôtes Claude BOISSIER
Le Mazeldan, 48400 BARRE DES CEVENNES
☎ 04 66 45 07 18
Situated at an altitude of 700 metres, Le Mazeldan is a small village. A warm welcome awaits at this sheep and cattle rearing farm with its traditional farmhouse with a magnificent view over the Cévennes. All rooms have en suite facilities. The sitting-dining room has an open fire and TV. There is a patio and parking. Halfboard prices: €66 two people; €94 three people. Open all year.
PRICES: s €34; d €40; t €55; extra person €11; HB €47; dinner €13 **NEARBY:** Bathing (17km) Canoeing (20km) Horse riding (7km) Golf (7km) Fishing (1km) Swimming pool (4km) Stretch of water (17km) Tennis (4km) Railway station (55km) Shops (4km) **NOTES:** Pets admitted

CHANAC

Le Jas J-Pierre et Sylvie DURAND
48230 CHANAC ☎ 04 66 48 22 93

Gorges du Tarn 12 km. Vallée du Lot 6 km. This farm is situated between the Gorges du Tarn and the Vallee du Lot. It offers three independent en suite guest rooms with space for eight guests in the proprietors' home. Also a conservatory, TV corner, washing machine, kitchen, baby equipment, barbecue and parking. Advanced booking is essential and all prices are inclusive. Children under two are free; children up to six are charged 30% for meals. Generous meals based on local specialities are available in July but not on Sundays, Wednesdays and Thursdays. No meals in August. Walking trips start from the doorstep. Open Easter to end of September.
PRICES: s €35; d €40; t €52; extra person €14; HB €34; dinner €13 **ON SITE:** Children's play area **NEARBY:** Bathing (6km) Canoeing (12km) Horse riding (6km) Fishing (7km) Stretch of water (7km) Tennis (6km) Railway station (7km) Shops (6km) **NOTES:** No pets

FONTANS

Les Sapins Verts Louis et M-Paule CRUEIZE
Chazeirollettes, 48700 FONTANS
☎ 04 66 48 30 23
Serverette 4 km. Saint-Alban 7 km. Lakes at Gavinet and Moulinet 15 km. In this old house guests are offered five en suite, centrally heated rooms for two or three people. Traditional family cooking includes local specialities including game, truffles etc. Half-board children €26; half-board €71 for 2 people for more than three days. Lots of activities in the area: walking, bison park 12 km, wolf park 20 km, Lac de Naussac 40 km . Open from beginning of April to mid October.
PRICES: (excludes drinks) s €33; d €45; t €62; extra person €17; HB €46; dinner €14 **NEARBY:** Bathing (4km) Canoeing (15km) Horse riding (7km) Fishing (4km) Swimming pool (18km) Stretch of water (4km) Tennis (4km) Railway station (18km) Shops (5km) Restaurant nearby **NOTES:** No pets

GATUZIERES

♦♦♦ ♥ ◯| Jontanels Alain BUONAMINI
48150 GATUZIERES
☎ 04 66 45 67 37

Situated in a peaceful village in the heart of the Cévennes National Park this typical house offers beautiful forest walks. The accommodation comprises two rooms with en suite bathroom, and a dining room, a sitting room with open fire and TV. There is also a washing machine, conservatory, patio and parking. Reservation is essential. Open all year.
PRICES: s €39; d €43; HB €69; dinner €13 **ON SITE:** Children's play area Fishing Forest walks **NEARBY:** Bathing (9km) Canoeing (20km) Horse riding (9km) Swimming pool (9km) Tennis (9km) Railway station (50km) Shops (9km) **NOTES:** No pets

GRANDRIEU

♦♦♦ ♥ ◯| Bellelande Eloi ASTRUC
48600 GRANDRIEU
☎ 04 66 46 30 53

This guest house offers two grade 2 rooms and two grade 3 rooms all with private wc and private or shared bath or shower room. The sitting room with TV is communal and there is an open fire in the dining room. Also a patio, a conservatory and parking. Reservation is essential and children up to three are free. Meals are served using local specialities. Open Easter to 1 November.
PRICES: s €20; d €38; HB €32; dinner €14 **NEARBY:** Bathing (5km) Canoeing (20km) Horse riding (20km) Golf (5km) Fishing (5km) Stretch of water (5km) Tennis (20km) Shops (5km) **NOTES:** No pets

LA CANOURGUE

♦♦♦ ♥ ◯| La Vialette Jean et Anne-Marie FAGES
en face la Capelle, 48500 LA CANOURGUE
☎ 04 66 32 83 00 & 04 66 32 94 62

A warm welcome awaits in this 15th-century Caussenarde farmhouse, with six guest rooms, all en suite and with TV. A fax is also available. Directions: from motorway take exit 40 towards la Canourgue. Take D998 and 12km after La Canourgue follow signs for Ste-Enimie opposite La Capelle. Open all year.
PRICES: d €42; HB €34 **NEARBY:** Bathing (15km) Canoeing (15km) Horse riding (20km) Golf (8km) Fishing (15km) Tennis (12km) Railway station (20km) Shops (12km) **NOTES:** Pets admitted

LA TIEULE

♦♦♦ ♥ Chambre d'hôtes Christine BASSET
48500 LA TIEULE
☎ 04 66 48 82 83 📠 04 66 48 89 23

A warm welcome awaits at this gîte with stables, where horse riders with their own horses are especially welcome. In this restored Caussenade farmhouse there are six spacious rooms with en suite bathrooms, a sitting room with TV and open fire, a swimming pool and patio. Meals include healthy produce from the local area. The farm is situated near the Gorges du Tarn. 3km from A41 (A75).
PRICES: d €52; t €67; extra person €15; HB €76; dinner €13 **ON SITE:** Bathing Swimming pool **NEARBY:** Canoeing (7km) Horse riding (5km) Golf (7km) Fishing (7km) Tennis (7km) Railway station (7km) Shops (7km) Restaurant nearby **NOTES:** Pets admitted English spoken

---

◯|

Places with this symbol serve table d'hôtes
evening meals - remember to book in advance

LAVAL-ATGER

♦♦♦ ♥ ◯| Mas de Bonnaude Chantal SCHWANDER
48600 LAVAL-ATGER
☎ 04 66 46 46 01
www.gite-equestre-lozere.com

This is a fascinating historic house which once belonged to the celebrated Abbot of Chayla who started the war of the Camisards under Louis XIV. It offers one double room with a view and bathroom with all facilities; two rooms on two levels with mezzanine double bed; one single room with en suite shower room on the ground floor. The house is centrally heated and the dining room has an open fire and TV. Evening meals offer local specialities. There is a private swimming pool and tennis court. Walking and riding are available and horse riders are especially welcome. 20% reduction except in July and August. Open all year.
PRICES: s €36-€63; d €43-€72; t €60-€90; HB €50-€77; babies free; children 3-8yrs -50%; dinner €15 **ON SITE:** Children's play area Bathing Horse riding Fishing Swimming pool Stretch of water **NEARBY:** Canoeing (15km) Golf (15km) Tennis (15km) Railway station (15km) Shops (5km) **NOTES:** Pets admitted English spoken

LE POMPIDOU

♦♦♦ ♥ ◯| Le Village Jean-Marie CAUSSE
48110 LE POMPIDOU
☎ 04 66 60 31 82
e-mail: j.m.causse@libertysurf.fr

Situated at the junction of two valleys in an area rich in history and spectacular scenery, this is a well appointed house, in a small village on the edge of the Cévennes. It offers four rooms for two to three people all with en suite bathroom. There is a sitting room with fridge and a terrace with conservatory and private garden with parking. Open all year except 22-30 June and 21 December-5 January.
PRICES: s €33; d €40; t €49-€57; extra person €9; HB €33; dinner €13 **ON SITE:** Tennis **NEARBY:** Canoeing (23km) Horse riding (10km) Fishing (10km) Swimming pool (30km) Stretch of water (10km) Railway station (60km) Restaurant nearby **NOTES:** No pets

LE PONT-DE-MONTVERT

♦♦♦ ◯| Maison Victoire Jacqueline GALZIN
Finiels, 48220 LE PONT-DE-MONTVERT
☎ 04 66 45 84 36

This restored house offers five comfortable rooms all with en suite bathroom. In the heart of the Cévennes National Park and on Stevenson's trail (GR 70) this peaceful little village on the slopes of the Mont Lozère offers guests a relaxing holiday in both summer and winter. Swimming, forest walks. Meals using home-made and local produce are served in front of the 16th-century fire. Half-board on the basis of two sharing €72. Open all year.
PRICES: HB €36; dinner €12 **ON SITE:** Fishing Stretch of water **NEARBY:** Bathing (6km) Canoeing (25km) Horse riding (10km) Swimming pool (15km) Tennis (6km) Railway station (30km) Shops (6km) **NOTES:** Pets admitted English spoken

♦♦♦ ♥ ◯| Le Merlet Philippe & Catherine GALZIN
48220 LE PONT-DE-MONTVERT
☎ 04 66 45 82 92 📠 04 66 45 80 78

This 16th-century farmhouse in the Cévennes National Park offers six double rooms with en suite bathrooms. Meals using local specialities are served. Mapped local walking routes are available.
PRICES: HB €40; Holiday Tax €0.30 pppd; single supplement €8; dinner €15 **ON SITE:** Bathing Fishing **NEARBY:** Canoeing (25km) Horse riding (25km) Golf (60km) Tennis (8km) Railway station (30km) Shops (8km) **NOTES:** No pets English spoken

LE ROZIER

♥♥♥ La Pause Francis ESPINASSE
route de Capluc, 48150 LE ROZIER
☎ 05 65 62 63 06
This property sits at the confluence of the Gorges du Tarn and La Jonte on the edge of the village. There are six guest rooms in the home of the proprietor: four double rooms, one room sleeping three and one room sleeping four, all with en suite facilities. There is a patio with conservatory and private pool. Walks start from the house. Charge for four: €67. Open all year.
PRICES: d €40; t €53; extra person €14 **ON SITE:** Bathing Canoeing Fishing Tennis **NEARBY:** Horse riding (5km) Railway station (20km)
NOTES: Pets admitted

LES VIGNES

♥♥♥ Chambre d'hôtes Hervé CAVALIER
route de Malène, 48210 LES VIGNES
☎ 04 66 48 83 87　🖷 04 66 48 83 87
In a picturesque village at the heart of the Gorges du Tarn four rooms with space for ten people with en suite bathroom in each are offered. There is a terrace and parking. Reservations in advance are recommended. Special package: one room and two days canoeing: €49 for two; €46 for four (prices per person). Pedal boats and walking available on site. Climbing 3 km from the house. Canoe trips €48,78 for two people and €45,73 for four. Open from 1 May to 30 September.
PRICES: d €37; t €45; extra person €13 **ON SITE:** Bathing Canoeing Fishing Tennis **NEARBY:** Horse riding (10km) Railway station (30km)
NOTES: Pets admitted

MARCHASTEL

♥♥♥ ÎOÎ Chambre d'hôtes André et Jeanine BOYER
48260 NASBINALS
☎ 04 66 32 53 79
Gévaudan wolf park 15 km. Thermal spa 20 km. Jeanine and André have furnished five en suite rooms with separate access in their old manor house, a family property. This charming home is situated in the heart of Aubrac in a pretty and very peaceful village with local walks on the doorstep. There is a dining room with a small kitchen and a washing machine. Meals feature local specialities.
PRICES: s €34; d €39; extra person €10; dinner €12 **NEARBY:** Bathing (15km) Horse riding (5km) Golf (30km) Fishing (2km) Swimming pool (30km) Stretch of water (2km) Tennis (20km) Railway station (23km) Shops (5km) **NOTES:** Pets admitted

MARVEJOLS

♥♥♥ Chambre d'hôtes Jacques et Maryse MIALANES
Château de Carrière, quartier de l'Empery, 48100 MARVEJOLS
☎ 04 66 32 02 27 & 04 66 32 28 14　🖷 04 66 32 49 60
This manor house, dating from the 17th and 18th centuries and situated in nine hectares of grounds, offers a range of accommodation - six en suite rooms sleeping from two to four people. One of the rooms has a mezzanine floor. There is a communal dining and sitting room with open fire and TV as well as a conservatory, swimming pool, park and parking. The bar is 50 metres away. Open from June to September.
PRICES: s €46-€47; d €53-€69; t €76-€84; extra person €15 **ON SITE:** Fishing Swimming pool **NEARBY:** Canoeing (28km) Horse riding (4km) Stretch of water (3km) Railway station (5km) Shops (4km) Restaurant nearby **NOTES:** No pets

MOISSAC-VALLEE-FRANCAISE

♥♥♥ ♥ ÎOÎ Le Cambon Hubert DIVOUX
48110 MOISSAC-VALLEE-FRANCAISE
☎ 04 66 44 73 13　🖷 04 66 44 73 15
Open all year round, this old restored farmhouse beside the park offers a warm welcome in a range of accommodation. On offer: one room for three (three single beds), one double room, one room for three (one double and one single bed), and one double room in a duplex apartment with an additional three single beds. All rooms have their own bathrooms. There is a swimming pool and farm produce is available. The farm specialises in bee keeping and has terraced gardens. Evening meals five days a week.
PRICES: s €23; d €46; HB €38 **ON SITE:** Fishing Swimming pool Stretch of water **NEARBY:** Canoeing (6km) Horse riding (20km) Tennis (6km) Railway station (17km) Shops (6km) **NOTES:** No pets

NAUSSAC

♥♥♥ ÎOÎ Chambre d'hôtes Michèle BANDON
Pomeyrols, 48300 NAUSSAC　☎ 04 66 69 17 47
e-mail: p.bandon@libertysurf.fr　lozereonline
Lake Naussac 2 km. Langogne 5 km. This beautifully decorated, newly renovated house situated between Langogne and Lake Naussac in the village of Pomeyrols offers five guest rooms, three double rooms, one three-bedded room and one four bedded-room, all with en suite shower and wc. There is a kitchen for guests' use, a sitting room with open fire and communal television, a conservatory and parking. Meals can be arranged and there is use of the telephone. Open all year.
PRICES: not supplied **NEARBY:** Bathing (3km) Canoeing (3km) Horse riding (5km) Golf (4km) Fishing (1km) Swimming pool (5km) Stretch of water (3km) Tennis (3km) Railway station (5km) Shops (5km)
NOTES: No pets

♥♥♥ ♥ ÎOÎ Chambre d'hôtes
Georges et Sylviane AUGUSTE
l'Escapade, Pomeyrols, 48300 NAUSSAC
☎ 04 66 69 25 91 & 06 80 08 40 28
Between Lake Naussac and the Allier border, at the heart of a forest and close to Langogne, the Ferme de Pomeyrols offers a peaceful, convivial environment. This traditional old building has been completely renovated to provide four guest rooms on the first floor of the owners' house, each with private bathroom. Communal lounge. Central heating. Horses, farm animals (dairy cows), walking and mountain biking. Halfboard for two people: 73.18 euros. Open February to November, Christmas holidays by reservation.
PRICES: s €28; d €43; dinner €15 **ON SITE:** Fishing **NEARBY:** Bathing (5km) Canoeing (10km) Horse riding (10km) Golf (10km) Swimming pool (5km) Tennis (8km) Railway station (8km) Shops (8km) Restaurant nearby **NOTES:** No pets English spoken

PREVENCHERES

♥♥♥ ♥ ÎOÎ Albespeyres Christine GALLAND
48800 PREVENCHERES
☎ 04 66 46 06 47 & 06 81 98 90 56　🖷 04 66 46 06 47
In a peaceful location this house is on the edge of the Gorges du Chassezac, 5km from the nearest village (access from the D906). Five rooms all with en suite bathroom are on offer. There is a communal sitting room, dining room and patio with garden and parking. Meals are served using local produce with lamb, and honey desserts are our specialities. It is essential to book in advance. Nearby honey farm and donkey sanctuary, horse riding and walking. Tennis with an instructor is also on offer. 10% reduction is available for children under ten. Open all year.
PRICES: s €21; d €43; t €64; HB €30; dinner €12 **NEARBY:** Bathing (1km) Canoeing (40km) Horse riding (10km) Golf (1km) Fishing (1km) Tennis (5km) Railway station (5km) Shops (5km) **NOTES:** Pets admitted

PRINSUEJOLS

♦♦♦ ⭑◎⭑ La Baume Haute Véronique DE LAS CASES
1 rue Louise Michel, 92300 LEVALLOIS
☎ 01 47 48 05 54 & 06 87 53 22 99
e-mail: francois.de.las.cases@libertysurf.fr
In the majestic grounds of the Château de la Baume this 17th-century building offers three spacious and tastefully decorated rooms (one with four-poster) with en suite bathrooms. Castle and grounds open to visitors. Parking available. This house lies on the route of St Jacques de Compostelle and guests can follow this trail on foot or on horseback. Open July and August.
PRICES: (2001) s €61; d €92; t €122; dinner €12 **ON SITE:** Fishing
NEARBY: Bathing (5km) Horse riding (15km) Golf (30km) Swimming pool (15km) Stretch of water (5km) Tennis (15km) **NOTES:** No pets

QUEZAC

♦♦♦ ⭑◎⭑ La Maison de Marius Danielle MEJEAN
8 rue du Pontet, 48320 QUEZAC
☎ 04 66 44 25 05 📠 04 66 44 25 05

Sainte-Enimie 16 km. Florac 12 km. La Maison de Marius welcomes you to the heart of the Gorges du Tarn. This traditional house offers a warm welcome and delightful local cooking, including the speciality nut gâteau. Tourist tax: €0.30 euros per person per day extra. Open all year.
PRICES: s €45-€61; d €45-€61; extra person €16; dinner €20
ON SITE: Bathing Fishing **NEARBY:** Canoeing (2km) Horse riding (1km) Golf (45km) Tennis (2km) Railway station (28km) Shops (2km) **NOTES:** Pets admitted

SAINT ANDRE DE LANCIZE

♦♦♦ 🐦 ⭑◎⭑ Le Valès Séverine KIEFFER
48240 SAINT ANDRE DE LANCIZE
☎ 04 66 45 93 20 📠 04 66 45 93 20
Parc National des Cévennes. This property is in a small peaceful hamlet. There is one triple room (one double and one single bed); and two family rooms (one double and two mezzanine single beds) all with en suite facilities. There is a garden, a conservatory and terrace. Nearby there are donkey and pony trips. Local farm products are on sale. Open all year.
PRICES: s €35; d €40-€45; t €60; extra person €10; HB €35; dinner €15; HB reduced prices for children. €7 for picnic basket **NEARBY:** Bathing (15km) Horse riding (12km) Fishing (1km) Stretch of water (1km) Tennis (15km) Shops (12km) **NOTES:** Pets admitted

SAINT PRIVAT DE VALLONGUE

♦♦♦♦ ⭑◎⭑ La Baume Philippe et Richard THEME
48240 SAINT PRIVAT DE VALLONGUE
☎ 04 66 45 58 89 📠 04 66 45 48 84
e-mail: bouges@club-internet.fr & labaume@cevennes.com
Parc National des Cévennes. A warm welcome awaits at this traditional Cévenole building dating to the 17th-century. Sleeps twelve in four guest rooms: 'Magnanerie' has a double bed, with en suite bathroom; the 'Bruyère Suite' has one double bed and two singles with en suite bathroom and sitting room alcove; 'La Clède' has, on the ground floor, a sitting room and private patio area, and on the first floor, one double bed with bathroom; 'Tilleul' has a hall with the option of a single sofa bed and a double bedroom with sitting room alcove and bathroom. Dining room, two sitting rooms and billiard room. Meals are served. There is parking, conservatory, and access to a telephone, terrace, and guided walks from La Baume. Open Easter to Christmas.
PRICES: s €40; d €70; t €84; extra person €16; HB €54; dinner €23
ON SITE: Tennis Swimming pool **NEARBY:** Railway station (40km) Shops (1.5km) Stretch of water (5km) Fishing (3km) Bathing (3km) Horse riding (10km) Canoeing (42km) **NOTES:** Pets admitted CC English spoken

STE-COLOMBE-DE-PEYRE

♦♦♦ 🐦 ⭑◎⭑ Lasfonds Georges PAUC
Le Chaudoudoux, 48130 STE-COLOMBE-DE-PEYRE
☎ 04 66 42 93 39 & 06 72 83 58 13
Lake Moulinet 3 km. Wolf park 7 km. Bison park 30 km. This small traditional farm offers four rooms all with en suite facilities and central heating. There is an open fire and garden. A garage is available for bikes; pick-up from the station if required. 1/2 board is on the basis of two people sharing. HB discount after 4 nights. €8 meal for children under twelve. Walking, mountain biking and cross-country skiing are available. Near GR65 (St. Jacques de Compostelle). Déroc waterfall 20 km. Open all year.
PRICES: s €34; d €43; extra person €13; HB €43; dinner €13
NEARBY: Bathing (3km) Horse riding (20km) Golf (35km) Fishing (3km) Swimming pool (20km) Stretch of water (3km) Tennis (20km) Railway station (8km) Shops (8km) **NOTES:** No pets

STE-ENIMIE

♦♦♦ ⭑◎⭑ Nissoulogres Annie et Patrice FOUQUEROLLE
48210 STE-ENIMIE
☎ 04 66 48 53 86 📠 04 66 48 58 43
e-mail: patrice.fouquerolle@wanadoo.fr
Situated on the Causse de Sauveterre above Sainte Enimie this establishment offers six rooms for two to four people (one room offers access for the less mobile) with private bathroom. Meals are served to the guests in a group. Both half and full board are available. Closed in January
PRICES: not supplied **NEARBY:** Canoeing (13km) Horse riding (11km) Fishing (13km) Swimming pool (30km) Stretch of water (13km) Railway station (22km) Shops (13km) **NOTES:** Pets admitted

ST-ETIENNE-VALLEE-FRANCAISE

♦♦♦ 🐦 ⭑◎⭑ Le Ranc des Avelacs
Bernard et Martine CHATIN
48330 ST-ETIENNE-VALLEE-FRANCAISE
☎ 04 66 45 71 80 📠 04 66 45 75 58
e-mail: chatinb@aol.com
This old renovated stone farmhouse, accessed by a forest track, has good views of La Corniche des Cévennes and Mount Aigoual. Six comfortable guest rooms with private terraces - three double rooms, one room with four single beds, two rooms with two single beds and all with central heating and en suite facilities. Meals are served in the communal dining room with open fire or on the covered terrace outside. Swimming pool in the grounds. Own home-produced honey is sold. Open all year by reservation only.
PRICES: HB €46 (€80 for 2); dinner €13 **ON SITE:** Swimming pool
NEARBY: Bathing (3km) Canoeing (50km) Horse riding (5km) Golf (70km) Fishing (3km) Stretch of water (3km) Tennis (5km) Railway station (43km) Shops (5km) **NOTES:** No pets English spoken

continued

ST-GERMAIN-DE-CALBERTE

♦♦♦ ❦ Ⱶⵔ Lou Pradel Nicole et Jean BECHARD
48370 ST-GERMAIN-DE-CALBERTE
☎ 04 66 45 92 46　🖥 04 66 45 92 46
e-mail: pradel.nbechard@wanadoo.fr
At the heart of the Cévennes this accommodation overlooking the valleys has three comfortable guest rooms with en suite facilities. There is a sitting room with open fire and a library. It is set beside the GR 67. Mountain bike hire. Donkey enclosure. Meals are served on request on Wednesday and Saturday and a bar is 1km away. Open all year.
NEARBY: Bathing (10km) Horse riding (2km) Fishing (10km) Swimming pool (12km) Tennis (12km) Railway station (30km) Shops (10km)
NOTES: No pets English spoken

♦♦♦ ❦ Ⱶⵔ Vernet Sabine LAMY
48370 ST-GERMAIN-DE-CALBERTE
☎ 04 66 45 91 94　🖥 04 66 45 93 36
e-mail: gerard.lamy@libertysurf.fr
We offer six guests rooms all with en suite shower room. There is a sitting room with open fire and central heating, a library and a terrace. Children's meals are €8. Guests have the chance to see the donkeys and the sheep, and at the right time of year collect raspberries with the farmer. Meals are prepared with garden and farm produce. Accessed via N106 and D984. Open all year.
PRICES: s €35; d €43; t €55; HB €34.50; extra person €15; dinner €13
NEARBY: Bathing (10km) Horse riding (12km) Fishing (2km) Swimming pool (10km) Stretch of water (10km) Railway station (35km) Shops (10km) **NOTES:** Pets admitted

ST-MARTIN-DE-LANSUSCLE

♦♦♦ Ⱶⵔ Le Cauvel Hubert et A-Sylvie PFISTER
Château de Cauvel, 48110 ST-MARTIN-DE-LANSUSCLE
☎ 04 66 45 92 75　🖥 04 66 45 94 76
Guests can enjoy peace and beautiful surroundings at this family home. There is a large library, an open fire, comfortable rooms and even the smell of hot bread and fresh jam! Interesting cuisine on offer. Open weekends from 11 November to 1 April.
PRICES: s €35–€40; d €70–€80; HB €38–€44; dinner €14
NEARBY: Bathing (4km) Canoeing (22km) Horse riding (9km) Fishing (4km) Swimming pool (12km) Stretch of water (4km) Tennis (12km) Railway station (45km) Shops (9km) **NOTES:** No pets English spoken

ST-PIERRE-DES-TRIPIERS

♦♦♦ ❦ Ⱶⵔ La Volpilière Danielle et Michel GAL
Le Choucas - La Volpilière, Saint-Pierre-des-Tripiers, 48150 MEYRUEIS
☎ 04 66 45 64 28　🖥 04 66 45 64 28
This privately owned house with splendid views is set on le Causse-Méjean above the Gorges du Tarn in the heart of the country. Three charming rooms sleeping two to four people with en suite facilities (wc and bathroom) are offered in this centrally heated house. There is a large sitting room with open fire and TV. Terrace. Walking on GR6. Cost: 1/2 board (more than three nights), 1 person: €50, two people: €70. Some English spoken. Open from 15 March to 15 November.
PRICES: s €42; d €49; extra person €13; dinner €13 **NEARBY:** Bathing (15km) Canoeing (20km) Horse riding (20km) Golf (40km) Fishing (10km) Stretch of water (10km) Tennis (17km) Railway station (38km) Shops (17km) **NOTES:** No pets

♦♦♦ ❦ Le Courby David et Catherine AVEN ARMAND
Saint-Pierre-des-Tripiers, 48150 MEYRUEIS
☎ 04 66 45 63 21 & 05 63 54 09 26　🖥 05 63 54 73 99
In a village location this old farmhouse is situated in 200 hectares of woodland. It is a centre for Prejwalsky horses and welcomes

horses to the eight boxes and paddock. There are six completely renovated rooms (three twin rooms and three double rooms) all with en suite shower. An additional bed is available in four of the rooms. Heated private pool. Walking, climbing and rafting 15km. Open from 1 April to 30 September.
PRICES: s €37; d €49; t €61; extra person €13; HB €46; FB €55; dinner €13–€21 **ON SITE:** Swimming pool **NEARBY:** Bathing (20km) Canoeing (20km) Horse riding (20km) Golf (20km) Fishing (20km) Tennis (20km) Railway station (35km) Shops (20km) Restaurant nearby **NOTES:** Pets admitted English spoken

TERMES

♦♦♦ ❦ Ⱶⵔ La Narce Alain CHALVET
48310 TERMES
☎ 04 66 31 64 12　🖥 04 66 31 64 12
The old traditionally restored farmhouse of La Narce guarantees peace and quiet. Access is by a private road and the farm is situated between Aubrac and Margeride in the heart of the country. Just 500m from the village and in three hectares of parkland. Accommodation is in twin rooms with private facilities. There is a large dining room and fitted kitchen with stove.
PRICES: d €41; single supplement €15; HB €34 **NEARBY:** Railway station (8km) Shops (5km) **NOTES:** Pets admitted

PYRÉNÉES-ORIENTALES

ARGELES-SUR-MER

♦♦♦ Ⱶⵔ Mas Senyarich Marina ROMERO
66700 ARGELES-SUR-MER
☎ 04 68 95 93 63　🖥 04 68 95 93 63
Collioure 7 km. Cloître d'Elne 7 km. This farmhouse, at the heart of the Mediterranean forest and only five minutes from the beach, offers five guest rooms. Overlooking the village the view extends to sea. Meals feature Catalan specialities. Outside there is a swimming pool and parking. Walks and mountain bike trips from the doorstep. There is a gîte in the grounds.
PRICES: s €46–€50; d €50–€55; t €64–€68; dinner €20 **ON SITE:** Wine tasting Bathing Hiking **NEARBY:** Horse riding (7km) Sea (5km) Fishing (5km) Spa (30km) Railway station (3km) Shops (5km) ARGELES SUR MER (5km) **NOTES:** No pets English spoken

CAMELAS

♦♦♦ Ⱶⵔ Mas Félix Lucie BOULITROP
66300 CAMELAS
☎ 04 68 53 46 71 & SR : 04 68 51 52 70　🖥 04 68 53 40 54
e-mail: lucie.boulitrop@wanadoo.fr
Castelnou 2 km. Thuir 7 km. This isolated farmhouse, perched high above Les Aspres, is ideal for those looking for a quiet and restful holiday. This is a non-smoking house. There are four guest rooms and a family suite available. The dining room and sitting room are reserved for guests and the meals are based on Mediterranean cooking.
PRICES: s €44; d €55; t €67–€78; suite €93; dinner €21 **ON SITE:** Hiking **NEARBY:** Bathing (10km) Horse riding (10km) Sea (35km) Fishing (10km) Railway station (25km) Shops (7km) THUIR (7km) **NOTES:** No pets English spoken

CASES-DE-PENE

♦♦♦ Les Oliviers de Virgina
M-Christine & Robert FAURE
66600 CASES-DE-PENE
☎ 04 68 38 91 46 & 06 08 07 53 15　🖥 04 68 38 91 48
e-mail: lesoliviersdevirgina@wanadoo.fr
Tautavel 7 km. Quéribus 18 km. Four guest rooms are available in this modern, quiet farmhouse on a 20-hectare farm with olives and vineyards. Each room has its own private access. Many delightful

continued　　　　　　　　　　　　　　　*continued*

sites nearby to discover. Perpignan airport is only 10km away (shuttle bus available).
PRICES: s €43-€49; d €43-€55; t €70; suite €85 **ON SITE:** Wine tasting Bathing Fishing Hiking **NEARBY:** Sea (20km) Spa (40km) Railway station (5km) RIVESALTES (5km) **NOTES:** Pets admitted English spoken

CASTELNOU

♥♥♥ ❦ ❍ Domaine de Querubi
R et F NABET-CLAVERIE
66300 CASTELNOU
☎ 04 68 53 19 08 ▤ 04 68 53 18 96
e-mail: contact@querubi.com www.querubi.com
Figuéras 35 km. Castelnou 35 km. Facing the Pyrenees this magnificently restored 12th-century farmhouse offers four guest rooms and two family suites. Situated on 200 hectares of moors amid olive trees. Walking, archery and hunting can be enjoyed here.
PRICES: s €61; d €73; t €82; suite €105; dinner €23
ON SITE: Bathing Hiking **NEARBY:** Horse riding (10km) Sea (30km) Fishing (15km) Spa (30km) Railway station (25km) Shops (7km) THUIR (10km) **NOTES:** Pets admitted English spoken

♥♥♥ La Figuera Patrick et Luc DEGREEF ET DIEZ
3 Carrer de la font d'Avall, 66300 CASTELNOU
☎ 04 68 53 18 42 & SR : 04 68 51 52 70 ▤ 04 68 53 18 42
e-mail: lafiguera@wanadoo.fr www.la-figuera.com

Prieuré de Serrabonne 20 km. Four comfortable and beautifully decorated rooms in a house full of character are available in one of the most beautiful villages of France. Breakfast is served outside on the terrace. The enclosed flower garden offers a solarium and garden furniture. Private parking at the entrance to the village.
PRICES: s €46; d €58-€65; t €75 **ON SITE:** Wine tasting Hiking
NEARBY: Bathing (5km) Horse riding (5km) Sea (25km) Fishing (25km) Spa (20km) Railway station (20km) Shops (5km) THUIR (5km)
NOTES: No pets English spoken

CERET

♥♥♥ Mas Terra Rosa Simone JOSSE-ROUX
Las Bourgueres, 66400 CERET
☎ 04 68 87 34 00 & 06 09 06 76 63
Spain 10 km. This quiet wooded property has three guest rooms. In fine weather breakfast is served on the sunny terrace with a splendid view over the Canigou Massif. Secure parking is available. Many routes for walking directly from the farmhouse.
PRICES: s €41; d €47; t €56 **NEARBY:** Bathing (3km) Horse riding (10km) Sea (30km) Fishing (3km) Hiking (3km) Spa (10km) Railway station (3km) Shops (4km) CERET (3km) **NOTES:** No pets

---

Prices are given in Euros €1 = £0.62
at the time of going to press

ELNE

♥♥♥ ❍ Can Oliba Florence LE CORRE
24 rue de la Paix, 66200 ELNE
☎ 04 68 22 11 09 & 06 09 35 67 44
e-mail: elna@club-internet.fr
Perpignan 12 km. This guesthouse offers five rooms and a family suite near the cathedral and its cloisters and only 5km from the beaches. Accommodation comprises a sitting room with open fireplace and piano. Mediterranean meals are served. There is a permanent exhibition of contemporary art and a swimming pool with a jacuzzi.
PRICES: s €50; d €55; t €59; suite €73; dinner €17 **ON SITE:** Bathing
NEARBY: Horse riding (1km) Sea (5km) Fishing (5km) Spa (20km) Railway station (1km) Shops (1km) ELNE **NOTES:** No pets

♥♥♥ ❦ ❍ Mas de la Roubine
Régine PIQUEMAL PASTRE, 66200 ELNE
☎ 04 68 22 76 72 ▤ 04 68 22 76 72
Collioure 4 km. This remote farmhouse offers three guest rooms tucked away on a forestry estate. Meals are served in the sitting room opening out onto a huge tree-lined lawn in a peaceful environment. Covered parking is offered on the property. Nearby you will find cultural and sporting venues.
PRICES: s €49; d €52; t €61; dinner €19 **ON SITE:** Hiking
NEARBY: Bathing (2km) Horse riding (4km) Sea (4km) Fishing (4km) Railway station (4km) Shops (4km) ELNE (3km) **NOTES:** Pets admitted

LATOUR-BAS-ELNE

♥♥♥ Chambre d'hôtes Colette ARMENGOL
Chemin des Horts, B.P. 17, 66200 LATOUR-BAS-ELNE
☎ 04 68 22 75 28 & SR : 04 68 51 52 70 ▤ 04 68 22 75 28
Argelès 6 km. Four tastefully appointed rooms in Catalan style in a rural gîte with private access. The sitting and dining rooms are reserved for breakfast and it is possible to picnic on the property. Parking is provided. Traditional meals are available in the nearby village.
PRICES: s €45; d €50 **NEARBY:** Bathing (1km) Horse riding (2km) Sea (4km) Fishing (3km) Hiking (7km) Spa (20km) Railway station (4km) CANET EN ROUSSILLON (6km) **NOTES:** No pets

LLO

♥♥♥ ❍ Cal Miquel Jean-Pierre MASSIE
66800 LLO
☎ 04 68 04 19 68
e-mail: calmiquel@wanadoo.fr www.calmiquel.com

Spain 4 km. Situated high up in the village of Llo this pretty farm offers five guest rooms. The decoration and the quality of the furnishings create a warm and pleasant atmosphere in the house. There is a beautiful music room with a piano, a library and an open fireplace. Beautiful views over the mountains from the terrace.

continued

PRICES: s €40; d €43; t €50; suite €64; dinner €14　**ON SITE:** Hiking
NEARBY: Bathing (1km)　Horse riding (1km)　Fishing (1km)　Spa (1km)
Railway station (4km)　Shops (4km)　SAILLAGOUSE (4km)　**NOTES:** Pets
admitted　English spoken

MONTESQUIEU-DES-ALBERES

Les Trompettes Hautes Norman et Jacqueline HAYES
13 rue du Tambori, 66740 MONTESQUIEU-DES-ALBERES
☎ 04 68 83 00 56 & SR : 04 68 51 52 70　🖹 04 68 83 00 56

Argelès 20 km. Collioure 26 km. This individually designed guest
house is set in a residential area and the five rooms are equipped
with TV. The sitting room is shared with the host family and has an
open fireplace. The enclosed tree-lined garden has a swimming
pool and outdoor furniture. Parking.
PRICES: d €56　**ON SITE:** Bathing　**NEARBY:** Horse riding (6km)　Sea
(20km)　Fishing (1km)　Hiking (1km)　Railway station (20km)　Shops (5km)
ARGELES SUR MER (15km)　**NOTES:** No pets　English spoken

MONTFERRER

Mas Can Ripe Adrianus CASTRICUM
Baynat d'en Galangau, 66150 MONTFERRER
☎ 04 68 39 81 08　🖹 04 68 39 81 08
Céret 20 km. Spain 50 km. The Dutch owners of this isolated
farmhouse on the slopes of Montferrer offer five comfortable
rooms and a family suite. The dining and sitting rooms, with a
library corner, are reserved for guests. The garden has a solarium.
Access to the property is via a rough track.
PRICES: s €40; d €50; t €66-€74; suite €82; dinner €13
ON SITE: Bathing　Horse riding　Hiking　**NEARBY:** Sea (51km)　Fishing
(7km)　Spa (14km)　Railway station (50km)　Shops (8km)　ARLES SUR
TECH (8km)　**NOTES:** Pets admitted　English spoken

MONT-LOUIS

La Volute Martine SCHAFF
1 place d'armes, 66210 MONT-LOUIS
☎ 04 68 04 27 21 & SR : 04 68 51 52 70　🖹 04 68 04 27 21
Spain 20 km. Andorra 50 km. Situated in the ramparts, this house
was once the residence of the governor of Louis XIV. The five guest
rooms have their own shower rooms, and there is a large
characterful attic room with lounge area, children's play area and
music. Log fire and fully equipped kitchen. The garden has
panoramic views over the mountain.
PRICES: s €43-€47; d €52-€59; t €67-€75　**ON SITE:** Fishing　Hiking　Spa
NEARBY: Bathing (2km)　Horse riding (2km)　Sea (80km)　Railway station
(1km)　MONT LOUIS　**NOTES:** No pets　English spoken

MOSSET

La Casa del Gat Aurélie D'HUYVETTER
Hameau Brezes, 66500 MOSSET
☎ 04 68 05 07 50　🖹 04 68 05 07 50
e-mail: joaurelie@hotmail.com
www.ehol.com/accommodation/1258014_fr.asp
Villefranche de Conflent 14 km. Two well appointed rooms and a
family suite are to be found in this isolated house in the middle of
the Castellane Valley. Meals are taken in the dining room with the
owner who also shares the sitting room. There is a large garden
with lots of trees and a patio. Enjoy walking and the peaceful
surroundings. Mediterranean meals are served; vegetarian meals
available by request.
PRICES: s €38; d €43-€46; t €58; extra person €4; suite €73; dinner €14
ON SITE: Bathing　Hiking　**NEARBY:** Horse riding (2km)　Sea (60km)
Fishing (1km)　Spa (2km)　Railway station (10km)　Shops (3km)　PRADES
(9km)　**NOTES:** No pets　English spoken

La Forge Judith CARMONA
Mas LuganasS, 66500 MOSSET
☎ 04 68 05 04 84 & SR : 04 68 51 52 70　🖹 04 68 05 04 08
e-mail: Maslluganas@aol.com
Yellow train 14 km. Serrabone 20 km. This former Catalan smithy has
been renovated to offer three guest rooms and one suite. Each room
has its own private access. There is a dining room with open fireplace,
a flower garden with furniture and a barbecue. A trout river flows past
the 2-hectare property. Meals can be taken in a nearby inn.
PRICES: s €35; d €42; suite €80　**ON SITE:** Horse riding　Fishing　Hiking
NEARBY: Bathing (2km)　Sea (63km)　Spa (5km)　Railway station (13km)
Shops (1km)　PRADES (13km)　**NOTES:** No pets　English spoken

PERPIGNAN

Domaine du Mas Boluix
Jean-Louis CEILLES, 66100 PERPIGNAN
☎ 04 68 08 17 70　🖹 04 68 08 17 71
www.domaine-de-boluix.com
Le Castillet 5 km. Jean-Louis, a winegrower, is happy to show
guests the 30-hectare vineyard during their stay in this 18th-
century renovated farmhouse. The five rooms and the family
suite are beautifully decorated and offer air conditioning and
TV with foreign stations. There is a dining room and separate
sitting room.
PRICES: s €58; d €64; t €73; suite €99　**NEARBY:** Bathing (3km)
Horse riding (3km)　Sea (8km)　Fishing (3km)　Hiking (15km)　Spa
(30km)　Railway station (5km)　Shops (2km)　PERPIGNAN (5km)
NOTES: Pets admitted

LANGUEDOC-ROUSSILLON

PRUGNANES

♦♦♦ ⏻◎⏻ Domaine de Cousseres Joo et Anne MAES
66220 PRUGNANES
☎ 04 68 59 23 55 & SR : 04 68 51 52 70 🖺 04 68 59 23 55
www.cousseres.com

Gorges de Galamus 7 km. Château de Quéribus 12 km. Total peace can be found here and views of cliffs, moors and vineyards can be enjoyed. The renovated country-house offers four guest rooms and a family suite with sitting room, day room, dining room and library and lots of terraces. Meals are served from a wide ranging menu.
PRICES: s €45-€50; d €55-€60; t €65-€70; suite €100-€110; dinner €20
ON SITE: Bathing Hiking **NEARBY:** Horse riding (7km) Sea (50km) Fishing (10km) Railway station (45km) Shops (5km) SAINT PAUL DE FENOUILLET (5km) **NOTES:** No pets English spoken

SERRALONGUE

♦♦♦ ⏻◎⏻ Case Guillamo E & P BRACCKEVELDT
66230 SERRALONGUE
☎ 04 68 39 60 50 & SR : 04 68 51 52 70
Céret 35 km. Dali Museum 50 km. A farm tucked away in a forest that promises peace and quiet, natural surroundings and good food. Accommodation consists of two rooms and a family suite with a shady terrace and parking. Fishing and walking. The farm is reached by a 1.8 kilometre rough track.
PRICES: s €46; d €54; t €69; suite €91; dinner €23 **ON SITE:** Bathing Fishing Hiking **NEARBY:** Horse riding (4km) Sea (55km) Spa (25km) Railway station (65km) Shops (4km) PRATS DE MOLLO LA PRESTE (18km) **NOTES:** No pets

ST-LAURENT-DE-CERDANS

♦♦♦ ⏻◎⏻ ⟨ Mas del Faig Emmanuelle PRATS
La forge del Mitg, 66260 ST-LAURENT-DE-CERDANS
☎ 04 68 39 53 91
e-mail: emmanuelle.prats@wanadoo.fr
Céret 25 km. Tours de Cabrens 8 km. A 19th-century Catalan farmhouse, amid 60 hectares of land, that offers three guest rooms, a family suite and a suite reserved for less mobile guests. There is a kitchen, and a sitting room with open fireplace, TV and video. Enclosed swimming pool, which is also suitable for use by the less mobile, a furnished garden and parking. Catalan dishes are served.
PRICES: s €38; d €46; t €61; suite €61-€76; dinner €15
ON SITE: Children's play area Bathing Horse riding Fishing Hiking **NEARBY:** Sea (50km) Spa (12km) Railway station (55km) Shops (5km) PRATS DE MOLLO LA PRESTE (16km) **NOTES:** No pets English spoken

> Use the atlas at the back of the guide to locate your chambre d'hôtes

TAURINYA

♦♦♦ ⏻◎⏻ Las Astrillas Bernard LOUPIEN
66500 TAURINYA
☎ 04 68 96 17 01 & SR : 04 68 51 52 70 🖺 04 68 96 17 01
e-mail: las.astrillas@libertysurf.fr
Pau Casals at Prades 5 km. St-Michel de Cuxa 2 km. In this renovated farmhouse, full of character, at the foot of the Canigou five guest rooms are offered plus a family suite. Guests share the dining room with open fireplace with the owner, but the sitting room is reserved for guests. The flower garden has outdoor furniture. There is also a small museum.
PRICES: d €42; t €53; dinner €16; suite €58 **ON SITE:** Fishing Hiking **NEARBY:** Bathing (5km) Horse riding (4km) Sea (50km) Spa (10km) Railway station (5km) Shops (1km) PRADES (5km) **NOTES:** No pets English spoken

THUIR

♦♦♦♦ Mas Petit Casa del Arte Joelle FOURMENT
Mas Petit, 66300 THUIR
☎ 04 68 53 44 78 & SR : 04 68 51 52 70
🖺 04 68 53 44 78
e-mail: casadelarte@wanadoo.fr
http://perso.wanadoo.fr/casa.del.arte/

Prieuré de Serrabone 22 km. A renovated, 11th-century farmhouse with four rooms and a family suite on offer. There is private access to some of the rooms and all are equipped with TV, telephone and a mini-bar. A communal sitting room with open fireplace and terrace are also available. There are large grounds with parking .
PRICES: s €61-€70; d €73-€76; suite €99 **ON SITE:** Bathing **NEARBY:** Horse riding (10km) Sea (22km) Fishing (22km) Hiking (22km) Railway station (15km) Shops (2km) THUIR (2km) **NOTES:** Pets admitted English spoken

VILLELONGUE-DE-LA-SALANQUE

♦♦♦ ⏻◎⏻ Le Clos Saint Jean Jean-Marie FAU
Avenue du Littoral, Mas Grand Jean,
66410 VILLELONGUE-DE-LA-SALANQUE
☎ 04 68 73 94 18 & SR : 04 68 51 52 70 🖺 04 68 73 97 93
Perpignan 8 km. Mediterranean Sea 4 km. Jackye and Jean-Marie offer a warm welcome to their home on the outskirts of the village and will be pleased to give lots of information about the area. The house is only five minutes from the beach and has four rooms and a family suite. It is set beside a leisure park with cycle paths. Sitting room with TV, games and books. Outside there is garden furniture, a shady terrace, a large enclosed garden and a porch. Catalan food is served.
PRICES: s €38; d €46; t €84; suite €91; dinner €15 **ON SITE:** Hiking **NEARBY:** Bathing (4km) Horse riding (5km) Sea (4km) Fishing (4km) Spa (40km) Railway station (12km) SAINT LAURENT DE LA SALANQUE (6km) **NOTES:** No pets Minimum 2 night stay English spoken

LIMOUSIN

CORRÈZE

AIX

🏫 🐓 🍽 Chalons d'Aix

Christian & Nathalie FAGEOLLE, 19200 AIX
☎ 05 55 94 31 17

Le Sancy 40 km. Ussel 15 km. Merlines 4 km. Nathalie and Christian welcome you to their Limousin cattle farm in a peaceful and verdant setting. Home cooking with farm produce includes pork, beef, cep mushrooms, and bilberries. The first-floor of the owners' house has been converted to three bedrooms with private shower-room, wc and a shared sitting room. 10% discount for five nights or more. Meals provided out of season by reservation only. Price for four people is 59 euros. Open all year.
PRICES: s €31; d €37; t €48; extra person €11; dinner €13
ON SITE: Fishing **NEARBY:** Bathing (4km) Horse riding (6km) Golf (35km) Swimming pool (15km) Hiking (5km) Tennis (4km) Sailing (25km) Railway station (4km) Shops (4km) **NOTES:** No pets

ALTILLAC

🏫 🍽 La Majorie Basse Michel et Christine GILLIERON

19120 ALTILLAC
☎ 05 55 91 28 70 🖷 05 55 91 28 70
e-mail: lamajorie@wanadoo.fr

This large house is in enchanting surroundings near the Dordogne. There are four bedrooms, an equipped kitchen, a living room and a terrace, plus a private swimming pool. The rate for two people per week is 519 euros with an additional 8 euros for an extra bed. A suite for four people is 519 euros per week. Out of season rates upon request. Open all year.
PRICES: s €40; d €49; t €56; dinner €15 **ON SITE:** Bathing Fishing Swimming pool Hiking **NEARBY:** Golf (10km) Tennis (1km) Railway station (5km) **NOTES:** No pets

ARGENTAT

🏫 🍽 La Maison du Pecheur

Florence et Eric LEBOUCHER
Chadiot, 19400 ARGENTAT
☎ 05 55 28 81 99 🖷 05 55 28 81 99
e-mail: ericlbchr@aol.com

Florence and Eric invite you to stay in their attractive residence dating from the end of the 18th century. Situated in the hollow of a sunny valley, La Maison du Pecheur (fisherman's house) offers guests the chance to enjoy tasty local dishes in the evening seated together around a large table. Eric, a registered fishing guide, can take you out on fly-fishing courses on the Dordogne.
PRICES: s €30; d €41; t €53; HB €38; FB €50; dinner €15
ON SITE: Fishing Hiking **NEARBY:** Bathing (1km) Golf (30km) Swimming pool (2km) Tennis (2km) Sailing (1km) Railway station (45km) Shops (2km) **NOTES:** No pets English spoken

ARNAC-POMPADOUR

🏫 Relais du Brifan Brigitte et François LEMOINE

Le Queyraud, 19230 ARNAC POMPADOUR
☎ 05 55 98 52 56

This country house of character is the home of Brigitte and François, who are pleased to offer their guests four bedrooms with shower room and wc plus a shared room containing a fridge and microwave. There is also an outside kitchen area with garden

furniture and a barbecue featuring an old converted oven. This property is situated three kilometres from the racecourse at Pompadour and for those keen on riding, new horse boxes can be rented for 8 euros a day, straw and hay included. Baby-sitting arrangements are possible on the premises.
PRICES: s €30; d €37; t €55 **ON SITE:** Fishing Hiking
NEARBY: Bathing (20km) Horse riding (3km) Golf (30km) Swimming pool (3km) Tennis (3km) Sailing (20km) Railway station (3km) Shops (3km) **NOTES:** No pets

BEAULIEU-SUR-DORDOGNE

🏫 🐓 Chambre d'hôtes J-Claude & Christine HENRIET

11, rue de la Gendarmerie,
19120 BEAULIEU-SUR-DORDOGNE
☎ 05 55 91 24 97 🖷 05 55 91 51 27

Situated a stone's throw away from the Dordogne in the heart of Beaulieu, this house offers four bedrooms that look out either onto an interior patio full of flowers or the garden with its swimming pool. Each one is unusually decorated - Indian, 1930s, bridal or bird themes. Guests also have the use of a large room with fireplace. Christine, who adores browsing in antique shops, will provide guests with the best places to visit. Rate for four people is 84 euros. Open 1 April to 30 September.
PRICES: s €38-€44; d €46-€56; t €61-€76 **ON SITE:** Bathing Fishing Swimming pool Hiking Tennis **NEARBY:** Horse riding (8km) Golf (17km) Sailing (30km) Railway station (7km) **NOTES:** No pets

BENAYES

🏫 🐓 Forsac Henry et Mireille DEMONTBRON

19510 BENAYES
☎ 05 55 73 47 78 🖷 05 55 73 47 78

Guest rooms situated on the first floor of this château, dating from the 13th century, are currently undergoing restoration. The château is on a farm with a hunting enclosure and fishing. Fifteen kilometres away is the Minoterie centre, offering archery, mountain biking and kayaks and within 10 km there is a go-karting track. Meals available on request. Open all year.
PRICES: s €29; d €34; t €40 **ON SITE:** Fishing Hiking
NEARBY: Bathing (6km) Horse riding (15km) Golf (30km) Swimming pool (15km) Tennis (6km) Railway station (15km) Shops (5km)
NOTES: Pets admitted English spoken

BILHAC

🏫 🐓 🍽 Mas-Vidal Pierre et Michele SIMBILLE

19120 BILHAC
☎ 05 55 91 08 74
http://www.multimania.com/masvidal/contacts.html

Situated on the south slopes overlooking the Dordogne Valley, this establishment is within easy reach of many tourist areas. Three bedrooms, one with loggia, are situated on the top floor. Each has a shower and wc, plus heating and extra beds. There is a lounge with television, reading material and access to a shady park with garden furniture. A riding school is only 500m away. Near Curemonte, Collonge-la Rouge, Turenne, Beaulieu and Argentat. Price for half board 69 euros for two people. Open all year.
PRICES: s €34; d €38; t €46; dinner €13-€16 **ON SITE:** Bathing Swimming pool Hiking **NEARBY:** Horse riding (1km) Golf (10km) Fishing (3km) Tennis (5km) Sailing (25km) Railway station (3km) Shops (3km) **NOTES:** Pets admitted English spoken

continued

BORT-LES-ORGUES

░░░ Chambre d'hôtes Jean-Claude BOURDOUX
51, boulevard de la Nation, place de l'Eglise,
19110 BORT-LES-ORGUES
☎ 05 55 96 00 58 📠 05 55 96 00 58
Le Sancy & the Puy-Mary 40 km. Accommodation in a small village
on the banks of the Dordogne on the borders of the Cantal,
offering two bedrooms, one with a view of Les Orgues rock
formations and garden, the other overlooking the church in Bort.
The bedrooms have full en suite facilities. There is a very spacious
lounge with large windows and, outside, garden furniture and a
barbecue. Microlight initiation lessons can be arranged, or you can
go walking, mountain-biking, or fishing in the dam and river three
kilometres away. Open all year.
PRICES: s €29; d €37; t €46 **NEARBY:** Bathing (3km) Horse riding
(5km) Golf (20km) Fishing (3km) Swimming pool (1km) Hiking (3km)
Tennis (1km) Sailing (3km) **NOTES:** Pets admitted by arrangement

CHAMBERET

░░░ Chambre d'hôtes
Jean-François DESMOULIN-CATONN
2, route du Mont Gargan, 19370 CHAMBERET
☎ 05 55 98 34 26 📠 05 55 97 90 66
Jean-François and Nicole welcome you to their village home dating
from the end of the 18th century. The property, in the centre of
seasonal tourist attractions, consists of three bedrooms, a small
garden with garden furniture, and an arbour of centennial yew
trees. All bedrooms have shower, wc and kitchenette. There is a
day room with television and books. Breakfast is served to guests
in their rooms, and there is a restaurant on the premises. Open all
year.
PRICES: s €30; d €38; t €49 **ON SITE:** Bathing Fishing Hiking Tennis
NEARBY: Horse riding (4km) Golf (35km) Swimming pool (4km) Sailing
(10km) Railway station (30km) **NOTES:** No pets

CLERGOUX

░░░ ❦ 🍴 Leix Sylvie SOUDANT
19320 CLERGOUX
☎ 05 55 27 75 49 📠 05 55 27 75 49
e-mail: asoudant@fr.packardbell.org
Château de Sédières 5 km. This peaceful farm with character
offers four ground-floor bedrooms joined to the owners' house,
each room having its own separate entrance, shower room and
wc. Evening meals using farm produce are served. Horse riding
and harnessing on the premises. Near a lake and three kilometres
from a village. Price is 64 euros for four people. Open all year.
PRICES: s €30; d €42; t €53; extra person €10; dinner €14
ON SITE: Horse riding Fishing Hiking **NEARBY:** Bathing (5km) Tennis
(8km) Sailing (8km) Railway station (21km) Shops (3km) **NOTES:** Pets
admitted English spoken

COLLONGES-LA-ROUGE

░░░ Domaine de la Raze Eliane TATIEN
19500 COLLONGES-LA-ROUGE
☎ 05 55 25 48 16 & 05 55 25 49 00
e-mail: domainedelaraze@yahoo.fr
www.correze.net/laraze-jardinlaraze.free.fr
An old smallholding belonging to Eliane and Jean-Pierre, a few
steps from Collonges-la Rouge, and overlooking the majestic
village towers. Bedrooms are pleasant and bright, and have
matching curtains and counterpanes in restful colours. Each has a
private shower and wc. Among the attractions here is a painter's
garden composed of flowering trees and old, scented roses. There
is a large sitting room with fireplace, library, telephone, kitchen
area and a private swimming pool. Open all year.

PRICES: s €30; d €40; t €50 **ON SITE:** Swimming pool Hiking
NEARBY: Horse riding (6km) Golf (15km) Fishing (4km) Tennis (2km)
Sailing (20km) Railway station (6km) Shops (1km) **NOTES:** Pets
admitted English spoken

░░░ La Vigne Grande Gabrielle DIGIANNI
19500 COLLONGES LA ROUGE
☎ 05 55 25 39 20
e-mail: La-vigne-grande@infonie.fr
A barn conversion in one of the most beautiful villages in France,
set in charming, tranquil surroundings. There are five upstairs
bedrooms, each with its own bathroom and wc, and a living room
with TV, fireplace, library and telephone. Electric and wood-fuelled
heating. Picnics can be provided. There is a large private
swimming pool. Open all year.
PRICES: s €27; d €37; t €47; extra person €8 **ON SITE:** Hiking
NEARBY: Bathing (5km) Horse riding (5km) Golf (25km) Fishing (5km)
Swimming pool (3km) Tennis (2km) Sailing (25km) Railway station
(20km) Shops (4km) **NOTES:** Pets admitted English spoken

COMBRESSOL

░░░ ❦ 🍴 Les Chaussades Marcelle MIGNON
19250 COMBRESSOL
☎ 05 55 94 27 89 📠 05 55 94 27 89
A stone house typical of the Plateau de Millevaches offering two
bedrooms with private showers and one bedroom with a
bathroom. Situated near Meymac, a centre of contemporary art.
Riders are welcome. This is a good area for hiking. Open all year.
PRICES: d €34-€37; t €50; extra person €8; dinner €14
ON SITE: Fishing Hiking **NEARBY:** Bathing (4km) Horse riding (5km)
Golf (15km) Swimming pool (5km) Tennis (3km) Sailing (5km) Railway
station (6km) Shops (2km) **NOTES:** No pets

CUBLAC

░░░ ❦ 🍴 La Farandole Marie-Pierre PRAUDEL
19520 CUBLAC
☎ 05 55 85 19 79 📠 05 55 85 19 79
e-mail: humbert.guy@wanadoo.fr
http://perso.wanadoo.fr/fermeaubergelafarandole/
Farmers Marie-Pierre and Guy, who specialise in duck and cattle
breeding, welcome you to their fine, stone-built house which
dominates a valley in the Périgord-Limousin area. Four bedrooms
are available, one is a suite. There is a swimming pool in the
grounds. Close to Lascaux, Sarlat, Padirac and Rocamadour.
PRICES: s €34; d €40; t €49; HB €37; FB €44-€50; dinner €12-€30
ON SITE: Fishing Swimming pool Hiking **NEARBY:** Bathing (8km)
Horse riding (1km) Golf (10km) Sailing (10km) Railway station (6km)
Shops (6km) **NOTES:** Pets admitted English spoken

CUREMONTE

░░░ 🐔 🍴 Chambre d'hôtes Fernande RAYNAL
Le Bourg, 19500 CUREMONTE
☎ 05 55 25 35 01
Accommodation offered in the heart of a medieval city in one of
the most beautiful areas of France. Fernande, a farmer, offers
guests three very comfortable rustic-style rooms in a former barn;
each has its own shower room. Calves and ducks are reared on
this farm. Open all year, reservations necessary.
PRICES: s €32; d €48; t €64; HB €41; dinner €11-€17 **ON SITE:** Hiking
NEARBY: Bathing (12km) Horse riding (25km) Golf (25km) Fishing
(12km) Swimming pool (12km) Tennis (10km) Sailing (25km) Railway
station (12km) Shops (12km) Restaurant nearby **NOTES:** Pets admitted

continued

FORGES

¶¶¶ {O¦ La Souvigne Ian et Jacquie HOARE
19380 FORGES
☎ 05 55 28 63 99　🖷 05 55 28 65 62
e-mail: La.souvigne@wanadoo.fr
http://perso.wanadoo.fr/souvigne
Argentat 10 km. Discover this restored period residence belonging to Ian and Jacquie. Three bedrooms are available, two upstairs with private showers and wc and one on the ground floor with private bathroom and wc. Living room available for guests' use. Electric heating and library. Easy parking. Evening meal by reservation only. Open all year.
PRICES: s €25-€28; d €28-€31; extra person €9; dinner €13
ON SITE: Fishing Hiking Tennis　**NEARBY:** Bathing (11km)　Horse riding (11km)　Golf (15km)　Swimming pool (11km)　Sailing (15km)　Railway station (16km)　Shops (11km)　**NOTES:** No pets　English spoken

MANSAC

¶¶¶ {O¦ Le Seuil-Bas Noël FRAYSSE
19520 MANSAC
☎ 05 55 85 27 14 & 05 55 85 11 69
Self-catering rural accommodation and campsite on a farm on the border of the Perigord. Bedrooms are in a converted farm building. There is a swimming pool, tennis court and children's play area on the premises. Open all year.
PRICES: s €29; d €35; t €41; dinner €14　**ON SITE:** Children's play area Bathing Swimming pool Hiking Tennis　**NEARBY:** Horse riding (6km) Golf (12km)　Fishing (6km)　Sailing (12km)　Railway station (6km)　Shops (4km)　**NOTES:** No pets English spoken

MARCILLAC-LA-CROISILLE

¶¶¶ La Teyssonnière Jean-Claude CLEMENT
19320 MARCILLAC-LA-CROISILLE
☎ 05 55 27 58 99 & 06 73 36 96 79
Discover the 'house near the lake' in a hamlet set in wonderful Corrèzian scenery in the Dordogne Valley, where rest and tranquillity are guaranteed. Only 600 metres from the lake, this friendly residence has an inglenook fireplace with a wood-burning fire and four comfortable, elegantly decorated bedrooms, each with its own bathroom. There are four restaurants offering regional specialities two kilometres away. Price for four people: 49 euros. Open all year.
PRICES: s €29; d €35; t €42　**ON SITE:** Bathing Fishing Hiking Tennis Sailing　**NEARBY:** Horse riding (6km)　Swimming pool (8km)　Railway station (19km)　Shops (2km)　**NOTES:** No pets

MEYSSAC

¶¶¶ Grand Rue Jean-Luc LEBAS
La Dame Blanche, 19500 MEYSSAC
☎ 05 55 84 05 96 & 06 83 30 53 99
Collonges-la-Rouge 1 km. Rocamadour and Padirac 20 mn. Jean-Luc and Valerie are delighted to welcome you to their residence built of red sandstone which features a 17th-century tower. Situated in the old village of Meyssac, near Turenne and Curemonte, the accommodation consists of four spacious bedrooms. Price for four people: 61 euros. Open all year.
PRICES: s €35; d €40-€45; t €50-€55　**ON SITE:** Swimming pool Hiking Tennis　**NEARBY:** Bathing (10km)　Horse riding (5km)　Golf (15km) Fishing (10km)　Sailing (20km)　Railway station (20km)　**NOTES:** No pets English spoken

MILLEVACHES

¶¶¶ Le Magimel Maryline DESASSIS
19290 MILLEVACHES
☎ 05 55 95 61 24　🖷 05 55 95 17 27
This detached property with upstairs bedrooms is peacefully situated in the heart of the Plateau de Millevaches. A reception room plus an exterior terrace with garden furniture is available. Two kilometres from a village, with fishing and pleasant woodland walks. Open from 1 May to 30 September.
PRICES: s €31; d €35　**ON SITE:** Fishing Hiking　**NEARBY:** Bathing (15km)　Horse riding (15km)　Golf (10km)　Swimming pool (30km)　Tennis (10km)　Sailing (15km)　Railway station (15km)　Shops (11km)
NOTES: No pets

MONCEAUX-SUR-DORDOGNE

¶¶¶ 🐓 Saulières Marie-José LAFOND
19400 MONCEAUX-SUR-DORDOGNE
☎ 05 55 28 09 22　🖷 05 55 28 09 22
Dordogne River 200 m. The heart of the Dordogne Valley is the site of Marie-Jo and Jean-Marie's farm (cows and walnuts). The individually decorated bedrooms are situated in an extension of their contemporary house, each with shower and private wc. An equipped kitchen, lounge with fireplace, dining room and terrace are at the guests' disposal. There is a picnic area on the riverbank. Price for four people: 60 euros. Open all year.
PRICES: s €30; d €40; t €50　**ON SITE:** Bathing Fishing Hiking
NEARBY: Horse riding (6km)　Golf (20km)　Swimming pool (6km)　Tennis (3km)　Sailing (6km)　Railway station (40km)　Shops (7km)　**NOTES:** Pets admitted　English spoken

NAVES

¶¶¶ {O¦ Gourdinot Brunhild & Jean-Marc PERROT
19460 NAVES
☎ 05 55 27 08 93
Uzerches 25 km. Tulle 12 km. Brunhild and Jean-Marc's home would seem to be at the end of the world! There are three tastefully refined bedrooms upstairs: one with a large canopied bed and comfortable lounge, one with a double bed overlooking a loggia, the third with two single beds. There is a living room, library and TV and large kitchen with an open fireplace, where evening meals are taken. At this charming, typical Corrèze house guests can appreciate both tranquillity and local gastronomy. Brunhild can also give bread-making lessons, the delicious smell of which will delight you. Open all year.
PRICES: s €29; d €35-€40; t €46-€50; dinner €14　**ON SITE:** Hiking
NEARBY: Bathing (4km)　Horse riding (3km)　Golf (25km)　Fishing (2km) Swimming pool (3km)　Tennis (7km)　Sailing (4km)　Railway station (12km) Shops (5km)　**NOTES:** No pets　English spoken

NESPOULS

¶¶¶ {O¦ Belveyre Eloi et Marie-France LALLE
19600 NESPOULS
☎ 05 55 85 84 47
The calm and warm welcome of this restored old residence could be just the ticket! Here you will be treated like old friends. Cosy nights are guaranteed in the four tastefully decorated bedroom, each with their own shower rooms and wc. Price for four people: 45 euros. Open from 1 May to 30 September.
PRICES: s €27; d €30-€38; t €38-€45; dinner €15　**ON SITE:** Bathing Hiking　**NEARBY:** Horse riding (5km)　Golf (10km)　Fishing (5km) Swimming pool (10km)　Tennis (5km)　Sailing (5km)　Railway station (15km)　Shops (2km)　**NOTES:** No pets

NEUVIC

♦♦♦ i⊙i **Ferme de Becherave** André CHASTAING
Ferme de Becherave, 19160 NEUVIC
☎ 05 55 95 97 60

In the upper Corrèze, in an area renowned for mushrooms, this establishment is just a stone's throw from a lake with an enchanting view of the Puy-du-Dome and Cantal Mountains. An ideal place to discover the region and gastronomic cooking. There are three guest rooms, plus lounge with fireplace, television and electric central heating. Open all year.

PRICES: s €30; d €53; dinner €13 **NEARBY:** Bathing (2km) Horse riding (2km) Golf (2km) Fishing (2km) Hiking (1km) Sailing (2km) Railway station (20km) Shops (1km) **NOTES:** Pets admitted

♦♦♦ i⊙i **Raulhac** Jean-Jacques LARIVIERE
19160 NEUVIC
☎ 05 55 95 09 14
e-mail: COLETTE.LARIVIERE@wanadoo.fr

Four entirely new guest rooms built in a barn, with living room, library, and gas central heating. Situated in 10 hectares of grounds, guests can enjoy walking and fishing. Very near to Bort-les-Orgues and a lake with watersports.

PRICES: s €29; d €40; t €53; dinner €13 **ON SITE:** Fishing
NEARBY: Bathing (4km) Horse riding (4km) Golf (5km) Swimming pool (30km) Tennis (4km) Sailing (4km) Railway station (30km) Shops (4km) **NOTES:** No pets English spoken

NOAILHAC

♦♦♦ i⊙i **La Maison des Etoiles** Jacqueline CICUREL
Le Genestal, 19500 NOAILHAC
☎ 05 55 25 31 46 & 06 12 23 86 24 📠 05 55 25 31 46
e-mail: la.maison.des.etoiles@wanadoo.fr
http://maison.etoiles.free.fr

On a hill, commanding an exceptional view, 1.5 km from the village of Noailhac stands La Maison des Etoiles. This very peaceful establishment is an old farmhouse with a red-stone outbuilding, carefully renovated in keeping with tradition. Each guest room is different and has been decorated to a high standard; all have a shower room and wc. Holiday tax is included in the price.

PRICES: s €32; d €40; t €48; extra person €8; HB €28-€45; dinner €16 **ON SITE:** Hiking **NEARBY:** Bathing (10km) Horse riding (10km) Golf (15km) Fishing (3km) Swimming pool (6km) Tennis (4km) Sailing (4km) Railway station (12km) Shops (6km) **NOTES:** No pets English spoken

OBJAT

♦♦♦ **Chambre d'hôtes** Henri Pierre GUIONY
10 avenue Georges Clémenceau, 19130 OBJAT
☎ 05 55 25 00 17 & 06 82 31 86 03
e-mail: guiony@club-internet.fr

Pierre Guiony provides a warm welcome to his fine mansard-style family home, dating from the beginning of the 20th century. This totally renovated property offers a choice of three spacious bedrooms; one double room can accommodate a couple plus three children. There is a large living room. Your host can help you plan various outings and walks around Objat. Close to Limousin, the Auvergne, the Quercy and Perigord. The prehistoric sites of the Dordogne and Vézère Valleys are less than one hour away.

PRICES: s €38; d €44; t €53; extra person €11 **ON SITE:** Bathing Fishing Swimming pool Hiking Tennis **NEARBY:** Horse riding (5km) Golf (15km) Sailing (15km) **NOTES:** No pets

Prices are given in Euros €1 = £0.62
at the time of going to press

PALAZINGES

♦♦♦ i⊙i **Chambre d'hôtes** Dominique et Nicole CURE
Le Bourg, 19190 PALAZINGES
☎ 05 55 84 63 44

An exceptional view and five spacious guest bedrooms are offered at this restored barn full of old-world charm, each equipped with shower and wc. Dinner is served for residents. Close to Tulle and Brive. 390 euros per week for two people.

PRICES: s €31; d €39; t €46; dinner €13 **ON SITE:** Hiking
NEARBY: Bathing (4km) Horse riding (4km) Golf (4km) Fishing (4km) Tennis (4km) Sailing (4km) Shops (4km) **NOTES:** Pets admitted English spoken

SARROUX

♦♦♦ 🐾 i⊙i **Puy de Bort** Roger VENNAT
19110 SARROUX
☎ 05 55 96 05 10

Stay on Roger and Odette's organic beef and dairy farm. Four guest rooms have been fitted out with private wc and shower rooms. There is a living room available and you can try some of the farm produce. Views of the Orgues rock formations, Puy Mary and le Sancy. Route from Bort-les-Orgues: D922 or D979, follow the circuit of the Orgues. Price for four people: 54 euros. Open all year.

PRICES: s €28; d €37; t €45; extra person €8; dinner €13
NEARBY: Bathing (5km) Horse riding (12km) Golf (30km) Fishing (5km) Swimming pool (5km) Hiking (1km) Tennis (5km) Sailing (5km) Railway station (5km) Shops (5km) **NOTES:** Pets admitted by arrangement

ST-BONNET-L'ENFANTIER

♦♦♦ 🐓 i⊙i **La Borde** Nadine BUGE
19410 ST-BONNET-L'ENFANTIER
☎ 05 55 73 72 44 📠 05 55 73 72 44

In a green and peaceful setting, five kilometres from the A20, Nadine will provide a warm welcome to her geese-rearing farm, surrounded by walnut groves. There are five upstairs bedrooms, each with full bathroom facilities. At the dining table you will discover a traditional cuisine in a warm and friendly family atmosphere. Treat yourself and recharge your batteries! Kitchen, board games and outdoor games on the premises. In winter Nadine organises foie gras weekends. Rate for two people starting from two nights is 36 euros (15% reduction). Rate for half board starting from two nights is 32 euros per person. Open all year except 10 September to 25 October.

PRICES: d €42; HB €35; dinner €14 **ON SITE:** Children's play area Hiking **NEARBY:** Bathing (10km) Horse riding (20km) Golf (20km) Fishing (10km) Swimming pool (10km) Tennis (3km) Railway station (15km) Shops (3km) **NOTES:** No pets

ST-CERNIN-DE-LARCHE

♦♦♦ i⊙i **Le Moulin Vieux de la Roche**
Michel et Danielle ANDRIEUX
19600 ST-CERNIN-DE-LARCHE
☎ 05 55 85 40 92 📠 05 55 85 34 66

There is independent access to the six bedrooms at this 13th-century cistercian mill belonging to Danielle and Michel. Each has a TV, bath and wc, and there is a suite with shower and wc. Each has been comfortably and tastefully decorated by Danielle. The large fireplaces and old earthenware tiles accentuate the charm of this old restored barn, dating from 1693. Copious breakfasts are served in the large dining room. The property overlooks the picturesque village of Laroche and the cliffs of the Cirque de la Doux. Open from 1 March to 31 October.

PRICES: s €43-€68; d €49-€68; t €61-€75; dinner €15-€19

continued

ON SITE: Hiking **NEARBY:** Bathing (1km) Horse riding (5km) Golf (5km) Fishing (1km) Swimming pool (1km) Tennis (3km) Sailing (1km) Railway station (3km) Shops (1km) **NOTES:** Pets admitted English spoken

ST-CHAMANT

⬛⬛⬛ ⫶◯⫶ ♿ Chambre d'hôtes
Madeleine et Germain COUTAL
Le Bourg, 19380 ST-CHAMANT
☎ 05 55 28 05 46 📠 05 55 28 84 03
Marie-Madeleine and Germain are the owners of this large house situated in a very quiet, old region of the village. There are six bedrooms with private shower and wc, one of which has access for guests with disabilities. Two have private living rooms. A communal lounge with TV is available, as are evening meals upon demand. Open from 1 April to 30 November.
PRICES: s €30; d €37; t €55; HB €33; dinner €14 **ON SITE:** Hiking
NEARBY: Bathing (6km) Horse riding (6km) Golf (25km) Fishing (6km) Swimming pool (6km) Tennis (4km) Sailing (20km) Railway station (24km) **NOTES:** No pets

ST-JULIEN-PRES-BORT

⬛⬛⬛ ⫶◯⫶ La Garenne à Nuzejoux Eric MESNIL
19110 ST-JULIEN-PRES-BORT
☎ 05 55 94 83 83 📠 05 55 94 83 83
e-mail: lagarenne@minitel.net www.la.garenne.fr.st
Bort-les-Orgues 6 km. In the heart of the Artense, on the borders of three departments, you will meet Eric and Martine. Their period residence, set in wooded parkland, has a completely renovated interior, comprising four tasteful bedrooms equipped with shower, private wc, veranda and living area. Guests also have use of a TV, games and the private swimming pool. Fans of fishing and nature, your hosts will help you discover local beauty spots and gastronomic delights. Variable rates. Low season reductions. Price for four people is 70 euros.
PRICES: s €35; d €45; t €56; dinner €14-€16 **ON SITE:** Children's play area Swimming pool Hiking **NEARBY:** Bathing (5km) Horse riding (3km) Golf (20km) Fishing (5km) Tennis (2km) Sailing (5km) Railway station (20km) Shops (7km) **NOTES:** No pets

ST-MATHURIN-LEOBAZEL

⬛⬛⬛ ♥ ⫶◯⫶ Mialaret Guy SEGOL
19430 ST-MATHURIN-LEOBAZEL
☎ 05 55 28 50 09 📠 05 55 28 54 00
This characterful house is situated in the centre of an equestrian farm. The six guest rooms each have their own shower and wc, and electric heating. There is a large dining room, lounge, phone and garden furniture. Price for four people: 69 euros. Open all year.
PRICES: s €35; d €47; t €58; HB €35; FB €44; dinner €11
ON SITE: Children's play area Horse riding Fishing Hiking
NEARBY: Bathing (5km) Swimming pool (10km) Tennis (5km) Railway station (24km) Shops (5km) **NOTES:** Pets admitted English spoken

TROCHE

⬛⬛⬛ ♥ ⫶◯⫶ La Petite Brunie
Jacques et Martine CROUZILLAC
19230 TROCHE
☎ 05 55 73 34 17 📠 05 55 73 57 25
e-mail: martine.crouzillac@netcourrier.com
www.isasite.net/la-petite-brunie
Pompadour 3 km. Right in the centre of the Limousin, near Périgord, Jacques and Martine, young farmers (cattle and apples), can accommodate you in an entirely renovated independent building. There are five rooms, all comfortably equipped with individual shower and wc and electric heating. Guests can sit

beside the open fireplace or in the shared living room. The village is three kilometres away. The grounds include a three-hectare lake for fishing. Price for four people: 58 euros. Open all year.
PRICES: s €29-€37; d €34-€41; dinner €16 **ON SITE:** Fishing Hiking
NEARBY: Horse riding (2km) Swimming pool (3km) Tennis (2km) Railway station (3km) Shops (3km) **NOTES:** Pets admitted

TUDEILS

⬛⬛⬛ ♥ Château de la Salvanie Edmond POUJADE
19120 TUDEILS
☎ 05 55 91 53 43
In this château, where one can appreciate the peace of the countryside and the period charm of the building, there are three guest rooms and one suite with wc, washbasin and shower. There is also a living room, TV, fireplace, lounge, microwave and refrigerator. Guests can sit out on the terrace. Price for four people: 68 euros. Open from 1 April to 1 December.
PRICES: s €41; d €50; t €59; extra person €9 **NEARBY:** Bathing (8km) Fishing (8km) Swimming pool (8km) Hiking (8km) Tennis (8km) Sailing (8km) Shops (8km) **NOTES:** No pets

TURENNE

⬛⬛⬛ Au Bontemps Jean-Pierre SOUSTRE
19500 TURENNE ☎ 05 55 85 97 72
Discover an old, peaceful, isolated farm in one of the most beautiful villages of France, on the edge of Quercy. Accommodation consists of six guest rooms with private shower rooms (washbasin, shower, wc) in a barn restoration, plus living room, TV and library. Breakfast served in the owners' dining room. Price is 60 euros for four people. Open all year.
PRICES: s €29; d €39; t €49; extra person €11 **ON SITE:** Hiking
NEARBY: Bathing (12km) Horse riding (13km) Golf (15km) Fishing (5km) Swimming pool (10km) Tennis (8km) Sailing (12km) Railway station (15km) Shops (3km) **NOTES:** No pets

⬛⬛⬛ La Croix de Belonie
Catherine COUVRAT-DESVERGNES
19500 TURENNE ☎ 05 55 85 97 07 & 06 10 61 46 92
e-mail: bcouvrat@aol.com
Come and stay in a recently restored former bell founder's residence just 400 metres from the historic town of Turenne, listed as one of the most beautiful in France. Here on the hill surrounded by meadows, is a refined residence, with antique furniture, tasteful décor and flower arrangements. Your hostess, being very fond of art, history and nature, will be able to guide you in your discovery of the region's treasures. Panoramic view, large garden, swimming pool, TV lounge, and local reading material. Open all year.
PRICES: s €38; d €45 **ON SITE:** Fishing Swimming pool Hiking
NEARBY: Bathing (10km) Horse riding (10km) Golf (10km) Tennis (5km) Sailing (10km) Railway station (17km) Shops (1km)
NOTES: No pets English spoken

VARS-SUR-ROSEIX

⬛⬛⬛ Le Logis Varsois Annick VAN CAUWENBERG
19130 VARS-SUR-ROSEIX ☎ 05 55 25 23 61
Jean and Annick welcome you into their completely restored 19th-century property. There are five upstairs rooms with individual shower and wc, a large room with open fireplace, a library, electric heating and a car park. The nearest restaurant is just 50 metres away. Price per week variable. Price for four people normally 61 euros. Open from 1 April to 30 October.
PRICES: s €32; d €38; t €46 **ON SITE:** Hiking **NEARBY:** Bathing (5km) Horse riding (8km) Golf (20km) Fishing (5km) Swimming pool (5km) Tennis (5km) Sailing (30km) Railway station (25km) Shops (3km)
NOTES: Pets admitted

continued

VOUTEZAC

꧁ ⫍⊘⫎ Sajueix Jean-Charles RELIER
Sajueix 14, 19130 VOUTEZAC
☎ 05 55 25 80 70 📠 05 55 25 80 70
Pompadour 14 km. 'La Gentilhommière' is the charming home of
Jean-Charles and is situated in a small village in the heart of the
Vézère and Loyre valley. There are three upstairs rooms, one with
a suite. This is the ideal place to laze around and enjoy good food.
Near Pompadour and Objat. Exit 45 from the A20 motorway
coming from Limoges or exit 50 coming from Toulouse. Canoes
and kayaks five kilometres away. Open all year.
PRICES: s €34-€35; d €37-€40; t €48-€51; extra person €11; HB €32-€34;
dinner €14 **ON SITE:** Hiking **NEARBY:** Bathing (6km) Horse riding
(15km) Golf (27km) Fishing (2km) Swimming pool (7km) Tennis (6km)
Sailing (30km) Railway station (7km) Shops (2km) **NOTES:** Pets
admitted

CREUSE

ALLEYRAT

꧁ ❦ Ourdeaux Patrice et Guylaine D'HIVER
23200 ALLEYRAT
☎ 05 55 66 29 65 & 06 72 46 44 63
Aubusson 7 km. In the weaving capital of Aubusson, Patrice and
Guylaine have converted an old farm building, on 75 hectares of
cattle-rearing ground. The accommodation on their traditional
farm consists of four double rooms on the ground floor and
upstairs two family rooms (one for 4 people, one for 3 people).
There is electric heating, a terrace and private parking. Meals are
prepared with their own farm produce. There is a pony for
children, swimming pool and bicycles. Price for four people is 75
euros. Open all year.
PRICES: s €41; d €43-€50; t €64-€69 **ON SITE:** Horse riding Fishing
Swimming pool Bicycle hire **NEARBY:** Tennis (7km) Railway station
(7km) Shops (7km) Restaurant nearby **NOTES:** Pets admitted

BANIZE

꧁ ⫍⊘⫎ Meyzoux Maryse GUY
Banize, 23120 VALLIERES
☎ 05 55 66 07 17
Four guest rooms have been created in an old manor house
situated in the middle of the countryside. These consist of one
room for four people with private bathroom, one single room with
private shower room, one double room with private bathroom and
one double room with private shower room. There is a living room
with a dining area, plus TV and library. There is also a TV in all the
rooms, and central heating. Set in parkland with cross-country
skiing 18 km away. Restaurant 10 km away with vegetarian menu
on demand. Children aged five upwards: 9 euros. Open from
February to October.
PRICES: s €27; d €44; extra person €17; dinner €15 **NEARBY:** Bathing
(25km) Horse riding (3km) Fishing (5km) Swimming pool (14km) Tennis
(5km) Sailing (25km) Bicycle hire (3km) Railway station (14km) Shops
(4km) **NOTES:** No pets

⫍⊘⫎
Places with this symbol serve table d'hôtes
evening meals - remember to book in advance

For further information on these and
other chambres d'hôtes, consult
the Gîtes de France website
www.gites-de-france.fr

BETETE

꧁ Château de Moisse Simone et Ignace DEBOUTTE
23270 BETETE
☎ 05 55 80 84 25 📠 05 55 80 84 25
This château, situated on a hill in wooded parkland of 25
hectares, with a fine view of the pastoral countryside of
Creuse, has four guest rooms to offer. Each bedroom has a
private bathroom and, in addition at the guests' disposal,
there is a dining room, a TV lounge, a terrace and a car park.
Gas heating. Restaurant 3.5 km away. Bikes to rent. Open
from 1 June to 30 September. Book in advance.
PRICES: s €69; d €76; t €105 **NEARBY:** Bathing (8km) Horse riding
(8km) Golf (16km) Fishing (1km) Tennis (4km) Shops (15km)
NOTES: No pets English spoken

BOUSSAC

꧁ ⫍⊘⫎ La Courtepointe Françoise GROS
3, rue des Loges, 23600 BOUSSAC
☎ 05 55 65 80 09 📠 05 55 65 80 09
e-mail: courtepointe@wanadoo.fr Pro.wanadoo.fr/courtepointe/

Discover this 18th-century residence converted into four guest
rooms. Downstairs there is a living room/lounge with TV and
library. Upstairs there is the 'Verdure' room with a double bed and
a child's bed, plus shower room and wc. Bedroom 2 'Rose' has
three single beds, bathroom and wc. Suite 3 is called 'Mauve and
Muguet' and has a double bed and two singles, bathroom and wc.
Bedroom 4 'Jardin d'artiste' is on the ground floor and has its own
entrance, a double bed, shower room and access to a kitchen is
possible. Central heating. There is a garage 200 metres away, and
a terrace with garden furniture. Guests may also use the garden
and car port. Restaurant close by. Evening meals available for
residents. Open all year.
PRICES: s €33; d €46; extra person €13; dinner €14 **ON SITE:** Children's
play area Tennis Bicycle hire **NEARBY:** Bathing (10km) Horse riding
(8km) Fishing (1km) Swimming pool (10km) Sailing (20km)
NOTES: Pets admitted CC English spoken

BUSSIERE-SAINT-GEORGES

꧁ Couchardon Edith GUILBERT
23600 BUSSIERE ST GEORGES
☎ 05 55 82 78 01 & 05 55 82 04 17
On the edge of two tree-lined lakes, you will discover Edith's
extremely comfortable guest rooms in a converted farm building
dating from the last century. The quality of the surroundings will
contribute to a very convivial stay. There are four bedrooms on the
ground floor - each has a double bed and private bathroom - and
a lounge-dining room with TV and library. Restaurants five
kilometres away. Open all year.
PRICES: s €38; d €46; t €53; extra person €8 **ON SITE:** Fishing
NEARBY: Bathing (30km) Horse riding (15km) Swimming pool (5km)
Shops (5km) **NOTES:** Pets admitted

CHAMBON-SAINTE-CROIX

♦♦♦ ⏲ Chambre d'hôtes Antoine PICARD
2 rue de la Mairie, Le Bourg, 23220
☎ 05 55 89 24 80 📠 05 55 89 24 80
Fresselines 7 km. Crozant 14 km. La Celle Dunoise 6 km. This old property dates from the last century, and is located near the sites where the impressionists of Crozant lived. There are two double rooms with child's beds and one room for four; each has a TV and private shower room. Guests can use the living room with lounge area, formal gardens and terrace (garden furniture). Central heating. Restaurants at six and twelve kilometres. Price for four: 69 euros. Children over 12 years: 7.5 euros. Open all year.
PRICES: s €38; d €41; t €49; dinner €15 **NEARBY:** Bathing (8km) Fishing (4km) Swimming pool (20km) Tennis (12km) Sailing (10km) Shops (12km) **NOTES:** Pets admitted

CHAMPSANGLARD CREUSE

♦♦♦♦ Le Villard Corinne et Gérard LEROY-HUET
23220 CHAMPSANGLARD CREUSE
☎ 06 82 07 14 15
In the heart of the three lakes area in the middle of a country park, you will find this former hunting lodge dating from the early 19th century. The four comfortable bedrooms have private bathrooms, TV and panoramic views over the countryside. Facilities include a heated swimming pool and private parking. Restaurant 3 km away. Open all year.
PRICES: s €68; d €76 **NEARBY:** Bathing (2km) Fishing (2km) Sailing (20km) Tennis (5km) Horse riding (5km) Shops (5km)

FRESSELINES

♦♦♦ ⏲ Confolent Danielle DEMACHY-DANTIN
23450 FRESSELINES
☎ 05 55 89 70 83
This very fine Creuse house dates from the 17th and 18th centuries, and is located on the site immortalised by Claude Monet, where the two Creuse rivers meet. There are two double rooms with bathroom and wc, and one single room with shower and wc. Central heating. Guests have use of a living room, lounge with TV and library, and the car park. Restaurant ten kilometres away. Open all year.
PRICES: s €53; d €60-€73; extra person €15; dinner €21
ON SITE: Bathing Fishing **NEARBY:** Horse riding (10km) Tennis (1km) Railway station (30km) Shops (10km) **NOTES:** Pets admitted English spoken

GENOUILLAC

♦♦♦ Montfargeaud Annie AUDOUX
20 Montfargeaud, Petite Marie, 23350 GENOUILLAC
☎ 05 55 80 85 60 📠 05 55 80 75 73

An old farm, on the border of the department, halfway between Guéret and La Chatter, has been converted into four rooms and a

suite. This property, in a peaceful village, comprises three rooms for three people, one double room and one suite for four people. Each of these has a bathroom, wc, telephone and TV. There is also a living room and electric heating. Car park. Open all year.
PRICES: s €40; d €44; t €56; 4 pers €61 **NEARBY:** Bathing (1km) Horse riding (10km) Golf (12km) Fishing (1km) Swimming pool (12km) Tennis (2km) Shops (2km) Restaurant nearby **NOTES:** Pets admitted English spoken

GENTIOUX

♦♦♦♦ ⏲ Pallier la Commanderie
Yolande et Yves GOMICHON
23340 GENTIOUX
☎ 05 55 67 91 73 📠 05 55 67 91 73
An old, 18th-century knights' fortress with five guest rooms. The ground floor consists of living room, lounge (TV, library), two double bedrooms with bathroom and wc. On the first floor there is one double room with bathroom and wc, plus a further double room with shower and wc. On the second floor there is one room with three single beds and a child's bed, bathroom and wc. Children aged 2-8 charged at half rate. Central heating and open fireplaces. In the landscaped grounds, there is a car park, medieval garden, lake and small fishing ground for children. Drinks not included in the price of meals. Restaurants 9 km away. Cross-country skiing nearby. Open from 1 April to 15 November.
PRICES: s €42; d €52; t €58; extra person €10; dinner €15
ON SITE: Children's play area Fishing **NEARBY:** Bathing (13km) Horse riding (10km) Golf (10km) Swimming pool (27km) Tennis (9km) Sailing (13km) Bicycle hire (9km) Shops (4km) **NOTES:** Pets admitted

GENTIOUX-PIGEROLLES

♦♦♦ ❦ ⏲ Ferme des Nautas
François et Danielle CHATOUX
Pigerolles, 23340
☎ 05 55 67 90 68 📠 05 55 67 93 12
e-mail: les_nautas@wanadoo.fr perso.wanadoo.fr/les.nautas
This character property is situated in shady grounds on the Plateau of Millevaches, on a farm which mainly rears livestock (cattle, sheep and saddleback pigs). There is one bedroom with two double beds, shower room and wc, and one bedroom with one double bed, two single beds, shower and wc. There is also one room sleeping four (two double beds) with shower room and wc in an independent house situated 20 metres from the main building. Guests may use the living room with TV and reading material.Central heating. Car park. Farm-inn on the premises. Cross-country skiing. Price for four people: 57 euros. Open all year.
PRICES: s €33; d €41; t €48; extra person €10; dinner €14
ON SITE: Fishing Bicycle hire **NEARBY:** Bathing (15km) Horse riding (15km) Golf (10km) Tennis (15km) Sailing (15km) Shops (7km) Restaurant nearby **NOTES:** Pets admitted English spoken

Prices are given in Euros €1 = £0.62
at the time of going to press

Ask the proprietor for directions
when booking

continued

LIMOUSIN

GUERET

♥♥♥ Beausoleil - Le Cottage Jeanine ROYER
23000 GUERET
☎ 05 55 81 90 96
Situated at Chabnières in the Parc à Loups, near the old village of Coussières, 300 metres from the lake of Courtille, is this individual house of character. There are four double bedrooms (one grade 2, three grade 3) and a living room with a lounge area, local reading material and central heating. The grounds are laid out, with a covered terrace and enclosed car park. A restaurant is 300 metres away. Evening meals are possible for residents if reserved (price 15 euros). Open all year.
PRICES: s €38; d €49; t €73 **ON SITE:** Bathing Fishing Tennis Sailing Bicycle hire **NEARBY:** Horse riding (3km) Swimming pool (2km) Railway station (3km) Shops (3km) **NOTES:** Pets admitted on request

JOUILLAT

♥♥♥ 🍽 Villecoulon Danielle et Gilbert GIRARDOT
23220 JOUILLAT
☎ 05 55 51 24 47 📠 05 55 51 24 47
e-mail: gi-gir@clubinternet.fr
Guéret 18 km. Villecoulon, near the lakes, is the location of this turn-of-the-century residence, featuring three double rooms (one double bed with a child's bed in each room) and en suite bathrooms and wc. There is a living room with fireplace and a lounge with TV, open fire and library. Central heating. Landscaped grounds. Car park. Restaurant 1 km away. Open all year.
PRICES: s €30; d €35; extra person €11 **NEARBY:** Bathing (2km) Horse riding (18km) Fishing (2km) Swimming pool (18km) Tennis (2km) Shops (11km) **NOTES:** Pets admitted English spoken

LA CELLE-DUNOISE

♥♥♥ 🍽 L'Age Henry et Béatrice N'GUYEN
L'Ecole Buissonnière, 23800 LA CELLE-DUNOISE
☎ 05 55 89 23 49 📠 05 55 89 27 62
e-mail: ecolebuissoniere@wanadoo.fr
www.ecole-buissoniere.tm.fr
Take time off at Béatrice and Henry's countryside property in the heart of the Creuse valley. There are three bedrooms with mezzanine on the ground floor. Bedrooms 1 and 3 have one single bed and two children's beds per room; bedroom 2 has two single beds and two children's beds. Upstairs there is a suite with one double bed and two children's beds. All have private bathrooms. There is a relaxing lounge with reading material and games, and a small kitchen. The garden has an ornamental pond and perennial plants. Restaurant four kilometres away. Enclosed car park. Fishing boats, canoes and bikes for rent. Ideal for families and activity holidays (walking, fishing, canoes, kayaks and cycling). Tariff varies according to length of stay. Reservations recommended. Price for four people: 65 euros. Open all year except Christmas.
PRICES: s €34; d €42; t €53; dinner €14 **ON SITE:** Bicycle hire **NEARBY:** Bathing (4km) Horse riding (4km) Fishing (1km) Swimming pool (18km) Tennis (4km) Sailing (6km) Shops (4km) **NOTES:** No pets English spoken

LA CHAPELLE-SAINT-MARTIAL

♥♥♥♥ Chambre d'hôtes Alain COUTURIER
Le Bourg, La Chapelle Saint-Martial, 23250 PONTARION
☎ 05 55 64 54 12 📠 05 55 64 54 12
This detached house has stacks of character. On the ground floor there is a living room and a double bedroom with a view of the garden and swimming pool. There are two further doubles on the first and second floors; all rooms have a colour TV, private shower and wc. Central heating. There is a terrace with garden furniture, and a restaurant 6 km away. Open all year.

PRICES: s €34-€53; d €40-€58; extra person €9
ON SITE: Swimming pool **NEARBY:** Bathing (10km) Horse riding (6km) Golf (30km) Fishing (4km) Tennis (4km) Sailing (25km) Bicycle hire (13km) Shops (8km) **NOTES:** Small pets by arrangement English spoken

LE GRAND-BOURG

♥♥♥ Montenon Michel et Martine LIMOUSIN
23240 LE GRAND-BOURG
☎ 05 55 81 30 00 📠 05 55 81 36 33
e-mail: montenon@wanadoo.fr ferme-de-montenon.com
Martine and Michel Limousin welcome you warmly to their character property situated on a hill overlooking the Gartempe valley. They are pleased to offer one bedroom for three people, two double rooms, and two rooms for four people. There is a shower and wc in each bedroom. There is also a living room (library, board games and TV), plus an adjoining area for table tennis. You can use the swimming pool, and in the evening you can enjoy local produce (cheeses, foie gras, and preserves), served at the country inn. Rates: children 5-11 euros according to age. Price for four people is 68 euros. Open all year except January.
PRICES: s €29; d €40; t €54; dinner €14 **ON SITE:** Swimming pool Bicycle hire **NEARBY:** Bathing (10km) Horse riding (15km) Fishing (1km) Tennis (5km) Sailing (15km) Railway station (15km) Shops (6km) Restaurant nearby **NOTES:** No pets English spoken

LUSSAT

♥♥♥ 🐑 🍽 Chambre d'hôtes
Claude et Nadine RIBBE
Puy-Haut, 23170 LUSSAT
☎ 05 55 82 13 07 📠 05 55 82 13 07
In the heart of the village of Puy-Haut is this fine 17th-century restoration of a 13th-century building. On the ground floor there is a living room, lounge (TV, library) and one double bedroom. Upstairs there are three double rooms and one room for three people. All have en suite bathrooms and wc. There is also electric heating. A small kitchen is available. The grounds are laid out with a children's play area and a private swimming pool surrounded by a garden equipped with sun beds. The casino at Evaux-les-Bains is 10 km away. Open from 1 April to 1 November. Other periods by reservation.
PRICES: s €49; d €54-€58; t €67; extra person €9; dinner €17 **ON SITE:** Children's play area Swimming pool **NEARBY:** Bathing (15km) Fishing (4km) Tennis (4km) Shops (7km) **NOTES:** Pets admitted

MERINCHAL

♥♥♥ 🐑 Le Montaurat Didier et Odile LABAS
23420 MERINCHAL
☎ 05 55 67 25 99 & 06 83 05 11 88 📠 05 55 67 25 99
Accommodation available in a detached stone house comprising a living room and one bedroom sleeping three with en suite bathroom and wc on the ground floor. Upstairs there is one double room and one room sleeping three people, each with separate bathrooms and wc. A lounge with TV and local reading material is available, as is a kitchen. Central heating, grounds, car park. Restaurant 3 km. Price for four people: 62 euros. Open all year.
PRICES: s €35; d €44; t €53; extra person €9 **ON SITE:** Children's play area **NEARBY:** Bathing (15km) Horse riding (10km) Fishing (4km) Swimming pool (30km) Tennis (4km) Bicycle hire (4km) Shops (4km) **NOTES:** Pets admitted

Use the atlas at the back of the guide to locate your chambre d'hôtes

continued

PONTARION

⚍ ♿ Château Gaillard Roger et Lorette MAYNE
3, Château-Gaillard, 23250 PONTARION
☎ 05 55 64 52 76
There is independent access to the three guest rooms at this property, comprising two grade 2 bedrooms for four people with shower and wc, plus one grade 3 room for three people, with access for guests with disabilities. Guests may use the living room and lounge (with TV and library) on the ground floor. Electric central heating. Car park and barbecue. Self catering is possible. Restaurant 500 metres away. Children from five years: 7.5 euros. Four people: 50 euros. Open all year.
PRICES: s €27; d €35; t €43; extra person €7.5 **ON SITE:** Fishing
NEARBY: Bathing (6km) Horse riding (12km) Swimming pool (23km)
Tennis (9km) Sailing (25km) Shops (1km) **NOTES:** No pets

ROCHES

⚍ ⎮◎⎮ La Vergnolle Nelly et Philippe BOURET
23270 ROCHES
☎ 05 55 80 81 97 & 06 63 42 23 14 ▤ 05 55 80 88 12
Nelly and Philippe are your hosts in this pleasant residence offering four delightful bedrooms, each with a TV. There are three double rooms (two rooms with double bed and one with two single beds), and one bedroom for three people (one double and one single bed). Guests may use the living room with TV and reading material, the formal gardens, car park and the children's play area. There is a swimming pool, lakes and several farm animals on the premises. Bicycles and fishing rods are available at no extra charge. Child's menu (less than 12 years): 6 euros. No charge for child's room under four years old. Prices varying according to season. Open all year.
PRICES: s €36; d €43; t €54; extra person €11; dinner €13-€17
ON SITE: Children's play area Fishing Swimming pool
NEARBY: Bathing (5km) Horse riding (12km) Golf (25km) Tennis (5km)
Sailing (20km) Bicycle hire (5km) Railway station (22km) Shops (5km)
NOTES: Pets admitted English spoken

ST-BARD

⚍ ⎮◎⎮ Château de Chazepaud
Patrick et Madeleine ALBRIGHT
23260 ST-BARD
☎ 05 55 67 33 03 & 06 83 12 58 61 ▤ 05 55 67 30 25
e-mail: albrightpatrick@aol.com
This neo-renaissance chateau set in a hundred-year-old park offers a period dining room and a Louis XVI lounge with TV on the ground floor. Upstairs there is one room with a double bed and shower room, two bedrooms with a double and a single bed with bathroom, plus a suite for four people. On the second floor there is one room for three people, offering one double bed, a single bed and bathroom. Central heating and car park. There is a covered, heated swimming pool, a gym and childrens' games. Restaurant 2 km away. Price for four people: 85-110 euros. Open from April to October and school holidays.
PRICES: s €45-€70; d €55-€80; t €70-€95; extra person €15; dinner €20
ON SITE: Children's play area Swimming pool Bicycle hire
NEARBY: Bathing (15km) Horse riding (8km) Fishing (1km) Tennis
(8km) Sailing (15km) Shops (8km) **NOTES:** Pets admitted

ST-DIZIER-LEYRENNE

⚍ Le Masbeau Jean-Pierre PELEGE
23400 ST-DIZIER-LEYRENNE
☎ 05 55 64 40 11 ▤ 05 55 64 46 42
e-mail: j-p.pelege@wanadoo.fr
Bourganeuf 10 km. Nicole and Jean-Pierre have converted an outbuilding on their bourgeois estate, dating from the beginning of

the 20th century, into three bedrooms of character. The ground floor provides a living room with TV, and on the first floor there is a living room with library, plus three bedrooms. The first two of these are double rooms, with two double beds and two children's beds in each, and the other has just a double bed. Both have private shower rooms and wc. There is electric heating, a games room and use of a kitchen. Outside there are landscaped grounds, a swimming pool, a garage and a car park. Restaurant 4 km away. Open from March to November.
PRICES: s €34; d €38; t €46; 4 pers €53 **ON SITE:** Swimming pool
NEARBY: Bathing (2km) Fishing (2km) Tennis (2km) Shops (2km)
NOTES: No pets English spoken

ST-ETIENNE-DE-FURSAC

⚍ ⎮◎⎮ Chambre d'hôtes
Dominique et Josette BASSE
44, Paulhac, 23290 St ETIENNE-DE-FURSAC
☎ 05 55 63 36 02 & 06 67 91 52 28
Fortified churches and castles, tour Roman Creuse. This 18th-century vicarage, restored in the early 20th century, belongs to Josette and Dominique, and is near the Templar knights' command post. It is set in a park protected from the outside world, with an uninterrupted view of the Monts d'Ambazac. Accommodation comprises four non-smoking bedrooms. On the first floor bedroom 1 has two single beds, a shower and wc, and bedroom 2 has one double bed, a shower and wc. Second floor rooms comprise bedrooms 3 and 4, each with double beds, bathroom and wc. Extra bed and TV on request. There is a non-smoking living room, a smokers' lounge, library and TV. Gardens laid out with terrace, garden furniture, children's games and car park. Price for children over four years: 12 euros. Open all year except February. Reservations only from 1 November to 31 March.
PRICES: s €54-€63; d €60-€69; dinner €17
ON SITE: Children's play area **NEARBY:** Bathing (5km) Horse
riding (5km) Fishing (3km) Swimming pool (5km) Tennis (4km)
NOTES: No pets

ST-HILAIRE-LE-CHATEAU

⚍ Le Thaurian M-Christine & Gérard FANTON
La Chassagne, 23250 ST-HILAIRE-LE-CHATEAU
☎ 05 55 64 55 75 & 05 55 64 50 12 ▤ 05 55 64 90 92
Le Thaurian is a magnificent 15th and 17th-century château overlooking the Thaurian valley, with a shady park of five hectares bordered by a trout river. There are four bedrooms (three double beds and two single beds) and one suite in the guard house (one double and one single bed). All rooms have wc and bathrooms. There is also a living room with TV lounge area and central heating. Excellent restaurants 3 km away. Open all year.
PRICES: s €69-€84; d €76-€91; t €91-€105 **NEARBY:** Bathing
(27km) Horse riding (3km) Fishing (3km) Sailing (27km) Shops
(3km) **NOTES:** Pets admitted

ST-MARTIAL-LE-MONT

⚍ ♥ ⎮◎⎮ Sainte-Marie Monique et Marc TORTERAT
23150 ST-MARTIAL-LE-MONT
☎ 05 55 81 43 36
This old coaching inn is situated in parkland of two hectares, and features welcoming paintings by the artist Monique. On the first floor there are three bedrooms: one double room (classed grade 2) with bathroom and private wc separate from the bedroom, and two bedrooms for three people (grade 3) with private bathroom and wc. There is a living room and lounge with TV on the ground floor. Car park. Open all year.

continued   *continued*

PRICES: d €34; t €46; dinner €14 **ON SITE:** Bicycle hire
NEARBY: Bathing (6km) Horse riding (5km) Fishing (1km) Swimming pool (15km) Tennis (2km) Shops (2km) **NOTES:** Pets admitted English spoken

ST-PARDOUX-LE-NEUF

Les Vergnes Patrick et Sylvie DUMONTANT
23200 ST-PARDOUX-LE-NEUF
☎ 05 55 66 23 74 📠 05 55 67 74 16
Aubusson 7 km (capital of tapestry). Six bedrooms are available in this 18th-century farmhouse, a beautiful Creuse house with private lake opposite the bedrooms. The bedrooms contain five double beds and two singles plus an en suite room with two single beds. Each room has its own shower and wc, one has a spa bath. There is a living room with open fireplace, lounge, TV and library, electric heating and an adjoining park and terrace. Restaurants 7 km away. Price for four people: 84 euros. Open from 1 April to the end of October.
PRICES: s €43-€61; d €52-€73; t €69; dinner €16 **ON SITE:** Children's play area Bathing Fishing Swimming pool **NEARBY:** Horse riding (15km) Tennis (6km) Sailing (45km) **NOTES:** Pets admitted Minimum 2 night stay English spoken

ST-PARDOUX-LES-CARDS

Le Mont Gapier Ghislaine JUHEL
23150 ST-PARDOUX-LES-CARDS
☎ 05 55 62 35 16
Sixteenth-century house of character built on the former site of the château of Villemonteix, in the Limousin cattle-raising area. On the ground floor there is a living room with lounge area, TV, library, and fireplace, a garden and children's games. Upstairs there is one bedroom with a double bed, and one suite with a double bed, one single and one child's bed, each having its own bathroom and wc. There are two double-bedded rooms and shower room on the second floor. There is a wc in each bedroom. Restaurants are 3 km away. Price for four people: 62 euros. Animals accepted but not in the bedrooms. Open all year.
PRICES: s €34-€36; d €46-€48; t €58; dinner €16 **ON SITE:** Children's play area Bicycle hire **NEARBY:** Bathing (2km) Horse riding (23km) Fishing (2km) Tennis (2km) Shops (3km) **NOTES:** No pets English spoken

ST-PIERRE-BELLEVUE

La Borderie Marc et Maryse DESCHAMPS
23460 ST-PIERRE-BELLEVUE
☎ 05 55 64 96 51 📠 05 55 64 94 11
www.gites-de-la-borderie.com
This large 19th-century stone house is situated in a village 20 km from cross-country skiing. There are five bedrooms: one room for four people, two grade 1 double rooms and two grade 3 double rooms). There is also a living room/lounge with TV, library and fireplace. Central heating, landscaped grounds and car park. Children's menu available at 7-9 euros. Price for four adults: 53 euros. Restaurant 1 km away. Open all year.
PRICES: s €30-€33; d €33-€40; t €43; extra person €10; dinner €15 **ON SITE:** Children's play area **NEARBY:** Bathing (12km) Horse riding (3km) Fishing (3km) Swimming pool (35km) Tennis (8km) Sailing (12km) Shops (8km) **NOTES:** Pets admitted English spoken

For further information on these and other chambres d'hôtes, consult the Gîtes de France website
www.gites-de-france.fr

ST-YRIEIX-LA-MONTAGNE

Gibouleaux Richard et Danièle DARDUIN
23460
☎ 05 55 66 03 27 📠 05 55 66 05 82
This individual house dates from 1863 and offers two double rooms with a child's bed, and one room for four. Each room has its own washbasin and wc. There is a living room/lounge with TV, electric heating, landscaped grounds and a car park. Children: 80 francs. Price for four people: 63 euros. Open all year.
PRICES: s €35; s €40; s €55 **NEARBY:** Bathing (8km) Horse riding (6km) Golf (30km) Fishing (8km) Swimming pool (20km) Tennis (6km) Sailing (25km) Railway station (20km) Shops (20km) **NOTES:** Pets admitted

La Valette Corinne et Charles KULUNKIAN
23460 ST-YRIEIX-LA-MONTAGNE
☎ 05 55 66 07 77 📠 05 55 66 04 08
Aubusson 20 km. Corinne and Charles are delighted to welcome guests to this old village, which was originally built by Creuse craftsmen and has recently been renovated as a tourist destination. There are two double rooms and one suite for four people with private bathroom. The living room has a TV and reading material. Central heating. Car park and garden. The games room and swimming pool are shared with two other gîtes.
PRICES: s €53; d €53 **ON SITE:** Swimming pool **NEARBY:** Bathing (7km) Horse riding (7km) Golf (25km) Fishing (7km) Tennis (7km) Sailing (7km) Bicycle hire (20km) Shops (20km) **NOTES:** Pets admitted

HAUTE-VIENNE

ARNAC-LA-POSTE

Chambre d'hôtes Yvonne ROUART
Rond Point du Marronnier, 87160 ARNAC-LA-POSTE
☎ 05 55 76 87 26
This old renovated property belonging to Madame Rouart is situated in a village, overlooking a shady garden and a small square with a large chestnut tree. In this house, where you can be assured of a warm welcome, there are two bedrooms on the first floor, and one on the second floor. Each of these is equipped with private bathrooms and convector heaters. There is also a lounge reserved for guests with a TV and library. Open from 1 June to 20 September.
PRICES: d €36; t €46; dinner €13 **ON SITE:** Hiking **NEARBY:** Bathing (10km) Fishing (10km) Swimming pool (11km) Tennis (1km) Railway station (12km) **NOTES:** No pets English spoken

BELLAC

Chambre d'hôtes Jean et Colette GAUTIER
Le Bourg, 20, rue Armand Barbes, 87300 BELLAC
☎ 05 55 68 74 45
The first and second floors of this old house in the historic centre of Bellac have been converted into bedrooms for two, three, or four people. Three rooms have their own individual showers and wc, and one has its wc and shower on the landing. There is a dining room and a lounge reserved for guests. Kitchen available. Small interior courtyard. Parking nearby with a closed garage. Open all year.
PRICES: s €26; d €34; t €42; extra person €7; dinner €13 **ON SITE:** Hiking **NEARBY:** Horse riding (4km) Fishing (1km) Swimming pool (1km) Tennis (1km) Railway station (1km) **NOTES:** Pets admitted

🍴
Places with this symbol serve table d'hôtes evening meals - remember to book in advance

▥ ⯅ Chambre d'hôtes Jean-Paul et Odile FONTANEL
8 rue du Docteur Vetelay, 87300 BELLAC
☎ 05 55 68 11 86 ▤ 05 55 68 78 96
e-mail: bellac@free.fr bellac.free.fr
This character house dating from the 17th century is located in the heart of old Bellac. There are three rooms for two, three or four people on the first and second floors, each with private bathroom. The house also offers a lounge, living room, private parking, interior courtyard and some land with a lawn. Evening meals are available if reserved in advance. Open all year.
PRICES: s €28; d €34; t €43; extra person €9; dinner €13
ON SITE: Hiking **NEARBY:** Horse riding (4km) Fishing (1km) Swimming pool (1km) Tennis (1km) Railway station (2km) **NOTES:** No pets English spoken

BERSAC-SUR-RIVALIER

▥ ⯅ Domaine du Noyer Jean et Anna MASDOUMIER
Bersac-sur-Rivalier, 87370 ST-SULPICE-LAURIERE
☎ 05 55 71 52 91 ▤ 05 55 71 51 48
e-mail: noyer.prats@cyberpoint.tm.fr
Four bedrooms are available in this 16th-century stately residence, in the heart of a property of 20 hectares, with gym, swimming pool and bicycles. There are four double rooms (three double beds and two single beds) with showers and private wc, and a living room, lounge, fireplace, library and games room. Anna, a doctor (acupuncturist and homeopathist), and Jean a sculptor, are happy to welcome you for either a weekend or a longer stay. In addition, there are loose boxes for horses and training areas. Lake for fishing on the estate. Half-board per person, 265 euros a week. Open all year.
PRICES: s €34; d €45; t €55; dinner €15 **ON SITE:** Fishing Swimming pool Hiking **NEARBY:** Bathing (2km) Tennis (3km) Railway station (6km) Shops (2km) **NOTES:** Pets admitted English spoken

▥ ⯅ Le Pré de Lafont Annie JACQUEMAIN
87370 BERSAC-SUR-RIVALIER
☎ 05 55 71 47 05 ▤ 05 55 71 47 05
The attic of a 17th-century thatched cottage has been converted into guest rooms in the centre of the Ambazac mountains. The three double bedrooms have a private shower and wc, and there is a living room and TV reserved for residents. Guests can also use the raised swimming pool and relaxation area in a covered courtyard, plus extensive grounds. Gérard will delight in sharing the rural delights of his birthplace, and with his wife, will suggest wonderful outings. Open from Easter to 1 November.
PRICES: s €30; d €38; t €47; extra person €9; dinner €14
ON SITE: Hiking **NEARBY:** Bathing (8km) Fishing (5km) Tennis (2km) Railway station (5km) Shops (5km) **NOTES:** Pets admitted English spoken

BESSINES-SUR-GARTEMPE

▥ ⯅ ▥ Morterolles-sur-Semme
Jean-Marie et Andrée TESSIER
Chez Doussaud, 87250 BESSINES-SUR-GARTEMPE
☎ 05 55 76 06 94 ▤ 05 55 76 09 17
The cattle farm of Jean-Marie and Andrée Tessier is situated in a small hamlet very close to the A20 (exits 23.1 or 24). Here, Jean-Marie will take you on a guided tour of the farm before suggesting you sample his home-made rabbit and chicken rillettes. Three very large, cheerful, bedrooms, opening onto a terrace and garden, have been built in an annexe separate from the house. Each accommodates two to four people and has an en suite shower and wc. An adjoining lounge is reserved for guests. Meals available for residents on demand, except for Sunday evenings. Open all year.
PRICES: s €28; d €34; t €42; extra person €8; dinner €13
NEARBY: Bathing (6km) Canoeing (7km) Fishing (4km) Hiking (5km) Tennis (5km) Shops (2km) **NOTES:** Pets admitted English spoken

BLANZAC

▥ ⯅ Chambre d'hôtes C et A KUBIAK LE QUERE
Rouffignac, 87300 BLANZAC
☎ 05 55 68 02 14 ▤ 05 55 68 86 89
This farm is close to the mountains of Blond, Bellac and Mortemart, and the centre of la Mémoire d'Oradour-sur-Glane. There are five very comfortable bedrooms (two split level) for four and five people, with en suite showers and wc. There is a TV mezzanine over a huge living room with modern décor, and a games room with billiard table, a TV lounge and piano. Catherine serves copious meals at the table of her farm-inn using her own farm produce. Open all year.
PRICES: s €33; d €40; t €49; extra person €9; dinner €15
ON SITE: Fishing Hiking **NEARBY:** Horse riding (8km) Swimming pool (4km) Tennis (4km) Railway station (4km) Shops (4km) Restaurant nearby **NOTES:** No pets English spoken

▥ Chambre d'hôtes Marcelle LEQUERE
Rouffignac, RN145, 87300 BLANZAC
☎ 05 55 68 03 38

Five comfortable bedrooms with private bathrooms are to be found in this fine bourgeois residence. In addition, there is also a living room, lounge and TV at the disposal of guests. Outside there is a meadow, games area and car park. The river is 1 km away and the lake 20 km away. Meals can be taken at the farm inn belonging to Madame Kubiak Le Quéré, or cold meals (7 euros) can be reserved when booking. Farm products on the premises. Open all year.
PRICES: s €31; d €38; t €48; extra person €6 **ON SITE:** Fishing Hiking **NEARBY:** Horse riding (8km) Swimming pool (4km) Tennis (4km) Railway station (4km) Shops (4km) Restaurant nearby **NOTES:** No pets English spoken

BOISSEUIL

▥ ⯅ Domaine de Moulinard Brigitte ZIEGLER
87220 BOISSEUIL
☎ 05 55 06 91 22 ▤ 05 55 06 98 28
e-mail: philippe.ziegler@wanadoo.fr

Near Moulinard, a sheep farm and tree cultivation business,

continued

Monsieur and Madame Ziegler have restored part of the 18th-century mansion near their home to provide five bedrooms. These are all light and spacious with antique furniture, private bathrooms, and views on the quiet, shady garden surrounding the house. Restaurants are two kilometres away and there is a challenging 18-hole golf course with heated swimming pool at a distance of six kilometres. This property is situated ten minutes south of Limoges in the middle of countryside, not far from the Paris/Toulouse motorway (access A20 exit 37). Ideal for discovering Limoges. Open from April to October.
PRICES: s €29; d €36 **NEARBY:** Horse riding (13km) Fishing (6km) Swimming pool (9km) Hiking (1km) Tennis (2km) Railway station (7km) Shops (2km) **NOTES:** No pets English spoken

BUJALEUF

♦♦♦ ⏇ Les Côtes du Maine
Natacha et Bertrand JACQUELINE
87460 BUJALEUF
☎ 05 55 69 51 45
This large house, the property of Natacha and Bertrand, is set amidst three hectares of wooded grounds, with a view of lake Bujalef and only 300 metres from the beach. There are five upstairs bedrooms, of which three are family suites, each with their own en suite shower and wc. Central heating, TV and lounge reserved for guests and terrace with a view of the lake. Meals feature farm produce and vegetables from the garden. Half board is 198 euros per person per week. Open all year.
PRICES: s €30; d €38; t €44; extra person €5; dinner €12 **ON SITE:** Fishing **NEARBY:** Bathing (1km) Canoeing (1km) Horse riding (3km) Swimming pool (14km) Hiking (3km) Tennis (3km) Railway station (6km) Shops (1km) **NOTES:** Pets admitted English spoken

CHAMPAGNAC-LA-RIVIERE

♦♦♦♦ ⏇ Château de Brie
Pierre DU MANOIR DE JUAYE
87150 CHAMPAGNAC-LA-RIVIERE
☎ 05 55 78 17 52 📠 05 55 78 14 02
e-mail: chateaudebrie@wanadoo.fr
www.chateaux-france.com

Fifteenth-century chateau set in three hectares of parkland with swimming pool and tennis court. There are four character bedrooms on the first and second floors with private bathroom and wc. Guests can use the lounge, dining room and library. Fishing, forest walks and cycling on the property. Open from 1 May to 1 November, and other months if booked in advance.
PRICES: d €95; dinner €40 **ON SITE:** Fishing Swimming pool Tennis **NEARBY:** Bathing (11km) Horse riding (11km) Hiking (2km) Railway station (8km) Shops (5km) **NOTES:** Pets admitted English spoken

CHATEAU-CHERVIX

♦♦♦ 🐐 ⏇ La Chapelle Patrick et Mayder LESPAGNOL
87380 CHATEAU-CHERVIX
☎ 05 55 00 86 67 📠 05 55 00 70 78
e-mail: lespagno@club-internet.fr
Discover this small traditional house on an organic goat farm, offering four bedrooms, each with individual shower and wc. Other amenities include a living room with reading material reserved for guests, a kitchen area and a garden, games corner, grounds and car park. There is a river three kilometres away and a forest on the property; however, a car is indispensable. Meals featuring farm produce can be arranged between 1 July and 15 August, if reserved in advance. Access by the A20, exit 41 at Magnac Bourg. Half board 208 euros per person per week. Open all year.
PRICES: s €30; d €38; t €43; dinner €14 **ON SITE:** Hiking **NEARBY:** Bathing (6km) Horse riding (6km) Fishing (6km) Tennis (4km) Shops (4km) **NOTES:** No pets English spoken

CHATEAUNEUF-LA-FORET

♦♦♦ La Croix du Reh Leigh ANDREWS
87130 CHATEAUNEUF-LA-FORET
☎ 05 55 69 75 37 📠 05 55 69 75 38
e-mail: lacroixdureh@aol.com www.la croixdureh.com
This opulent-looking residence is situated in a park of hundred-year-old trees, among banks of roses and rhododendrons, and provides four tastefully decorated bedrooms for two to four people with private bathrooms. Your hostess, Leigh, has chosen to live in a small village close to a large forest of 700 hectares. After relaxing a little in the park surrounding the house, you can finish your evening by the fireside in a very comfortable lounge featuring fine oak beams. Close to the Vassivière lake (1000 hectares), the plateau of Millevaches (springs) and Saint-Léonard-de-Noblat and Eymoutiers, old cities on the Vienne. Open all year.
PRICES: s €61; d €68; t €76 **NEARBY:** Bathing (1km) Fishing (1km) Swimming pool (14km) Hiking (1km) Tennis (1km) Railway station (14km) **NOTES:** Pets admitted English spoken

CIEUX

♦♦♦ ⏇ Les Volets Bleus Kathy et Tony FRENCH
l'Etang, 8/10 rte d'Oradour-sur-Glane, 87520 CIEUX
☎ 05 55 03 26 97 📠 05 55 03 26 97
Kathy and Tony fell in love at first sight with this small village situated at the foot of the Monts de Blond. Here they have bought a house looking out on a garden of flowers and trees, bordered by a stream, near lake Cieux (43 hectares, bathing possible). There are three carefully decorated bedrooms on the first floor, each with their own shower and wc. In addition, a dining room and lounge area with fireplace, library and TV are reserved for guests. Meals, including a vegetarian menu, are available if booked in advance. No smoking is requested in the house. Discover the legendary standing stones nearby by taking the numerous footpaths, and horse and bike trails. Open from 1 May to 15 October.
PRICES: s €32; d €40; dinner €17 **ON SITE:** Bathing Fishing **NEARBY:** Horse riding (6km) Hiking (1km) Tennis (1km) Shops (1km) **NOTES:** No pets English spoken

COUSSAC-BONNEVAL

♦♦♦ 🐐 ⏇ Le Moulin de Marsaguet
Renaud et Valérie GIZARDIN
87500 COUSSAC-BONNEVAL
☎ 05 55 75 28 29 📠 05 55 75 28 29
Three bedrooms can be found in this old mill, on the banks of a fine 13-hectare lake. These are for two to three people, with bath or shower and wc. Come and meet your hosts, Valérie and

continued

Renaud, in their large ironmongers house, where you can sample their farm produce (foie gras, conserves, duck fillet), and vegetables from the garden. Ask about the special foie gras weekends. Open all year but advance bookings recommended.
PRICES: s €35; d €39; dinner €17 **ON SITE:** Fishing Hiking
NEARBY: Bathing (14km) Horse riding (14km) Swimming pool (14km) Tennis (3km) Railway station (12km) Shops (3km) **NOTES:** Pets admitted English spoken

♦♦♦ ✿ ♨ Marsac Catherine et Thierry CHIBOIS
87500 COUSSAC-BONNEVAL
☎ 05 55 75 95 61 🖷 05 55 75 95 61
www.france-bonjour.com/marsac/
Pompadour, château de Coussac Bonneval. Discover this small stock breeding farm, set in the middle of the countryside in the centre of the Pays Arédien, where Thierry raises free-range saddleback pigs, in the open air. Here, there are two ground floor bedrooms, each with en suite facilities, and one mezzanine bedroom in an independent house for two to four people. Living room and lounge area reserved for guests. You will have the chance to enjoy pork, the local speciality, at table d'hôte meals (prior reservation necessary). Open all year.
PRICES: s €34; d €39; t €47; extra person €9; dinner €14
ON SITE: Fishing Hiking **NEARBY:** Bathing (14km) Horse riding (14km) Swimming pool (14km) Tennis (3km) Railway station (14km) Shops (3km) **NOTES:** Pets admitted English spoken

CUSSAC

♦♦♦ ♨ Fayolas Margaret et Cliff BENTLEY
87150 CUSSAC
☎ 05 55 70 96 46 🖷 05 55 70 96 46
e-mail: cliff.mag@wanadoo.fr
From this property, owned by Cliff and Margaret, you have easy access to Richard the Lionheart's route, which links the main architectural sites, the Brie châteaux, the medieval fortresses of Chalus Chabrol and Montbrun, and the remarkable frescoes of the Saint-Eutrope churches. It is also near the bike track at Bussière Galant. Accommodation consists of three bedrooms with en suite facilities on the first floor of an independent house, with a living room on the ground floor. The property also enjoys a large terrace, extensive lawns and a pleasant view of the mountains of Chalus and Puyconnieux. Open all year.
PRICES: s €35; d €42; dinner €11–€15 **ON SITE:** Hiking
NEARBY: Bathing (8km) Horse riding (3km) Fishing (8km) Swimming pool (14km) Tennis (2km) Railway station (20km) Shops (2km) **NOTES:** No pets English spoken

DOURNAZAC

♦♦♦ ♨ Les Tilleuls C et P MERLE-PANI
87230 DOURNAZAC
☎ 05 55 78 68 47 🖷 05 55 78 68 47

Discover this fine 19th-century residence belonging to Catherine and Pierre, situated in a peaceful village in the Périgord-Limousin

continued

regional park. Upstairs there are four bedrooms, two of which are family suites (one double bed and two single beds), each with en suite shower and wc. Downstairs there is a large lounge overlooking the garden, with reading material, games and TV. Garden furniture, a swing and a hammock are also at your disposal. Your hosts will be delighted to show you the highlights of Richard the Lionheart's route, such as the Chalus tower and the Montbrun medieval fort. Meals prepared with tasty local produce must be booked in advance. Open all year except from 7-31 January and 18 November-15 December).
PRICES: s €31; d €39; t €49; extra person €12; dinner €13
ON SITE: Children's play area Hiking **NEARBY:** Bathing (10km) Horse riding (11km) Fishing (1km) Swimming pool (7km) Tennis (7km) Railway station (7km) **NOTES:** Pets admitted

FEYTIAT

♦♦♦ ♨ Chambre d'hôtes Mady et Gérard CHASTAGNER
Allée du Puy Marot, 87220 FEYTIAT
☎ 05 55 48 33 97 🖷 05 55 30 31 86
e-mail: gerardchastagner@wanadoo.fr
Let this 16th-century priory transport you peacefully back in time. Situated ten minutes from Limoges and overlooking the Valoine valley, there are three bedrooms, one a family suite and one a luxury bedroom, on the first and second floors. All of these have en suite facilities, open out onto the park which surrounds the house, and enjoy the vast panoramic view of the valley. Mady and Gérard, your welcoming hosts, are passionate about porcelain and will delight in helping you to discover the history of table china. Easy access to Limoges, the capital of kiln arts with its porcelain and enamel museums. Open all year.
PRICES: s €54–€92; d €61–€100; dinner €16–€28 **ON SITE:** Tennis
NEARBY: Canoeing (9km) Horse riding (4km) Fishing (7km) Swimming pool (5km) Hiking (2km) Railway station (6km) Shops (1km)
NOTES: No pets English spoken

♦♦♦ Le Vieux Crezin Danielle et Bernard BRULAT
87220 FEYTIAT
☎ 05 55 06 34 41 🖷 05 55 48 37 16
Limoges town centre 5 mins. A spacious barn conversion owned by Danielle and Bernard in a small, peaceful hamlet, offers three mezzanine bedrooms above a living room with billiard table. Each room has its own shower or bathroom and wc. Access by the A20 motorway (exit 35). Open all year.
PRICES: s €40; d €48; t €57; extra person €9 **NEARBY:** Horse riding (5km) Swimming pool (3km) Hiking (4km) Tennis (2km) Railway station (6km) Shops (2km)

FROMENTAL

♦♦♦ ♨ Montautre Norma RIVA SCHIPPER
Château de Montautre, 87250 FROMENTAL
☎ 05 55 76 69 81 & 06 72 30 22 20 🖷 05 55 76 69 81
e-mail: Normarini@compuserve.com
Dance, yoga, and cookery courses are offered in this 15th-century manor house. The square keep and machiolated walls of this dwelling have been renovated by Norma and Rini, a cabinetmaker, and are situated amidst meadows and woods on the banks of the Creuse. Accommodation comprises four rooms of character with en suite shower and wc. There is also a living room, lounge and library. Within access of the Gartempe valley, museum of Chateauponsac, lake of Saint-Pardoux and Limoges with its porcelain art. Meals and courses to be booked in advance. Open from May to December.
PRICES: s €45; d €54; t €61; dinner €13 **ON SITE:** Hiking
NEARBY: Horse riding (6km) Fishing (8km) Swimming pool (9km) Tennis (7km) Railway station (10km) Shops (4km) **NOTES:** No pets English spoken

ISLE

╫╫╫ Château de la Chabroulie B & Philippe DE LA SEL
87170 ISLE
☎ 05 55 36 13 15 📠 05 55 36 13 15
e-mail: dls@chateau-chabroulie.com
www.chateau-chabroulie.com
The château, la Chabroulie, is set in grounds of 70 hectares, and offers the warmth and quality of an old family home. It is an excellent place to stopover. Four bedrooms with private bathrooms and wc have been built for guests, plus a lounge, library area and fireplace. It is possible to explore the property by bicycle. Situated six kilometres from Limoges. Open all year.
PRICES: s €58; d €61; t €71 **ON SITE:** Hiking **NEARBY:** Canoeing (8km) Horse riding (6km) Fishing (1km) Swimming pool (8km) Tennis (2km) Railway station (8km) Shops (2km) **NOTES:** Pets admitted English spoken

╫╫╫ ⚪ Verthamont Edith BRUNIER
Pic de l'Aiguille, 87170 ISLE
☎ 05 55 36 12 89
e-mail: brunieredith@yahoo.fr
This beautiful modern house, set out in the country yet only a stone's throw from Limoges, enjoys a panoramic view of the Vienne valley and features a private swimming pool and landscaped flower garden. Here there are three bedrooms, two of which have large French windows leading onto a terrace with garden furniture. All have their own en suite facilities. Central heating. Town centre ten minutes away. Restaurants two kilometres away. Open all year.
PRICES: s €29; d €37; t €44; extra person €12; dinner €15
ON SITE: Swimming pool Hiking **NEARBY:** Canoeing (4km) Horse riding (6km) Fishing (1km) Tennis (4km) Railway station (8km) Shops (3km) **NOTES:** Pets admitted English spoken

LA CHAPELLE-MONTBRANDEIX

╫╫╫ ⚪ Doumailhac Benoît et Laurence de RADIGUES
87440 LA CHAPELLE-MONTBRANDEIX
☎ 05 55 78 57 06 📠 05 55 78 57 06
e-mail: radi.ben@free.fr
This small manor house, dating from the 17th century, stands apart from the village in the Périgord-Limousin regional park. On the first floor there are three bedrooms with en suite shower or bathroom and wc (two double rooms and one family suite for four). On the ground floor there is a large living room with old granite flagstones where meals are served, and a shared lounge. Laurence and Benoît, who have recently moved into this pleasant residence, will be delighted to suggest walks or mountain bike trails (bikes available on the premises) in the numerous forest paths near their gîte. Open all year.
PRICES: s €34; d €43; t €56; extra person €9; dinner €13
ON SITE: Hiking **NEARBY:** Bathing (6km) Swimming (15km) Horse riding (5km) Fishing (3km) Tennis (6km) Railway station (19km) Shops (7km) **NOTES:** No pets

╫╫╫ ⚪ Lartimache Evelyne et Bernard GUERIN
87440 LA CHAPELLE-MONTBRANDEIX
☎ 05 55 78 75 65
Evelyne and Bernard are ready to give you a warm welcome to their 15th-century renovated farm building, in a verdant setting with two private lakes in the centre of the Périgord-Limousin regional park. There are four upstairs bedrooms with exposed beams, and one family suite for four to six people, all with private shower or bathroom and wc. In addition there is a large room with a fireplace, terrace, washing machine, kitchen area for guests' use, table tennis and board games. Bicycles can be rented and fishing lessons can be organised. Walkers and horses welcomed. Family atmosphere. Half board 640 euros for four per week. Open all year.
PRICES: s €28; d €38; t €45; extra person €10; dinner €12
ON SITE: Children's play area Fishing Hiking **NEARBY:** Bathing (4km) Swimming (15km) Horse riding (5km) Tennis (5km) Railway station (20km) Shops (9km) **NOTES:** Pets admitted English spoken

LE CHALARD

╫╫╫ ⚪ Le Petit Masvieux Y CLARIJS et K PINTARIC
87500 LE CHALARD
☎ 05 55 09 94 14 📠 05 55 09 20 81
e-mail: le-petit-masvieux@wanadoo.fr
perso.wanadoo.fr/le-petit-masvieux
Périgord Vert 5 km. Four bedrooms sleeping either two or three people and a lovely suite for four, all with private shower and wc, can be found in this 19th-century manor house. There is also a large dining room, lounge with library, billiard table and lake for carp fishing. Yoland and Kaspar have fallen for this property, which is like a little bit of paradise on earth. Meals can be booked in advance. Bicycles can be rented. Open all year.
PRICES: s €43; d €55; t €60; extra person €35; dinner €17
ON SITE: Fishing Hiking **NEARBY:** Bathing (3km) Horse riding (11km) Swimming pool (11km) Tennis (2km) Railway station (12km) Shops (3km) **NOTES:** No pets English spoken

MAGNAC-LAVAL

╫╫╫ ⚪ l'Age Jean-Paul et Annie ALBESPY
87190 MAGNAC-LAVAL
☎ 05 55 68 26 03
www.France-bonjour.com/albespy/
Five spacious and airy bedrooms have been built on the first and second floors of this manor house, within walking distance of a good country inn at the bottom of a hill. Each bedroom is for two to four people and has its own facilities (three rooms with showers and two with bathrooms). There is a large lounge with billiard table, snug open fire area and reading material on the ground floor. Your hosts, Annie and Jean-Paul, are specialist teachers of the Middle East. Sheltered in an attractive hundred-year-old park, their large residence enjoys a vast panorama of the low-lying countryside. Open all year.
PRICES: s €31; d €43; t €54; extra person €11; dinner €15
ON SITE: Hiking **NEARBY:** Fishing (2km) Swimming pool (14km) Tennis (2km) Shops (2km) **NOTES:** Pets admitted English spoken

MASLEON

╫╫╫ 🐓 Chambre d'hôtes F et M CHARBONNI
Le Bourg, 87130 MASLEON
☎ 05 55 57 00 63 📠 05 55 57 00 63
e-mail: Marylene.CHARBONNIAUD@wanadoo.Fr
Marylène and Frédéric are Limousin cattle breeders, and offer guest accommodation in a village seven kilometres from the lakes at Bujalef and Châteauneuf-la-Forêt, which are ideal for swimming. There are three bedrooms upstairs and one downstairs, each with

continued

their own private showers or bath and wc. In addition, downstairs there are two living rooms with fireplace, TV and reading matter, and a kitchen with refrigerator and washing machine. Outside there is a terrace, garden furniture, pétanque and table tennis. This spot is an ideal holiday destination and is situated between Limoges and Vassivière on the D979.
PRICES: s €33; d €37-€45; t €54; extra person €15 **NEARBY:** Bathing (8km) Canoeing (8km) Horse riding (10km) Fishing (3km) Hiking (7km) Tennis (8km) Railway station (10km) **NOTES:** Pets admitted

NEXON

♥♥♥ ⦿ Domaine des Landes Jean-François CANE
87800 NEXON
☎ 06 07 08 80 20 & 05 55 58 25 25
e-mail: jf.cane@irisnet.fr nexon.irisnet.fr
This contemporary thatched outbuilding provides three bedrooms with en suite facilities and TV in a ten-hectare park with mature chestnut trees and large swimming pool. A family suite for four people has been incorporated in the owners' own home, featuring sauna and hammam. Near the châteaux of Nexon, Coussac and Bonneval, the roman colleges at Solignac and Saint-Yrieix-la-Perche, and the national stud farms at Pompadour. Open all year.
PRICES: s €64; d €69; dinner €27.5 **NEARBY:** Bathing (5km) Horse riding (5km) Fishing (5km) Hiking (2km) Tennis (5km) Railway station (5km) Shops (5km) **NOTES:** Pets admitted English spoken

PANAZOL

♥♥♥ ⦿ Chambre d'hôtes
Henri et Maryse CHAMOULAUD
4, allée de Courbiat, 87350 PANAZOL
☎ 05 55 30 81 37 & 06 82 96 05 83   05 55 31 00 98
e-mail: henri.parry@libertysurf.fr
Limoges 6 km. This 19th-century property is set in woods of three hectares, and has its own swimming pool. Henri, your host, is a specialist in porcelain decoration and would be delighted to share his passion with guests. Henri has converted the attic of the house into two bedrooms, with three others in an adjoining building. All have private showers and wc. There is also a large rustic living room with a reading room on a mezzanine level. Situated in the porcelain capital, close to enamel and pottery museums, with its old city and cathedral. Near the centre of the Mémoire d'Oradour-sur-Glane. Open all year.
PRICES: s €43; d €49; t €57; dinner €19 **NEARBY:** Bathing (6km) Canoeing (6km) Horse riding (3km) Fishing (3km) Swimming pool (6km) Hiking (2km) Tennis (2km) Railway station (6km) Shops (2km) **NOTES:** No pets English spoken

PENSOL

♥♥♥ ⦿ La Vieille Maison
Agnès et J-François FOURGEAUD
87440 PENSOL
☎ 05 55 78 75 14
Three cosy bedrooms, each with en suite facilities, have been incorporated in the attic of an old house with plenty of character, in the small, quiet village of Pensol. On the ground floor there is a lounge and living room with a heraldic crest dating from 1662. Terrace and barbecue for fine weather. Situated in the Périgord-Limousin regional park. The food is varied and healthy, with vegetables from the garden. Only good organic produce is served. Price half board for one week.
PRICES: s €31; d €40; t €50; dinner €13 **ON SITE:** Hiking **NEARBY:** Bathing (9km) Horse riding (7km) Fishing (7km) Tennis (3km) Shops (8km) **NOTES:** Pets admitted English spoken

♥♥♥ ♥ Le Moulin Catherine BERTHELOT
87440 PENSOL
☎ 05 55 78 21 31   05 55 78 21 31
This old mill, situated on the banks of the Bandiat in the national park, has been converted to provide three first-floor rooms for two and four people, with private showers and wc. Downstairs there is a small room where the meals of the farm-inn are served. Be prepared for your tastebuds to be tantalised by the delicious rabbit, chicken and organic fruit products served at table. Open all year.
PRICES: s €31; d €38; t €43; extra person €11; dinner €13 **ON SITE:** Fishing Hiking **NEARBY:** Bathing (9km) Horse riding (10km) Swimming pool (15km) Tennis (5km) Railway station (16km) Shops (15km) Restaurant nearby **NOTES:** Pets admitted English spoken

PEYRAT-DE-BELLAC

♥♥♥ ♥ ⦿ La Lande Georges et Marie QUESNEL
87300 PEYRAT-DE-BELLAC
☎ 05 55 68 00 24 & 05 55 68 31 83
Not far from Bellac, towards Poitiers, there is a little road on the left, after the 'brocante', which leads to Marie and Georges's sheep farm. At table, after a house-special apéritif, you will be able to sample such Limousin specialities as home-reared lamb, potato paté and *flognarde*, prepared by Marie, a fine cordon bleu cook. There are three bedrooms with en suite facilities in this attractive period residence, plus a large communal room with fireplace. This is on the ground floor and opens out onto a terrace and garden with private swimming pool. Three kilometres from the main Poitiers-Limoges road (N147). Open from Easter to the end of October.
PRICES: s €34; d €40; t €47; dinner €15 **ON SITE:** Swimming pool **NEARBY:** Horse riding (1km) Fishing (3km) Hiking (5km) Tennis (5km) Railway station (5km) Shops (5km) **NOTES:** No pets

PEYRAT-LE-CHATEAU

♥♥♥ ⦿ Villards Bernard LEPORCHER
87470 PEYRAT-LE-CHATEAU
☎ 05 55 69 21 36
Lac de Vassivière 8 km. A beautiful stone building, set in wooded grounds and meadows of 30 hectares, has been converted to provide one bedroom downstairs and four upstairs. The rooms sleep two to four people and all have private showers and wc. There is also a room with fireplace, reading material, TV and billiard table. Mountain-bike rental is possible. You are invited to discover the unspoilt countryside of the Millevaches area by magnificent walks, or horse and bike trails. Open all year.
PRICES: s €34; d €41; t €48; extra person €8; dinner €14 **ON SITE:** Children's play area Horse riding Hiking Tennis **NEARBY:** Bathing (2km) Canoeing (12km) Fishing (2km) Swimming pool (12km) Sailing (8km) Railway station (12km) Shops (2km) **NOTES:** Pets admitted

PEYRILHAC

♥♥♥ La Boisserie Louis et Josette SAVATTE
87510 PEYRILHAC
☎ 05 55 75 69 68
An individual house has been converted by craftsmen to provide three spacious and comfortable bedrooms with private bathrooms, plus a living room and lounge area. For longer stays, a kitchen is available. This property can be found in La Boisserie, a tranquil hamlet just two kilometres from the main Limoges/Poitiers road. Restaurants three kilometres away. An ideal base for walking holidays in the Blond mountains. Open from 1 April to 31 October.
PRICES: s €33; d €38; t €51 **NEARBY:** Bathing (11km) Fishing (7km) Hiking (3km) Tennis (3km) Railway station (2km) Shops (3km) **NOTES:** No pets

REMPNAT

▦ ○I Château de la Villeneuve Jean-Claude AEN
87120 REMPNAT
☎ 05 55 69 99 28   🖷 05 55 69 99 26
e-mail: jean-claude.aen@wanadoo.fr

Lac de Vassivière 15 km. Classes in silk painting and painting miniatures are a feature of the holidays in this 19th-century manor house, in the foothills of the plateau de Millevaches (springs). The three bedrooms, one of which is a suite, with private en suite facilities, open out onto either the river or the extensive park surrounding the house. On the ground floor there is a lounge with fireplace, a dining room, a snooker table and an indoor heated swimming pool. There is private fishing (killing of fish prohibited) on the Vienne, and you can enjoy the tasty meals prepared by the master of the house. Open all year.
PRICES: s €59; d €75; t €90; dinner €23-€38 **ON SITE:** Fishing Swimming pool Hiking **NEARBY:** Bathing (15km) Canoeing (15km) Horse riding (8km) Tennis (5km) Sailing (15km) Railway station (15km) Shops (5km) **NOTES:** No pets English spoken

RILHAC-LASTOURS

▦ Rilhac Alexis DEBORD
87800 RILHAC-LASTOURS
☎ 05 55 58 22 43
Monsieur Debord has turned the upstairs of the next door house into three bedrooms, each sleeping three people, with private shower rooms and wc. In addition, he has renovated two terraced houses in a neighbouring village to provide accommodation for five people. These also have private en suite facilities and a kitchen, and can be rented by the week. Open all year.
PRICES: s €31; d €37; t €46 **NEARBY:** Bathing (5km) Horse riding (5km) Fishing (5km) Swimming pool (5km) Hiking (5km) Tennis (5km) Railway station (5km) Shops (5km) **NOTES:** Pets admitted

ST-AUVENT

▦ ❦ ○I Coufiegeas Geoffroy et Päivi TILLEUL
87310 ST-AUVENT
☎ 05 55 48 16 12   🖷 05 55 48 16 12
On a hill overlooking the Gorre, between Rochechouart and Saint-Junien, you will find this charming farm renovated by a Franco-Finnish couple. The property, which is welcoming and calm, is set in green countryside. Four bedrooms have been built upstairs with en suite facilities. At mealtimes you will be able to enjoy the farm produce, such as rillette, patés, ham and local dishes. There is a reduction of ten per cent after the third night. Open all year.
PRICES: s €31; d €36; t €40; extra person €5; dinner €13
ON SITE: Hiking **NEARBY:** Bathing (10km) Horse riding (11km) Fishing (10km) Tennis (1km) Railway station (7km) Shops (7km) **NOTES:** Pets admitted English spoken

ST-HILAIRE-BONNEVAL

▦ ○I La Forge Dominique et Aude BATAILLER
Le Bourg, 87260 ST-HILAIRE-BONNEVAL
☎ 05 55 00 68 57
e-mail: la_forge@mail.dotcom.fr france-bonjour.com/batailler

Limoges 17 km. Dominique and Aude have converted an old forge into three bedrooms with private showers and wc, and the adjoining blacksmith's house into one guest room. All the rooms look out onto a flowery, green park and there is a large lounge with fireplace downstairs. The owners hope you will share their love of the setting, in a small village typical of the Briance valley. Meals to be booked in advance. Open all year.
PRICES: s €29; d €36; t €42; dinner €12 **ON SITE:** Hiking Tennis **NEARBY:** Bathing (16km) Horse riding (3km) Fishing (2km) Swimming pool (16km) Railway station (4km) Shops (5km) **NOTES:** Pets admitted

ST-JUNIEN-LES-COMBES

▦ ○I Château de Sannat
C et Jacques de SAINTE-CROIX
87300 ST-JUNIEN-LES-COMBES
☎ 05 55 68 13 52   🖷 05 55 68 13 52
e-mail: labelette@aol.com
Discover this 18th-century château built on an ancient stronghold with panoramic views of the Blond mountains, where you can enjoy the tennis court and private swimming pool. Accommodation consists of four spacious double rooms, with private shower or bathroom, one of which is classed grade 3. There is also a large lounge with TV, and dining room. The property is set in a huge wooded park of 500 hectares, with a French-style hanging garden. Open during July, August, September and the November half-term holidays.
PRICES: d €100; dinner €23 **ON SITE:** Fishing Swimming pool Hiking Tennis **NEARBY:** Horse riding (3km) Railway station (9km) Shops (9km) **NOTES:** Pets admitted

ST-LEONARD-DE-NOBLAT

▦ Chambre d'hôtes Françoise BIGAS
20, rue Jean Jaures, 87400 ST-LEONARD-DE-NOBLAT
☎ 05 55 56 19 47   🖷 05 55 56 19 47
In the remarkable medieval village of St-Léonard-de-Noblat, you will find two grade 1 bedrooms in a house with shared shower and wc, and three bedrooms with private facilities in an adjoining house, linked by a garden full of flowers. At guests' disposal, there is a lounge and washing-machine, with a dining room and kitchen area for longer stays. Françoise will tell you all about the area and her hobbies including enamel work and dried flower arranging. A special welcome is reserved for cyclists; champion cyclist Raymond Poulidor hails from this area. Open all year.
PRICES: s €29; d €40; t €53; extra person €14 **NEARBY:** Bathing (15km) Horse riding (11km) Fishing (2km) Swimming pool (1km) Tennis (1km) Railway station (1km) **NOTES:** No pets

ST-MARTIN-TERRESSUS

♦♦♦ ❦ ⦿Ⅰ La Gasnerie Paul et Marie POUSSIN

87400 ST-MARTIN-TERRESSUS
☎ 05 55 57 11 64 🖷 05 55 57 12 65
If you like the sweet pleasures of the countryside, tranquillity, nature, animals and hilly scenery, this is the place for you. Marie and Paul invite you to share the charm of la Gasnerie, where they offer three upstairs wood-panelled rooms with bathroom and private wc, and one bedroom downstairs with shower, wc and cot if required. In addition there is a lounge, and electric and central heating. Meals can be provided if booked in advance. Half board for two people per week is 381 euros. Open all year.
PRICES: s €28; d €34; t €42; dinner €13 **NEARBY:** Bathing (6km) Horse riding (8km) Fishing (3km) Swimming pool (12km) Tennis (3km) Railway station (12km) Shops (3km) **NOTES:** Pets admitted

ST-PARDOUX

♦♦♦ ⦿Ⅰ Vaugueniges Alain et Marick CLAUDE

Château de Vauguenige, 87250 ST-PARDOUX
☎ 05 55 76 58 55 🖷 05 55 76 57 11
e-mail: vauguenige@voila.fr
Marick, a yoga teacher, Gestalt practitioner and dietician, together with Alain, a PE teacher and lifeguard, organise themed holidays at this 19th-century chateau. These could be based on swimming, fitness, relaxation or health, taking advantage of the heated covered swimming pool, sauna, jacuzzi and equestrian centre on the premises. There are five large bedrooms with private facilities, and lounges with TV, library, and piano. A space is reserved for smokers. Open from 1 April to 1 November.
PRICES: s €54-€57; d €67-€70; t €80-€83; extra person €93-€96; dinner €22 **ON SITE:** Horse riding Fishing Swimming pool **NEARBY:** Bathing (3km) Hiking (3km) Tennis (6km) Sailing (10km) Railway station (38km) Shops (3km) **NOTES:** No pets Minimum 2 night stay English spoken

ST-SYLVESTRE-GRANDMONT

♦♦♦ ⦿Ⅰ Bois Sauvage Edith et Lorenzo RAPPELLI

Les Chênes, Les Sauvages par Grandmont,
87240 ST-SYLVESTRE
☎ 05 55 71 33 12 🖷 05 55 71 33 12
e-mail: les.chenes@wanadoo.fr
www.haute-vienne.com/chenes.htm
Three charming and comfortable bedrooms sleeping two to four people, with en suite bathroom and private wc, have been installed in this fine, wooden house in the heart of the Ambazac mountains. This is ideal for restful holidays, with healthy, family cooking (vegetarian meals available). Painting exhibition on the premises. Close to horse riding centres, tennis courts and well placed for wild-mushroom picking and walking. For stays longer than one night the price for one to two people is 42 euros, 57 euros for three people, and 72 euros for four. Open all year.
PRICES: s €46; d €46; t €62; extra person €16; dinner €14
ON SITE: Hiking **NEARBY:** Bathing (8km) Horse riding (8km) Fishing (8km) Tennis (8km) Railway station (8km) Shops (8km)
NOTES: No pets English spoken

ST-VICTURNIEN

♦♦♦ ⦿Ⅰ Chambre d'hôtes Philippe et Angela DEBERNARD

32 rue Alluaud la Maison, de Maître Dony,
87420 ST-VICTURNIEN
☎ 05 55 03 19 99 🖷 05 55 03 54 50
e-mail: debernardphil@aol.com
A fine miller's house, built in 1850 and recently restored, is the home of Philippe and Angela, who reserve you a warm Franco-Irish welcome. Here there are two double rooms and one suite of two rooms for five people, each with private bathroom. The

garden and terrace enjoy a panoramic view of the Vienne valley, and there is a swimming pool, pétanque, badminton, billiard table and barbecue. Open all year.
PRICES: s €39-€45; d €45-€60; t €68; extra person €7; dinner €14
ON SITE: Canoeing Hiking **NEARBY:** Bathing (8km) Horse riding (15km) Fishing (1km) Swimming pool (10km) Tennis (1km)
NOTES: No pets English spoken

♦♦♦ ❦ ⦿Ⅰ Chambre d'hôtes

Anne-Marie et Marcel LALOYAUX
La Chapelle Blanche, 87420 ST-VICTURNIEN
☎ 05 55 03 58 20
In their farm, which is typical of the region, Marcel and Anne-Marie produce "Baronnet" lamb. Here they have built a family room with one double bed and two single beds, and two double rooms. Each room has en suite facilities. There is also a large enclosed courtyard and table tennis. Meals must be booked in advance. Various pretty walks can be enjoyed through the farm lanes. Open from 15 April to 31 October.
PRICES: s €30; d €38; t €50; extra person €5; dinner €13
NEARBY: Bathing (12km) Canoeing (4km) Fishing (2km) Hiking (4km) Tennis (4km) Railway station (13km) Shops (3km) **NOTES:** No pets

♦♦♦ Le Loubier Michel DAURIAC

87420 ST-VICTURNIEN ☎ 05 55 03 29 22
This large 19th-century residence, opens onto a park planted with hundred-year-old trees. Upstairs you can find three spacious bedrooms for two to four people, characterful furniture and private shower and wc. On the ground floor there is a family suite with access for guests with disabilities. There is a reduction for stays of over one week. Close to restaurants. Open all year.
PRICES: s €31; d €42; t €49; extra person €6 **NEARBY:** Bathing (11km) Canoeing (3km) Horse riding (14km) Fishing (3km) Swimming pool (11km) Hiking (3km) Tennis (3km) Railway station (3km) Shops (3km)
NOTES: Pets admitted

VERNEUIL-MOUSTIERS

♦♦♦ ⦿Ⅰ Domaine du Fan Suzanne NOZARI

87360 VERNEUIL-MOUSTIERS
☎ 05 55 68 25 30 🖷 05 55 60 14 56
e-mail: contact@domainedufan.de www.domainedufan.de
A fine drive of oak trees leads to this 18th-century manor house situated in 60 hectares. Suzanne Nozari has fallen in love with this idyllic spot in the Brenne National Park and offers accommodation of five bedrooms for two to four people with private shower and wc. There is also a living room, reading room and a video room.
PRICES: s €37; d €46; t €55; dinner €13 **ON SITE:** Fishing Swimming pool Hiking Tennis **NEARBY:** Bathing (18km) Canoeing (7km) Horse riding (15km) Railway station (19km) Shops (4km) **NOTES:** No pets English spoken

VEYRAC

♦♦♦ Grand Moulin Guy et Gisèle DORIDANT

87520 VEYRAC
☎ 05 55 03 11 87 🖷 05 55 03 11 87
Limoges 15 km. Monsieur and Madame Doridant have converted their old Limousin barn, situated near their home, into three spacious bedrooms with shower or bath and private wc. There is also a dining room, mezzanine lounge, and a beautiful swimming pool. Closed on Tuesday evenings. Close to the porcelain and enamel museums. Open March to October.
PRICES: s €38; d €46; t €55; extra person €8
NEARBY: Bathing (12km) Canoeing (16km) Horse riding (10km) Fishing (6km) Swimming pool (16km) Hiking (1km) Tennis (1km) Railway station (16km) Shops (1km) **NOTES:** No pets English spoken

continued

ARIÈGE

AX-LES-THERMES

♦♦♦♦ Chambre d'hôtes Pierre SERRES
2E Bazerques, l'Adret, 09110 AX-LES-THERMES
☎ 05 61 64 05 70

Margreth and Pierre welcome guests to their home perched high in the mountains, an ideal base for hiking or skiing holidays. Ax-les-Thermes is a spa town popular with rheumatic and ENT patients. The accommodation comprises two ground floor and three first floor guest rooms, all twin-bedded and with en suite shower-room/wc. There is a large living/dining room with a stone fireplace, a lounge with an attractive fireplace and, outside, a barbecue in the courtyard. Open all year except November.
PRICES: s €30; d €42 **ON SITE:** Fishing **NEARBY:** Horse riding (5km) Golf (70km) Swimming pool (3km) Place of interest (20km) Downhill skiing (10km) Tennis (3km) Spa (2km) Railway station (4km) Shops (2km) **NOTES:** Pets admitted

BENAC

♦♦♦♦ ⏏ Château de Benac Serge et Sylvie DOUMENC
09000 BENAC
☎ 05 61 02 65 20

Foix 8 km. Château de Bénac is a 17th-century château situated in the Barguillère valley. Serge and Sylvie offer the following accommodation: three double guest rooms and three rooms with one double and one single bed. All rooms are on the second floor and have a bathroom/wc and electric heating. On the ground floor guest living rooms have a TV, an open fireplace, books and children's games. Open 1 February to 16 November.
PRICES: s €38; d €49-€52; t €58; extra person €11; HB €37-€40; dinner €16 **ON SITE:** Children's play area **NEARBY:** Horse riding (5km) Golf (20km) Swimming pool (2km) Place of interest (15km) Tennis (2km) Spa (20km) Railway station (8km) Shops (8km) **NOTES:** Pets admitted

COS

♦♦♦♦ ⏏ ⏏ Caussou Paulette BABY
09000 COS
☎ 05 61 65 34 42

Caussou is a renovated farmhouse. On the first floor are two double bedrooms, two rooms with one double and one single bed, two triple rooms and one twin-bedded room. All rooms have en suite shower-room/wc and two have a balcony. Living room, dining room and lounge with fireplace and library. An extra bed can be provided. There are accompanied visits to the mountain pastures weekly. A reduced rate applies on bookings of two nights or more (except in July and August). Open all year, except 15 December to 15 January.
PRICES: d €43; t €55; extra person €14; HB €64-€73; dinner €14 **ON SITE:** Swimming pool Tennis **NEARBY:** Horse riding (2km) Golf (12km) Fishing (3km) Place of interest (18km) Downhill skiing (45km) Spa (30km) Railway station (2km) Shops (2km) Restaurant nearby **NOTES:** No pets

GAUDIES

♦♦♦♦ ⏏ Certes Jeanne GOSSELIN
09700 GAUDIES
☎ 05 61 67 01 56 📠 05 61 67 42 30

This property has been completely renovated and is situated

amongst the hills in spacious grounds near the owners' house. On the ground floor there is a living room and a lounge, upstairs there are four bedrooms (one of which is in the process of being graded), comprising one double and two rooms sleeping three, all with en suite bathroom/wc and heating. Programmes for craft courses are available on request. Open all year.
PRICES: s €21-€26; d €30-€39; t €46; HB €27-€30; dinner €14 **ON SITE:** Fishing **NEARBY:** Horse riding (15km) Swimming pool (13km) Place of interest (45km) Tennis (4km) Railway station (13km) Shops (4km) **NOTES:** Pets admitted English spoken

LE BOSC

♦♦♦♦ ⏏ ⏏ Madranque Birgit et J-Claude LOIZANCE
09000 LE BOSC
☎ 05 61 02 71 29 📠 05 61 02 71 29

Foix 15 km. Col des Marous 2 km. Situated in a mountain hamlet in the "Green Valley" with splendid views, this renovated old farmhouse offers the following accommodation: three guest rooms, two with en suite shower-room/wc and private entrance, and one family room with a double bed, two beds in an annexe and en suite shower-room/wc, costing €66 for four people. Facilities include a washing machine and a tumble dryer. Pets are accepted by prior arrangement. Packed lunches are available. Courses in weaving and dyeing. In winter, accompanied cross country skiing. Open all year.
PRICES: s €35; d €40; t €53; dinner €14 **NEARBY:** Horse riding (6km) Golf (20km) Fishing (2km) Swimming pool (6km) Place of interest (25km) Downhill skiing (4km) Tennis (6km) Spa (35km) Railway station (15km) Shops (6km) **NOTES:** Pets admitted English spoken

LE VERNET

♦♦♦♦ ⏏ Saint-Paul Marie-France TOULIS
09700 LE VERNET
☎ 05 61 68 32 93 & 05 61 68 37 63 📠 05 61 68 31 53

Le Vernet 1 km. This lovely, large renovated farmhouse is situated in five acres of woodland bordered by the River Ariège and by a small stream. Its position is rural and peaceful, yet easily accessible from the RN20. There are four double guest rooms with a private entrance and each with bathroom/wc. A lounge and a dining room with open fireplace and books are at guests' disposal. Open all year.
PRICES: s €28; d €36 **ON SITE:** Fishing **NEARBY:** Horse riding (10km) Golf (40km) Swimming pool (4km) Place of interest (20km) Downhill skiing (60km) Tennis (1km) Spa (40km) Railway station (1km) Shops (4km) **NOTES:** No pets English spoken

LERAN

♦♦♦♦ ⏏ ⏏ Bon Repos Marie-Anne DE BRUYNE
Ferme Bon Repos, 09600 LERAN
☎ 05 61 01 27 83 📠 05 61 01 27 83

Lac de Montbel 3 km. The three first floor guest rooms, all with en suite bathroom/wc, are located on a working dairy/breeding farm. Dining room, lounge with open fireplace and piano. Facilities include private swimming pool, table tennis, picnic area and shady garden. Mountain biking or microlighting available. Local tourist attractions include go-karting (3km), textile museum (8km), museum of agricultural machinery (3km) and the historic sites at Montségur, Mirepoix, Camon, Foix and Puivert. The all-inclusive price for two people is €458 per week. Open all year.

continued

continued

PRICES: s €37; d €42; t €54; extra person €12; dinner €16
NEARBY: Horse riding (5km) Fishing (5km) Swimming pool (3km)
Place of interest (25km) Downhill skiing (25km) Tennis (14km) Railway
station (37km) Shops (3km) **NOTES:** No pets English spoken

⁂ ⍟ Chambre d'hôtes John et Lee-Anne FURNESS
Impasse du Temple, 09600 LERAN
☎ 05 61 01 50 02 & SR : 05 61 02 30 80 📠 05 61 01 50 02
e-mail: john.furness@wanadoo.fr www.chezroo.com
Lac de Léran (beach) 2 km. Mirepoix (13th-century village) 14 km.
This 18th-century house has been restored by an Australian couple
and sits by a small stream. On the ground floor is a lounge and
living room with access on to a courtyard, where breakfast and
evening meals are served. On the first floor there are one double
room, one room with a double and a single bed, and a suite of
two rooms (one double, one twin-bedded). On the second floor
are two double rooms. All have en suite facilities. Guests are
invited to sample regional specialities and Australian cuisine.
Open all year.
PRICES: s €46; d €53; t €67; extra person €14; dinner €18
ON SITE: Tennis **NEARBY:** Golf (50km) Fishing (2km) Swimming pool
(17km) Place of interest (40km) Downhill skiing (45km) Railway station
(50km) **NOTES:** No pets English spoken

LUDIES

⁂ ⍟ Château de Ludies L et J-P BOGULINSKI-FINES
09100 LUDIES
☎ 05 61 69 67 45 & SR : 05 61 02 30 80
Mirepoix, medieval town 10 km. Vals 5 km. Montségur 50 km.
The Château de Ludies has recently been completely rebuilt using
authentic materials. Four guest rooms and one family suite costing
€69 -76 are available, comprising one double room, two rooms
with king-sized beds, one twin-bedded room and another twin-
bedded room with an extra bed in an alcove. Table d'hôte meals
using local produce are available. TV lounge, library, painting
studio, garden with swimming pool, tennis courts, terrace and
gazebo are provided. Games room with billiard table. Open all
year (by reservation only).
PRICES: s €46-€69; d €61-€76; t €76; HB €91; dinner €19
ON SITE: Swimming pool Tennis **NEARBY:** Horse riding (4km) Golf
(50km) Fishing (2km) Place of interest (5km) Downhill skiing (45km)
Spa (65km) Railway station (6km) Shops (3km) **NOTES:** No pets

MAZERES

⁂ ⍟ Chambre d'hôtes Emmanu GUYBERT
10, rue Martimor, 09270 MAZERES
☎ 05 61 69 42 81 & SR : 05 61 02 30 80
This listed mansion, built in 1740, is in the heart of Mazères. There
are five double bedrooms, all combining period charm with
modern comforts. Two of the rooms have a spare single bed, two
have adjoining twin-bedded rooms and one has a private
entrance. All rooms have en suite bathroom/wc. Dining room,
library and lounge with games and a TV. Private wooded garden,
and inner courtyard. Open all year (by reservation only).

continued

PRICES: s €38; d €43-€53; t €69; extra person €15; HB €84; dinner €15
NEARBY: Horse riding (6km) Swimming pool (1km) Downhill skiing
(70km) Tennis (1km) Spa (50km) Railway station (7km) **NOTES:** No
pets English spoken

MONTAUT

⁂ Chambre d'hôtes Casimir & Bernadette GIANESINI
Royat, 09700 MONTAUT
☎ 05 61 68 32 09 📠 05 61 68 32 09
This house has four first floor guest rooms, comprising one grade
2 double room with an adjoining single bedroom and two grade 3
rooms, one double and one twin-bedded. All rooms are equipped
with en suite shower-room/wc. On the ground floor there is a
living room reserved for guests and a kitchen. Guests are free to
enjoy the shade of the trees found in the 24-acre parkland, which
overlooks a lake. Open all year.
PRICES: s €28; d €36-€40 **ON SITE:** Fishing **NEARBY:** Horse riding
(2km) Swimming pool (6km) Tennis (1km) **NOTES:** Pets admitted
English spoken

SALSEIN

⁂ ⍟ La Maison de la Grande Ourse
Judith MATULOVA 09800 SALSEIN
☎ 05 61 96 16 51
Castillon 3 km. Saint-Crions 12 km. Judith welcomes guests to her
home in a small mountain village. On the ground floor are two
double rooms, each with en suite bathroom/wc and opening
directly on to the garden. There are also two guest rooms on the
first floor, one a suite with a picture window, accommodating
three guests, the other a double room with spare bed, balcony and
en suite facilities. Guest lounge with open fireplace, books and a
picture library is available. Judith is happy to advise guests on local
places of interest. Open all year (by reservation only).
PRICES: d €45; dinner €15 **NEARBY:** Horse riding (15km) Swimming
pool (3km) Tennis (3km) Spa (30km) Railway station (40km) Shops
(3km) **NOTES:** Pets admitted English spoken

SERRES-SUR-ARGET

⁂ 🐓 ⍟ Le Poulsieu Bob et Jenny BROGNEAUX
09000 SERRES-SUR-ARGET
☎ 05 61 02 77 72 📠 05 61 02 77 72
Foix 12 km. This 173 acre mountain estate enjoys magnificent
views. It offers five guest rooms, two with one double and one
single bed, one double room, one twin-bedded room and one
room incorporating a double bed and a mezzanine with twin beds.
All rooms have en suite shower-room/wc. There is a dining room,
a lounge with open fireplace and TV, also a kitchen, which is
available at lunchtime. Large terrace, games area and private
swimming pool. Open 1 April to 1 October.
PRICES: s €30-€33; d €37-€40; extra person €8; dinner €12
ON SITE: Horse riding Fishing Swimming pool **NEARBY:** Golf (14km)
Place of interest (20km) Downhill skiing (20km) Tennis (3km) Railway
station (12km) Shops (4km) **NOTES:** Pets admitted English spoken

STE-CROIX-VOLVESTRE

⍟⍟⍟ 🍽 La Maison du Bout du Pont Josette PERE
09230 STE-CROIX-VOLVESTRE
☎ 05 61 66 73 73
This charming house is situated near a lake and provides the
following accommodation: one double room with two adjoining
grade 3 single rooms and en suite shower-room/wc; one grade 3
apartment with one double and one single bed, a lounge and en
suite shower-room/wc; one grade 2 double room with en suite
shower-room/wc. Facilities include a living room, a lounge with TV,
piano and open fireplace, billiards, a garden with a terrace,
minigolf and a children's farm. Open all year.
PRICES: s €25; d €36; dinner €13 **ON SITE:** Horse riding Fishing Tennis
NEARBY: Golf (35km) Swimming pool (20km) Railway station (13km)
Shops (1km) **NOTES:** No pets

ST-GIRONS

⍟⍟⍟ Le Relais d'Encausse Lysette CATHALA
09200 ST-GIRONS
☎ 05 61 66 05 80
In a rural setting, yet only 1.5km from the nearest town, this house
offers comfortable accommodation. One family room with
bathroom, two double and two single beds, also two double
rooms, each with en suite bathroom and a washbasin in an
annexe. There is also a small apartment comprising a lounge with
open fireplace, a kitchen, a bathroom and a double bed. Other
facilities include a large guest lounge with television, piano and
open fireplace, also use of a kitchen. The price for four people is
€61. Open all year.
PRICES: s €31; d €38; t €51 **NEARBY:** Horse riding (2km) Golf (25km)
Fishing (2km) Swimming pool (2km) Place of interest (23km) Downhill
skiing (35km) Tennis (2km) Spa (4km) Railway station (2km) Shops
(2km) **NOTES:** Pets admitted English spoken

ST-PAUL-DE-JARRAT

⍟⍟⍟ Chambre d'hôtes Paul SAVIGNOL
09000 ST-PAUL-DE-JARRAT
☎ 05 61 64 14 26
Foix 7 km. This delightful, detached house is surrounded by forests
and fields. It offers one very spacious double guest room with en
suite shower-room/wc and two further rooms on the ground floor,
one a double and the other a twin-bedded room, each with en
suite shower-room/wc. Two of the rooms are classified grade 3,
the other grade 2. A cot is available on request. Lounge with TV
and kitchenette are provided. Local activities include hang-gliding
(8 km) and water-skiing (4 km). Open 1 May to 30 September.
PRICES: s €34; d €40 **ON SITE:** Swimming pool Tennis
NEARBY: Horse riding (10km) Golf (15km) Fishing (3km) Place of
interest (30km) Downhill skiing (30km) Spa (30km) Railway station (6km)
Shops (3km) **NOTES:** No pets English spoken .

TARASCON-SUR-ARIEGE

⍟⍟⍟ 🍽 Domaine Fournie Pierre MARIE
Route de Saurat, 09400 TARASCON-SUR-ARIEGE
☎ 05 61 05 54 52 📠 05 61 02 73 63
e-mail: Contact@domaine-fournie.com
www.domaine-fournie.com
Tarascon 1 km. A variety of rooms to suit all needs is offered in
this large 17th-century mansion, which is surrounded by parkland
and conservation woodland. There are three double rooms with
en suite bathroom/wc, also one room with a king-sized bed and
two single beds, another with a double and two single beds, both
bedrooms consisting of two large rooms with additional en suite
shower-room/wc. Table d'hôte meals and half board bookings for
two people are available on request. Prices for four people range

from €75 -82. Indoor swimming pool. Open all year.
PRICES: s €40; d €49; t €61-€69; HB €53; dinner €15
ON SITE: Swimming pool **NEARBY:** Downhill skiing (20km) Tennis
(1km) Spa (2km) Railway station (1km) Shops (1km) **NOTES:** No pets

AVEYRON

ALPUECH

⍟⍟⍟⍟ 🍽 ♿ La Violette Danielle et Gilbert IZARD
BDG Air Aubrac, 12210 ALPUECH
☎ 05 65 44 33 64 & 05 65 68 52 36 📠 05 65 44 33 64
france-bonjour.com/air-aubrac·
Laguiole 8 km. Large stretches of pasture land are the setting
for these five rooms with separate access. Four doubles, with
shower or bathroom and wc. One family suite of two
adjoining rooms sleeping four, with private bathroom and wc.
Lounge for guests, with open fire and TV. Living room. Terrace;
garden furniture; table tennis. One room with access for the
less mobile. Hot air ballooning can be arranged. Reduced
rates for longer stay on half board. Open 27 April to
23 September; 28 October to 4 November; 27 December to
3 January.
PRICES: s €46-€50; d €54-€57; t €73; extra person €14; dinner €17
ON SITE: Fishing **NEARBY:** Canoeing (16km) Horse riding (8km)
Swimming pool (8km) Stretch of water (20km) Downhill skiing
(15km) Tennis (8km) Railway station (60km) Shops (3km)
NOTES: No pets

BOURNAZEL

⍟⍟⍟ 💚 La Borde Pilar et Roland MATHAT
12390 BOURNAZEL
☎ 05 65 64 41 09
Belcastel 10 km. Villefranche-de-Rouergue 25 km. Expect a warm
welcome at the Borde farmhouse. This old sheep farm has guest
rooms in an annexe on two levels, with independent entrances.
Two rooms for two/three, with shower and wc. Two family rooms
with mezzanine for two to four, with shower and wc. Communal
living room with open fire and TV. Open grounds; summer kitchen;
barbecue; table tennis; spare bed and cot available. Camping on
farm. Farm-auberge 200m. Open all year.
PRICES: s €30; d €35; t €44; extra person €9 **ON SITE:** Tennis
NEARBY: Canoeing (20km) Horse riding (7km) Fishing (1km)
Swimming pool (7km) Stretch of water (2km) Railway station (9km)
Shops (7km) **NOTES:** No pets

CASTELNAU-DE-MANDAILLES

⍟⍟⍟ La Molière Chantal & Denis LOMBARDO
12500 CASTELNAU DE MANDAILLES
☎ 06 65 48 72 17 📠 05 65 48 72 17
Plateau de l'Aubrac: 20km; Vallée du Lot: 12km. Open countryside
is the setting for La Molière, a small group of farm buildings
tucked away on the hillside between Aubrac and the Lot Valley,

continued   *continued*

near the pilgims' route to St Jacques de Compostelle (GR65). Its pleasant rooms are in an old barn - five rooms with independent access - four doubles and a triple, all with shower or bathroom and wc and TV. Communal salon and kitchenette. Garden, garden furniture, table tennis, parking. Private swimming pool. Open 1st March to 31st October.
PRICES: s €37; d €44; t €59; extra person €15 **ON SITE:** Fishing Swimming pool **NEARBY:** Canoeing (9km) Horse riding (4km) Stretch of water (2km) Cross-country skiing (10km) Downhill skiing (10km) Tennis (4km) Railway station (40km) Shops (4km) **NOTES:** No pets English spoken

COLOMBIES

Ancienne Ecole Françoise et Claude GALAMPOIX
Combrouze, 12240 COLOMBIES
☎ 05 65 69 97 07
Françoise and Claude are your hosts in this old school in a hamlet of Ségala. The bedrooms are comfortable and there are orchards behind the house. Three guest rooms in the owners' home, with independent access; one double and two triples, each with shower or bathroom and wc. Lounge and living room are communal (open fires and library). Courtyard and garden; garden furniture; barbecue. Cots available. 10% discount for stays over two days. Open 15th April to 15th September.
PRICES: s €40; d €55; t €65 **NEARBY:** Horse riding (16km) Fishing (10km) Swimming pool (6km) Stretch of water (40km) Tennis (6km) Railway station (32km) Shops (6km) **NOTES:** No pets

COMPEYRE

Quiers J et V LOMBARD-PRATMARTY
12520 COMPEYRE
☎ 05 65 59 85 10 ▤ 05 65 59 80 99
e-mail: QUIERS@wanadoo.fr www.ifrance.com/quiers
Six guest rooms in an annexe to the farmhouse at Quiers, clinging to the foothills of the Causse cliffs. The Tarn Gorges are nearby. Five double rooms each with private shower or bathroom and wc; one room for four to five people with shower and wc. Spare beds. TV in each room. Garden furniture. Half board. No dinners Sunday evening after 7th August, or Monday evening throughout season. Open 1st April to 11th November.
PRICES: d €43; t €53; extra person €10; dinner €13 **NEARBY:** Canoeing (5km) Horse riding (15km) Fishing (5km) Swimming pool (12km) Stretch of water (40km) Tennis (5km) Shops (12km) Restaurant nearby **NOTES:** Pets admitted

COUPIAC

Lapaloup Rosette SLUIMAN
12550 COUPIAC
☎ 05 65 99 71 49 ▤ 05 65 99 72 63
This farm is dedicated to raising horses and black sheep and offers a magnificent vista over meadows and forests. Walk, ride or cycle in the Parc Naturel Régional des Grands Causses. Three guest rooms for two to three on the first floor of the home of the proprietor. Each with private shower and wc. Communal lounge and sitting room with open fire and TV. Courtyard and covered terrace; garden furniture; barbecue; table tennis. Abbaye de Sylvanes 50km. Vegetarian food can be arranged. Open all year.
PRICES: s €29; d €37; t €55; dinner €16 **ON SITE:** Horse riding **NEARBY:** Canoeing (12km) Swimming pool (13km) Stretch of water (4km) Tennis (4km) Railway station (45km) Shops (4km) **NOTES:** Pets admitted English spoken

ESTAING

Cervel André et Madeleine ALAZARD
Route de Vinnac, 12190 ESTAING
☎ 05 65 44 09 89 ▤ 05 65 44 09 89
In this small hamlet in the Lot Valley at the foot of the Aubrac, Madeleine and André open their doors. Stay in the first floor rooms of their farmhouse, with traditional furniture, and a view over the shady courtyard and flowery terrace. Four guest rooms - two double rooms, and two family triple rooms. Dual queen beds, shower, wc and TV. Spare beds available. Panelled salon for use of guests, with open fire, piano, bookshelves, TV. Garden furniture. Open 1st April to 15th November.
PRICES: s €37; d €45; t €58; extra person €13; HB €34; dinner €14 **NEARBY:** Canoeing (5km) Horse riding (7km) Fishing (2km) Swimming pool (5km) Stretch of water (7km) Cross-country skiing (30km) Downhill skiing (30km) Tennis (5km) Railway station (35km) Shops (5km) **NOTES:** Pets admitted

GISSAC

Saint-Etienne Anne-Marie & Gilbert BOSC
12360 GISSAC
☎ 05 65 99 59 27 & 06 84 11 38 96 ▤ 05 65 99 59 27
Abbaye de Sylvanés 10 km. This countryside family mansion opens onto a paved courtyard, surrounded by old vaulted buildings. The rooms have stone paving slabs and white-washed walls. The hosts can help visitors discover south Aveyron and the Parc des Grands Causses. Two double rooms and two rooms for two to four people on the second floor, each with shower and wc. Lounge with open fire and living room for guests. Courtyard and garden with outdoor furniture. Reduced rates for half board longer stays. Open 15th January to 15th December.
PRICES: s €37; d €46; t €61; extra person €15; dinner €16 **NEARBY:** Horse riding (10km) Fishing (10km) Swimming pool (23km) Tennis (10km) Railway station (35km) Shops (10km) **NOTES:** No pets

LACROIX-BARREZ

Vilherols Jean LAURENS
12600 LACROIX-BARREZ
☎ 05 65 66 08 24 ▤ 05 65 66 19 98
In the house of the proprietors: one family room for three people with shower and wc, access to a sitting room with open fire and TV. In an annexe, three double rooms with TV, shower and wc; one with private terrace. Cooking areas in the bedrooms. Garden and meadowland; garden furniture; parking. Disabled access. A terrific vista over the wild valley of the Truyère. Restaurants 4 and 6km. Keep fit centre 6km. Open July and August and school holidays.
PRICES: s €38-€53; d €46-€61; t €61-€76; extra person €15 **NEARBY:** Horse riding (10km) Swimming pool (6km) Stretch of water (16km) Tennis (4km) Shops (8km) **NOTES:** No pets

LAGUIOLE

Bouet Evelyne et Michel CHAYRIGUES
12210 LAGUIOLE
☎ 05 65 44 33 33 & 06 77 00 53 87
Delightful small château with spacious guest rooms. Four rooms with separate access, for three/four people, each with shower or bathroom, wc and TV. Communal lounge with open fire; washing machine; refrigerator. Courtyard and herb garden; garden furniture; barbecue. Open 1st April to 15th November. Tariff: €71/four persons; reduction for longer stays.
PRICES: s €40; d €48; t €59 **NEARBY:** Horse riding (2km) Fishing (1km) Stretch of water (8km) Downhill skiing (6km) Tennis (1km) Railway station (56km) Shops (1km) **NOTES:** No pets

♯♯♯ ♥ Moulhac Claudine et Philippe LONG
12210 LAGUIOLE
☎ 05 65 44 33 25 & 06 07 30 55 77 ▤ 05 65 44 33 25
www.france-bonjour.com/moulhac/
Laguiole 3 km. On the Aubrac plateau on a cattle farm in the open
country, these guest rooms are in a converted barn adjacent to the
family house. The decoration, mixing traditional and modern
materials, gives a distinct charm to the place. Three double rooms
and one sleeping four, all with shower or bathroom and wc.
Private living room on the ground floor with open fire. Cooking
area available. Garden. Animals accepted by prior booking (dogs
€3.81/night). Small lake in the grounds. Open all year.
PRICES: s €39; d €49; extra person €13 **ON SITE:** Fishing
NEARBY: Horse riding (11km) Stretch of water (10km) Cross-country
skiing (8km) Downhill skiing (8km) Tennis (3km) Railway station (65km)
Shops (3km) **NOTES:** Pets admitted English spoken

LAPANOUSE

♯♯♯ Chambre d'hôtes Armelle et Henri COSTES
Rue des Rosiers, 12150 LAPANOUSE
☎ 05 65 71 64 40 ▤ 06 65 71 64 40
e-mail: COSTES@net.np.com
Gorges du Tarn 25 km. Lapanouse, a small village in the Parc
Naturel Régional des Grands Causses, clusters around its 11th-
century church. Three guest rooms in a converted barn next to the
house. One double room; one room with mezzanine sleeping four;
one duplex for five. Cooking facilities, shower and wc for each.
Private lounge with open fire and TV. Terrace, small garden,
outdoor furniture, barbecue. No smoking rooms. Restaurant 100m.
Baby equipment. Open all year.
PRICES: s €32-€38; d €38; t €50; extra person €12 **NEARBY:** Canoeing
(35km) Horse riding (8km) Fishing (1km) Swimming pool (3km) Stretch
of water (48km) Tennis (3km) Railway station (3km) Shops (3km)
NOTES: Pets admitted English spoken

MILLAU

♯♯♯ ♥ Montels Henriette CASSAN
12100 MILLAU
☎ 05 65 60 51 70

In the proprietor's house, one family room (for four) with shower
and wc; and two double rooms with shower and wc, and
independent access. TV in each room. Communal lounge. Garden,
courtyard and terrace; outdoor furniture; barbecue. This farm
clings to the slopes of the plateau which surrounds Millau, and
enjoys a spectacular view over the town and the foothills of Larzac.
Good area for walking and hang-gliding. Open all year.
PRICES: s €34-€37; d €37-€40; t €46-€49 **NEARBY:** Canoeing (5km)
Fishing (7km) Swimming pool (5km) Stretch of water (35km) Tennis
(5km) Railway station (5km) Shops (5km) **NOTES:** No pets

ONET-LE-CHATEAU

♯♯♯ ♥ Les Cabaniols Nadine CONSTANS
12850 ONET-LE-CHATEAU
☎ 05 65 42 68 33 & 06 82 08 57 63 ▤ 05 65 42 68 33
Whether strolling on the nearby Causses, or on longer hikes
towards the Conques, the Lakes of Levezou or Aubrac, or golfing at
nearby Fontanges - you won't be short of things to do here. Three
bedrooms (for two, three or four) in a converted barn; one room
for two in a separate small building. Private shower rooms and wcs.
Private kitchen corner and lounge with TV and books. Garden,
outdoor furniture, barbecue. Cot available. Open all year.
PRICES: s €37-€41; d €41-€46; t €56; extra person €9 **NEARBY:** Horse
riding (10km) Fishing (7km) Swimming pool (4km) Stretch of water (30km)
Tennis (2km) Railway station (4km) Shops (4km) **NOTES:** No pets

PEYRELEAU

♯♯♯ ♥◯♥ l'Ermitage Doris et Philippe GARSI
12720 PEYRELEAU
☎ 05 65 62 61 91 & 06 08 51 23 65
L'Ermitage is a vast old convent that overlooks the listed village of
Peyreleau, at the confluence of the Gorges of the Tarn and the
Jonte. Three bedrooms: two doubles and a suite for two or three,
each with shower or bathroom and wc. Vaulted dining room and
private TV lounge. Terrace, garden furniture, mountain bikes,
organic breakfast. Dinners may be booked (Friday and Saturday
evening only). Out of season reduced rates for stays over four
nights. Open 20th March to 12th November.
PRICES: s €46; d €50-€73; t €73-€88; extra person €15; dinner €21
ON SITE: Canoeing Fishing Tennis **NEARBY:** Horse riding (4km)
Swimming pool (9km) Cross-country skiing (40km) Downhill skiing
(40km) Railway station (20km) **NOTES:** No pets English spoken

PONT-DE-SALARS

♯♯♯ ♥◯♥ La Coste Michel et Mireille BEDOS
12290 PONT-DE-SALARS
☎ 05 65 46 84 14 & 06 83 46 42 71 ▤ 05 65 46 84 14
e-mail: mireillebedos@fr.st www.mireillebedos.fr.st
Micropolis, the city of insects. 20 km. Three guest rooms in the
proprietors' house opposite the gendarmerie. On the ground floor,
with separate entrance: two double rooms and a twin, each with
shower, wc and satellite TV. Communal lounge. Lovely garden with
outdoor furniture. River and sailing. Restaurant 500m. Animals
must be booked. Dinner only if booked (not available Sunday
evening). Reduction for longer stays out of season. Mireille, a
tourist guide, has prepared routes for you to follow. Open all year.
PRICES: s €38; d €45; extra person €17; dinner €17 **ON SITE:** Fishing
Stretch of water Tennis **NEARBY:** Canoeing (13km) Horse riding (4km)
Swimming pool (3km) Railway station (20km) **NOTES:** Pets admitted

PRADES-DE-SALARS

♯♯♯ ♥ Boulouis Annie et David CLUZEL
12290 PRADES-DE-SALARS
☎ 05 65 46 34 55 ▤ 05 65 46 34 55
Beside the Lac de Pareloup, is this pretty farmhouse. Five guest
rooms in a converted stone barn with separate access. Three
double rooms and two for four (one a family room), all with
shower and wc. Cot available. Private lounge, library, terraces,
garden, outdoor furniture, table tennis. Meals can be booked in
the farm-auberge (no lunches on Monday). Reduction for longer
stays. Open 1st June to 30th September and weekends in May.
PRICES: s €34; d €40; t €53; extra person €12; dinner €14
ON SITE: Fishing Stretch of water **NEARBY:** Horse riding (3km) Tennis
(3km) Railway station (36km) Shops (3km) Restaurant nearby
NOTES: Pets admitted English spoken

RIGNAC

♯♯♯ ♥ La Garrissonie André et Monique PRADEL
12390 RIGNAC ☎ 05 65 64 53 25 📄 05 65 64 53 25
La Garrissonie is near to Rodez, and you can explore its lanes, which lead to the cathedral, visit Belcastel and sample the local wine in the producer's home. Three rooms with mezzanine, exposed beams and covered terrace. Two double rooms with private shower/wc. One room for three (grade 2) with separate bathroom and wc. Shady garden with outdoor furniture. Barbecue and picnicking possible. Two horses available for guests. Animals accepted with prior booking. Restaurants 4km. Farm-auberge 2km. Tariff: €51.83 for four persons. Open all year.
PRICES: d €34; t €41; extra person €8 **NEARBY:** Horse riding (15km) Fishing (5km) Swimming pool (5km) Tennis (5km) Railway station (25km) Shops (5km) **NOTES:** Pets admitted

RIVIERE-SUR-TARN

♯♯♯ ⁄⊙⁄ l'Arcade Jeannine et Francis FABRE
rue Beausoleil, 12640 RIVIERE-SUR-TARN
☎ 05 65 59 85 88 & 06 08 65 01 90 📄 05 65 59 85 88

L'Arcade is a large house on the way to the Tarn Gorges. Five rooms with independent access. Three upstairs double rooms; two rooms for two or three at ground level. All have shower and wc. TV in one room. Communal lounge. Terrace. Lawn with surrounding hedges and garden furniture. Parking. Regional cuisine, using produce from the garden. No evening meal on Sunday. Animals admitted if pre-booked. Children's games, table tennis. Leisure centre 1km. Open 15 March to 15 November.
PRICES: s €33; d €40; t €49; extra person €9; dinner €13
ON SITE: Children's play area Canoeing Horse riding Fishing Tennis **NEARBY:** Swimming pool (1km) Railway station (12km) **NOTES:** Pets admitted English spoken

♯♯♯ ⁄⊙⁄ Les Salles Jean et Jeanine MELJAC
12640 RIVIERE-SUR-TARN
☎ 05 65 59 85 78 📄 05 65 59 85 78
Millau 12 km. On the road to the Tarn Gorges, is this winegrower's farm - a large stone house right in the middle of the hamlet. Four double rooms and one sleeping three, each with shower and wc, and independent access. Games area, table tennis, terrace, parking, barbecue, pétanque. Lovely swimming pool. No dinner on Sunday. Beach 1km on the Tarn. Reduction for longer stays (not July and August). Open all year.
PRICES: s €30; d €40; t €55; dinner €13 **ON SITE:** Children's play area Canoeing Horse riding Fishing Swimming pool **NEARBY:** Tennis (1km) Railway station (12km) **NOTES:** Pets admitted

SANVENSA

♯♯♯ ⁄⊙⁄ Monteillet Pierre et Monique BATESON
12200 SANVENSA ☎ 05 65 29 81 01 📄 05 65 65 89 52
e-mail: pbc.@wanadoo.fr
Monique and Pierre welcome guests to this house in a hamlet.

Three rooms for two to four people (two on the ground floor with independent access). Two double rooms with shower or bathroom and wc, and shared terrace. In an annexe, one bedroom for two to four, with kitchenette, bathroom and wc, and terrace. Shared facilities include a lounge with TV and open fire, open courtyard, garden furniture, barbecue, table tennis. No evening meal on Tuesday, Thursday or Sunday unless booked. Open all year, except 9-24 August.
PRICES: s €35; d €38; t €46; dinner €15 **ON SITE:** Tennis
NEARBY: Canoeing (15km) Horse riding (1km) Fishing (5km) Swimming pool (11km) Stretch of water (20km) Railway station (11km)
NOTES: Pets admitted English spoken

SAUVETERRE-DE-ROUERGUE

♯♯♯ ⁄⊙⁄ Lou Cambrou Marcel et Maguy PRIVAT
Jouels, 12800 SAUVETERRE-DE-ROUERGUE
☎ 05 65 72 13 40
In this old convent in the village, guests will find bedrooms in individual styles. Four bedrooms on the first floor, with separate access. One family room for four or five people, and three doubles, all with private shower and wc. Living room and TV lounge reserved for guests. Terrace, garden furniture, parking. Nearby are the royal house at Sauveterre, the village of Belcastel and the Château du Bosc. No evening meals on Friday and Saturday in July and August. Open all year.
PRICES: s €34; d €42-€53; t €57-€67; dinner €14 **ON SITE:** Fishing
NEARBY: Horse riding (4km) Swimming pool (4km) Stretch of water (10km) Tennis (2km) Railway station (10km) Shops (4km) **NOTES:** No pets

ST-REMY

♯♯♯ ⁄⊙⁄ Mas de Jouas Guy et Christel TAILLET
12200 ST-REMY
☎ 05 65 81 64 72 📄 05 65 81 50 70
Near to Villefranche de Rouergue, the Mas du Jouas nestles in serene countryside. Below the bedrooms in the old sheepfold, the pool and waterfall dominate the view. On two floors: five double rooms each with bath and wc; one room for three, again with bath and wc. TV in every room. Living room on ground floor. Extensive open grounds. Garden furniture. Small pond. Free tennis. Telephone. Reduced rates for longer stays. Open from 1st March to 31st December.
PRICES: s €43; d €58-€61; t €72-€75; extra person €14; dinner €19
ON SITE: Fishing Swimming pool **NEARBY:** Canoeing (20km) Horse riding (7km) Tennis (1km) Railway station (7km) Shops (7km)
NOTES: Pets admitted English spoken

VILLEFRANCHE-DE-ROUERGUE

♯♯♯ ♥ Le Mas de Comte Agnès JAYR
Les Pesquies, 12200 VILLEFRANCHE-DE-ROUERGUE
☎ 05 65 81 16 48 📄 05 65 81 16 48
Whether you sleep in the Provençal bedroom or the African, you will love the charm and the ambiance of the Mas de Comte, and the welcome of your hosts, M and Mme Jayr. Two double rooms, with private bathroom and wc, and a room for three with shower and wc. Kitchenette/living room and lounge with open fire and TV. Spare bed and cot available. Garden, outdoor furniture. Reduced rates for extended stay. Open 1st February to 31st December.
PRICES: s €34; d €44; t €54; extra person €10 **NEARBY:** Canoeing (12km) Horse riding (6km) Fishing (1km) Swimming pool (6km) Stretch of water (15km) Tennis (6km) Railway station (6km) Shops (6km)
NOTES: Pets admitted English spoken

continued

GERS

AUCH

♦ ❧ Le Castagne Véronique SEMEZIES-DUPUY
Route de Toulouse, 32000 AUCH

☎ 05 62 63 32 56 & SR : 05 62 61 79 00 🖹 05 62 63 32 56

Véronique welcomes you to her restored house at the gates of Auch, with impressive views over the castle and the countryside. Four rooms, two with double and single beds, one with three single beds and one with a double and twin beds. All have own shower and wc. Upstairs is a lounge with corner kitchen (fridge), living room with fireplace and TV. Baby cot available, laundry and heating. Leisure activities: mini-golf, mountain biking, camping, pool and games room. Proprietor's mobile phone: 06 07 97 40 37. Open all year.

PRICES: s €31; d €40; t €54; extra person €11   **ON SITE:** Fishing Swimming pool   **NEARBY:** Horse riding (8km) Golf (8km) Theme park (25km) Tennis (8km) Sailing (25km) Railway station (4km) Shops (4km) **NOTES:** No pets English spoken

BELMONT

♦ Les Figuiers Violette et John SMITH
Couté, 32190 BELMONT

☎ 05 62 06 58 33 & SR : 05 62 61 79 00 🖹 05 62 06 58 33

John and Violette welcome guests to their large Gascon home opening out onto a flower garden, with panoramic views of the hills. The upstairs guestrooms, all with shower and wc, offer one double, one with three single beds, and one with a double and a child's bed, and there is a small lounge nook on the landing. On the ground floor there is a living/dining room, TV, library and a large garden with pool. Open 1 April to 31 December.

PRICES: s €43; d €49; extra person €15   **ON SITE:** Swimming pool **NEARBY:** Horse riding (11km) Golf (25km) Fishing (11km) Tennis (11km) Sailing (11km) Railway station (32km) Shops (11km) **NOTES:** No pets CC English spoken

BIRAN

♦ Betaire-Sud Henri et Jeannette BARBE
32350 BIRAN

☎ 05 62 64 63 73

Three guestrooms are available in this house dominating the village and its hills, with a sheltered park and large meadow. One double and one twin room with TV on the ground floor with bathroom facilities and a corner kitchen for use. Upstairs is a family double room with bathroom and wc along a private corridor. Extra child's bed for €7.5. Private lake 1km, golf at Auch/Embats 12km, boules 500m, Lavardens 12km. Price for four: €70. Open all year.

PRICES: s €28; d €38; t €50; extra person €14   **NEARBY:** Horse riding (15km) Golf (12km) Theme park (12km) Fishing (3km) Swimming pool (15km) Tennis (15km) Sailing (12km) Railway station (15km) Shops (8km) **NOTES:** No pets

CASTELNAU-D'AUZAN

♦ ❧ 🍽 Domaine de la Musquerie
Michel et Bernadette DENIS
Le Juge, 32440 CASTELNAU-D'AUZAN

☎ 05 62 29 21 73 & SR : 05 62 61 79 00 🖹 05 62 29 28 47
e-mail: michel.denis@guideo.fr

Eauze 8 km. Barbotan 12 km, Séviac. Michel and Bernadette welcome you to their mansion which has a wooded garden with furniture. Ten hectares of the 30 ha estate is made up of vineyards. Three upstairs rooms, two with two double beds and one with three single, all have own shower and wc facilities. Communal living areas with TV, washing machine and cot available on request. Gastronomic meal supplement: €9. Children's meal: €7.5. Walks, own wine on sale. Proprietor's mobile phone: 06 83 97 89 19. Open all year.

PRICES: s €40; d €49; t €63.5; extra person €18 **NEARBY:** Horse riding (4km) Golf (4km) Theme park (12km) Fishing (10km) Swimming pool (3km) Tennis (3km) Sailing (12km) Railway station (65km) Shops (3km) **NOTES:** No pets English spoken

CAUSSENS

♦ ❧ Le Vieux Pressoir Christine et Laurent MARTIN
Saint-Fort, 32100 CAUSSENS

☎ 05 62 68 21 32 & SR : 05 62 61 79 00 🖹 05 62 68 21 32

Large 17th-century stone building with flower garden containing pool and jacuzzi. The dining room opens out onto a terrace, and there are pleasant views over the hills. Three upstairs rooms, one family sized, one twin, and two large singles. All have bathroom facilities. TV, central heating, communal lounge. Washing machine €7.5 per load. Gastronomic meal supplement: €8.5. Children's meal: €7. Price based on four people: €61/75. Reductions for stays longer than three nights. Local farm produce including foie gras. Open all year.

PRICES: s €38; d €47; t €53-€66; HB €38; FB €49; dinner €15 **ON SITE:** Swimming pool **NEARBY:** Horse riding (6km) Golf (28km) Theme park (15km) Fishing (1km) Tennis (8km) Sailing (15km) Railway station (40km) Shops (8km) Restaurant nearby **NOTES:** No pets CC English spoken

EAUZE

♦ Hourcazet Claude LEJEUNNE
32800 EAUZE

☎ 05 62 09 99 53 & SR : 05 62 61 79 00 🖹 05 62 09 99 53
e-mail: claude.lejeunne@mageos.com   site.voila.fr/hourcazet

Eauze 6 km. This old timbered farmhouse sits amongst vines and a flower garden with hundred year old oaks. Upstairs in the owner's house, there are two double rooms with extra single beds, each with TV, shower room and wc, and in the annexe, two double rooms en suite on the ground floor. There is heating, a communal lounge with TV, fireplace and library, terrace and large park. Open 1 April to 30 November, other dates upon reservation.

PRICES: s €45; d €55; extra person €20   **NEARBY:** Horse riding (6km) Golf (6km) Theme park (13km) Fishing (13km) Swimming pool (6km) Tennis (6km) Sailing (13km) Railway station (60km) Shops (6km) **NOTES:** Pets admitted English spoken

♦ ❧ 🍽 Mounet Bernard et Monique MOLAS
32800 EAUZE

☎ 05 62 09 82 85 & SR : 05 62 61 79 00 🖹 05 62 09 77 45

Manor house surrounded by parkland. One double room on the ground floor and two more upstairs, one with an extra bed for third person, all with washing facilities. Family dining room with TV and fireplace on the ground floor and upstairs, a den and lounge with TV and library. Visit the farm and buy farm produce. Spa 12km away. Gastronomic meal supplement: €18 extra/person. Open Easter to 1 November.

continued

PRICES: ; d €45-€53; HB €42.5-€46.5; dinner €20 **NEARBY:** Horse riding (3km) Golf (3km) Theme park (12km) Fishing (4km) Swimming pool (3km) Tennis (3km) Sailing (12km) Railway station (55km) Shops (4km) Restaurant nearby **NOTES:** No pets English spoken

FOURCES

₩₩ Château du Garros Anne CARTER
32250 FOURCES
☎ 05 62 29 47 89 ▤ 05 62 29 47 89
e-mail: chateaudugarros@wanadoo.fr
http:/perso.wanadoo.fr/chateaudugarros/
Fources 0.5 km, 14th-century circular bastide town. In a large charming home surrounded by parkland, Anne offers you three rooms of which two are family sized with en suite facilities. You will have use of lounge, dining room, library and fireplace. The rooms are spacious and decorated with antique furniture. Outside are garden furniture and a barbecue. Reduced price for children under 12. Open from May to October.
PRICES: s €69-€92; d €76-€99; t €122 **ON SITE:** Fishing
NEARBY: Horse riding (5km) Golf (16km) Swimming pool (10km) Tennis (1km) Railway station (55km) Shops (13km) **NOTES:** No pets

GALIAX

₩₩ Au Hameau Pierre et Michele METAYER
32160 GALIAX
☎ 05 62 69 34 23
Three double guestrooms arranged upstairs in the owners' house with en suite facilities, dining and living rooms on the ground floor, fireplace and heating. Spa 35km away. Special price for three nights or more. Open 8th January to 20th December.
PRICES: s €24; d €38; extra person €10 **NEARBY:** Horse riding (15km) Golf (35km) Theme park (18km) Fishing (1km) Swimming pool (4km) Tennis (2km) Sailing (10km) Railway station (7km) Shops (3km)
NOTES: No pets

GAZAUPOUY

₩₩ ⎆ Domaine de Polimon
Philippe & Catherine BOLAC
32480 GAZAUPOUY
☎ 05 62 28 82 66 ▤ 05 62 28 82 88

Adjacent to the property, a small orangery offers a family room with lounge and shower and wc. One twin and one double room each with shower and wc and central heating upstairs in a wing of the main house, and two more family rooms in an outbuilding with shower, wc and electric heating. Lounge, library, TV, fireplace, kitchenette. Cot available on request. Meals available on request in July and August, children's meal: €9. Price for 4 €90. Open all year.
PRICES: s €35-€45; d €50-€60; t €75; extra person €15; dinner €18
ON SITE: Children's play area Swimming pool Tennis **NEARBY:** Horse riding (10km) Golf (30km) Theme park (8km) Fishing (8km) Sailing (8km) Railway station (26km) Shops (10km) **NOTES:** Pets admitted English spoken

IDRAC-RESPAILLES

₩₩ ⎆ ⎝Ol Au Noby Alain et Hélène FILLOS
Les Quatre Saisons, 32300 IDRAC-RESPAILLES
☎ 05 62 66 60 74 & SR : 05 62 61 79 00
Mirande (bastide, museum, country music festival in July) 3 km. Alain and Hélène welcome you to their recently built home overlooking the countryside and lake, near a farm, with four double rooms en suite. At your disposal, corner kitchen with fridge, washing machine, heating and lounge. Gastronomic meal supplement: €4.5. Special prices for stays of three days or more. Open all year.
PRICES: s €28; d €34; t €43; dinner €14 **NEARBY:** Horse riding (6km) Golf (25km) Theme park (17km) Fishing (3km) Swimming pool (3km) Tennis (3km) Sailing (17km) Railway station (21km) Shops (3km)
NOTES: No pets English spoken

JEGUN

₩₩ ⎝Ol Chambre d'hôtes Rolande MENGELLE
28 Grand rue, 32360 JEGUN
☎ 05 62 64 55 03 & SR : 05 62 61 79 00
Auch 15 km. Rolande welcomes guests to a stone house with panoramic views. Four rooms on the second floor, one family with canopied double and a single bed, two with double and twin beds, each with shower and wc, and another double room with seating area and bathroom with wc. Lounge with TV and hi-fi, and a kitchenette. One grade 2 double room on the ground floor with own shower and wc. Laundry service available. Gastronomic meal supplement: €9. Half-board available on reservation. Open 1st March to 31st October.
PRICES: s €42; d €45; t €55; extra person €20; dinner €20
ON SITE: Tennis **NEARBY:** Horse riding (13km) Golf (15km) Theme park (4km) Fishing (4km) Swimming pool (13km) Sailing (4km) Railway station (15km) **NOTES:** No pets

JUILLAC

₩₩ ⎆ ⎝Ol Au Château
Yves et Hélène DE RESSEGUIER
32230 JUILLAC
☎ 05 62 09 37 93 & SR : 05 62 61 79 00
Marciac jazz festival 5 km (August). Yves and Hélène welcome guests to this 18th-century monastery which has a large sheltered park with flowers and century old trees. Two double and one twin room upstairs in a side wing adjoining the owners' home, on the ground floor a day-room with fireplace and corner kitchenette. Electric heating, laundry service, cot and child's bed available and bicycles. Gastronomic meal supplement: €8. Children's meal: €9. Proprietor's mobile phone:- 06 15 90 25 31. Open all year.
PRICES: s €43; d €46; extra person €11; HB €39; dinner €16
ON SITE: Fishing **NEARBY:** Horse riding (5km) Golf (10km) Theme park (5km) Swimming pool (5km) Tennis (5km) Sailing (5km) Railway station (40km) Shops (5km) **NOTES:** No pets

JUILLES

₩₩₩ Au Soulan de Laurange
Gérard CROCHET et Alain PETIT
Chemin de Ladeveze, 32200 JUILLES
☎ 05 62 67 76 62 & SR : 05 62 61 79 00
▤ 05 62 67 76 62
Gimont 5 km. Toulouse 60 km. Gérard and Alain welcome guests to their 18th-century home, with park, terraces, panoramic views of the hillsides and three comfortable rooms. One double and twin room with an extra single bed and one room with three single beds, shower, wc and double washbasin each. A family suite includes one double room with shower, wc and double washbasin, and another room has a

continued

three-quarter bed, bathroom and wc opposite. Heating, pool and laundry service available. Meals available on request. Off-peak rates available. Open all year. Price for 4: €158. Minimum 2 nights stay in July/August.
PRICES: s €75; d €83; t €103-€150; dinner €20
ON SITE: Swimming pool **NEARBY:** Horse riding (6km) Golf (25km) Theme park (17km) Fishing (6km) Tennis (6km) Sailing (17km) Railway station (6km) Shops (5km) **NOTES:** No pets English spoken

LAAS

₩₩ ¡O¡ Marchou Paul et Odette DUFFAR
32170 LAAS ☎ 05 62 67 57 14 & SR : 05 62 61 79 00
Four upstairs rooms in an old terraced farmhouse with a shady flower garden. One grade 3 double room with private wc and bathroom, two grade 2 double rooms with own shower and two wcs on the landing. Finally one grade 3 family room with a double, twin beds, a fold-up and a cot with shower and wc. There is a dining room. Living room with fireplace and TV, and an outside canopy for alfresco dining. Children's meal: €7. Price for four: €64.5. Open all year.
PRICES: s €25-€29; d €34-€39; t €52; extra person €13; HB €33-€35; dinner €16 **ON SITE:** Tennis **NEARBY:** Horse riding (3km) Golf (4km) Theme park (3km) Fishing (3km) Swimming pool (10km) Sailing (3km) Railway station (35km) Shops (4km) **NOTES:** Pets admitted

LARTIGUE

₩₩ 🐓 Garrigas Marie-Claire FORGET
32450 LARTIGUE
☎ 05 62 65 42 10 & SR : 05 62 61 79 00 🖷 05 62 65 49 25
Marie-Claire and Jean welcome guests to an annexe of their house opening out onto a large wooded garden, with flowers and garden furniture, overhanging the valley of Arratz. Three rooms on the ground floor, one double, one twin and another small double with shower and wc each. In the house there is a dining room and TV lounge. Cot available, hunting, walking and fishing excursions, views onto the hillsides of Haut Astarac and farmhouse inn 5km away. Open 1st April to 15th December.
PRICES: s €40; d €44; extra person €20 **NEARBY:** Horse riding (10km) Golf (20km) Theme park (6km) Fishing (6km) Swimming pool (10km) Tennis (6km) Sailing (6km) Railway station (17km) Shops (6km) **NOTES:** Pets admitted English spoken

₩₩ ¡O¡ Chambre d'hôtes Nicole et Philippe DEVAUX
Hameau de Mazeres, 32450 LARTIGUE
☎ 05 62 65 80 72 & SR : 05 62 61 79 00 🖷 05 62 65 80 75
Nicole and Philippe welcome guests to a renovated wing of their house giving onto large shaded and flowered grounds with outdoor furniture. Two twin rooms on the ground floor opening out onto a terrace, two double rooms upstairs with balconies. All rooms have shower and wc. Lounge with TV, piano and fireplace, washing machine, cot, photocopy and minitel, ping-pong. Gastronomic meal supplement: €7. Children's meal: €7. Fishing, hunting, hiking around Haut Astarac, and the Pyrenees are 1km away. Open all year.
PRICES: s €42; d €46; t €57; HB €37; dinner €14 **NEARBY:** Horse riding (6km) Golf (25km) Theme park (7km) Fishing (1km) Swimming pool (17km) Tennis (7km) Sailing (30km) Railway station (20km) Shops (7km) **NOTES:** Pets admitted English spoken

₩₩ ¡O¡ Moulin de Mazeres Régine BERTHEAU
32450 LARTIGUE
☎ 05 62 65 98 68 🖷 05 62 65 83 50
Located on the D40, four rooms in an old watermill and lovely buildings among lawn, meadows and trees. One double, one twin and one room with three singles, all with own shower and wc, and "The Owl Barn"- a double room with shower, wc, seating area and

fireplace. Heating, on site pool and ping-pong. Open all year.
PRICES: s €51; d €57; t €63; dinner €19 **ON SITE:** Fishing Swimming pool **NEARBY:** Horse riding (15km) Golf (20km) Theme park (7km) Tennis (12km) Sailing (7km) Railway station (20km) Shops (7km) **NOTES:** Pets admitted English spoken

LAUJUZAN

₩₩ 🦃 Domaine du Verdier
J-Pierre & Geneviève SANDRIN
32110 LAUJUZAN
☎ 05 62 09 06 57
Geneviève and Jean-Pierre welcome guests to their Napoleon III home on the hillsides of Armagnac in Gascony. One twin and one double room opening out onto a park, and a large room with a double and two wide single beds in the alcove, all with own bathroom and wc. Summer dining room/TV lounge and kitchen. Access to shaded park with flowers, pond, three bikes, ping-pong, croquet, volleyball, boules and pool. Price for large room: €90. Open 15th June to 15th September.
PRICES: s €41; d €49; extra person €8 **ON SITE:** Children's play area Fishing Swimming pool **NEARBY:** Horse riding (13km) Golf (25km) Theme park (20km) Tennis (9km) Sailing (20km) Railway station (35km) Shops (9km) **NOTES:** Pets admitted English spoken

LAURAET

₩₩₩ Au Bernes Léa HERBINIERE
La Bastidoun, 32330 LAURAET
☎ 05 62 68 29 49 🖷 05 62 68 29 49
Léa greets guests to her Gascon home amidst the Armagnac vineyards. One double and one twin room on the second floor with mansard roof, bathroom and wc each. On the first floor, one twin and one double with shared bathroom and lounge with TV fireplace and books on the region, separate wcs. Heating, telephone, fax, minitel, garden, terraces, outdoor furniture, barbecue, boules, ping-pong and mountain biking. Price for four: €80. Open all year.
PRICES: s €40; d €48; t €70 **NEARBY:** Horse riding (14km) Golf (18km) Theme park (8km) Fishing (2km) Swimming pool (5km) Tennis (3km) Sailing (27km) Railway station (55km) Shops (5km) **NOTES:** No pets English spoken

₩₩₩ Peillot Dominique MORARDET
32330 LAURAET
☎ 05 62 29 51 85 & SR : 05 62 61 79 00 🖷 05 62 29 51 85
e-mail: franck.morardet@wanadoo.fr
Dominique and Pierre welcome guests to their Gascon farmhouse, completely restored, in a green setting of four hectares. Five rooms with shower and wc, two on the ground floor. Two doubles, one room with two large singles and sofabed, and two family rooms each with double and twin beds. Private living and dining rooms, large reception room in the annexe, pool and paddling pool for kids. Local interest: museum of Armagnac, cathedral. Price for four: €90. Open all year.
PRICES: s €49; d €57; t €73; extra person €17 **ON SITE:** Swimming pool **NEARBY:** Horse riding (10km) Golf (12km) Fishing (5km) Tennis (6km) Railway station (40km) Shops (5km) **NOTES:** No pets English spoken

LAVARDENS

₩₩₩ 🐓 Mascara Roger et Monique HUGON
32360 LAVARDENS
☎ 05 62 64 52 17 & SR : 05 62 61 79 00 🖷 05 62 64 58 33
Monique and Roger welcome guests to their large country house, which has a flower garden. Three upstairs rooms with en suite facilities, double and twin rooms. On the ground floor, dining room, lounge with TV and fireplace, piano and library for guest use. There is a pool, terrace, lawn, garden furniture, mountain

continued

continued

biking and ping-pong. Sale of local produce. On the D103. Open 1st February to 31st December.
PRICES: s €45-€50; d €54-€61; extra person €16 **ON SITE:** Swimming pool **NEARBY:** Horse riding (15km) Golf (12km) Theme park (14km) Fishing (4km) Tennis (14km) Sailing (14km) Railway station (15km) Shops (10km) **NOTES:** No pets English spoken

LE HOUGA

♦♦♦ |O| Le Glindon Brigitte DUCHENE
32460 LE HOUGA
☎ 05 62 08 97 61 & SR 05 62 61 79 10 ▤ 05 62 08 97 61
Nogaro racing circuit (15 km). Brigitte and Daniel welcome you to their restored 17th-century Gascon timbered farmhouse. There are two double rooms with en suite facilities and another grade 2 double room with an extra single bed, bathroom and wc, all on the ground floor. Large lounge with TV, garden furniture on the patio, dining room with fire and library shared with the owners. At the edge of the forest, guests may spot deer. Games, volleyball and pool. Foie gras-making course. Open all year.
PRICES: s €40; d €48; t €58; HB €39; dinner €15 **ON SITE:** Fishing **NEARBY:** Horse riding (2km) Golf (20km) Swimming pool (6km) Tennis (4km) Railway station (32km) Shops (4km) **NOTES:** No pets English spoken

L'ISLE-JOURDAIN

♦♦♦ ❤ |O| Au Pigeonnier de Guerre Eliane BAJON
32600 L'ISLE-JOURDAIN
☎ 05 62 07 29 17 & SR : 05 62 61 79 00 ▤ 05 62 07 31 70
Eliane welcomes guests to the converted cowshed adjoining her home, near a pigeon house typical of the area, with views of the valley. There are three rooms with shower and wc each, two double, and one double and single. Groups of up to eight are received. Living room with TV and fireplace, library, terrace and outdoor furniture. Gastronomic meal supplement: €14. Special price for stays of three nights or more.
Mobile phone: 05 62 07 29 04. Open 1st January to 24th December.
PRICES: s €38; d €42; t €54; HB €36; dinner €15 **ON SITE:** Fishing **NEARBY:** Horse riding (7km) Golf (4km) Theme park (3km) Swimming pool (3km) Tennis (3km) Sailing (3km) Railway station (2km) Shops (2km) Restaurant nearby **NOTES:** No pets English spoken

♦♦♦ ❤ |O| Le Fiouzaire
Jacques et M-Claude CHAUVIGNE
Chemin de Ninets, Route de Grenade,
32600 L'ISLE-JOURDAIN
☎ 05 62 07 18 80 & SR : 05 62 61 79 00 ▤ 05 62 07 08 24
A single storey farmhouse. One double room with lounge, TV, shower and wc, central heating in the owner's house, and in the annexe, one double, and another with an extra single, both en suite. Also two rooms with double and twin beds, kitchenette, mezzanine and TV each, one extra single available. Terrace, barbecue, dining corner, fireplace and communal pool. In the annexe, shared lounge, TV and washing machine. Specialist foie gras producing farmer. Mountain biking, walks and cookery course. Price for four people: €65. Gastronomic meal supplement: €10. Reductions for stays of four nights or more.
PRICES: s €31; d €40; t €52; extra person €5; HB €36; dinner €16 **ON SITE:** Swimming pool **NEARBY:** Horse riding (4km) Golf (4km) Theme park (4km) Fishing (4km) Tennis (4km) Sailing (4km) Railway station (4km) Shops (4km) **NOTES:** Pets admitted

MARSOLAN

♦♦♦ |O| Le Nauton Michèle VINCENT
Saint-Jacques, 32700 MARSOLAN
☎ 05 62 68 99 82 & SR : 05 62 61 79 00 ▤ 05 62 68 99 81
e-mail: lenauton@aol.com

Lectoure 6 km. Michèle greets her guests in this 17th and 18th-century property set in a three hectare park. Five ground floor rooms in a building near the host's own home. Three double, two with bathroom and wc, and one with shower and wc. Two twin, one with bath and the other with shower room. Nice old furniture, central heating, lounge with TV and open fire, dining room, pool, ping-pong, boules, fortified villages nearby. Dinner by request. Children's meal: €11. Half-board based on two sharing. Minimum of two nights in July and August. Open all year.
PRICES: s €69; d €73; extra person €23; dinner €23
ON SITE: Swimming pool **NEARBY:** Horse riding (17km) Golf (18km) Theme park (8km) Fishing (5km) Tennis (2km) Sailing (8km) Railway station (40km) Shops (6km) **NOTES:** No pets English spoken

MAUPAS

♦♦♦ |O| Le Pouy Germaine et Béatrice DUCASSE
32240 MAUPAS
☎ 05 62 09 60 68 & SR : 05 62 61 79 00 ▤ 05 62 09 60 68
Germaine and daughter Béatrice greet guests in their 17th-century renovated house, located on a sandy bank by an oak forest. On the ground floor, a double room with an extra three-quarter sized bed with shower and wc, another double with extra single, bathroom and wc. Two more double rooms, one with empire style canopy, bathroom and wc, the other with shower and wc. Kitchen/diner with fireplace, lounge with TV, central heating, pool and games pitch on site. Open from Easter to mid-November.
PRICES: s €40-€43; d €45-€50; t €60-€65; extra person €15
ON SITE: Children's play area Swimming pool **NEARBY:** Horse riding (10km) Golf (20km) Theme park (14km) Fishing (1km) Tennis (3km) Sailing (14km) Railway station (35km) Shops (3km) **NOTES:** Pets admitted English spoken

MAUROUX

♦♦♦ |O| Moulin au Pouteou Bernhard et Ingrid HILPERT
32380 MAUROUX
☎ 05 62 66 33 82 & SR : 05 62 61 79 00 ▤ 05 62 66 33 82
Saint-Clar 4 km. Lectoure 19 km. Renovated farmhouse with flower garden, dining room with fireplace and espresso bar, modern kitchen, lounge and living room with fireplace TV, library, hi-fi, fax, washer-dryer, pool and outdoor furniture. On the ground floor, two rooms with a double and a single bed, another with two double beds and lastly, a double room upstairs, all with en suite facilities. Spa and gym 19km. Special price for stays of three nights or more. Gastronomic meal supplement: €25. Children's meal: €14. Price for four: €99. Open 1st February to 31st December.
PRICES: d €75; t €84-€87; HB €66; FB €94; dinner €28
ON SITE: Swimming pool **NEARBY:** Horse riding (20km) Golf (15km) Theme park (4km) Fishing (4km) Tennis (4km) Sailing (4km) Railway station (55km) Shops (4km) **NOTES:** No pets

MIRADOUX

♦♦♦ Maison Lou Casaù A et B LANUSSE CAZALE
5 place de la halle, 32340 MIRADOUX
☎ 05 62 28 73 58 ▤ 05 62 28 73 17
Lectoure 17 km. A warm welcome awaits at this 18th-century property in the heart of a small tranquil village, with quality furniture and decor, dining room, living room, garden and terrace, pool with power jets. Three elegant and spacious rooms, one double with shower and wc on the ground floor, upstairs one twin with bathroom and wc, and a family suite with a double and three single beds with bathroom and wc. Open 1st April to 15th November.
PRICES: s €55; d €65; t €85; extra person €20 **ON SITE:** Swimming pool Tennis **NEARBY:** Horse riding (13km) Golf (24km) Fishing (3km) Railway station (30km) **NOTES:** No pets English spoken

continued

MIDI-PYRÉNÉES

MIRANDE

♥ Le Président Marie-Hélène PIQUEMIL
Route d'Auch, 32300 MIRANDE
☎ 05 62 66 64 06 & SR : 05 62 61 79 00   🖷 05 62 66 64 06
Mirande Country Music Festival (week of 14 July). Marie-Hélène
and Jacques receive guests in their large renovated house opening
out onto a big flower garden with views of the Pyrenees. There are
two double rooms with sofabed, shower and wc, each with own
access through a small garden and terrace, on the ground floor.
Upstairs there is a family room with mansard roof, double and
twin beds, two showers and wc. There is a games room with
billiards. Nearby: golfing at Pallane or jazz in Marciac during the
first two weeks of August. Open all year.
PRICES: s €35-€42; d €40-€46; extra person €12   **NEARBY:** Horse riding
(4km) Golf (20km) Fishing (2km) Swimming pool (2km) Tennis (2km)
Sailing (15km) Railway station (25km) Shops (1km) **NOTES:** No pets
English spoken

Moulin de Régis Gisèle et Pierre TREMONT
32300 MIRANDE
☎ 05 62 66 66 29 & SR : 05 62 61 79 00   🖷 05 62 66 51 06
A restored 12th-century watermill surrounded by shaded lawn and
flowers at the edge of the canal in Pays d'Astarac. Four rooms on
the second floor, three double and one twin, all with shower or
bathroom facilities and separate wcs, TV and phone. Living room
with fireplace, sauna, jacuzzi. Canoeing, kayaking, horses and
stables. Country Music Festival in July at Mirande.
Price for four: €114. Open all year.
PRICES: ; d €84; t €99   **ON SITE:** Fishing Swimming pool
NEARBY: Horse riding (2km) Golf (20km) Theme park (14km) Tennis
(1km) Sailing (14km) Railway station (20km) Shops (1km) **NOTES:** No
pets

MONFERRAN-PLAVES

♥ IOI Les Merisiers Louisette LEBRUN
32260 MONFERRAN-PLAVES
☎ 05 62 66 20 90 & SR : 05 62 61 79 00
At the top of a hill, Louisette and Auguste offer rooms in their
small Gascon farmhouse. Upstairs one twin and one double with
fold-up, both with bathroom and separate wc, opening out onto a
terrace. On the ground floor, another double room with shower
and wc. Lounge with TV, fireplace, library, hi-fi, washing machine,
heating, cot bed and bedding available, outdoor furniture, terrace
with dining area in summer and hunting trips or foie gras courses.
Gastronomic meal: €12. Children's meal: €8.Open 1st January to
25th December.
PRICES: s €35-€38; d €41-€46; extra person €12; HB €39-€41; dinner €18
NEARBY: Golf (13km) Theme park (20km) Fishing (10km) Swimming
pool (3km) Tennis (3km) Sailing (20km) Railway station (23km) Shops
(3km) **NOTES:** No pets English spoken

MONFERRAN-SAVES

♥ IOI Le Meillon Anne-Marie LANNES
32490 MONFERRAN-SAVES
☎ 05 62 07 83 34 & SR : 05 62 61 79 00   🖷 05 62 07 83 57
Anne-Marie and Jean-Raymond greet guests at their farmhouse
with large garden and views of the valleys. There are three double
and one twin room with own shower or bathroom and wc on the
first floor, on the ground floor are the dining and living rooms.
Laundry service, pool, jacuzzi and lake fishing. Gastronomic meal
supplement: €9. Children's meal: €9. Open all year.
PRICES: s €44; d €54; extra person €17; dinner €17   **ON SITE:** Swimming
pool **NEARBY:** Horse riding (7km) Golf (7km) Fishing (7km) Tennis
(7km) Sailing (7km) Railway station (30km) Shops (7km) **NOTES:** No
pets CC English spoken

MONTAMAT

♥ IOI Caufepe Lucien et Monique JONCKEAU
32220 MONTAMAT
☎ 05 62 62 37 55 & SR : 05 62 61 79 00   🖷 05 62 62 32 10
Upstairs, the Blue Room and the Green Room are doubles and the
Old Room is double with a single. All have shower and wc in this
18th-century farmhouse on the hillsides of Gers, run by Monique
and Lucien. Dining/TV room, central heating, garden, summer
dining area with kitchen, laundry service and picnic baskets.
Homegrown farm produce. Gastronomic meal supplement: €5.5.
Open all year.
PRICES: s €30; d €41; t €55; HB €37; dinner €16   **ON SITE:** Children's
play area **NEARBY:** Horse riding (10km) Golf (30km) Theme park (7km)
Fishing (7km) Swimming pool (5km) Tennis (5km) Sailing (7km) Railway
station (28km) Shops (5km) **NOTES:** No pets

MONTESQUIOU

Maison de la Porte Fortifiée Marie-Thérèse KOVACS
Au village, 32320 MONTESQUIOU
☎ 05 62 70 97 59 & SR : 05 62 61 79 00   🖷 05 62 70 97 59
www.france-bonjour.com/gascogne/

This 18th-century house adjoins a 13th-century city gate. Four
individual rooms on the first floor, one twin and one double both
with own shower and wc. On the second floor, one twin and one
double with extra single, with en suite facilities. Living room for
guests opening out onto a terrace. Pay-phone. Small charge for
children under 12. Special price for stays of five nights or more
except in season. Proprietor's mobile phone: 06 87 89 31 02.
Open 1st to 9th January and 6th February to 31st December.
PRICES: s €34-€48; d €42-€61; extra person €18   **NEARBY:** Horse riding
(5km) Theme park (7km) Fishing (7km) Swimming pool (10km) Tennis
(1km) Sailing (20km) Railway station (29km) Shops (1km) **NOTES:** No
pets

POLASTRON

♥ IOI Lou-Cantou Louis et Lise BENEDET
32130 POLASTRON
☎ 05 62 62 53 39 & 05 62 62 41 71   🖷 05 62 62 41 71
Lise and Louis welcome guests to their renovated house in the
heart of the village of Polastron with four bedrooms on the ground
and first floors. "The Blue Roses" is a twin, "The Thirties",
"Countryside" and "At Grandma's" are all doubles, and all have
their own shower and wc. Dining room with open fire, washing
machine. Farm produce for sale. Visits to the preserve factory.
Meals on request, gastronomic meal supplement: €7.5 a head.
Open 15th January to 30th November, except 15th to 30th
September.
PRICES: s €27; d €38; t €49; extra person €11; HB €33; dinner €14
NEARBY: Horse riding (8km) Golf (30km) Theme park (5km) Fishing
(5km) Swimming pool (8km) Tennis (4km) Sailing (5km) Railway station
(12km) Shops (8km) **NOTES:** Pets admitted

RISCLE

Ⓦ Ⓦ Bidouze Georgette et Daniel DUBOS
32400 RISCLE
☎ 05 62 69 86 56 ▤ 05 62 69 75 20
Between the Landes and the Pyrenees, a restored farmhouse with
five guestrooms upstairs. One family room with mezzanine and
two double beds with bathroom and wc, one double, one twin,
one double and twin, and one double and single, all with shower
and wc each. Central heating, washer-dryer, lounge with TV and
kitchenette. Gastronomic meal supplement: €23. Open all year.
PRICES: d €47-€50; t €63-€66; dinner €11 **NEARBY:** Horse riding
(18km) Theme park (2km) Fishing (2km) Swimming pool (2km) Tennis
(2km) Sailing (15km) Railway station (50km) Shops (2km) Restaurant
nearby **NOTES:** No pets

SAMATAN

Ⓦ Ⓦ ⓘ◎ⓘ Latrillote Monique MORVAN
32130 SAMATAN
☎ 05 62 62 31 17 & SR : 05 62 61 79 00 ▤ 05 62 62 31 17
Three guestrooms in a small farmhouse with views of the Pyrenees,
3km northwest of Samatan. Two grade 3 double rooms with
bathroom and wc each, and one grade 2 double room with own
shower and wc down the hall. Dining room, lounge, central heating,
covered terrace, camping on the grounds and extra children's room
(two singles). Traditional Gascon cuisine, children's meal: €7.5.
Supplement for gastronomic meals: €7.5. Special price for stay of
three nights or more. Open 5th January to 20th December.
PRICES: s €27-€30; d €32-€40; HB €36; dinner €16 **NEARBY:** Horse
riding (3km) Golf (35km) Theme park (3km) Fishing (3km) Swimming
pool (3km) Tennis (3km) Sailing (2km) Railway station (15km) Shops
(3km) **NOTES:** Pets admitted

SARRAGACHIES

Ⓦ Ⓦ La Buscasse Fabienne et J-Michel ABADIE
32400 SARRAGACHIES
☎ 05 62 69 76 07 & SR : 05 62 61 79 00 ▤ 05 62 69 79 17
e-mail: Buscasse@aol.com
Fabienne, Jean-Michel and their children offer guests their
beautiful 18th-century house within parkland with magnificent
views of farmland and vineyards. Three pretty rooms upstairs, one
large double, one double and one twin, all with en suite facilities.
Dining/living room with fireplace, kitchen and washing machine.
Several sites and monuments, leisure parks nearby, pool, bicycles,
archery and visits to wine cellars. Open all year.
PRICES: s €42; d €45; extra person €15 **ON SITE:** Swimming pool
NEARBY: Horse riding (15km) Golf (20km) Theme park (15km) Fishing
(5km) Tennis (2km) Sailing (15km) Railway station (40km) Shops (5km)
NOTES: Pets admitted CC English spoken

SIMORRE

Ⓦ Ⓦ ⓘ◎ⓘ La Ferme du Rey
Marie et Pascal CONSIGLIO
32420 SIMORRE
☎ 05 62 65 35 91 & SR : 05 62 61 79 00 ▤ 05 62 65 36 42
Marie and Pascal welcome guests to their restored mansion house
with shaded flower gardens, pool and walking nearby. There are
four upstairs rooms furnished with antiques, one twin, one double
and two large doubles, all with shower and wc. Lounge with sofa,
TV and video, library. On the ground floor, a living room with
fireplace. Laundry service, central heating and cot available.
Hunting 8km away. Gastronomic meal supplement: €7. Children's
meal: €8. Open 15th March to 30th November.
PRICES: s €31; d €42; extra person €14; HB €37; dinner €16
ON SITE: Swimming pool **NEARBY:** Horse riding (3km) Golf (4km)
Theme park (7km) Fishing (2km) Tennis (4km) Sailing (7km) Railway
station (35km) Shops (3km) **NOTES:** No pets English spoken

ST-CLAR

Ⓦ Ⓦ ⓘ◎ⓘ Chambre d'hôtes Nicole COURNOT
La Garlande., Place de la Mairie, 32380 ST-CLAR
☎ 05 62 66 47 31 & SR : 05 62 61 79 00 ▤ 05 62 66 47 70
e-mail: nicole.cournot@wanadoo.fr
Stone mansion house with 13th-century hall on site, and walled
garden. Rooms are upstairs, one double with fold up for child,
own entrance and shower and wc. Another double with single
room attached, shower and wc, and a room with single and large
single, shower and wc. Also an extra twin room for children, with
shower and basin. Large lounge and shared kitchen, dining room
with fireplace. Meals available on request except Tuesdays and
Thursdays. Children's meal: €8. Open March to December.
PRICES: s €37; d €46-€55; t €70; HB €39-€44; dinner €16
NEARBY: Horse riding (4km) Golf (10km) Theme park (4km) Fishing
(1km) Swimming pool (10km) Tennis (1km) Sailing (4km) Railway
station (50km) **NOTES:** No pets English spoken

STE-DODE

Ⓦ Ⓦ ⓘ◎ⓘ Au Manot le Village
C LALANNE et A LAVERDURE
32170 STE-DODE
☎ 05 62 67 11 31 ▤ 05 62 67 11 31

Anne and Claudine offer a restored wing of their traditional house
with large shaded garden. Five rooms with own entrance via
terrace or gallery. One twin on the ground floor with shower and
wc, three twins and one double upstairs each with own shower
and wc. Living room, TV lounge, washing machine, fax, central
heating and cot available. Bicycles, mountain biking and ping-
pong. Meals available 1st July to 30th September. Children's
meal: €7. Open all year.
PRICES: s €35; d €40; extra person €11; dinner €14 **ON SITE:** Swimming
pool **NEARBY:** Horse riding (20km) Golf (16km) Theme park (8km)
Fishing (8km) Tennis (6km) Sailing (8km) Railway station (40km) Shops
(6km) **NOTES:** No pets English spoken

ST-LARY

Ⓦ Ⓦ ⓘ◎ⓘ Le Cousteau Yann MALARET
32360 ST-LARY
☎ 05 62 64 53 50 & SR : 05 62 61 79 00
Jegun 6 km. Five guestrooms in a Gascon house with rustic
furnishings. Living room, terrace, private pool and central heating.
On the first floor, two doubles with shower and wc each, and two
more doubles with bathroom and wc each. On the ground floor, a
room for four with private bathroom and wc. Spa 11km away. At
weekends there is Gascon cooking and foie gras. Open 1st January
to 2nd September and 21st September to 31st December.
PRICES: s €31; d €38; t €53; HB €36; FB €51; dinner €17
ON SITE: Swimming pool **NEARBY:** Horse riding (20km) Golf (15km)
Theme park (11km) Tennis (15km) Sailing (11km) Railway station (14km)
Shops (6km) Restaurant nearby **NOTES:** No pets

ST-MAUR

⚓ 🐓 Domaine de Loran Jean et Marie NEDELLEC
32300 ST-MAUR
☎ 05 62 66 51 55 & SR : 05 62 61 79 00 ▤ 05 62 66 78 58
Marie and Jean welcome guests to their large home in beautiful
parkland. On the first floor, two family rooms with double and
twin beds, own bathroom and wc each, one double with shower
and wc and another double with shower and wc down the hall.
Living room, games room with billiards and ping-pong, and library.
Extra heating and cot available. Price for four: €70. Open from
Easter to 1 November.
PRICES: s €31-€34; d €40-€45; t €55-€60; extra person €15
NEARBY: Horse riding (3km) Golf (12km) Theme park (5km) Fishing
(1km) Swimming pool (3km) Tennis (3km) Sailing (5km) Railway station
(28km) Shops (3km) **NOTES:** Pets admitted

⚓ 🐓 Noailles Marthe SABATHIER
32300 ST-MAUR
☎ 05 62 67 57 98 & SR : 05 62 61 79 00
Three guest rooms arranged on the first floor of the owners'
house. One double and one twin room, shower and wc each, one
family room with two double beds and shower and wc. There is a
dining room, living room, corner kitchen, shaded walled garden
and barbecue. Walks on site. Working farm. Price for four: €66.
Open all year.
PRICES: s €30; d €35; t €61 **NEARBY:** Horse riding (4km) Golf (12km)
Theme park (4km) Fishing (4km) Swimming pool (8km) Tennis (1km)
Sailing (4km) Railway station (32km) Shops (8km) **NOTES:** Pets
admitted

ST-PUY

⚓ 🍴 La Lumiane J-Louis et C SCARANTINO
32310 ST-PUY
☎ 05 62 28 95 95 & SR : 05 62 61 79 00 ▤ 05 62 28 59 67
e-mail: LA.LUMIANE@wanadoo.fr
Flaran 10 km (Cistercian Abbey). Castéra-Verduzan 9 km.
Jean-Louis and Catherine welcome guests to their 18th-century
property in the heart of the village. Pool, barbecue and outdoor
furniture. There is one double room in the owners' house with
bathroom and wc, and in the annexe four double rooms, two
upstairs, two on the ground floor, two with shower and wc and
two with bathroom and wc. All rooms have telephone and TV.
Communal lounge with fireplace and TV, heating, washing
machine, fax and cot. Meals on request. Gastronomic meal
supplement: €7.5. Closed in school holidays - February.
PRICES: s €53; d €61; extra person €23; dinner €23
ON SITE: Swimming pool Tennis **NEARBY:** Horse riding (11km) Golf
(18km) Theme park (9km) Fishing (9km) Sailing (9km) Railway station
(34km) **NOTES:** No pets English spoken

TERMES-D'ARMAGNAC

⚓ 🐓 🍴 Domaine de Labarthe
Christiane & Marlène LARDENOIS
32400 TERMES-D'ARMAGNAC
☎ 05 62 69 24 97 & SR : 05 62 61 79 00 ▤ 05 62 69 24 97
Marlène and her mother welcome guests to their farm in the
valley of Adour, once part of the Tour de Termes d'Armagnac.
There are three double rooms upstairs, two with extra single beds,
each with own bathroom and wc or shower. There are two seating
areas on the first floor and living and dining rooms on the ground
floor. The garden is surrounded by fish ponds, ancient moats and
fortresses. Foie gras made on the farm. Children's meals: €7.5.
Open all year.
PRICES: s €37; d €43; t €54; HB €35; dinner €13 **NEARBY:** Horse riding
(20km) Fishing (2km) Swimming pool (7km) Tennis (7km) Sailing
(10km) Railway station (50km) Shops (7km) **NOTES:** No pets

⚓ 🐓 🍴 Sempe Ariane LAINE
32400 TERMES-D'ARMAGNAC
☎ 05 62 69 25 13 & SR : 05 62 61 79 00 ▤ 05 62 69 25 13

Ariane welcomes guests to her farm with garden, outdoor
furniture, ping-pong and mountain biking. Four rooms in an
outbuilding attached to the owner's home contain one double, one
double with a large single, one with three singles and one with a
double and a single, each with own shower and wc. Lounge with
TV, corner kitchen with fridge and central heating. Two more
rooms for three with shower and wc each. Farm produce for sale,
jazz festival in Marciac. Price for 4: €61. Supplement for
gastronomic meals: €4. Open all year.
PRICES: s €37; d €42; t €57; extra person €61; HB €34; dinner €17
ON SITE: Swimming pool **NEARBY:** Horse riding (20km) Golf (34km)
Theme park (10km) Fishing (3km) Tennis (1km) Sailing (10km) Railway
station (54km) Shops (9km) **NOTES:** Pets admitted

TOURNECOUPE

⚓ 🐓 🍴 Chambre d'hôtes Jean et Jacqueline MARQUE
En Bigorre, 32380 TOURNECOUPE
☎ 05 62 66 42 47 & SR : 05 62 61 79 00
Six rooms in a wing of the owners' house, each with own shower
and wc. On the ground floor, two double rooms, and three more
with an extra single bed in each. Upstairs there is another double
room. Central heating at no extra cost, washing machine, pool,
bicycles, fishing and putting green. Lunch can be prepared under
the canopy, in the shaded garden. There is a lounge with TV and
dining room with fireplace. Open all year.
PRICES: s €34; d €46; t €64; extra person €18; HB €35; dinner €12
ON SITE: Swimming pool Tennis **NEARBY:** Horse riding (15km) Golf
(15km) Theme park (15km) Fishing (1km) Sailing (15km) Railway station
(45km) Shops (5km) **NOTES:** Pets admitted

HAUTE-GARONNE

ANAN

⚓ Le Moulin de Samaran Marc et Odile MOTTE
31230 ANAN
☎ 05 61 94 14 43
L'Isle-en Dodon 4 km. A renovated house on the edge of the
Gascony region. There is a kitchen, dining area and further room
on the ground floor. A pink and green bedroom has one double
and one single bed. There is also a 1930s single bedroom. Each
bedroom has its own bathroom facilities. Electric heating. Many
historic sites in the area, neighbouring markets. Open from May
until October.
PRICES: s €33; d €39; t €54 **ON SITE:** Fishing **NEARBY:** Horse riding
(10km) Swimming pool (4km) Tennis (4km) Railway station (35km)
Shops (4km) **NOTES:** No pets

> Prices are given in Euros €1 = £0.62
> at the time of going to press

AUTERIVE

✦✦✦ ⍥ La Maison de Pierrette Pierrette BOURDEAU
Rue Michelet, 31190 AUTERIVE
☎ 05 61 50 81 31 & 06 08 01 28 98 ▤ 05 61 50 81 31
Toulouse 35 km. Guestrooms in a small suburban tavern, restored by the hosts. Dining room and shared areas on the ground floor. The bedrooms are on the first floor and can be reached via an external staircase. Three twin bedrooms, all with bathroom facilities. Gas central heating, swimming pool and parking. Lovely views of the countryside, and a shaded garden. Open all year.
PRICES: s €39; d €43; t €55; extra person €13; dinner €13 **ON SITE:** Children's play area Swimming pool **NEARBY:** Horse riding (4km) Golf (15km) Fishing (1.5km) Stretch of water (10km) Tennis (1.5km) Railway station (2km) Shops (1km) **NOTES:** No pets English spoken

✦✦✦ ⍥ La Manufacture Valérie BALANSA
2 rue des Docteurs Basset, 31190 AUTERIVE
☎ 05 61 50 08 50 & 06 74 12 60 10 ▤ 05 61 50 08 50
www.pyrenet.fr/manufacture
Bedrooms in an 18th century building that once manufactured sheets for royalty. On the ground floor is a dining room, another room with a stove and a TV shared with the hosts. On the first floor are one bedroom with a double and a single bed, a twin bedroom, a triple bedroom and two double bedrooms. All have bathroom facilities. Two bedrooms have TV points. Garden, courtyard and park. Swimming pool, bikes, porch, table tennis, games and parking are all available. Open April to end of October.
PRICES: s €45-€50; d €60-€75; t €80-€95; extra person €20; dinner €24 **ON SITE:** Children's play area Fishing Swimming pool Hiking **NEARBY:** Horse riding (8km) Stretch of water (15km) Tennis (1km) Railway station (1km) **NOTES:** No pets English spoken

✦✦✦ 🐾 ♿ Les Murailles Hélène TOURNIANT
Route de Grazac, 31190 AUTERIVE
☎ 05 61 50 76 98 ▤ 05 61 50 76 98
e-mail: helene.tourniant@wanadoo.fr
A renovated Toulouse poultry farm with five bedrooms, situated 2.5km from the village. There are two triple rooms, each with bathroom facilities. On the ground floor, there are three bedrooms with three double beds, each with bathroom facilities. One bedroom has access for the less mobile. All bedrooms are non-smoking. Lounge with TV, bookcase and indoor games. Breakfast rooms on the first floor. Local produce for sale. Open all year upon reservation.
PRICES: d €43; extra person €17; dinner €16 **ON SITE:** Hiking **NEARBY:** Horse riding (3km) Swimming pool (3km) Stretch of water (10km) Tennis (3km) Railway station (2km) Shops (3km) Restaurant nearby **NOTES:** No pets

AUZAS

✦✦✦ 🐾 Chambre d'hôtes Angeline et André SCHMITT
31360 AUZAS
☎ 05 61 90 23 61 ▤ 05 61 90 23 61
Situated on a working farm. Large room with fireplace and TV reserved for guests, three bedrooms and one bedroom with one double bed and two single beds. Each bedroom has private bathroom facilities. Swimming pool. Farm produce for sale. Visit the farm and take part in bread making. Open all year.
PRICES: s €32; d €38; t €52; dinner €13 **ON SITE:** Swimming pool Hiking **NEARBY:** Horse riding (5km) Fishing (1km) Tennis (1km) Railway station (10km) Shops (5km) Restaurant nearby **NOTES:** Pets admitted

Use the atlas at the back of the guide to locate your chambre d'hôtes

AZAS

✦✦✦ En Tristan Gérard et Chantal ZABE
31380 AZAS
☎ 05 61 84 94 88 ▤ 05 61 84 94 88
e-mail: en.tristan@free.fr http://en.tristan.free.fr
An old restored farm, 2 km from the village in the direction of Garrigues. Large lounge with fireplace and TV on the ground floor. On the first floor are four bedrooms with private bathroom facilities. There is one twin bedroom, and three triple bedrooms. Reading room, lounge area for guests. Garden, courtyard, barbecue, games area and patio. Open all year.
PRICES: s €32-€37; d €37-€41; t €53 **ON SITE:** Hiking **NEARBY:** Horse riding (5km) Golf (7km) Fishing (3km) Swimming pool (8km) Stretch of water (10km) Tennis (5km) Shops (8km) **NOTES:** No pets English spoken

BRETX

✦✦✦ 🐾 ⍥ Domaine de Fleyres
André et Sylvie DELPRAT
31530 BRETX
☎ 05 61 85 39 53 & 06 15 42 75 12 ▤ 05 61 85 39 53
A beautiful house with a large flowery park situated 100m from the farm. There is a dining room, lounge with a fireplace, TV area and kitchen on the ground floor. There is also a triple bedroom. On the first floor there is a double bedroom with a cot, two triple bedrooms and a double bedroom. All bedrooms have bathroom facilities. Open 1st April to 31st October.
PRICES: s €40; d €45; t €55; dinner €13 **ON SITE:** Horse riding Fishing Hiking **NEARBY:** Golf (12km) Swimming pool (4km) Stretch of water (15km) Tennis (4km) Railway station (20km) Shops (2km) **NOTES:** Pets admitted

CABANAC-SEGUENVILLE

✦✦✦✦ ⍥ Château de Séguenville
Jean-Paul et Marie LARENG
31480 CABANAC SEGUENVILLE
☎ 05 62 13 42 67 ▤ 05 62 13 42 68
e-mail: info@chateau-de-seguenville.com
www.chateau-de-seguenville.com
Toulouse 45 km. Guestrooms full of character, situated at the heart of the Gascony region. The park has hundred-year-old trees and is very tranquil. The ground floor is solely for the use of guests and has a TV room, a large room with a fireplace, a dining room and a patio. On the first floor is a suite of three non-smoking bedrooms. Each en suite bedroom has a large double bed. Open 15th January to 15th December.
PRICES: d €90-€95; t €100-€110; dinner €20 **ON SITE:** Children's play area Swimming pool Hiking **NEARBY:** Golf (24km) Fishing (5km) Stretch of water (12km) Tennis (7km) Railway station (45km) Shops (12km) **NOTES:** No pets English spoken

CARAMAN

✦✦✦ Château de Croisillat GUERIN
Le Croisillat, 31460 CARAMAN
☎ 05 61 83 10 09 ▤ 05 61 83 30 11
e-mail: chateau.du.croisillat@wanadoo.fr
Guestrooms in a 14th and 18th-century château, 2.5km from the village. There are three double bedrooms, a single bedroom and a bedroom with one double and two single beds. All rooms have bathroom facilities and authentic period furniture. There is also a room with a fireplace. Dining room, garden, parking and swimming pool. Open 15 March to 15 November.
PRICES: s €61; d €77-€92; t €92-€99; dinner €16 **ON SITE:** Swimming pool Hiking **NEARBY:** Horse riding (3km) Golf (29km) Fishing (3km) Stretch of water (3km) Tennis (3km) Railway station (30km) Shops (3km) **NOTES:** Pets admitted English spoken

CASTELNAU-D'ESTRETEFONDS

♦♦♦ Saint-Guilhem Esméralda & Philippe LADUGUIE

31620 CASTELNAU-D'ESTRETEFONDS

☎ 05 61 82 12 09 & 06 85 20 54 18 ▤ 05 61 82 65 59

Fronton 2.5 km. Toulouse 24 km. Four guestrooms in a wine-makers residence, situated 2.5km from the village. There is a triple bedroom, two twin bedrooms and a triple bedroom with a cot. All bedrooms are non-smoking, and have independent access, private bathroom facilities and a fireplace. There is a lounge with a TV. Large wooded area and an outdoor swimming pool. Open all year.
PRICES: s €34-€46; d €41-€49; extra person €12 **ON SITE:** Wine tasting Swimming pool Hiking **NEARBY:** Horse riding (4km) Golf (15km) Fishing (12km) Stretch of water (15km) Tennis (3km) Railway station (8km) Shops (3km) **NOTES:** No pets English spoken

CINTEGABELLE

♦♦♦ ❦ ⑩ Serres d'en Bas

Danielle DESCHAMPS-CHEVREL

Route de Nailloux, 31550 CINTEGABELLE

☎ 05 61 08 41 11 ▤ 05 61 08 41 11

Situated on the edge of Lauragais, in an old renovated farm. One double bedroom on the ground floor. On the first floor are one triple bedroom, one twin bedroom and one suite with one double and three single beds. Each bedroom has private bathroom facilities. Lounge, TV area and another room reserved for guests. Table tennis, children's games and a laundry are all available to guests. Open from Easter until 30th September.
PRICES: s €38; d €42-€46; t €60-€60; extra person €15; dinner €15 **ON SITE:** Children's play area Swimming pool Hiking Tennis **NEARBY:** Horse riding (4km) Golf (40km) Fishing (3km) Stretch of water (10km) Railway station (4km) Shops (4km) **NOTES:** No pets

FIGAROL

♦♦♦ ⑩ Chourbaou BORDERES MARQUAIS

31260 FIGAROL

☎ 05 61 98 25 54

An old farm, full of character dating from 1878, which has been entirely renovated. There is an 180° view over the Pyrenees. Dining room with fireplace and TV area on the ground floor. On the first floor, there are two twin bedrooms, a double bedroom and a family suite, all with bathroom facilities. There is an enclosed flowery, shaded area and parking. Picnics in the garden. Open all year.
PRICES: s €31-€34; d €38-€43; t €52; extra person €13; dinner €13 **ON SITE:** Children's play area Hiking **NEARBY:** Horse riding (7km) Fishing (2km) Swimming pool (7km) Stretch of water (7km) Tennis (4km) Railway station (10km) Shops (5km) **NOTES:** Pets admitted

FRANCON

♦♦♦ ⑩ La Bastide Vidiane DUCLAUD

31420 FRANCON

☎ 05 61 98 67 25

A very large old house on the edge of the village. Three bedrooms on the first floor with two double beds and two single beds. There is one further twin bedroom. All bedrooms have private bathroom facilities. On the ground floor, there is a large lounge/dining room with a fireplace. Garden with heated swimming pool, shaded patio and summer kitchen. Parking is available. Open from April until October.
PRICES: s €38; d €45; t €61; dinner €15 **ON SITE:** Swimming pool Hiking **NEARBY:** Horse riding (8km) Fishing (15km) Stretch of water (15km) Tennis (5km) Railway station (30km) Shops (8km) **NOTES:** No pets

GRENADE

♦♦♦ Domaine de Vivès Monique FAUVARQUE

31330 GRENADE

☎ 05 61 82 65 30 & 06 85 04 76 87

Toulouse 25 km. The Domaine de Vivès is an ideal base from which to explore the cultural treasures of Toulouse. On the first floor, 'Bouton d'Or' is a double room with shower room and wc. There is also a family room comprising a double room, 'Marguerite', and a twin room, 'Berger', with bathroom and separate wc. Guests are welcome to share the proprietor's lounge on the ground floor. Open all year.
PRICES: s €37; d €40; t €55; extra person €70 **ON SITE:** Children's play area Fishing **NEARBY:** Horse riding (15km) Golf (10km) Swimming pool (1km) Stretch of water (15km) Tennis (1km) Railway station (7km) **NOTES:** No pets

JUZET-DE-LUCHON

♦♦♦ ⑩ Le Poujastou Elodie et Thierry COTTEREAU

Rue du Sabotier, 31110 JUZET DE LUCHON

☎ 05 61 94 32 88 & 06 88 30 00 20

e-mail: lepoujastou@wanadoo.fr

www.lepoujastou.com

Bagnères-de-Luchon 2 km. Elodie and Thierry welcome guests to their renovated former café, near Luchon. Dining room and room with a fireplace on the ground floor. On the first floor, there are two single bedrooms and one triple bedroom. The second floor has a bedroom with four single beds and a further triple bedroom. Each bedroom has bathroom facilities. There is an enclosed garden and a garage. Open all year.
PRICES: s €30; d €44; t €64; extra person €20; dinner €13 **NEARBY:** Horse riding (2km) Golf (3km) Fishing (2km) Swimming pool (2km) Stretch of water (2km) Tennis (2km) Railway station (2km) Shops (2km) **NOTES:** No pets English spoken

LABROQUERE

♦♦♦ ⑩ Château de Vidaussan Christiane SIPIETER

31510 LABROQUERE

☎ 05 61 95 05 68

Saint-Bertrand-de-Comminges 4 km. The Château de Vidaussan is on the edge of the Garonne region. Large dining room with fireplace and shared room on the ground floor. The first floor has two double bedrooms, one triple bedroom, a single bedroom and a twin double bedroom, with two additional single beds. All bedrooms have private bathroom facilities. Large wooded park and swimming pool. Fishing and cultural visits are available nearby. Open all year.
PRICES: s €37; d €41; t €53; extra person €15; dinner €14 **ON SITE:** Fishing Swimming pool Tennis **NEARBY:** Horse riding (1km) Golf (5km) Stretch of water (5km) Railway station (5km) Shops (5km) **NOTES:** Pets admitted English spoken

LATOUR

♦♦♦ ❦ ⑩ Namaste Marie-Paule REVEILLES

Primoulas, 31310 LATOUR

☎ 05 61 97 46 87 & 06 84 19 42 64 ▤ 05 61 90 33 57

e-mail: namaste.primoulas@wanadoo.fr

Carbonne 20 km. Toulouse 60 km. Marie-Paule welcomes guests into a four-bedroom guesthouse. There is one triple bedroom with access to the garden and a separate washroom and wc. There are three triple bedrooms with private bathroom facilities. Large communal dining room with huge fireplace and TV, video and hi-fi. The garden has beautiful views over the Pyrénées. Dance, yoga and pottery classes available. Open all year.

continued

PRICES: s €30; d €39; t €52; dinner €14 **ON SITE:** Swimming pool Hiking **NEARBY:** Horse riding (12km) Golf (50km) Fishing (7km) Stretch of water (12km) Tennis (7km) Railway station (50km) Shops (7km) **NOTES:** No pets Minimum 2 night stay English spoken

LAVALETTE

⊪⊪ ΙΟΙ La Poterie Jean-Loup THIBAUD
Route de Lavaur - D112, 31590 LAVALETTE
☎ 05 61 84 34 49 🖹 05 61 84 99 19
e-mail: lapoterie@free.fr lapoterie.free.fr

Toulouse 15 km. This former pottery has been completely restored with comfortable guest rooms. Dining room with fireplace, kitchen and wc. The four bedrooms are distributed around a central corridor and each has access to the garden. There are two twin bedrooms, one bedroom with a double and two single beds and a double bedroom. Each bedroom has bathroom facilities. Open all year.
PRICES: s €38; d €46; t €58; extra person €16; dinner €16
ON SITE: Hiking **NEARBY:** Horse riding (2km) Golf (10km) Fishing (5km) Swimming pool (5km) Stretch of water (8km) Tennis (1km) Railway station (5km) Shops (5km) **NOTES:** No pets Minimum 2 night stay English spoken

MONTBERAUD

⊪⊪ ❦ ΙΟΙ Toubies B et P ALBRECHT ET LAGENDIJK
31220 MONTBERAUD
☎ 05 61 98 14 35 🖹 05 61 98 14 35
Cazères 12 km. Toulouse 60 km. An isolated renovated old farm offering guests hospitality in guestrooms arranged around a patio area. There is a communal lounge with a fireplace on the ground floor. The first floor has two double bedrooms, one bedroom with a double and two single beds. Each bedroom has private bathroom facilities. Kitchenette, table tennis and games are available. There is a lovely view over the Pyrenees. Open all year.
PRICES: s €28; d €40; extra person €20; dinner €14
ON SITE: Swimming pool Hiking **NEARBY:** Golf (30km) Fishing (5km) Stretch of water (5km) Tennis (5km) Railway station (12km) Shops (5km) **NOTES:** No pets English spoken

MONTBRUN-BOCAGE

⊪⊪ ❦ ΙΟΙ Pavé Josette PARINAUD
31310 MONTBRUN-BOCAGE
☎ 05 61 98 11 25
A small-enclosed farm amidst warm surroundings. There are two double bedrooms and a triple on the ground floor, and on the first floor, there is a bedroom with two single beds and one double bed. All bedrooms have bathroom facilities. There is a dining room with a fireplace, where the evening meals are served around the family table. Open all year upon reservation.
PRICES: s €31; d €37; t €53; dinner €14 **ON SITE:** Hiking
NEARBY: Horse riding (20km) Fishing (1km) Swimming pool (20km) Stretch of water (10km) Tennis (5km) Railway station (20km) Shops (10km) **NOTES:** No pets Minimum 2 night stay English spoken

MONTESQUIEU-LAURAGAIS

⊪⊪ ❦ Bigot Irène et Joseph PINEL
31450 MONTESQUIEU-LAURAGAIS
☎ 05 61 27 02 83 🖹 05 61 27 02 83
e-mail: joseph.pinel@libertysurf.fr
http://persolibertysurf.fr/hotebigot
Toulouse 25 km. Villefranche-Lauragais 6 km. An entirely renovated farm, surrounded by a garden in flowery countryside. Large reception room with kitchen on the ground floor. The first floor has a double bedroom, one bedroom with a double and a single bed and a power shower and Jacuzzi. There are three further bedrooms with three double beds and two single beds. Each bedroom has separate bathroom facilities. There is a guest room with a TV and bookcase. Lawn, covered patio and car shelter. Patchwork demonstrations. Open all year.
PRICES: s €40; d €45; t €57; extra person €12 **ON SITE:** Fishing Swimming pool Hiking **NEARBY:** Horse riding (7km) Golf (20km) Water sports (10km) Tennis (1km) Railway station (25km) Shops (1km)
NOTES: No pets Minimum 2 night stay English spoken

MONTESQUIEU-VOLVESTRE

⊪⊪ ΙΟΙ La Halte du Temps Marie-Andrée GARCIN
72 rue Mage, 31310 MONTESQUIEU-VOLVESTRE
☎ 05 61 97 56 10 🖹 05 61 97 56 10
e-mail: lahaltedutemps@free.fr
A 17th century building with access through a charming central courtyard. There is a dining room with a large fireplace on the ground floor. The first floor has three double bedrooms, one single bedroom and one triple bedroom. All bedrooms have private bathroom facilities. There is a music room, a patio and an enclosed garden. A Louis XIII staircase leads to the bedrooms. Every room has a fireplace. Open all year.
PRICES: s €46; d €54; t €69; dinner €18 **ON SITE:** Swimming pool Hiking **NEARBY:** Horse riding (5km) Golf (15km) Fishing (1km) Stretch of water (5km) Tennis (1km) Railway station (11km) **NOTES:** Pets admitted Minimum 2 night stay CC English spoken

MONTPITOL

⊪⊪ Stoupignan Claudette FIEUX
31380 MONTPITOL
☎ 05 61 84 22 02
A large Louis XIII style house, set in the Toulouse countryside, surrounded by a large wooded park. There are two twin bedrooms and one double bedroom, all with bathroom facilities and a TV. There is a large room and garden available to guests, in which seminars can be catered for, up to ten people. Open all year.
PRICES: s €46; d €77; t €92 **ON SITE:** Hiking **NEARBY:** Horse riding (18km) Golf (4km) Swimming pool (5km) Stretch of water (26km) Tennis (5km) Shops (4.5km) **NOTES:** No pets Minimum 2 night stay English spoken

SAMOUILLAN

♦♦♦ IOI Le Moulin Steve CALLEN
31420 SAMOUILLAN
☎ 05 61 98 86 92 ▤ 05 61 98 86 92
e-mail: kris.steve@free.fr www.moulin-vert.net
An old mill close to the village, by a small stretch of water in shaded terrain. Dining room with fireplace on the ground floor. The first floor has two bedrooms with two doubles and one single bed. These have shared facilities and are rated as grade 1. There are also two bedrooms with two double and two single beds, with private facilities. Vegetarian meals are available on request. There is a car shelter. Open all year.
PRICES: s €30; d €42; dinner €14 **ON SITE:** Fishing **NEARBY:** Horse riding (15km) Swimming pool (15km) Stretch of water (10km) Tennis (15km) Railway station (20km) Shops (15km) **NOTES:** Pets admitted English spoken

ST-LEON

♦♦♦ ✿ Pagnard Anne-Marie LAMOUROUX
31560 ST-LEON
☎ 05 61 81 92 21 ▤ 05 61 81 92 21
A large 18th century renovated house. There is a ferme-auberge dining room with a fireplace on the ground floor. The first floor has a small private room with a TV. There are five bedrooms above the ferme-auberge containing four double beds and five single beds. All bedrooms have private bathroom facilities. Covered swimming pool. Open all year.
PRICES: s €39; d €39; t €54; dinner €10 **ON SITE:** Fishing Swimming pool **NEARBY:** Golf (40km) Stretch of water (5km) Water sports (5km) Tennis (5km) Railway station (10km) Shops (5km) Restaurant nearby
NOTES: No pets Minimum 2 night stay English spoken

ST-PAUL-D'OUEIL

♦♦♦ Maison Jeanne Michèle GUERRE
31110 SAINT-PAUL-D'OUEIL
☎ 05 61 79 81 63 ▤ 05 61 79 81 63
e-mail: www.locations-luchon.com/B/guerre
Bagnères de Luchon 6 km. This exposed stone house welcomes guests into warmly decorated surroundings. Dining room and another room on the ground floor. The first floor has a family room with a double and two single beds. The second floor has two bedrooms with one double and two single beds. Each bedroom has private facilities and TV. Skiing and walking nearby. Large enclosed garden. Open all year.
PRICES: s €49; d €55; t €73 **ON SITE:** Fishing **NEARBY:** Horse riding (6km) Golf (6km) Swimming pool (6km) Stretch of water (15km) Tennis (6km) Railway station (6km) Shops (6km) **NOTES:** No pets

VERNET

♦♦♦ Domaine de Dussède Modesta TROUCHE
31810 VERNET
☎ 05 61 08 39 30 ▤ 05 61 08 39 30
Toulouse 22 km. On the edge of Toulouse, Dussède welcomes guests into enchanting surroundings. Dining room, small and large rooms, billiards room and patio on the ground floor. On the first floor there is a breakfast room, two double bedrooms, Louis XIII and Louis XVI, a 'Rétro' double bedroom and a Louis XV suite. Each bedroom has its own bathroom facilities. Relax in the park, by the swimming pool, or play tennis on the private court. Open April to September.
PRICES: s €125-€245; d €135-€255; t €265 **ON SITE:** Swimming pool Tennis **NEARBY:** Horse riding (6km) Golf (12km) Fishing (1km) Stretch of water (0.5km) Railway station (2km) Shops (2km) **NOTES:** No pets English spoken

ANERES

♦♦♦ IOI Les Sorbiers Valérie ROGE
65150 ANERES
☎ 05 62 39 75 41
You will be welcomed to this old house by the young owners who live next door. There are three bedrooms available, each with shower room and wc. Dining room, sitting room, TV and library. Central heating and private parking. There are a number of leisure activities and caves nearby. In winter, you can enjoy skiing from the Nistos-Cap-Nestes. Communal courtyard shared with the owners. Regional cooking on request.
PRICES: d €37; t €46; extra person €10; dinner €13 **ON SITE:** Hunting Fishing Hiking **NEARBY:** Horse riding (6km) Golf (6km) Swimming pool (9km) Tennis (2km) Railway station (12km) Shops (2km)
NOTES: No pets

ANSOST

♦♦♦ ✿ IOI Chambre d'hôtes Charles LOUIT
65140 ANSOST
☎ 05 62 96 62 63 ▤ 05 62 96 62 63
Fronton 5 km. This renovated farm lies within a small village. There are five bedrooms available on the first floor: four double bedrooms, and one bedroom with a double bed and bunk beds. There is a wc, shower and washbasin in each bedroom. An extra bed can be provided on request. Central heating, TV, cot. Outside, there is a courtyard with both shade and a lawn. Sailing can be enjoyed at a lake 18km away. Rooms available throughout the year.
PRICES: s €26; d €32; dinner €13 **NEARBY:** Hunting (10km) Horse riding (5km) Fishing (3km) Swimming pool (7km) Tennis (3km) Railway station (25km) Shops (7km) **NOTES:** No pets

ARCIZAC-EZ-ANGLES

♦♦♦ Chambre d'hôtes Amélie TARBES
Arcizac ez Angles, 65100 LOURDES
☎ 05 62 42 92 63
Lourdes 4 km. Situated in a small village of 150 people, there are three guest rooms available on the ground floor of the owner's house: three double beds, one single bed and a possible extra bed, each with a private bathroom. There is an enclosed courtyard with a lawn and a parking area. Sailing is available at a lake 5km away. The rate for two people (twin beds) is 37.50 euros. The rooms are available throughout the year.
PRICES: s €28; d €35; t €43 **ON SITE:** Hunting Fishing Hiking **NEARBY:** Horse riding (10km) Golf (5km) Swimming pool (5km) Tennis (5km) Railway station (5km) Shops (4km) **NOTES:** No pets

ARCIZANS-AVANT

♦♦♦ ✿ Chambre d'hôtes Maïté VERMEIL
3 rue du Château, 65400 ARCIZANS-AVANT
☎ 05 62 97 55 96 ▤ 05 62 97 55 96
Pyrénées National Park 10 km. Frédérick (a mountain guide) and Maïté, welcome you to their old 1855 Bigourdane house which lies in a small quiet village. There are three bedrooms for one, three and five people, each with shower, sink and wc. Kitchen area with TV and terrace with a lovely view over the mountains. There are two restaurants in the village, a thermal spa 2km away and a ski resort (alpine and cross country), 10 km away. The house is available throughout the year.
PRICES: s €28; d €39; t €51; extra person €13 **NEARBY:** Hunting (3km) Horse riding (2km) Golf (2km) Fishing (1km) Swimming pool (2km) Hiking (1km) Tennis (2km) Railway station (10km) Shops (2km)
NOTES: No pets English spoken

ARIES-ESPENAN

♯♯♯ 🍴 Moulin d'Aries Dorit WEIMER-VD-WEYDEN
Aries Espenan, 65230 CASTELNAU-MAGNOAC
☎ 05 62 39 81 85 🖹 05 62 39 81 85

Pyrenees & Spain 1 h. Atlantic Coast 2 h. Although near the D929, the atmosphere is quiet in this renovated 14th century mill, on the borders of the Gers region. There is one double and four twin bedrooms (two bedrooms are on the ground floor). Two bedrooms can sleep two adults and two children or three adults (using an extra double bed). Each room has a shower and wc. There are two lounges, one with a library, satellite TV, video, board games and children's games. Bicycles are available. The rooms are available between 15 May and 15 January or on reservation.
PRICES: s €41; d €52; t €61; extra person €9; dinner €18 **ON SITE:** Wine tasting Children's play area Hunting Horse riding Fishing Hiking **NEARBY:** Golf (22km) Swimming pool (1km) Tennis (1km) Railway station (22km) Shops (2km) **NOTES:** Pets admitted Minimum 2 night stay English spoken

ARRENS-MARSOUS

♯♯♯ 🍴 Maison Sempé Sylvie GUILLET
3 rue Marque de Dessus, 65400 ARRENS-MARSOUS
☎ 05 62 97 41 75

Lourdes 25 km. Cauterets 40 km. Gavarnie 45 km. Sylvie and Michel welcome you to one of the most beautiful houses in the village, in a valley that offers cross-country skiing, mountain biking, etc. There are four guest bedrooms (a family room can be made from two linked bedrooms) in this 18th century home. Each bedroom has a private bathroom. Lounge and dining room shared with the owners. Fireplace with a wood burning stove, library, TV. Terrace, garden and garden furniture. 10% discount after the third night and children's meals are 7 euros. No charge for children under four; children between four and twelve - 8 euros per night. Evening meals using regional specialities available. Open all year.
PRICES: s €35; d €45; t €55; HB €50-€125; dinner €15
ON SITE: Hunting Fishing Hiking **NEARBY:** Horse riding (5km) Swimming pool (1km) Tennis (1km) Railway station (25km) Shops (1km) **NOTES:** No pets English spoken

ARTIGUES

♯♯♯ 🍃 Chambre d'hôtes Colette CAPDEVIELLE
65100 ARTIGUES
☎ 05 62 42 92 42
e-mail: colette.capdevielle@wanadoo.fr
www.pyrenees-online.fr/Capdevielle
Lourdes 5 km. Bagnères-de-Bigorre 18 km. Situated in a small village of only thirty people, this farmhouse is typical of the Bigourd region. There are three bedrooms on the ground floor, with independent access and a view of the fields, including a double bedroom and a suite of a double bedroom with single sofa bed and a twin bedroom. First floor: bedroom with independent

entrance (a double bed and a double sofa bed, with a fireplace). Each bedroom has a shower room. Kitchen area, terrace with garden furniture and a barbecue. Communal sitting room shared with the owners. Rooms available throughout the year.
PRICES: s €31; d €39; t €61; extra person €8 **ON SITE:** Children's play area Hiking **NEARBY:** Hunting (5km) Horse riding (5km) Golf (5km) Fishing (5km) Swimming pool (5km) Tennis (5km) Railway station (5km) Shops (5km) **NOTES:** No pets

ASPIN-EN-LAVEDAN

♯♯♯ 🍃 🍴 Ferme Mongeat
Famille BOYRIE-LAMARQUE
1 chemin du Turoun Debat, 65100 ASPIN-EN-LAVEDAN
☎ 05 62 94 38 87 & 06 81 35 53 01
e-mail: s.boyrie_lamarque@libertysurf.fr
http://perso.libertysurf.fr/boyrie
Cauterets 30 km. Argeles 12 km. Gavarnie 49 km. A farm in a small village, 3km from Lourdes. Two grade 2 bedrooms with three double beds, private shower, washbasin and communal wc. There are four grade 3 bedrooms (one is a family room) with seven double beds in total, and private bathrooms. A TV is provided in each bedroom and extra beds may be installed. Lawn, patio, enclosed parking area. Four people: €46/61. Evening meals made from farm produce are available, and farm produce can be purchased on site. Children's meal (under seven) €7. Gourmet meal €20-€26.Farm visits can be arranged. Open all year.
PRICES: s €26-€31; d €31-€37; t €40-€46; extra person €10; dinner €12 **ON SITE:** Children's play area Fishing **NEARBY:** Hunting (3km) Horse riding (12km) Golf (3km) Swimming pool (3km) Tennis (3km) Railway station (3km) Shops (3km) Restaurant nearby **NOTES:** No pets

AYROS

♯♯♯ Chambre d'hôtes Raymonde et J-Marie PAMBRUN
3 Camin Dera Hont, 65400 AYROS
☎ 05 62 97 04 00 🖹 05 62 97 04 00
Lourdes 10 km. Cauterets 17 km. Gavarnie 35 km. Tourmalet 39 km. An old family boarding house that has been turned into guest rooms. On the second floor there are three bedrooms with a double bed, single bed and full bathroom in each one. Private lounge, sitting room area and TV on the ground floor. Garden, garden furniture and a parking area. Lying at the foot of the Hautacam, enjoy a quiet stay in this small village, typical of the Hautes-Pyrénées. There are lovely views of the mountains and there is a restaurant 300m away. Rooms available throughout the year.
PRICES: s €29; d €39; t €46 **ON SITE:** Hunting Hiking **NEARBY:** Horse riding (5km) Golf (11km) Fishing (2km) Swimming pool (3km) Tennis (2km) **NOTES:** Pets admitted English spoken

BARTRES

♯♯♯ 🍃 Chambre d'hôtes Daniel LAURENS
3 route d'Ade, 65100 BARTRES
☎ 05 62 42 34 96 🖹 05 62 94 58 06
A house on a farm, offering five guest bedrooms, one of which is accessible to the less mobile. There are three double beds, six single beds and two sofa beds. Dining room, communal sitting room shared with the owners, with a fireplace, TV and library. Courtyard, enclosed garden with garden furniture, parking area and a restaurant 80m away. This working farm is in the heart of a village with lots of character and close to the great sites of the Pyrénées. Rooms available throughout the year.
PRICES: s €26; d €34; t €41 **ON SITE:** Hunting Hiking **NEARBY:** Horse riding (5km) Golf (3km) Fishing (3km) Swimming pool (3km) Tennis (3km) Railway station (3km) Shops (3km) **NOTES:** No pets

continued

MIDI-PYRÉNÉES

BEAUCENS

⊞ ⏐◯⏐ Eth Béryè Petit Henri et Ione VIELLE
15 route de Vielle, 65400 BEAUCENS
☎ 05 62 97 90 02 ▤ 05 62 97 90 02
www.beryepetit.com
Argeles-Gazost 5 km. Lourdes 15 km. There are three guest rooms
with lots of character, each with a double bed and a single bed
(an extra bed is also possible). First floor: large bedroom with 19th
century furniture, bathroom, wc and balcony. Second floor: two
beautiful bedrooms with shower and wc. Large sitting room with a
chimney, TV and library. A microwave and fridge can also be used
by guests. Shady terrace, garden, kitchen garden, field and private
parking area. Restaurants nearby. Evening meals between
November and April, at weekends or on request. Open all year.
PRICES: d €42-€49; t €52-€60; extra person €11; dinner €14
ON SITE: Children's play area Hiking **NEARBY:** Horse riding (5km)
Golf (15km) Fishing (2km) Swimming pool (5km) Tennis (5km) Railway
station (15km) Shops (5km) **NOTES:** No pets English spoken

BETPOUEY

⊞ ❧ ⏐◯⏐ Chambre d'hôtes Christine LASSALLE
65120 BETPOUEY
☎ 05 62 92 88 50
Barèges (spa resort) 3 km. There are four guest rooms with a
shower room and wc in this restored barn, in a mountain village,
at the foot of Tourmalet: one bedroom on the ground floor sleeps
four, the first floor bedroom sleeps three and there are also two
bedrooms that sleep two. Lounge with fireplace and TV and
private parking outside. The home is owned by a young couple
from the valley, who provide a warm welcome. The house is in a
small village, typical of the region. Rooms are available all year.
PRICES: s €31; d €39; t €48; extra person €11; dinner €13
ON SITE: Hunting Fishing Hiking **NEARBY:** Golf (4km) Swimming
pool (4km) Tennis (3km) Railway station (25km) Shops (3km)
NOTES: No pets

BOO-SILHEN

⊞ ❧ ⏐◯⏐ Les Aillans Franck BROUILLET
Silhen Débat, 65400 BOO-SILHEN
☎ 05 62 97 59 22 ▤ 05 62 97 59 22
A renovated barn, near the owners' 15th century house, in an
isolated hamlet in the middle of green countryside. Three guest
rooms (one is a family room with two communicating rooms) with
private bathrooms for each bedroom. Dining room and separate
sitting room, fireplace, TV, library, video and hi-fi. Courtyard,
enclosed parkland, garden furniture and garage. Franck will be
happy to help you discover the Hautes Pyrénées in his 4 x 4.
(Rate for two: €46, four: €77, picnic included). Children's meals
(under fives): 8 euros. Available all year.
PRICES: s €31; d €45; t €57; dinner €16 **ON SITE:** Hunting
NEARBY: Horse riding (8km) Golf (10km) Fishing (1km) Swimming
pool (2km) Hiking (2km) Tennis (2km) Railway station (12km) Shops
(3km) **NOTES:** Pets admitted English spoken

BORDERES-LOURON

⊞ ⏐◯⏐ Chambre d'hôtes A L BRACHET & H CHAMARY
Le Village, 65590 BORDERES-LOURON
☎ 05 62 99 98 89 ▤ 05 62 99 98 89
Genos Loudenvielle 10 km. St-Larry 18 km. Anne-Lise and Henri
welcome you to their renovated farm, which has five bedrooms
on the first and second floors. One double bedroom and four
bedrooms with a double bed and a single bed. All have private
bathrooms. Communal dining room and sitting room. Garden,
lawn and garden furniture. Set in a valley offering diverse

activities: skiing, paragliding, walking, mountain biking, etc. Rooms
are available throughout the year.
PRICES: s €31; d €43; t €54; dinner €14 **ON SITE:** Hiking Tennis
NEARBY: Horse riding (2km) Golf (32km) Swimming pool (10km)
NOTES: Pets admitted

CAMPAN

⊞ ⏐◯⏐ La Laurence Marian MASSON
65710 CAMPAN
☎ 05 62 91 84 02 & 05 62 91 84 21 ▤ 05 62 91 84 21
e-mail: lalaurence@wanadoo.fr
http://perso.wanadoo.fr/lalaurence
A comfortable chalet with panoramic views over the valley and
mountains, offering independent guest rooms with shower room
and wc, lounge area, balcony or terrace. Three of the bedrooms
have a kitchen area (one room is classed as grade 2). Communal
dining room shared with the owners, sitting room, library and TV.
Picnic baskets: 8 euros; heating: 4 euros per day/per room.
Reductions possible for groups (out of season). Open 1 December
to 30 October.
PRICES: s €35; d €44; t €60; extra person €14; HB €27; dinner €15
ON SITE: Hunting Fishing Hiking **NEARBY:** Horse riding (3km) Golf
(18km) Swimming pool (1km) Tennis (4km) Railway station (15km)
Shops (3km) **NOTES:** Pets admitted English spoken

CAMPARAN

⊞ ❧ Chambre d'hôtes Marie-Thérèse MOREILHON
La Couette de Bieou, 65170 CAMPARAN
☎ 05 62 39 41 10
St-Lary-Soulan 4 km. There are three bedrooms in this mountain
farm, at the entrance to a small village: one double bedroom, one
twin and one bedroom with a double bed and twin beds, each
with private shower room. Mezzanine level and communal dining
room, shared with the owners. Courtyard and balcony, with
garden furniture, parking area, lounge area, TV and fireplace.
There are beautiful views over the Aure valley and surrounding
peaks. Ski resorts and spas nearby. The house retains much of its
original character. Rate for four: 61 euros. Open all year.
PRICES: s €31; d €39; t €52; extra person €14 **ON SITE:** Hiking
NEARBY: Horse riding (4km) Golf (30km) Fishing (2km) Swimming
pool (4km) Tennis (4km) Railway station (30km) Shops (3km)
NOTES: No pets

CASTELNAU-MAGNOAC

⊞ ❧ ⏐◯⏐ Au Verdier Nathalie CARRILLON-FONTAN
route de Lamarque, 65230 CASTELNAU-MAGNOAC
☎ 05 62 99 80 95 ▤ 05 62 39 85 45
There are three beautiful bedrooms (four double beds and one
single bed) with private bathrooms in this converted grain store. In
the lounge the large locally-made table has pride of place, where
you can enjoy breakfasts and meals made from fresh farm
produce. TV, telephone and library. From the balcony, you can
admire the park and the flowerbeds. Fishing lake and terrace.
Available from April to October, advance bookings only.
PRICES: s €31; d €39; t €46; extra person €11; dinner €14
ON SITE: Fishing Hiking **NEARBY:** Hunting (1km) Horse riding (5km)
Golf (23km) Swimming pool (13km) Tennis (3km) Railway station (25km)
Shops (2km) **NOTES:** Pets admitted

Manoir de la Grange

⊞ Manoir de la Grange Bernard VERDIER
65230 CASTELNAU-MAGNOAC
☎ 05 62 99 85 33 & 06 89 10 00 73 ▤ 05 62 99 85 33
e-mail: mandelagrange@wanadoo.fr www.castelmagnoac.com
Auch 40 km. Spa resort 20 km. There are three bedrooms in this
16th century manor house between Gascony and the Pyrénées.

continued   continued

MIDI-PYRÉNÉES

One room is a suite for three people. Each bedroom has a private bathroom. Dining room, sitting room, library and small kitchen reserved for guests. Enclosed parkland, swimming pool, garden furniture and private parking. One hour from the Pic du Midi; walking, horse riding, tennis and aerial sports are all available on the doorstep. Available from 1 January to 5 November.
PRICES: s €52; d €61; t €76 **ON SITE:** Swimming pool Hiking **NEARBY:** Hunting (3km) Horse riding (3km) Golf (24km) Fishing (3km) Tennis (1km) Railway station (24km) Shops (1km) **NOTES:** No pets English spoken

CASTELNAU-RIVIERE-BASSE

♦♦♦♦ ⏹ Le Château du Tail
Andrew et Maria HEDLEY
65700 CASTELNAU-RIVIERE-BASSE
☎ 05 62 31 93 75 🖷 05 62 31 93 72
e-mail: chateau.du.tail@wanadoo.fr
www.sudfr.com/chateaudutail

The outbuildings of this chateau house the bedrooms, each with a four-poster bed (except one ground floor room). On the ground floor there are two double bedrooms with a bathroom, and a twin room with shower room and wc. An extra bed is available on request. First floor: double bedroom with shower room and wc, plus a suite with a double bed and adjoining room with 2/3 beds, bathroom and wc. Communal lounge/sitting room. Library, swimming pool, garden and garden furniture, old vineyard. Evening meals on request. Available throughout the year on reservation.
PRICES: s €58-€80; d €58-€85; extra person €19; dinner €20 **ON SITE:** Swimming pool Hiking **NEARBY:** Horse riding (5km) Golf (25km) Fishing (1km) Tennis (1km) Railway station (45km) Shops (1km) **NOTES:** Pets admitted English spoken

♦♦♦ ❧ ⏹ Chambre d'hôtes
Nicole et Jean-Louis GUYOT
Hameau de Mazeres, 65700 CASTELNAU-RIVIERE-BASSE
☎ 05 62 31 90 56 🖷 05 62 31 92 88
Nicole and Jean-Louis rear and keep Pyrénées donkeys on this 18th century Gascony farm. Ground floor: a double bedroom, and a suite for two people with wc and fireplace. First floor bedroom sleeping two, with shower, wc and fireplace. There is another double bedroom and a suite for three, with shower and wc. Sitting room with TV, fireplace and library, dining room with fireplace. Central heating. Rate for four: 64 euros. Children's meals (under 12): 7 euros. Babies free. Enclosed courtyard and garden. Evening meals on request. Open all year.
PRICES: s €40; d €43; t €55; dinner €14 **ON SITE:** Hunting Fishing Hiking **NEARBY:** Horse riding (2km) Golf (15km) Swimming pool (2km) Tennis (2km) Railway station (40km) Shops (2km) **NOTES:** Pets admitted English spoken

CHEZE

♦♦♦ Le Palouma Marie-Hélène THEIL
Cheze, 65120 LUZ-ST-SAUVEUR
☎ 05 62 92 90 90 🖷 05 62 92 90 90
This house is next to the owners' house, situated in a small village in the mountains, with a beautiful view over the Luz-Saint-Sauveur valley. There are three bedrooms: two double beds and three single beds. Two rooms have washbasin, shower and wc and one has a basin and shower (wc nearby). Dining room and communal sitting room with fireplace, TV, library, shared with the owners. Outside: enclosed garden with flowerbeds and children's toys. Terrace with garden furniture and communal parking. Rooms available throughout the year.
PRICES: s €28; d €34; t €46 **ON SITE:** Children's play area Hiking **NEARBY:** Horse riding (15km) Golf (30km) Fishing (5km) Swimming pool (5km) Tennis (6km) Railway station (30km) Shops (5km) **NOTES:** No pets

CHIS

♦♦♦ ❧ Ferme St-Féreol Jacques DALAT
1 chemin du Camparces le Buron, 65800 CHIS
☎ 05 62 36 21 12
Lourdes 25 km. In this old, restored house on a farm, there are three bedrooms (one double bedroom) and a bathroom with a wc, lounge and sitting room. There is also a private garage, table tennis and ponies in the grounds. Nearby there is a restaurant and sailing can be enjoyed on the lake, 20 km away. There are cows, horses, donkeys and poultry on the farm and farm produce can be sampled. Open all year.
PRICES: s €31; d €41; extra person €13 **ON SITE:** Hunting Fishing Hiking Tennis **NEARBY:** Horse riding (2km) Golf (10km) Swimming pool (7km) Railway station (7km) Shops (1km) **NOTES:** Pets admitted

FONTRAILLES

♦♦♦ ⏹ Chambre d'hôtes
Nicolas et Dominique COLLINSON
Jouandassou, 65220 FONTRAILLES
☎ 05 62 35 64 43 🖷 05 62 35 66 13
e-mail: dom@collinson.fr www.collinson.fr
Situated in south Gascony, on the Pyrénées coast, in the middle of protected countryside. First floor: two double rooms, and a bedroom with a double bed and a single bed. Each bedroom has a private bathroom. Sitting room and a day room/dining room with a library, piano and games. Park with a swimming pool and table tennis. Bike hire can be arranged and tennis can be played in the village. Contact for directions. Open all year.
PRICES: s €43; d €50-€57; extra person €20; dinner €20 **ON SITE:** Children's play area Fishing Swimming pool Hiking **NEARBY:** Horse riding (3km) Golf (15km) Tennis (1km) Railway station (29km) Shops (2km) **NOTES:** No pets English spoken

GARDERES

♦♦♦ ❧ ⏹ Chambre d'hôtes Joseph et Josette LABORDE
27 route de Seron, 65320 GARDERES
☎ 05 62 32 53 86
There are four bedrooms in this stylish former barn, separate from the owners' house: three double beds and two single beds, with private bathrooms. Other features include exposed beams, soundproofed rooms, a covered terrace, a courtyard and a garage. Farm produce features in the evening meals. Table tennis and a TV. Farm visits can also be arranged. There are views over the Pyrénées and the house is available throughout the year.
PRICES: s €26; d €34; t €43; extra person €10; dinner €11 **NEARBY:** Horse riding (10km) Golf (20km) Swimming pool (5km) Hiking (30km) Tennis (5km) Railway station (18km) Shops (5km) **NOTES:** No pets

GEZ-ARGELES

♦♦♦ ⭐ ⏀ Chambre d'hôtes Jean DOMEC
65400 GEZ-ARGELES
☎ 05 62 97 28 61

Argeles-Gazost 2 km (spa resort). An old, restored farm, near the owners' home in the heart of the Pyrénées, in a peaceful setting. There are four bedrooms on the first floor, and one on the ground floor with access for the less mobile. (Two double rooms, two bedrooms with two double beds, and one room with a double bed and two singles, shower room and wc.) Dining room, sitting room with a TV and private parking. Lawn, garden furniture, pergola, barbecue. This is a comfortable house with many lakes, walks, etc. nearby. Rooms available 1st May - 30th September.
PRICES: s €29; d €37; t €51; extra person €14; dinner €13
ON SITE: Hunting Horse riding Fishing Hiking **NEARBY:** Golf (12km) Swimming pool (3km) Tennis (3km) Railway station (12km) Shops (2km)
NOTES: No pets

JUNCALAS

♦♦♦ ⭐ Chambre d'hôtes Daniel COUMES
65100 JUNCALAS
☎ 05 62 94 76 26

Lourdes 7 km. There are three bedrooms in the owners' house, with private bathrooms: three double beds and one single. TV, library, lounge room, communal sitting room for guests and an enclosed courtyard. Outside, there is garden furniture, a parking area and courtyard. The rate for four is 55 euros. In the village, you will find a swimming pool, golf, horse riding and fishing. The property is available throughout the year.
PRICES: s €27; d €37; t €46 **ON SITE:** Hunting Fishing Hiking
NEARBY: Horse riding (12km) Golf (7km) Swimming pool (7km) Tennis (7km) Railway station (7km) Shops (7km) **NOTES:** No pets

♦♦♦ ⏀ Maison Monseigneur Laurence
Robert ASSOUERE
65100 JUNCALAS
☎ 05 62 42 02 04   🖷 05 62 94 13 91

Monseigneur Laurence, the priest of the Lourdes apparitions, spent part of his childhood at this characterful house. Ground floor: dining room, lounge area. First floor: double bedrooms. Second floor: two bedrooms with private bathrooms, a small sitting room, fireplace, TV. Dining room with lots of character, sitting room, TV, garage, parking area, private courtyard, garden furniture and barbecue. Shady park with stream, mountain biking. Fishing trips, mountain trips, evening grills. Lourdes nearby, sailing 7km. Open all year.
PRICES: s €31; d €39-€45; t €54; HB €47; dinner €16 **ON SITE:** Fishing Hiking **NEARBY:** Horse riding (10km) Golf (7km) Swimming pool (3km) Tennis (7km) Railway station (7km) Shops (7km) **NOTES:** No pets

LABASTIDE

♦♦♦ ⭐ ⏀ Lauga Alain et Evelyne DASQUE
Les Granges du Col de Coupe, Route d'Esparros RD26,
65130 LABASTIDE
☎ 05 62 98 80 27 & 06 87 48 53 21   🖷 05 62 98 20 57

This old shepherd's house has four bedrooms on the first floor, for two/four people, with a private bathroom in each. There is a lounge for guests with a fireplace, a sitting room with billiard table and a TV room. Outside, there is a covered, heated swimming pool, a covered tennis court, a gym, courtyard, garden and parking area. The house is available from June to September and over the winter holidays.
PRICES: s €46; d €60; HB €46; dinner €16 **ON SITE:** Children's play area Hunting Swimming pool Hiking Tennis **NEARBY:** Horse riding (8km) Golf (14km) Fishing (2km) Railway station (12km) Shops (2km)
NOTES: Pets admitted

LABATUT-RIVIERE

♦♦♦ ⭐ ⏀ Chambre d'hôtes Daniel SOUQUET
rue du Manoir Souquet, Labatut Rivière,
65700 MAUBOURGUET
☎ 05 62 96 34 12   🖷 05 62 96 95 92

On this cereal farm, in a renovated wing of the manor house, there are five bedrooms on the first floor: two with a communal bathroom and two with a private shower room. Fridge, bar and TV. Parking area, spa and sauna. Ponies, bicycles and mountain bikes are all available on site. Restaurant 1km, farm inn 3km and a lake for sailing 7km. Tennis court, swimming pool, boule pitch and a games room. Open all year.
PRICES: s €42; d €39-€46; t €55; HB €69; dinner €13 **ON SITE:** Hunting Horse riding Fishing Swimming pool Hiking Tennis **NEARBY:** Golf (35km) Railway station (30km) **NOTES:** Pets admitted English spoken

LABORDE

♦♦♦ ⏀ Chambre d'hôtes Gi et Jean VIDAL
Les Couettes, 65130 LABORDE
☎ 05 62 39 07 53   🖷 05 62 39 07 53

Gouffre d'Esparros 3 km. Lourdes 50 km. Spain 65 km. Situated in the heart of a valley, offering an impressive view, this old renovated house from 1854 is opposite the church. There are four guest rooms, each with private bathroom and wc. Lounge area, fireplace, library, games, garden, enclosed parking. Traditional cooking. Activity holidays possible: cooking, drawing, watercolours, pottery. Open all year.
PRICES: s €39; d €46; t €54; extra person €8; dinner €14-€17
ON SITE: Hiking **NEARBY:** Horse riding (20km) Golf (20km) Fishing (2km) Swimming pool (20km) Tennis (16km) Railway station (20km) Shops (3km) **NOTES:** No pets

♦♦♦ ⏀ Le Petit Château Petra ENGLISCH
65130 LABORDE
☎ 05 62 40 90 16   🖷 05 62 40 90 18
e-mail: Petit.Chateau@wanadoo.fr

Small chateau in the heart of the Baronnies, owned by a Canadian/German couple. Five stylish bedrooms (two are suites) with balconies and private shower rooms. Communal lounge, sitting room area, library. Pretty parkland and 1.5 hectares of grounds, with selection of old and exotic trees and a river containing trout. Large terrace, courtyard and garden furniture. Playground, table tennis, boules pitch, small lake. Traditional or exotic cooking. Day nursery, dances and parties. Guided walks, language courses. Discounts for children. Family atmosphere. Open all year.
PRICES: s €39-€85; d €49-€60; extra person €15-€22; dinner €18
ON SITE: Children's play area Hunting Horse riding Fishing Swimming pool Hiking **NEARBY:** Golf (15km) Tennis (7km) Railway station (15km) Shops (1km) **NOTES:** No pets English spoken

LAYRISSE

♦♦♦ ⭐ ⏀ La Ferme Davanches Thierry SALLES
65380 LAYRISSE
☎ 05 62 45 47 22

Situated on an old farm, owned by a young farming couple and their daughter, in the small village of Layrisse, typical of the Lourdes region. Three guest rooms on the first floor attached to the owners' house. Each has private shower room, exposed beams and antique furniture. Dining room, sitting room, garden furniture, children's toys, private parking. Evening meals available. Children's meals (under fives): 5 euros. 49 euros for four people. Half-board based on two people sharing. Open all year.
PRICES: s €25; d €34; t €42; extra person €8; HB €55; dinner €11
ON SITE: Children's play area Hunting Fishing Hiking **NEARBY:** Golf (10km) Swimming pool (12km) Tennis (12km) Railway station (12km) Shops (2km) Restaurant nearby **NOTES:** Pets admitted

LOUBAJAC

♥♥♥ ♥ ⦿I Chambre d'hôtes Nadine et Jean-Marc VIVES
28 route de Bartres, 65100 LOUBAJAC
☎ 05 62 94 44 17 & 06 08 57 38 95 🖅 05 62 42 38 58
e-mail: Nadine.Vives@wanadoo.fr www.anousta.com
In a house typical of the Bigourd region, surrounded by a garden, Nadine and Jean-Marc offer two double bedrooms, one room with a double bed and a single bed, and two bedrooms with two double beds. Each room has a bathroom and wc. Private sitting room with TV and library. Garden furniture. 46 euros for four people. Sailing and lake 5km away. Open all year.
PRICES: s €28; d €34; t €43; HB €29; dinner €13 **ON SITE:** Hunting Hiking **NEARBY:** Golf (5km) Fishing (10km) Swimming pool (5km) Tennis (5km) Railway station (5km) Shops (5km) **NOTES:** No pets

MAUBOURGUET

♥♥♥ ♥ ⦿I Domaine de la Campagne
F et Henri-Paul NOUVELLON
65700 MAUBOURGUET
☎ 05 62 96 45 71 🖅 05 62 96 02 29
Maubourguet 1 km. Pyrénées. Relax in a deckchair or hammock with views of the Pyrénées. Ground floor: two large (grade 3) bedrooms, each with private bathroom, and two large (grade 2) bedrooms with private bathrooms, communal wc. Lounge/sitting room area, games. Sailing and lake 13km away. Swimming pool, private parking. Good evening meals available. Marciac Jazz Festival in August. Reductions for children under ten. Contact for directions. Available from Easter to 1 November.
PRICES: s €20-€23; d €36-€39; t €39-€46; HB €60; dinner €11
ON SITE: Hunting Swimming pool Hiking **NEARBY:** Horse riding (13km) Golf (30km) Fishing (50km) Tennis (2km) Railway station (30km) Shops (1km) **NOTES:** No pets

MOMERES

♥♥♥ ♥ Chambre d'hôtes Arlette CABALOU
65360 MOMERES
☎ 05 62 45 99 34 & 06 07 96 31 04 🖅 05 62 45 31 57
Lourdes 18 km. Six guest bedrooms in a ferme-auberge, typical of the Bigourd region, near the thermal spa of Bagnères-de-Bigorre. Three double bedrooms, three bedrooms with two double beds, each with a bathroom. Park, garden, courtyard, terrace, stretch of water, mountain biking, table tennis. Farm produce available. Farm specialises in duck rearing. Rate for four people: 53 euros. Couple half-board: 60 euros. Open all year.
PRICES: s €30; d €36; t €43; extra person €8; HB €43; dinner €13
ON SITE: Hunting Fishing Hiking Tennis **NEARBY:** Horse riding (5km) Golf (2km) Swimming pool (5km) Railway station (5km) Restaurant nearby **NOTES:** No pets

MONTGAILLARD

♥♥♥ ⦿I Maison Buret Jean-Louis et Jo CAZAUX
67 La Cap de la Veille, 65200 MONTGAILLARD
☎ 05 62 91 54 29 & 06 11 77 87 74 🖅 05 62 91 52 42
Three guest bedrooms, one of which is a suite, in a 1791 family manor house that has kept its original character. Ground floor: one bedroom with double bed and single bed, shower and wc. First floor: one suite of two bedrooms, a double bed, two single beds, bathroom and wc. One bedroom with two double beds, shower and wc. Lawn, barbecue, garden furniture. Private parking area. The lounge and one bedroom have a fireplace. There is a small museum of 17th century country life. Open all year.
PRICES: s €35-€46; d €35-€46; extra person €8; dinner €16
ON SITE: Hunting Fishing Hiking **NEARBY:** Horse riding (6km) Golf (6km) Swimming pool (6km) Tennis (6km) Railway station (6km) Shops (1km) **NOTES:** No pets English spoken

OMEX

♥♥♥♥ ⦿I Les Rocailles Murielle FANLOU
Cami Deths Escourets, 65100 LOURDES-OMEX
☎ 05 62 94 46 19 🖅 05 62 94 33 35
e-mail: muriellefanlou@aol.com www.lesrocailles.com
In a small Pyrénées village, Murielle has used her talents as a former costumier for the Paris Opera to decorate and revive this old stone and wood farmhouse, typical of the region. 'La Couturière' is a ground floor twin bedroom with terrace and bathroom. On the first floor, 'Tourmalet' has a double bed and single bed. 'Bigorre' has twin beds and a single bed, bathroom. Telephone and TV in each room. Lounge, fireplace, safe, air conditioning. Lawn, garden furniture, swimming pool, shed, fruit trees, private parking area. Available from February to October.
PRICES: s €40; d €54; t €65; extra person €11; dinner €17
ON SITE: Hunting Fishing Swimming pool Hiking **NEARBY:** Golf (6km) Tennis (3km) Railway station (4km) Shops (4km)
NOTES: No pets English spoken

ORINCLES

♥♥♥ ⦿I Chambre d'hôtes Françoise GRIMBERT
Passage du Moulin, 65380 ORINCLES
☎ 05 62 45 40 65 🖅 05 62 45 60 50
e-mail: moulindo@free.fr
Lourdes 12 km. Bagnères (spa town) 15 km. Near to Lourdes, there is easy access to the different valleys of the Pyrénées from this old renovated mill. The sound of the water is calming and peaceful. There are two bedrooms with a double bed and a single bed, and one double bedroom with a mezzanine with twin beds. Each bedroom has a private bathroom. Hiking possible nearby with qualified guides. Cycling, fishing and bathing also available. Open all year.
PRICES: s €42; d €49; t €60; extra person €11; HB €59; dinner €17
ON SITE: Hunting Fishing Hiking **NEARBY:** Golf (10km) Swimming pool (10km) Tennis (10km) Railway station (10km) Shops (4km)
NOTES: Small animals only English spoken

OSSUN-BOURG

♥♥♥ ⦿I Chambre d'hôtes Michel et Marinette ABADIE
38 rue Henri Maninat, 65380 OSSUN
☎ 05 62 32 89 07
Between Tarbes and Lourdes, in a small peaceful village, with a view over the Pyrénées, there are four simple and welcoming bedrooms with private shower rooms. Independent entrance. Courtyard, garden, terrace, boules, table tennis, mountain biking, private parking. Sailing and a lake 10km away. Half rate for children under ten. Open by reservation only.
PRICES: s €28; d €34; t €42; extra person €8; dinner €13
ON SITE: Horse riding Fishing Hiking Tennis **NEARBY:** Hunting (3km) Golf (5km) Swimming pool (5km) **NOTES:** No pets

OUEILLOUX

☶☶☶ ▯◯▮ Chambre d'hôtes Rachel et Alain GUIDICI
15 Cami Deth Barboutou, 65190 OUEILLOUX
☎ 05 62 35 07 66 🖷 05 62 35 07 66
Bagnères-de-Bigorre 13 km. Abbaye de l'Escaladieu 15 km. In the old stable and granary of the owners' house, in the foothills of the Pyrénées, there are three first floor bedrooms, each with four single beds, shower and wc. Dining room and sitting room reserved to guests. Open fireplace. Shady lawn, private parking, garden furniture, TV, kitchen area. €54 for four people. Open all year.
PRICES: s €31; d €39; t €46; dinner €13 **ON SITE:** Hiking
NEARBY: Horse riding (12km) Golf (7km) Swimming pool (7km) Tennis (7km) Railway station (7km) Shops (7km) **NOTES:** No pets

OUZOUS

☶☶☶ Chambre d'hôtes Pierre NOGUEZ
Chemin de l'Eglise, 65400 OUZOUS
☎ 05 62 97 24 89 & 05 62 97 26 69 🖷 05 62 97 29 87
In a small mountain village, in the Argeles valley, there are four bedrooms on the first and second floor of this large, 18th century farmhouse with lots of character. Two twin beds, four double beds, and two extra beds. Each bedroom has private bathroom. Lounge, sitting room and library. Gazebo with garden furniture and a lovely view over the whole valley. Peaceful flower garden. Restaurant typical of the region. Owner's mobile: 06.08.51.77.62. Open all year.
PRICES: s €32; d €40; t €52 **ON SITE:** Hunting Fishing Hiking
NEARBY: Horse riding (3km) Golf (13km) Swimming pool (4km) Tennis (4km) Railway station (4km) Shops (4km) **NOTES:** Pets admitted English spoken

PIERREFITTE-NESTALAS

☶☶☶ ▟ ▯◯▮ Chambre d'hôtes Claire et Noël DUBARRY
21 rue Parmantier, 65260 PIERREFITTE-NESTALAS
☎ 05 62 92 74 77
Argeles 5 km. Tarbes 37 km. Four bedrooms in this former barn with a courtyard shared by the owners. On the first floor: one double bedroom, one bedroom with two double beds, one twin bedroom, one bedroom with a double bed and a double bed on a mezzanine. Each bedroom has a private bathroom. On the ground floor: a large lounge/sitting room with a fireplace and kitchen attached. 52 euros for four people. Contact for directions. Available between 1st February and 31st October.
PRICES: s €28; d €36; t €44; extra person €8; dinner €11
ON SITE: Fishing Hiking Tennis **NEARBY:** Horse riding (7km) Golf (18km) Swimming pool (4km) Railway station (12km)
NOTES: No pets

PINAS

☶☶☶ Domaine de Jean-Pierre Marie COLOMBIER
route de Villeneuve, 65300 PINAS
☎ 05 62 98 15 08 🖷 05 62 98 15 08
e-mail: marie.colombier@wanadoo.fr
In a peaceful setting, on the Lannemezan plateau, this large house has lots of character and a shady park. There are three beautiful bedrooms with private wcs and bathrooms. Charming stopover place, with pretty interior décor, sitting room, library and piano. Your hostess and her small dog are very welcoming. Restaurant 3km away.
PRICES: s €40; d €45; t €60; extra person €15 **ON SITE:** Fishing
NEARBY: Horse riding (3km) Golf (3km) Swimming pool (5km) Hiking (20km) Tennis (1km) Railway station (5km) Shops (1km) **NOTES:** Pets admitted English spoken

SALIGOS

☶☶☶ ▯◯▮ La Munia Monique LABIT
65120 SALIGOS
☎ 05 62 92 84 74
Luz-St-Sauveur 3 km. Small, calm, restful village of 81 people, with a lovely view over the mountains. There are three bedrooms on the first floor with a mezzanine (three double beds, four single beds). Each room has a washbasin, shower and wc. TV, telephone, library and board games. Terrace, garden furniture, barbecues, private parking. 50 euros for four people. Open all year.
PRICES: s €23; d €32; t €41; dinner €11 **ON SITE:** Fishing
NEARBY: Horse riding (9km) Swimming pool (3km) Hiking (9km) Tennis (3km) Railway station (25km) Shops (2km) **NOTES:** No pets

SALLES-ARGELES

☶☶☶ ▯◯▮ Le Belvédère Jean-Marc CRAMPE
6 rue de l'Eglise, 65400 SALLES-ARGELES
☎ 05 62 97 23 68 🖷 05 62 97 23 68
e-mail: le.belvedere@wanadoo.fr
Looking out over the three valleys of Luz, Cauterêts, Arrens, the Belvédère is ideally situated and bathed in sun and tranquillity. Enjoy sitting around the large table, on the terrace opposite the Pyrénées. There are four bedrooms: one bedroom with a double bed and bunk beds, two twin bedrooms and one bedroom with three single beds. Each bedroom has a private bathroom. Dining room and sitting room. Children under five free. Available all year, except November.
PRICES: d €43-€48 extra person €14; HB €35-€38; dinner €15
ON SITE: Hunting Fishing Hiking **NEARBY:** Horse riding (1km) Swimming pool (4km) Tennis (4km) Railway station (8km) Shops (4km)
NOTES: No pets English spoken

☶☶☶ ▯◯▮ Chambre d'hôtes Sandra MARIN
Can Sano, 65400 SALLES
☎ 05 62 97 92 08
Argelès-Gazost 4 km. Sandra and Bruno welcome you to their 1884 Bigourd house, which has four bedrooms. On the first and second floors: one bedroom with a double bed and a single bed, one double bedroom, two bedrooms for three people. Each bedroom has a private bathroom. Large dining room with lounge area, terrace, garden, private parking and panoramic view.
PRICES: s €36; d €48; t €60; dinner €15 **ON SITE:** Hiking
NEARBY: Horse riding (1km) Golf (8km) Swimming pool (4km) Tennis (4km) Railway station (4km) Shops (4km) **NOTES:** No pets English spoken

SOMBRUN

☶☶☶ ▯◯▮ Château de Sombrun
Josette et Gilles BRUNET
65700 SOMBRUN
☎ 05 62 96 49 43 🖷 05 62 96 01 89
e-mail: http://www.sudfr.com/chateaudesombrun/
The château of this charming small village offers one bedroom and a suite of two bedrooms (twin bedroom and a double bedroom) with bathroom and wc. Further twin bedroom and double bedroom, each with bathroom and wc, in an outbuilding. On the ground floor: sitting room, piano, billiard room, library, TV and music room, dining room. Outside: park, swimming pool, pond. Dinner on reservation (except Sunday). Childrens' meals: 10 euros. On the Maridan wine route, the château is situated within six hectares of parkland. 83 euros for four people. Available from 1st February to 30th November.
PRICES: s €55-€56; d €57-€60; t €71; dinner €20
ON SITE: Hunting Swimming pool **NEARBY:** Horse riding (4km) Golf (25km) Fishing (2km) Hiking (1km) Tennis (1km) Railway station (27km) Shops (2km) **NOTES:** No pets English spoken

ST-ARROMAN

▦ ◉ Domaine Vega Jacques MUN
65250 ST-ARROMAN
☎ 05 62 98 96 77   ⬒ 05 62 98 96 77
In this old manor house with lots of history, there are five renovated bedrooms each with a double bed, private bathroom and a child's bed (on request). The rooms are decorated with stencils. Communal lounge, shared with the owners, sitting room/library, piano. Old parkland, garden furniture, country swimming pool with lovely view, three hectares of grounds. Warm welcome provided by the owner, whose principal activity is rearing pigeons.
PRICES: s €37; d €46; extra person €8; HB €83; dinner €19
ON SITE: Swimming pool Hiking **NEARBY:** Horse riding (5km) Golf (12km) Fishing (2km) Tennis (5km) Railway station (12km) Shops (5km) **NOTES:** No pets English spoken

ST-LAURENT-DE-NESTE

▦ ◉ Chambre d'hôtes Fabienne GARCIA
4 rue de l'Ancienne Poste, La Souleillane,
65150 ST-LAURENT-DE-NESTE
☎ 05 62 39 76 01 & 06 87 13 19 45
e-mail: fjl.garcia@wanadoo.fr
St-Bertrand-de-Comminges 10 km. Lourdes 60 km. Spain 40 km.
At the foot of the Pyrénées, this old manor farm house dates from 1822, and is located in the centre of a village. There are three spacious and comfortable bedrooms. One bedroom in the owner's house has a double bed and twin beds. A further two bedrooms in an adjoining annexe have double beds, a bathroom and wc each. There is a garden outside for relaxation and meals. Evening meals featuring local produce can be provided on reservation, (Wednesdays, Fridays, and Sundays).
PRICES: s €35; d €43; t €51; extra person €8; dinner €14
ON SITE: Hunting Fishing Hiking Tennis **NEARBY:** Horse riding (4km) Golf (8km) Swimming pool (8km) Railway station (8km) **NOTES:** No pets

ST-PE-DE-BIGORRE

▦▦ Le Grand Cèdre Christian PETERS
6 rue du Barry,
65270 ST-PE-DE-BIGORRE
☎ 05 62 41 82 04   ⬒ 05 62 41 85 89
e-mail: chp@grandcedre.com   www.grandcedre.com
Pau 25 km. Lourdes 8 km. Le Grand Cèdre is a 17th century manor house, in the heart of Saint-Pé-de-Bigorre. There are four bedrooms with one double bed and one single bed and private bathroom in each. The house has stylish furniture and a large lounge/dining room with a library and TV. There is also a fireplace in each room. Park with large trees, garden, enclosed parking on site, garden furniture, french kitchen garden and a flower bed with a fountain. Children under five are welcome free. Open all year.
PRICES: s €48; d €60; t €72 **ON SITE:** Fishing Swimming pool Tennis **NEARBY:** Hunting (3km) Horse riding (5km) Golf (8km) Hiking (1km) Railway station (1km) **NOTES:** Pets admitted English spoken

🐓 Places with this symbol are farmhouses

▦ 🐓 ◉ Ferme Campseisillou
Marie-Luce ARRAMONDE
Quartier du Mousques, 65270 ST-PE-DE-BIGORRE
☎ 05 62 41 80 92   ⬒ 05 62 41 80 92
e-mail: camparaa@clubinternet.fr
Lourdes 13 km. 3km from the centre of the village, in the middle of the mountains and forests, there are three bedrooms with private bathrooms attached. (Three double beds and two single beds.) There is a lounge with TV and sitting room. Terrace, garden furniture. Evening meal featuring farm produce. Each bedroom has a lovely view. Open all year.
PRICES: s €27; d €35; t €44; extra person €9; dinner €13
ON SITE: Hunting Fishing Hiking **NEARBY:** Horse riding (1km) Golf (13km) Swimming pool (3km) Tennis (3km) Railway station (13km) Shops (3km) **NOTES:** Pets admitted English spoken

▦ 🐓 ◉ Ferme Versailles Michel et Lucienne AZENS
65270 ST-PE-DE-BIGORRE
☎ 05 62 41 80 48
In this large Bigourd house, built by the owner's grandparents in 1863, there are three comfortable bedrooms, each with private shower room and wc. Central heating. TV room. Large dining room with antique furniture. Parking is available in the farm courtyard. Sailing and lake, 10km away. Well located for access and relaxation. Evening meals featuring farm produce are available. Walking, excursions, and local visits are all possible. Half rate is charged for children under 12. Available from 1st March to 15th December.
PRICES: d €31; HB €30; dinner €13 **ON SITE:** Hunting Fishing **NEARBY:** Horse riding (4km) Golf (10km) Swimming pool (1km) Hiking (1km) Tennis (1km) Railway station (1km) Shops (1km) **NOTES:** No pets English spoken

▦▦ La Calèche Françoise et Luc L'HARIDON
6 rue du Barry, 65270 ST-PE-DE-BIGORRE
☎ 05 62 41 86 71 & 05 62 94 60 17   ⬒ 05 62 94 60 50

Lourdes, Betharram caves 10 km. At the foot of the Pyrénées, in the old village of St-Pé-de-Bigorre, la Calèche is a 17th century manor house. There are four Louis XIII-style, tastefully decorated romantic bedrooms, each with bathroom and wc. A large breakfast of croissants, fruit juice, home-made jams and house specialities is served in the old stables. Secure parking. Evening meals of fish, duck or quiche can be served in the old stables. Private park with swimming pool. Available all year.
PRICES: s €39; d €39-€46; t €59; extra person €14 **ON SITE:** Hunting Swimming pool **NEARBY:** Horse riding (4km) Golf (10km) Fishing (10km) Hiking (10km) Tennis (10km) **NOTES:** No pets English spoken

MIDI-PYRÉNÉES

TOSTAT

¶¶¶ ⫴◯⫴ Chambre d'hôtes Catherine RIVIERE D'ARC
allée du Château, 65140 TOSTAT
☎ 05 62 31 23 27 📠 05 62 31 23 27

In the old stables of the 18th century château, classed as a historic site, there is one twin bedroom on the ground floor, accessible to less mobile guests. On the first floor, there is a bedroom with a double bed and a single bed, and two twin bedrooms, each with private bathroom. The bedrooms retain all the character of the old stables, whilst the exterior fits in with the setting of the Ardour plains. Half-board. Available all year.
PRICES: s €43; d €46; extra person €14; dinner €14 **ON SITE:** Fishing Hiking **NEARBY:** Hunting (10km) Horse riding (5km) Golf (12km) Swimming pool (10km) Tennis (10km) Railway station (10km) Shops (6km) **NOTES:** Pets admitted

VIC-EN-BIGORRE

¶¶¶ ⫴◯⫴ Chambre d'hôtes Lucienne BROQUA
rue Osmin Ricau, 65500 VIC-EN-BIGORRE
☎ 05 62 96 26 29 & 06 87 22 75 54
Madiran vineyard 15 km. There are three bedrooms and a kitchen, next to the owners' house. Two double beds, twin beds and bunks with a shower room and wc in each one. One double bedroom with shower room and wc in the owners' house. Courtyard, enclosed parkland, garden furniture, barbecue and parking area. Sand pit, park with lots of flowers, summer dining room for guests. Available on site: mountain biking, boule and model aircraft making. Stretch of water 10km away. Archery 5km. Interesting monuments nearby. Open in the school holidays.
PRICES: s €30; d €34; t €42; extra person €9; dinner €14
NEARBY: Horse riding (1km) Fishing (1km) Swimming pool (1km) Hiking (1km) Tennis (1km) Railway station (17km) **NOTES:** No pets Minimum 2 night stay

VIDOU

¶¶¶ ⫴◯⫴ Chambre d'hôtes Chantal MANSOUX
Las Peloches, 65220 VIDOU ☎ 05 62 35 65 04
http://perso.wanadoo.fr/coteaux-bigorre/peloches/index.htm
This old Bigourd farmhouse lies near the coast: there are three bedrooms with private bathrooms. Ground floor: large double bedroom, possibility of two bunks, shower room. First floor: one attic double bedroom and shower, a twin bedroom with mezzanine level with a bathroom. Two sitting rooms, lounge. Swimming pool, children's play area. Garden furniture and barbecue. The windows open over the Pyrenees, the vegetable garden and countryside views. Evening meals feature fresh garden produce. Half board: 206 euros/week (children under ten 103 euros). Available throughout the year.
PRICES: s €28; d €37; extra person €14; dinner €14 **ON SITE:** Children's play area Fishing Swimming pool Hiking **NEARBY:** Hunting (5km) Horse riding (7km) Golf (25km) Tennis (5km) **NOTES:** Pets admitted English spoken

VIELLA

¶¶¶ 🐓 ⫴◯⫴ Les Cabanes Marcel et Jocelyne LAPORTE
Eslias, 65120 VIELLA
☎ 05 62 92 84 58
Tourmalet, Pic du Midi 10 km. Gavarnie, Pont d'Espagne 30 km. There are three guest rooms in this peaceful setting, 300m from the Tourmalet road, in a small mountain village. First floor, one bedroom with a double bed and twin beds, shower room and wc. Ground floor: two double bedrooms, shower room and wc. Dining room, TV, library area, fireplace. Large terrace area, garden furniture and barbecue. Rate for four people: €54. Very pretty views over the surrounding mountains. Available throughout the year.
PRICES: s €28; d €37; t €46; extra person €10; HB €30; dinner €12
NEARBY: Hunting (1km) Horse riding (5km) Fishing (1km) Swimming pool (2km) Hiking (1km) Tennis (2km) Railway station (30km) Shops (2km) **NOTES:** No pets

VIELLE-AURE

¶¶¶ Chambre d'hôtes Claude FOURCADE-ABBADIE
65170 VIELLE-AURE
☎ 05 62 39 42 33
Ski and spa resort of St-Lary 1.5 km. Spain 20 km. In the heart of the Aure valley, at an altitude of 800m, there are three peaceful rooms in the owners' typical Pyreneen house. Shower room and wc in each bedroom. Dining room for breakfast, garden furniture and parking area. Rate for four: 70 euros. Near to the nature reserve of Néouvielle (20km) and numerous ski resorts. Walking (GR10), horse riding, mountain biking, paragliding, canyoning, rafting and climbing all possible nearby. Open May to September.
PRICES: s €35; d €40; t €55 **ON SITE:** Fishing Hiking **NEARBY:** Horse riding (3km) Golf (35km) Swimming pool (2km) Tennis (2km)
NOTES: No pets

¶¶¶ Chambre d'hôtes Pauline BEYRIE
65170 VIELLE-AURE
☎ 05 62 39 52 68 & 05 62 39 59 78
Three bedrooms in a former barn attached to the owners' house. First floor: three double bedrooms, shower room and wc. Garden furniture, terrace, private parking. Very calm comfortable bedrooms with beautiful views over the surrounding mountains. Separate dining room. Large meadow in front of the house. Typical lively Aure valley village. Available all year.
PRICES: s €35; d €40; extra person €13 **ON SITE:** Children's play area Hunting Fishing Hiking **NEARBY:** Horse riding (1km) Golf (15km) Swimming pool (1km) Tennis (1km) Railway station (30km) Shops (1km)
NOTES: Pets admitted

VIGNEC

¶¶¶ 🐓 Chambre d'hôtes Daniel VERDOT
65170 VIGNEC
☎ 05 62 39 54 53
Four bedrooms in the owner's house. One twin bedroom, three double bedrooms with shower room and wc. Small sitting room and large room with fireplace. Small, tree lined park. Situated on a farm, with a small campsite, in a typical small village. Visit the herds or haymaking in the summer. Rooms available all year.
PRICES: d €36 **NEARBY:** Golf (1km) Fishing (1km) Swimming pool (1km) Tennis (1km) Shops (1km) **NOTES:** No pets

For further information on these and
other chambres d'hôtes, consult
the Gîtes de France website
www.gites-de-france.fr

LOT

ALBAS

♦♦♦ Chambre d'hôtes Max GRAVES
Crespiat, 46140 ALBAS
☎ 05 65 20 18 04 & 06 08 60 60 09 ▯ 05 65 30 75 20
e-mail: maxgrav@aol.com
Cahors 24 km. Upstairs in an annexe of the owners' house: one room sleeping four in single beds (bath and wc); one double room (bath and wc); one room sleeping three in single beds (bath and wc). Summer kitchen (with refrigerator). Private swimming pool. Hiking trails nearby. A 4ha estate in the heart of vineyards. Tariff: €70 for four persons. Open 1 May to 30 October.
PRICES: s €38-€40; d €43-€44; t €56 **ON SITE:** Swimming pool **NEARBY:** Horse riding (16km) Fishing (3km) Stretch of water (3km) Tennis (4km) Railway station (24km) Shops (4km) **NOTES:** No pets English spoken

♦♦♦ ⏚ La Méline Edouard et Nel VOS
Route de Sauret. D37, 46140 ALBAS
☎ 05 65 36 97 25 ▯ 05 65 36 97 25
e-mail: ednel.vos@wanadoo.fr
A lovely isolated house with views over forests and vineyards. One room sleeping three (shower and wc). One twin room with disabled access (bathroom and wc). One double room (shower and wc). TV in every room. Central heating. Terrace, garden furniture, wooded park. Beautiful walking trails. Open 1 April to 30 September, and by reservation at other times.
PRICES: s €30; d €44; t €55; dinner €17 **NEARBY:** Bathing (4km) Canoeing (9km) Horse riding (9km) Fishing (4km) Swimming pool (7km) Stretch of water (4km) Tennis (4km) Railway station (20km) Shops (7km) **NOTES:** No pets English spoken

♦♦♦ Le Soleil M.Thérèse et J.François FERRON
Rivière Haute, 46140 ALBAS
☎ 05 65 30 91 90 & 06 22 17 38 07 ▯ 05 65 30 91 90
e-mail: le-soleil@wanadoo.fr

This character house offers guest rooms with separate entrances. Room 1 (double bed, shower, wc); room 2 (double bed, extra double bed, shower, wc); room 3 (double bed, two single beds, adjoining shower and wc). Terrace, garden furniture, barbecue, boules pitch, wooded park. TV in each room, washing machine, refrigerator, central heating. Rooms are no smoking. Evening events, piano. Covered swimming pool. Tariff: €61-€70 for four persons. Open all year.
PRICES: s €43; d €46; t €50-€54 **ON SITE:** Fishing Swimming pool Stretch of water **NEARBY:** Horse riding (8km) Tennis (3km) Railway station (22km) Shops (3km) **NOTES:** No pets English spoken

ALVIGNAC

♦♦♦ Le Roc Marie et Yves LASCOSTE
46500 ALVIGNAC ☎ 05 65 33 70 18 ▯ 05 65 33 70 18
This traditional house is between Rocamadour and Padirac and is

set in open countryside. Rooms are on the first floor, with separate access. 'Safranée' (double bed with shower and wc); 'Primevère' (twin beds with shower and wc); 'Cannelle' (double bed with spare double bed, bathroom and wc); 'Eté Indien' (double bed and single, bathroom and wc). Breakfast served on the terrace in summer. Home-made patisseries. Fresh platter available €9. Rest guaranteed. Four people: €47-€53. Open all year.
PRICES: s €30; d €35; t €41-€47 **NEARBY:** Horse riding (8km) Swimming pool (8km) Tennis (2km) Railway station (2km) Shops (3km) **NOTES:** Pets admitted

♦♦♦ ⏚ ⏚⏚ Chambre d'hôtes Elie LASCOSTE
Route de Rocamadour, Mazeyrac, 46500 ALVIGNAC
☎ 05 65 33 61 16
Rocamadour and Padirac 8 km. Rooms in a Quercynois house of 1818. On the ground floor: double room with spare bed, shower and wc (separate entrance). Two upstairs rooms, one sleeping four, the other a double, each with shower and wc. Extra heating, fridge. Tariff: €47-€53 for four persons. Meals must be booked in advance. Open all year.
PRICES: s €30; d €35; t €41-€47; extra person €8; dinner €15 **ON SITE:** Fishing **NEARBY:** Canoeing (8km) Horse riding (8km) Swimming pool (8km) Stretch of water (10km) Tennis (2km) Railway station (8km) Shops (2km) **NOTES:** Pets admitted

AUTOIRE

♦♦♦ ⏚ ⏚⏚ La Rivière Christiane GRAVES
46400 AUTOIRE
☎ 05 65 38 18 01 ▯ 05 65 38 00 50
Caves at Padirac 6 km. A house of character 1.5km from the village. One double room and one triple, each with bathroom and wc; one twin room with shower and wc. Lounge with TV. Central heating. Local produce on sale. 9 hole golf course 3km. Tourist tax €0.5 per person per day. Child's meal €7. Open all year.
PRICES: s €30; d €34; t €46; extra person €8; dinner €14 **NEARBY:** Bathing (5km) Horse riding (4km) Fishing (1km) Swimming pool (4km) Stretch of water (5km) Tennis (4km) Railway station (14km) Shops (4km) **NOTES:** Pets admitted

BELAYE

♦♦♦ ⏚⏚ Marliac Véronique STROOBANT
46140 BELAYE ☎ 05 65 36 95 50 ▯ 05 65 31 99 04
Five guest rooms (two in a duplex) on a lovely 18th-century farm. One room with six single beds, and four double rooms (queen size beds), all with shower and wc and private access. Terrace, barbecue, washing machine, electric heating. Private swimming pool. Children's games, table tennis, boules. Tourist tax €0.15 per person per day. Tariff: €91-€92 for four persons. Child's meal 9€. Open all year.
PRICES: s €46; d €55-€61; t €69-€76; extra person €15; dinner €17 **ON SITE:** Children's play area Swimming pool **NEARBY:** Bathing (8km) Horse riding (6km) Fishing (8km) Stretch of water (8km) Tennis (8km) Railway station (30km) Shops (10km) **NOTES:** No pets

BOUSSAC

♦♦♦ ⏚ ⏚⏚ Domaine des Villedieu Martine VILLEDIEU
46100 BOUSSAC
☎ 05 65 40 06 63 ▯ 05 65 40 09 22
e-mail: villedi@aol.com www.villedieu.com
At ground level, with individual access in annexes to the owners' house, three double rooms and two twins, with extra bed available. Shower and wc in each room. Sitting room, library. Extra electric heating. Garden furniture. Private swimming pool, shared with customers of the adjacent farm-auberge. Farm produce for sale. Tariff: €105 for four persons. Open all year.

continued   *continued*

PRICES: s €43-€49; d €43-€76; t €90; extra person €11; dinner €19 **ON SITE:** Swimming pool **NEARBY:** Bathing (2km) Canoeing (2km) Horse riding (10km) Fishing (2km) Stretch of water (2km) Tennis (10km) Railway station (10km) Shops (10km) Restaurant nearby **NOTES:** Pets admitted English spoken

BRENGUES

⊪ **Merlet** Thérèse CHANUT
46320 BRENGUES
☎ 05 65 40 05 44 🖹 05 65 40 05 44
On the first floor of the owners' house, 100m from the River Célé. Two double beds, three singles, baby cot. Bathroom or shower and wc in each room. Heating. Restaurant 1km. Open all year.
PRICES: s €30; d €40; t €46 **ON SITE:** Bathing Canoeing Fishing Stretch of water **NEARBY:** Horse riding (12km) Swimming pool (1km) Tennis (1km) Railway station (15km) Shops (1km) **NOTES:** No pets

BRETENOUX

⊪ ❤ **Ferme de Borie** Jeanine RIGAL
46130 BRETENOUX
☎ 05 65 38 41 74 & 05 65 38 61 49
Music festival at the Château de Castelnau 2.5 km from 20/07 to 15/08. Guest rooms in a 14th-century farmhouse of character, each with private entrance. Four twin rooms and two doubles, each with shower and wc. Small sitting room. Panoramic terrace overlooks 12ha grounds. Electric heating. Shady park with picnic tables. Restaurants 300m. Open all year.
PRICES: s €27; d €34 **ON SITE:** Bathing Canoeing Fishing Stretch of water **NEARBY:** Horse riding (8km) Swimming pool (1km) Tennis (1km) Railway station (2km) **NOTES:** No pets English spoken

CABRERETS

⊪ **Chambre d'hôtes** Patrick BESSAC
Place de la Mairie, 46330 CABRERETS
☎ 05 65 31 27 04 🖹 05 65 30 25 46

Upstairs rooms in the owners' house. Three double beds, three singles. Shower and wc in each room. Extra pull-out bed available. Cooking area. Extra heating. Tariff: €59 for four persons. Open 1st February to 30th October.
PRICES: s €27; d €35-€38; t €46-€49; extra person €11
ON SITE: Bathing Canoeing Fishing Stretch of water Tennis
NEARBY: Horse riding (1km) Swimming pool (8km) Railway station (32km) **NOTES:** No pets English spoken

CAHORS

⊪ ᑔ **Chambre d'hôtes** Noël MASCHERETTI
Saint-Henri, 46000 CAHORS
☎ 05 65 22 56 47 & 06 81 55 55 36
In the owners' home are these three double beds and four singles. One room with double bed plus spare double bed. Bath or shower and wc in each room. Colour TV in each bedroom. Electric heating.

Private swimming pool. Tariff: €53 for four persons. Open all year.
PRICES: s €30; d €38; t €46; dinner €15 **ON SITE:** Swimming pool Tennis **NEARBY:** Horse riding (5km) Fishing (5km) Stretch of water (5km) Railway station (5km) Shops (5km) **NOTES:** Pets admitted

CALES

⊪ ❤ ᑔ **Chambre d'hôtes** Alain VERGNES
Lac Boutel, 46350 CALES
☎ 05 65 37 95 70 🖹 05 65 41 90 89
Rooms at ground level in an annexe of the owners' house. Four double beds and three singles. Private shower and wc for each room. Heating. Each room has its own terrace. Refrigerator available. Extra double bed available. Private swimming pool. Tariff: €61 for four persons. Open all year.
PRICES: s €34; d €38; t €50; dinner €12 **ON SITE:** Swimming pool **NEARBY:** Bathing (7km) Canoeing (7km) Horse riding (7km) Fishing (7km) Stretch of water (7km) Tennis (9km) Railway station (12km) Shops (9km) **NOTES:** Pets admitted English spoken

CASTELNAU-MONTRATIER

⊪ ᑔ **La Combe** Michèle LELOUREC
46170 CASTELNAU-MONTRATIER
☎ 05 65 21 84 16 🖹 05 65 21 84 49
e-mail: michele.lelourec@free.fr
Cahors 25 km. Guest rooms in a typical Quercynois house and its associated buildings, each with private entrance and terrace. 'Le Figuié' double room with shower and wc; 'Les Chênes' triple room with shower and wc; 'La Source' with two double beds, shower, separate wc. Heating and TV in each room. Garden. Private covered swimming pool. Four people: €98. Open all year.
PRICES: ; d €58-€76; t €78-€90; dinner €21 **NEARBY:** Bathing (12km) Horse riding (6km) Fishing (1km) Stretch of water (12km) Tennis (3km) Railway station (25km) Shops (3km) **NOTES:** Pets admitted

DEGAGNAC

⊪ **La Cabane** Occo BINNENDIJK
La Cabane - Poudens, 46340 DEGAGNAC
☎ 05 65 41 49 74 🖹 05 65 41 49 74
e-mail: lacabane@wanadoo.fr

Gourdon 6 km. Spacious rooms are available, upstairs at this house. One suite with double bed and kitchen/living room, bathroom and wc. One double room (160cm bed) with shower and wc. One twin room with cooking area, shower and wc. Extra beds available. Garden furniture, terrace, garden and meadow, covered swimming pool. View over the valley of the Céou. Four people: €85. Open all year.
PRICES: ; d €46-€55; t €70; extra person €15 **ON SITE:** Swimming pool **NEARBY:** Horse riding (6km) Stretch of water (14km) Tennis (4km) Railway station (6km) Shops (6km) **NOTES:** No pets CC English spoken

continued

DURAVEL

⫽⫽⫽ ◯ Chambre d'hôtes Philippe et Isabelle DUCOUM
46700 DURAVEL
☎ 05 65 36 54 27 & 05 65 36 40 99 ▤ 05 65 36 44 14
Rooms in a castle in Cahors wine country. Ground floor: a suite sleeping two in single beds, with bathroom and wc. Upstairs, the Yellow Room (double bed, shower, wc); Green Room (double bed, bath, wc); Pink Room (double bed, bathroom, wc, private sitting room, extra double bed). Central heating. Lounge with satellite TV. Library. Extensive park. Open all year.
PRICES: d €69-€105; extra person €19; dinner €20 NEARBY: Bathing (4km) Canoeing (7km) Horse riding (3km) Fishing (4km) Stretch of water (10km) Tennis (3km) Railway station (14km) Shops (7km)
NOTES: No pets

⫽⫽⫽ ❤ La Roseraie Denis et Patricia RIGAL
46700 DURAVEL
☎ 05 65 24 63 82 ▤ 05 65 30 89 75
At the heart of a Cahors vineyard with a view over the Lot valley. Three double rooms and one twin room, each with private shower room and wc. TV room. Electric heating. Private swimming pool shared with the occupants of two gîtes. Tourist tax €0.31 per person per day. Ostrich rearing. Meals for guests staying over three nights. 1km from village shops. Private park. Open all year.
PRICES: s €30; d €40; extra person €10; dinner €14 ON SITE: Swimming pool NEARBY: Bathing (1km) Canoeing (1km) Horse riding (1km) Fishing (1km) Stretch of water (1km) Tennis (1km) Railway station (11km) Shops (1km) Restaurant nearby NOTES: No pets English spoken

FONS

⫽⫽⫽ ◯ La Piale Charlotte VIPREY
La Piale, 46100 FONS
☎ 05 65 40 19 52
One large double room with its own sitting room at ground floor level in the proprietors' house, with separate bathroom and wc. Gourmet dining possible. €22.9. This 18th-century house has a 7ha park and a swimming pool. The owners have preserved original features of the dining room. Open all year.
PRICES: s €48-€55; d €53-€60; dinner €14 NEARBY: Bathing (10km) Canoeing (10km) Horse riding (10km) Fishing (10km) Stretch of water (10km) Tennis (10km) NOTES: No pets English spoken

FRANCOULES

⫽⫽⫽ ◯ Le Mas de Jaillac Eric BELLEMANS
46090 FRANCOULES
☎ 05 65 36 02 36 ▤ 05 65 36 02 35
e-mail: e.bellemans@wanadoo.fr
Cahors 21 km. Three rooms for guests in an old barn restored with care. Very fine view. One room has a double bed and a single, bathroom and wc. There are also two double rooms with bath and wc. Central heating; courtyard; garden and 2ha of meadowland; large swimming pool. A lovely quiet spot. Four people: €75-€90. Open all year.
PRICES: s €40-€55; d €45-€60; t €60-€75; dinner €19 NEARBY: Bathing (10km) Horse riding (8km) Fishing (10km) Swimming pool (10km) Stretch of water (10km) Railway station (21km) Shops (10km) NOTES: No pets

GINDOU

⫽⫽⫽ ◯ Le Ségalard Monique DELAUNOIT
46250 GINDOU
☎ 05 65 21 62 71 ▤ 05 65 21 62 71
http://www.gites-de-france-lot/segalard/
Gourdon 19 km. Two ground floor rooms with independent access and one room upstairs, in the home of the owners. 'La Pergola'

has a 160cm double bed, as does 'Cocoon'. 'La Source' has twin beds. All have shower room and wc. Heating. Swimming pool shared with owners. Sitting room. One bedroom has TV. Open 30th March to 15th November.
PRICES: s €42-€46; d €46-€52; t €68-€72; dinner €19
ON SITE: Swimming pool NEARBY: Bathing (4km) Canoeing (20km) Horse riding (10km) Fishing (4km) Stretch of water (4km) Tennis (4km) Railway station (19km) Shops (4km) NOTES: No pets

GOURDON

⫽⫽⫽ ◯ Le Paradis Jacquie JARDIN
Route de Salviac D 673, 46300 GOURDON
☎ 05 65 41 09 73 & 06 72 18 05 44
The owner's house accommodates guests in four rooms. A double room with private shower and own wc on landing; two rooms sleeping three each with shower room and wc; a twin room with shower room and private wc on landing. Private swimming pool and paddling pool shared with visitors to a nearby campsite. Tax: €0.3 per person per day. Open all year.
PRICES: s €32; d €37; t €49; dinner €13 ON SITE: Swimming pool NEARBY: Canoeing (11km) Horse riding (4km) Fishing (1km) Tennis (1km) Railway station (4km) Shops (1km) NOTES: No pets

GRAMAT

⫽⫽⫽ ❤ ◯ Ferme du Gravier Patrice et Lydia RAVET
Le Gravier, 46500 GRAMAT
☎ 05 65 33 41 88 ▤ 05 65 33 73 75
Rocamadour & Padirac 9 km. In a small farmhouse typical of the Causse three upstairs rooms and two downstairs. In total four double beds, three singles and two bunks. Each room has its own shower and wc. Electric heating. Extra beds available. Library. Terrace with garden furniture. Tariff: €59 for four persons. Child's meal €8. Open all year.
PRICES: s €38; d €38-€41; t €49; extra person €11; dinner €15 NEARBY: Bathing (20km) Canoeing (20km) Horse riding (2km) Fishing (20km) Swimming pool (2km) Stretch of water (20km) Tennis (2km) Railway station (1km) Shops (2km) NOTES: No pets English spoken

⫽⫽⫽ ◯ Domaine du Cloucau
Francine BOUGARET
Cavagnac, 46500 GRAMAT
☎ 05 65 33 76 18 & 06 12 90 03 28 ▤ 05 65 33 76 18
e-mail: lecloucau@caramail.com
A huge 18th-century house in the heart of the Causse de Gramat. Two double rooms, 'L'Hortensia' and 'Le Pigeonnier' with shower or bathroom and wc. Two suites, 'La Caussanette' (double room on ground floor and two single beds upstairs, with bathroom and wc) and 'La Brocantine' (double bed, twin beds in adjoining room, shower and wc). Swimming pool with diving board. TV. Piano. Rooms are non-smoking. Heating. Rambling trails nearby. Four people: €72-€80. Open all year.
PRICES: ; d €52-€56; t €71; extra person €11; dinner €18
ON SITE: Swimming pool NEARBY: Canoeing (15km) Horse riding (4km) Fishing (5km) Tennis (4km) Railway station (4km) Shops (4km) NOTES: Pets admitted

⫽⫽⫽ ◯ Montanty Brigitte DUMAS
46500 GRAMAT
☎ 05 65 33 41 65 ▤ 05 65 33 41 66
www.montanty.com
Rocamadour & Padirac 13 km. The proprietors live in a converted barn. Upstairs they offer four guest rooms, each with a double bed, shower room and wc. Cot and spare bed available. Two more rooms are in the process of construction. Open from 1st April to 15th October.
PRICES: s €30-€31; d €37; t €49; extra person €9; dinner €14

continued　　　continued

Montanty, Gramat

NEARBY: Bathing (20km) Canoeing (20km) Horse riding (4km) Swimming pool (4km) Stretch of water (20km) Tennis (4km) Railway station (4km) Shops (4km) **NOTES:** No pets English spoken

♦♦♦♦ ⏀ Moulin de Fresquet Claude RAMELOT
46500 GRAMAT
☎ 05 65 38 70 60 & 06 08 85 09 21 ▤ 05 65 33 60 13
e-mail: moulindefresquet@ifrance.com
Rocamadour & Padirac 9 km. A house of character and charm in a genuine 17th-century Quercynois water mill. Five guest rooms (four double and one with two double beds) of which three have direct access to the 3ha shady park and private courtyard. Each room has private shower and wc. Heating. Terrace. Library. TV lounge/reading room. Fishing on private stretch of water. Tariff: €87 for four persons. Child's meal 60F.
PRICES: s €50-€54; d €50-€67; t €81; dinner €18 **ON SITE:** Bathing Fishing **NEARBY:** Canoeing (15km) Horse riding (1km) Swimming pool (1km) Stretch of water (1km) Tennis (1km) Railway station (1km) Shops (1km) **NOTES:** No pets

LACHAPELLE-AUZAC

♦♦♦ Lachapelle Basse René LOURDJANE
46200 LACHAPELLE-AUZAC
☎ 05 65 37 82 77 ▤ 05 65 37 82 77
e-mail: lourdjanerene@wanadoo.fr.
www.france-bonjour.com/lachapelle-auzac/
Accommodation for up to twelve in rooms in part of the owners' house (three double beds in total and six single). Each room has shower and wc. Large salon with TV. Garden furniture, terrace. Private swimming pool, shared with the owners. Tariff: €61-€69 for four persons. Golf 3km. Open all year.
PRICES: s €37; d €43; t €53-€58 **ON SITE:** Swimming pool
NEARBY: Bathing (5km) Canoeing (5km) Horse riding (5km) Fishing (5km) Stretch of water (5km) Tennis (5km) Railway station (5km) Shops (5km) **NOTES:** No pets

LAMOTHE-FENELON

♦♦♦ ⏀ Gatignol Eliane MONTARNAL
46350 LAMOTHE-FENELON
☎ 05 65 37 60 24
Ground level rooms with separate access. One room in an annexe with a double bed and a single. Two rooms in the house of the owners, each with a double bed. Rooms have shower or bath and wc. Central heating. Garden furniture, small private terraces. Children's meals (under 10): €8. No meals on Sunday. Open all year.
PRICES: s €30; d €37; t €44; dinner €14 **NEARBY:** Bathing (2km) Canoeing (7km) Horse riding (13km) Fishing (2km) Swimming pool (4km) Stretch of water (2km) Tennis (4km) Railway station (13km) Shops (4km) **NOTES:** No pets English spoken

LE BASTIT

♦♦♦ ♥ ⏀ Bel-Air Francine CHAMBERT
46500 LE BASTIT
☎ 05 65 38 77 54 ▤ 05 65 38 85 18
In a Quercynois house of character, two twin rooms, one triple room and three doubles. Each room has its own shower or bathroom and wc. Central heating. Salon, TV, refreshment room, shaded terrace. Boules area, garden furniture, caving, paths. Minitel. Cooking area. Near the sites of Rocamadour and Padirac. Tariff: €56 for four persons. Child's meal €8. Open all year.
PRICES: s €32; d €41; t €49; dinner €14 **NEARBY:** Horse riding (8km) Swimming pool (8km) Tennis (8km) Railway station (9km) Shops (8km)
NOTES: Pets admitted English spoken

LE MONTAT

♦♦♦ ⏀ Domaine Les Tuileries André CARRIER
46090 LE MONTAT-CAHORS
☎ 05 65 21 04 72 ▤ 05 65 21 04 72
e-mail: domainelestuileries@yahoo.fr
www.multimania.com/domlestuileries
South of Cahors by 5km, three self-contained guest rooms at ground level. One room sleeping four, one room sleeping three, and a double room, all with shower, wc and TV. Heating. Garden furniture. Marked walking trails; stop-off point on the St Jacques de Compostelle pilgrim route. Paddock for horses. Winter truffle hunts. The rooms are non-smoking. Tariff: €67 for four persons. Gourmet dinner: €15. Open all year.
PRICES: s €38-€41; d €44; t €53-€56; extra person €6; dinner €14
NEARBY: Horse riding (4km) Fishing (10km) Swimming pool (8km) Stretch of water (10km) Tennis (1km) Railway station (8km) Shops (5km)
NOTES: No pets English spoken

LE VIGAN-SUR-GOURDON

♦♦♦♦ ⏀ Manoir de la Barrière
Michel et Christiane AUFFRET
46300 LE VIGAN-SUR-GOURDON
☎ 05 65 41 40 73 ▤ 05 65 41 40 20
e-mail: manoirauffret@aol.com
www.france-bonjour.com/manoir-la-barrière/

Large rooms with independent access, in a 13th-century manor house now entirely restored. The rooms are named 'La Quercy', 'l'Occitane', 'La Régence' (all double rooms with bathroom and wc); and 'Le Pigeonnier' (one double bed plus two singles, bathroom and wc). Kitchen area in each room. Shaded 1ha park with stream. Private swimming pool. Tariff: €115 for four persons. Open 1st April to 20th October.
PRICES: s €55; d €75; t €95; extra person €20; dinner €30
ON SITE: Fishing Swimming pool Stretch of water Tennis
NEARBY: Horse riding (3km) Railway station (6km) **NOTES:** No pets English spoken

LEBREIL

♥♥♥ ⚞◯⚟ Labrugade Madeleine BIBARD
46800 LEBREIL
☎ 05 65 31 84 66

Attractive countryside location among flowers and woods. Three rooms, with separate access. Three double beds, one single, one spare, one cot. All rooms have shower and wc. Central heating. Courtyard, sitting room, library. In summer enjoy the shady terrace with its outdoor furniture; in winter head for the warmth of the open fire inside. Child's meal €7. Open all year.
PRICES: s €29; d €37; t €46; extra person €9; dinner €13
ON SITE: Fishing **NEARBY:** Bathing (4km) Horse riding (4km) Swimming pool (4km) Stretch of water (4km) Tennis (4km) Railway station (25km) Shops (4km) **NOTES:** Pets admitted

LES QUATRE-ROUTES

♥♥♥ ⚞◯⚟ Chambre d'hôtes René EYMAT et J CHABOY
Saint-Julien, 46110 LES QUATRE-ROUTES
☎ 05 65 32 11 82

Turenne & Colonge-la-Rouge 10 km. Guest rooms in the proprietors' home, with separate access. On the ground floor, 'Tilleul', a double room with TV, shower and wc; 'Tournesol' with two double beds, shower, wc and TV. Upstairs is 'Lavande' with a double bed, shower and wc. Heating. Terrace. At the appropriate time of year, Josette offers demonstrations of truffle hunting and expeditions. Tariff: €58 for four persons. Open all year.
PRICES: s €30-€35; d €35-€40; t €53; extra person €8; dinner €14
NEARBY: Bathing (1km) Canoeing (6km) Horse riding (10km) Fishing (1km) Swimming pool (10km) Stretch of water (6km) Tennis (1km) Railway station (1km) Shops (1km) **NOTES:** No pets

LIMOGNE-EN-QUERCY

♥♥♥ Bastide de Vinel Jean-Pierre GAVENS
46260 LIMOGNE-EN-QUERCY
☎ 05 65 24 37 32

Cahors 35 km. This old religious school has been recently restored. Four rooms, all on the first floor: one room with double bed and two singles; two rooms each with three single beds; one room with a double bed and a single. All have shower and wc. Garden and courtyard. Four people: €56. Open all year.
PRICES: s €30; d €37-€41; t €47-€52; extra person €11
NEARBY: Bathing (11km) Horse riding (2km) Swimming pool (1km) Stretch of water (12km) Tennis (1km) Railway station (35km) **NOTES:** Pets admitted

♥♥♥ ⚞◯⚟ Le Clos des Chênes Verts Patrice PONSOLLE
Route de Cahors, 46260 LIMOGNE-EN-QUERCY
☎ 05 65 31 50 03   ▤ 05 65 31 50 03
e-mail: ponsolle@club-internet.fr
Cahors 35 km. Guest rooms in an old family mansion. On the first floor, the Room of Birds (double bed, sitting area, bathroom and shower); The Polished Room (double bed, shower and wc); and

the Vaulted Room (double bed, lounge, child's bed, bathroom and wc). On the ground floor, with separate access, The Old Study (three single beds, lounge area, bathroom and wc). Heating. Country garden. Very shady, walled park. Open all year.
PRICES: ; d €46-€53; t €64; extra person €8; dinner €15
NEARBY: Bathing (9km) Horse riding (1km) Fishing (9km) Swimming pool (1km) Stretch of water (8km) Tennis (1km) Railway station (35km) **NOTES:** No pets English spoken

LISSAC-ET-MOURET

♥♥♥ 🐾 ⚞◯⚟ L'Oasienne Clavies Gérard et Nicole GAY
46100 LISSAC-ET-MOURET
☎ 05 65 34 40 98 & 06 76 07 87 26   ▤ 05 65 34 40 98

Upstairs rooms for guests in the owners' house. Three double beds, two singles and a child's bed in total. Private showers and wcs. There is also a gîte and camping on the farm. Two swimming pools and a jacuzzi, shared with the campers and gîte visitors. Trampoline, mini-golf, refreshment room, table tennis. Restaurant 7km. Tariff: €41 for four persons. Open all year.
PRICES: s €29; d €32; t €37; dinner €14 **ON SITE:** Swimming pool **NEARBY:** Bathing (8km) Canoeing (8km) Horse riding (4km) Fishing (5km) Stretch of water (3km) Tennis (2km) Railway station (8km) Shops (8km) **NOTES:** No pets English spoken

MARCILHAC-SUR-CELE

♥♥♥ ⚞◯⚟ La Caussenarde Colette BESSY
Cap de la Coste, 46160 MARCILHAC-SUR-CELE
☎ 05 65 40 69 10

One ground floor double room with bath and wc. Upstairs, one double room and a second room form a family suite with two single beds and a double, shower and wc. Heating. Private swimming pool. Lakes 1km. Walking trails. Dinner may be available for walkers. Garden. Tariff: €67 for four persons. Open all year.
PRICES: s €35; d €41; t €55; dinner €15 **ON SITE:** Swimming pool **NEARBY:** Bathing (1km) Horse riding (3km) Fishing (1km) Tennis (1km) Railway station (20km) Shops (15km) **NOTES:** Pets admitted

♥♥♥ Les Tilleuls Michèle MENASSOL
Maison Falret, 46160 MARCILHAC-SUR-CELE
☎ 05 65 40 62 68   ▤ 05 65 40 74 01
http://www.les-tilleuls.fr.st
This 18th-century residence offers upstairs rooms with accommodation for eleven. Seven single beds, two doubles and a cot. Electric heating. Living room reserved for guests. Shady park with paddling pool, swings, garden furniture, barbecue. Refrigerator. Nearby restaurant. Four people: €62. Open 1st January to 15th November.
PRICES: s €27; d €37-€39; t €52-€56 **ON SITE:** Bathing Canoeing Fishing Stretch of water **NEARBY:** Horse riding (4km) Swimming pool (4km) Tennis (1km) Railway station (8km) **NOTES:** Pets admitted

♥♥♥ ⚞◯⚟ Lou-Cayrou Peter REUSEMANN
46160 MARCILHAC-SUR-CELE
☎ 05 65 31 28 41   ▤ 05 65 31 28 41
Near the Valley of Celé, this house is a little isolated. The rooms are: 'Fer à Cheval' (two single beds, bath and wc); 'La Chouette' (double bed, shower and wc); 'Le Chapeau' (two singles, bath and wc); 'La Paille' (double bed, bath and wc). Heating. Restaurant 3km (15 minutes on foot). Lakes 3km. Walking trails. Open all year.
PRICES: s €30; d €43; dinner €12 **NEARBY:** Bathing (3km) Horse riding (7km) Fishing (3km) Swimming pool (7km) Stretch of water (3km) Tennis (3km) Railway station (20km) Shops (3km) **NOTES:** Pets admitted

continued

MARTEL

♦♦♦ ⏀ Domaine de la Vaysse Christiane GASPARD
46600 MARTEL
☎ 05 65 32 49 87 📠 05 65 32 49 87
Martel 2 km. Rooms named after butterflies on the first floor of the proprietors' home. 'Les Papillons Roses' has a double bed; 'Les Papillons Bleus' has a double and a single; 'Les Papillons Verts' has a double bed and a sofa; 'Les Papillons Jaunes' has four single beds. All have shower and wc. Heating, terrace, garden, boules ground, private swimming pool, library, table tennis, hunting, bike hire. Weekend and week-long theme holidays out of season.
PRICES: ; d €43-€55; extra person €11; dinner €14 **NEARBY:** Bathing (6km) Canoeing (5km) Horse riding (4km) Fishing (5km) Tennis (6km) Railway station (11km) Shops (2km) **NOTES:** No pets

♦♦♦ ⏀ Chambre d'hôtes Liliane MACAINE
Croix Mathieu, 46600 MARTEL
☎ 05 65 37 41 78 & 05 65 27 13 03
Four guest rooms available. Upstairs there is a triple room with private shower and wc. A double bed and cot in an adjoining room may be used. Three downstairs rooms with separate access in an annexe: two triple rooms and a twin room, each with shower or bathroom and wc. Extra beds possible. Lounge/living room with TV and open fire. Picnicking in the grounds. Private swimming pool shared with the owners. Covered terrace with barbecue. Four people: €72. Gourmet meals: €23. Child's meal: €7.7. Open all year.
PRICES: s €32; d €38-€53; t €59-€63; extra person €12; dinner €15 **NEARBY:** Bathing (5km) Canoeing (5km) Horse riding (8km) Fishing (5km) Swimming pool (13km) Stretch of water (5km) Tennis (1km) Railway station (8km) Shops (1km) **NOTES:** No pets English spoken

♦♦♦ La Cour au Tilleul Myriam JOUVET
Avenue du Capitani, 46600 MARTEL
☎ 05 65 37 34 08
In the little medieval village of Martel are these three charming guest rooms with independent access opening on to the interior courtyard of this Lotois house. One room sleeping three (one double bed and a single, shower and wc); one sleeping four (double and two singles, shower and wc); one double room (shower and wc). Central heating. Breakfast served on the terrace in the summer. Four people: €53-€73. Open all year.
PRICES: s €38-€43; d €43; t €46-€58 **NEARBY:** Bathing (4km) Canoeing (4km) Horse riding (4km) Fishing (4km) Swimming pool (10km) Stretch of water (4km) Tennis (4km) Railway station (5km) **NOTES:** Pets admitted

MAUROUX

♦♦♦ ⏀ Mas de Laure Laure TREBOSSEN
46700 MAUROUX
☎ 05 65 30 67 39 📠 05 65 30 67 39
e-mail: mas de laure@infonie.fr

Puy l'Evèque 11 km. In an old farmhouse of character, rooms with their own access (and romantic names).'Couché de Soleil' and

'Abri des Vents' have two single beds; 'Sous Ciel Etoilé' has a double bed and two singles on a mezzanine; 'Plain Sud' sleeps three; and 'Brise d'Antan' has a double bed. All have shower and wc. Heating. Private swimming pool. 4 x 4 tracks (except July and August). Lakes 8km. Walking trails. Gourmet dining: €27. Child's meal €9.15. Theme weekends. Four people: €79-€89. Open all year (reservations required from October to February).
PRICES: s €55-€65; d €55-€65; t €67-€77; extra person €12; dinner €20 **ON SITE:** Swimming pool **NEARBY:** Bathing (8km) Horse riding (2km) Fishing (8km) Stretch of water (6km) Tennis (1km) Railway station (13km) Shops (1km) **NOTES:** No pets

MERCUES

♦♦♦♦ ⏀ Le Mas Azemar Claude PATROLIN
46090 MERCUES
☎ 05 65 30 96 85 📠 05 65 30 53 82
e-mail: masazemar@aol.com www.masazemar.com
A beautiful home in the heart of Cahors wine territory. One room with a double and single bed; two double rooms; one room sleeping five (two doubles and a single); one twin room; and one room with three single beds. All have shower or bathroom and wc. Sitting room. Central heating. Tax: €0.61 per person per day. Child's meal: €12.2. Tariff: €105.2 for four persons. Gourmet dinner: €30. Open all year, booking required.
PRICES: s €60-€78; d €60-€78; t €93; extra person €15; dinner €24 **ON SITE:** Swimming pool **NEARBY:** Canoeing (5km) Fishing (5km) Stretch of water (5km) Tennis (1km) Railway station (10km) Shops (1km) **NOTES:** Pets admitted English spoken

MIERS

♦♦♦ Le Vieux Séchoir Josiane LAVERGNE
Grezes, 46500 MIERS
☎ 05 65 33 68 33 📠 05 65 33 68 33
e-mail: levieuxsechoir@wanadoo.fr
www.site.voila.fr/levieuxsechoir
Rocamadour 10 km. Padirac 5 km. Upstairs rooms in an old restored barn by the owners' house. In total, five double beds, one single bed, two bunks, one spare bed, and a cot. All rooms have shower and wc. Electric heating, garden furniture, barbecue, security. Tariff: €50 for four persons, 10% reduction for a week. Tax included. Golf 18km. Open 1st April to 30th September.
PRICES: s €28; d €35; t €42 **ON SITE:** Children's play area **NEARBY:** Bathing (4km) Canoeing (8km) Horse riding (10km) Fishing (8km) Swimming pool (3km) Stretch of water (8km) Tennis (2km) Railway station (10km) Shops (2km) **NOTES:** No pets

MILHAC

♦♦♦ ❧ ⏀ Château-Vieux Christian BOUDET
46300 MILHAC
☎ 05 65 41 02 11 & 06 86 74 69 83 📠 05 65 41 02 11
e-mail: chateau_vieux@hotmail.com
www.internet46.fr/chateau_vieux.html
Gourdon 7 km. Caves at Cougnac 4 km. Sarlat 15 km. Rocamadour 20 km. One ground floor room with access for the less mobile (two double beds, with shower and wc). Upstairs: three rooms sleeping three and one double room, all with shower and wc. Heating. Table d'hôtes on request; gourmet meal supplement €23. Children catered for. Lake 3km. Tariff: €64 for four persons. Open all year.
PRICES: s €31; d €37; t €45; dinner €14 **NEARBY:** Bathing (4km) Canoeing (4km) Horse riding (2km) Fishing (4km) Swimming pool (7km) Stretch of water (4km) Tennis (1km) Railway station (7km) Shops (7km) **NOTES:** Pets admitted

continued

MONTBRUN

¶¶¶ 🐾 🐄 La Treille Emmanuel PRADINES
46160 MONTBRUN
☎ 05 65 40 77 20
Beside the River Lot stands this house with upstairs guest rooms, all with independent access. Two double rooms, one twin room and one sleeping four (double and two single beds), each with shower and wc. Cots and spare bed available. Heating. Private lounge. Garden furniture. Tariff: €49 for four persons. Open all year.
PRICES: s €27; d €34; t €40; extra person €8 **ON SITE:** Fishing Stretch of water **NEARBY:** Bathing (8km) Canoeing (8km) Horse riding (8km) Swimming pool (8km) Tennis (8km) Railway station (8km) Shops (8km) **NOTES:** No pets

PADIRAC

¶¶¶ 🐾 🍴 Latreille Philippe et M-Joëlle LESCALE
46500 PADIRAC
☎ 05 65 33 67 57 📠 05 65 33 67 57
Rocamadour 15 km. Padirac 1 km. In the proprietors' house, four upstairs guest rooms. Three rooms sleeping three and one double, all with shower and wc. Three spare beds. Heating. Tariff: €50 for four persons, tax included. Child's meal €8. Open all year.
PRICES: s €26; d €32; t €40; dinner €13 **ON SITE:** Swimming pool **NEARBY:** Bathing (8km) Canoeing (8km) Horse riding (10km) Fishing (8km) Stretch of water (8km) Tennis (10km) Railway station (9km) Shops (10km) **NOTES:** Pets admitted

PAYRIGNAC/GOURDON

¶¶¶ 🐾 🍴 Le Syndic Marie-France CAPY
46300 PAYRIGNAC
☎ 05 65 41 15 70 📠 05 65 41 15 70
Rooms each with separate access. On the second floor: one room with a double bed and three singles; three double rooms. On the ground floor: one double room; one suite with two double beds. All have shower and wc. Heating. Garden furniture and swings. Picnicking. Refrigerator shared between two rooms. Tariff: €67-73 for four persons. Child's meal €7.6.
PRICES: s €34; d €38-€43; t €52; extra person €14; dinner €14
ON SITE: Children's play area **NEARBY:** Bathing (6km) Canoeing (6km) Horse riding (5km) Fishing (1km) Swimming pool (5km) Stretch of water (6km) Tennis (1km) Railway station (7km) Shops (5km) **NOTES:** No pets

PEYRILLES

¶¶¶ 🐾 Trespecoul André et Jacqueline CHRISTOPHE
46310 PEYRILLES
☎ 05 65 31 00 91 & 06 80 81 86 15 📠 05 65 31 00 91
e-mail: j-et-a-christophe@wanadoo.fr
www.internet46.fr/trespecoul.html
Three rooms in total, two double and one sleeping three, each with bath or shower and wc. Extra bed can be put up in any room (supplement payable). Electric heating. Garden furniture, barbecue, cooking area, table tennis. Restaurant 2km. Tariff: €50 for four persons. Open Easter to All Saints' Day.
PRICES: s €27; d €30-€35; t €35-€46 **ON SITE:** Fishing **NEARBY:** Horse riding (15km) Swimming pool (2km) Tennis (2km) Railway station (17km) Shops (2km) **NOTES:** Pets admitted English spoken

PUY-L'EVEQUE

¶¶¶ 🍴 Domaine de Cazes Jean-Louis BARRAUD
46700 PUY-L'EVEQUE
☎ 05 65 30 69 74 📠 05 65 30 85 05
Puy l'Evèque 3 km. Rooms in a large house. Two double rooms

with shower and wc; one room sleeping three with shower and wc; one suite with double bed and large sitting room, bathroom, wc; one room with double bed, bath and wc. TV lounge. Large garden. Open 15th April to 15th October.
PRICES: d €61-€91; t €90; extra person €14; dinner €18 **NEARBY:** Bathing (4km) Canoeing (7km) Horse riding (3km) Fishing (4km) Swimming pool (3km) Stretch of water (10km) Tennis (3km) Railway station (14km) Shops (3km) **NOTES:** No pets

¶¶¶ 🐾 Maison Rouma Bill ARNETT
2, rue du Docteur Rouma, 46700 PUY-L'EVEQUE
☎ 05 65 36 59 39 📠 05 65 36 59 39
e-mail: williamarnett@hotmail.com
Guest rooms on the first and second floors of this house in Puy-l'Evèque next to the river. The Blue Room and Nicki's Room have double beds, bathroom and wc. Henry's Room has twin beds, bathroom and wc. Courtyard, terrace for breakfast. Parking. Open air swimming pool. Open all year.
PRICES: s €42; d €46; t €53 **ON SITE:** Fishing **NEARBY:** Canoeing (1km) Horse riding (8km) Swimming pool (1km) Tennis (1km) Railway station (33km) **NOTES:** No pets English spoken

ROCAMADOUR

¶¶¶ 🐾 L'Hospitalet Marguerite LARNAUDIE
46500 ROCAMADOUR
☎ 05 65 33 62 60 📠 05 65 33 62 60
Upstairs rooms for guests in the owners' home, not far from Rocamadour, the Forêt des Singes and Rocher des Aigles. Two rooms sleeping three with bathroom and shower. One double bedroom with bathroom and shower. Restaurants adjacent and at a short distance. Farm produce for sale. Barbecue. Tax: €0.3 per day. Tariff: €54.9-€64 for four persons. Open all year.
PRICES: s €32; d €39-€43; t €52 **ON SITE:** Tennis **NEARBY:** Bathing (10km) Canoeing (10km) Horse riding (10km) Fishing (10km) Swimming pool (6km) Stretch of water (10km) Railway station (10km) **NOTES:** No pets

¶¶¶ 🐾 Maison-Neuve Odette ARCOUTEL
46500 ROCAMADOUR
☎ 05 65 33 62 69
Rocamadour, Rocher des Aigles, Forêts des Singes 1 km. Rooms with individual entrances and private showers and wc. One double room; one room with double bed and single bed plus spare single bed; one room with double and single bed; possible extra ground floor double room. Electric heating. Possible spare single bed. Tourist tax €0.30 per person per day. Tariff: €54 for four persons. Open all year.
PRICES: s €30; d €34-€40; t €44 **NEARBY:** Bathing (10km) Canoeing (10km) Horse riding (10km) Fishing (10km) Swimming pool (10km) Stretch of water (10km) Tennis (1km) Railway station (10km) Shops (1km) **NOTES:** Pets admitted

SAIGNES

¶¶¶ 🍴 La Mazotière Véronique DUMONT
46500 SAIGNES
☎ 05 65 33 75 31 & 06 71 44 35 21 📠 05 65 33 75 31
In an annexe to the owners' home, ground floor rooms with independent access. One double room with access for the less mobile, shower and wc. One triple room with shower and wc. Another triple room, with bathroom and wc. Living room/lounge reserved for guests with TV and video recorder. Terrace and garden. Open from 1st May to 30th September.
PRICES: s €31; d €37; t €46; dinner €14 **NEARBY:** Bathing (17km) Canoeing (17km) Horse riding (8km) Fishing (3km) Swimming pool (8km) Tennis (8km) Railway station (8km) Shops (8km) **NOTES:** Pets admitted

continued

SARRAZAC

♦♦♦ |◯| Château de Couzenac Louise MAC CONCHIE
46600 SARRAZAC

☎ 05 65 37 78 32 & 05 55 91 00 30   🖹 05 55 91 00 30

Upstairs guest rooms in an entirely renovated 18th-century castle. One twin room and three doubles, all with bathroom and wc. Large TV lounge. Central heating. Shady and flower-filled parkland. Open all year.

PRICES: s €46; d €53; t €61; dinner €15   **NEARBY:** Bathing (15km) Canoeing (15km) Horse riding (10km) Fishing (15km) Swimming pool (10km) Stretch of water (15km) Tennis (3km) Railway station (6km) Shops (6km) **NOTES:** No pets English spoken

SAULIAC-SUR-CELE

♦♦♦ |◯| Les Fargues Claude RONCIN
46330 SAULIAC-SUR-CELE

☎ 05 65 31 29 96   🖹 05 65 31 29 96

This is a 16th-century Quercynois house, offering three rooms on the ground floor, all with independent access and private terraces which look over the valley of the Célé. One room with two single beds and a sofa bed, shower and wc; one double plus child's bed, bath and wc; one double with shower and wc. Fine view from the garden over the castle of Sauliac and the cliffs. Open all year.

PRICES: s €31; d €37-€38; t €44-€46; dinner €13   **NEARBY:** Bathing (1km) Canoeing (1km) Horse riding (14km) Fishing (1km) Swimming pool (14km) Stretch of water (1km) Tennis (9km) Railway station (40km) Shops (9km) **NOTES:** Pets admitted

SOUILLAC

♦♦♦ Le Prieuré LANDMAN
Cieurac-Lanzac, 46200 SOUILLAC

☎ 05 65 32 74 61

e-mail: contact@le-prieure.net   www.le-prieure.net

Souillac 2.5 km. This former priory still has its chapel. One room has a double bed plus a single in an adjoining room, shower and wc; one room with double bed plus sofa bed, shower and wc; one double room with bath and wc; one double room with shower and wc. Heating.

PRICES: s €38-€45; d €44-€50; t €56-€60   **NEARBY:** Bathing (1km) Canoeing (3km) Horse riding (3km) Fishing (1km) Swimming pool (3km) Tennis (3km) Railway station (3km) Shops (3km) **NOTES:** Pets admitted English spoken

ST-CHAMARAND

♦♦♦ |◯| Les Cèdres de Lescaille André CHAMPEAU
46310 ST-CHAMARAND

☎ 05 65 24 50 02   🖹 05 65 24 50 78

e-mail: lescaillé46@.com

Four upstairs rooms, each with one double and one single bed, and one double room, all with shower and wc. Spare bed available. Heating. Terrace and garden; private swimming pool shared with owners. Tariff: €51.8-€59.5 for four persons, with reduced rates depending on season. Child's meal €6.10. Open Easter to 1st November. Groups out of season.

PRICES: s €30; d €35-€45; t €45-€55; extra person €9; dinner €15 **ON SITE:** Swimming pool **NEARBY:** Horse riding (7km) Fishing (2km) Stretch of water (4km) Tennis (1km) Railway station (12km) Shops (4km) **NOTES:** No pets

ST-CIRGUES

♦♦♦ |◯| Roudergue Véronique THIBAUDEAU
Roudergue, 46210 ST-CIRGUES

☎ 05 65 40 37 40 & 06 89 30 13 88   🖹 05 65 40 49 83

e-mail: philippe.thibaudeau@wanadoo.fr

St Cirgues is at the edge of three departments, Cantal, Aveyron

and Lot. Hosts Véronique and Philippe are honey producers. They offer three named guest rooms on the second floor of their house. 'La Rouge' with 160cm double, and 'La Blanche' and 'La Dorée' each sleeping three in a double plus a single bed. All rooms have shower and wc. Central heating. Lakes 15km. Hiking trails. Shaded park. Open all year.

PRICES: s €40; d €44; t €64; dinner €14   **NEARBY:** Bathing (15km) Horse riding (12km) Fishing (1km) Swimming pool (12km) Stretch of water (1km) Tennis (12km) Railway station (12km) Shops (12km) **NOTES:** No pets

ST-DENIS-LES-MARTEL

♦♦♦ 🐾 |◯| Chambre d'hôtes Jean-Paul ANDRIEUX
Cabrejou, 46600 ST-DENIS-LES-MARTEL

☎ 05 65 37 31 89   🖹 05 65 37 31 89

Upstairs rooms in a converted barn adjacent to the owners' house. Three double rooms and one twin room, all with shower or bathroom and wc. Spare single bed available. Large lounge with open fire. Electric heating. Kitchen area. Dinner available from Easter to 1st November only. Open all year.

PRICES: s €28; d €35; t €40; dinner €13   **NEARBY:** Bathing (6km) Canoeing (6km) Horse riding (5km) Fishing (6km) Swimming pool (5km) Stretch of water (6km) Tennis (5km) Railway station (5km) Shops (4km) **NOTES:** No pets

♦♦♦ 🐾 |◯| Chambre d'hôtes
Roger et Marinette ANDRIEUX
Cabrejou, 46600 ST-DENIS-MARTEL

☎ 05 65 37 31 89   🖹 05 65 37 31 89

Two ground floor rooms and a first floor room with its own sitting room. Two rooms sleep three (one double and one single bed), and one twin room. All have shower or bathroom and wc. Central heating or electric heating. Shaded park. Garden furniture. Dinner available from Easter to 1 November only. Tariff: €46 for four persons. Open all year.

PRICES: s €28; d €35; t €40; dinner €13   **NEARBY:** Bathing (6km) Canoeing (6km) Horse riding (5km) Fishing (6km) Swimming pool (5km) Stretch of water (6km) Tennis (5km) Railway station (5km) Shops (4km) **NOTES:** No pets

ST-GERY

♦♦♦ Domaine du Porche Jean-Claude LADOUX
46330 ST-GERY

☎ 05 65 31 45 94   🖹 05 65 31 45 94

In a house in the village, with separate access, two upstairs and two downstairs rooms. One double room with bathroom and wc. Three rooms sleeping three in a double plus single bed, each with shower and wc. Cot available. Summer kitchen. Swimming pool. Shaded terrace. Garden for picnics. Open all year.

PRICES: s €26-€30; d €30-€37; t €37-€43 **ON SITE:** Bathing Canoeing Fishing Swimming pool Stretch of water Tennis **NEARBY:** Horse riding (8km) Railway station (20km) **NOTES:** No pets

ST-MARTIN-LE-REDON

♦♦♦ |◯| Castel du Bouysset Jean-Luc MEYER
46700 ST-MARTIN-LE-REDON

☎ 05 65 30 34 00   🖹 05 65 30 34 09

Upstairs are three double rooms each with bath or shower and wc. At ground level with disabled access, two rooms - one twin with shower and wc, and one room with a double bed plus, on a mezzanine, another double and two singles, with shower and wc. Central heating. Terrace with outdoor furniture, and grounds. Garage and private parking. Private swimming pool shared with owners. Tariff: €120 for four persons. Open all year.

PRICES: s €55; d €61; dinner €18 **ON SITE:** Horse riding Swimming pool **NEARBY:** Stretch of water (5km) Tennis (1km) Railway station (10km) Shops (5km) **NOTES:** Pets admitted English spoken

continued

ST-PANTALEON

♦♦♦ ⃝ Chambre d'hôtes Françoise CARDINET
Preniac, 46800 ST-PANTALEON
☎ 05 65 31 88 51 ▤ 05 65 31 88 51
Right in the heart of White Quercy (on GR65), in the outbuildings of a lovely 18th-century farmhouse, there are four guest rooms, two of them on the ground floor. Two rooms sleeping three (three singles or double and single beds); one double room; and one twin room. All have shower and wc. Heating, kitchen area, washing machine, refrigerator, barbecue, garden, terrace, ornamental lake. Four people: €59. Open all year.
PRICES: s €30; d €40; t €49; dinner €13 **NEARBY:** Bathing (4km) Horse riding (4km) Fishing (4km) Swimming pool (4km) Tennis (4km) Railway station (20km) Shops (4km) **NOTES:** No pets English spoken

ST-SIMON

♦♦♦ ⃝ Les Moynes Frank LE CERF
46320 ST-SIMON
☎ 05 65 40 48 90 ▤ 05 65 40 48 90
e-mail: les.moynes@free.fr
Five rooms on an old restored sheepfarm on a 12ha estate in the middle of the Causses de Quercy Regional Park. One room is at ground level, with disabled access. Two double rooms, one triple and two sleeping four, all with private shower and wc. Swimming pool and paddling pool; park; terrace; boules; table tennis; piano; billiards; library; TV lounge; hiking trails. Four people €63. Open 1st April to 31st December.
PRICES: s €38; d €46-€52; t €53-€56; extra person €12; dinner €17 **NEARBY:** Canoeing (18km) Horse riding (1km) Fishing (12km) Swimming pool (12km) Stretch of water (12km) Tennis (8km) Railway station (9km) Shops (6km) **NOTES:** Pets admitted English spoken

ST-SOZY

♦♦♦ Le Mas Rambert Françoise TIERCE
46200 ST-SOZY
☎ 05 65 37 14 07 ▤ 05 65 37 14 07
Souillac 10 km. The owner's house accommodates three guest rooms upstairs. Room 1 with double bed, shower and wc. Room 2 has a double bed with a possible two extra single beds in an adjoining room, shower and wc. Room 3 sleeps four, with shower and wc. TV point in each room. The property is on the Causse de Martel, close to numerous interesting sites. Four people: €79. Open all year.
PRICES: s €42; d €49; t €64; extra person €11 **NEARBY:** Bathing (2km) Canoeing (2km) Horse riding (7km) Swimming pool (2km) Tennis (2km) Railway station (10km) Shops (2km) **NOTES:** No pets CC

THEDIRAC

♦♦♦♦ ⃝ Manoir de Surgès Joëlle DELILLE
46150 THEDIRAC
☎ 05 65 21 22 45 & 06 75 26 79 44
e-mail: manoirdesurges@multimania.com
Rooms upstairs in a 17th-century manor. One duplex with double four-poster plus two single beds; one room with double four-poster; one room with double and a single bed. Each bedroom has its own bathroom and wc. Two spare beds available. Central heating. TV lounge with open fire. Terrace with garden furniture. Plenty of walks in 36ha grounds. Private swimming pool shared with owners. Tariff: €91 for four persons. Gourmet dining supplement €27. Child's meal €7. Open all year.
PRICES: s €46-€53; d €53-€61; t €69-€76; extra person €15; dinner €21 **ON SITE:** Swimming pool **NEARBY:** Horse riding (20km) Tennis (2km) Railway station (20km) Shops (8km) **NOTES:** No pets

THEMINETTES

♦♦♦ ⃝ La Gaoulière Isabelle NGUYEN-THANH
Friaulens Haut, 46120 THEMINETTES
☎ 05 65 40 97 52 & 06 81 04 14 21 ▤ 05 65 40 97 52
e-mail: gîtes-de-france-lot.com/la-gaoulière/
On the ground floor of the owner's house, three double rooms and one twin with separate access, each with shower and wc. Three spare beds available. Walks in the locality. Child's meal €8. Fax. Open all year.
PRICES: s €38; d €38; extra person €11; dinner €14 **NEARBY:** Horse riding (3km) Swimming pool (7km) Tennis (7km) **NOTES:** Pets admitted English spoken

TOUR-DE-FAURE

♦♦♦ ⃝ Combe de Redoles Philippe DRUOT
46330 TOUR-DE-FAURE
☎ 05 65 31 21 58 ▤ 05 65 31 21 58
e-mail: druot@club-internet.fr www.quercy.net/com/redoles/
A typical Quercynois farmhouse on the edge of the forest. Each bedroom has private shower and wc. Central heating; dining room and lounge for guests; piano, summer kitchen, barbecue, garden furniture, outdoor games. Swimming pool and children's pool. Tariff: €50 for four persons. Child's meal €6. Open all year.
PRICES: s €32; d €37; t €44; extra person €11; dinner €12 **NEARBY:** Bathing (1km) Canoeing (1km) Horse riding (3km) Fishing (1km) Swimming pool (3km) Stretch of water (1km) Tennis (1km) Railway station (35km) Shops (1km) **NOTES:** Pets admitted English spoken

UZECH-LES-OULES

♦♦♦♦ ⃝ Le Château Dominique BRUN
46310 UZECH-LES-OULES
☎ 05 65 22 75 80 ▤ 05 65 22 75 80

Two restored towers inside the castle walls. One duplex with double bed and 120cm bed, bathroom, wc and private sitting room. One double room with bathroom, wc, private sitting room and terrace. Second duplex with king-size double and single bed, with shower and wc. One single room with shower and wc. Heating. Private swimming pool. Gourmet dinner €30.5. Open all year.
PRICES: s €46; d €76; t €91; dinner €23 **ON SITE:** Swimming pool **NEARBY:** Canoeing (30km) Horse riding (20km) Tennis (7km) Railway station (25km) Shops (10km) **NOTES:** Pets admitted English spoken

VERS

♦♦♦ ⃝ Le Bois-Noir Jacques DUFLOS
46090 VERS
☎ 05 65 31 44 50 ▤ 05 65 31 47 10
A large house in the midst of an oak forest. Six rooms each with shower or bathroom and wc. Electric heating. Garden furniture.

continued

MIDI-PYRÉNÉES

Terrace. Swimming pool. Board games, library, table tennis. Tourist tax payable. Tariff: €47.2 for four persons. Child's meal €9.15. Open all year.
PRICES: s €29-€36; d €29-€36; t €45; dinner €12 **ON SITE:** Swimming pool **NEARBY:** Canoeing (20km) Horse riding (2km) Fishing (2km) Stretch of water (2km) Tennis (2km) Railway station (15km) Shops (2km) **NOTES:** Pets admitted English spoken

VIRE-SUR-LOT

▦ ⚇ La Maison du Port André-Louis BIANCO
Port de Vire, 46700 VIRE-SUR-LOT
☎ 05 65 24 67 38
Puy l'Evêque 4 km. Ground floor rooms with separate access, in the proprietors' house. One double room with shower and wc; four rooms each with double bed plus - on mezzanine - twin beds, with shower and wc. Terrace, garden. On the banks of the Lot. Four people: €79. Open all year.
PRICES: d €49; t €64; dinner €15 **ON SITE:** Fishing **NEARBY:** Horse riding (6km) Tennis (4km) Railway station (10km) Shops (4km) **NOTES:** No pets

TARN

AIGUEFONDE

▦ ♥ ⚇ Le Fourchat Roger et Simone LELIEVRE
81200 AIGUEFONDE
☎ 05 63 61 22 67 & 05 63 98 12 62
Mazamet 5 km. Lac des Montagnès 10 km. This renovated traditional building on a farm is in a quiet and attractively wooded setting. Private sitting room with TV. Five first floor bedrooms, two doubles, one twin, one double plus double bunk, all with own wc and shower. Meals using farm produce can be provided. Courtyard, garden. Simone, Roger and Véronique will give you a friendly welcome and will do their best to make your farmhouse holiday an enjoyable one. Pony riding for children, lots of things to do in the area. Open 1 March to 20 September.
PRICES: s €27; d €34; t €43; extra person €9; dinner €13 **ON SITE:** Forest **NEARBY:** Bathing (10km) Horse riding (10km) Golf (4km) Fishing (2km) Swimming pool (5km) Stretch of water (10km) Place of interest (20km) Water sports (40km) Tennis (5km) Railway station (5km) Shops (5km) MAZAMET (5km) **NOTES:** No pets

ALGANS

▦ ⚇ Montplaisir en Rose Thierry MAZZIA
81470 ALGANS
☎ 05 63 75 02 33 🖎 05 63 75 02 33
Lavaur 12 km. Puylaurens 12 km. This 17th-century gentleman's stone and half-timbered residence has been attractively restored and is in a wonderful setting in the heart of the Cocagne countryside with the Pyrenees in the distance. There are five bedrooms, one twin, two doubles plus a single bed, two triples, all with own wc and shower. Dining room with corner sitting area and TV. Washing machine and fridge available. Large garden with space for games, swimming pool, table tennis, badminton. Mountain bikes can be borrowed. Meals by prior arrangement. Baby-sitting on request. Open all year.
PRICES: s €46; d €51; t €69; dinner €17 **ON SITE:** Children's play area Swimming pool **NEARBY:** Bathing (15km) Horse riding (6km) Forest (25km) Golf (12km) Fishing (10km) Stretch of water (15km) Place of interest (5km) Water sports (25km) Tennis (6km) Railway station (12km) Shops (6km) CUQ TOULZA (6km) **NOTES:** No pets English spoken

BELLEGARDE

▦ ⚇ La Borie Neuve Jacqueline RICHARD
81430 BELLEGARDE
☎ 05 63 55 33 64

Albi 12 km. In quiet countryside but only 400 metres from the village, this restored 16th century farmhouse has two twin-bedded rooms and three doubles, all with own wc and bath or shower. Linen (€3) and TV can be provided and creche and kitchenette facilities are available. Evening meal. Swimming pool. The surrounding area with its bastides and woodlands attracts many visitors and the ancient cathedral city of Albi with its Toulouse-Lautrec museum is nearby. The village has music and drama festivals. Open all year.
PRICES: s €39-€48; d €43-€52; extra person €12; dinner €18 **ON SITE:** Swimming pool Tennis **NEARBY:** Bathing (10km) Horse riding (20km) Forest (15km) Golf (12km) Fishing (6km) Stretch of water (6km) Place of interest (12km) Water sports (6km) Railway station (12km) Shops (4km) VILLEFRANCHE D'ALBI (4km) **NOTES:** No pets English spoken

CAGNAC-LES-MINES

▦ ♥ ⚇ Las Campagnes D et V JOLY - VALENTIN
81130 CAGNAC-LES-MINES
☎ 05 63 53 92 97 & SR : 05 63 48 83 01 🖎 05 63 53 92 97
Cordes 12 km. Cagnac 5 km. Albi 10 km. This traditional stone house near the tiny town of Cordes is set in its own two-hectare vegetable garden. There are three bedrooms, one on the ground floor with three single beds, two on the first floor with one double and two single beds, all with own wc and shower or bath. Dining room, TV, living room with open fireplace, conservatory, library, music. BBQ, play area, swimming pool, private parking. Meals by arrangement except on Thursdays and Fridays, using organic traditional vegetable varieties. Picnics prepared. Low season reductions. Open all year.
PRICES: s €46; d €57; t €72; dinner €16 **ON SITE:** Swimming pool **NEARBY:** Bathing (15km) Horse riding (15km) Forest (2km) Golf (10km) Fishing (1km) Stretch of water (1km) Place of interest (12km) Water sports (15km) Tennis (5km) Railway station (10km) Shops (5km) ALBI (12km) **NOTES:** No pets CC English spoken

CAHUZAC-SUR-VERE

▦ ⚇ Chambre d'hôtes Claudine MIRAILLE
Place de l'Eglise, 81140 CAHUZAC-SUR-VERE
☎ 05 63 33 91 53 🖎 05 63 33 99 59
Gaillac 12 km. Cordes 10 km. Attractively furnished in country style, Claudine's well-restored house is in the little village of Cahuzac on the Route des Bastides between Cordes and Gaillac. There are three bedrooms on the first floor, two doubles and one with a double and two single beds, all with own shower and wc. Cot available on request. Meals (except between 14 July and 15 August) made with local ingredients, pretty garden room and terrace. Open all year.
PRICES: s €31; d €39; extra person €11; dinner €13 **ON SITE:** Fishing Swimming pool Tennis **NEARBY:** Bathing (15km) Horse riding (12km) Forest (10km) Golf (10km) Stretch of water (15km) Place of interest (10km) Water sports (10km) Railway station (8km) CASTELNAU DE MONTMIRAL (10km) **NOTES:** No pets

▦ ⚇ La Ventresque Aurore CUQUEL
81140 CAHUZAC-SUR-VERE
☎ 05 63 33 29 94 🖎 05 63 33 29 94
e-mail: laventresque@wanadoo.fr
http://perso.wanadoo.fr/laventresque/
Cordes 12 km. Gaillac 12 km. Five prettily-decorated rooms are available in this traditional house, two on the first floor, three in a wing. There are two doubles, two rooms with a double and two single beds and one room with three single beds. Four rooms have en suite shower and wc, the other has its own separate bathroom. Three cots and other baby gear available. Sitting room with TV. Evening meals with local specialities. Picnics can be provided. Reduced rates for longer stays. No charge for babies. 5m x 10m

continued

continued

swimming pool, 2 mountain bikes, play-space. Open all year.
PRICES: s €39-€42; d €45-€49; t €57; extra person €14; dinner €14
ON SITE: Children's play area Swimming pool **NEARBY:** Bathing
(13km) Horse riding (14km) Forest (15km) Golf (20km) Fishing (2km)
Stretch of water (13km) Place of interest (7km) Water sports (13km)
Tennis (1km) Railway station (12km) Shops (1km) CASTELNAU DE
MONTMIRAL (7km) **NOTES:** No pets English spoken

CAMBOUNET-SUR-LE-SOR

🍴 Château de la Serre
C DE LIMAIRAC BERTHOUMIEUX
81580 CAMBOUNET-SUR-SOR
☎ 05 63 71 75 73 📠 05 63 71 76 06
e-mail: reservations@la-serre.com http://www.la-serre.com
*Castres 10 km. Toulouse 60 km. Albi 40 km. Carcassonne 60
km.* The Limairac family invite you to join them in their
charming and historic 16th-century chateau in its extensive
park. There are two characterful bedrooms, one double, one
twin, both with own bathroom and wc, and a suite in an
adjoining tower with one double and one single bed and
bathroom and wc. Breakfast served in the family dining room.
Evening meal on request. Billiard room and swimming pool.
Open 1 May to 30 October.
PRICES: s €92-€122; d €92-€122; t €122; dinner €23-€28
ON SITE: Swimming pool **NEARBY:** Bathing (4km) Horse riding
(4km) Forest (15km) Golf (15km) Fishing (4km) Stretch of water
(15km) Place of interest (15km) Water sports (15km) Tennis (2km)
Railway station (6km) Shops (1km) PUYLAURENS (8km)
NOTES: No pets English spoken

🍴 Le Bois des Demoiselles Alice ANDRE
La Serre, 81580 CAMBOUNET-SUR-LE-SOR
☎ 05 63 71 73 73 📠 05 63 71 74 37
Castres 10 km. Puylaurens 10 km. Toulouse 60 km. Among fields
and woods, Le Bois des Demoiselles is full of character and has
four attractive bedrooms, one on the ground floor with two double
beds (one on a mezzanine) and own bathroom and wc, two
doubles with own shower and wc. Another room may be available.
Shared living and sitting room. Evening meal available except
weekends. Reduced rates for stays of more than five days. The
owner's son farms the surrounding land and will be happy to
show you round. Open all year.
PRICES: s €22-€26; d €25-€29; t €37-€39; extra person €10; dinner €11
NEARBY: Bathing (3km) Horse riding (4km) Forest (15km) Golf (15km)
Fishing (1km) Swimming pool (8km) Stretch of water (3km) Place of
interest (15km) Water sports (15km) Tennis (1km) Railway station (6km)
Shops (1km) PUYLAURENS (10km) **NOTES:** Pets admitted

CASTANET

🍴 Naussens Jean-Michel MALBREIL
81150 CASTANET
☎ 05 63 55 22 56
Albi 15 km. In wine-growing country a few kilometres from both
Albi and Cordes, the house belonging to Jean-Michel and
Catherine has two rooms, one double and one with one double
and two single beds, with separate entrance and terrace. In the
adjacent converted barn, two doubles and one room with a double
and a single bed. All with own shower and wc. Evening meal using
local ingredients. Babies welcome (8 euros for under-threes).
Open 1 March to 30 October.
PRICES: s €32; d €32; t €47; extra person €16; dinner €13
ON SITE: Forest Swimming pool **NEARBY:** Bathing (6km) Horse riding
(3km) Golf (6km) Fishing (6km) Stretch of water (6km) Place of interest
(15km) Water sports (15km) Tennis (6km) Railway station (5km) Shops
(6km) GAILLAC (12km) **NOTES:** No pets

CASTELNAU-DE-MONTMIRAL

🍴 La Croix du Sud Catherine SORDOILLET
Mazars, 81140 CASTELNAU-DE-MONTMIRAL
☎ 05 63 33 18 46 📠 05 63 33 18 46
e-mail: catherine@la-croix-du-sud.com
http://www.la-croix-du-sud.com
Gaillac 12 km. Cordes 18 km. Three comfortable rooms are
available in this renovated house, deep in wine-growing and
bastide country. Ground floor room with one double and one
single bed, bathroom and wc. One first floor room has one double
and one single bed, the other one double, both with shower and
wc. Extra single beds, cot and bedroom TV on request. Living and
sitting room. Swimming pool, petanque and ping-pong. Gourmet
meals or local specialities by arrangement. Picnic meals on
request. Reduced rates for longer stays. Open all year.
PRICES: s €40; d €49; t €60; extra person €12; dinner €19
ON SITE: Swimming pool **NEARBY:** Bathing (4km) Horse riding (12km)
Forest (6km) Golf (20km) Fishing (3km) Stretch of water (4km) Place of
interest (1km) Water sports (15km) Tennis (4km) Railway station (10km)
Shops (1km) CASTELNAU DE MONTMIRAL (1km) **NOTES:** No pets
English spoken

CORDES

🍴 Aurifat Ian et Pénélope WANKLYN
81170 CORDES
☎ 05 63 56 07 03 📠 05 63 56 07 03
e-mail: aurifat@wanadoo.fr
http://www.jcjdatacomm.co.uk/france
Cordes 1 km. On a sunny slope with fine views, this characterful
house is peaceful and quiet, despite being only five minutes walk
from the centre of Cordes. Ian and Penelope are happy to welcome
you here and invite you to share their large garden and swimming
pool. There are two twin rooms, one in a lookout tower, a double
room in the old dovecote, and a four-bed suite, all with own
entrance and own facilities, most with a balcony or attractive
terrace where breakfast is served. Living room with library, cooking
and barbecue facilities. Rates according to season.
PRICES: s €37-€49; d €50-€64; t €80-€99; extra person €19
ON SITE: Swimming pool **NEARBY:** Bathing (3km) Horse riding (20km)
Forest (5km) Golf (22km) Fishing (1km) Stretch of water (16km) Place of
interest (1km) Water sports (16km) Tennis (1km) Railway station (4km)
Shops (1km) CORDES (1km) **NOTES:** No pets English spoken

🐾 La Bouriette Jean ALUNNI-FEGATELLI
La Bouriette - Campes, 81170 CORDES
☎ 05 63 56 07 32 📠 05 63 56 23 76
Cordes 3 km. Run by Nadine and Jean-Marc, the Auberge de la
Bourriette is in a quiet setting on an arable farm in Cathar country,
3 km from the tiny medieval town of Cordes. There are three
comfortable rooms in an annexe with its own entrance, one twin
(additional single bed if required) and four doubles (one with a
single bed). All have TV, bathroom and wc. Swimming pool with
private terraces. Half-board by arrangement. 10% reduction in low
season. Mountain bikes. Open all year.
PRICES: s €47-€52; d €49-€54; t €68-€73; extra person €19
ON SITE: Forest Swimming pool **NEARBY:** Bathing (15km) Horse
riding (10km) Golf (20km) Fishing (1km) Stretch of water (15km) Place
of interest (3km) Water sports (15km) Tennis (7km) Railway station (7km)
Shops (9km) Restaurant nearby CORDES (3km) **NOTES:** No pets CC
English spoken

🍴 La Vedillerie Famille KERJEAN
Les Cabannes, 81170 CORDES
☎ 05 63 56 04 17 & 06 82 83 94 78 📠 05 63 56 18 56
e-mail: le.kerglas@wanadoo.fr
Cordes 4 km. You will get a warm welcome from the Kerjean
family in their farmstead dating from 1730. Outbuildings have been

continued

converted to give five guest rooms, all with either a kingsize bed, or 1 or 3 singles, and all with own wc, bath or shower, and private entrance. Some rooms have a panoramic view over the little medieval town of Cordes, others overlook the verdant and tranquil countryside all around. There is a garden. Pets welcome (€5). Evening meal. Mountain bikes. Long-distance footpaths GR 36 and 46 nearby. Open all year.
PRICES: s €37-€44; d €41-€47; t €61-€67; dinner €19 **ON SITE:** Forest **NEARBY:** Bathing (3km) Horse riding (12km) Golf (30km) Fishing (3km) Swimming pool (3km) Stretch of water (20km) Place of interest (3km) Water sports (15km) Tennis (3km) Railway station (6km) Shops (3km) CORDES (3km) **NOTES:** Pets admitted

♦♦♦ ♥ ♨ Les Tuileries Annie et Christian RONDEL
81170 CORDES   ☎ 05 63 56 05 93   ▤ 05 63 56 05 93
e-mail: christian.rondel@wanadoo.fr
Cordes 0.6 km. This gentleman's residence and working farm in a quiet and leafy setting near Cordes has five spacious two, three and four-bed guest rooms, all with own shower and wc. There are shady chestnut trees, wonderful views, and an attractive swimming pool. Evening meals featuring produce from the farm are served in a convivial atmosphere, by the fireside in winter, outdoors in summer. Garage, play-space, sitting room with TV, ping-pong, additional children's beds available. Open all year.
PRICES: s €40-€47; d €48-€55; t €56-€64; extra person €10; dinner €17 **ON SITE:** Children's play area Forest Fishing Swimming pool Tennis **NEARBY:** Bathing (3km) Horse riding (12km) Golf (22km) Stretch of water (15km) Place of interest (1km) Water sports (15km) Railway station (3km) Shops (1km) CORDES (1km) **NOTES:** Small dogs only English spoken

DONNAZAC

♦♦♦♦ ♨ Les Vents Bleus
Isabelle et Laurent PHILIBERT
Rue de la Caussade, 81170 DONNAZAC
☎ 05 63 56 86 11 & SR : 05 63 48 83 01
▤ 05 63 56 86 11
e-mail: lesventsbleus@free.fr
Cordes 7 km. In the Gaillac countryside, this house offers five spacious guest rooms, all with TV, own bath and wc. Of the two on the ground floor, one has three single beds, the other is a double. On the first floor is a suite with three single beds and a bunk bed, one room with three beds and another with a double and single. Fridge, crockery. Walled garden and swimming pool, play-space, ping-pong, badminton, four adult bikes. Meals available (not Monday, Tuesday, Thursday in July/August). Two gîtes. Open all year.
PRICES: s €66-€85; d €69-€85; t €81-€97; extra person €12; dinner €26 **ON SITE:** Children's play area Swimming pool **NEARBY:** Bathing (8km) Horse riding (11km) Forest (20km) Golf (22km) Fishing (5km) Stretch of water (15km) Place of interest (7km) Water sports (15km) Tennis (5km) Railway station (8km) Shops (7km) CORDES (7km) **NOTES:** No pets English spoken

ESCOUSSENS

♦♦♦ ♨ Mont St-Jean Marie-Thérèse ESCAFRE
81290 LES ESCOUSSENS   ☎ 05 63 73 24 70
At the foot of the Black Mountain. Castres 15 km. Marie-Thérèse looks forward to welcoming you to her farmhouse which once belonged to the Carthusians and is located on the old pilgrim route to Santiago de Compostela. There is a ground floor room with a double and single bed and two first floor rooms, one twin and one double plus a single bed and child's bed. All have own facilities. Additional family room with double bed and single bed and wash-basin. Cot available. Living room with TV and open fireplace. Meals. Covered terrace, garden, barbecue, ping-pong. Open all year.

PRICES: s €31; d €34; t €46; extra person €12; dinner €14 **ON SITE:** Forest Fishing **NEARBY:** Bathing (12km) Horse riding (14km) Golf (14km) Swimming pool (7km) Stretch of water (12km) Place of interest (20km) Tennis (1km) Railway station (7km) Shops (7km) LABRUGUIERE (7km) **NOTES:** Pets admitted English spoken

ESPERAUSSES

♦♦♦ ♨ La Maison de Jeanne Florence ARTERO
Le Bourg, 81260 ESPERAUSSES
☎ 05 63 73 02 77
Lacaune 15 km. Sidobre 15 km. The Maison de Jeanne is a 350-year-old house in the village centre. It has been completely restored, exposing the original beams and stonework, and now provides four first-floor guest rooms. There are two doubles and two rooms with a double and a single bed. Each has a private shower and wc. Communal lounge and living room, fireplace, TV, billiards. Terrace, garden furniture, barbecue. Table d'hôte (gastronomic meals can be served). No charge for babies. Fishing nearby. Reduced rates for longer stays. Closed 15 December - 15 January.
PRICES: s €31; d €35; t €46; extra person €13; dinner €14 **ON SITE:** Fishing **NEARBY:** Bathing (25km) Horse riding (10km) Forest (2km) Golf (35km) Swimming pool (11km) Stretch of water (25km) Water sports (25km) Tennis (11km) Railway station (35km) Shops (11km) LACAUNE (15km) **NOTES:** No pets

GAILLAC

♦♦♦ Chambre d'hôtes Lucile PINON
8 place St-Michel, 81600 GAILLAC
☎ 05 63 57 61 48   ▤ 05 63 41 06 56
Cordes 22 km. Albi 23 km. This fine old 17th century residence deep in the Gaillac countryside has fine views over the Abbey of St-Michel, the River Tarn and the roofs of the old town. There are six double rooms with a total of five double beds and three single beds. All have TV, own bathroom and wc. The house is furnished with antiques, there is a splendid stone staircase, a prettily planted courtyard, and fine outbuildings. Sitting rooms with TV. Breakfast served in the rooms or on a covered terrace. Open all year.
PRICES: s €38; d €43; t €61 **ON SITE:** Fishing Swimming pool Place of interest Tennis **NEARBY:** Bathing (12km) Horse riding (10km) Forest (12km) Golf (12km) Stretch of water (12km) Railway station (1km) GAILLAC **NOTES:** Pets admitted English spoken

♦♦♦ ♥ ♨ Domaine de Gradille
Lyne et Denis SOULIE
D 999, 81310 LISLE-SUR-TARN
☎ 05 63 41 01 57   ▤ 05 63 57 43 73
e-mail: lynesoulie@wanadoo.fr

Gaillac 5 km. Albi 28 km. Close to Albi and to Cordes, this wine-growing property has a quiet and charmingly rustic setting with panoramic views. There are three rooms, one double on the ground floor, two doubles plus single bed on the first floor, all with own bathroom and wc and central heating. Own sitting room, TV, library, open fireplace. Attractive terrace, shared 5 metre x 10 metre

continued

continued

swimming pool. Tasty meals. Shady park and pleasant 15-minute walk to a lake. Three gites in another building. Open all year.
PRICES: s €41; d €41; t €54; extra person €13; dinner €14
ON SITE: Swimming pool Stretch of water **NEARBY:** Bathing (12km) Horse riding (1km) Forest (1km) Golf (12km) Fishing (1km) Place of interest (5km) Water sports (25km) Tennis (5km) Railway station (5km) Shops (5km) GAILLAC (5km) **NOTES:** No pets CC English spoken

♦♦♦ Le Mas de Sudre Philippa RICHMOND-BROWN
81600 GAILLAC
☎ 05 63 41 01 32 ▣ 05 63 41 01 32
e-mail: georgerbrown@free.fr
Gaillac 4 km. Cordes 20 km. In a tranquil setting among the Gaillac vineyards, this large country house has hospitable English owners. Of the four bright and spacious rooms, two (one double, one twin) are in the annexe, two (one double, one twin) in the main house, all with private shower and wc. Shared sitting and living room. TV, telephone and piano. Large garden with terrace, tennis court, swimming pool, boules, table tennis etc. Open all year.
PRICES: s €42; d €55; extra person €20 **ON SITE:** Swimming pool Tennis **NEARBY:** Bathing (8km) Horse riding (8km) Forest (7km) Golf (7km) Fishing (4km) Stretch of water (8km) Place of interest (4km) Water sports (35km) Railway station (4km) Shops (4km) GAILLAC (4km) **NOTES:** Pets admitted English spoken

GARREVAQUES

♦♦♦ iO¹ Château de Gandels
Martine et Philippe DUPRESSOIR
81/00 GARREVAQUES
☎ 05 63 70 27 67 & 06 07 14 11 55 ▣ 05 63 70 27 67
e-mail: dupressoir@chateau-de-gandels.com
http://www.chateau-de-gandels.com

Revel 3 km. Bassinde St-Ferréol 6 km. Near Revel, deep in the Lauragais countryside between Toulouse and Castres, the charming Château de Gandels is set in a five-hectare park designed by the 18th century landscape architect Le Notre, with terrace, pools and fountains. Five spacious and very comfortable rooms for between two and four people, all with TV and own bathroom and wc. Private sitting and living room and antique furniture. Gourmet meals. Stables. Receptions and seminars. Open all year.
PRICES: d €107–€183; extra person €16; dinner €29
ON SITE: Swimming pool **NEARBY:** Bathing (9km) Horse riding (13km) Forest (10km) Fishing (1km) Stretch of water (9km) Place of interest (6km) Water sports (9km) Tennis (6km) Railway station (3km) Shops (6km) DOURGNE (18km) **NOTES:** Pets admitted CC English spoken

GIROUSSENS

♦♦♦ ❦ iO¹ Le Pepil Jean-Paul RAYNAUD
81500 GIROUSSENS ☎ 05 63 41 62 84
Lavaur 6 km. Marie-Joséc, Jean-Paul and their family look forward to welcoming guests to their traditional farm. Of the four rooms, all with own shower and wc, two are doubles, one has one

continued

double and one single bed, and one is a twin plus bunk bed. Big sitting room with open fireplace. TV, fridge, washing machine, library. Kitchen available (€31 per week). Garden, outside bread oven and barbecue. Bikes, ping-pong. Meals featuring farm produce, home-made bread and local wine. Open all year except between 28 August and 5 September and between 29 December and 4 January.
PRICES: d €38; t €52–€66; extra person €10; dinner €14
NEARBY: Bathing (5km) Horse riding (4km) Forest (4km) Golf (10km) Fishing (10km) Swimming pool (6km) Stretch of water (5km) Place of interest (6km) Tennis (3km) Railway station (6km) Shops (3km) LAVAUR (6km) **NOTES:** Pets admitted English spoken

LACAUNE

♦♦♦ iO¹ Couloubrac Claude et Christine SERENO
81230 LACAUNE
☎ 05 63 37 14 94 ▣ 05 63 37 14 94
Lac de Laouzas 15 km. Tucked away in a wooded mountain setting with many springs, the 55-hectare Relais de Couloubrac at Lacaune-les-Bains is owned by Claude and Christine who look forward to welcoming you. The five rooms include one double, one suite with one double and two single beds, and three rooms with one double and one single bed, all with own shower and wc. Corner sitting room with open fire and TV. Garden, fishing lake, barbecue, wood stove. Mountain bikes, ping-pong, volley-ball, badminton. Meals feature farm produce. Good walking country. Open all year.
PRICES: s €36; d €43; t €57; dinner €15 **ON SITE:** Forest Fishing Stretch of water **NEARBY:** Bathing (15km) Horse riding (15km) Golf (45km) Swimming pool (6km) Place of interest (5km) Water sports (45km) Tennis (5km) Railway station (45km) Shops (5km) LACAUNE (5km) **NOTES:** No pets

LACAZE

♦♦♦ ❦ La Borie de Ganoubre Jean-Pierre BRUS
81330 LACAZE
☎ 05 63 50 44 23
Lacaune 18 km. Castres 45 km. Albi 40 km. The three rooms on this 34-hectare sheep and poultry farm in the Gijou valley among the Lacaune hills, close to Sidobre, include one double, one twin and one double plus a single bed. Breakfast terrace, living room, fridge, washing machine. Private entrance. Farm cooking. Waymarked footpaths. Open all year except between mid-September and mid-October.
PRICES: s €25; d €34; t €40; extra person €8; HB €28; dinner €11
ON SITE: Forest **NEARBY:** Bathing (25km) Horse riding (12km) Golf (45km) Fishing (2km) Swimming pool (12km) Stretch of water (25km) Place of interest (45km) Water sports (45km) Tennis (12km) Railway station (45km) Shops (8km) Restaurant nearby VABRE (12km) **NOTES:** No pets

LACROUZETTE

♦♦♦ Auberge de Cremaussel Gilbert HOULES
81210 LACROUZETTE
☎ 05 63 50 61 33 ▣ 05 63 50 61 33
Castres 17 km. In the Sidobre area, this listed inn has a welcoming atmosphere and fine views. Its five guest rooms include one three-bed room, one four-bed room and three doubles, all with own shower and wc. Regional cooking and gourmet meals. Sitting room with open fireplace. Garden and conservatory.
PRICES: s €35; d €39; t €50; extra person €12; dinner €14
ON SITE: Forest **NEARBY:** Bathing (17km) Horse riding (3km) Golf (17km) Fishing (3km) Swimming pool (9km) Stretch of water (3km) Place of interest (17km) Water sports (10km) Tennis (17km) Railway station (17km) Shops (4km) Restaurant nearby ROQUECOURBE (11km) **NOTES:** Pets admitted

LAMONTELARIE

♦♦♦ ꙶ◯ꙶ La Tranquille Denis et Sophie SAILLARD
81260 LAMONTELARIE
☎ 05 63 74 56 54 🖹 05 63 74 56 54
e-mail: la-tranquille@worldonline.fr
La Salvetat-sur-Agoût 12 km. Lac de la Raviège 1 km. Sophie and
Denis invite you to their home deep in the leafy countryside of the
Haute-Languedoc regional park, just a step from Lake la Raviège.
Four double rooms and additional room with bunk bed, own
shower and wc. Cots and additional beds available. Living and
sitting room with open fireplace. Washing machine. Terrace and
large garden, ping-pong. Open from 15 February to 1 November.
PRICES: s €30; d €37; t €48; extra person €11; dinner €11
ON SITE: Forest Fishing Place of interest **NEARBY:** Bathing (1km)
Horse riding (12km) Golf (15km) Swimming pool (12km) Stretch of water
(1km) Water sports (1km) Tennis (12km) Railway station (50km) Shops
(12km) ANGLES (10km) **NOTES:** No pets English spoken

LARROQUE

♦♦♦ ꙶ♥ꙶ Les Chênes Serge et Cécile CAZEAUX
Peyre Blanque, 81140 LARROQUE
☎ 05 63 33 10 92 🖹 05 63 33 17 28
Gaillac 26 km. Cécile and Serge live in bastide country in the
Grésigne forest between Larroque and Bruniquel. They offer a
warm welcome to their home with its five guest rooms with
separate entrance; one room has a double and a single bed, the
rest are doubles, and all have own shower and wc. Additional
beds can be provided. Reception room. Country-style inn serving
meals made with local farm produce. Farm shop, grounds, terrace.
Open all year except Sunday evening and Monday.
PRICES: s €34; d €34; t €53; extra person €10; dinner €16
ON SITE: Forest Swimming pool **NEARBY:** Bathing (12km) Horse riding (8km) Fishing
(5km) Swimming pool (20km) Stretch of water (12km) Place of interest
(10km) Water sports (10km) Tennis (8km) Railway station (22km) Shops
(15km) Restaurant nearby CASTELNAU DE MONTMIRAL (15km)
NOTES: Pets admitted English spoken

LAVAUR

♦♦♦ ꙶ◯ꙶ En Roque N et L D'ESTIENNE D'ORVES
81500 LAVAUR
☎ 05 63 58 04 58 & SR : 05 63 48 83 01 🖹 05 63 58 39 83
e-mail: enroque@wanadoo.fr
http://perso.wanadoo.fr/enroque/DomaineDesPlatanes
Lavaur 3.5 km. Ideal for a weekend stay or longer, this house
between Toulouse, Castres and Albi has five guest rooms all with
TV, own bathroom and wc. Three are suites with a double bed and
between two and four single beds, the other two rooms have a
double and two single beds. Two cots available. Sitting room and
private living room. Three-hectare grounds, shady courtyard,
terrace, secluded 14 x 7 metre swimming pool, ping-pong,
playspace, riding stables. Meals (except Wednesdays in July &
August). Airport transfer. Reduced rates for stays of more than one
night. Open all year.
PRICES: s €40–€78; d €55–€78; t €70–€78; extra person €12; dinner €19
ON SITE: Children's play area Horse riding Fishing Swimming pool
Place of interest **NEARBY:** Bathing (3km) Forest (8km) Golf (10km)
Stretch of water (1km) Tennis (4km) Railway station (4km) Shops (4km)
LAVAUR (4km) **NOTES:** Pets admitted English spoken

LEMPAUT

♦♦♦ ꙶ◯ꙶ La Bousquetarie Charles SALLIER
81700 LEMPAUT
☎ 05 63 75 51 09 🖹 05 63 75 51 09
Puylaurens 9 km. Bassin de St-Ferréol 10 km. Standing among
ancient oaks, this château offers a particularly warm welcome.

There are two suites, both with bathroom and wc, one with a
double and large single bed, one with a double, three singles and
a child's bed, and two rooms, also with own bathroom and wc;
one is a double, the other has two single beds which can be
attached. Living room, TV, washing machine. Family meals
featuring local produce available. Swimming pool, tennis court,
ping-pong and bike hire. Reduced rates for stays of one week or
more. Open 15 January to 1 December.
PRICES: s €48–€53; d €60–€68; t €83; extra person €16; dinner €20–€23
ON SITE: Swimming pool Tennis **NEARBY:** Bathing (10km) Horse
riding (4km) Forest (15km) Golf (22km) Fishing (2km) Stretch of water
(10km) Place of interest (20km) Railway station (18km) Shops (2km)
PUYLAURENS (9km) **NOTES:** No pets English spoken

♦♦♦ La Rode Catherine DE FALGUEROLLES
81700 LEMPAUT
☎ 05 63 75 51 07 🖹 05 63 75 51 07
e-mail: larode@wanadoo.fr http://perso.wanadoo.fr/larode
Puylaurens 6 km. Castres 18 km. A friendly welcome is assured at
this grand former priory. There are two suites; one with double
bed, own bathroom and wc plus an adjoining room with two
single beds and cot, the other has a canopied double bed and a
single bed, own bathroom and wc plus an adjoining room with
twin beds and washbasin. Another room has three single beds,
own shower and wc. Shared kitchen. Games room, library, piano,
and summerhouse. Ping-pong. Small private swimming pool.
Reductions for stays of more than three days (except in July and
August). Open 15 March to 30 October.
PRICES: s €39; d €46; t €61; extra person €15 **ON SITE:** Swimming pool
NEARBY: Bathing (10km) Horse riding (5km) Forest (3km) Golf (30km)
Fishing (3km) Stretch of water (15km) Place of interest (30km) Water
sports (25km) Tennis (5km) Railway station (18km) Shops (6km)
PUYLAURENS (6km) **NOTES:** Pets admitted English spoken

LOMBERS

♦♦♦ ꙶ◯ꙶ Le Moulin d'Ambrozy Jacques et Annick NOVAK
81120 LOMBERS
☎ 05 63 79 17 12 & SR : 05 63 48 83 01 🖹 05 63 79 17 12
e-mail: moulin.ambrozy@free.fr http://moulin.ambrozy.free.fr

Albi 15 km. Réalmont 5 km. In a peaceful riverside location on the
road to Castres, this establishment has three guest rooms, one
with its own entrance. One room has a double and a single bed,
two spacious rooms have a double and three single beds. Shared
living and sitting rooms. Washing machine if required and use of
fridge. Meals and picnic baskets. Garden room, large garden,
barbecue, private swimming pool, bikes. Good walking and fishing.
PRICES: s €39–€51; d €43–€54; t €55–€66; extra person €12; dinner €18
ON SITE: Fishing Swimming pool **NEARBY:** Bathing (13km) Horse
riding (5km) Forest (25km) Golf (18km) Stretch of water (15km) Place of
interest (18km) Water sports (25km) Tennis (5km) Railway station (18km)
Shops (5km) REALMONT (5km) **NOTES:** No pets English spoken

continued

MEZENS

⊞ ⫶◎⫶ Le Cambou Régine SAULLE
81800 MEZENS
☎ 05 63 41 82 66

Rabastens 7 km. Toulouse 30 km. Expect a warm welcome in this restored traditional farmstead, which enjoys lovely views over green hills and a medieval chateau. There are three rooms, all with shower and wc. One has a double and a single bed, one two single beds which can be attached, and one is a double with an optional adjoining twin room. Cots and other baby gear. Sitting room, TV, kitchenette, piano. Weaving and sculpture studios. Meals served on the terrace or around the fireplace. Bikes. Reductions according to length of stay. Open 2 January to 23 December.
PRICES: s €28; d €35; t €45; extra person €8; dinner €13
NEARBY: Bathing (10km) Horse riding (15km) Forest (1km) Golf (10km) Fishing (2km) Swimming pool (4km) Stretch of water (10km) Place of interest (4km) Tennis (4km) Railway station (4km) Shops (4km) RABASTENS (7km) **NOTES:** No pets English spoken

MONTANS

⊞ ⫶❦⫶ ⫶◎⫶ Bois Moysset Philippe et Sylvie MAFFRE
81600 MONTANS
☎ 05 63 40 41 12
Gaillac 7 km. Lisle-sur-Tarn 3 km. Sylvie, Philippe and their family invite you to their traditional farmstead in Montans, an archeologically important village. There are four rooms, two doubles and two with a double and a single bed, all with own shower and wc. Run on organic lines, their farm has vines, cereals, poultry and horses. Meals feature farm produce (poultry and wine) and local recipes (please reserve by 2pm). Good walking and recreation nearby. Open all year.
PRICES: s €29; d €34; t €38; dinner €13 **NEARBY:** Bathing (12km) Horse riding (6km) Golf (20km) Fishing (2km) Swimming pool (3km) Stretch of water (3km) Place of interest (3km) Tennis (3km) Railway station (7km) Shops (3km) GAILLAC (7km) **NOTES:** Pets admitted English spoken

MONTDURAUSSE

⊞ ⫶◎⫶ La Vinatière Evelyne et Alain BENITTA
81630 MONTDURAUSSE
☎ 05 63 40 54 34
Salvagnac 12 km. On the borders of Tarn and Tarn-et-Garonne, this tastefully restored house in its own grounds has a panoramic view over the surrounding countryside. There are three rooms, all with shower and wc, one on the ground floor with a double and a single bed, two on the first floor with a double bed, a double folding bed and a cot. Sitting room with TV and open fireplace, shared dining room, evening meals. Library. Terrace. Bikes. Complete set of baby gear, children's games. Small pets by arrangement. Open all year.
PRICES: s €25-€28; d €31-€34; t €42; extra person €11; dinner €12
ON SITE: Children's play area **NEARBY:** Bathing (2km) Horse riding

(2km) Forest (10km) Golf (10km) Fishing (2km) Swimming pool (2km) Stretch of water (2km) Place of interest (18km) Water sports (17km) Tennis (2km) Railway station (25km) Shops (2km) SALVAGNAC (12km) **NOTES:** No pets English spoken

MONTROC

⊞ Chambre d'hôtes Mme CLOUZET VIARD Henri
14 place du Village, 81120 MONTROC
☎ 05 63 55 77 00
Montredon Labessonnié and the Sidobre region 12 km. Albi 30 km. This hundred-year-old gentleman's residence stands on a village square close to the popular Sidobre area and close to the Rassisse lake. There are four spacious and comfortable first floor rooms, two with one double and one single bed, and two twins, all with own shower and wc. Shared TV. Private garden, garden room, garage and car spaces. Terrace. Picnic lunches and suppers provided. Washing machine available. The GR 36 long-distance footpath passes nearby. Open all year.
PRICES: s €33; d €38; t €48 **ON SITE:** Tennis **NEARBY:** Bathing (10km) Horse riding (5km) Forest (10km) Golf (30km) Fishing (2km) Swimming pool (11km) Stretch of water (5km) Place of interest (10km) Water sports (5km) Railway station (30km) Shops (10km) MONTREDON LABESSONNIE (12km) **NOTES:** No pets

MURAT-SUR-VEBRE

⊞ ❦ Félines Christiane ROQUE
81320 MURAT-SUR-VEBRE
☎ 05 63 37 43 17 🖷 05 63 37 19 85
Lacaune 15 km. Lac de Laouzas 6 km. A little hamlet in the Lacaune hills is the setting for this farm with four recently converted first floor guest rooms with their own entrance. There is a two-room suite with a double bed and two singles and its own bath and wc, a double with own shower and wc, and a room with mezzanine with two doubles, own bath and wc. Private parking, garden with garden room and barbecue. Swimming pool shared with owners. You are welcome to look round the farm, which specialises in ewe's-milk cheese.
PRICES: s €29-€32; d €32-€39; t €46; extra person €16 **ON SITE:** Forest Swimming pool Place of interest **NEARBY:** Bathing (6km) Horse riding (6km) Golf (65km) Fishing (1km) Stretch of water (6km) Tennis (1km) Railway station (65km) Shops (2km) MURAT SUR VEBRE (2km) **NOTES:** No pets

PAULINET

⊞ ❦ ⫶◎⫶ Domaine Equestre des Juliannes
M et N HUDSWELL
S.A.R.L. Domaine des Juliannes, 81250 PAULINET
☎ 05 63 55 94 38 & SR : 05 63 48 83 01 🖷 05 63 55 97 49
e-mail: nicholas.hudswell@wanadoo.fr
http://perso.wanadoo.fr/juliannes/
Tarn Valley 20 km. Oulas Gorges 5 km. The Hudswell family welcome guests to their 17th century farm. There are three rooms (two doubles, one triple) and two suites (one sleeps four, the other sleeps six), all with own bathroom and wc, and an additional room with its own entrance. Dining room overlooking shady terrace, sitting room with fireplace. Gîte for ten people. Shared swimming pool. Games room and children's toys. Traditional cooking. Pets by arrangement. Stables with horses and ponies. Transport can be arranged to and from Albi station. Price reductions for longer stays. Open 16 March to 9 November.
PRICES: s €43; d €49-€73; t €63-€86; extra person €13; HB €122; FB €183; dinner €11-€19 **ON SITE:** Children's play area Horse riding Forest Swimming pool **NEARBY:** Bathing (30km) Golf (40km) Fishing (1km) Stretch of water (15km) Place of interest (40km) Water sports (15km) Tennis (6km) Railway station (35km) Shops (6km) ALBAN (6km) **NOTES:** No pets CC English spoken

continued

MIDI-PYRÉNÉES

PUYCALVEL

♯♯♯ ‡◎‡ **Plaisance** Minerve CAYLA
81440 PUYCALVEL
☎ 05 63 75 94 59
Lautrec 7 km. Castres 18 km. In the Cocagne countryside near the medieval village of Lautrec, this old farmstead stands among 13 hectares of woods and meadows. Overlooking a sheltered terrace from the first floor are three rooms, all with own entrance and shower and wc. Two are doubles, one a triple. Additional beds can be provided. Spacious dining room with open fireplace, library and TV. Evening meals, lunches by arrangement, reductions for children, themed evenings. Riders welcome (horses available), and courses in leatherworking. Open all year.
PRICES: s €30; d €40; t €50; extra person €10; dinner €13
NEARBY: Bathing (7km) Horse riding (12km) Forest (5km) Golf (17km) Fishing (5km) Swimming pool (7km) Stretch of water (25km) Place of interest (7km) Water sports (25km) Tennis (7km) Railway station (10km) Shops (7km) LAUTREC (7km) **NOTES:** Pets admitted English spoken

PUYCELCI

♯♯♯ ‡◎‡ **Laval** Josette ROQUES
81140 PUYCELCI ☎ 05 63 33 11 07
Gaillac 23 km. Louis and Josette welcome you to their large stone-built residence. Built in 1872, it stands in the fortified village of Puycelci in the valley of the River Vère. There are three rooms, all with own shower and wc, one with a double and a single bed, one twin and one triple. A suite with twin beds may be available. Sitting and living room with TV. Fireplace. Fridge. Garden. Evening meals available Monday, Wednesday and Friday in July and August (by arrangement out of season). Ping-pong. Open all year.
PRICES: s €24; d €30-€31; t €39; extra person €8; dinner €11
ON SITE: Fishing **NEARBY:** Bathing (6km) Horse riding (3km) Forest (3km) Golf (6km) Swimming pool (20km) Stretch of water (6km) Place of interest (3km) Water sports (18km) Tennis (3km) Railway station (23km) Shops (10km) CASTELNAU DE MONTMIRAL (10km)
NOTES: Pets admitted

SALVAGNAC

♯♯♯ ‡◎‡ **Domaine de Lagarrigue**
Michèle et Jean-Jacques VEDY
81630 SALVAGNAC
☎ 05 63 33 29 72 📠 05 63 33 29 72
e-mail: info@chambre_hotes_tarn.com
www.chambre_hotes_tarn.com
Gaillac 20 km. Montauban 30 km. Albi 40 km. Toulouse 50 km. This 18th century farmhouse one kilometre from the village has five attractive first floor rooms; there is one triple, two doubles, and two rooms with a double and two single beds, all with own shower and wc. Cots and additional beds available. TV. Evening meals. Picnic lunches can be provided. Shady terrace, extensive garden, 8 x 5 metre swimming pool, ping-pong, boules, play-space, mountain bikes. 10% reduction for stays of one week or more, 15% for two weeks or more. Open all year.
PRICES: s €34; d €34; t €45; extra person €9-€10; dinner €14
ON SITE: Children's play area Swimming pool **NEARBY:** Bathing (12km) Horse riding (12km) Forest (3km) Golf (28km) Fishing (1km) Stretch of water (12km) Place of interest (12km) Water sports (12km) Tennis (2km) Railway station (18km) Shops (2km) SALVAGNAC (1km)
NOTES: No pets English spoken

ST-LIEUX-LES-LAVAUR

♯♯♯ **Château** Lizette DORVAL
Château, 81500 ST-LIEUX-LES-LAVAUR
☎ 05 63 41 60 87 📠 05 63 41 61 23
Lavaur 9 km. Toulouse 30 km. This 19th-century chateau is in

quiet and attractive surroundings in the village of St Lieux in the heart of the Cocagne country. There are five second floor double rooms all with TV, own bath and wc. Cot available. Private sitting room, dining room. Large, well-wooded garden with raised round swimming pool. Ping-pong, billiard room. Restaurants and other facilities nearby. Open all year except Christmas week.
PRICES: s €46; d €46 **ON SITE:** Swimming pool **NEARBY:** Bathing (1km) Horse riding (2km) Forest (1km) Golf (10km) Fishing (1km) Stretch of water (1km) Place of interest (9km) Water sports (1km) Tennis (1km) Railway station (6km) Shops (1km) LAVAUR (9km) **NOTES:** Pets admitted English spoken

TREBAS

♯♯♯ ‡◎‡ **La Goudoufie** Claude et Josette BERTHOUT
Route de Requista, 81340 TREBAS
☎ 05 63 55 96 01 📠 05 63 55 96 01
e-mail: http://www.web-de-loire.com/c/81H2146.htm
www.web.de.loire.com
Trébas 3 km. In Tarn Valley. In a quiet setting this old stone-built farmstead is on a five hectare property crossed by a little stream. There is one ground-floor double room with own bath and wc, and two first floor rooms, one with a double and two single beds, the other with three single beds, both with own shower and wc. Cot available. Washing machine. Sitting room, TV, library. Garden. Cats welcome. Evening meals by arrangement. Two mountain bikes. Reductions for stays of four days or longer; special out-of-season weekend rates. Chestnut collection and mushroom picking. Open all year.
PRICES: s €30; d €35; t €46; extra person €11; dinner €12
ON SITE: Forest **NEARBY:** Bathing (3km) Horse riding (20km) Golf (35km) Fishing (3km) Swimming pool (11km) Stretch of water (10km) Place of interest (15km) Water sports (3km) Tennis (3km) Railway station (35km) Shops (3km) VALENCE D'ALBI (13km) **NOTES:** No pets English spoken

VAOUR

♯♯♯ 🐓 ‡◎‡ **Serene** Brigitte et Francis BESSIERES
81140 VAOUR
☎ 05 63 56 39 34 & SR : 05 63 48 83 01 📠 05 63 56 39 34
Cordes 15 km. St-Antonin-Noble-Val 12 km. Brigitte and Francis invite you to their farmhouse in lovely countryside. The old stone building which once belonged to the Knights Templar has three rooms and a suite, all with own facilities. There is a ground floor twin (with disabled access), and on the first floor two doubles plus the suite with a double bed and a sitting room with two single beds. Cot available. Living room and large sitting room with fireplace. Shared swimming pool. Terrace. Evening meals. Botanical trail. Good walking. Open March to late December.
PRICES: s €40-€66; d €48-€66; t €74; extra person €8; dinner €15
ON SITE: Forest Swimming pool **NEARBY:** Bathing (18km) Horse riding (8km) Golf (35km) Fishing (10km) Stretch of water (12km) Place of interest (15km) Water sports (10km) Tennis (12km) Railway station (12km) Shops (15km) VAOUR (2km) **NOTES:** No pets CC

VIANE

♯♯♯ 🐓 ‡◎‡ **La Bessière** Myriam BARDY et Philippe CROS
81530 VIANE
☎ 05 63 37 01 26 & 05 63 37 51 00
Lacaune 12 km. Among green and wooded hills on the edge of the valley, this cattle farm is run by Myriam and her brother Philippe who will do their best to make you welcome. There are three first floor rooms, one double with bath and wc, one triple with shower and wc, and one room with two double beds, shower and wc. Washing machine. Living room with TV, sitting room with fireplace. Garden and outdoor furniture. Meals using farm produce. Farm tours. Mushroom picking in season. Lovely walks.

continued

continued

Trout fishing nearby. Open all year.
PRICES: s €32; d €39-€41; t €48; extra person €11; dinner €12-€20
ON SITE: Forest Place of interest **NEARBY:** Bathing (27km) Horse riding (27km) Golf (50km) Fishing (1km) Swimming pool (12km) Stretch of water (27km) Water sports (27km) Tennis (3km) Railway station (50km) Shops (3km) LACAUNE (12km) **NOTES:** Pets admitted English spoken

TARN-ET-GARONNE

BEAUMONT-DE-LOMAGNE

⚞⚞⚞ 🐓 🍽 L'Arbre d'Or Tony ELLARD
16 rue Despeyrous, 82500 BEAUMONT-DE-LOMAGNE
☎ 05 63 65 32 34 & 06 87 13 50 31 ▤ 05 63 65 29 85
Large house in Beaumont-de-Lomagne. Ground floor: one bedroom with disabled access, double bed, shower, wc. First floor: one family room with double bedroom, shower room and wc, one room with double bed, bathroom and wc. One double bedroom with bathroom and wc. Twin bedroom with shower room and wc. Lounge with TV on ground floor. TV in bedroom on request (€3). Half board on the basis of two people sharing for a minimum of three days. Reduction after three days. Special weekend rates out of season. Open all year.
PRICES: s €37-€43; d €45-€50; t €60-€66; extra person €15; FB €38-€40; dinner €15-€18 **ON SITE:** Stretch of water **NEARBY:** Bathing (1km) Horse riding (7km) Fishing (1km) Swimming pool (1km) Tennis (1km) **NOTES:** Pets admitted English spoken

See advert on this page

BRASSAC

⚞⚞⚞ 🐓 🍽 La Marquise Gilbert et Michèle DIO
82190 BRASSAC
☎ 05 63 94 25 16 & SR : 05 63 21 79 61 ▤ 05 63 94 25 16
A warm welcome is assured at this farm, offering four bedrooms on the first floor of the owner's house. One room with a double bed and twin beds, two double bedrooms, one bedroom with double bed and single bed. Shower room and wc in each bedroom. Shade, veranda and garden furniture. Flowers, walks and pond fishing. Half board based on two people for a minimum of three days. Quality evening meals. Mountain biking. Fishing on site. Open all year.
PRICES: s €32; d €38; t €48; extra person €10; HB €32; FB €46; dinner €14 **ON SITE:** Fishing Hiking **NEARBY:** Bathing (14km) Canoeing (29km) Horse riding (17km) Swimming pool (11km) Stretch of water (14km) Tennis (6km) Railway station (20km) Shops (8km) **NOTES:** Pets admitted English spoken

CASTANET

⚞⚞⚞ 🐓 🍽 Cambayrac Daniel et Myriam VIDAL
82160 CASTANET
☎ 05 63 24 02 03 ▤ 05 63 24 01 68
e-mail: DVIDAL@wanadoo.fr www.cambayrac.com
The slate roof and stone walls of this rustic house are typical of old barns. You will love the calm of the countryside. Evening meals in front of the fireplace, featuring local cuisine are carefully prepared by Myriam. Daniel will guide you on beautiful walks on a number of footpaths. There are four bedrooms with private shower room and bathroom/wc. Three double bedrooms, one twin bedroom. Half board on the basis of two sharing. Swimming pool, mountain biking, table tennis on site. Open all year.
PRICES: s €30; d €40; extra person €12; HB €32; dinner €13
ON SITE: Fishing Swimming pool Hiking **NEARBY:** Bathing (4km) Canoeing (11km) Horse riding (9km) Tennis (4km) Railway station (33km) Shops (6km) **NOTES:** No pets English spoken

L'Arbre d'Or

View of rear garden

A former gentleman's residence dating back to the 17th century is located in the 13th century Bastide town of Beaumont-de-Lomagne. In the summer meals can be enjoyed in a tree shaded garden. Regional produce is used for the traditional Gascon cooking. All of the bedrooms have en-suite facilities. Bicycles can be hired.

A62 Bordeaux/Toulouse, exit Castelsarrasin, Beaumont de Lomagne is on the D928 between Montauban/Auch. A20 Paris/Toulouse exit Montauban in direction of Auch

16 rue Déspéyrous, 82500 Beaumont-de-Lomagne
Tel: 00 33 5 63 65 32 34 Fax: 00 33 5 63 65 29 85

CASTELSARRASIN

⚞⚞⚞ Dantous Sud Christiane GALEA ☎ 05 63 32 26 95
82100 CASTELSARRASIN
Five bedrooms on the first floor of a pretty house. Four with a single bed and a double bed in each; and one with twin beds and a double bed. Shower room and wc in each. Two comfortable attic bedrooms. Enclosed shady garden. Games area. Private entrance. Boules pitch, garden furniture, colour TV. Garonne canal 100m. Numerous tourist sites nearby. Open all year.
PRICES: s €35; d €40; extra person €14 **ON SITE:** Children's play area Swimming pool **NEARBY:** Bathing (17km) Horse riding (6km) Fishing (4km) Stretch of water (8km) Tennis (3km) Railway station (3km) Shops (3km) **NOTES:** No pets

CAZES-MONDENARD

⚞⚞⚞ 🍽 Martissan Claude MAURET
82110 CAZES-MONDENARD
☎ 05 63 95 83 71 / 06 33 61 66 00 & SR : 05 63 21 79 61
▤ 05 63 95 83 71
e-mail: claude.mauret@free.fr www.montauban.cci.fr/grange/
The family home of the Maurets, each bedroom evokes a style, a country or a tradition. First floor: a large corridor leads to the 'Heritage' bedroom with three antique single beds, bathroom, wc. 'Julie' is a modern room with a double bed a single bed, shower room and wc. 'Melissa' is has a double bed and single bed, bathroom and wc. Ground floor: guest sitting room and dining room. Garden with garden furniture, sun loungers, swimming pool. Children's meals 7 euros. Open all year.
PRICES: s €43-€45; d €55-€58; t €58-€61; extra person €16; HB €78-€87; dinner €16 **ON SITE:** Swimming pool Hiking **NEARBY:** Bathing (12km) Canoeing (30km) Horse riding (15km) Fishing (4km) Stretch of water (8km) Tennis (8km) Railway station (24km) Shops (6km) **NOTES:** Pets admitted CC

ESCATALENS

Chambre d'hôtes Claudine CHOUX
Place de la Mairie, 82700 ESCATALENS
☎ 05 63 68 71 23 & SR : 05 63 21 79 61
🖷 05 63 68 71 23

*Montauban (Ingres museum) 20 km, Moissac (10 km),
Toulouse (45 km).* Relax in the large rooms or around the
swimming pool of this 18th century building. First floor: the
suite, 'des Chevaliers' has one double and one single room,
bathroom and wc. 'Les Romantiques' has a double bed and a
twin bed, bathroom and wc. 'Côté Sud' has a double room,
twin room, bathroom and wc. 'Romeo and Juliette' has a
bedroom with three single beds, bathroom, shower and wc.
Private sitting room, TV, library, shady garden, children's
games room. Kitchen, dining room and sitting room in the
cellars. Available 1st April - 31st October.
PRICES: s €38-€50; d €49-€61; t €61-€76; dinner €15-€20
ON SITE: Swimming pool Hiking Tennis **NEARBY:** Bathing (16km)
Horse riding (10km) Fishing (1km) Railway station (8km) Shops
(2km) **NOTES:** Pets admitted English spoken

FENEYROLS

Les Clauzels Sonia AHARCHAOU
Feneyrols, 81140 ROUSSAYROLLES
☎ 05 63 56 30 98 & SR : 05 63 21 79 61 🖷 05 63 56 22 92
Situated in wooded, hilly, countryside, a calm atmosphere is
assured on this farm. Two grade three bedrooms (twin beds,
double bed and a cot) with private bathroom. Three grade one
bedrooms: one twin bedroom, two double bedrooms. Cot
available and there is a washbasin in each bedroom. Bathroom.
Half board based on two people sharing. Children's meals: €7.
Available 15th February-15th December.
PRICES: s €22-€28; d €28-€35; t €39; dinner €13 **ON SITE:** Horse riding
Hiking **NEARBY:** Bathing (18km) Canoeing (18km) Swimming pool
(18km) Stretch of water (18km) Tennis (10km) Railway station (10km)
Shops (8km) **NOTES:** Pets admitted English spoken

GRAMONT

Les Garbes P et S GAILLARD et VARGAS
82120 GRAMONT ☎ 05 63 94 07 81 & SR : 05 63 21 79 61
An authentic small farmhouse where each room is named after a
wild flower. First floor: one twin bedroom, one double bedroom,
one bedroom with a double bed and a single bed, one bedroom
with two double beds, shower room and wc. Half board based on
two people sharing. Table tennis, mountain biking, toys, large
grounds and terrace with an exceptional view. Free children's
meals (under 4), reduced rate for under 10 (€8). Rate for four:
€65. Open all year.
PRICES: s €30; d €38; t €47; extra person €10; dinner €13.5
ON SITE: Children's play area **NEARBY:** Bathing (8km) Horse riding
(17km) Fishing (2km) Swimming pool (17km) Stretch of water (8km)
Tennis (7km) Shops (7km) **NOTES:** Pets admitted English spoken

LABARTHE

Le Soyc Richard GROB
82220 LABARTHE
☎ 05 63 67 70 66 & SR : 05 63 21 79 61 🖷 05 63 67 70 66
Montpezat-de-Quercy 15 km. Moissac (8 km). Lauzerte 20 km.
A 13th century manor house, made from white stone, with rooms
with lovely views over the countryside. First floor: two twin
bedrooms, shower room and wc. One double bedroom, large
bathroom with private wc. Two bedrooms with a double bed and a
single bed. Ground floor: communal sitting
room and dining room. Two communal wcs. Second floor: games
room (table tennis), kitchen (microwave, fridge and baby bottle
heater). Covered terrace, swimming pool, bowling pitch, bicycles,
volleyball. Open all year.
PRICES: s €39-€43; d €45-€47; t €59-€62; extra person €15; dinner €17
ON SITE: Swimming pool **NEARBY:** Bathing (6km) Fishing (1km)
Hiking (1km) Tennis (6km) Railway station (22km) Shops (6km)
NOTES: Pets admitted

LAFRANCAISE

Chambre d'hôtes Christa HORF
Coques Lunel, Le Platane, 82130 LAFRANCAISE
☎ 05 63 65 92 18 🖷 05 63 65 88 18
This farm has a great atmosphere: stables, riding school, pigeon
loft, wonderfully restored manor house, parkland with a lake and a
13 x 7m swimming pool. First floor: two double bedrooms, sitting
room area with shower room and wc. One double bedroom with
shower room. TV, shower room and wc in each bedroom. Bikes.
Rate for children: 8 euros.
PRICES: s €50-€58; d €55-€60; extra person €13; dinner €16
ON SITE: Horse riding Fishing Swimming pool **NEARBY:** Hiking (5km)
Tennis (4km) Railway station (22km) Shops (5km) **NOTES:** Pets
admitted

Trouilles MM GUFFROY
82130 LAFRANCAISE
☎ 05 63 65 84 46 & SR : 05 63 21 79 61 🖷 05 63 65 97 14
Six bedrooms await you for a very enjoyable stay. Ground floor:
four bedrooms with independent access (double bed and single
bed in each one), shower room and wc. First floor: one bedroom
with a double bed and a single bed; one double bedroom, shower
room and wc. Half board based on two people sharing for longer
than three days. Swimming pool.
PRICES: s €31; d €43; t €54; extra person €10; dinner €14
ON SITE: Fishing Swimming pool Hiking **NEARBY:** Bathing (3km)
Horse riding (2km) Stretch of water (2km) Tennis (2km) Shops (2km)
Restaurant nearby **NOTES:** Pets admitted CC English spoken

LAVIT

La Ferme de Floris
Joseph et Danielle BORGOLOTTO
Route de Saint-Clar, 82120 LAVIT
☎ 05 63 94 03 26 & SR : 05 63 21 79 61 🖷 05 63 94 05 45
Five pastel bedrooms on the first floor. Two double rooms, one
twin room, two rooms with a double bed and twin beds in each,
shower room and wc. Small sitting room on the first floor. Single
bed available on request. Dining room, sitting room with fireplace
on ground floor. Table tennis, board games, library, Rate for four
people: €63. Farm produce, mushroom picking (when in season).
Evening meals made from local produce. Guests will love the calm
of the countryside. Open all year.
PRICES: s €30; d €41; t €52; HB €35; FB €47; dinner €14
ON SITE: Children's play area Hiking **NEARBY:** Bathing (10km)
Canoeing (15km) Horse riding (15km) Fishing (1km) Swimming pool
(3km) Stretch of water (15km) Tennis (3km) Railway station (24km)
Shops (3km) **NOTES:** Pets admitted

MAUBEC

⚑⚑⚑ |◎| ⬥ Le Jardin d'en Naoua Michèle ROUX
82500 MAUBEC
☎ 05 63 65 39 61 & SR : 05 63 21 79 61   🗏 05 63 65 39 61
At the foot of the fortified village of Maubec, Le Jardin de Naoua is an old 13th century farm which has been recently restored. Ground floor: one family suite: (double room and twin room), shower room, wc and disabled access. One grade two bedroom with twin beds, shower room and wc. First floor: two double bedrooms, one with a cot and one with and extra single bed, shower room and wc. One bedroom with three single beds, bathroom and wc. Garden, terrace, bikes. Evening meals on reservation. Price for 4: €69. Children's meals: €8. Open April to October.
PRICES: s €29-€33; d €35-€45; t €54; HB €33 **ON SITE:** Hiking
NEARBY: Bathing (2km) Horse riding (6km) Fishing (2km) Swimming pool (10km) Tennis (2km) Railway station (45km) Shops (2km)
NOTES: Small pets by arrangement CC English spoken

MONTAUBAN

⚑⚑⚑ 🐓 Ramierou Jean-Pierre PERE
960 chemin du Ramierou, 82000 MONTAUBAN
☎ 05 63 20 39 86   🗏 05 63 20 39 86

Montauban (Ingres museum) 2 km. Moissac 25 km. A lovely green space, and a building full of character. In one building: private sitting room (colour TV, fireplace, a sofa bed) opening onto a double bedroom and spacious bathroom with separate wc. Private terrace with garden furniture, barbecue and leafy garden. In another building: two bedrooms with private sitting rooms, one double bed and one sofa bed in each, shower room and wc. Communal terrace with garden furniture. Use of the kitchen. Rate for four people: 55/59 euros. Available throughout the year.
PRICES: s €34-€38; d €43-€47; t €50-€55 **ON SITE:** Hiking
NEARBY: Bathing (10km) Horse riding (2km) Fishing (4km) Swimming pool (2km) Stretch of water (10km) Tennis (2km) Railway station (4km) Shops (2km) **NOTES:** Pets admitted English spoken

MONTPEZAT-DE-QUERCY

⚑⚑⚑ |◎| Le Barry
Francis BANKES et Lothar JAROSS
Faubourg Saint-Roch,
82270 MONTPEZAT-DE-QUERCY
☎ 05 63 02 05 50 & SR : 05 63 21 79 61   🗏 05 63 02 03 07
On the ramparts of the medieval city of Montpezat-de-Quercy, Le Barry is a stone house with five bedrooms. Garden level: one double bedroom, bathroom/wc. Ground floor: one twin bedroom, bathroom and wc. First floor: two double bedrooms, shower and wc. Second floor: one bedroom with a double bed and single bed, bathroom and wc. Sitting room, TV and library. Half board supplement per person: €18. Children's meals: €7.5. Garden, terrace with swimming pool, lawn and flowers. Exceptional views over the Quercy hillsides. Available throughout the year.

continued

PRICES: s €46; d €58; t €69; HB €46; dinner €19 **ON SITE:** Swimming pool **NEARBY:** Bathing (2km) Canoeing (24km) Horse riding (15km) Fishing (2km) Stretch of water (2km) Hiking (1km) Tennis (2km) Railway station (12km) **NOTES:** Pets admitted English spoken

⚑⚑⚑⚑ |◎| Domaine de Lafon Micheline PERRONE
Pech de Lafon, 82270 MONTPEZAT-DE-QUERCY
☎ 05 63 02 05 09 & SR : 05 63 21 79 61
🗏 05 63 27 60 69
e-mail: Micheline.perrone@domainedelafon.com
www.domainedelafon.comx
Montpezat-de-Quercy 4 km. This beautiful pink 19th century manor house overlooks the fragrant Quercy countryside. The house has lovely paintings. First floor: the 'Indienne' room has a double bed and a single bed; the 'Perroquets' room has a double bed and a single bed; and the 'Baldaquin' room has two single beds. Each bedroom has a shower room and wc. Large sitting room with TV and fireplace, guest dining room. Painting courses. Evening meals on reservation. Pets on request. Open 1st April to 1st November.
PRICES: s €45-€48; d €58-€64; t €69-€77; extra person €13; HB €49-€52; dinner €20 **ON SITE:** Hiking **NEARBY:** Bathing (10km) Canoeing (28km) Horse riding (30km) Swimming pool (4km) Stretch of water (4km) Tennis (4km) Railway station (16km) Shops (4km) **NOTES:** Pets admitted Minimum 2 night stay

NEGREPELISSE

⚑⚑⚑ |◎| Les Brunis Johnny ANTONY
4965 route de Montricoux, 82800 NEGREPELISSE
☎ 05 63 67 24 08 & SR : 05 63 21 79 61   🗏 05 63 67 24 08

This is a beautiful house, situated at the entrance to the Aveyron Gorges. Ground floor: a family suite comprising a twin bedroom linked to an attic room with bunkbeds, and a double bedroom, each with shower room and wc. First floor: spacious twin bedroom leading to a balcony, with superb bathroom and wc. One twin bedroom with shower room and wc. One double bedroom with shower room and wc. Sitting room with lounge area. Rate for four: €64/72. Swimming pool, TV in each bedroom. Evening meals in July/August on reservation. Available throughout the year.
PRICES: s €35-€41; d €41-€53; t €55-€63; extra person €10; dinner €17 **ON SITE:** Swimming pool **NEARBY:** Bathing (13km) Canoeing (2km) Horse riding (3km) Fishing (1km) Stretch of water (13km) Hiking (2km) Tennis (1km) Railway station (24km) Shops (1km) **NOTES:** Pets admitted English spoken

MIDI-PYRÉNÉES

PARISOT

¶¶¶ Belvésé Colette NORGA
82160 PARISOT
☎ 05 63 67 07 58

Caylus (medieval village) 10 km. A beautifully restored building in a lovely country location. There are three double guest rooms on the first floor, each with a lounge area, bath or shower room and wc. On the ground floor there is a lounge, fireplace and kitchen area. Open all year.

PRICES: s €36; d €54 **ON SITE:** Hiking **NEARBY:** Bathing (3km) Horse riding (4km) Fishing (3km) Swimming pool (10km) Tennis (3km) Railway station (31km) Shops (3km) **NOTES:** No pets English spoken

SAINT-ETIENNE-DE-TULMONT

¶¶¶ Le Ramier Nadine LAFLORENTIE
3833 Vieille route de Montauban,
82410 SAINT-ETIENNE-DE-TULMONT
☎ 05 63 64 64 25 & 06 76 25 25 99
Montauban 5 km. Aveyron Gorges 15 km. This lovely place is five minutes from Montauban and very near the Aveyron Gorges. The park around the house guarantees calm and rest. Two of the three bedrooms have direct access onto the terrace, one double bed with shower room and wc; one double bedroom with shower room and wc in the corridor. Child's bed and extra bed also available. Colour TV in each bedroom, communal sitting room and dining room (colour TV and fireplace). Open all year.
PRICES: s €35; d €38; extra person €8 **ON SITE:** Hiking **NEARBY:** Bathing (16km) Fishing (2km) Swimming pool (5km) Tennis (4km) Railway station (5km) Shops (4km) **NOTES:** No pets English spoken

‖○‖
Places with this symbol serve table d'hôtes
evening meals - remember to book in advance

SERIGNAC

¶¶¶ ✿ Le Vieux Chêne Yves MIRAMONT
82500 SERIGNAC
☎ 05 63 20 70 32 & SR : 05 63 21 79 61 🖹 05 63 20 74 39
Moissac 30 mn. Ingres Museum at Montauban 30 mn. An authentic farm on the hillside, bordered by old oak woods, with a stream and pond. One family room with a double bed, a twin bedroom and a small lounge area, shower room and wc. Ground floor: bedroom with double and single beds, bedroom with three single beds, and a shower room and wc in each. Kids' meals half the adult rate. Four people: €60. Good meals served at the ferme-auberge. Table tennis, fishing, table football, bike hire, walking. Warm, friendly welcome. Available all year.
PRICES: s €30; d €40; t €50; extra person €10; HB €35; dinner €15-€30
ON SITE: Children's play area Fishing Swimming pool Hiking
NEARBY: Bathing (5km) Horse riding (2km) Tennis (2km) Railway station (15km) Shops (5km) Restaurant nearby **NOTES:** Pets admitted English spoken

ST-ANTONIN-NOBLE-VAL

¶¶¶ ✿ ‖○‖ Chambre d'hôtes Joseph COSTES
Du Bes de Quercy, 82140 ST-ANTONIN-NOBLE-VAL
☎ 05 63 31 97 61
Typical stone house, near the owner's home, in a lovely relaxing setting. Bedrooms on the first floor: one family suite with two double bedrooms and a bathroom and wc in each. Two double bedrooms, one with an extra single bed, and one bedroom with a double bed and a single bed. Bathroom and wc in each bedroom. Garden. Open all year.
PRICES: s €30; d €40; t €50; dinner €13 **ON SITE:** Hiking **NEARBY:** Bathing (9km) Canoeing (9km) Horse riding (9km) Fishing (9km) Swimming pool (8km) Tennis (8km) Railway station (14km) Shops (8km) **NOTES:** Pets admitted

ST-NAUPHARY

¶¶¶ ✿ Domaine du Roussillon David FRESQUET
82370 ST-NAUPHARY
☎ 05 63 67 85 47 & 06 76 86 21 21 🖹 05 63 67 85 47
www.domaineroussillon.com
Montauban (Ingres Museum) 8 km. This beautiful farm lies in the Roussillon area. On the first floor, one (grade 2) double bedroom with shower room, wc on the landing. One bedroom with a double and a single bed, shower room and wc. Lovely, comfortable space, private sitting room with TV. Ground floor: a grade three bedroom with independent access, double bed and bunkbeds, shower room and wc. Covered terrace with garden furniture. Large grounds and green, tree lined space. Communal swimming pool. Breakfast served in front of the fireplace (in season). Four people: 68 euros. Open all year.
PRICES: s €35-€38; d €38-€48; t €58 **ON SITE:** Fishing Swimming pool Hiking **NEARBY:** Bathing (10km) Horse riding (8km) Tennis (1km) Railway station (8km) Shops (1km) **NOTES:** No pets

NORD-PAS-DE-CALAIS

NORD

BAIVES

††† ȮÎ Les Pres de la Fagne
C. CHAUVEAU & P. MELLE POUL
2 rue Principale, 59132 BAIVES
☎ 03 27 57 02 69　▤ 03 27 57 02 69
e-mail: la.fagne@wanadoo.fr
Val Joly 8 km. Fourmies 15 km. Avesnes/Helpe 20 km. Chimay 8 km. In the area known as Little Switzerland, this establishment is in contemporary style but with plenty of traditional exposed timbers. It was built in 1880 but renovated in 1993. Separate from the owners' dwelling are five charming double rooms all on the first floor, three with own shower and wc, two with own bath and wc. Meals provided, drinks extra. Riding stables, guests' horses welcome.
PRICES: s €34-€49; d €37-€52; dinner €15　**NEARBY:** Swimming pool (8km) Hiking (1km) Tennis (8km) Sailing (8km) Railway station (15km) Shops (8km) AVESNES SUR HELPE (20km)　**NOTES:** Pets admitted English spoken

BANTEUX

††† 🐓 Ferme de Bonavis Thérèse DELCAMBRE
Bonavis, 59266 BANTEUX
☎ 03 27 78 55 08　▤ 03 27 78 55 08
e-mail: c.delcambre@club-internet.fr
There are three attractive guest rooms on the first floor of the Bonavis farmstead 2km north of the village, all with TV and own shower and wc. One is a double with balcony, one is a triple, one has two double and two single beds. Central heating and double glazing. Children's toys, table football, boules. Enclosed parking, garage. Restaurants 500m away. Footpaths and cycle tracks to Vaucelles Abbey 2km. Aerodrome with gliding 9km. Open all year.
PRICES: s €35-€40; d €42-€55; t €61-€67; extra person €69-€79
ON SITE: Children's play area　**NEARBY:** Forest (15km) Golf (6km) Sea (140km) Swimming pool (10km) Hiking (2km) Tennis (13km) Sailing (12km) Railway station (12km) Shops (4km) MARCOING (5km)
NOTES: No pets

BEAUCAMPS-LIGNY

††† ȮÎ Chez Julie Claire TILMANT-DANJOU
8, rue de Radinghem, 59134 BEAUCAMPS-LIGNY
☎ 03 20 50 33 82　▤ 03 20 50 34 35
e-mail: CTILMANT@wanadoo.fr
Lille 12 km. Next to the owners' house, this old farmstead in the village square has three guest rooms and its own entrance. There is a double room on the ground floor, while the first floor has a triple and a room with a double and two single beds. All have own telephone, shower and wc. Cot available. TV on request. Living and sitting room with wood stove. 100 square metre terrace, garden room. Table tennis. Enclosed parking. Garage if required. Restaurant and shop 50m. Tennis courts, riding 8km. Children under 12 €5.5. Open all year.
PRICES: s €30; d €41; t €52　**NEARBY:** Forest (12km) Golf (10km) Sea (70km) Swimming pool (8km) Hiking (50km) Tennis (3km) Sailing (11km) Railway station (5km) LILLE (12km)　**NOTES:** No pets English spoken

BIERNE

††† 🐓 & Chambre d'hôtes (Route de Watten)
Alain VEREECKE
GITES DE FRANCE-SERVICE RESERVATION, 5 allée Sully, 29322 QUIMPER Cedex
☎ 03 20 14 93 93 & PROP: 03 28 68 66 98　▤ 03 20 14 93 99
Dunkerque 10 km. Bray-Dunes 15 km. Belgium 20 km. Gravelines 25 km. This mixed farm, 2km from the fortified town of Bergues, has four guest rooms separate from the owners' dwelling. There is a ground floor twin with disabled access and own shower, and on the first floor a double with own bath, a twin with own shower, and a double with own shower. All rooms have own wc. Ground floor breakfast room and kitchenette. Sitting area with TV. Garden. Restaurant 800m. Children €9
PRICES: s €32; d €37　**NEARBY:** Forest (20km) Golf (4km) Sea (10km) Swimming pool (2km) Hiking (6km) Tennis (2km) Sailing (6km) Railway station (1km) Shops (2km) BERGUES (2km)　**NOTES:** No pets CC

BOLLEZEELE

††† ȮÎ & Le Pantgat-Hof
Jean-François CHILOUP-GEY
27, rue de Metz, 59470 BOLLEZEELE
☎ 03 28 68 00 87 & 03 28 68 04 91　▤ 03 28 68 00 87
e-mail: chiloup@net-up.com
Bergues, Cassel 15 km. Saint-Omer 18 km. Gravelines 20 km. Close to the Marais Audomarois Nature Park is this old farmstead. Rooms, all with own shower and wc, are in a building next to the owners' house. There is one double with TV and telephone, one double with telephone, one double, one triple and a twin-bedded suite. Gardens, woodland. Artist's studio. Lace-making instruction. Special weekend guided walking tours. Loose boxes to let May-October. Parking. Ponies and donkeys. 8ha grounds. Village centre 2km. €66/4 persons; €73/5 persons. Special weekend rates October-March: two nights, €72 per couple, €132 for a 5-person family.
PRICES: s €32; d €40; t €50; dinner €16　**NEARBY:** Forest (15km) Golf (20km) Sea (20km) Swimming pool (10km) Hiking (1km) Tennis (11km) Sailing (15km) Railway station (7km) Shops (2km) WORMHOUT (13km)
NOTES: No pets

BOURBOURG

††† ȮÎ Le Withof Bernard BATTAIS
Chemin du Château, 59630 BOURBOURG
☎ 03 28 62 32 50　▤ 03 28 62 38 88
Dunkerque 18 km. Calais, Saint-Omer 30 km. This fortified farmstead with its pony, geese, ducks and chickens dates from the 16th century. Guest rooms on the first floor of the owners' house include a suite with two double beds, own bath, and own wc on the landing, two doubles and two triples, all with own bath and wc. TV. Ground floor sitting and living room with antique furniture. €70/4 persons; children €10. Cot available. Garden with extensive lawn, garden room, 3ha of grazing, fishing. Channel Tunnel 30km.
PRICES: s €40; d €50; t €60; dinner €17　**NEARBY:** Forest (12km) Golf (20km) Sea (10km) Swimming pool (1km) Hiking (1km) Tennis (1km) Sailing (10km) Railway station (2km) Shops (1km) Restaurant nearby DUNKERQUE (18km)　**NOTES:** No pets

COMINES

♦♦♦ ❦ ⚐ Relais de la Vielle Garde
SCI LE VIEUX SOLDAT
GITES DE FRANCE-SERVICE RESERVATION, 5 allée Sully,
29322 QUIMPER Cedex
☎ 03 20 14 93 93 & PROP: 03 20 78 91 31 ▤ 03 20 14 93 99
*Belgium 5 km. Lille 13 km. Roubaix-Tourcoing 17 km. Bruges
60 km.* This farmhouse with ducks and chickens has three guest
rooms on the first floor with their own entrance. There is one
room with two double beds, two showers and two wcs, another
room is a double with own shower and wc, another is a triple with
own bath, shower and wc. TV points. Card telephone. Ground
floor breakfast room. Garden room. Children €13. €45/4 persons.
Gourmet meals €16/22. Enclosed parking. Walking and riding.
Fishing. Skiing. Bus service to Lille and Comines 300m. Guest
should arrive before 9pm.
PRICES: s €30; d €35; t €40; dinner €16-€22 **ON SITE:** Hiking
NEARBY: Forest (15km) Golf (8km) Sea (60km) Swimming pool (1km)
Tennis (2km) Sailing (15km) Railway station (2km) Shops (2km)
QUESNOY SUR DEULE (2km) **NOTES:** No pets CC English spoken

CYSOING

♦♦♦ Chambre d'hôtes Annette LAUMET
192 rue du Maréchal Leclerc, Le Quennaumont,
59830 CYSOING ☎ 03 20 79 51 45
Villeneuve d'Ascq, Tournai, Orchies 10 km. Lille 15 km. This little
farmhouse dating from 1875 has three first floor guest rooms, all
doubles, one with TV, one with child's bed, TV and video, all with
own shower and wc. Leisure corner with TV and library. Sitting
room with open fireplace. Parking. Swimming pool in extensive
garden. Good walking. Chemist 400m, restaurants and shops 2km.
200m to bus service linking with tram to Lille.
PRICES: s €36; d €39 **ON SITE:** Hiking **NEARBY:** Forest (5km) Golf
(10km) Sea (100km) Swimming pool (10km) Tennis (15km) Sailing
(5km) Railway station (10km) Shops (1km) CYSOING **NOTES:** No pets

ESTAIRES

♦♦♦ ⚐ La Quénèque Bernard HUYGHE
1822 rue de l'Epinette, 59940 ESTAIRES
☎ 03 28 40 84 69

Bailleul 12 km. Lille 30 km. Bruges, Gand 80 km. The Huyghe
family are happy to welcome guests to stay for one or more days
with them in the pleasant countryside of the valley of the River Lys
close to the Belgian border. They have four rooms, one part of a
gîte, all with separate facilities, on the first floor of a separate
building which has been sensitively restored in local style. There
are two doubles, one twin and one triple. Vegetarian cooking. Use
of garden. Enclosed parking.
PRICES: s €28; d €39-€42; t €51; dinner €14 **ON SITE:** Hiking
NEARBY: Forest (12km) Golf (20km) Sea (60km) Swimming pool
(12km) Tennis (12km) Sailing (10km) Railway station (10km) Shops
(4km) MERVILLE (12km) **NOTES:** No pets English spoken

FAUMONT

♦♦♦ Chambre d'hôtes Renée DEWAS
1143 rue du Général de Gaulle, 59310 FAUMONT
☎ 03 20 59 27 74
Lesquin 15 km. Belgium 18 km. Saint-Amand 20 km. This old farm
has three first floor guest rooms adjacent to a gîte and with a
separate entrance from the main house. There is a twin and a
double both with own shower and wc, and a triple with own
shower and wc on the landing. Ground floor reception room with
TV, fridge, microwave and coffee-maker. Breakfast served in main
building. Lawn and paved courtyard. Covered parking. Farm shop
1km, restaurants 1.5km. Historic mining centre.
PRICES: s €28; d €36-€38; t €45 **NEARBY:** Forest (10km) Golf (8km)
Sea (80km) Swimming pool (8km) Hiking (1km) Tennis (2km) Sailing
(10km) Railway station (8km) Shops (1km) ORCHIES (8km)
NOTES: No pets

FOURNES-EN-WEPPES

♦♦♦ ❦ ⚐ Ferme de Rosembois Francine BAJEUX
Hameau du Bas Flandres, 59134 FOURNES-EN-WEPPES
☎ 03 20 50 25 69 ▤ 03 20 50 60 75
e-mail: FAMILLEBAJEUX@wanadoo.fr
Belgium 10 km. Lille 15 km. Orchies 40 km. Francine and
Emmanuel Bajeux welcome guests to their mixed farm in a quiet
setting 10km from Armentières. Their farmhouse has three first
floor guest rooms, one double, one twin, and one triple, all with
own facilities. Sitting room with TV and open fireplace. Garden
room. Restaurant in the village. Armentières leisure centre 10km.
Tennis courts and gym 2km. Golf course 5km.
PRICES: s €28; d €36-€38; t €45; dinner €13 **NEARBY:** Golf (5km) Sea
(80km) Swimming pool (6km) Tennis (2km) Sailing (10km) Railway
station (15km) Shops (2km) LA BASSEE **NOTES:** No pets English
spoken

HALLUIN

♦♦♦ ❦ Ferme du Nid de Mousse
Marie-Joseph DELESALLE
GITES DE FRANCE-SERVICE RESERVATION, 5 allée Sully,
29322 QUIMPER Cedex
☎ 03 20 14 93 93 & PROP: 03 20 37 02 05 ▤ 03 20 14 93 99
*Roubaix, Tourcoing 12 km. Lesquin, Courtrai 18 km. Tournai 30
km.* This mixed farm with chickens and horses has three guest
rooms on the first floor above two gîtes with entrance separate
from the owners' house. There is a triple, a double and a twin with
a suite with two single beds. Shared sitting room with TV and living
room with TV corner and library. Ground floor breakfast room.
Parking. Terrace and small shared open area. Garden room. €49/4
persons. Lille 20 minutes by expressway.
PRICES: s €25; d €31; t €38 **ON SITE:** Hiking **NEARBY:** Forest (5km)
Golf (10km) Sea (60km) Swimming pool (2km) Tennis (3km) Railway
station (10km) Shops (2km) TOURCOING (12km) **NOTES:** No pets CC

HONDSCHOOTE

♦♦♦ ♿ La Xavière Serge ROUFFELAERS
1200 Chemin du Clachoire, 59122 HONDSCHOOTE
☎ 03 28 62 61 04 ▤ 03 28 68 31 27
This old farm building on the Belgian border 5km from the village
has six guest rooms with an entrance separate from the owners'
residence. On the ground floor is a double with disabled access
and a triple, on the first floor two doubles, a twin, and a triple, all
with own shower and wc (one with bath) and telephone. Adjacent
inn. Coast 18km, and within 40km are Bruges, Furnes/Veurne,
Ypres, the Monts de Flandres hills and the ports of Dunkirk and
Ostend. Tourist tax. Open all year. Children €9
PRICES: s €35; d €43; t €55; dinner €17-€30 **ON SITE:** Children's play

continued

NORD-PAS-DE-CALAIS

area **NEARBY:** Forest (40km) Golf (18km) Sea (18km) Swimming pool (11km) Hiking (5km) Tennis (5km) Sailing (18km) Railway station (15km) Shops (5km) Restaurant nearby HONDSCHOOTE (5km) **NOTES:** No pets English spoken

JENLAIN

♦♦♦♦ Château d'En Haut Michel DEMARCQ
59144 JENLAIN
☎ 03 27 49 71 80 📠 03 27 35 90 17
e-mail: mdemarcq@nordnet.fr

Valenciennes 10 km. Belgium 12 km. Standing in extensive parkland, this 18th-century château has six first floor guest rooms. There are four doubles, another double with a single bed in an adjoining room, and a triple. Three rooms have own bath and wc, three have own shower and wc. Sitting room and open fireplace. Telephone box 800m. Garden room. Restaurants in the village.
PRICES: s €42-€50; d €45-€64; t €67 **NEARBY:** Forest (10km) Golf (10km) Sea (130km) Swimming pool (10km) Hiking (10km) Tennis (10km) Sailing (17km) Railway station (6km) Shops (1km) VALENCIENNES (10km) **NOTES:** No pets English spoken

JOLIMETZ

♦♦♦ ⏐◯⏐ Chambre d'hôtes
Marie-Anne GUILLET-MASSON
GITES DE FRANCE-SERVICE RESERVATION, 5 allée Sully, 29322 QUIMPER Cedex
☎ 03 20 14 93 93 & PROP: 03 27 26 41 81 📠 03 20 14 93 99
Valenciennes 27 km. In the middle of the village and only 100m from the Mormal forest, this house has five guest rooms with their own entrance. There are four doubles and one twin, all with own bath and wc. TV available. Sitting and living room and open fireplace on ground floor. Meals by arrangement. Adjacent to country inn. Large lawn and garden room. Spacious courtyard with parking. Bikes for hire.
PRICES: s €38; d €43; HB €49; dinner €15 **ON SITE:** Forest **NEARBY:** Golf (2km) Sea (150km) Swimming pool (19km) Hiking (2km) Tennis (2km) Sailing (17km) Railway station (2km) Shops (2km) Restaurant nearby LE QUESNOY (2km) **NOTES:** Pets admitted CC English spoken

LE QUESNOY

♦♦♦ Chambre d'hôtes Christophe TELLIER
GITES DE FRANCE-SERVICE RESERVATION, 5 allée Sully, 29322 QUIMPER Cedex
☎ 03 20 14 93 93 & PROP: 03 27 26 29 06 📠 03 20 14 93 99
Valenciennes 16 km. Maubeuge 30 km. This large farm shop has five guest rooms on its upper floor. There are two family rooms with desk, own bath and wc, and three doubles with own shower and wc, all with TV. Ground floor sitting room in wing. Breakfast made with local produce. View over the valley of the River Rhonelle. Recreational and sporting facilities, restaurants and

guided tours at the fortified town of Le Quesnoy, one kilometre. Large dining hall for hire (capacity 150 people).
PRICES: s €35-€38; d €38-€46; t €58 **NEARBY:** Forest (8km) Golf (8km) Sea (170km) Swimming pool (10km) Hiking (10km) Tennis (2km) Sailing (40km) Railway station (3km) Shops (2km) LE QUESNOY **NOTES:** No pets CC

LOCQUIGNOL

♦♦♦ La Touraille Odette RENARD-FREMY
2, La Touraille, 59530 LOCQUIGNOL
☎ 03 27 34 20 65 & SR : 03 20 14 93 93 📠 03 27 34 20 65
e-mail: renardmc@free.fr http://:www.chez.com/latouraille
Maroilles 7.5 km. Berlaimont 6 km. Avesnes 17 km. This residence in the Mormal forest has four rooms. On the first floor is a double with own shower, plus a suite with a single bed and another double with own bath, on the second floor a double with own bath, and a family room with own wc. All rooms have own wc. Breakfast room with open fireplace. Leisure corner with TV. Garden and conifer park. Enclosed parking. Mountain bikes for hire. Bridle paths and equestrian centre. Restaurants 1km.
PRICES: s €38-€43; d €43-€46; t €61 **ON SITE:** Forest Hiking **NEARBY:** Golf (10km) Sea (180km) Swimming pool (10km) Tennis (8km) Sailing (35km) Railway station (10km) Shops (10km) LE QUESNOY (9km) **NOTES:** No pets CC

LOMPRET

♦♦♦ Ferme Blanche de Lassus Olivier DELEVAL
Rue Pasteur, 59840 LOMPRET
☎ 03 20 92 99 12 & 03 20 54 29 82 📠 03 20 92 99 12
e-mail: dadeleval@nordnet.fr
Lambersart 2 km. Lille 5 km. Belgium 10 km. Bruges 45 km. With its own entrance, the accommodation in this 18th-century building consists of three charming rooms. There are two doubles, one with a sitting area, both with own bath and wc, and a twin with own shower and wc and sitting area. Living room with fireplace. Large secluded grassed area. Bikes, table tennis, private lake. Garage. Lille Metro stop 1km. Restaurants 4km. Close to Lille Ouest expressway. Prés du Hem leisure centre 2km.
PRICES: s €40; d €44-€45 **ON SITE:** Swimming pool Tennis **NEARBY:** Forest (10km) Golf (5km) Sea (80km) Sailing (5km) Railway station (2km) Shops (1km) QUESNOY SUR DEULE (4km) **NOTES:** Pets admitted English spoken

MAROILLES

♦♦♦ Vert Bocage M-France et J-Noël VILBAS
555 rue des Juifs, 59550 MAROILLES
☎ 03 27 77 74 22 & 06 85 17 68 32 📠 03 27 77 74 22
e-mail: jean-noel.vilbas@wanadoo.fr
Landrecies 5 km. Avesnes/Helpe 12 km. Maubeuge 20 km. Val Joly 30 km. This old farmhouse has three guest rooms, two with their own entrance. On first floor: one double with additional room with single bed, and one triple. The third room is a twin. All have own shower and wc. Sitting room, library, TV, guests' billiard room. Ground floor breakfast room with wood fire, games, table football. Large shared leafy garden with views over the countryside. No smoking on upper floor. Parking. Restaurants 600m. Mormal forest 2km. Mormal golf course. Belgian border 40km. Valenciennes 45km.
PRICES: s €33; d €42-€44; t €50-€53 **NEARBY:** Forest (3km) Golf (30km) Sea (160km) Swimming pool (20km) Hiking (2km) Tennis (3km) Sailing (30km) Railway station (5km) Shops (3km) LANDRECIES (5km) **NOTES:** No pets English spoken

continued

MASNIERES

♣♣♣ 🐓 Ferme des Ecarts Gérard et Jeannette CATTEAU
59241 MASNIERES
☎ 03 27 37 51 10 📠 03 27 37 51 10
e-mail: gcatteau@free.fr
Marcoing 3 km. Cambrai 8 km. This arable and pig farm on the village outskirts has four rooms. There is a double on the ground floor, and on the first floor a triple and two doubles, one with small child's bed, all with own shower and wc. Central heating and double glazing. Parking, garage on request. Telephone box 1km. Large lawn, garden room. Château d'Esnes, Vaucelles Abbey 5km, Cambrai 8km. Leisure park 5km. Children €8.
PRICES: s €32; d €40-€42; t €55 **NEARBY:** Forest (45km) Golf (45km) Sea (120km) Swimming pool (7km) Hiking (1km) Tennis (7km) Sailing (6km) Railway station (8km) Shops (1km) MARCOING (3km)
NOTES: No pets

QUAEDYPRE

♣♣♣ 🐓 Ferme du Cheval Noir
Ghislaine et Gérard REUMAUX, 59380 QUAEDYPRE
☎ 03 28 68 68 85 📠 03 28 68 54 96
e-mail: reumaux@multimania.com http://www.reumaux.net
Dunkerque, Belgium 15 km. Bruges 1 hour. Calais 30 mn. This farm growing traditional local crops (potatoes, flax, raspberries and strawberries) has four first floor guest rooms with their own entrance. There is a double, a twin, and two triples. Cot available. Supplement payable for pets. Ground floor breakfast room with open fireplace. Kitchen may be used. Sitting room with TV (satellite and cable). Outdoor furniture. Courtyard. Farm produce for sale.
PRICES: s €29; d €39; t €43 **NEARBY:** Forest (20km) Golf (10km) Sea (15km) Swimming pool (5km) Hiking (5km) Tennis (5km) Sailing (8km) Railway station (5km) Shops (4km) BERGUES (6km) **NOTES:** Pets admitted English spoken

RAIMBEAUCOURT

♣♣♣ 🐓 Chambre d'hôtes Marie-Ange LIEGEOIS
GITES DE FRANCE-SERVICE RESERVATION, 5 allée Sully,
29322 QUIMPER Cedex
☎ 03 20 14 93 93 & PROP: 03 27 80 12 56 📠 03 20 14 93 99
Douai 12 km. Orchies 15 km. Saint-Amand 20 km. Lille, Tournai 30 km. This mixed farm with its dairy herd has four guest rooms with their own entrance and all with TV. Three have their own bath and wc, one has own shower and wc. Cot available. Breakfast room in main house. Villeneuve d'Ascq 25km, Valenciennes, Cambrai 30km, Lens 35km, Béthune 40km. Sale of farm produce. Three self-catering gîtes.
PRICES: s €26; d €30 **NEARBY:** Forest (2km) Golf (10km) Sea (80km) Swimming pool (5km) Hiking (15km) Tennis (2km) Railway station (5km) Shops (1km) DOUAI (12km) **NOTES:** No pets CC

SAINGHIN-EN-MELANTOIS

♣♣♣ 🐓 🍽️ Chambre d'hôtes Dominique POLLET
832 rue Pasteur, 59262 SAINGHIN-EN-MELANTOIS
☎ 03 20 41 29 82 & SR : 03 20 14 93 93 📠 03 20 79 06 99
Villeneuve d'Ascq 4 km. Cysoing 5 km. Lesquin 6 km. Belgium 10 km. Only a few steps from Noyelle Wood and the Rivière de la Marque, this working farm dating from the 18th century specialises in cattle breeding and strawberry growing. The four guest rooms, all with TV, own shower and wc and with their own entrance comprise two doubles, a twin and a triple. Kitchenette. Breakfast room in main building. Meals by arrangement. Charge for pets. Telephone box 1.5km. Lawn, garden room. Metro stop 5km.
PRICES: s €31; d €37; t €45; dinner €13 **ON SITE:** Forest Hiking **NEARBY:** Golf (6km) Sea (80km) Swimming pool (5km) Tennis (2km) Railway station (6km) Shops (2km) CYSOING (5km) **NOTES:** Pets admitted CC English spoken

SEBOURG

♣♣♣ Chambre d'hôtes Pierre DELMOTTE
23 rue du Moulin, 59990 SEBOURG
☎ 03 27 26 53 31 📠 03 27 26 50 08
Valenciennes, Le Quesnoy 9 km. Roisin (Belgium) 3 km. Onnaing 5 km. Five guest rooms are available in this establishment, all with TV and telephone. On the ground floor there is a double with own bath and wc and an additional room with two single beds, on the first floor a double with own bath and wc, two doubles with own hip bath and wc, and a triple with own shower and wc. Small child's bed available. First floor sitting area, library. Ground floor sitting room and breakfast room. €68/4 persons. Shops 500m. Park and small lake. Parking for three cars. Good walking.
PRICES: s €35; d €41; t €53 **NEARBY:** Forest (3km) Golf (8km) Sea (160km) Swimming pool (9km) Hiking (5km) Tennis (1km) Sailing (50km) Railway station (9km) Shops (1km) VALENCIENNES (9km)
NOTES: Pets admitted

SOLRE-LE-CHATEAU

♣♣♣ Chambre d'hôtes Pierrette MARIANI
5 Grand'Place, 59740 SOLRE-LE-CHATEAU
☎ 03 27 61 65 30 📠 03 27 61 63 38
Val Joly 10 km. Belgium 5 km. This 19th-century gentleman's residence has three guest rooms. On the first floor there is a double with own shower and wc, on the second floor a twin with own bath and wc. Cot and additional single bed if required. On the ground floor is a double with its own entrance, shower, wc and kitchenette. Sitting room with TV. Guests have use of garden and grounds. Bikes available. Good walking, riding and cycling.
PRICES: s €34; d €40-€44; t €57 **ON SITE:** Children's play area **NEARBY:** Forest (5km) Golf (30km) Swimming pool (13km) Hiking (1km) Tennis (5km) Sailing (10km) Railway station (15km) SOLRE LE CHATEAU **NOTES:** No pets English spoken

ST-PIERRE-BROUCK

♣♣♣♣ 🍽️ Le Château Nathalie DUVIVIER-ALBA
287 route de la Bistade, 59630 ST-PIERRE-BROUCK
☎ 03 28 27 50 05 & 03 28 27 58 30 📠 03 28 27 50 05
e-mail: nduvivier@nordnet.fr www.lechateau.fr.st

Dunkerque, Calais, Saint-Omer 20 km. Character residence with antique furniture, and three charming guest rooms. First floor twin with own bath and wc, second floor double with own shower and wc, and suite with canopied double bed and single bed, own shower and two wcs. Additional double with own shower. Sitting room with open fireplace. Terrace and extensive grounds. No smoking establishment. Children €15. Twenty minutes from coast. Nearby: Cap Gris Nez, fortified towns, Belgian border. Open all year.
PRICES: s €42; d €49-€54; t €64; dinner €17 **NEARBY:** Forest (6km) Golf (6km) Sea (15km) Swimming pool (7km) Hiking (1km) Tennis (6km) Sailing (15km) Railway station (7km) Shops (1km) BOURBOURG (6km) **NOTES:** No pets English spoken

TETEGHEM

⫴ ⫼Ⓞ⫼ Le Galgouck Thérèse PEINTE
157 rue des Pierres, 59229 TETEGHEM
☎ 03 28 26 00 35 & SR : 03 20 14 93 93　▤ 03 28 26 00 35
http://www.itea-dev.com/59/1660

Dunkerque, Malo-les-Bains 7 km. Belgium 7 km. This establishment has three guest rooms on the first floor. There is a twin with shower and wc, a twin with small child's bed, shower, bath and wc, and a triple with shower and wc. Gîte. Terrace and large grassed area, garden room. Meals featuring flans, terrines, preserves and Flemish specialities. Gravelines (Sportica) 10km, Bergues (canoeing) 7km. Menu for children under 10: €9. Open all year.
PRICES: s €37; d €43; t €51; dinner €16　**NEARBY:** Forest (3km)　Golf (3km)　Sea (7km)　Swimming pool (7km)　Hiking (5km)　Tennis (1km)　Sailing (5km)　Railway station (5km)　Shops (1km)　DUNKERQUE (5km)
NOTES: No pets CC

TOUFFLERS

⫴ Chambre d'hôtes Nicole et J-Pierre DURIEUX
75, rue de la Festingue, 59390 TOUFFLERS
☎ 03 20 83 65 99 & 06 12 18 53 34
Lannoy 3 km. Courtrai 14 km. Roubaix 8 km. Château Estainbourg 10 km. The owners of this house have three guest rooms available on their first floor. There are two twins with shower and wc and a double with bath and wc, all with TV and gas central heating. Sitting room and living room on ground floor. Attractive garden with lawn. Parking. Telephone box 10m. Bus service to Lille and Villeneuve d'Ascq 700m. Snack bar 100m. Restaurant 1km. Lille 15 minutes, Villeneuve 10 minutes.
PRICES: s €30; d €37　**NEARBY:** Forest (1km)　Golf (3km)　Sea (90km)　Swimming pool (5km)　Tennis (1km)　Sailing (3km)　Railway station (8km)　LANNOY (3km)　**NOTES:** Pets admitted English spoken

VIEUX-CONDE

⫴ ✔ Mont de Péruwelz. M-Paule et Albert MATHYS
935 rue de Calonne, 59690 VIEUX-CONDE
☎ 03 27 40 16 13
Valenciennes 18 km. Onnaing 17 km. Tournai 25 km. Lille 35 km. This working farm has three guest rooms on the first floor of the owners' house. There is a double, a twin and a family room, all with own shower and wc. Small child's bed available. Two gîtes. Shared terrace. Shops 2km, station 15km, Amaury leisure centre in Bonsecours in Belgium 4km, Parc St-Amand spa 15km, Beloeil Chateau. €54/4 persons.
PRICES: s €24; d €30; t €42　**NEARBY:** Forest (5km)　Golf (4km)　Sea (120km)　Swimming pool (4km)　Hiking (15km)　Tennis (2km)　Sailing (2km)　Railway station (15km)　Shops (2km)　CONDE SUR ESCAUT
NOTES: No pets

AIX-EN-ISSART

⫴ Chambre d'hôtes Gilberte SANTUNE
42 rue Principale, 62170 AIX-EN-ISSART
☎ 03 21 81 39 46
Montreuil 10 km. Le Touquet 24 km. In a quiet spot by the river in a green valley, this house offers five guest rooms. There are two doubles and a triple, all Grade 3 with own shower and wc (2 folding beds available), plus a double and a twin with shared shower and wc, both Grade 1. Child's bed available. Sitting room, TV. No charge for children under two. Restaurant 2km. Garden, garage. Free use of kitchen in another building. Waymarked footpaths. Bras de Brosne (Seven Valleys). Open all year.
PRICES: s €27-€32; d €35-€40; t €52; extra person €8-€12
ON SITE: Fishing Hiking Tennis　**NEARBY:** Horse riding (15km)　Sea (24km)　Swimming pool (10km)　Sailing (24km)　**NOTES:** Pets admitted

ALEMBON

⫴ ✔ ⫼Ⓞ⫼ Les Volets Bleus Véronique BRETON
1 A, rue du Cap Gris Nez, 62850 ALEMBON
☎ 03 21 00 13 17
e-mail: D.Breton2@libertysurf.fr
Licques 3 km. Boulogne-sur-Mer 20 km. This little farmhouse in the middle of the village has five guest rooms. There are three doubles and two twins, all with own shower and wc, TV on request. Sitting room, living room, TV and library. Breakfast and other meals served in the sitting room in front of a wood stove or on the sunny terrace. Evening meal by arrangement. Garden, outdoor furniture, parking. Two child's beds available. Mountain bikes. Restaurant 5km, lake 3km, forest 3km. Riding stables in the village. Open all year.
PRICES: s €32; d €43; dinner €17　**ON SITE:** Children's play area　Horse riding Hiking　**NEARBY:** Golf (18km)　Sea (22km)　Fishing (3km)　Swimming pool (18km)　Tennis (18km)　Sailing (22km)　**NOTES:** No pets

ARDRES

⫴ ✔ Ferme de la Cense Hebron Jean-Louis LELIEUR
Bois-en-Ardres, 62610 ARDRES
☎ 03 21 35 43 45　▤ 03 21 85 87 62

Calais 10 km. Ardres 3 km. Three guest rooms with their own entrance are available in this establishment outside the village. On the ground floor is a triple plus a family room with a kitchenette, both Grade 3 and with own shower and wc. The first floor double is Grade 2 and has own shower and wc outside the room. TV in all rooms. Shared sitting room. Parking, garage. Garden. Contact establishment for directions. Restaurants 4km. Open all year.
PRICES: s €30; d €43; t €55; extra person €12　**NEARBY:** Horse riding (15km)　Golf (15km)　Sea (12km)　Fishing (1km)　Swimming pool (5km)　Hiking (10km)　Tennis (3km)　Sailing (1km)　Shops (3km)　**NOTES:** No pets

♦♦♦♦ Le Manoir de Bois en Ardres Françoise ROGER
1530, rue de Saint-Quentin,62610 ARDRES
☎ 03 21 85 97 78 & 06 15 03 06 21 ▤ 03 21 36 48 07
e-mail: roger@aumanoir.com www.aumanoir.com

Ardres 2 km. Calais 12 km. Guests are warmly welcomed to this
recently restored manor house in its five hectare park in a quiet
countryside setting. Guest rooms comprise a triple, a twin, and a
suite of two rooms with one double and two single beds. Cot
available free of charge. Parking. Garden, ping pong. €74 per four
sharing. Twenty minutes from Channel Tunnel. Open all year.
PRICES: s €45; d €52; t €67 **ON SITE:** Hiking **NEARBY:** Horse riding
(2km) Golf (15km) Sea (12km) Fishing (2km) Swimming pool (8km)
Tennis (2km) Sailing (2km) Shops (2km) **NOTES:** No pets

AUCHY-AU-BOIS

♦♦♦♦ ✌ ﯽⵔ Chambre d'hôtes
Brigitte DE SAINT LAURENT
13 rue Neuve, 62190 AUCHY-AU-BOIS
☎ 03 21 25 80 09

Lillers 7 km. Aire-sur-la-Lys 9 km. In the middle of the village, this
brick-built farmhouse has four guest rooms with their own
entrance and one suite. There is a double, a twin, and two triples.
The suite has twin beds. All rooms have own bath and wc. Sitting
room and kitchenette for use of guests, living room, games room,
open fireplace, TV, library. Parking. Garden. €61 per four sharing.
Contact establishment for directions. Open all year.
PRICES: s €30; d €39; t €49; dinner €14 **NEARBY:** Horse riding (4km)
Sea (60km) Fishing (6km) Swimming pool (7km) Hiking (5km) Tennis
(2km) Sailing (10km) **NOTES:** No pets

AUDINGHEN

♦♦♦♦ 🐓 Ferme des 4 Vents Danielle et J.Claude MAERTEN
62179 CAP-GRIS-NEZ - AUDINGHEN
☎ 03 21 32 97 64 ▤ 03 21 83 62 54
e-mail: ferme.des.quatre.vents@wanadoo.fr
pro.wanadoo.fr/ferme4vents/
Marquise 8 km. Boulogne-sur-Mer 15 km. This farmhouse outside
the village has six guest rooms, four of them with sea views. The

accommodation includes a suite with two doubles, a twin, a suite
with one double and two singles, a double with sitting room,
kitchenette and TV, and a triple with living room, kitchenette, TV
and sitting area. All have own shower and wc. Convertible double
bed available. Living room, sitting room, fully equipped kitchen.
Garden. Parking. €73 per four sharing. Open all year.
PRICES: s €31-€36; d €40-€47; extra person €13 **ON SITE:** Sea Hiking
NEARBY: Horse riding (10km) Fishing (5km) Swimming pool (16km)
Tennis (5km) Sailing (2km) **NOTES:** No pets

♦♦♦♦ ✌ Le Repos des Mouettes Sylvie DUTERTE
Haringzelle, 62179 AUDINGHEN
☎ 03 21 32 97 20 ▤ 03 21 32 97 20
Wissant 10 km. Boulogne-sur-Mer 20 km. Outside the village and
only three kilometres from Cap Gris Nez, this detached house is
next to a pig farm. On the ground floor are three double rooms
with TV point, kitchenette and own shower and wc, while on the
first floor there is a family room with a double and two twin beds,
TV point, kitchenette and own bath and wc. Garden. Parking. €73
per four sharing. Adjacent restaurant. Tourist tax payable. Between
Audinghen and Audresselles on D940. Open all year.
PRICES: s €30; d €40; t €55 **ON SITE:** Hiking **NEARBY:** Horse riding
(3km) Sea (1km) Fishing (5km) Swimming pool (20km) Tennis (10km)
Sailing (15km) **NOTES:** Pets admitted

AZINCOURT

♦♦♦♦ La Gacogne Patrick & Marie-José FENET
62310 AZINCOURT
☎ 03 21 04 45 61 ▤ 03 21 04 45 61

Hesdin 20 km. Fruges 6 km. This house of character stands on the
site of the Battle of Agincourt, and has four guest rooms with their
own entrance, and all with own shower and wc. There is a
kitchenette and a sitting room with open fireplace. Breakfast
served in the owners' part of the house. Medieval atmosphere.
Attractive garden, wooded park. Parking.
PRICES: d €46; t €53 **ON SITE:** Hiking **NEARBY:** Horse riding (20km)
Sea (50km) Fishing (10km) Swimming pool (20km) Tennis (1km)
NOTES: No pets

BAYENGHEN-LES-SENINGHEN

♦♦♦♦ Chambre d'hôtes Alain DESVIGNES
32 rue Principale, 62380 BAYENGHEN-LES-SENINGHEN
☎ 03 21 95 71 36
Lumbres 2 km. Saint-Omer 15 km. In a quiet location, these three
comfortable rooms in restored outbuildings all have their own
entrance. There are two doubles and a triple, all with own shower
and wc. Sitting room, living room, TV, garden. Restaurant 2km.
Courtyard parking. Open 1 March to Christmas, in January and
February by arrangement.
PRICES: s €28; d €35-€38; t €43; extra person €11 **ON SITE:** Golf
Hiking **NEARBY:** Horse riding (3km) Sea (40km) Fishing (3km)
Swimming pool (3km) Tennis (3km) Sailing (40km) **NOTES:** Pets
admitted

continued

BEUSSENT

♦♦♦♦ Le Ménage Josiane BARSBY
124 route d'Hucqueliers, 62170 BEUSSENT
☎ 03 21 90 91 92   🖷 03 21 86 38 24

*Le Touquet 15 km. Etaples & Boulogne-sur-Mer 20 km.
Montreuil 13 km.* In a quiet and leafy setting beyond the
village in its own 9ha park, this 19th-century manor house has
five guest rooms, each a double with TV, sitting area, own
bath and wc. Child's bed available. Sitting room. Fax. Garden.
Covered parking. Guests are welcome to visit the owner's
studio and sculpture gallery. No charge for children under five.
Open all year.
PRICES: s €61; d €69; extra person €8 **ON SITE:** Horse riding
Hiking **NEARBY:** Sea (22km) Fishing (3km) Tennis (3km) Sailing
(22km) Railway station (13km) **NOTES:** No pets English spoken

BEZINGHEM

♦♦♦ 🐓 Ferme-Auberge des Granges José DACQUIN
62650 BEZINGHEM
☎ 03 21 90 93 19   🖷 03 21 90 93 19
Desvres 12 km. Montreuil-sur-Mer 15 km. This farmhouse outside
the village has six guest rooms with their own entrance. On the
ground floor there are two doubles with own shower and wc, and
on the first floor a triple and two doubles, all with own shower and
wc. Guests' living room with sitting area and TV. Games available.
Garden. Parking. 15 mountain bikes for hire €4 an hour or €8 per
half-day. Etaples station 20km. Open all year.
PRICES: s €30; d €38; t €52 **ON SITE:** Hiking **NEARBY:** Horse riding
(5km) Sea (20km) Fishing (2km) Swimming pool (12km) Tennis (6km)
Sailing (20km) **NOTES:** Pets admitted   *See advert on this page*

BLANGY-SUR-TERNOISE

♦♦♦ Chambre d'hôtes Bernard DECLERCQ
3, rue de la Gare, 62770 BLANGY-SUR-TERNOISE
☎ 03 21 47 29 29 & SR : 03 21 10 34 40
Hesdin 12 km. Saint-Pol 15 km. Fruges 14 km. This gentleman's
residence has four guest rooms. All are doubles, three with own
shower and wc, one with own bath and wc. Additional beds can
be provided, child's bed €9. Sitting room. Garaging for two cars by
arrangement. No charge for children under two. Open all year.
PRICES: d €42; extra person €18 **ON SITE:** Hiking **NEARBY:** Horse
riding (10km) Sea (45km) Fishing (5km) Swimming pool (20km) Tennis
(12km) Sailing (45km) Railway station (12km) Restaurant nearby
NOTES: Pets admitted

BRIMEUX

♦♦♦ 🐓 Ferme du Saule Germain TRUNNET
20 rue de l'Eglise, 62170 BRIMEUX
☎ 03 21 06 01 28 & 06 08 93 77 91   🖷 03 21 81 40 14
Montreuil 6 km. Hesdin 18 km. Touquet 18 km. Four guest rooms
in the centre of the village, comprising one triple with own bath

Ferme-Auberge
des Granges

Situated outside the village, the accommodation consists
of six bedrooms in a separate building within the farm and
all en-suite. Guests have use of their own living room with
kitchenette, TV, games and garden. It is possible to eat at
Ferme-Auberge des Granges and sample produce from
the farm. Private parking. Opposite a river and meadows
an ideal spot for calm. Open all year. Montreuil sur Mer
15 km, Boulogne sur Mer 30 kms.

62650 Bezinghem
Tel and fax: 03 21 90 93 19

and wc in the owners' house, and two triples and one double on
the farm, all with TV, own shower and wc. Extra bed and child's
bed available. Garden, courtyard and enclosed parking. Adjacent
restaurant. Pedalos. Beach 18km. Contact establishment for
directions. Open all year.
PRICES: s €40; d €46; t €60 **ON SITE:** Fishing Hiking Tennis
NEARBY: Golf (18km) Sea (18km) Swimming pool (6km) Sailing (18km)
NOTES: No pets English spoken

CAMPAGNE-LES-BOULONNAIS

♦♦♦ Chambre d'hôtes BAILLIEU-TERLUTTE
4, rue des Croisettes, 62650 CAMPAGNE-LES-BOULONNAIS
☎ 03 21 86 58 55
Desvres 15 km. Boulogne-sur-Mer & Saint-Omer 30 km. With its
own entrance, this village centre accommodation includes a
double with kitchenette, own shower and wc, and a double plus a
suite with two single beds and kitchenette, own shower and wc.
Additional bed available. Sitting and living room for sole use of
guests in owners' house. Shared TV. Parking. €53 per four sharing.
Open all year.
PRICES: s €27; d €38; t €46; extra person €8 **ON SITE:** Hiking
NEARBY: Horse riding (5km) Sea (40km) Fishing (5km) Swimming pool
(16km) Tennis (15km) Sailing (40km) **NOTES:** Pets admitted

CONCHIL-LE-TEMPLE

♦♦♦ Chambre d'hôtes Nicole FROISSART
51 rue de la Mairie, 62180 CONCHIL-LE-TEMPLE
☎ 03 21 81 11 02   🖷 03 21 81 88 32
Berck 6 km. Boulogne-sur-Mer & Montreuil 10 km. This old
property of great character has been renovated and contains four
guest rooms. There is a double with cot, a family room with a
double and two single beds, and two triples, all with own shower

continued   *continued*

and wc. Child's bed available. Sitting and living room with TV. Garden. Restaurant 3km. €61 per four sharing. Open all year. **PRICES:** s €42; d €46; t €55; extra person €10 **ON SITE:** Fishing Hiking Sailing **NEARBY:** Horse riding (6km) Golf (3km) Sea (6km) Swimming pool (6km) Tennis (6km) Shops (3km) **NOTES:** Pets admitted English spoken

CONTES

▦ ❧ ⫯⦙ Chambre d'hôtes Thérèse-Marie LECERF
2, rue de la Creuse, 62990 CONTES
☎ 03 21 86 80 50
Montreuil-sur-Mer 18 km. Hesdin 7 km. In the middle of the village, this miller's house has a family room with a double and two single beds with own bath and wc. Child's bed available. Sitting room, library. Restaurant 2km. Good walking in the Seven Valleys. Open all year.
PRICES: s €35; d €42; t €53; extra person €11; dinner €15
ON SITE: Hiking **NEARBY:** Horse riding (7km) Sea (30km) Fishing (1km) Swimming pool (7km) Tennis (7km) Sailing (30km) Railway station (7km) **NOTES:** Pets admitted

ECHINGHEN

▦ ❧ Chambre d'hôtes Jacqueline BOUSSEMAERE
Rue de l'Eglise, 62360 ECHINGHEN
☎ 03 21 91 14 34   ▤ 03 21 31 15 05
e-mail: jp-boussemaere@wanadoo.fr

Hardelot 10 km. Boulogne-sur-Mer 4 km. In a quiet and attractive setting, this little 18th-century farmhouse in the middle of the village has four guest rooms. There is a double with microwave, fridge, private terrace and own bath and wc, and a twin, a triple, and a double, all with own shower and wc. Kitchenette, living and sitting room. Garden, courtyard, parking. Stabling. Reductions for stays of more than two nights. Restaurant 500m. Open all year except Christmas to late January.
PRICES: s €32; d €41-€49; t €50-€58; extra person €9 **ON SITE:** Hiking Tennis **NEARBY:** Horse riding (2km) Sea (5km) Fishing (5km) Swimming pool (5km) Sailing (5km) Railway station (4km) Shops (4km) **NOTES:** No pets

EPERLECQUES

▦ Château du Ganspette Gérard PAUWELS
62910 EPERLECQUES
☎ 03 21 93 43 93   ▤ 03 21 95 74 98
Saint-Omer 10 km. Watten 3 km. This 19th-century château in the heart of the Audomarois countryside stands in its own parkland outside the village. There are three guest rooms, two twins with own shower and wc and a double with shower and wc on the landing. Games room. Parking. Garden. One room is Grade 2, the others Grade 3. Restaurant in the village. Swimming pool, tennis court. Open May to September.

PRICES: d €46; extra person €13 **ON SITE:** Swimming pool Hiking Tennis **NEARBY:** Horse riding (3km) Sea (50km) Fishing (1km) Sailing (30km) **NOTES:** No pets

ESCALLES

▦ ❧ La Grand'Maison Marc BOUTROY
Hameau de la Haute Escalles,
62179 ESCALLES
☎ 03 21 85 27 75   ▤ 03 21 85 27 75

Calais 12 km. Wissant 7 km. In a verdant setting on the little square in the hamlet of Haute Escalles, this charming house with its 18th-century dovecot has six guest rooms. There are three triples, a family room with two double beds, a suite with a double bed and a double with kitchenette. All rooms have own shower or bath and wc and three have TV. Washing machine available. Games room. Garden. Parking. Garage. Horses welcome. Four restaurants 1km. Contact establishment for directions. Open all year.
PRICES: s €33-€40; d €40-€50; t €53-€70; extra person €13
ON SITE: Hiking **NEARBY:** Horse riding (20km) Sea (1km) Swimming pool (12km) Tennis (1km) Sailing (7km) Railway station (10km) **NOTES:** No pets English spoken

▦ ❧ Ferme de l'Eglise Eric BOUTROY
62179 ESCALLES
☎ 03 21 85 20 19   ▤ 03 21 85 12 74
e-mail: ferme.eglise@libertysurf.fr
perso.libertysurf.fr/ferme.eglise/
Calais 15 km. This traditional farmstead in the Boulonnais countryside has five guest rooms. There are two doubles, one twin, and two triples, all with own bath or shower and wc. Sitting room, kitchenette, living room with TV. Garden. Parking. Restaurant nearby. €55 per four sharing plus tourist tax. Special weekend rates between 1 September and 30 June (minimum two nights): 1 person €65, 2 people €75, 3 people €95, four people €100. Open all year.
PRICES: s €35; d €40; t €50 **ON SITE:** Sea Fishing Hiking Tennis **NEARBY:** Horse riding (12km) Swimming pool (15km) Sailing (4km) Railway station (15km) **NOTES:** No pets

continued

FAUQUEMBERGUES

♥♥♥ La Rîverie Annie et Gilles MILLAMON
19 rue Jonnart, 62560 FAUQUEMBERGUES
☎ 03 21 12 12 38 ◻ 03 21 12 18 66
Saint-Omer 20 km. Hesdin 30 km. This gentleman's residence of character stands in a park in the centre of the village. There are three guest rooms, a ground floor twin with own bath and wc, and two family rooms with two double beds on the first floor, both with own shower and wc. TV in all rooms. Sitting and living room with open fireplace and wood fire, conservatory. Parking. No charge for children under three. Restaurant in village.
PRICES: s €40; d €46 **ON SITE:** Fishing Hiking Tennis
NEARBY: Horse riding (15km) Golf (15km) Sea (40km) Swimming pool (15km) Sailing (40km) Railway station (20km) **NOTES:** No pets

FILLIEVRES

♥♥♥ ◻◻◻ Chambre d'hôtes Bernadette LEGRAND
16, rue de Saint-Pol, 62770 FILLIEVRES
☎ 03 21 41 13 20 & 06 82 62 30 15
http://aufildeleau.free.fr/
Hesdin 12 km. Saint-Pol 15 km. An 18th-century mill building in village centre with three rooms and one suite. There is a double with own shower and wc, a family room and a suite, each with one double and two single beds, own shower and wc, and a triple with separate shower and wc. Child's bed available. Shared sitting and living room with TV and library. Garden. Restaurant nearby. Nearby lake and river, forest 12km. Mountain bikes, canoeing. No charge for children under five. Table d'hôte with drinks/apéritif included. Open all year.
PRICES: d €46-€49; t €56-€59; extra person €11; dinner €16
ON SITE: Fishing Swimming pool Hiking **NEARBY:** Horse riding (12km) Sea (45km) Sailing (45km) Railway station (12km) **NOTES:** Pets admitted

FOSSEUX

♥♥♥ ◻◻ Chambre d'hôtes Geneviève DELACOURT
3 rue de l'Eglise, 62810 FOSSEUX ☎ 03 21 48 40 13
Arras 17 km. Close to woodland, this house of character in its attractive garden has three guest rooms. There are two doubles and a twin, all with own bath and wc. Child's bed available. Sitting and living room with TV and library. Garage. Restaurant 5km. No charge for children under five.
PRICES: s €26; d €30; t €38; extra person €8 **ON SITE:** Hiking
NEARBY: Horse riding (7km) Golf (18km) Sea (80km) Fishing (12km) Swimming pool (17km) Tennis (17km) Sailing (80km) Railway station (17km) Shops (5km) **NOTES:** No pets English spoken

GAUCHIN-VERLOINGT

♥♥♥ Chambre d'hôtes Philippe VION
550 rue de Montifaux, 62130 GAUCHIN-VERLOINGT
☎ 03 21 03 05 05 ◻ 03 21 41 26 76
e-mail: McVion.Loubarre@wanadoo.fr

Arras 35 km. The five guest rooms in the outbuildings of this 19th-century manor house include two doubles and three twins, all with own shower and wc. Guests have exclusive use of sitting room with open fireplace, TV and library. No charge for children under five. Park with outdoor furniture. Parking, garage. Croix-en-Ternois car and motorcycle racing circuit 3km. Restaurant 2km. Open all year.
PRICES: s €32; d €38; t €50 **ON SITE:** Hiking **NEARBY:** Horse riding (3km) Golf (18km) Sea (70km) Fishing (12km) Swimming pool (13km) Tennis (2km) Sailing (70km) **NOTES:** Pets admitted English spoken

GUISY

♥♥♥ ♥ La Hotoire Martine et Marc W. GARREL
2 place de la Mairie, 62140 GUISY
☎ 03 21 81 00 31 ◻ 03 21 81 00 31
e-mail: a.la.hotoire@wanadoo.fr

Forêt de Hesdin 3 km. Montreuil 18 km. This old farmstead in the centre of the village has four ground floor guest rooms with their own entrance. There is a double, a twin with kitchenette, a triple with kitchenette, and a double plus two single mezzanine beds and kitchenette. All rooms have own shower and wc. Sitting and living room shared with owners. TV. Garden room, barbecue. Pets welcome by prior arrangement. Pétanque, darts, bike hire, and donkey rides in the forest. €61 per four sharing. Access via D113. Open all year.
PRICES: s €37; d €42; t €53 **ON SITE:** Fishing Hiking **NEARBY:** Horse riding (3km) Sea (30km) Swimming pool (18km) Tennis (5km) Sailing (30km) **NOTES:** No pets

HARDELOT

♥♥♥ La Claire Eau Sylvie DELASSUS
Rond-Point du Centre Equestre, No 25, 62152 HARDELOT
☎ 03 21 83 43 89 & 06 22 70 70 08 ◻ 03 21 83 43 89
e-mail: laclaireau@wanadoo.fr
Boulogne-sur-Mer & le Touquet 12 km. On the way into the resort, this old but newly renovated building has five guest rooms with their own entrance. All are doubles with own bath and wc. Child's bed available. No charge for children under five. Sitting and living rooms, TV, reading. Garden, terrace. Parking. Table tennis nearby. Restaurant nearby. Open all year.
PRICES: d €55 **ON SITE:** Horse riding Golf Sea Fishing Swimming pool Hiking Tennis Sailing **NOTES:** No pets

♥♥♥ La Colo Sabine DECROIX LUITAUD
131, avenue Princesse Louise, 62152 HARDELOT
☎ 03 21 83 88 54 ◻ 03 21 83 88 54
Boulogne-sur-Mer 12 km. Le Touquet 15 km. In the middle of the Hardelot pine wood, this house has five guest rooms. There is a double with own shower, a double with own shower outside the room, a double with own bath, a double with own shower and separate kitchenette, and a double with own bath and separate kitchenette. All rooms come with private wc. Extra beds can be provided. Sitting room with TV, living room shared with owners.

continued

continued

Garage for two vehicles, parking. Table tennis, barbecue, badminton. Open all year.
PRICES: s €46-€53; d €50-€57; extra person €15 **ON SITE:** Hiking **NEARBY:** Horse riding (1km) Golf (1km) Sea (1km) Fishing (1km) Swimming pool (15km) Tennis (15km) Sailing (1km) Railway station (15km) Shops (1km) **NOTES:** No pets

HAUTEVILLE

♥ La Solette Jeannine et J-Marie DEBAISIEUX
La Solette, 10 rue du Moulin, 62810 HAUTEVILLE
☎ 03 21 58 73 58 ▤ 03 21 58 73 59
e-mail: lasolette@yahoo.fr www.lasolette.com
Arras 15 km. Avesnes-le-Comte 3 km. On the edge of the village, this house of character has three guest rooms with their own entrance. One room is on the ground floor, two on the first floor. All have double beds (convertible into twin) and own shower and wc. Child's bed available. Breakfast served in family dining room. Sitting area with TV and kitchenette. Garden, courtyard, open-air games. On the Six Chateaux walking route. Mountain bikes. Free use of kitchen in annexe. Restaurant 3km. Forest 15km. Open all year.
PRICES: s €30; d €46; extra person €11 **ON SITE:** Children's play area Hiking **NEARBY:** Horse riding (4km) Golf (15km) Sea (80km) Fishing (20km) Swimming pool (17km) Tennis (15km) Sailing (80km) **NOTES:** No pets

HERVELINGHEN

♥ ◉ La Leulène Catherine PETITPREZ
708, rue Principale, 62179 HERVELINGHEN
☎ 03 21 82 47 30 e-mail: LALEULENE@aol.com
Channel Tunnel 5 minutes. Wissant 3 km. Calais 12 km. This attractive restored farmhouse has three guest rooms. There is a triple with own shower and wc, a double with own bath and wc, and a room plus suite with four single beds, two bathrooms and two wcs. Child's bed available. Sitting and living room shared with owners, TV, library, grand piano. Garden, barbecue, outdoor furniture, open fireplace, children's games. Parking. Meals by arrangement. Tourist tax payable. €72 per four sharing. Contact establishment for directions. Closed between Christmas and New Year.
PRICES: s €37; d €43; t €61; extra person €13; dinner €15 **ON SITE:** Children's play area Hiking **NEARBY:** Horse riding (3km) Sea (3km) Swimming pool (15km) Tennis (3km) Sailing (3km) **NOTES:** No pets

HUCQUELIERS

Le Clos Isabelle et Alain BERTIN
19 rue de l'Eglise, 62650 HUCQUELIERS
☎ 03 21 86 37 10 ▤ 03 21 86 37 18
e-mail: abertin@club.internet.fr
Desvres 11 km. Montreuil 8 km. This 19th-century residence standing in landscaped gardens in the middle of the village has six guest rooms with their own entrance. Four are apartments each with twin beds, kitchenette, sitting room, shower and wc, two are suites with own bath and wc. Child's bed available. Two sitting rooms, one with open fireplace, bread oven, plus dining room for exclusive use of guests. TV. Outdoor furniture, barbecue, children's games. €81 for four sharing.
PRICES: s €50-€60; extra person €11 **ON SITE:** Children's play area Horse riding Hiking Tennis **NEARBY:** Golf (25km) Sea (25km) Fishing (5km) Swimming pool (11km) Sailing (25km) **NOTES:** No pets

See advert on opposite page

LA COUTURE

La Pilaterie Jean-Michel DISSAUX
2129 route d'Estaires, 62136 LA COUTURE
☎ 03 21 26 77 02
Lestrem 4 km. Béthune 10 km. This establishment is outside the

village and has four guest rooms with their own entrance. There are three doubles and one twin, all with TV, own shower and wc. Child's bed available. Sitting and living room reserved for exclusive use of guests. Garden. Parking. No charge for children under two. Restaurant 2km. Open all year.
PRICES: s €30; d €34 **ON SITE:** Hiking **NEARBY:** Horse riding (1km) Sea (80km) Fishing (5km) Swimming pool (10km) Tennis (4km) Sailing (80km) Railway station (10km) **NOTES:** No pets CC

LOCON

Chambre d'hôtes Maxime NOULETTE
464 rue du Pont d'Avelette, 62400 LOCON
☎ 03 21 27 41 42 ▤ 03 21 27 80 71
Béthune 5 km. In the middle of the hamlet, this is a restored house with six guest rooms. There are two doubles (Grade 2) with shared shower, and four doubles (Grade 3) all with own shower and TV. Sitting and living room, TV. Garage for six vehicles and parking. Kitchen available. No charge for children under three in parents' room. Restaurant 2km. All-year skiing facilities 15km. Open all year.
PRICES: s €23-€31; d €39 **ON SITE:** Hiking **NEARBY:** Horse riding (5km) Golf (10km) Sea (80km) Fishing (8km) Swimming pool (5km) Sailing (80km) Railway station (6km) Shops (2km) **NOTES:** No pets CC

LOISON-SUR-CREQUOISE

La Commanderie Marie-Hélène FLAMENT
3, allée des Templiers, 62990 LOISON-SUR-CREQUOISE
☎ 03 21 86 49 87

Montreuil-sur-Mer 13 km. Hesdin 13 km. In the village centre, this building was once a residence of the Knights Templar. The three guest rooms include a twin and a double with kitchenette and veranda, both with own shower and wc, a twin and a suite with double bed separated by bathroom and wc. Cot available without charge. Sitting room, games room, library, TV. Open wood fire. Garden, outdoor furniture. Parking. River. Forest 13km. €84 for four sharing. Beaurainville station 3km. Open all year.
PRICES: s €43-€54; d €54-€61 **ON SITE:** Children's play area Hiking **NEARBY:** Horse riding (3km) Sea (25km) Fishing (3km) Swimming pool (13km) Tennis (3km) Sailing (25km) **NOTES:** No pets

LONGVILLIERS

♥ La Longue Roye DELAPORTE
3 rue de l'Abbaye, 62630 LONGVILLIERS
☎ 03 21 86 70 65 ▤ 03 21 86 71 32
Montreuil 10 km. Le Touquet 14 km. Originally built by the Cistercians, this farmstead has been restored and has six guest rooms with their own entrance. On the ground floor there is a twin, on the first floor four doubles, all with own shower and wc, TV, telephone and sitting room. Another room is a twin with own bath and wc. Additional beds including child's bed available. Shared living room. Open fireplace. Outdoor furniture. Mountain bikes. Pets welcome (no cats). Restaurant 3km. Open all year.
PRICES: s €47; d €52; extra person €13 **ON SITE:** Hiking

continued

continued

NEARBY: Horse riding (4km) Golf (12km) Sea (10km) Fishing (5km) Swimming pool (10km) Tennis (4km) Sailing (10km) **NOTES:** Pets admitted

MAMETZ

††† ¡O¡ Chambre d'hôtes Jean-Pierre QUETU
49 Grand'Rue, 62120 MAMETZ
☎ 03 21 39 02 76 📠 03 21 38 12 69
e-mail: chambres.hotes.mametz@wanadoo.fr
www.citeweb.net/mametz/
Aire-sur-la-Lys 5 km. Saint-Omer 15 km. Béthune 30 km. Four comfortable ground floor guest rooms have their own entrance in the quiet courtyard of this former brewery. There are two doubles and two twins, all with own shower and wc. Electric central heating. Sitting room, library, living room, TV. Enclosed parking. Garden, barbecue. Restaurant nearby. No charge for children under five. Open all year.
PRICES: s €26; d €37; extra person €11; dinner €15 **ON SITE:** Fishing Hiking Tennis Sailing **NEARBY:** Horse riding (5km) Golf (15km) Sea (60km) Swimming pool (5km) Railway station (12km) **NOTES:** Pets admitted

MARCK

††† Le Manoir du Meldick Jean et Danièle HOUZET
2528, Ave, du Gal de Gaulle le Fort Vert, 62730 MARCK
☎ 03 21 85 74 34 📠 03 21 85 74 34
e-mail: jeandaniele.houzet@Free.92
Calais 7 km. Gravelines 12 km. This manor house outside the village has five guest rooms. There is a twin, another twin with table and armchairs, a double, a family room with a double bed and two singles, all with own shower and wc, and a double with bureau, armchairs, own bath and wc. Child's bed available. Sitting room and living room with TV and library for exclusive use of guests. Another sitting room with open fireplace on ground floor. Card phone, fax and minitel. Restaurant 7km. Airfield 3km.
PRICES: s €42; d €50; extra person €9 **ON SITE:** Hiking
NEARBY: Horse riding (2km) Sea (4km) Swimming pool (7km) Tennis (7km) Sailing (3km) **NOTES:** No pets

MARLES-SUR-CANCHE

††† Manoir Francis Dominique LEROY
1 rue de l'Eglise, 62170 MARLES-SUR-CANCHE
☎ 03 21 81 38 80 📠 03 21 81 38 56

Montreuil 5 km. Le Touquet 20 km. Etaples 15 km. This fine old 17th-century manor house in the Boulonnais countryside has three guest rooms. There are two doubles and a suite with one double and two single beds, all with own sitting area, bath and wc. Sitting room. Parking for cars and horse-boxes. Garden. Restaurant and canoeing 4km. Forest 20km. Leisure centre 20km. Open all year.
PRICES: s €40; d €50; extra person €10 **ON SITE:** Hiking
NEARBY: Horse riding (4km) Golf (20km) Sea (20km) Fishing (2km) Swimming pool (4km) Tennis (4km) Sailing (20km) **NOTES:** No pets English spoken

LE CLOS
HUCQUELIERS

**Bed & Breakfast –
Self catering
apartments –
Sleeps 16**

Maison de Maître in the scenic Course Valley. Stylish place to relax and soak up French atmosphere. Ideally located for short breaks or more (Calais/Montreuil/Hesdin/Le Touquet/St. Omer/Agincourt/Picardie).

Four independent apartments with private kitchenette, lounge, toilets, bathroom (shower), bedroom with twin beds. Two romantic deluxe rooms (double bed, bath and shower) Guests' lounges with fireplace. Walled garden, barbecue. Private car park. Large buffet breakfasts. Midweek and 7 nights special prices. Honeymoon special welcome. Apartments also available for self catering. Easy reach of Calais, ideal stop on your way to holidays. Special arrangements for groups. No pets.

**Tel: 00 33 3 21 86 37 10. Fax: 00 33 3 21 86 37 18
E-mail: abertin@club-internet.fr**

Bed and breakfast from €55 night for two

Mr et Mme LOUCHEZ
77, rue Pierre-Ledent
62 170 MONTREUIL-SUR-MER

*Tel: 03.21.81.54.68
E-mail: Louchez.Anne@wanadoo.fr*

Situated in the city centre, this is a XVIII century house of character with a garden. There are three bedrooms: one twin and two double rooms, all en-suite, with television and well furbished. A lounge is at your disposal. An additional bed is available.

Prices =
2 people:
€46 (FF301.70);
added bed:
€15 (FF98.40)

*Access =
A16, exit
Le Touquet
(15 km), RN1.
12 km from
Etaples*

MONTREUIL-SUR-MER

♥♥♥ Chambre d'hôtes Michel LOUCHEZ
77, rue Pierre Ledent, 62170 MONTREUIL-SUR-MER
☎ 03 21 81 54 68
e-mail: Louchez.Anne@wanadoo.fr
Le Touquet 15 km. Etaples 12 km. In the centre of town, this is an 18th-century brick and stone house of character with three guest rooms. There is a twin and two doubles, all with sitting area and TV and own bath and wc. Sitting room. Garden. Canoeing. Open all year.
PRICES: d €46; extra person €15 **ON SITE:** Fishing Swimming pool Hiking Tennis **NEARBY:** Horse riding (8km) Sea (15km) Sailing (12km)
NOTES: No pets   *See advert on previous page*

NEUFCHATEL-HARDELOT

♥♥♥ ⁉⃝ Fields Fairway Alan FIELD
91 rue du Chemin, D119, 62152 NEUFCHATEL-HARDELOT
☎ 03 21 33 85 23 📠 03 21 33 85 24
e-mail: fields.fairway@wanadoo.fr
Boulogne-sur-Mer 12 km. Le Touquet 15 km. This large house in a peaceful setting outside the village and close to the Hardelot forest has four twin-bedded guest rooms (non-smoking) with own shower and wc. Sitting and living room, TV, veranda. Oil-fired central heating. Evening meals for eight or more by arrangement except July and August. Large landscaped garden, terrace, garden furniture. Parking. Mountain bikes. Green fee reductions for golfers. Tourist tax. Open early January to November.
PRICES: s €38; d €53; dinner €14 **ON SITE:** Hiking **NEARBY:** Horse riding (3km) Golf (2km) Sea (4km) Fishing (3km) Swimming pool (12km) Tennis (2km) Sailing (3km) Railway station (12km) Shops (3km)
NOTES: No pets English spoken

NIELLES-LES-ARDRES

♥♥♥ ❧ ⁉⃝ Chambre d'hôtes CAILLIERET
130, route Départementale, 62610 NIELLES-LES-ARDRES
☎ 03 21 82 86 22 📠 03 21 82 86 22
e-mail: bruno.caillieret@wanadoo.fr
http://perso.wanadoo.fr/caillieret
Ardres 3 km. Calais 17 km. This restored brick farmhouse built around a courtyard has three guest rooms with separate entrance. There is a double with TV, kitchenette, own shower and wc, a triple with kitchenette, own shower and wc, and a twin with own shower and wc. No charge for cot (up to 3 years), additional child's bed (4 to 10 years) €7.6. Shared sitting and living room with TV. Evening meal during the week by arrangement including drinks. Contact establishment for directions. Open all year.
PRICES: s €30; d €43; t €55; extra person €12; dinner €15
ON SITE: Hiking **NEARBY:** Horse riding (6km) Golf (18km) Sea (20km) Fishing (3km) Swimming pool (8km) Tennis (3km) Sailing (3km) Shops (2km) **NOTES:** No pets

NUNCQ-HAUTECOTES

♥♥♥ La Pommeraie Eric MORVAN
13, route Nationale, 62270 NUNCQ-HAUTECOTES
☎ 03 21 03 69 85 📠 03 21 47 28 02
e-mail: eric.morvan01@infonie.fr
www.multimania.com/chambredhote
Frevent 3 km. Saint-Pol 10 km. Four guest rooms with their own entrance are available in this village centre establishment standing in its tree-filled garden. On the ground floor is a double with own shower and wc, a triple with own bath, shower and wc, and on the first floor two doubles with own shower and wc. Child's bed (five years plus) available. Sitting room, fridge, gas cooker, washing machine and drier, TV, library. Garden furniture, barbecue. Restaurant 3km. Racing circuit 10km. Open all year.

PRICES: s €31; d €38; t €47; extra person €15 **ON SITE:** Hiking Children's play area **NEARBY:** Horse riding (7km) Sea (60km) Fishing (8km) Swimming pool (3km) Tennis (3km) Sailing (60km) Railway station (10km) **NOTES:** No pets

PIHEN-LES-GUINES

♥♥♥ Chambre d'hôtes Guy DECLEMY
227 route de Guines, 62340 PIHEN-LES-GUINES
☎ 03 21 85 92 61 & 06 87 07 15 62
Guines 5 km. Wissant 9 km. Calais 12 km. This house in the centre of the village has three guest rooms, all doubles with own shower and wc. Living room and sitting area, well-equipped kitchen. Garden. Parking. Restaurant 5km. Open all year.
PRICES: d €35; t €46 **ON SITE:** Hiking **NEARBY:** Horse riding (3km) Sea (10km) Swimming pool (10km) Tennis (10km) Sailing (18km)
NOTES: No pets

QUELMES

♥♥♥ ❧ Chambre d'hôtes Eric HUYSENTRUYT
110 rue de la Place, 62500 QUELMES
☎ 03 21 95 60 62 📠 03 21 93 20 88
Saint-Omer 10 km. The four guest rooms in this 18th-century farmhouse include a triple and three doubles, all with own shower and wc. Shared kitchen. Sitting and living room. Garden, outdoor furniture. Parking. Open all year.
PRICES: d €40; t €53 **NEARBY:** Horse riding (5km) Golf (7km) Sea (45km) Fishing (15km) Swimming pool (5km) Hiking (2km) Tennis (5km) Sailing (35km) **NOTES:** No pets

QUESTRECQUES

♥♥♥ Chambre d'hôtes Bruno HALLEY DES FONTAINES
740, route de Samer, 62830 QUESTRECQUES
☎ 03 21 87 06 56 📠 03 21 87 06 56
Boulogne-sur-Mer 15 km. Montreuil 18 km. This 16th-century manor house has four guest rooms in an old farm building with its own entrance and wood fire (charge for fuel). There is a double with own bath and two wcs, a twin, a Grade 2 double with own shower and wc, and a family room with one double bed and two singles on a mezzanine, own bath and wc. TV in the Grade 3 rooms. Shared sitting and living room. Telephone available. Restaurant 2km. Contact establishment for directions. Open 1 February to 31 December.
PRICES: d €69; extra person €23 **ON SITE:** Fishing Hiking
NEARBY: Horse riding (8km) Sea (15km) Swimming pool (8km) Tennis (1km) Sailing (15km) **NOTES:** No pets

RAMECOURT

♥♥♥ ❧ Ferme du Bois Quesnoy François DELEAU
62130 RAMECOURT
☎ 03 21 41 66 60
e-mail: François.deleau@wanadoo.fr
Saint-Pol 2 km. Frévent 8 km. This stone farmstead outside the village has four guest rooms with their own entrance, all with own facilities. Kitchenette for guests' use. Parking. Soft fruit picking in season. Specialities: jams and syrups, pickled onions. Motor racing circuit 4 km. Open all year.
PRICES: s €35; d €40; extra person €8 **ON SITE:** Hiking
NEARBY: Horse riding (10km) Sea (70km) Fishing (20km) Swimming pool (2km) Tennis (1km) Sailing (20km) **NOTES:** No pets

> Prices are given in Euros €1 = £0.62
> at the time of going to press

continued

NORD-PAS-DE-CALAIS

RICHEBOURG

††† 🐓 ❤ Ferme les Caperies André et Christiane BAVIERE
106 rue des Charbonniers, 62136 RICHEBOURG
☎ 03 21 26 07 19 📠 03 21 02 79 95
Béthune 12 km. Armentières 16 km. La Bassée 8 km. This fine old
farmstead has four guest rooms on the first floor of a building
adjacent to the owners' residence. There is a single, a double and
two triples, all with own shower and wc. No charge for children
under five. Shared ground floor sitting room and kitchen. TV.
Garden furniture, veranda, barbecue. Leisure centre 6km.
Restaurant 2km. Open all year.
PRICES: s €26; d €35; t €43 **ON SITE:** Hiking Tennis **NEARBY:** Horse
riding (2km) Golf (5km) Sea (80km) Fishing (5km) Swimming pool
(10km) Sailing (15km) **NOTES:** No pets

††† ❤ La Niche Renée LE MAT
2355/31, rue Marsy, Vieille-Chapelle, 62136 RICHEBOURG
☎ 03 21 65 33 13 📠 03 21 66 89 04
e-mail: CJB@easynet.fr http://Laniche.free.fr
Béthune 10 km. Lens à 15 km. Lille 27 km. La Bassée 10 km. In
lovely countryside outside the village, this building has four first
floor guest rooms with own entrance. There are three doubles and
a single, all with TV, telephone, own shower and wc. One room is
Grade 2. Extra bed available. Guests have their own kitchen, dining
area, living room, library and games. Mountain bikes. Shop selling
local products. Fax and internet. No charge for children under five.
Reduced rates for longer stays. Forest 10km. Open all year.
PRICES: s €34; d €38; extra person €8 **ON SITE:** Horse riding Fishing
Hiking Tennis **NEARBY:** Golf (12km) Sea (80km) Swimming pool
(12km) Sailing (15km) **NOTES:** No pets

SAMER

††† Chambre d'hôtes Joëlle MAUCOTEL
127 rue du Breuil, 62830 SAMER
☎ 03 21 87 64 19 & 06 77 83 04 74 📠 03 21 87 64 19
Hardelot 12 km. Boulogne-sur-Mer 15 km. This fine village centre
residence has three guest rooms. There is a twin and a triple, both
with own shower and wc, and a twin with own bath and wc.
Child's bed available. Sitting and living room, library, TV. Garden,
outdoor furniture, terrace. Parking. Restaurant nearby. Children
over six: €10. Open all year.
PRICES: s €32; d €40; t €55; extra person €10 **ON SITE:** Hiking Tennis
NEARBY: Horse riding (2km) Sea (12km) Fishing (2km) Swimming pool
(6km) Sailing (12km) **NOTES:** No pets

See advert on this page

SAULTY

††† Chambre d'hôtes Emmanuel et Sylvie DALLE
Verger de Saulty, 62158 SAULTY
☎ 03 21 48 24 76 📠 03 21 48 18 32
Arras & Doullens 18 km. Standing in a leafy park, this 19th-century
château has five guest rooms. There is a double with own shower,
a double with own bath, two triples with own bath and wc, and a
family room with a double, two twin beds, own bath and wc.
Sitting and living rooms, open fireplace, kitchenette, TV, library.
Garden furniture. Parking. Waymarked walk through the orchards.
Children's rate €12. Contact establishment for directions. Open all
year except January.
PRICES: s €38; d €46; t €59; extra person €13 **ON SITE:** Hiking
NEARBY: Golf (18km) Sea (80km) Fishing (6km) Swimming pool
(18km) Tennis (7km) Sailing (80km) Railway station (18km) **NOTES:** No
pets English spoken

Bed and Breakfast
Hardelot 12kms   Boulogne sur Mer 15kms
127 rue du Breuil
62830 Samer
Tel: 03 21 87 64 19
Fax: 03 21 87 64 19

Centrally situated in this small market village of Samer
with a listed church is an old style house of character.
Recently refurbished the three bedrooms are en-suite
and available for bed and breakfast. Guests have use of
a lounge with TV and garden with shaded patio and
garden chairs. Private parking. Restaurant nearby.

SORRUS

††† Ferme du Colombier HENOT
171 rue Saint-Riquier, 62170 SORRUS
☎ 03 21 06 07 27
Le Touquet 15 km. Montreuil 4 km. Standing apart from the
owners' residence and with its own entrance, this newly-
constructed building has six guest rooms. There are four rooms
with a double bed and a double sofa-bed, all with own shower
and wc, and two Grade 1 rooms with a double bed and a double
sofa-bed with shared shower and wc. Breakfast is taken with the
family. Sitting room with TV. Microwave, fridge, sofas. Parking. No
charge for children under three. Garden rooms. Restaurant 3km.
Open all year.
PRICES: s €20-€27; d €27-€35; t €34-€41; extra person €6
ON SITE: Hiking **NEARBY:** Golf (14km) Sea (12km) Fishing (10km)
Swimming pool (4km) Sailing (15km) Railway station (4km) Shops (4km)
NOTES: Pets admitted English spoken

ST-AUBIN

††† Les Buissonnets Marie-Thérèse HOREL
67 chemin des Corps Saints, 62170 ST-AUBIN
☎ 03 21 84 12 12 & 06 83 13 82 62 📠 03 21 84 12 12
Le Touquet & Montreuil-sur-Mer 8 km. The three guest rooms in
this house located near the village comprise two triples with own
shower and wc (one wc on the landing), and a double with own
shower and wc. Sitting and living room for exclusive use of guests.
Garden. Parking. Restaurant nearby. Etaples station 8km. Open all
year.
PRICES: s €40; d €45; t €57; extra person €12 **ON SITE:** Hiking
NEARBY: Horse riding (8km) Sea (8km) Fishing (8km) Swimming pool
(8km) Tennis (8km) Sailing (8km) Railway station (8km) **NOTES:** Pets
admitted

STE-CECILE

Chambre d'hôtes Marie-Chantal DELMAR
343, chemin des Bateaux, La Halte,
62176 STE-CECILE-PLAGE
☎ 03 21 84 94 51 & 06 11 05 09 09 🖳 03 21 84 94 51
jfdelmar.free.fr
Etaples 6 km. Boulogne-sur-Mer 17 km. Le Touquet 13 km. This newly restored old house outside the village has four guest rooms, all non-smoking. There are two Grade 1 ground floor twins with shared bath and wc, and two first floor doubles both with own shower and wc. Shared sitting and living room with TV. Evening meals by arrangement. Oil-fired central heating. Garden. Inside parking. Restaurant 1km. Open all year.
PRICES: s €28-€34; d €31-€38; extra person €11; dinner €12
ON SITE: Horse riding Sea Fishing Hiking Sailing **NEARBY:** Golf (10km) Swimming pool (6km) Tennis (6km) Railway station (6km)
NOTES: No pets

ST-JOSSE-SUR-MER

Ferme du Tertre Sabine et Alain PRETRE
77 Chaussée de l'Avant Pays, 62170 ST-JOSSE-SUR-MER
☎ 03 21 09 09 13 & 06 07 42 07 90 🖳 03 21 09 09 13
e-mail: pretrealain@hotmail.com
Montreuil-sur-Mer & Etaples 8 km, Le Touquet/Berck 10 km. This old farmhouse has four guest rooms with separate entrance. There are two doubles, a triple, and a family room for four with kitchenette, own bath and wc. Sitting room with kitchenette. Parking. Landscaped park with lake. Restaurant 1km. Four golf courses and two fishing lakes nearby. €75 for four sharing. Reduced rates for stays of two nights or more: €37 one person, €45 for two, €59 for three and €71 for four. Open all year.
PRICES: s €41; d €49; t €63 **ON SITE:** Fishing Hiking **NEARBY:** Horse riding (8km) Golf (8km) Sea (8km) Swimming pool (8km) Tennis (8km) Sailing (8km) **NOTES:** No pets

Les Peupliers Alain LEPRETRE
8, allée des Peupliers, 62170 ST-JOSSE-SUR-MER
☎ 03 21 94 39 47 🖳 03 21 94 03 08
Montreuil, Le Touquet & Beck 10 km. This new building has first floor guest rooms. There are five doubles and a twin, all with own shower and wc. Cooking facilities in room if required. Sitting room, TV. Parking. No charge for children under five. Restaurant nearby. Mountain bike hire in the village. Open all year.
PRICES: s €37; d €43; extra person €11 **ON SITE:** Fishing Hiking
NEARBY: Horse riding (8km) Golf (8km) Sea (8km) Swimming pool (8km) Tennis (8km) Sailing (8km) Shops (3km) **NOTES:** No pets

ST-TRICAT

Chambre d'hôtes Nelly CORNILLE
774, Manoir Haute de Leulingu, 62185 ST-TRICAT
☎ 03 21 85 92 58 🖳 03 21 85 92 58
Guines 4 km. Calais 9 km. This fine old 17th-century manor house in the middle of the village has four guest rooms. There is a family room with a double and three single beds, a room with a double and two singles, and a double, all with TV, fridge, own shower and wc. Sitting and living room, TV, library. Garden. Parking. Meals available, rates excluding drinks. Mountain bikes. Contact establishment for directions. €61 for five sharing. Carriage rides and tours in a convertible. Open all year.
PRICES: d €38; t €46; extra person €8; dinner €8-€23 **ON SITE:** Hiking
NEARBY: Horse riding (8km) Sea (4km) Fishing (6km) Swimming pool (9km) Tennis (9km) Sailing (4km) Railway station (9km) **NOTES:** Pets admitted

TENEUR

Chambre d'hôtes M et J VENIEZ-QUENIART
11 rue Marcel Dollet, 62134 TENEUR
☎ 03 21 41 62 34 🖳 03 21 41 62 34
e-mail: jcveniezi@france.com www.ifrance.com/jcveniez
Azincourt 7 km. Croix-en-Ternois circuit 10 km. A green and peaceful valley in the Ternois countryside is the setting for this old barn that has been converted into three guest rooms. All are doubles with own shower, wc, and sitting area. Child's bed available. Kitchen for use of guests. Garden, barbecue. Parking. Mountain bikes. No charge for children under five. Restaurant 5km. On GR21 long-distance footpath. Open all year.
PRICES: s €33; d €38; t €50; extra person €9; dinner €16
ON SITE: Fishing Hiking **NEARBY:** Horse riding (10km) Sea (50km) Swimming pool (15km) Tennis (5km) Sailing (7km) **NOTES:** No pets

TIGNY-NOYELLE

Le Prieuré Roger DELBECQUE
Impasse de l'Eglise, 62180 TIGNY-NOYELLE
☎ 03 21 86 04 38 🖳 03 21 81 39 95
Berck 12 km. Montreuil 14 km. Abbaye de Valloire 6 km. This charming house outside the village has five guest rooms, one of them a suite. There is a double, a family room with a double and two single beds, two twins, and a suite with a double and two single beds, all with TV, own bath and wc. Child's bed available. Sitting room, garden. Off-site parking. Meals by arrangement. Restaurant 2km. Suite: Marquenterre bird sanctuary 20km. Open all year.
PRICES: s €43; d €52-€64; t €64-€77; extra person €16; dinner €21.5
ON SITE: Fishing **NEARBY:** Horse riding (12km) Golf (2km) Sea (12km) Swimming pool (12km) Hiking (2km) Tennis (12km) Sailing (12km) **NOTES:** Pets admitted CC

TUBERSENT

Chambre d'hôtes Marie-Claire DELAPORTE
140, route de Frencq, 62630 TUBERSENT
☎ 03 21 81 26 48
Le Touquet 10 km. Montreuil 10 km. This village centre house has four guest rooms, all with TV. There is a double with own shower and wc, a tower room with double bed, own shower and wc, a double with own bath, wc, and a kitchenette shared with a triple (one alcove bed) with own bath and wc. Guests' first floor breakfast room. Garden. Parking. Open all year.
PRICES: s €43; d €49; t €59; extra person €11 **ON SITE:** Fishing Hiking
NEARBY: Horse riding (5km) Sea (10km) Swimming pool (5km) Tennis (5km) Sailing (10km) **NOTES:** No pets

Les Coquennes Anne-Marie et Alain BOITREL
59 rue de Frencq, 62630 TUBERSENT
☎ 03 21 86 73 53 🖳 03 21 86 09 78

Le Touquet 8 km. Etaples 6 km. Outside the village, this house has five guest rooms. There are two Grade 3 doubles with own shower

continued

and wc, one Grade 3 triple with own bath and wc, and two Grade 1 doubles with own washbasin and shared shower and wc. Ground floor sitting room, TV. Garden, outdoor furniture, barbecue. Parking. Open all year.
PRICES: d €39–€40; t €50 **ON SITE:** Children's play area Hiking
NEARBY: Horse riding (6km) Sea (8km) Fishing (1km) Swimming pool (6km) Tennis (12km) Sailing (8km) **NOTES:** No pets

VERTON

La Chaumière Geneviève et Christian TERRIEN
19 rue du Bihen, 62180 VERTON
☎ 03 21 84 27 10
www.perso.worldonline.fr/lachaumière
Berck 4 km. Le Touquet 15 km. In the middle of a quiet and peaceful village, this delightful thatched house stands in a lovely, tree-lined garden. There are four double rooms, all with TV, own shower and wc. Parking. Restaurant 3km. Leisure centre 5km. Open all year.
PRICES: s €39; d €48 **ON SITE:** Hiking **NEARBY:** Horse riding (5km) Golf (15km) Sea (5km) Fishing (5km) Swimming pool (5km) Tennis (5km) Sailing (5km) Railway station (3km) **NOTES:** No pets

Villa Marie Viviane BROCARD
12, rue des Ecoles, 62180 VERTON
☎ 03 21 94 05 49
e-mail: phbrocar@wanadoo.fr http://site.wanadoo.fr/villamarie/
Berck 3 km. Le Touquet 13 km. This detached house stands in a large walled garden and has four guest rooms, three of them in a separate building. There are two doubles and a twin, all with own shower and wc, and a suite of two rooms with a double and two single beds with own bath and wc. TV in all rooms. Extra bed available. Shared cooking facilities. Parking. €74 to €84 per four sharing. Cot available without charge. Contact establishment for directions. Open all year.
PRICES: s €39; d €48–€52; t €61–€73; extra person €13 **ON SITE:** Hiking
NEARBY: Horse riding (3km) Golf (13km) Sea (5km) Fishing (5km) Swimming pool (5km) Tennis (5km) Sailing (5km) Railway station (3km)
NOTES: Pets admitted

WAIL

Ferme de la Wawette Anielle COURQUIN
1 rue de Wawette, 62770 WAIL
☎ 03 21 41 88 38 📠 03 21 41 88 38

Hesdin 7 km. Berck 40 km. Only 30 minutes from the coast, this old farmhouse has been completely renovated and has four ground floor guest rooms with separate entrance. There is a twin, a double, and two triples, all with own shower and wc. Two additional single beds available. Sitting and living room, wood fire, exclusively for use of guests. Parking, garage. Restaurant. Croix-en-Ternois motor-racing circuit 20km. Open all year.
PRICES: s €38; d €42; t €54; extra person €13 **ON SITE:** Children's play area Horse riding Fishing Hiking **NEARBY:** Sea (45km) Swimming pool (14km) Tennis (6km) Sailing (4km) Railway station (8km) Shops (8km)
NOTES: No pets

WAILLY-LES-ARRAS

Chambre d'hôtes Denise DESSAINT
18, rue des Hochettes, 62217 WAILLY-LES-ARRAS
☎ 03 21 51 64 14 📠 03 21 51 64 14

Arras 7 km. Amiens 40 km. This old building in the centre of the village has been completely restored. The four rooms, two ground floor and two first floor, include two twins and two doubles, all with own shower and wc. Child's bed available. Parking, garage. Inn 4km. Open all year.
PRICES: s €28; d €35; extra person €14 **ON SITE:** Hiking
NEARBY: Sea (70km) Fishing (20km) Swimming pool (4km) Sailing (70km) Railway station (7km) **NOTES:** No pets

WIMILLE

Chambre d'hôtes Patrick BOUTROY
2, route d'Etiembrique, 62126 WIMILLE
☎ 03 21 87 10 01
Marquise & Wimereux 5 km. Outside the village, this house has three guest rooms with their own entrance. There are two doubles and a triple with kitchenette, all with own shower and wc. Cot available, €10 per week. Shared sitting room. Restaurant 3km. Open all year.
PRICES: d €40; t €50 **ON SITE:** Hiking **NEARBY:** Horse riding (1km) Sea (5km) Fishing (6km) Swimming pool (10km) Tennis (3km) Sailing (3km) **NOTES:** No pets

WIRWIGNES

Ferme du Blaizel Hervé NOEL
Rue de la Lombardie, 62240 WIRWIGNES
☎ 03 21 32 91 98
e-mail: rvnoel@clubinternet.fr
www: fermeaubergedublaisel.com
Boulogne-sur-Mer 12 km. Desvres 4 km. This old village centre building has been renovated and has three ground floor guest rooms with separate entrance and shared kitchenette. There is a double, a triple, and a family room with one double and two single beds, all with TV, own shower and wc. Guests' sitting area in hall. Parking. Ferme-auberge on site, meals from €10 (drinks not included). €70/4 persons. Open all year.
PRICES: s €30; d €40; t €55 **ON SITE:** Hiking **NEARBY:** Horse riding (15km) Sea (16km) Fishing (6km) Swimming pool (4km) Tennis (4km) Sailing (16km) Restaurant nearby **NOTES:** No pets

> 🐓 Places with this symbol are farmhouses

> 🍽 Places with this symbol serve table d'hôtes evening meals - remember to book in advance

NORMANDY

CALVADOS

AMBLIE

♦♦♦ Chambre d'hôtes Lydie FIQUET
28 Rue des Porets, 14480 AMBLIE ☎ 02 31 80 57 97
This house offers three guest rooms housed in a separate building.
Two double rooms and one triple room, all with shower and wc.
Ground floor lounge. Garden. Open all year.
PRICES: s €27; d €38; t €46 **ON SITE:** Wine tasting **NEARBY:** Horse
riding (2km) Golf (15km) Sea (5km) Swimming pool (5km) Tennis
(1km) Sailing (5km) Railway station (15km) Shops (4km) COURSEULLES
S/MER (6km) **NOTES:** No pets

AUTHIE

♦♦♦ Chambre d'hôtes Annick LEMOINE
2 rue Henri Brunet, 14280 AUTHIE
☎ 02 31 26 00 35 & 06 63 09 69 88

This attractive stone house offers spacious, tasteful guest rooms
with private showers. Two double rooms and one triple room;
extra beds available. Garden with furniture. The Côte de Nacre
beaches and Caen are only 15 minutes away. Open all year.
PRICES: s €29; d €37; t €49 **ON SITE:** Wine tasting Tennis
NEARBY: Canoeing (6km) Horse riding (2km) Golf (10km) Sea (15km)
Fishing (12km) Swimming pool (5km) Sailing (15km) Railway station
(10km) CAEN (5km) **NOTES:** No pets

BANVILLE

♦♦♦ 🐓 Ferme le Petit Val Gérard LESAGE
24 rue du Camp Romain, 14480 BANVILLE
☎ 02 31 37 92 18 📠 02 31 37 92 18

Two double or triple rooms with private shower or bathroom are
offered in the main part of this property. Two double rooms with

private shower and one suite consisting of two double rooms,
again with private shower, are housed in an independent building.
Lounge with TV. Open Easter to 1 November.
PRICES: s €34; d €41-€47; t €53 **ON SITE:** Wine tasting
NEARBY: Horse riding (3km) Golf (10km) Sea (3km) Fishing (3km)
Swimming pool (3km) Tennis (3km) Sailing (3km) Railway station (20km)
COURSEULLES S/MER (2km) **NOTES:** No pets English spoken

BERNIERES D'AILLY

♦♦♦ 🐓 🍽️ Ferme d'Ailly André et Arlette VERMES
14170 BERNIERES D'AILLY
☎ 02 31 90 73 58 📠 02 31 40 89 39
e-mail: andre.vermes@wanadoo.fr

This farmhouse offers attractive, stylish guest rooms in a rustic
environment. In the main building there are three guest rooms,
one double room and two suites consisting of double or triple
rooms with connecting double rooms. All have private shower
facilities. Games room and lounge. Open Easter to 1 November.
PRICES: s €27; d €34; t €40; dinner €14 **ON SITE:** Wine tasting Fishing
NEARBY: Horse riding (10km) Swimming pool (10km) Tennis (10km)
Railway station (10km) Shops (10km) FALAISE (10km) **NOTES:** No pets
English spoken

BERVILLE L'OUDON

♦♦♦ Le Pressoir Annick DUHAMEL
route de l'église, 14170 BERVILLE L'OUDON
☎ 02 31 20 51 26 📠 02 31 20 03 03
Three elegant guest rooms are available in this historic house,
once used as a cider press. One double room with private shower
facilities and separate entrance and two triple rooms with
bathroom. Reception room at guests' disposition. Open all year.
PRICES: s €34; d €41; t €53 **ON SITE:** Wine tasting Fishing
NEARBY: Canoeing (3km) Horse riding (1km) Golf (6km) Sea (35km)
Swimming pool (3km) Tennis (3km) Railway station (3km) Shops (3km)
ST PIERRE S/DIVES (3km) **NOTES:** No pets

BEUVILLERS

♦♦♦ Cour de la Tour Yvette MANCEL
9 rue de la Liberte, 14100 BEUVILLERS
☎ 02 31 62 18 32 & 06 09 90 95 92 📠 02 31 62 18 32
e-mail: mancel.michel@wanadoo.fr
This newly built house offers two double rooms and one triple
room, each with private shower or bathroom. Terrace and garden
with furniture. Very close to the nearby basilica, this house is
extremely comfortable. Open April to September.

continued

continued

PRICES: s €33; d €40; t €55 ON SITE: Wine tasting Fishing Tennis
NEARBY: Horse riding (13km) Golf (12km) Sea (28km) Swimming pool
(2km) Sailing (17km) Railway station (2km) Shops (2km) LISIEUX (2km)
NOTES: No pets

BONNEVILLE LA LOUVET

▓▓▓ IOI Ferme des Tostes Isabelle MONCLERC
Route de Blangy, 14130 BONNEVILLE-LA-LOUVET
☎ 02 31 64 37 74 & 06 80 42 25 44 ▤ 02 31 64 95 47
e-mail: ferme.tostes@wanadoo.fr http://www.ferme.tostes.com

Part of a farm complex made up of several fully restored
traditional houses, this annexe offers comfortable and quiet guest
rooms with open views over the surrounding countryside. Two
double rooms, one split-level room for four people, with TV, and
two double or triple rooms are available. All rooms have private
shower or bathroom. TV, lounge and garden with furniture. Local
Norman specialities and vegetarian dishes available. Open all year.
PRICES: s €38; d €45; t €57; dinner €15 ON SITE: Wine tasting
NEARBY: Canoeing (14km) Horse riding (3km) Golf (8km) Sea (25km)
Fishing (8km) Swimming pool (18km) Tennis (2km) Sailing (14km)
Railway station (14km) Shops (2km) PONT L'EVEQUE (14km)
NOTES: Pets admitted English spoken

BOURGEAUVILLE

▓▓▓ ❧ La Belle Epine Vincent et Stéphanie CLOUET
14430 BOURGEAUVILLE
☎ 02 31 65 27 26 & 06 61 17 83 82 ▤ 02 31 65 27 26
In the heart of the Auge region, between the seaside resorts of
Cabourg and Deauville, this farmhouse offers four spacious rooms
housed in a former cider press. Four double, triple or four person
rooms with private shower facilities are available. Garden with
furniture. Set in green and peaceful surroundings. Open all year.
PRICES: s €30; d €40; t €50 ON SITE: Wine tasting Children's play area
Horse riding NEARBY: Golf (13km) Sea (8km) Fishing (10km)
Swimming pool (2km) Tennis (2km) Sailing (8km) Railway station (10km)
Shops (3km) DEAUVILLE (10km) NOTES: No pets

BRETTEVILLE SUR LAIZE

▓▓▓▓ IOI Château des Riffets Alain CANTEL
Les Riffets, 14680 BRETTEVILLE-SUR-LAIZE
☎ 02 31 23 53 21 ▤ 02 31 23 75 14
e-mail: acantel@free.fr
This majestic château offers guests the choice of two double
or triple rooms and two family suites with private bathrooms.
Lounge with TV. Covered swimming pool, which is heated in
season. Wooded 15 hectare park. Open all year.
PRICES: d €90; t €116; dinner €40 ON SITE: Wine tasting
Swimming pool NEARBY: Canoeing (20km) Horse riding (4km)
Golf (5km) Sea (24km) Fishing (1km) Tennis (1km) Sailing (24km)
Railway station (15km) Shops (1km) CAEN (15km) NOTES: No pets
English spoken

BUCEELS

▓▓▓ ❧ Chambre d'hôtes Daniel et M. Agnès HARIVEL
Hameau de la Croix, 14250 BUCEELS
☎ 02 31 80 38 11 ▤ 02 31 80 20 53

Near Bayeux, this attractive house built from local stone offers
one triple room and, housed in a connecting building with
separate entrance, one family room and one triple room. All
rooms have private shower and wc facilities. Lounge and kitchen
are at guests' disposition. Garden with furniture. The guest rooms
are comfortable and distinctively decorated. Discover the local
cuisine by trying the evening meals (served on reservation).
Closed 15 December to 15 January.
PRICES: s €29; d €38; t €50 ON SITE: Wine tasting NEARBY: Horse
riding (4km) Golf (10km) Sea (19km) Fishing (10km) Swimming pool
(10km) Tennis (1km) Sailing (19km) Railway station (10km) Shops (2km)
BAYEUX (10km) NOTES: No pets

BURES SUR DIVES

▓▓▓ Manoir des Tourpes M et M LANDON-CASSADY
3 rue de l'Eglise, 14670 BURES-SUR-DIVES
☎ 02 31 23 63 47 ▤ 02 31 23 86 10
e-mail: mcassady@mail.cpod.fr
http://www.cpod.com/monoweb/mantourpes
Three tastefully decorated double rooms, all with private shower,
are available in this 17th-century manor house. The River Dives
flows through the garden. Garden with furniture, and lounge with
library and fireplace. Open Easter to 1 November.
PRICES: s €43; d €46-€61; t €72 ON SITE: Fishing NEARBY: Horse
riding (12km) Golf (12km) Sea (12km) Swimming pool (12km) Tennis
(12km) Sailing (12km) Railway station (15km) Shops (2km) TROARN
(2km) NOTES: No pets English spoken

CAMBREMER

▓▓▓ Les Marronniers Jean et Chantal DARONDEL
Englesqueville, 14340 CAMBREMER
☎ 02 31 63 08 28 ▤ 02 31 63 92 54
e-mail: Chantal.Darondel@wanadoo.fr
http://www.les-marronniers.com
One double room and two rooms sleeping three to four people
are available in a wing of this 17th-century house. Rooms all have
private bathroom facilities. Two further double rooms are housed
in a separate building, the former cider press. Private entrances,
and kitchen for guests' use in the summer. Garden with furniture.
Surrounded by a park, this house offers rooms decorated with a
personal touch. Wonderful views of the Dives valley. Open all year.
PRICES: s €35; d €42-€52; t €65 NEARBY: Horse riding (7km) Sea
(22km) Swimming pool (17km) Tennis (5km) Sailing (22km) Railway
station (17km) Shops (5km) LISIEUX (17km) NOTES: No pets English
spoken

♦♦♦ Manoir de Cantepie Arnaud et Christine GHERRAK
14340 CAMBREMER
☎ 02 31 62 87 27
The well-balanced and distinctive décor of this 17th-century Norman manor forms a large part of its charm. Three double or triple rooms with private bathroom facilities are available. Open 1 March to 15 November.
PRICES: s €40; d €45-€55; t €60 NEARBY: Horse riding (6km) Golf (17km) Sea (25km) Swimming pool (11km) Tennis (1km) Sailing (25km) Railway station (11km) Shops (1km) LISIEUX (11km) NOTES: No pets English spoken

CLECY-LE VEY

♦♦♦ ♥ |⊙| La Ferme du Manoir Louise PELLIER
14570 LE VEY
☎ 02 31 69 73 81
Madame Pellier welcomes guests to stay at this restored Norman manor house. In the main building, a suite consisting of one double room and one single room is offered, and one triple room, is also available. An annexe houses an additional family room for four people, with an independent entrance. Guest rooms are comfortable and pleasant and breakfast is served in a rustic setting. All rooms have private shower or bathroom facilities. Boules equipment for guests' use. Open all year.
PRICES: s €26; d €35; t €44; dinner €13 NEARBY: Canoeing (2km) Horse riding (3km) Golf (3km) Sea (50km) Fishing (2km) Swimming pool (10km) Tennis (2km) Railway station (40km) Shops (3km) THURY-HARCOURT (9km) NOTES: No pets

♦♦♦ ♥ La Ferme du Vey SCS LEBOUCHER-BRISSET
14570 CLECY/LE VEY
☎ 02 31 69 71 02 📠 02 31 69 69 33
e-mail: pbrisset@9online.fr
This farm, very close to the tourist attractions of Clécy, offers three double rooms with private shower facilities, housed in a separate building close to the farmhouse itself. Cot available. Private guest entrance and the kitchen is at guests' disposition. Garden with furniture. The rooms are comfortable and welcoming. Open all year.
PRICES: s €29; d €33 NEARBY: Canoeing (1km) Horse riding (1km) Golf (3km) Sea (50km) Fishing (1km) Swimming pool (11km) Tennis (1km) Railway station (25km) Shops (1km) THURY-HARCOURT (9km) NOTES: Pets admitted CC

♦♦♦ Le Manoir de Miette André et Denise LEBOUCHER
14570 LE VEY
☎ 02 31 69 45 80 📠 02 31 69 69 33
This unique house is surrounded by an attractive garden. The accommodation offered consists of two double or triple rooms with private shower or bathroom facilities and one double room housed in an independent cottage with private shower and kitchen corner. The lounge with TV is at guests' disposition and there is a garden with furniture. The area offers many diverse attractions. Open all year.
PRICES: s €30; d €38-€46; t €46 NEARBY: Canoeing (1km) Horse riding (1km) Golf (3km) Sea (50km) Fishing (1km) Swimming pool (10km) Tennis (1km) Railway station (35km) Shops (1km) THURY-HARCOURT (9km) NOTES: No pets

CLINCHAMPS SUR ORNE

♦♦♦ Chemin du Courtillage Annick HERVIEU
14320 CLINCHAMPS-SUR-ORNE
☎ 02 31 23 87 63
This elegant and charming house offers two double rooms and one triple room, all with private bathroom facilities and each decorated according to a certain theme, be it the 17th-century

atmosphere of the Beaumarchais room, the literary style of the writer's room or the vibrant Mediterranean colours of the Provençal room. Lounge with sofa and fireplace. Leafy park and garden with furniture. Open all year.
PRICES: s €46; d €61; t €76 ON SITE: Tennis NEARBY: Canoeing (17km) Horse riding (8km) Golf (8km) Sea (27km) Swimming pool (15km) Sailing (27km) Railway station (15km) Shops (6km) CAEN (15km) NOTES: No pets English spoken

COLLEVILLE SUR MER

♦♦♦ ♥ |⊙| Ferme du Clos Tassin
Daniel et M-Thérèse PICQUENARD
14710 COLLEVILLE-SUR-MER
☎ 02 31 22 41 51 📠 02 31 22 29 46
http://www.multimania.com/clostassin

In the main building of this farm, one grade 2 double room with private bathroom and three grade 3 rooms (double room, triple room and four-person family room) with private bathrooms are available. One grade 3 suite with double room and connecting twin room is housed in an annexe. Private shower facilities. Evening meals are available on reservation. This working farm is only five minutes away from the sea and the D-Day beaches. Open all year.
PRICES: s €29; d €34; t €49; dinner €14 NEARBY: Horse riding (7km) Golf (7km) Sea (2km) Fishing (2km) Swimming pool (15km) Tennis (1km) Sailing (2km) Railway station (15km) Shops (3km) PORT-EN-BESSIN (7km) NOTES: No pets

COMMES

♦♦♦ Chambre d'hôtes Michel et Lilou CAIRON
L'église, 14520 COMMES
☎ 02 31 21 71 08 📠 02 31 21 95 87
Two grade 3 double rooms with shower and one suite with two connecting double rooms and bathroom are available in this modern house with pleasant terrace. Perfect for families and a warm welcome guaranteed. Close to the D-Day beaches. Open all year.
PRICES: s €30; d €35-€38; t €50 NEARBY: Horse riding (2km) Golf (3km) Sea (2km) Fishing (2km) Swimming pool (9km) Tennis (2km) Sailing (2km) Railway station (10km) Shops (2km) PORT-EN-BESSIN (2km) NOTES: No pets

♦♦♦ ♥ Ferme d'Escures
Charles & Christiane HAELEWYN
Hameau d'Escures, 14520 COMMES
☎ 02 31 92 52 23 📠 02 31 92 52 23
This traditional Norman house has two double rooms, one family room and one suite sleeping four people. All rooms have private bathroom facilities. This comfortable house is close to a pretty fishing town and the D-Day beaches. Open all year.
PRICES: s €30-€34; d €35-€40; t €50-€55 NEARBY: Horse riding (3km) Golf (2km) Sea (2km) Fishing (2km) Swimming pool (7km) Tennis (2km) Sailing (2km) Railway station (8km) Shops (2km) PORT-EN-BESSIN (2km) NOTES: No pets English spoken

continued

NORMANDY

⚜️ 🌱 Le Logis Florence et Gilles HAELEWYN
Escures Village, 14520 COMMES
☎ 02 31 21 79 56 📠 02 31 21 79 56
Close to the fishing town of Port en Bessin, this farmhouse offers one triple room, two double rooms and one suite consisting of two connecting double rooms, with hand basin and wc. All rooms have private bathroom or shower facilities. A supplementary bed is available. Garden with furniture. Comfortable house with lounge, close to the D-Day beaches. Open all year.
PRICES: s €30; d €35-€38; t €46　**NEARBY:** Horse riding (2km)　Golf (2km)　Sea (2km)　Swimming pool (6km)　Tennis (2km)　Sailing (2km)　Railway station (7km)　Shops (2km)　PORT-EN-BESSIN (2km)　**NOTES:** No pets　English spoken

COURSEULLES SUR MER

⚜️ Chambre d'hôtes Gérard & Marie-Noëlle WILLE
1 rue Arthur Leduc, 14470 COURSEULLES-SUR-MER
☎ 02 31 37 86 46 & 06 78 26 70 07
This very attractive house in the centre of a seaside resort offers three triple rooms, one of which is very large, and one double room. All rooms have private shower facilities and are tastefully decorated. Garden with furniture. Only 400 metres from the beach. Open all year.
PRICES: s €34; d €41-€46; t €52-€56　**ON SITE:** Sea　**NEARBY:** Horse riding (1km)　Golf (20km)　Swimming pool (1km)　Tennis (1km)　Sailing (1km)　Railway station (17km)　CAEN (15km)　**NOTES:** Pets admitted English spoken

COURSON

⚜️ 🌱 🍴 La Plaine Postel Daniel et Elisabeth GUEZET
14380 COURSON
☎ 02 31 68 83 41 📠 02 31 68 83 41
This working farm offers one grade 1 double room and one grade 1 room for four people, with communal bathroom. The house also has three grade 3 double rooms with private shower facilities. Billiard table. Guests can enjoy the calm atmosphere of the Norman countryside and try the local specialities. Private swimming pool. Open all year.
PRICES: s €21-€26; d €26-€35; t €32-€44; dinner €14　**ON SITE:** Fishing　**NEARBY:** Horse riding (7km)　Golf (17km)　Sea (40km)　Swimming pool (3km)　Tennis (3km)　Railway station (15km)　Shops (3km)　SAINT SEVER (3km)　**NOTES:** Pets admitted

CREPON

⚜️ Manoir de Crépon Anne-Marie POISSON
Route d'Arromanches, 14480 CREPON
☎ 02 31 22 21 27 📠 02 31 22 88 80

Surrounded by a large park planted with trees, this 18th-century manor house offers four superior guest rooms, consisting of two 3-4 person suites with private bathrooms, and two double rooms with private shower facilities. Lounge and garden with furniture. Bicycles can be borrowed and the

continued

D-Day beaches are nearby. Open all year.
PRICES: s €53; d €69; t €84　**NEARBY:** Horse riding (12km)　Golf (12km)　Sea (4km)　Fishing (12km)　Swimming pool (10km)　Tennis (4km)　Sailing (4km)　Railway station (10km)　BAYEUX (12km)　**NOTES:** Pets admitted

CRESSEVEUILLE

⚜️ Longueval Jeanne DE LONGCAMP
14430 CRESSEVEUILLE
☎ 02 31 79 22 01
e-mail: philippe.de-longcamp@wanadoo.fr

This attractive manor house offers three large and comfortable guest rooms and has a telephone and a lounge with TV. One double room with shower is situated in the main building, and one triple room with private bathroom and TV is housed in an adjoining building with separate entrance. A further double room with private bathroom and TV is situated in another annexe. The house has a garden with furniture and is surrounded by a leafy park. Open all year.
PRICES: s €32; d €41-€53; t €61　**NEARBY:** Horse riding (5km)　Golf (14km)　Sea (9km)　Fishing (1km)　Swimming pool (1km)　Tennis (1km)　Sailing (9km)　Railway station (16km)　Shops (5km)　DOZULE (4km)　**NOTES:** No pets　English spoken

CRICQUEBOEUF

⚜️ A la Villa des Rosiers
Benoit et Sandrine HAUCHECORNE
14113 CRIQUEBOEUF
☎ 02 31 98 25 22 & 06 81 01 11 03
This guest house offers two double rooms and two triple or double rooms, all grade 3 accommodation with private shower facilities. One grade 2 double room is also available, with private shower and wc on the landing. Extra single bed available. Benoit and Sandrine invite guests into their home, situated between Honfleur and Deauville. Open all year.
PRICES: s €30; d €50; t €60　**NEARBY:** Canoeing (7km)　Horse riding (2km)　Golf (7km)　Sea (1km)　Fishing (999km)　Swimming pool (7km)　Tennis (1km)　Sailing (7km)　Railway station (7km)　Shops (1km)　HONFLEUR (6km)　**NOTES:** No pets　English spoken

DOUVILLE EN AUGE

⚜️ 🌱 Ferme de l'Oraille Louis et Gisèle HOULET
Chemin de Deraine, 14430 DOUVILLE-EN-AUGE
☎ 02 31 79 25 49
This farmhouse offers three rooms, one double, one triple and one family room, all with private shower facilities. Separate guest entrance and garden with furniture. The rooms, which look over the countryside, are situated at the heart of this working farm, which has many enjoyable walks nearby. Open all year.
PRICES: s €30; d €38; t €46　**NEARBY:** Horse riding (7km)　Golf (7km)　Sea (7km)　Fishing (3km)　Swimming pool (15km)　Tennis (5km)　Railway station (15km)　Shops (6km)　CABOURG (9km)　**NOTES:** No pets

ECRAMMEVILLE

▮▮▮ ❧ Ꜿ Ferme de l'Abbaye Annick FAUVEL
14710 ECRAMMEVILLE
☎ 02 31 22 52 32 🗎 02 31 22 47 25
Large rooms and good country cooking featuring local produce
are offered in this farmhouse, close to the fishing port of
Grandcamp-Maisy. Accommodation includes one suite consisting
of one double room and one single room with private shower, one
suite with two connecting double rooms and private bathroom,
and one family room with private shower and separate entrance.
There is a garden with furniture and boat trips leave from the
nearby Hoc Point. Evening meals available on reservation. Open all
year.
PRICES: s €34; d €40; t €50; dinner €14 **NEARBY:** Horse riding (4km)
Golf (20km) Sea (7km) Fishing (1km) Swimming pool (20km) Tennis
(4km) Railway station (20km) Shops (4km) GRANDCAMP-MAISY (10km)
NOTES: No pets

EQUEMAUVILLE

▮▮▮ ❧ La Ferme Chevalier
J-Yves et Françoise GREGOIRE
14600 EQUEMAUVILLE
☎ 02 31 89 18 14
This 18th-century house, a former horseman's rest, offers two
double rooms, two triple rooms and one room sleeping five, with
mezzanine. All rooms have private shower and wc facilities and
separate entrances. Garden with furniture and courtyard
dominated by a magnificent 18th-century well. Hosts Françoise and
Jean Yves welcome guests into their family home. Open all year.
PRICES: s €30; d €38; t €46 **NEARBY:** Horse riding (3km) Golf (4km)
Sea (4km) Swimming pool (4km) Tennis (1km) Railway station (12km)
Shops (1km) HONFLEUR (4km) **NOTES:** No pets

FORMIGNY

▮▮▮ ❧ Ferme du Mouchel Odile LENOURICHEL
14710 FORMIGNY
☎ 02 31 22 53 79 🗎 02 31 21 56 55
e-mail: odile.lenourichel@libertysurf.fr
This large dairy farm offers attractively decorated rooms, including
three rooms for two to four people, with private shower facilities
and one suite with two connecting double rooms, housed in an
annexe to the main building. Lounge and garden with furniture.
Close to the D-Day beaches. Open all year.
PRICES: s €34; d €38-€41; t €49-€58; extra person €9 **NEARBY:** Horse
riding (5km) Golf (15km) Sea (4km) Fishing (4km) Swimming pool
(15km) Tennis (4km) Sailing (4km) Railway station (15km) Shops (5km)
TREVIERES (3km) **NOTES:** No pets

GEFOSSE FONTENAY

▮▮▮ ❧ Ꜿ La Rivière Gérard et Isabelle LEHARIVEL
14230 GEFOSSE FONTENAY
☎ 02 31 22 64 45 🗎 02 31 22 01 18
e-mail: manoirdelariviere@mageos.com
http://chez.com/manoirdelariviere
This fortified farmhouse dates from medieval times and benefits
from spacious, meticulously decorated rooms, with exposed beams
and antique furniture. One double room and two triple rooms, all
with private shower facilities, are offered. Evening meals are
available on reservation and are served in the vaulted dining room
with fireplace and baker's oven. Open all year.
PRICES: s €43; d €46; t €60; dinner €18 **NEARBY:** Horse riding (12km)
Golf (25km) Sea (2km) Fishing (3km) Swimming pool (20km) Tennis
(3km) Sailing (3km) Railway station (20km) Shops (3km) GRANDCAMP-
MAISY (5km) **NOTES:** No pets CC English spoken

▮▮▮ ❧ Manoir de l'Hermerel
Agnès et François LEMARIE
14230 GEFOSSE FONTENAY
☎ 02 31 22 64 12 🗎 02 31 22 64 12
e-mail: lemariehermerel@aol.com
Three guest rooms retaining traditional character are available in
this 15th-century farmhouse. The rooms are all decorated in blue,
green or pink and consist of one ground floor double room, and
one suite accommodating four people. Also offers one attic room
with mezzanine which sleeps four to five people. Private shower
facilities for each room. Cot and extra bed available. Independent
guest entrance, picnic corner and garden with furniture. Breakfast
is served in front of the impressive fireplace. Open 1 April to
1 November
PRICES: s €42; d €50; t €67 **NEARBY:** Horse riding (15km) Golf (30km)
Sea (1km) Fishing (4km) Swimming pool (20km) Tennis (4km) Sailing
(4km) Railway station (20km) Shops (4km) GRANDCAMP-MAISY (5km)
NOTES: No pets English spoken

GONNEVILLE SUR MER

▮▮▮ ❧ Ferme des Glycines Hugues et Elizabeth EXMELIN
Carrefour Manerbe, 14510 GONNEVILLE-SUR-MER
☎ 02 31 28 01 15
Surrounded by orchards, this typical Norman farm complex offers
large rooms, decorated with a personal touch. One room for four
people (including a mezzanine for two), one triple room and one
double room, all with private wc and shower. Guest rooms benefit
from independent entrances, which open onto the attractive
garden with furniture, planted with trees and flowers. Open April
to November.
PRICES: s €30; d €43; t €55 **NEARBY:** Canoeing (15km) Horse riding
(4km) Golf (1km) Sea (3km) Fishing (3km) Swimming pool (4km)
Tennis (3km) Sailing (5km) Railway station (6km) Shops (4km)
HOULGATE (4km) **NOTES:** No pets

LA BIGNE

▮▮▮ ❧ La Vauterie Simone LAIMAN
14260 LA BIGNE
☎ 02 31 77 95 21 🗎 02 31779521

This country house, set in four hectares of land, has two double
rooms and one family room (two connecting double rooms) with
private shower facilities. Cot and extra bed available. Garden with
furniture. Simone and Jean-Pierre (who is an artist) promise guests
a warm welcome. Large house with romantic bedrooms and
creative courses in clay modelling, drawing, painting and
watercolours are on offer. Horse-riding also available. Open all
year.
PRICES: s €29; d €38; t €47 **ON SITE:** Wine tasting **NEARBY:** Horse
riding (8km) Fishing (1km) Swimming pool (9km) Tennis (9km) Railway
station (24km) Shops (9km) AUNAY SUR ODON (8km) **NOTES:** Pets
admitted English spoken

NORMANDY

LA BOISSIERE

♦♦♦ Le Manoir Paul et Thérèse DELORT
D 103, 14340 LA BOISSIERE
☎ 02 31 62 25 95 & 02 31 32 20 81
This 17th-century manor house surrounded by a leafy park, offers three distinctive guest rooms. One family room for four people with private shower and wc facilities, one double room with bathroom and one triple room with bathroom are available. Garden with furniture. Open all year.
PRICES: s €34; d €40-€46; t €50 **ON SITE:** Wine tasting
NEARBY: Horse riding (7km) Golf (30km) Sea (35km) Swimming pool (7km) Tennis (7km) Railway station (7km) Shops (1km) LISIEUX (6km)
NOTES: No pets

LE TRONQUAY

♦♦♦ Chambre d'hôtes Denise DEBIEU
Hameau de Montirly, 14490 LE TRONQUAY
☎ 02 31 92 34 48
Three comfortable and distinctive double rooms with private shower facilities are available in this newly restored house. The hostess, Mme Debieu, will be pleased to help guests to discover the joys of the region. Fishing possible in the private pond. Open all year.
PRICES: s €24; d €34 **ON SITE:** Fishing **NEARBY:** Horse riding (10km) Golf (15km) Sea (20km) Swimming pool (10km) Tennis (7km) Railway station (10km) Shops (3km) BAYEUX (10km) **NOTES:** No pets

LES AUTHIEUX S/CALONNE

♦♦♦ Les Bélières François & Françoise LE ROUX
Route de Blangy le Chât.,
14130 LES AUTHIEUX-SUR-CALONNE
☎ 02 31 64 67 28 🗎 02 31 64 67 28
e-mail: les-belières@wanadoo.fr
Peaceful and comfortable rooms housed in a modern building with an attractive garden. One double room with an independent entrance and two double or triple rooms, each connecting with a further double room. All rooms have private shower or bathroom. Garden with furniture. Open all year.
PRICES: s €42; d €46; t €61 **ON SITE:** Wine tasting
NEARBY: Canoeing (8km) Horse riding (4km) Golf (6km) Sea (18km) Fishing (2km) Swimming pool (18km) Tennis (6km) Sailing (8km) Railway station (8km) Shops (8km) PONT-L'EVEQUE (8km) **NOTES:** No pets

LINGEVRES

♦♦♦ ♥ 🍴 Chambre d'hôtes Charles et Marie POLIDOR
Hameau de Verrieres, 14250 LINGEVRES
☎ 02 31 80 91 17 🗎 02 31 08 37 78
e-mail: lelandey.p@libertysurf.fr
http://www.perso.libertysurf.fr/lelandey
In the main building of this farmhouse, three double or triple guest rooms are available, all with private shower facilities. In an adjoining building with separate entrance there are two further triple rooms with private showers. Charles and Marie invite guests to join them at the dinner table. Open all year.
PRICES: s €29; d €35; t €45; dinner €14 **NEARBY:** Horse riding (5km) Sea (20km) Swimming pool (12km) Tennis (3km) Railway station (12km) Shops (3km) TILLY SUR SEULLES (3km) **NOTES:** No pets

LIVRY

♦♦♦ ♥ 🍴 La Suhardière Alain et Françoise PETITON
14240 LIVRY ☎ 02 31 77 51 02 🗎 02 31 77 51 02
This restored 17th-century farmhouse offers one triple room with private shower facilities, and two double or triple rooms with a connecting double room. Private shower. Independent entrance, lounge and garden with furniture. The rooms enjoy a restful country setting with fishing and horse-riding available on site. Open all year.
PRICES: s €30; d €40; t €50; dinner €18 **ON SITE:** Fishing
NEARBY: Canoeing (15km) Horse riding (1km) Sea (20km) Swimming pool (10km) Tennis (1km) Railway station (23km) Shops (1km) CAUMONT L'EVENTE (1km) **NOTES:** Pets admitted

LONGUES SUR MER

♦♦♦ Ferme de la Tourelle J-M et J LECARPENTIER
Hameau de Fontenailles, 14400 LONGUES-SUR-MER
☎ 02 31 21 78 47 🗎 02 31 21 84 84
e-mail: lecarpentier2@wanadoo.fr
http://www.multimania.com/tourelle
Housed in an annexe to the main building of this 17th-century former farmhouse, are three rooms accommodating three to four people with private shower facilities and an independent entrance. Lounge with kitchen, keep-fit room and garden with furniture. This Norman farmhouse, close to the sea, offers guest rooms with exposed stone walls and has internet access. Open all year.
PRICES: s €32; d €40; t €50 **NEARBY:** Horse riding (7km) Golf (7km) Sea (1km) Fishing (4km) Swimming pool (7km) Tennis (4km) Sailing (7km) Railway station (7km) Shops (2km) ARROMANCHES (5km)
NOTES: Pets admitted

LONGVILLERS

♦♦♦ 🍴 La Nouvelle France Anne-Marie GODEY
14310 LONGVILLERS
☎ 02 31 77 63 36 🗎 02 31 77 63 36
e-mail: anne-marie.godey@wanadoo.fr
Three double rooms with private shower facilities are available in this former barn which is built from local stone, and forms part of a farm complex. The rooms are decorated in a comfortable rustic style and there is also a large, shady lawn. Calm environment and footpaths for walkers. Open all year.
PRICES: s €26; d €34 **NEARBY:** Canoeing (18km) Horse riding (8km) Golf (24km) Sea (35km) Fishing (4km) Swimming pool (3km) Tennis (3km) Sailing (4km) Railway station (30km) Shops (4km) VILLERS-BOCAGE (4km) **NOTES:** No pets English spoken

♦♦♦ ♥ Chambre d'hôtes
Jean et Anne-Marie DE MATHAN
Mathan, 14310 LONGVILLERS
☎ 02 31 77 10 37 🗎 02 31 77 49 13
e-mail: jdemathan@fr.packardbell.org
This 15th-century manor house offers two suites, both consisting of two connecting double rooms with private bathrooms, and one double room with private bathroom. Second-floor lounge with fireplace and private guest entrance. Ideally situated for stopovers between Normandy and Brittany, this house offers large, pleasant and distinctive guest rooms with king size beds. Open all year.
PRICES: s €30; d €40; t €49 **NEARBY:** Horse riding (15km) Golf (35km) Sea (35km) Swimming pool (15km) Tennis (4km) Sailing (35km) Railway station (30km) Shops (4km) VILLERS BOCAGE (4km) **NOTES:** No pets English spoken

MAISONS

♦♦♦ Ferme des Goupillières Annie LABBE
14400 MAISONS ☎ 02 31 92 53 47
Housed in an annexe to a holiday cottage, these guest rooms are meticulously decorated and feature walls of exposed stone. Two double or triple rooms and one triple room are available, all with private shower facilities. Lounge and kitchen for guests' use. Set in a rural environment close to the D-Day beaches. Open Easter to 1 November.

continued

continued

NORMANDY

PRICES: s €32; d €40; t €50 **NEARBY:** Golf (3km) Sea (3km) Fishing (4km) Swimming pool (5km) Tennis (1km) Sailing (3km) Railway station (6km) Shops (3km) PORT EN BESSIN (4km) **NOTES:** Pets admitted

MANERBE

⚑⚑⚑ La Katounette Micheline VALETTE
14340 MANERBE
☎ 02 31 61 14 66
This half-timbered Norman house surrounded by greenery offers two double rooms with private shower and a further connecting double room. One double room and one family room, also with connecting double room, are housed in a separate building. All rooms have TV and are welcomingly decorated with a personal touch. Garden with furniture. Open all year.
PRICES: s €32; d €39; t €49 **NEARBY:** Canoeing (7km) Horse riding (4km) Golf (14km) Sea (16km) Fishing (3km) Swimming pool (4km) Tennis (3km) Sailing (16km) Railway station (6km) Shops (1km) LISIEUX (7km) **NOTES:** Pets admitted

MANVIEUX

⚑⚑⚑ La Breholière Sandrine PASTRE
14117 MANVIEUX
☎ 02 31 22 19 66 & 06 73 68 71 64 📠 02 31 22 93 48
This pretty stone house located between Arromanches and Port en Bessin offers three charming guest rooms set in a peaceful environment. Two double or triple rooms and one split-level family room for four people are available. Rooms all have private shower facilities and there is a cot available. Independent guest entrance and garden with furniture. Open all year.
PRICES: s €30; d €38; t €46 **NEARBY:** Horse riding (6km) Golf (8km) Sea (2km) Swimming pool (8km) Tennis (3km) Sailing (2km) Railway station (8km) Shops (3km) ARROMANCHES (3km) **NOTES:** No pets English spoken

⚑⚑⚑ La Gentilhommière Patricia & Isabelle ROTTIER
L'Eglise, 14117 MANVIEUX
☎ 02 31 51 97 91

One double room with private entrance and three further double rooms are available in this attractive stone house which dates from the 18th century and is close to the D-Day beaches. Rooms are comfortable and all have a lounge corner and private shower. Garden with furniture. Open all year.
PRICES: s €43; d €49 **NEARBY:** Horse riding (6km) Golf (8km) Sea (2km) Fishing (2km) Swimming pool (8km) Tennis (3km) Sailing (2km) Railway station (8km) Shops (3km) ARROMANCHES (3km) **NOTES:** No pets English spoken

---

For further information on these and other chambres d'hôtes, consult the Gîtes de France website
www.gites-de-france.fr

MAROLLES

⚑⚑⚑ Chambre d'hôtes Lucien et Christiane SIX
Route de Fumichon, 14100 MAROLLES
☎ 02 31 63 64 39
This large, traditional half-timbered house offers two double rooms and one triple room, all with private shower. Independent entrance and garden with furniture. The dining room benefits from a large fireplace which is lit at breakfast and in the evenings, during the winter months. Discover the rich heritage of the local Norman villages, easily accessible on foot or by bicycle. Open all year.
PRICES: s €30; d €38; t €46 **NEARBY:** Canoeing (18km) Horse riding (1km) Golf (18km) Sea (30km) Fishing (18km) Swimming pool (9km) Tennis (2km) Sailing (30km) Railway station (9km) Shops (3km) LISIEUX (9km) **NOTES:** Pets admitted English spoken

⚑⚑⚑ 🐓 la Ferme aux Alpines Evelyne PILON
le Mont Hérault, 14100 MAROLLES
☎ 02 31 61 96 11
This stone farmhouse offers three very comfortable guest rooms, consisting of three double rooms with private bathrooms or shower rooms. Cot and extra bed available. The inviting and restful lounge is for guests and there is a garden with furniture. Extensive opportunity for walking nearby. Open all year.
PRICES: s €27; d €35; t €43 **NEARBY:** Canoeing (20km) Horse riding (5km) Golf (27km) Sea (35km) Swimming pool (12km) Tennis (1km) Sailing (35km) Railway station (12km) Shops (4km) LISIEUX (12km) **NOTES:** Pets admitted English spoken

MONCEAUX EN BESSIN

⚑⚑⚑ 🍽 Manoir les Equerres
M-Catherine/Didier CHAMBRY
14400 MONCEAUX-EN-BESSIN
☎ 02 31 92 03 41 & 06 80 33 01 03 📠 02 31 92 03 41
Close to Bayeux, this charming Norman house has comfortable and welcoming guest rooms, warmly decorated and all with private shower facilities. Four double rooms are available and there is a billiard room and garden with furniture. The house is set in two hectares of wooded park with a freshwater spring. Breakfast is served on the veranda. Open all year.
PRICES: s €46; d €54; dinner €28 **NEARBY:** Horse riding (3km) Golf (9km) Sea (10km) Swimming pool (2km) Tennis (2km) Sailing (10km) Railway station (2km) Shops (2km) BAYEUX (2km) **NOTES:** No pets

MONDRAINVILLE

⚑⚑⚑ Manoir de Colleville Monique GROSS
14210 MONDRAINVILLE ☎ 02 31 80 96 75
This house, typical of the local area, offers three double bedrooms with private shower facilities. Lounge and garden with furniture. Guest rooms are spacious and tastefully furnished. Open Easter to 1 November.
PRICES: s €27; d €34 **NEARBY:** Horse riding (6km) Sea (25km) Fishing (1km) Swimming pool (12km) Tennis (1km) Railway station (12km) Shops (1km) CAEN (12km) **NOTES:** No pets

MONTREUIL EN AUGE

⚑⚑⚑ Ferme du Manoir Henri et Janine GESBERT
14340 MONTREUIL-EN-AUGE ☎ 02 31 63 00 64
e-mail: alain.gesbert@libertysurf.fr
Accommodation available in this house consists of four rooms for two to five people, all with private shower or bath facilities. The rooms are warmly decorated in tones of pink or green and the house has wood panelling, exposed beams and fireplaces. Lounge and garden with furniture. Open all year.
PRICES: s €30; d €40; t €52 **NEARBY:** Horse riding (4km) Sea (26km) Swimming pool (15km) Tennis (3km) Sailing (17km) Railway station (15km) Shops (3km) CAMBREMER (3km) **NOTES:** Pets admitted

MONTS EN BESSIN

♥♥♥ La Varinière Philippa EDNEY

La Vallee, 14310 MONTS-EN-BESSIN
☎ 02 31 77 44 73 📠 02 31 77 11 72
e-mail: pippa.edney@free.fr

Two double rooms, two triple rooms and one suite with two double rooms, all with private shower or bathroom, are available in this large house built at the end of the 19th century. Cot available. Philippa and David welcome guests into their peaceful and comfortable house which has charmingly decorated rooms, garden with furniture and lounge with fireplace. Closed 20 December to 31 January.

PRICES: s €38; d €61; t €69 **NEARBY:** Horse riding (4km) Golf (25km) Sea (30km) Fishing (15km) Swimming pool (6km) Tennis (6km) Sailing (30km) Railway station (18km) Shops (6km) VILLERS BOCAGE (6km)
NOTES: No pets English spoken

MONTVIETTE

♥♥♥ Domaine des Sources Margaret LOVE et Philippe KALK

Les Vignes, 14140 MONTVIETTE
☎ 02 31 20 35 35 & 06 15 72 15 15 📠 02 31 20 36 35
e-mail: DesSources@aol.com
http://www.le-domaine-des-sources.com

This enchanting property offers three double rooms with private shower facilities, which are housed in an annexe to the main building. The guest rooms available in this fully restored 18th-century manor house feature independent access and lounge corners for each room. Communal lounge, garden with furniture and charming pond. Bicycles for hire. Open all year.

PRICES: s €46; d €53 **NEARBY:** Horse riding (9km) Golf (40km) Sea (40km) Fishing (12km) Swimming pool (18km) Tennis (5km) Railway station (18km) Shops (5km) LIVAROT (5km) **NOTES:** No pets English spoken

NOYERS BOCAGE

♥♥♥ ♥ Ferme de la Cordière

Philippe et A-Marie FLAGUAIS
La Cordière, 14210 NOYERS BOCAGE
☎ 02 31 77 18 64 📠 02 31 77 18 64
e-mail: ferme.la.cordiere@wanadoo.fr

This equestrian farm offers five south-facing rooms accommodating two, three and five people, all with private shower facilities. Lounge with TV and fireplace. Leafy garden with swimming pool. Numerous equestrian activities are available, on horses or ponies, all accompanied and with instructor. Riding school, sandpit and clubhouse with eating area. Inn on site. Open all year.

PRICES: s €30; d €41; t €49 **ON SITE:** Horse riding Swimming pool
NEARBY: Golf (15km) Sea (25km) Fishing (5km) Tennis (1km) Sailing (25km) Railway station (20km) Shops (1km) VILLERS BOCAGE (7km)
NOTES: Pets admitted English spoken

ORBEC

♥♥♥ Le Manoir de l'Engagiste

Christian et Annick DUBOIS
15 Rue Saint Remy, 14290 ORBEC
☎ 02 31 32 57 22 📠 02 31 32 55 58

In the centre of Orbec, this beautiful 16th-17th-century manor house offers comfortable en suite guest rooms. There is one double on the first floor of the main house and, in an adjacent building, one double on the ground floor, and a double and a duplex room for four people on the first floor. Very attractive dining room, lounge, billiards room, TV, table tennis, garden furniture. Open all year.

PRICES: s €53; d €69; t €91 **NEARBY:** Horse riding (2km) Golf (10km) Sea (50km) Fishing (2km) Tennis (2km) Sailing (50km) Railway station (16km) ORBEC **NOTES:** Pets admitted   *See advert on this page*

Manoir de l'Engagiste

The beauty of this 15th-century Norman manor house seduces all its visitors

Tel: 231325722 Fax: 231325558

14 rue de Géolé, 14290 ORBEC, Calvados

Recommended in the area:

Local delicacies–
Pork with apples, cider, Pont l'Evêque and Camembert cheeses

Activities–
Table-tennis, billiards, walking, bicycles available

Visits–
Bernay, Giverny (one hour)

Once through the impressive porch of this ancient building, you will forget you are right in the heart of Orbec, a small town mid-way between Paris and Caen. The recently-restored house is sheltered by high walls covered in rambling roses and clematis. The garden of lawns and apple trees reflects the attributes of the Normandy countryside. These peaceful surroundings, combined with Annick Dubois' warm welcome and the comfort of the centrally-heated bedrooms, will ensure a memorable stay. Breakfast is served in a gallery lined with paintings. Open parking is available, and English and Spanish are spoken.

5 rooms, no smoking in 2 bedrooms

¶¶¶ ❧ Le Chêne Sec Michel PLASSAIS
14700 PERTHEVILLE NERS ☎ 02 31 90 17 55
Not far from Falaise, birthplace of William the Conqueror, Michel welcomes you to his 15th-century farm of great character. The spacious guest rooms have authentic decor and private shower rooms and wcs. There is one double room on the ground floor, and two rooms for three and four people on the first floor. Open March to October.
PRICES: s €30; d €44; t €50 **NEARBY:** Horse riding (7km) Golf (7km) Sea (45km) Fishing (3km) Swimming pool (7km) Tennis (7km) Railway station (20km) Shops (7km) FALAISE (7km) **NOTES:** No pets

PONT D'OUILLY

¶¶¶ ⦿ Arclais Claudine LEBATARD
14690 PONT D'OUILLY ☎ 02 31 69 81 65 🖷 02 31 69 81 65
This house is situated on a hillside in south-east Normandy, and benefits from panoramic views of the countryside. Two double rooms and one suite with two connecting double rooms are available, all with private shower facilities. Lounge, veranda and garden with furniture. Close to the tourist attractions of Pont d'Ouilly, with its kayaking and canoeing facilities and designated hiking routes. Open April to October.
PRICES: s €30; d €35; t €45; dinner €13 **NEARBY:** Canoeing (4km) Horse riding (1km) Golf (4km) Sea (50km) Fishing (1km) Swimming pool (15km) Tennis (4km) Railway station (20km) Shops (4km) CLECY (6km) **NOTES:** No pets

REVIERS

¶¶¶ La Malposte J-Michel et Patricia BLANLOT
15 rue des Moulins, 14470 REVIERS
☎ 02 31 37 51 29 🖷 02 31 37 51 29
This former mill set on the edge of the sea has been fully restored and offers two double rooms and one suite consisting of two double rooms, all with shower facilities. Rooms are equipped with TVs. Lounge and kitchen at guests' disposition. The surrounding village retains its authentic architecture. Garden with furniture. Open all year.
PRICES: s €37; d €49; t €66 **ON SITE:** Fishing Tennis **NEARBY:** Horse riding (3km) Golf (15km) Sea (3km) Swimming pool (3km) Sailing (3km) Railway station (18km) Shops (3km) COURSEULLES S/MER (3km) **NOTES:** Pets admitted English spoken

ROBEHOMME

¶¶¶ Chambre d'hôtes Monique KONCEWIECZ
Hameau de Bricqueville, 9 Rue Vitrée,
14860 ROBEHOMME/BAVENT ☎ 02 31 78 84 90

This modern house in the heart of the Marais area enjoys a south-facing terrace that opens to the well-kept and attractive garden. Two double rooms with private bathroom and one double room with private shower are available. Garden with furniture. Guests

will enjoy exploring the surrounding area on foot or by bicycle. Open all year.
PRICES: s €27; d €34-€37 **NEARBY:** Horse riding (8km) Sea (8km) Fishing (1km) Swimming pool (8km) Tennis (10km) Sailing (10km) Railway station (18km) Shops (3km) CABOURG (10km) **NOTES:** No pets

SECQUEVILLE EN BESSIN

¶¶¶ Chambre d'hôtes Vincent et Annick LE RENARD
rue des Lavoirs, 14740 SECQUEVILLE-EN-BESSIN
☎ 02 31 80 39 42

This farmhouse offers tastefully restored, restful guest rooms and a warm welcome. The accommodation available consists of one double room with shower, one suite with a double room, single room and shower facilities, and a further suite with two double rooms and bathroom. Garden with furniture. Open all year.
PRICES: s €28; d €43; t €55 **NEARBY:** Horse riding (6km) Golf (20km) Sea (15km) Swimming pool (15km) Tennis (1km) Sailing (15km) Railway station (15km) Shops (4km) CAEN (15km) **NOTES:** No pets

ST AUBIN LEBIZAY

¶¶¶¶ Cour l'Epée M-Claire et Andre TESNIERE
14340 ST-AUBIN-LEBIZAY
☎ 02 31 65 13 45 🖷 02 31 65 13 45
e-mail: aj.tesniere@wanadoo.fr
Two grade 4 double or triple rooms with private bathroom facilities are available in this charming house, surrounded by a wonderful garden with furniture. A further grade 3 double room with private shower is housed in a connecting building. The guest rooms are elegantly decorated and the house enjoys very pretty views. Open all year.
PRICES: s €46-€54; d €54-€61; t €73 **NEARBY:** Horse riding (5km) Golf (15km) Sea (15km) Swimming pool (15km) Tennis (15km) Sailing (15km) Railway station (25km) Shops (5km) DOZULE (5km) **NOTES:** No pets English spoken

ST CHARLES DE PERCY

¶¶¶ Le Château Jacques DESORMEAU
14350 ST-CHARLES-DE-PERCY
☎ 02 31 66 91 03
e-mail: jacques.desormeau@wanadoo.fr
http://www.perso.wanadoo.fr/chateau-saint-charles/
This 18th-century château has architecture reminiscent of Tuscany, and offers two double or triple rooms and one suite consisting of two double rooms. The rooms have exposed floorboards and are equipped with private shower facilities. Inviting and relaxing lounge. Garden with furniture and park planted with trees. Open Easter to 1 November.
PRICES: s €40; d €49-€52; t €64 **NEARBY:** Canoeing (10km) Horse riding (4km) Golf (15km) Sea (45km) Fishing (15km) Swimming pool (14km) Tennis (4km) Sailing (50km) Railway station (14km) Shops (4km) VIRE (14km) **NOTES:** No pets English spoken

continued

ST DESIR DE LISIEUX

🏵🏵 ♿ La Cour St-Thomas Brigitte BESNEHARD
14100 SAINT-DESIR-DE-LISIEUX
☎ 02 31 62 87 46 & 06 82 99 12 37 📠 02 31 62 87 46
Annabelle the donkey will be on hand to charm children staying here. The accommodation itself will charm their parents. Two double rooms and one suite of two double rooms are offered, all with private bathroom or shower facilities. Extra beds are available. This house has wheelchair access. The kitchen and the lounge with TV and fireplace are also for guest use. Open all year.
PRICES: s €41; d €46-€49; t €64 **NEARBY:** Horse riding (15km) Golf (15km) Sea (32km) Fishing (1km) Swimming pool (5km) Tennis (4km) Sailing (32km) Railway station (4km) Shops (3km) LISIEUX (3km)
NOTES: No pets

ST ETIENNE LA THILLAYE

🏵🏵 Le Friche St-Vincent Guy et Monique BARATTE
14950 SAINT-ETIENNE-LA-THILLAYE
☎ 02 31 65 22 04 📠 02 31 65 10 16
Four double and triple rooms with private shower facilities are available in this modern house, built in the typical local style, which creates a perfect mix of comfort and calm. The garden is equally charming and its furniture is for guests' use. Open all year.
PRICES: s €32; d €40; t €46 **NEARBY:** Canoeing (4km) Horse riding (3km) Golf (4km) Sea (8km) Fishing (3km) Swimming pool (8km) Tennis (3km) Sailing (3km) Railway station (3km) Shops (3km)
DEAUVILLE (9km) **NOTES:** No pets

ST GERMAIN DE LIVET

🏵🏵 Route du Château Astrid MARLET
14100 ST-GERMAIN-DE-LIVET
☎ 02 31 31 18 24
Set on a hillside, which forms part of a wonderful valley in the Auge area, this house offers two triple rooms and one double room, all with private shower facilities. Garden with furniture. Nearby château. Open all year.
PRICES: s €35; d €43; t €52 **NEARBY:** Horse riding (7km) Sea (40km) Fishing (1km) Swimming pool (7km) Tennis (7km) Railway station (7km) Shops (3km) LISIEUX (7km) **NOTES:** No pets

ST GERMAIN DU PERT

🏵🏵 🌱 Ferme de la Rivière Paulette MARIE
14230 SAINT-GERMAIN-DU-PERT
☎ 02 31 22 72 92 📠 02 31 22 01 63
This 16th-century fortified farm offers two double rooms with private shower and wc facilities and one suite consisting of a triple room and connecting double room, with private bathroom. Nature lovers will enjoy the nature walk and the views of the marshland. Close to the D-Day beaches. Open Easter to 1 November.
PRICES: s €30; d €43; t €59 **NEARBY:** Horse riding (11km) Golf (25km) Sea (7km) Fishing (2km) Swimming pool (25km) Tennis (7km) Sailing (7km) Railway station (15km) Shops (2km) GRANDCAMP-MAISY (6km)
NOTES: No pets

ST LAURENT DU MONT

🏵🏵 La Vignerie Marie-France HUET
14340 ST-LAURENT-DU-MONT
☎ 02 31 63 08 65 📠 02 31 63 08 65
e-mail: mfhuet@club-internet.fr
Once used as a cider press, this independent building houses one double room, one family room and three triple rooms, all with private bathrooms. Communal lounge with fireplace and TV. Garden with furniture. The building is part of a 17th-century complex and features spacious guest rooms. Bicycles and

mountain bikes available on loan. Open all year.
PRICES: s €30; d €37; t €46 **NEARBY:** Canoeing (20km) Horse riding (2km) Sea (25km) Swimming pool (15km) Tennis (3km) Sailing (25km) Railway station (15km) Shops (3km) CAMBREMER (2km) **NOTES:** Pets admitted English spoken

ST LOUET SUR SEULLES

🏵🏵 🍽 Manoir de la Rivière Aurélien HOUDRET
14310 ST-LOUET-SUR-SEULLES
☎ 02 31 77 96 30 📠 02 31 77 96 30
e-mail: manoir-de-la-rivière@wanadoo.fr
Set in a 15-hectare park through which the Seulles River flows, this establishment offers elegant guest rooms whose décor incorporates family memorabilia. The guest accommodation, which is situated in an annexe to the main house, consists of double, triple and family rooms all with private bathrooms. Wander among the trees of the large park, which benefits from garden furniture. Open all year.
PRICES: s €53-€69; d €69-€84; t €99; dinner €23 **ON SITE:** Fishing
NEARBY: Canoeing (22km) Horse riding (2km) Golf (30km) Sea (30km) Swimming pool (3km) Tennis (3km) Sailing (30km) Railway station (22km) Shops (3km) VILLERS BOCAGE (3km) **NOTES:** No pets English spoken

ST MARTIN AUX CHARTRAINS

🏵🏵 Manoir Le Mesnil Françoise/J.François HOM
Le Mesnil, 14130 ST-MARTIN-AUX-CHARTRAINS
☎ 02 31 64 71 01 & 06 87 64 49 38 📠 02 31 64 70 46
e-mail: mmm.hom@voila.fr
Three large and attractive double rooms are available in this pleasant house only ten minutes from Deauville. The rooms all have private bathroom facilities. Open all year.
PRICES: s €53; d €61 **NEARBY:** Horse riding (8km) Golf (8km) Sea (8km) Fishing (1km) Swimming pool (8km) Tennis (5km) Sailing (8km) Railway station (8km) Shops (2km) DEAUVILLE (8km) **NOTES:** No pets English spoken

ST MARTIN DES ENTREES

🏵🏵 Chambre d'hôtes Pierre et Muriel LAUMONNIER
9, route de Caen, 14400 SAINT-MARTIN-DES-ENTREES
☎ 02 31 92 76 31 & 06 70 30 08 44
Three triple rooms with private shower facilities are available in this house close to the D-Day beaches and only five minutes from the historical town of Bayeux. The guest rooms have an independent entrance and benefit from additional facilities such as the picnic area. Open all year.
PRICES: s €32; d €38; t €47 **NEARBY:** Horse riding (2km) Golf (8km) Sea (8km) Fishing (4km) Swimming pool (2km) Tennis (1km) Sailing (8km) Railway station (1km) Shops (1km) BAYEUX (1km) **NOTES:** No pets

ST PIERRE DU MONT

🏵🏵 🍽 Chambre d'hôtes Kaï et Isabelle WEIDNER
Hameau Lefèvre, 14450 SAINT-PIERRE-DU-MONT
☎ 02 31 22 96 22 📠 02 31 22 96 22
Two grade 3 double rooms and one grade 2 family room with cot are offered in this house, situated close to the sea and coast path. The rooms all have private shower facilities. Large, open garden with furniture. Open all year.
PRICES: s €30; d €38; t €46; dinner €14 **ON SITE:** Sea **NEARBY:** Golf (12km) Fishing (4km) Swimming pool (10km) Tennis (4km) Sailing (4km) Railway station (25km) Shops (4km) GRANDCAMP-MAISY (4km)
NOTES: No pets English spoken

continued

NORMANDY

SURVILLE

♦♦♦♦ Le Prieuré Boutefol Bernard et Laetitia COLIN
Route de Rouen, 14130 SURVILLE
☎ 02 31 64 39 70

One triple room with private bathroom is available in the main building of this typical local property. In a separate building, hosts Bernard and Laetitia also offer two double rooms with bathroom and one suite of two rooms which can accommodate five people. The suite also has a private bathroom. Lounge and garden with furniture. Open all year.
PRICES: s €50; d €55-€80; t €93 **NEARBY:** Canoeing (1km) Horse riding (1km) Golf (2km) Sea (12km) Fishing (1km) Swimming pool (12km) Tennis (1km) Sailing (2km) Railway station (1km) Shops (1km) PONT L'EVEQUE (1km) **NOTES:** No pets English spoken

TILLY SUR SEULLES

♦♦♦♦ 🐾 🍴 Chambre d'hôtes Michel et Nelly BARATTE
Route d'audrieu, 14250 TILLY-SUR-SEULLES
☎ 02 31 80 82 10 📠 02 31 80 82 10
Set in a small hamlet, this traditional Norman farmhouse offers two double rooms, one triple room and one family room for four people, all with private bathroom facilities. The kitchen is for guests' use and the hostess, Nelly, has a seemingly inexhaustible stock of recipes! She and Michel welcome guests into this charming rustic setting. Open all year.
PRICES: s €29; d €35; t €45; dinner €14 **NEARBY:** Horse riding (8km) Sea (20km) Fishing (1km) Swimming pool (12km) Tennis (1km) Sailing (20km) Railway station (12km) Shops (1km) TILLY SUR SEULLES (1km) **NOTES:** No pets

TOUR EN BESSIN

♦♦♦♦ 🍴 La Vignette Bertrand & Catherine GIRARD
Route de Crouay, 14400 TOUR-EN-BESSIN
☎ 02 31 21 52 83 📠 02 31 21 52 83
e-mail: relais.vignette@wanadoo.fr
http://perso.wanadoo.fr/Relais.Vignette/
Two double rooms and two family rooms, all with private shower facilities, are available in this restored farmhouse. Enjoy the architecture, typical of the region, and relax in the attractive guest rooms which all have TV. There are an extra bed and cot available and evening meals are served on reservation. Lounge and garden with furniture. Open all year.
PRICES: s €40; d €40; t €55; dinner €20 **NEARBY:** Horse riding (10km) Golf (6km) Sea (5km) Swimming pool (6km) Tennis (5km) Railway station (6km) Shops (2km) BAYEUX (5km) **NOTES:** Pets admitted English spoken

---

CC - credit cards accepted

VERSAINVILLE

♦♦♦♦ Le Dernier Sou Paulette RALU
14700 VERSAINVILLE
☎ 02 31 90 27 82

This newly built house offers spacious, very comfortable guest rooms. There is a ground floor double room with bath and wc, and two rooms for three and four people on the first floor, plus an additional double room, with private shower rooms and wcs. Lounge with TV available. This is the ideal base from which to explore Falaise and the riches of la Suisse Normande. Open all year.
PRICES: s €24; d €34; t €41 **NEARBY:** Canoeing (18km) Horse riding (3km) Golf (15km) Sea (50km) Fishing (3km) Swimming pool (3km) Tennis (3km) Railway station (35km) Shops (3km) FALAISE (3km) **NOTES:** Pets admitted

VILLY BOCAGE

♦♦♦♦ Le Manoir du Cèdre
Bahram et Josette MOGHTADER
Maizerais, 14310 VILLY-BOCAGE
☎ 02 31 77 81 19
This establishment, set in peaceful countryside, offers bright, spacious rooms which successfully combine themed décor and comfort. The rooms, decorated either in oriental, retro or romantic styles, include two double rooms and one suite consisting of one double room and one single room. All rooms either have private bath or shower facilities. Open June to September.
PRICES: s €35; d €58; t €69; extra person €12 **NEARBY:** Canoeing (25km) Horse riding (5km) Golf (30km) Sea (30km) Fishing (7km) Swimming pool (2km) Tennis (2km) Sailing (30km) Railway station (25km) Shops (2km) VILLERS BOCAGE (2km) **NOTES:** No pets

VIRE

♦♦♦♦ Manoir du Pont des Vaux
Patrick et Martine JAUNATRE
14500 VIRE
☎ 02 31 66 14 93 📠 02 31 66 14 92
e-mail: Le-Manoir-du-Pont-des-Vaux@wanadoo.fr
Three double rooms and two triple rooms, all with private shower facilities, are offered in this restored 18th-century manor house with a leafy park. Hosts Martine and Patrick welcome guests to their property, surrounded by woodlands and bordered by a river. Bungee jumping and the Dathée Lake are nearby. Close to Vire and only 40 minutes from Granville and Mont Saint Michel. Open all year.
PRICES: s €32; d €38; t €46 **NEARBY:** Horse riding (10km) Golf (5km) Sea (50km) Fishing (5km) Swimming pool (1km) Tennis (1km) Sailing (50km) Railway station (2km) Shops (1km) VIRE (1km) **NOTES:** No pets English spoken

NORMANDY

VOUILLY

♥♥♥♥ ♥♥ Le Château James et Marie-José HAMEL
14230 VOUILLY
☎ 02 31 22 08 59   📠 02 31 22 90 58
Two double rooms, one triple room and two family suites are
available in this 18th-century château, still encircled by its
moat. There is independent access to the guest rooms, which
all have private bathroom facilities, look over the park, and
are spacious and comfortable. Lounge and garden with
furniture and picnic area. Fishing possible in the private pond.
Open March to November.
PRICES: s €47-€55; d €54-€62; t €77 **ON SITE:** Wine tasting
Fishing **NEARBY:** Canoeing (999km) Horse riding (28km) Golf
(28km) Sea (8km) Swimming pool (28km) Tennis (8km) Sailing
(10km) Railway station (9km) Shops (8km) ISIGNY S/MER (8km)
NOTES: No pets CC

See advert on this page

EURE

ACQUIGNY

♥♥♥♥ La Roseray Claude et Michèle HEULLANT
Quartier Saint Mauxe, 27400 ACQUIGNY
☎ 02 32 50 20 10   📠 02 32 50 20 10

M and Mme Heullant welcome guests to their peaceful home just
a few steps from the gardens of the Château at Acquigny. They
have four guest rooms on the first floor and one on the ground
floor. There are three doubles, a twin, and a single, all with own
facilities. Cot available. Kitchenette, open fireplace, living room
with billiard table for guests' use. Secure parking. Open all year.
PRICES: s €32-€34; d €37-€43 **ON SITE:** Fishing Hiking Tennis
NEARBY: Bathing (90km) Horse riding (5km) Golf (12km) Swimming
pool (5km) Water sports (1km) Railway station (12km) LOUVIERS (5km)
NOTES: Pets admitted

AIZIER

♥♥♥ Les Sources Bleues M.Thérèse et Yves LAURENT
Route de vieux port, 27500 AIZIER
☎ 02 32 57 26 68   📠 02 32 57 42 25
On the "Route des chaumières" and overlooking the River Seine,
this fine 19th-century brick building belongs to M and Mme
Laurent who live in the nearby thatched house. There are two first
floor double rooms with a single bed in a separate little room,
easily reached by the stair lift for anyone with restricted mobility,
and a double and a single on the second floor. All rooms have
their own facilities. Sitting and living room. 3ha garden. Open all
year.
PRICES: s €39; d €45-€54; t €54; extra person €9; dinner €14
ON SITE: Fishing Hiking **NEARBY:** Bathing (20km) Horse riding (10km)
Swimming pool (15km) Water sports (15km) Tennis (3km) Railway station
(40km) Shops (5km) PONT AUDEMER (15km) **NOTES:** Pets admitted
See advert on this page

APPEVILLE-ANNEBAULT

¶¶¶ ΪΟΪ Les Aubépines
Yves et Françoise CLOSSON MAZE
Aux Chauffourniers, 27290 APPEVILLE ANNEBAULT
☎ 02 32 56 14 25   📠 02 32 56 14 25

Completely restored by M and Mme Closson-Maze, this 18th-
century Norman farmstead stands in lovely gardens with views
over the valley of the River Risle. There are two rooms with double
or twin beds and a family suite with two doubles in separate
rooms, all with own facilities including facilities for babies. The
dining room has an open fireplace. Parking. Montfort Forest
nearby. Explore the Risle Valley by canoe or mountain bike. Open
April to September, at other times by arrangement.
PRICES: s €37-€40; d €42-€45; t €55; extra person €17; dinner €18
NEARBY: Bathing (40km) Horse riding (3km) Golf (30km) Fishing
(3km) Swimming pool (13km) Hiking (2km) Water sports (13km) Tennis
(3km) Railway station (45km) Shops (3km) HONFLEUR (30km)
NOTES: No pets English spoken

BARNEVILLE-SUR-SEINE

¶¶¶ Chambre d'hôtes Arnaud et Francoise BILLY
La Ferronnerie, 27310 BARNEVILLE SUR SEINE
☎ 02 32 56 08 87   📠 02 32 56 08 87

This half-timbered house in Norman style belongs to M and Mme
Billy whose riverside residence is nearby. Within the Regional
Nature Park of the Lower Seine, the location is unsurpassed, with
unforgettable views over the river from the hang-glider launching
area only 200 metres away. There is a double on the ground floor
and two triples on the first floor, all with own shower and wc.
Reception room and kitchenette for use of guests. Open all year.
PRICES: s €28; d €34-€36; t €44; extra person €5 **ON SITE:** Hiking
NEARBY: Bathing (60km) Horse riding (5km) Golf (12km) Swimming
pool (12km) Water sports (12km) Tennis (1km) Railway station (30km)
Shops (1km) BOURG ACHARD (5km) **NOTES:** No pets English spoken

BOSC-BENARD-COMMIN

¶¶¶ 🐓 Les Noés Jacques AUVARD
27520 BOSC BENARD COMMIN
☎ 02 32 56 26 24
This charming house belonging to M and Mme Auvard has apple
orchards and dairy cows grazing all around. Their house has two
ground floor doubles and a first floor triple, all with own wc and
bath or shower. A corner of the kitchen is for exclusive use of
guests. Open all year.
PRICES: s €28; d €36; t €44 **NEARBY:** Bathing (60km) Horse riding
(3km) Golf (20km) Fishing (15km) Swimming pool (12km) Hiking (2km)
Water sports (25km) Tennis (6km) Railway station (30km) Shops (2km)
ROUEN (30km) **NOTES:** No pets

BOSC-ROGER-EN-ROUMOIS

¶¶¶ ΪΟΪ La Queue-Bourguignon
Nicole et Pierre FONTAINE
1034 chemin du Bas Boscherville,
27670 BOSC-ROGER-EN-ROUMOIS
☎ 02 35 87 75 16   📠 02 35 87 75 16

Nicole and Pierre Fontaine welcome guests to their lovely home in
the middle of an orchard. On the ground floor there is a Grade 2
double with own shower and wc and (by arrangement) a suite
with double bed and hand-basin. On the first floor are two Grade
3 triples with own facilities plus a single-person suite (by
arrangement). Sitting room, open fireplace, veranda. Stabling can
be provided. Open all year.
PRICES: s €26-€27; d €32-€35; t €43; dinner €15 **NEARBY:** Bathing
(60km) Horse riding (3km) Golf (10km) Fishing (8km) Swimming pool
(8km) Hiking (3km) Water sports (8km) Tennis (2km) Railway station
(8km) Shops (3km) ROUEN (18km) **NOTES:** Pets admitted English
spoken

BOURG-BEAUDOUIN

¶¶¶ 🐓 Ferme du Coquetot
Bénédicte & J.Luc DELAVOYE
46 rue du Coq, 27380 BOURG BEAUDOUIN
☎ 02 32 49 09 91 & 06 16 09 05 00   📠 02 32 49 09 91
Bénédicte and Jean-Luc have taken great pride in restoring their
farmstead with its splendid dovecote. The three guest rooms on
the second floor of their spacious traditional gentleman's residence
include two doubles and a triple, all with own facilities and
individual décor. Sitting room with open fireplace and kitchenette
for guests' use. Only 2km from RN 14 but complete peace and
quiet. Several châteaux nearby. Open all year.
PRICES: s €29; d €36; t €49 **NEARBY:** Bathing (50km) Horse riding
(15km) Golf (24km) Fishing (4km) Swimming pool (12km) Hiking (2km)
Water sports (20km) Tennis (4km) Railway station (20km) Shops (5km)
ROUEN (20km) **NOTES:** No pets English spoken

BOURGTHEROULDE

Château de Boscherville Bernadette DU PLOUY
27520 BOURTHEROULDE
☎ 02 35 87 62 12 & 02 35 87 61 41   ▤ 02 35 87 62 12

Bernadette du Plouy has devoted herself to restoring this elegant 18th-century château and its peaceful parkland, and offers guests the choice of five guest rooms. On the first floor are two doubles and a triple, on the second floor a twin and a triple, all with own facilities. Farm produce for sale. Several abbeys nearby. Lower Seine Regional Nature Park 10km. Open all year.
PRICES: s €38; d €46; t €53   **NEARBY:** Bathing (70km) Horse riding (3km) Golf (10km) Fishing (12km) Swimming pool (12km) Hiking (1km) Water sports (15km) Tennis (3km) Railway station (8km) Shops (2km) ROUEN (25km) **NOTES:** Pets admitted English spoken

BRIONNE

Le Coeur de Lion Pete et Hazel BAKER
14, Bl de la Republique, 27800 BRIONNE
☎ 02 32 43 40 35   ▤ 02 32 46 95 31
e-mail: coeurdelion27800@aol.com
Mr and Mrs Baker look forward to welcoming guests to their charming, centrally located home. There are five first floor guest rooms, including a twin, three doubles, and a triple, all with own facilities. Sitting room, garden with a stream, large terrace. Parking. Meals €19 including wine. Open February to November.
PRICES: s €38; d €45-€48; t €56; dinner €19   **NEARBY:** Bathing (50km) Horse riding (7km) Golf (15km) Fishing (1km) Swimming pool (15km) Hiking (1km) Water sports (1km) Tennis (1km) Railway station (16km) BERNAY (15km) **NOTES:** No pets English spoken

See advert on this page

CAMPIGNY

Le Clos Mahiet Régine VAUQUELIN
27500 CAMPIGNY
☎ 02 32 41 13 20
In a peaceful setting, the three guest rooms in this charming half-timbered house belonging to M and Mme Vauquelin include a ground floor twin and two first floor doubles, all with own shower and wc. Extra single bed if needed. Sitting room with open fireplace and garden room. Lovely leafy garden. Parking. Riders welcome (loose boxes and fodder). Good local walking, riding and mountain biking. Open all year.
PRICES: s €30; d €37; extra person €14; dinner €???   **ON SITE:** Hiking **NEARBY:** Bathing (30km) Horse riding (5km) Golf (37km) Fishing (3km) Swimming pool (5km) Water sports (8km) Tennis (6km) Railway station (25km) Shops (6km) PONT AUDEMER (6km) **NOTES:** Pets admitted

CONDE-SUR-RISLE

Chambre d'hôtes Corinne et Claude EYPERT
La Vallée - Le Village, 27290 CONDE-SUR-RISLE
☎ 02 32 56 46 71

Claude and Corinne welcome guests to their fully restored 19th-century half-timbered residence. On the ground floor there is a triple with own entrance plus a double with disabled access, and on the first floor a double with own entrance and a family suite with a double bed plus two singles in the second room. All rooms have own shower. Guests' dining room and sitting room. Table tennis, boules. Meals featuring Normandy specialities by arrangement. Lake, river and forest nearby. Open all year.
PRICES: s €41; d €46; t €58; extra person €15; dinner €18
ON SITE: Fishing Hiking Tennis   **NEARBY:** Bathing (40km) Horse riding (12km) Golf (40km) Swimming pool (10km) Water sports (12km) Railway station (25km) Shops (10km) HONFLEUR (30km) **NOTES:** No pets

CONTEVILLE

⫲⫲⫲ Chambre d'hôtes Laurence ROUICH
Route d'Honfleur, 27210 CONTEVILLE
☎ 02 32 56 09 71 & 06 88 35 98 17

Laurence Rouich invites guests to this Norman residence in a peaceful setting at the gateway to Honfleur. There is a double with own ground floor entrance, shower and wc, and three rooms in an outbuilding, also in Norman style, comprising two triples and a first floor family room with a double and a single bed plus a children's corner with two single beds and own facilities. Breakfast featuring home-made pastries and jams are served in the sitting room with open fireplace. Parking. Open all year.
PRICES: s €38; d €43; extra person €9   **NEARBY:** Bathing (20km) Horse riding (4km) Golf (30km) Fishing (1km) Swimming pool (10km) Hiking (1km) Water sports (20km) Tennis (10km) Railway station (30km) HONFLEUR (13km)   **NOTES:** Pets admitted

⫲⫲⫲ ❦ Le Clos Potier Pierre et Odile ANFREY
27210 CONTEVILLE
☎ 02 32 57 60 79 & 06 33 37 43 35   🖹 02 32 57 60 79

Guests are welcomed by the friendly atmosphere of this Norman-style country home with its antique furniture and, in season, its profuse display of flowers. There is a ground floor double, a first floor double with own facilities, and two doubles with own facilities in an annexe. Sitting room with TV, garden, 17th-century cider press. Farm produce for sale. Open all year.
PRICES: s €45; d €50   **NEARBY:** Bathing (19km) Horse riding (4km) Golf (30km) Fishing (3km) Swimming pool (4km) Hiking (1km) Water sports (10km) Tennis (4km) Railway station (13km) Shops (2km) HONFLEUR (14km)   **NOTES:** No pets English spoken

EMANVILLE

⫲⫲⫲ Saint-Léger Michel et Josiane FRAUCOURT
27190 EMANVILLE   ☎ 02 32 35 44 32
This house deep in the countryside belongs to M and Mme Fraucourt who offer their guests an especially warm welcome. Their four first floor guest rooms include three doubles and a twin, all with own shower and wc. Sitting room, living room with TV. Lovely garden. Open all year.

PRICES: s €27-€29; d €32-€35   **NEARBY:** Bathing (65km) Horse riding (14km) Golf (9km) Fishing (14km) Swimming pool (7km) Hiking (5km) Water sports (25km) Tennis (7km) Railway station (19km) Shops (7km) LE NEUBOURG (7km)   **NOTES:** Pets admitted

EPEGARD

⫲⫲⫲ ♿ La Paysanne Maurice et Edith LUCAS
8, rue de l'Eglise, 27110 EPEGARD
☎ 02 32 35 08 95   🖹 02 32 35 08 95
M and Mme Lucas offer a warm welcome to guests in their spacious and well-restored 17th-century Norman home. On the ground floor there is a twin and a triple with disabled access, both Grade 3, on the first floor a Grade 3 triple and double, and a Grade 2 twin. All rooms have own shower and wc. Guests' sitting room and kitchen. Large wooded garden. Open all year.
PRICES: s €29; d €35; t €43   **NEARBY:** Bathing (80km) Horse riding (1km) Golf (2km) Fishing (20km) Swimming pool (30km) Hiking (1km) Water sports (30km) Tennis (5km) Railway station (30km) Shops (5km) LE NEUBOURG (5km)   **NOTES:** Pets admitted English spoken

FERRIERES-SAINT-HILAIRE

⫲⫲⫲ La Fosse Nardière Madeleine DROUIN
27270 FERRIERES SAINT HILAIRE
☎ 02 32 43 26 67
Mme Drouin's house is set in a lovely garden on the edge of the forest. There are three Grade 2 first floor rooms, two doubles, one with own bath, the other with own shower, and a triple with own shower. Shared wc. Another room, a double with own bath and wc, is on the ground floor. The Risle Valley is nearby and there are many châteaux and manor houses in the surrounding area. Open all year.
PRICES: s €32-€34; d €38-€47; t €53   **ON SITE:** Fishing Hiking **NEARBY:** Bathing (50km) Horse riding (1km) Golf (30km) Swimming pool (6km) Water sports (15km) Tennis (6km) Railway station (6km) Shops (6km) BERNAY (6km)   **NOTES:** No pets

FOURGES

⫲⫲⫲ Chambre d'hôtes Paul et Josette STEKELORUM
24 rue du Moulin, 27630 FOURGES
☎ 02 32 52 12 51   🖹 02 32 52 13 12

This centrally located house is built from the local chalky limestone. There is a ground floor double (beds can be joined), and two more rooms in a separate building, a double and a triple, all with own shower and wc. Sitting room. Parking with separate access. The owner has been inspired by Monet's garden at nearby Giverny to create two lovely gardens for guests to enjoy. Open March to October.
PRICES: s €32-€40; d €40-€49; t €64   **ON SITE:** Fishing Hiking **NEARBY:** Bathing (130km) Horse riding (6km) Golf (9km) Swimming pool (14km) Water sports (30km) Tennis (4km) Railway station (15km) VERNON (15km)   **NOTES:** No pets

continued

FOURMETOT

♯♯♯♯ ʲΟʲ L'Aufragère

Régis et Nicky DUSSARTRE
La-Croisée, 27500 FOURMETOT
☎ 02 32 56 91 92 ▤ 02 32 57 75 34
e-mail: retn@laufragere.com www.laufragere.com

The fine half-timbered residence of M and Mme Dussartre stands in a leafy setting deep in the countryside. There are two first floor doubles and, on the second floor, a triple, a double, and a family room with a double and two single beds, all with own bath and wc. All the comfortable rooms have a distinct identity, Thai, Mexican, Indian etc. Sitting room with open fireplace. Open all year.

PRICES: s €46; d €61; t €76; extra person €15; dinner €23
NEARBY: Bathing (45km) Horse riding (1km) Golf (40km) Fishing (4km) Swimming pool (6km) Hiking (2km) Water sports (6km) Tennis (6km) Railway station (40km) Shops (1km) PONT-AUDEMER (6km)
NOTES: No pets English spoken

GIVERNY

♯♯♯♯ Chambre d'hôtes Marie-Claire BOSCHER

1, rue du Colombier, Le Bon Maréchal, 27620 GIVERNY
☎ 02 32 51 39 70 ▤ 02 32 51 39 70

Mme Boscher welcomes guests to what used to be a family pension in the middle of Monet's Giverny. The three first floor rooms with their own entrance include a double, a twin with a single convertible, and a triple with sitting area with satellite TV in a converted artist's studio. All rooms have own facilities. Breakfast served in sitting room or in the garden. Parking. Mountain bikes. Open all year.

PRICES: s €39-€53; d €46-€62; t €64-€79 **ON SITE:** Fishing Hiking
NEARBY: Bathing (110km) Horse riding (15km) Golf (10km) Swimming pool (4km) Water sports (25km) Tennis (4km) Railway station (4km) PARIS (85km) **NOTES:** Pets admitted English spoken

♯♯♯♯ ᕴ La Réserve M.L et Didier BRUNET

27620 GIVERNY
☎ 02 32 21 99 09 ▤ 02 32 21 99 09
www.giverny.org/hotels/brunet

Overlooking Giverny's woods and orchards, the hilltop manor house belonging to M and Mme Brunet has been decorated with taste and care. There are three doubles and two twins, two on the ground floor (one with access for the less mobile) and three on the first floor, all with own bath and wc. Sitting and breakfast room with billiard table. Reduced rates for longer stays. Giverny 2km. Open April to November, in winter by arrangement.

PRICES: s €76-€137; d €84-€145 **ON SITE:** Hiking
NEARBY: Bathing (130km) Horse riding (15km) Golf (15km) Fishing (2km) Swimming pool (3km) Water sports (25km) Tennis (3km) Railway station (4km) Shops (2km) PARIS (85km)
NOTES: No pets English spoken

27490 La Croix Saint-Leufroy

La Boissière
Hameau La Boissaye
Tel: 02 32 67 70 85   Fax: 02 32 67 03 18

This delightful Manoir from the 15th Century is a perfect reason for a short stop in order to discover this beautiful region. Five smart bedrooms, all with en-suite private bathrooms are available all year long. Wide lounge with fireplace, tables d'hotes meals with cider included: Cider cooking, tarts, pancakes "Normandy style". The old Porch, the little lake and the garden with numerous plants make it an enjoyable place to relax. Restaurants are situated at 3 km. Attractions neaby are the castle Gaillard and the castle Bizy with golf and swimming pool at 9 km; the American Museum and the Monet Museum at 20 km. Rouen is at 40 km, Paris and Honfleur at 100 km. Open-Air games base at Lery-Poses with private woods. Access: Motorway A13 exit at Chauffour, follow Pacy-Sur-Eure for 20 km on the National road D836.
1 pers: 32€ – 2 pers: 41€ – 3 pers: 54€
Meal: 16€

JUMELLES

♯♯♯♯ ᕴ La Huguenoterie Daniel POITRINEAU

27220 JUMELLES
☎ 02 32 37 50 06 ▤ 02 32 37 83 36
e-mail: jpoitrineau@hotmail.com
http://www.chez.com/huguenoterie

This old farm building has been converted by M and Mme Poitrineau to house five comfortable guest rooms. There is a ground floor double and twin and a first floor twin and two triples, all with own shower and wc. Gourmet start to the day in guests' own breakfast room. Open all year.

PRICES: s €32; d €40-€43; t €50-€53 **NEARBY:** Bathing (115km) Horse riding (10km) Golf (15km) Fishing (15km) Swimming pool (14km) Hiking (10km) Water sports (45km) Tennis (4km) Railway station (14km) Shops (4km) EVREUX (14km) **NOTES:** No pets

LA CROIX-SAINT-LEUFROY

♯♯♯♯ ᕴ ʲΟʲ La Boissière Clothilde & Gérard SENECAL

Hameau de la Boissaye,
27490 LA CROIX SAINT LEUFROY
☎ 02 32 67 70 85 ▤ 02 32 67 03 18

This 15th-century manor house is the home of M and Mme Sénécal and has five guest rooms, including two ground floor doubles and a double and two twins on the first floor, all with own shower and wc. Lovely sitting room with open fireplace, kitchenette and TV. Pond with ornamental fowl. Meals by arrangement. Games room. Open all year.

PRICES: s €32; d €41; t €54; dinner €16 **ON SITE:** Fishing
NEARBY: Bathing (100km) Horse riding (10km) Golf (8km) Swimming pool (8km) Hiking (1km) Water sports (22km) Tennis (3km) Railway station (1km) Shops (3km) EVREUX (15km) **NOTES:** No pets
See advert on this page

LA NEUVILLE-DU-BOSC

††† iOi Chambre d'hôtes Nicole et Bernard WILKIE
47, route du Bec Hellouin, 27890 LA NEUVILLE-DU-BOSC
☎ 02 32 46 53 40 · 02 32 46 53 40

This fine house is owned by M and Mme Wilkie. There is a first floor double and a second floor twin plus a double with an additional single bed, all with own shower and wc. Ground floor sitting and dining room. Extensive gardens. Parking. Several tourist attractions nearby, château and golf course 4km. Open all year.
PRICES: s €40; d €44; extra person €15; dinner €17 **NEARBY:** Bathing (70km) Horse riding (5km) Golf (4km) Fishing (4km) Swimming pool (8km) Hiking (1km) Water sports (7km) Tennis (7km) Railway station (20km) Shops (4km) LE NEUBOURG (8km) **NOTES:** No pets English spoken

LE BEC-HELLOUIN

††† Chambre d'hôtes Sylvie CARON
Place Guillaume le Conquérant, 27800 LE BEC HELLOUIN
☎ 02 32 46 19 36 · 02 32 46 19 36
An authentic stone-built and half-timbered Norman home in the middle of the village of Le Bec Hellouin, just a few steps from the famous Abbey. The three first floor rooms include two doubles and a family room with a double bed plus two single beds on a mezzanine, all with own facilities. Open all year.
PRICES: s €46; d €52; t €67; extra person €9 **ON SITE:** Fishing Hiking **NEARBY:** Bathing (45km) Horse riding (1km) Golf (25km) Swimming pool (20km) Water sports (5km) Tennis (5km) Railway station (20km) HONFLEUR (45km) **NOTES:** No pets English spoken

LES PREAUX

††† iOi Prieuré des Fontaines
Jacques et M.Hélène DECARSIN
Route de Lisieux, 27500 LES PREAUX
☎ 02 32 56 07 78 · 02 32 57 45 83
e-mail: jacques.decarsin@wanadoo.fr
http://www.prieure-des-fontaines.fr
M and Mme Decarsin welcome guests to their home, which is said to date from the time of the abbey at Les Préaux. There is a ground floor triple with own bath and wc, and four first floor rooms including a double, a triple, a twin and a family room with a double bed plus two singles in an adjoining little room, all with own bath and wc. Telephone in every room. Guests' sitting room. Large garden, heated covered swimming pool. Open all year.
PRICES: s €53; d €59-€69; t €73-€82; extra person €18; dinner €24 **ON SITE:** Swimming pool Hiking **NEARBY:** Bathing (25km) Horse riding (3km) Golf (15km) Fishing (5km) Water sports (5km) Tennis (5km) Railway station (23km) Shops (5km) PONT-AUDEMER (5km) **NOTES:** No pets English spoken

See advert on opposite page

LONGCHAMPS

††† ❧ Chambre d'hôtes Reine THIBERT
Route Principale, 27150 LONGCHAMPS
☎ 02 32 55 54 39 · 02 32 27 59 60
This restored house is close to the residence of the owners, M and Mme Thibert. The four rooms include a ground floor triple and a first floor single, double and triple, all with own shower and wc. Living room, kitchenette for exclusive use of guests. Attractive garden. Open all year.
PRICES: s €25-€28; d €34; t €46 **NEARBY:** Bathing (80km) Fishing (3km) Swimming pool (3km) Hiking (8km) Tennis (3km) Railway station (16km) Shops (6km) GISORS (16km) **NOTES:** No pets

MAINNEVILLE

††† ❧ Ferme Sainte-Geneviève
J.C & Jeannine MARC
27150 MAINNEVILLE
☎ 02 32 55 51 26 · 02 32 55 82 27
The farmstead belonging to M and Mme Marc stands in a peaceful setting amid leafy parkland. The five rooms, all with own shower and wc, include two doubles and three triples. Two rooms have access to a kitchenette in an annexe. Parking. Good walking and cycling. Open all year.
PRICES: s €32; d €37; t €47 **NEARBY:** Bathing (80km) Horse riding (10km) Fishing (6km) Swimming pool (10km) Hiking (5km) Water sports (20km) Tennis (10km) Railway station (15km) Shops (15km) GISORS (15km) **NOTES:** No pets English spoken

MANTHELON

††† ❧ Le Nuisement Daniel GARNIER
27240 MANTHELON
☎ 02 32 30 96 90
www.normandy-tourism.org
Guests will receive a warm welcome at this Norman farmstead. The four rooms, one ground floor and three first floor, include a double with own whirlpool bath and wc, two doubles with own massage shower and wc, and a single in an adjacent room. Spacious living room with open fireplace, kitchen, and sitting and breakfast room. TV if required. Billiard room, fitness room, bikes. Farmhouse foie gras, rillettes and duck confit. Good local walking. Open all year.
PRICES: s €35-€38; d €40-€43; t €47-€50 **NEARBY:** Bathing (100km) Horse riding (2km) Golf (20km) Fishing (6km) Swimming pool (8km) Hiking (8km) Water sports (10km) Tennis (8km) Railway station (8km) Shops (6km) EVREUX (17km) **NOTES:** No pets

MARTAGNY

††† ❧ La Rouge Mare M.F et Jacques LAINE
21, rue de la Chasse, 27150 MARTAGNY
☎ 02 32 55 57 22 · 02 32 55 14 01
This restored house on a farm is close to the owners' home. There is a ground floor triple and a first floor triple plus a family room with two double beds. Shared shower and wc. Living room, kitchenette, attractive garden. Close to Lyons-la-Forêt. €61 for four sharing. Open all year.
PRICES: s €30; d €38; t €46 **ON SITE:** Hiking **NEARBY:** Bathing (100km) Horse riding (4km) Golf (15km) Fishing (6km) Swimming pool (10km) Water sports (10km) Tennis (10km) Railway station (18km) Shops (4km) GISORS (18km) **NOTES:** No pets

MISEREY

♯♯♯ ♥ ⵔ◯ⵝ La Passée d'Août

D.Y et V. GAEC BERTOUT
1 rue du stade, 27930 MISEREY
☎ 02 32 67 06 24   ▤ 02 32 34 97 95
e-mail: passeedaout@wanadoo.fr
http://www.ifrance.com/passeedaout

The Bertout family lives in a large house built of local stone and offer four guest rooms on the first floor of their converted barn. There is a twin, a double, a triple and a family suite with a double and three single beds, all with own shower and wc. Cot available. Sitting room with open fireplace and TV. Home-made jams served. Meals featuring regional dishes made with farm produce. Attractive garden. Open all year.

PRICES: s €30; d €41; t €49-€53; extra person €11; dinner €13
NEARBY: Bathing (120km) Horse riding (5km) Golf (10km) Fishing (8km) Swimming pool (10km) Tennis (10km) Railway station (10km) Shops (5km) EVREUX (10km) **NOTES:** No pets English spoken

NOJEON-EN-VEXIN

♯♯♯ ♥ Chambre d'hôtes Jules & Marie Louise DELEU

27150 NOJEON EN VEXIN
☎ 02 32 55 71 03   ▤ 02 32 55 71 03

M and Mme Deleu have four guest rooms in an annexe on their farm in this little village, plus a Grade 2 family room on the first floor of their house with a double and two single beds and own shower and wc. The annexe rooms include a Grade 3 ground floor double with own facilities, and on the first floor, a Grade 2 double with own facilities and a Grade 1 double and a triple with shared facilities. Sitting room. Garden. Microlight field 12km. Open all year.

PRICES: s €23-€30; d €27-€35; t €38-€43; extra person €10
NEARBY: Bathing (90km) Horse riding (12km) Golf (18km) Fishing (6km) Swimming pool (7km) Hiking (4km) Tennis (7km) Railway station (16km) Shops (5km) ETREPAGNY (6km) **NOTES:** No pets

NOTRE-DAME-DE-L'ILE

♯♯♯ ⵔ◯ⵝ Au Champ du Renard

A et Jean-Luc DAUCHY- DESWARTE
14, rue de Mezières, Pressagny-le-Val,
27940 NOTRE-DAME-DE-L'ILE
☎ 02 32 52 64 01   ▤ 02 32 77 47 30
e-mail: jeanluc.deswarte@free.fr
http://www.multimania.com/auchampdurenard

A warm welcome awaits guests at this fine old farmhouse built in local stone. There are three first floor rooms in the farmhouse with own entrance and another room in the old dovecote. Two are twins, two doubles, and all have own shower and wc. Reception room with library, sitting room with open fireplace where meals and breakfast are served. The building overlooks the Seine Valley between the Vernon and Andelys forests and is on the GR2 long-distance footpath. Open all year.

Prieuré des Fontaines
Route de Lisieux
27500 Les Preaux

A 17thC manor house set in 15 acres of woodland, which has been tastefully restored and furnished with country furniture, now offers bed and breakfast. Once the former village abbey, it is the perfect place to stay for nature lovers and those seeking a quiet and relaxing break. Five spacious en-suite bedrooms each individually named and furnished. The large living room with fireplace has a piano, TV and games all for the guest's use. Traditional, generous French breakfasts are served either in the dining room or on the patio with views over the garden. Typical Normandy cooking is served in the evening, packed lunches prepared by your host from traditional food can be ordered should you choose to discover the surrounding countryside. Pont Audemer a typical market town 5kms or within a stone's throw from the cider and calvados route and Mont St Michel is just 2hrs away.

Tel: 02 32 56 07 78   Fax: 02 32 57 45 83

PRICES: s €36; d €43; extra person €8; dinner €17 **ON SITE:** Hiking
NEARBY: Bathing (120km) Horse riding (10km) Golf (10km) Fishing (8km) Swimming pool (10km) Water sports (4km) Tennis (4km) Railway station (10km) Shops (4km) GIVERNY (10km) **NOTES:** Pets admitted English spoken

PONT-SAINT-PIERRE

♯♯♯ ♥ ⵔ◯ⵝ ⵅ Le Cardonnet E et E BOQUET THIBERT

27380 PONT SAINT PIERRE
☎ 02 35 79 88 91   ▤ 02 32 55 97 92
e-mail: emmanuel.eliane@voonoo.net http://ticketvert.com
Eliane and Emmanuel offer four guest rooms in a separate building on a farm in quiet and peaceful surroundings on the edge of woodland. There is a ground floor triple with access for the less mobile, and three first floor rooms including a family suite with two double beds and four singles, all with own facilities (two showers and two bathrooms with whirlpool baths). Spacious sitting room with open fireplace. Stabling for horses available. Close to Rouen, the Seine Valley, Lyons-la-Forêt, and fishing. Open all year.

PRICES: s €33; d €37-€42; t €46-€51; extra person €10; dinner €13
ON SITE: Horse riding Hiking **NEARBY:** Bathing (100km) Golf (25km) Fishing (5km) Swimming pool (5km) Water sports (25km) Tennis (5km) Railway station (25km) Shops (5km) ROUEN (25km) **NOTES:** Pets admitted English spoken

REUILLY

♯♯♯ Clair Matin J.P et Amaia TREVISANI

19, rue de l'Eglise, 27930 REUILLY
☎ 02 32 34 71 47   ▤ 02 32 34 97 64
This delightful manor house is owned by Mr and Mme Trévisani. On the ground floor with an entrance from the courtyard is a

continued   continued

double plus a family room with twin beds and two single beds on a mezzanine, and on the first floor a two-room suite with a double and two single beds. Lovely garden. Open all year.
PRICES: s €34-€41; d €41-€49; t €49; extra person €8 **ON SITE:** Hiking Tennis **NEARBY:** Bathing (100km) Horse riding (3km) Golf (10km) Fishing (5km) Swimming pool (10km) Water sports (25km) Railway station (10km) Shops (5km) EVREUX (10km) **NOTES:** No pets English spoken

ST-AUBIN-LE-GUICHARD

††† 🦢 **Manoir du Val** Michel et Mauricette PARENT
27410 SAINT-AUBIN-LE-GUICHARD
☎ 02 32 44 41 04 🖷 02 32 45 36 50
Michel and Mauricette promise their guests a warm welcome in their 16th-century residence with its dovecote. All on the first floor, the comfortable and spacious rooms include two doubles and a family suite with a double bed and a single bed in a small adjoining room, all with own facilities. Breakfast served in living and dining room with open fireplace. Cider for sale. Open all year.
PRICES: s €42; d €49; t €65 **ON SITE:** Hiking **NEARBY:** Bathing (60km) Horse riding (3km) Golf (25km) Fishing (9km) Swimming pool (15km) Water sports (9km) Tennis (2km) Railway station (15km) Shops (2km) BERNAY (15km) **NOTES:** No pets

ST-CLAIR-D'ARCEY

††† 🍽️ **Domaine du Plessis** Antoine GOUFFIER
27300 ST CLAIR D'ARCEY
☎ 02 32 46 60 00 & 06 13 31 56 57 🖷 02 32 46 60 00
e-mail: rodriguez.henri@wanadoo.fr
http://perso.wanadoo.fr/henri.rodriguez

An 18th-century gentleman's residence, where every window offers a different view over the park. Three bright and spacious first floor rooms opening off a corridor include a double and two triples, all with own facilities. Sitting room and garden room. Meals by arrangement. Dogs admitted on lead to the formal five-hectare park with peacocks, decorative waterfowl, and the owner's sculpture studio. Open 16 February to 30 November.
PRICES: s €41-€47; d €47-€53; t €56-€63; dinner €15 **ON SITE:** Hiking **NEARBY:** Bathing (60km) Horse riding (4km) Golf (25km) Fishing (6km) Swimming pool (7km) Water sports (20km) Tennis (7km) Railway station (7km) Shops (7km) BERNAY (7km) **NOTES:** Pets admitted English spoken

ST-CYR-LA-CAMPAGNE

††† **Chambre d'hôtes** MAIRIE /Laure DEBARRE
Mairie Saint Cyr-la-Campagne,
27370 SAINT-CYR-LA-CAMPAGNE
☎ 02 35 81 90 98 🖷 02 35 87 80 86
Guests are offered rooms on the first and second floor of this old brick-built town hall which has been renovated in contemporary style, and is located in the green and leafy valley of the River Oison. Each double room has telephone and own bath and wc.

Additional beds can be provided. TV in shared sitting room. Four garages. Several long-distance footpaths. Open all year.
PRICES: s €29; d €34; t €41 **ON SITE:** Hiking **NEARBY:** Bathing (75km) Horse riding (10km) Golf (15km) Fishing (5km) Swimming pool (7km) Water sports (20km) Tennis (1km) Railway station (8km) Shops (4km) ELBEUF (4km) **NOTES:** No pets English spoken

ST-DENIS-LE-FERMENT

††† **Chambre d'hôtes** G et M-Jose BOURILLON-VLIEGHE
29, rue de Saint Paer, 27140 SAINT-DENIS-LE-FERMENT
☎ 02 32 55 27 86
Surrounded by trees and flowers in the Levriére Valley, this property has four spacious first floor guest rooms. They include three doubles and a triple, all with own shower and wc. Sitting room and cooking area for exclusive use of guests. Living room with open fireplace. Parking. Open all year.
PRICES: s €30; d €34; t €47; extra person €13 **NEARBY:** Bathing (100km) Horse riding (2km) Golf (18km) Fishing (1km) Swimming pool (6km) Hiking (1km) Water sports (12km) Tennis (6km) Railway station (6km) Shops (1km) GISORS (6km) **NOTES:** Pets admitted

ST-DIDIER-DES-BOIS

††† **Le Vieux Logis** Annick AUZOUX
1, Place de l'Eglise, 27370 SAINT-DIDIER-DES-BOIS
☎ 02 32 50 60 93 & 06 70 10 35 76 🖷 02 32 25 41 83

In the middle of the village, the fine property belonging to Mme Auzoux dates from the 17th century and has a lovely garden. The three guest rooms in a separate attractive building include a ground floor double and two first floor triples, all with own facilities. Sitting and living room, open fireplace. Telephone. Open all year.
PRICES: s €37; d €41; t €53 **ON SITE:** Hiking **NEARBY:** Bathing (80km) Horse riding (10km) Golf (25km) Fishing (10km) Swimming pool (10km) Water sports (10km) Tennis (1km) Railway station (15km) Shops (1km) ELBEUF (6km) **NOTES:** No pets

ST-GEORGES-DU-VIEVRE

††† **La Pommeraie** Marie et Patrick BELACEL
Route de Giverville, 27450 SAINT-GEORGES-DU-VIEVRE
☎ 02 32 42 53 92 & 06 83 64 08 52
e-mail: marie.belacel@wanadoo.fr
Marie and Patrick welcome guests to their lovely 19th-century property in Anglo-Norman style set in peaceful surroundings. There is a double on the first floor of a completely renovated little Norman building with own facilities, and a double and a twin with own facilities on the ground floor of another building with separate entrance. Shared sitting and dining rooms. Stabling and feed for horses. Baby-sitting by arrangement. Cot €8. Good riding. Open all year.
PRICES: s €35; d €42 **ON SITE:** Horse riding **NEARBY:** Bathing (40km) Golf (20km) Fishing (6km) Swimming pool (1km) Hiking (1km) Water sports (6km) Tennis (1km) Railway station (20km) BRIONNE (14km) **NOTES:** Pets admitted

continued

NORMANDY

ST-GERMAIN-LA-CAMPAGNE

†††† **♥** **Le Grand Bus** Bruno et Laurence DE PREAUMONT
27230 SAINT-GERMAIN-LA-CAMPAGNE
☎ 02 32 44 71 14   📠 02 32 46 45 81
e-mail: bruno.laurence.depreaumont@libertysurf.fr
This fine 18th-century residence is set in a lovely wooded park. The two first floor rooms include a double and a double linked with a twin, and the second floor rooms include a twin and a suite with a double plus two single beds in an adjoining room. All rooms have own facilities. Games room and French billiards. Bike hire 10km. GR26 long-distance footpath 1.5km. Small pets welcome. Open all year.
PRICES: s €40; d €46; t €56; extra person €9 **NEARBY:** Bathing (55km) Horse riding (3km) Golf (40km) Fishing (6km) Swimming pool (16km) Hiking (2km) Water sports (35km) Tennis (1km) Railway station (16km) Shops (6km) LISIEUX (18km) **NOTES:** Pets admitted English spoken

ST-MACLOU

†††† **Le Pressoir du Mont** Monique et Jean BAUMANN
Hameau le Mont, 27210 SAINT-MACLOU
☎ 02 32 41 42 55 & 06 73 57 65 83   📠 02 32 41 42 55
www.location-honfleur.com
Jean and Monique welcome guests to their 17th-century thatched home in its lovely landscaped setting. There is a first floor double with own facilities and, in an adjoining little thatched building, a ground floor double (alternatively twin) and a first floor double (alternatively twin plus single), reached by external staircase, all with own facilities. Living room with open fireplace, sitting room. Huge garden with brick-paved tennis court. Open all year.
PRICES: s €43; d €54; t €69 **ON SITE:** Hiking Tennis
NEARBY: Bathing (15km) Horse riding (4km) Golf (15km) Fishing (5km) Swimming pool (10km) Water sports (5km) Railway station (20km) Shops (5km) HONFLEUR (15km) **NOTES:** No pets English spoken

ST-OUEN-DES-CHAMPS

†††† **Le Vivier** Alice BLONDEL
La Vallee, 27680 SAINT-OUEN-DES-CHAMPS
☎ 02 32 42 17 25
This Norman-style house owned by Mme Blondel is in a conservation area. The three guest rooms on the first floor include two Grade 3 doubles with own facilities and a Grade 2 double with own shower and wc on the landing. Small first floor sitting room for exclusive use of guests, ground floor living room. Easy access to the Vernier Marsh nature reserve and its Great Lake. Open all year.
PRICES: s €27; d €30 **NEARBY:** Bathing (30km) Horse riding (8km) Golf (45km) Fishing (10km) Swimming pool (10km) Hiking (3km) Water sports (15km) Tennis (10km) Railway station (10km) Shops (4km) PONT AUDEMER (10km) **NOTES:** No pets

ST-QUENTIN-DES-ILES

†††† **La Ferme de la Grondière**
Albert et Thérèse LEBRUN
27270 SAINT-QUENTIN-DES-ILES
☎ 02 32 43 10 61 & 06 14 19 17 09
This inviting haven of peace and quiet in the heart of the Normandy countryside is the home of Albert and Thérèse, who have converted a half-timbered 17th-century outbuilding to house three guest rooms. All on the first floor and with own shower and wc, they include a family room and a room with four double beds and separate entrance. Sitting room with open fireplace, shared dining room. €62 per four sharing. Open all year.
PRICES: s €33; d €38; t €58 **ON SITE:** Hiking **NEARBY:** Bathing (55km) Horse riding (2km) Golf (25km) Fishing (4km) Swimming pool (5km) Water sports (20km) Tennis (2km) Railway station (5km) Shops (5km) BERNAY (5km) **NOTES:** No pets

TOURNEDOS-SUR-SEINE

†††† **Chambre d'hôtes** Nelly et Michel TELLIER
2 ruelle des Marronniers, 27100 TOURNEDOS SUR SEINE
☎ 02 32 61 08 15 & 06 16 66 74 11   📠 02 32 61 12 96
e-mail: nelly.tellier@wanadoo.fr   www.gite-in-normandie.com
Nelly and Michel look forward to welcoming guests to their property on the banks of the Seine. The converted stable close to their house has three guest rooms, including a ground floor twin with kitchen, own shower and wc, and two first floor doubles with own bath and wc. Lovely river views from one of the rooms. Bikes for hire, two gîtes. 3km from the Poses watersports leisure centre. Open all year.
PRICES: s €35-€46; d €38-€46; extra person €11 **ON SITE:** Fishing Hiking **NEARBY:** Bathing (90km) Horse riding (4km) Golf (5km) Swimming pool (1km) Water sports (1km) Tennis (4km) Railway station (3km) Shops (8km) LOUVIERS (8km) **NOTES:** No pets

VERNON

†††† **Le Val d'Aconville** Sophie DE GRAVE
7, rue du Val-d'Aconville, Le Val, 27200 VERNON
☎ 02 32 21 98 06 & 06 15 10 25 66
Sophie de Grave invites guests to stay in her house built of local Vernon stone in fine surroundings on its 3ha estate. The three first floor rooms include a double, a twin and a family suite with a double bed and two singles in a small adjoining room, all with own shower and wc. Cots available. Sitting room with lovely open fireplace and living room. Dressage arena. Open all year.
PRICES: s €33-€38; d €40-€44; t €67; extra person €14
ON SITE: Fishing Hiking **NEARBY:** Bathing (100km) Horse riding (5km) Golf (13km) Swimming pool (2km) Water sports (2km) Tennis (2km) Railway station (3km) Shops (2km) GIVERNY (8km) **NOTES:** No pets

MANCHE

AUCEY-LA-PLAINE

†††† **♥** **La Jouvenelle** Pierre et Janine DESCAMPS
La Rue, 50170 AUCEY-LA-PLAINE
☎ 02 33 48 60 01
Mont Saint-Michel 12 km. Pierre and Janine welcome guests to their newly-restored stone-built house in a little village on Mont-St-Michel Bay. The four centrally-heated first floor rooms with their own entrance include a double, two triples and a family room for four, all with own shower and wc. Large living room with open fireplace and kitchenette. €61 per four sharing, no charge for additional guests sharing. 20% reduction for families with children. Guests may be interested in the owners' unusual snail farm. Open all year.
PRICES: s €30; d €38; t €53 **NEARBY:** Horse riding (10km) Sea (40km) Fishing (3km) Swimming pool (20km) Hiking (10km) Tennis (3km) Sailing (40km) Railway station (5km) Shops (5km) **NOTES:** No pets

BARNEVILLE-CARTERET

†††† **La Tourelle** Gérard LEBOURGEOIS
5, rue du Pic Mallet, 50270 BARNEVILLE-CARTERET
☎ 02 33 04 90 22 & 06 82 98 95 06
Briquebec 15 km. Valognes 25 km. A local history enthusiast, M Lebourgeois, has a 16th-century house in the centre of Barneville. There are two first floor guest rooms including a triple with an additional room and a second floor family room for four with an additional room, all with separate entrance, own bath or shower and wc. Sitting room, garage for bikes and motorbikes. Restaurant nearby. Guided tours and walks for groups can be arranged except in July and August. €60 per four sharing. Open all year.
PRICES: s €34; d €38-€42; t €50 **ON SITE:** Hiking **NEARBY:** Horse riding (2km) Golf (2km) Sea (2km) Fishing (1km) Swimming pool (16km) Tennis (2km) Sailing (3km) Railway station (28km) **NOTES:** No pets

BEAUVOIR

👬 ❤ Polder St-Joseph Michel et M-Brigitte FAGUAIS
50170 BEAUVOIR
☎ 02 33 60 09 04 & 06 84 17 17 38 ▤ 02 33 48 62 25
e-mail: mbfaguais@wanadoo.fr
http://www.chez.com/fermesaintjoseph
Mont Saint-Michel 5 km. This small-holding stands on land
reclaimed from the sea and all its guest rooms have superb views
of Mont-Saint-Michel directly opposite. There is a ground floor
triple with kitchenette, separate entrance and own shower and wc,
and on the first floor a triple plus a suite with one double and two
single beds, both with own shower and wc. Large first floor sitting
room with kitchenette. €60 per four sharing. Additional beds €10.
GR34 long-distance footpath nearby. Open all year.
PRICES: s €30; d €40; t €50; extra person €10 **ON SITE:** Fishing Hiking
NEARBY: Horse riding (4km) Golf (25km) Sea (30km) Swimming pool
(15km) Tennis (2km) Sailing (30km) Railway station (7km) Shops (2km)
NOTES: No pets

BLAINVILLE-SUR-MER

👬 Chambre d'hôtes Robert et Jacqueline SEBIRE
11, rue du Vieux Lavoir, Village Grouchy,
50560 BLAINVILLE-SUR-MER
☎ 02 33 47 20 31 ▤ 02 33 47 20 31
Agon-Coutainville 1.5 km. Coutances 12 km. Jacqueline and Robert
welcome guests to their 17th-century stone-built family house in
this old fishing village. The four first floor guest rooms include a
triple and two doubles, all with own shower and wc, and a double
with own bath and wc. Sitting room for exclusive use of guests.
Large garden, summer kitchen, table tennis, bikes, volleyball.
Open from 16 March to 31 December.
PRICES: s €29; d €35; t €43; extra person €8 **ON SITE:** Golf
NEARBY: Horse riding (2km) Sea (1km) Fishing (2km) Swimming pool
(12km) Hiking (1km) Tennis (2km) Sailing (2km) Railway station (12km)
Shops (1km) **NOTES:** No pets

BRICQUEBEC

👬 Chambre d'hôtes Denise MESNIL
La Butte, 14, rue de Bricqueville, 50260 BRICQUEBEC
☎ 02 33 52 33 13 ▤ 02 33 52 33 13
Landing beaches 25 km. Valognes 13 km. Cherbourg 24 km.
Facing the 11th-century castle in the centre of the little town, this
old farmhouse stands in spacious gardens. There is a ground floor
double with own bath and wc, a first floor suite with two double
beds, own shower and wc, and in a separate little building, a
double room with kitchenette, own shower and wc. Sitting room.
€55 per four sharing. Shops and restaurants nearby. Courtyard
locked at night. Open all year.
PRICES: s €24; d €33; t €44; extra person €11 **NEARBY:** Horse riding
(6km) Golf (17km) Sea (15km) Fishing (2km) Swimming pool (13km)
Hiking (2km) Tennis (1km) Sailing (16km) Railway station (13km)
NOTES: Pets admitted

CAMPROND

👬 La Chapelle Annick LEBRUN
50210 CAMPROND-BELVAL
☎ 02 33 45 13 90 ▤ 02 33 45 71 40
e-mail: michel.lebrun2@free.fr
Coutances 7 km. Landing beaches 45 km. This modern
establishment in a leafy setting halfway between Mont-St-Michel
and the Normandy beaches is owned by Annick and her husband.
The three first floor rooms include a double, a triple and another
double plus sofa-bed and a terrace. All rooms have central
heating, own shower and wc. Billiards and bikes. Restaurant 50m.
Reduced rates for stays of more than five days. Open between

Easter and 1 November.
PRICES: s €27; d €32-€35; t €40; extra person €9 **ON SITE:** Tennis
NEARBY: Horse riding (7km) Golf (20km) Sea (20km) Fishing (4km)
Swimming pool (7km) Hiking (7km) Sailing (20km) Railway station (7km)
Shops (1km) **NOTES:** No pets

CATTEVILLE

👬 ❤ 🍴 Le Haul Gérard et Odile LANGLOIS
50390 CATTEVILLE
☎ 02 33 41 64 69 ▤ 02 33 41 64 69
e-mail: lehaul@free.fr
St-Sauveur-le-Vicomte 6 km. Landing beaches 30 km. Odile and
Gérard welcome guests to their estate where they breed saddle
horses. They have four guest rooms with separate entrance. One is
a suite with two double beds and one a Grade 2 room with own
shower and wc. There is another triple on the first floor of an old
bakery with own shower and wc and ground floor sitting area and
kitchenette. Games room, mountain bikes, private footpaths,
daytime hunting, and marshland observation hide. Six loose boxes
for visiting riders. Climbing and canoeing 6km. Open all year.
PRICES: s €27; d €33-€46; t €47-€55; extra person €9; dinner €14
ON SITE: Fishing Hiking **NEARBY:** Horse riding (10km) Golf (20km)
Sea (10km) Swimming pool (20km) Tennis (6km) Sailing (10km) Railway
station (20km) Shops (6km) **NOTES:** No pets English spoken

CAVIGNY

👬 La Vimonderie Sigrid HAMILTON
50620 CAVIGNY
☎ 02 33 56 01 13
*Saint-Lô 11 km. Carentan-sur-St-Côme-du-Mont 18 km. Bayeux
40 km.* This old farmhouse in the countryside has been restored by
Sigrid Hamilton, who has decorated it in a restful and romantically
English style. There are two doubles and a single room, all with
own shower and wc. Pets €2. 20% reduction for stays of more
than three days (excluding official holidays). Open all year.
PRICES: s €27; d €32-€34; extra person €9 **ON SITE:** Hiking
NEARBY: Horse riding (3km) Golf (20km) Sea (30km) Fishing (2km)
Swimming pool (7km) Tennis (1km) Sailing (30km) Railway station
(10km) Shops (2km) **NOTES:** Pets admitted English spoken

CEAUX

👬 ❤ Le Mée Provost Henri et Agnès DELAUNAY
50220 CEAUX
☎ 02 33 60 49 03
Mont St-Michel 12 km. Val-St-Père 3 km. This attractive 18th-
century farmstead has five guest rooms. On the first floor is a
double with another double bed in an adjacent room plus a
ground floor family room (double) with its own entrance. A
separate building has three rooms (six beds) on the first floor. All
rooms have own shower and wc. Sitting room and kitchen.
Breakfasts feature home-made farm produce. €52 per four
sharing. Open all year.
PRICES: s €25; d €36; t €46 **ON SITE:** Hiking **NEARBY:** Horse riding
(7km) Sea (25km) Fishing (1km) Swimming pool (10km) Tennis (1km)
Sailing (25km) Railway station (10km) Shops (7km) **NOTES:** No pets

👬 Le Pommeray Marie et Fernand MOREL
Route du Mont St-Michel, 11, le Pommeray, 50220 CEAUX
☎ 02 33 70 92 40
Mont St-Michel 12 km. Val-St-Père 7 km. This modern house in its
pretty garden has four guest rooms including a ground floor family
room (double and bunk bed), and on the second floor three
doubles and a family room (double and bunk bed), all with own
shower and wc. Sitting rooms and kitchen. Electric heating. €49
per four sharing. Restaurants 1km. Access via D43 towards Mont-

continued

continued

St-Michel. Open 15 February to 15 November.
PRICES: s €26; d €34; t €43; extra person €8 **NEARBY:** Horse riding
(6km) Sea (25km) Fishing (1km) Swimming pool (10km) Hiking (1km)
Tennis (2km) Sailing (30km) Railway station (10km) Shops (2km)
NOTES: No pets

FRESVILLE

♦♦♦ Manoir de Grainville Bernard et Rolande BRECY
50310 FRESVILLE
☎ 02 33 41 10 49 📠 02 33 21 59 23
e-mail: b.brecy@wanadoo.fr http://perso.wanadoo.fr/grainville/
In the Cotentin Marshes Regional Park, this fine 18th-century
residence is the home of Bernard and Rolande. The three guest
rooms with own shower or bath and wc accommodate eight
people. Central heating. Open all year.
PRICES: s €33; d €46; extra person €11 **ON SITE:** Fishing Hiking
NEARBY: Horse riding (6km) Golf (8km) Sea (8km) Swimming pool
(12km) Tennis (6km) Sailing (9km) Railway station (12km) **NOTES:** Pets
admitted English spoken

GENETS

♦♦♦ Le Moulin Louis DANIEL
50530 GENETS
☎ 02 33 70 83 78 📠 02 33 70 83 78

Avranches 9 km. Centrally located watermill with three second
floor doubles and a twin, all with own shower and wc and with
separate entrance. Sitting room for exclusive use of guests.
Crêperie nearby. Open all year.
PRICES: s €27; d €33; extra person €8 **ON SITE:** Hiking Tennis
NEARBY: Horse riding (2km) Sea (5km) Swimming pool (9km) Sailing
(9km) Railway station (9km) **NOTES:** No pets English spoken

GRAIGNES

♦♦♦ ✿ Domaine du Mémorial
Denise et Marcel DELAUNAY
3, place de la Libération, 50620 GRAIGNES
☎ 02 33 56 80 58 📠 02 33 56 80 58
Carentan 12 km. Landing beaches 21 km. In the Cotentin Marshes
Regional Park, this residence is on an estate used for breeding
horses. The four first floor rooms include two doubles with own
wc and shower or bath and a double and a twin with own shower
or bath and own wc on the landing. There is also a Grade 2
double in a converted loose box close to the house which should
appeal to more adventurous guests. €67 per four people.
Restaurants 5km. Special accommodation offers available. Open all
year.
PRICES: s €33-€36; d €36-€43; t €55; extra person €15 **ON SITE:** Hiking
NEARBY: Horse riding (16km) Golf (12km) Sea (25km) Fishing (2km)
Swimming pool (1km) Tennis (12km) Sailing (12km) Railway station
(12km) Shops (1km) **NOTES:** Pets admitted

HOUESVILLE

♦♦♦ Chambre d'hôtes Gilbert MOUCHEL
4, village de la Pierre, 50480 HOUESVILLE
☎ 02 33 42 38 12 📠 02 33 42 38 12
Sainte-Mère-Eglise 6 km. This restored house in its leafy park has
a ground floor double with own bath and wc and veranda kitchen,
and a first floor suite (two doubles) with kitchen and own shower
and wc, all with separate entrances. Central heating. Library.
Garden rooms. Bikes. €53 for four people. Boat trips around the
marshland 3km. Open all year.
PRICES: s €27; d €32; t €46; extra person €8 **ON SITE:** Hiking
NEARBY: Horse riding (10km) Sea (8km) Fishing (4km) Swimming pool
(7km) Tennis (6km) Railway station (7km) Shops (6km) **NOTES:** No
pets English spoken

HUISNES-SUR-MER

♦♦♦ ♿ Le Moulin de la Butte Béatrice RABASTE
11 rue du Moulin de la Butte, 50120 HUISNES-SUR-MER
☎ 02 33 58 52 62 📠 02 33 58 52 62
Mont St-Michel 7 km. This large new house has a marvellous hillside
location in a charming village, and all its guest rooms enjoy views of
Mont-St-Michel. The two ground floor twin rooms include one with
access for the less mobile, and there are three first floor doubles.
All rooms have own shower and wc. Breakfast and sitting room.
Summertime carriage rides. 10% reduction in low season.
Open all year.
PRICES: s €26; d €35; extra person €8 **ON SITE:** Hiking
NEARBY: Horse riding (6km) Sea (30km) Swimming pool (17km)
Tennis (3km) Railway station (7km) Shops (8km) **NOTES:** No pets
English spoken

ISIGNY-LE-BUAT

♦♦♦ Le Bourg de Naftel Marguerite FORESTIER
50540 ISIGNY-LE-BUAT
☎ 02 33 48 00 68
Avranches 20 km. Mont St-Michel 30 km. In a peaceful location
and set in a lovely garden, this well-restored house has three first
floor guest rooms (double or twin) with own shower and wc and
separate entrance. Sitting room with open fireplace for exclusive
use of guests. Restaurants 3km. Open all year.
PRICES: s €30; d €33; extra person €11 **ON SITE:** Hiking
NEARBY: Horse riding (3km) Sea (40km) Fishing (3km) Swimming pool
(20km) Tennis (3km) Sailing (5km) Railway station (20km) Shops (3km)
NOTES: No pets

JUILLEY

♦♦♦ ✿ Ferme du Grand Rouet
Christian & Isabelle FARDIN
50220 JUILLEY
☎ 02 33 60 65 25 📠 02 33 60 02 70
e-mail: C.fardin@wanadoo.fr
http://perso.wanadoo.fr/christian.fardin
Saint-James 6 km. Mont Saint-Michel 18 km. Avranches 12 km.
Isabelle and Christian welcome guests to their farm. They have a
first floor guest room and three second floor rooms including a
family room, all with own shower and wc and with a separate
entrance. Kitchenette for exclusive use of guests. Views of garden
and pool. Country inn 3km. €53 for four people. 10% reduction for
stays of more than four days except in August. Open all year.
PRICES: s €29; d €36-€38; t €45; extra person €9 **NEARBY:** Horse riding
(6km) Golf (12km) Sea (20km) Fishing (3km) Swimming pool (13km)
Hiking (6km) Tennis (4km) Railway station (13km) Shops (6km)
NOTES: No pets English spoken

♥ La Lande Martel Bernard COCMAN
17, la Lande Martel, 50220 JUILLEY
☎ 02 33 60 65 48   📠 02 33 58 29 73
e-mail: cocman@ifrance.com
Mont Saint-Michel 18 km. Avranches 10 km. This establishment
has two first floor doubles and a twin with own showers and wc
and separate entrance. Sitting room and kitchenette for exclusive
use of guests. Local farm produce for sale. Restaurants 5km.
Reduced rates for stays of more than five days. Open all year.
PRICES: s €26; d €35; extra person €10 **NEARBY:** Horse riding (2km)
Sea (30km) Fishing (3km) Swimming pool (10km) Hiking (10km) Tennis
(5km) Sailing (35km) Railway station (10km) Shops (5km) **NOTES:** No
pets

JUVIGNY-LE-TERTRE

♥ ⚫ Le Logis Marylène FILLATRE
50520 JUVIGNY-LE-TERTRE
☎ 02 33 59 38 20   📠 02 33 59 38 20
e-mail: FILLATRE.CLAUDE@wanadoo.fr
Mortain 7 km. Moulin de la Sée 6 km. Museum at Ger 15 km.
Marylène welcomes guests to her 17th-century farmstead with its
old dovecote which has been converted into two guest rooms with
their own entrances. There is a ground floor double and a first
floor family room. Sitting room and kitchenette. There is another
family room on the first floor of the owner's house. All come with
own shower and wc. Meals by arrangement. €53 for four people.
€1 reduction for stays of more than four days. Children's meals
€8. Bikes. Climbing 7km. Restaurants 2km. Open all year.
PRICES: s €30; d €37; t €45; extra person €8; dinner €12
NEARBY: Horse riding (6km) Golf (20km) Sea (35km) Fishing (1km)
Swimming pool (7km) Hiking (3km) Tennis (2km) Sailing (20km)
Railway station (28km) Shops (2km) **NOTES:** Pets admitted English
spoken

LA BESLIERE

♥ Le Manoir Michel et Marguerite BENSET
50320 LA BESLIERE
☎ 02 33 61 32 23
Villedieu les Poëles 14 km. Granville (casino, spa.) 14 km. In a
quiet and leafy setting, this old farmhouse has three guest rooms
with separate entrance. There is a ground floor double with
kitchenette and a first floor double plus a triple, all with own
shower and wc. Restaurant 1km. Gîte available adjacent to owners'
house. Open all year.
PRICES: s €29; d €35; t €46; extra person €11 **ON SITE:** Hiking
NEARBY: Horse riding (6km) Golf (10km) Sea (10km) Fishing (1km)
Swimming pool (10km) Tennis (4km) Sailing (10km) Railway station
(12km) Shops (1km) **NOTES:** No pets

LA CROIX-AVRANCHIN

♥ ⚫ Mouraine Evelyne MESLIN
50240 LA CROIX-AVRANCHIN
☎ 02 33 48 35 69   📠 02 33 48 35 69
e-mail: bnb@nooplanet.com http://www.nooplanet.com.
Mont Saint-Michel 15 km. This old farmhouse has been restored
and has a Grade 2 first floor double with own shower and shared
wc, and two doubles/triples with separate entrance and own bath
and wc. Electric heating. Meals made with local ingredients
according to availability. Open all year.
PRICES: s €30; d €36; extra person €12; dinner €13 **ON SITE:** Hiking
NEARBY: Horse riding (5km) Golf (40km) Sea (40km) Fishing (5km)
Swimming pool (18km) Tennis (5km) Sailing (30km) Railway station
(9km) Shops (2km) **NOTES:** No pets English spoken

LA MEURDRAQUIERE

♥ ⚫ ⚫ Ferme de la Butte
Roland et M-Thérèse VENISSE
14 rue St-Martin, 50510 LA MEURDRAQUIERE
☎ 02 33 61 31 52 & 06 84 19 78 93   📠 02 33 61 17 64
Bréhal 9 km. Granville & Villedieu 15 km. On the 'Cider Route', this
establishment's three guest rooms with separate entrance include
a ground floor double room with easy access and a first floor
double and triple, all with own shower and wc. Sitting room and
kitchen. Mezzanine kitchenette. Cider for sale. Tour of orchards,
cellars, and free tasting. 5% reduction for stays of five days or
more. Restaurants 2km. Champrépus Zoo 8km. Open all year.
PRICES: s €27; d €32-€36; t €40; extra person €8 **ON SITE:** Wine tasting
Fishing Hiking **NEARBY:** Horse riding (9km) Golf (15km) Sea (15km)
Swimming pool (15km) Tennis (2km) Sailing (20km) Railway station
(6km) Shops (5km) **NOTES:** No pets

♥ La Grenterie Bruno et Delphine VASTEL
10, route de St-Martin, 50510 LA MEURDRAQUIERE
☎ 02 33 90 26 45 & 06 81 47 51 78   📠 02 33 90 45 85
Delphine and Bruno invite guests to their 17th-century farmhouse
only a few minutes from the coast. The three spacious first floor
rooms with their own entrance have individual names: the "mille
fleurs" is a double, the "capucine" has a canopied double bed, and
both have own shower and wc. The "cosmos" is a triple (another
single bed can be provided - €11) with own shower and wc.
Kitchen and sitting room. 10% reduction for stays of more than
five days (excluding school holidays). Restaurants 2km.
Open all year.
PRICES: s €35; d €40-€43; t €56; extra person €11 **ON SITE:** Hiking
NEARBY: Horse riding (9km) Golf (10km) Sea (14km) Fishing (9km)
Swimming pool (15km) Tennis (1km) Sailing (15km) Railway station
(6km) Shops (3km) **NOTES:** No pets English spoken

LA ROCHELLE-NORMANDE

♥ La Belangerie Jean et Marie-Jo MESENGE
50530 LA ROCHELLE-NORMANDE
☎ 02 33 60 90 40
e-mail: mj.mesange@wanadoo.fr
Villedieu-les-Poîles 20 km. Abbaye de la Lucerne d'Outremer 5 km.
This fine house on a dairy farm has three guest rooms furnished in
country style and with their own entrance. There is a double with
optional separate room for two, another double, and a family
room with a double and two single beds, all with own shower and
wc. Superior breakfasts. Laundry room. €56 for four, 10%
reduction for stays of more than three days except in August.
Restaurants 3km. Inn serving local dishes 3km. Granville 20km.
Open all year.
PRICES: s €30; d €38-€41; t €47-€50; extra person €9-€12
ON SITE: Children's play area Hiking **NEARBY:** Horse riding (5km)
Golf (25km) Sea (10km) Fishing (10km) Swimming pool (12km) Tennis
(3km) Sailing (13km) Railway station (10km) Shops (4km) **NOTES:** Pets
admitted English spoken

LAMBERVILLE

♥ Le Château E & F DE BRUNVILLE
50160 LAMBERVILLE
☎ 02 33 56 15 70 & 06 80 40 96 02   📠 02 33 56 35 26
Saint-Lô 17 km. The De Brunvilles invite guests to stay on their
ancestral property midway between Mont-St-Michel and the
invasion beaches. There are three spacious first floor rooms (two
doubles) with own shower and wc, separate entrance, and views
over the park and lake. Baby equipment. Sitting room with open
fireplace and kitchen for the exclusive use of guests. Daytime
hunting. Bikes. Fishing and boating. Canoeing 12km. Open 1
March to 30 November.

continued

PRICES: s €41; d €49; extra person €13 **ON SITE:** Fishing Hiking
NEARBY: Horse riding (15km) Golf (40km) Sea (45km) Swimming pool
(17km) Tennis (7km) Sailing (45km) Railway station (17km) Shops (9km)
NOTES: No pets

LE MESNIL-AUBERT

⑂⑂ ❦ Ferme de la Peurie Antoinette DAVENEL
4, rue du Calvaire, 50510 LE MESNIL-AUBERT
☎ 02 33 51 96 31
Gavray 4 km. A restored farmstead in peaceful countryside. The
first floor rooms include two doubles and a twin, all with own
shower and wc, and a particularly spacious room with a canopied
double bed and a single bed on a mezzanine, with own shower
(hydro-massage) and wc. Sitting room for exclusive use of guests.
Open all year.
PRICES: s €28-€39; d €31-€43; extra person €9 **ON SITE:** Fishing
Hiking **NEARBY:** Horse riding (5km) Golf (12km) Sea (12km)
Swimming pool (12km) Tennis (5km) Sailing (12km) Railway station
(10km) Shops (2km) **NOTES:** No pets

LE VAL-ST-PERE

⑂⑂ ❦ La Maraicherie René et Simone DESGRANGES
50300 LE VAL-ST-PERE
☎ 02 33 58 10 87
Mont Saint-Michel 20 km. Val St Père 2 km. The 18th-century
farmhouse belonging to Simone and René stands on the edge of
Mont-St-Michel Bay. The three guest rooms in a separate building
include one on the ground floor and two on the first floor, all with
own shower and wc. Kitchen for exclusive use of guests.
Restaurant 3km. Open all year.
PRICES: s €30; d €38; extra person €10 **ON SITE:** Hiking
NEARBY: Horse riding (1km) Sea (20km) Fishing (1km) Swimming pool
(5km) Tennis (5km) Sailing (25km) Railway station (4km) Shops (5km)
NOTES: No pets

LE VAST

⑂⑂ La Dannevillerie Benoit et Françoise PASSENAUD
route de Quettehou, 50630 LE VAST
☎ 02 33 44 50 45   ▤ 02 33 44 50 45
e-mail: CH.HOTES.PASSENAUD@wanadoo.fr
Saint-Vaast-la-Hougue 7 km. Ile de Tatihou 7 km. This old
farmhouse is in deep countryside in the delightful Saire Valley.
There is a ground floor room with a room beyond (double bed
and bunk) and two first floor rooms (total six people), all with own
shower, wc and entrance. Sitting room and dining area for use of
guests. Electric central heating. €58 for four. Restaurants 2km. On
GR223 long distance footpath. Open all year.
PRICES: s €29; d €35-€40; t €43-€49 **ON SITE:** Hiking
NEARBY: Horse riding (7km) Golf (15km) Sea (6km) Fishing (2km)
Swimming pool (17km) Tennis (4km) Sailing (7km) Railway station
(17km) Shops (2km) **NOTES:** No pets English spoken

LES CHAMPS-DE-LOSQUES

⑂⑂ ❦ ⑂◯⑂ Les Rondchamps Georges et Irène VOISIN
50620 LES CHAMPS-DE-LOSQUES
☎ 02 33 56 21 40
Tourist train 15 km. Landing beaches 25 km. Irène and Georges
are happy to invite guests to their farm in the Cotentin Marshes
Regional Park. There are four guest rooms, all with own shower.
Small kitchen for use of guests. Central heating. Meals by
arrangement, featuring local produce in a family setting. Lake,
pedalos 8km. Racecourse 10km. Open all year.
PRICES: s €25-€27; d €32-€34; t €40-€42; extra person €9; dinner €14
ON SITE: Hiking **NEARBY:** Horse riding (3km) Golf (7km) Sea (26km)
Fishing (2km) Swimming pool (6km) Tennis (3km) Sailing (15km)
Railway station (15km) **NOTES:** No pets English spoken

LES VEYS

⑂⑂ ❦ ⑂◯⑂ Haras du Vieux Château
Denis et Myriam AVENEL
50500 LES VEYS
☎ 02 33 71 00 38   ▤ 02 33 71 63 38
e-mail: Denis.AVENEL@wanadoo.fr
Isigny-sur-Mer 5 km. Myriam and Denis invite guests to their stud
farm, with its 16th-century turreted residence and remains of a
moat. Own entrance. Sitting room for exclusive use of guests.
Norman-style family dinner by arrangement. Meals served
between Easter and 1 November. Open all year.
PRICES: s €47; d €50; dinner €18 **NEARBY:** Horse riding (13km) Golf
(30km) Sea (4km) Fishing (1km) Swimming pool (8km) Hiking (1km)
Tennis (4km) Sailing (8km) Railway station (8km) Shops (4km)
NOTES: No pets

LIEUSAINT

⑂⑂ Chambre d'hôtes André et Ghislaine MOUCHEL
Le Haut Pitois, 50700 LIEUSAINT
☎ 02 33 40 19 92
Valognes 5 km. Landing beaches 25 km. Guests are invited to stay
in this residence which has many fascinating associations with
local and regional history. The five first floor guest rooms have a
separate entrance and include a family room and another with a
connecting room, all with own shower and wc. Fully fitted kitchen
and sitting room with open fireplace for exclusive use of guests.
Bikes and games. Restaurants 5km. €55 for four people.
Open all year.
PRICES: s €31; d €36; t €46 **ON SITE:** Fishing **NEARBY:** Horse riding
(15km) Golf (16km) Sea (16km) Swimming pool (5km) Hiking (2km)
Tennis (5km) Sailing (16km) Railway station (5km) Shops (5km)
NOTES: No pets

LINGREVILLE

⑂⑂ Blanche pré Christine et Thierry GAUTIER
Village Hue, 7, rue des Chouers, 50660 LINGREVILLE
☎ 02 33 07 91 24 & 06 82 75 49 89
e-mail: blanchepre@chez.com www.chez.com/blanchepré

Granville 15 km. The stylish, newly-built white house owned by
Christine and Thierry stands in attractively landscaped garden.
There is a ground floor double opening onto the garden with a
further room (twin), while on the first floor are two doubles.
All rooms have own bath or shower and wc. Baby equipment.
Kitchen. Games area. €50 for four people. Restaurants 3km.
Open all year.
PRICES: s €30; d €30; t €42; extra person €10 **ON SITE:** Children's play
area **NEARBY:** Horse riding (3km) Golf (10km) Sea (2km) Fishing
(6km) Swimming pool (15km) Hiking (1km) Tennis (3km) Sailing (3km)
Railway station (15km) Shops (1km) **NOTES:** No pets English spoken

LONGUEVILLE

Château de Longueville
Ludovic et Sandrine BOUCHART
50290 LONGUEVILLE ☎ 02 33 50 66 60
Granville (spa, casino) 4 km. Mont Saint-Michel 60 km.
This 18th-century residence with its park and lakes offers guests
the chance to relax. Refined décor and modern facilities. The first
floor rooms include a twin and a suite (bedroom and sitting room,
double and single bed), and there is a large second floor suite
(two bedrooms and sitting room, double and two single beds).
Luxury bathrooms include one with jacuzzi, hammam and hydro-
massage. Non-smoking. Villedieu-les-Poëles is famous for its
copperware and bell-foundry. Open all year.
PRICES: s €76; d €76-€99; t €91; extra person €15 **ON SITE:** Fishing
NEARBY: Horse riding (2km) Golf (2km) Sea (2km) Swimming pool
(4km) Hiking (2km) Tennis (2km) Sailing (4km) Railway station (4km)
Shops (2km) **NOTES:** No pets

MONTCHATON

Le Quesnot Jacques et Ginette GERMANICUS
3, rue du Mont César, 50660 MONTCHATON
☎ 02 33 45 05 88
Coutances 6 km. With its landscaped garden, this attractive stone
house is close to a traditional village, from whose hilltop church
there are lovely views of the surrounding countryside. With own
showers and wcs, there are three first floor double rooms in a
separate building with its own sitting and breakfast room.
Canoeing 500m. Restaurants 1km. Open Easter to late September.
PRICES: s €35; d €40 **ON SITE:** Hiking **NEARBY:** Horse riding (6km)
Golf (6km) Sea (4km) Fishing (1km) Swimming pool (6km) Tennis (4km)
Sailing (6km) Railway station (6km) Shops (3km) **NOTES:** No pets

MONTGARDON

Le Mont Scolan Yves et Nicole SEGUINEAU
50250 MONTGARDON
☎ 02 33 46 11 27
La Haye-du-Puits 3 km. Midway between coast and countryside,
this working farm is owned by Yves and Nicole. There are two first
floor guest rooms (doubles) with separate entrance, shower and
wc. Sitting room for use of guests. Another building has two
ground floor triples, one with two beds on a mezzanine, both with
own shower and wc. Meals by arrangement. Children's meal €7.
Pets €3. Games room, table football, billiards. Open all year.
PRICES: s €29; d €35; extra person €11; dinner €13 **NEARBY:** Horse
riding (2km) Sea (6km) Fishing (11km) Swimming pool (25km) Hiking
(2km) Tennis (3km) Sailing (14km) Railway station (29km) Shops (2km)
NOTES: Pets admitted

MONTVIRON

Le Manoir de la Croix Patrice WAGNER
Le Gros Chêne, 50530 MONTVIRON
☎ 02 33 60 68 30 📠 02 33 60 69 21
Granville (casino, spa) 16 km. Located on Mont-St-Michel Bay,
Patrice Wagner's 19th-century manor house offers comfortable
rooms. On the first floor there are two individually named
suites, 'Rebecca' and 'Marie-Louise', with canopied bed plus a
single bed and private terrace, and on the second floor two
charming doubles, 'Pauline' and 'Eugénie'. All rooms have
own bath and wc and are non-smoking. Sitting and living
room. Wooded park. Open all year.
PRICES: s €43-€46; d €49-€65; t €79; extra person €12
NEARBY: Horse riding (10km) Golf (10km) Sea (10km) Fishing
(2km) Swimming pool (7km) Hiking (1km) Tennis (2km) Sailing
(13km) Railway station (8km) Shops (4km) **NOTES:** No pets
English spoken

MORSALINES

Chambre d'hôtes Maurice et Michele BERGER
8, hameau les Masses, 50630 MORSALINES
☎ 02 33 54 21 50 📠 02 33 54 21 50
e-mail: berger.michele@wanadoo.fr
Saint-Vaast-la-Hougue 6 km. Landing beaches 10 km. Lovers of
classical music, river fishing, and genealogy, Michele and Maurice
invite guests to their well-restored farmhouse standing in a lovely
garden. There is a ground floor double with own bath and wc, and
on the first floor a double plus a family room for four, both with
own shower and wc. Walkers and riders welcome. €55 for four.
Tatihou Island (August music festival) 6km. Open all year.
PRICES: s €34; d €37; t €46; extra person €9 **NEARBY:** Horse riding
(7km) Golf (10km) Sea (2km) Swimming pool (15km) Hiking (2km)
Tennis (6km) Sailing (6km) Railway station (15km) Shops (4km)
NOTES: No pets

POILLEY-SUR-LE-HOMME

Le Logis François et Martine LAMBERT
50220 POILLEY-SUR-LE-HOMME
☎ 02 33 58 35 90 & 06 62 63 35 90 📠 02 33 58 35 90
e-mail: francois.lambert2@libertysurf.fr
Mont Saint-Michel 17 km. Avranches 9 km. Le Val-St-Père 6 km.
This residence of character standing in its own park with a kitchen
garden, has two spacious doubles on the first floor and another
double on the second floor, all with own bath and wc. Sitting
room. Central heating. Central location opposite the church.
Fishing on foot at spring tides. Restaurant 1km. Open all year.
PRICES: s €46; d €50; extra person €15 **ON SITE:** Hiking
NEARBY: Horse riding (3km) Golf (30km) Sea (25km) Fishing (1km)
Swimming pool (8km) Tennis (1km) Sailing (25km) Railway station (8km)
Shops (1km) **NOTES:** No pets English spoken

RAUVILLE-LA-PLACE

La Cour Monique TARDIF
50390 RAUVILLE-LA-PLACE
☎ 02 33 41 65 07
Valognes 14 km. Forêt de Saint-Sauveur-le-Vicomte 5 km. Guests
receive a warm welcome at this completely restored manor house.
Originally dating from the 16th-century, the building has tiled
floors, and stone staircases, one of which gives access to a tower
room with double bed. There are two other rooms, one with two
double beds, the other with a double and children's bunk bed.
Luxurious own showers and wcs. Breakfast served in room with
monumental fireplace. Sitting room. Separate entrance. €59 for
four people, fifth night free except July and August. Open all year.
PRICES: s €30-€35; d €35-€40; t €52 **NEARBY:** Horse riding (14km)
Golf (20km) Sea (16km) Swimming pool (14km) Hiking (1km) Tennis
(3km) Sailing (16km) Railway station (14km) Shops (3km) **NOTES:** Pets
admitted

REVILLE

Ferme de Maltot Sophie DUBOST
50760 REVILLE
☎ 02 33 43 38 32 & 06 82 83 82 15 📠 02 33 43 38 87
e-mail: ferme.maltot@wanadoo.fr http://ferme.maltot@free.fr
Barfleur, St-Vaast-la-Hougue 7 km. Ile de Tatihou 6 km. In the
heart of the picturesque Saire Valley only 400m from the beach,
this old stone 18th-century outbuilding has been completely
restored by Sophie and has four bright and spacious guest rooms.
There is a ground floor twin with disabled access, own shower and
wc, and two first floor doubles and another double with canopied
bed, all with own shower or bath and wc. Meals served in a large
sitting room with granite fireplace. Children's meals €8. Bikes
available. Open all year.

continued

PRICES: s €44; d €49; extra person €13; dinner €15 **ON SITE:** Sea Hiking **NEARBY:** Horse riding (2km) Golf (30km) Fishing (3km) Swimming pool (20km) Tennis (5km) Sailing (5km) Railway station (20km) Shops (3km) **NOTES:** No pets English spoken

SERVON

Chambre d'hôtes Fabienne et Patrick BAUBIGNY
30, rue du Pont Morin, 50170 SERVON
☎ 02 33 60 34 14 & 06 82 14 55 71
Mont Saint-Michel 10 km. Val St Père 7 km: WWII museum. This old inn connected to their own stone-built residence has been converted by Fabienne and Patrick to house four bright and spacious guest rooms. On the first floor a family room (two doubles) and a triple, and on the second floor two doubles, all with own shower and wc. Breakfast served in sitting room with kitchenette, living room for guests. Garden available for picnics. Restaurant 1km. €53 for four. Open all year.
PRICES: s €29; d €35-€40; t €46; extra person €8 **NEARBY:** Horse riding (5km) Golf (30km) Sea (25km) Fishing (1km) Swimming pool (12km) Hiking (4km) Tennis (1km) Railway station (10km) Shops (10km) **NOTES:** No pets

ST-AUBIN-DES-PREAUX

Le Hamel Edith THOMAS
50380 ST-AUBIN-DES-PREAUX
☎ 02 33 51 42 65 & 06 14 25 38 22

Granville 7 km. Mont St-Michel Bay 10 km. Val-St-Père 5 km. On an old farm in a peaceful setting and with a well planted garden, this large stone building has three first floor guest rooms including two doubles and a family room for four, all with own facilities and separate entrance. Kitchenette for use of guests. €52 for four. Extra beds €8. Fifth night free between 1 October and 15 March. Lucerne Abbey 5km, Second World War Museum at Val-St-Père, Channel Islands ferry and seawater therapy at Granville. Open all year.
PRICES: s €29; d €35-€40; t €44-€47; extra person €8 **ON SITE:** Hiking **NEARBY:** Horse riding (5km) Golf (3km) Sea (5km) Fishing (4km) Swimming pool (7km) Tennis (3km) Sailing (7km) Railway station (8km) Shops (4km) **NOTES:** No pets

ST-AUBIN-DE-TERREGATTE

Ferme de la Patrais
J-Pierre et Hélène CARNET
3, Ferme de la Patrais, 50240 ST-AUBIN-DE-TERREGATTE
☎ 02 33 48 43 13 📠 02 33 48 59 03
Ducey 5 km. Mont Saint-Michel 20 km. This farmstead's four guest rooms include a ground floor double and a family room for four with disabled access, and there are two first floor family rooms for four (one with double bed and bunks and sitting area), all with own entrance, shower and wc. A separate building has a kitchenette, sitting area and games room for use of guests. Meals by arrangement. Children's meals €8. Additional beds €9. €53 per four. 10% reduction for stays of more than four days. Open all year.
PRICES: s €26; d €35; t €44; extra person €9; dinner €13
ON SITE: Hiking **NEARBY:** Horse riding (9km) Sea (4km) Fishing (3km) Swimming pool (15km) Tennis (1km) Sailing (6km) Railway station (18km) Shops (5km) **NOTES:** No pets English spoken

ST-CYR-DU-BAILLEUL

Chambre d'hôtes
Jean et Antoinette HARDY
Le Bourg, 50720 ST-CYR-DU-BAILLEUL
☎ 02 33 59 43 89 📠 02 33 59 39 85
Mont St-Michel 60 km. Climbing at la Fosse Arthour 8 km. This stone-built house is in the middle of a village in the Mortain countryside. There is a first floor double (plus separate room with twin beds), and a Grade 2 double, both with own shower and wc. A separate building houses a double (plus separate room with twin beds) with own bath and wc. Kitchenette and sitting area. Baby equipment, games, and children's mountain bikes. Mountain bike hire. The pear orchards are in spectacular blossom from mid-April. €48/50 for four. Children under 14 €8. Dogs €4. Open all year.
PRICES: s €22; d €28-€30; t €39-€41; extra person €6 **ON SITE:** Hiking **NEARBY:** Horse riding (7km) Golf (30km) Sea (50km) Fishing (8km) Swimming pool (14km) Tennis (5km) Railway station (30km) Shops (1km) **NOTES:** Pets admitted

STE-GENEVIEVE

Manoir de la Fevrerie Marie-France CAILLET
4, route d'Arville, 50760 STE-GENEVIEVE
☎ 02 33 54 33 53 & 06 80 85 89 01 📠 02 33 22 12 50

Barfleur 3 km. Cherbourg 25km. Ile de Tatihou 10 km. Marie-France will be delighted to welcome guests to her family's manor house dating from the 16th and 17th centuries. Reached by a stone staircase and charmingly decorated, the guest rooms include a double and two twins, all with own bath or shower and wc. Breakfast served in a room with a magnificent open fireplace in granite. Stabling for horses available. Open all year.
PRICES: s €42-€53; d €46-€58 **ON SITE:** Hiking **NEARBY:** Horse riding (5km) Golf (17km) Sea (3km) Fishing (2km) Swimming pool (20km) Tennis (3km) Sailing (3km) Railway station (20km) Shops (3km) **NOTES:** Pets admitted

STE-MERE-EGLISE

¶¶¶ Chambre d'hôtes Anne LEMARINEL
Musée de la Ferme, 1, chemin de Beauvais,
50480 STE-MERE-EGLISE
☎ 02 33 95 40 20 & 02 33 95 40 22 ▤ 02 33 95 40 24
Lovers of rural life will enjoy staying in this fine 17th and 18th century house which is in the grounds of the Farm Museum. There are four first floor guest rooms with separate entrance and own bath and wc, accommodating a total of eight people. Centrally heated. €50 per four. Restaurant 2km. Canoeing 17km. Free entry to museum. Closed December.
PRICES: s €30; d €36; t €40; extra person €9 **ON SITE:** Hiking
NEARBY: Horse riding (10km) Golf (10km) Sea (10km) Fishing (3km) Swimming pool (13km) Tennis (1km) Sailing (13km) Railway station (17km) Shops (1km) **NOTES:** No pets CC

¶¶¶ ✿ Ferme Riou Victor et Madeleine DESTRES
1, Ferme Riou, 50480 STE-MERE-EGLISE
☎ 02 33 41 63 40
Sainte-Mère-Eglise 1.5 km. Landing beaches 10 km. Madeleine and Victor welcome guests to their farm where cattle and horses graze. There are two ground floor rooms accommodating a total of five, both with own shower and wc, and a first floor double in the main building with own shower and wc. Picnicking. Pets €1. Restaurant 1km. Open all year.
PRICES: s €27; d €35-€38; t €47; extra person €10 **ON SITE:** Hiking
NEARBY: Horse riding (10km) Golf (10km) Sea (10km) Fishing (5km) Swimming pool (15km) Tennis (2km) Sailing (10km) Railway station (15km) Shops (2km) **NOTES:** Pets admitted

ST-GEORGES-DE-MONTCOCQ

¶¶¶ La Dainerie Thérèse et Pierre DROUET
122, avenue du Cotentin,
50000 ST-GEORGES-DE-MONTCOCQ
☎ 02 33 72 22 80
On the edge of the Marshlands Regional Nature Park, this attractively decorated modern home with its traditional country furniture belongs to Thérèse and Pierre. There is a ground floor double and two first floor triples, all with own bath or shower and wc, microwave and fridge. Good range of baby equipment. Generous breakfast with local ingredients. Bikes. Restaurant 2km. One night free for stays of five days or more in low season. Fortified St-Lô 4km. Open all year.
PRICES: s €27; d €35-€38; t €43-€46; extra person €9 **ON SITE:** Hiking
NEARBY: Horse riding (2km) Golf (15km) Sea (32km) Fishing (5km) Swimming pool (5km) Tennis (2km) Sailing (35km) Railway station (4km) Shops (2km) **NOTES:** Pets admitted

ST-JAMES

¶¶¶ ✿ ⬤ La Gautraie François & Catherine TIFFAINE
50240 ST-JAMES ☎ 02 33 48 31 86 ▤ 02 33 48 58 17

Mont Saint-Michel 21 km. In a leafy setting on a farm, this

establishment is attractively furnished in country style and has two first floor family rooms (one with kitchenette) and two doubles, all with own bath or shower and wc. Central heating. Good range of baby equipment. Dinners served by the open fireplace. Table tennis. €53 for four. Children's meal €8. 5% reduction for stays of more than three nights. Open all year.
PRICES: s €28; d €36-€41; t €46; extra person €8; dinner €14
ON SITE: Children's play area **NEARBY:** Horse riding (1km) Sea (35km) Fishing (4km) Swimming pool (20km) Hiking (1km) Tennis (2km) Railway station (14km) Shops (1km) **NOTES:** No pets English spoken

ST-LEGER

¶¶¶ ♿ Le Clos Serena Jacqueline MICONNET
50320 ST-LEGER
☎ 02 33 90 63 46 ▤ 02 33 90 63 46
e-mail: jac.serena@wanadoo.fr
http://www.France-bonjour.com/serena/

Granville 10 km. Abbaye de la Lucerne d'Outremer 900m. The hosts welcome guests to their residence standing in an attractive garden. There is a first floor triple with own bath and wc, and in a separate building a ground floor double with disabled access and own shower and wc, a first floor double with own bath and wc on the landing, and a family room for four with own bath and wc. Another double available on this floor. Separate entrances. Small ground floor kitchen. Spacious sitting room with French billiards. €52/67. Restaurant 5km. Open all year.
PRICES: s €26; d €33; t €43-€52; extra person €12 **NEARBY:** Horse riding (5km) Golf (15km) Sea (7km) Fishing (1km) Swimming pool (10km) Hiking (1km) Tennis (4km) Sailing (12km) Railway station (12km) Shops (3km) **NOTES:** Pets admitted English spoken

ST-MARTIN-DES-CHAMPS

¶¶¶ La Bourdonniere Raymond et Elisabeth TRUBLET
50300 ST-MARTIN-DES-CHAMPS
☎ 02 33 48 88 53
Avranches 2 km. Mont Saint-Michel 20 km. Guests are made welcome in the completely restored house furnished in Norman style and standing in its attractive garden. There are two first floor doubles and a triple, all with own shower and wc. Open all year.
PRICES: s €29; d €33; t €44; extra person €9 **NEARBY:** Horse riding (4km) Golf (30km) Sea (20km) Fishing (4km) Swimming pool (2km) Hiking (2km) Tennis (2km) Sailing (25km) Railway station (4km) Shops (2km) **NOTES:** No pets

---

⬤

Places with this symbol serve table d'hôtes
evening meals - remember to book in advance

---

continued

TAMERVILLE

♥♥♥ Manoir de Bellauney J & C ALLIX-DESFAUTEAUX
50700 TAMERVILLE
☎ 02 33 40 10 62

Valognes le Petit Versailles Normand 4 km. Overlooking its own park, this 15th and 16th century manor house residence has kept its character and is near the sea and well placed for the Cotentin peninsula. With separate entrance and all with individual names relating to the house's history ('Normande' on the ground floor, 'Louis XV' and 'Médiéval' on the first floor), there are three doubles with own bath or shower and wc. Sitting room for use of guests. Table tennis. Zoo park 3km. Invasion beaches 15km. Open 15 March to 15 November.
PRICES: s €34-€42; d €42-€54; extra person €15 **NEARBY:** Horse riding (7km) Golf (15km) Sea (12km) Fishing (1km) Swimming pool (4km) Hiking (1km) Tennis (4km) Sailing (15km) Railway station (4km) Shops (1km) **NOTES:** No pets English spoken

TESSY-SUR-VIRE

♥♥♥ ♥ La Poterie Roger et M-Thérèse DESVAGES
50420 TESSY-SUR-VIRE
☎ 02 33 56 31 76
Marie-Thérèse and Roger look forward to making their guests' acquaintance and impressing them with produce from their farm. There are three first floor guest rooms (total six people), all with own shower and wc. Sitting room with kitchenette for use of guests. Electric central heating. Reduced rates for stays of more than one night: €25 one person, €33 for two. Open all year.
PRICES: s €30; d €38 **ON SITE:** Hiking **NEARBY:** Horse riding (17km) Sea (40km) Fishing (3km) Swimming pool (20km) Tennis (3km) Railway station (17km) **NOTES:** No pets

TOURLAVILLE

♥♥♥ Manoir Saint-Jean Honoré et Simone GUERARD
par le Château des Ravalet, 50110 TOURLAVILLE
☎ 02 33 22 00 86
Collignon (leisure centre) 4 km. Musées Valognes 20 km. In a conservation area just a step away from the Les Ravelets Château, this family home is set among shady footpaths and enjoys a panoramic view over Cherbourg and its harbour. There are three rooms (total six people) with own bath or shower and wc. Harbour terminal 5km. Restaurant 3km. GR223 long-distance footpath passes nearby. Cherbourg and its museums 6km. Open all year.
PRICES: s €33-€38; d €40-€45; extra person €12 **ON SITE:** Hiking **NEARBY:** Horse riding (3km) Golf (2km) Sea (4km) Fishing (1km) Swimming pool (4km) Tennis (4km) Sailing (4km) Railway station (6km) Shops (2km) **NOTES:** No pets

> Prices are given in Euros €1 = £0.62
> at the time of going to press

VAUDRIMESNIL

♥♥♥ ♥ La Rochelle Alain et Olga BERTHOU
12, route de Coutances, 50490 VAUDRIMESNIL
☎ 02 33 46 74 95
Coutances 10 km. An old farmhouse in a peaceful rural setting close to the Cotentin Marshlands Regional Park. The three first floor guest rooms include two doubles and a triple, all with own shower, wc, and separate entrance. Central heating. Breakfast served on veranda overlooking a leafy landscape. Table tennis, billiards and boule. Pond and medieval dovecot. Invasion beaches 30km. Open all year.
PRICES: s €30; d €36; t €47; extra person €11 **NEARBY:** Horse riding (13km) Golf (9km) Sea (15km) Fishing (1km) Swimming pool (12km) Hiking (1km) Tennis (3km) Sailing (15km) Railway station (12km) Shops (3km) **NOTES:** No pets

VERGONCEY

♥♥♥♥ Château de Boucéel Régis DE ROQUEFEUIL
50240 VERGONCEY
☎ 02 33 48 34 61 📠 02 33 48 16 26
e-mail: chateaudebouceel@wanadoo.fr
www.chateaudebouceel.com

Mont Saint-Michel 16 km. Granville 37 km. M and Mme Régis de Roquefeuil invite guests to the Boucéel estate which goes back to the 12th century. The present château dates from 1763 and has been tastefully decorated and furnished and features a number of family portraits. Ground floor suite for three with own bath and wc, and a first floor suite for three with own shower and wc and two doubles with own spacious bathroom and wc. Non-smoking. Sitting room, billiards, library. Separate entrance. Park, lakes and chapel. Open all year.
PRICES: s €105-€135; d €115-€145; t €135-€145; extra person €20 **ON SITE:** Hiking **NEARBY:** Horse riding (15km) Golf (38km) Sea (28km) Fishing (2km) Swimming pool (16km) Tennis (6km) Sailing (38km) Railway station (38km) Shops (6km) **NOTES:** No pets CC English spoken

♥♥♥ ♥ ⭘⭥ Ferme de l'Etang Bouceel
Jean-Paul & Brigitte GAVARD 50240 VERGONCEY
☎ 02 33 48 34 68 📠 02 33 48 48 53
e-mail: jpgavard@club-internet.fr
Mont Saint-Michel 18 km. In tranquil countryside, this farm boasts a large farmhouse covered in creeper. There are four first floor guest rooms (total 12 people) all with own bath or shower and wc. Central heating. Sitting room with open fireplace. Children's games. Table tennis, billiards, table football. Children's meals €8. €53 per four. Woodland, ponds, footpaths, farm tours. Open all year.
PRICES: s €33; d €38-€41; t €47; extra person €8; dinner €14 **ON SITE:** Hiking **NEARBY:** Horse riding (5km) Golf (15km) Sea (35km) Fishing (3km) Swimming pool (16km) Tennis (5km) Sailing (15km) Railway station (10km) Shops (6km) **NOTES:** No pets English spoken

VESSEY

♦♦♦♦ ❦ ⦿¡ La Butte François TRINCOT
50170 VESSEY
☎ 02 33 60 20 32 ▤ 02 33 58 48 84
Mont Saint-Michel 14 km. Château de Fougères 28 km. This farm on Mont-St-Michel Bay will appeal to those who love horses and shore-walking. The owners have converted a separate building close to the farmstead to house three first floor rooms including a double and two twins, all with own shower and wc. Sitting room with kitchenette and open fireplace. Meals by arrangement. Meals for children under 10: €7. Open all year.
PRICES: s €27; d €35; extra person €8; dinner €13 **ON SITE:** Hiking
NEARBY: Horse riding (10km) Golf (25km) Sea (35km) Fishing (1km) Swimming pool (25km) Tennis (1km) Sailing (20km) Railway station (8km) Shops (10km) **NOTES:** No pets

VIDECOSVILLE

♦♦♦♦ Manoir Saint-Laurent Annick LEVAILLANT
50630 VIDECOSVILLE
☎ 02 33 54 17 58
Valognes 10 km. Quettehou 5 km. This house of character has three first floor rooms including two doubles and a triple, all with own shower and wc. Restaurant 5km. Saint-Vaast-la-Hougue, Tatihou Island 8km. Open all year.
PRICES: s €27; d €36-€38; t €48; extra person €10 **NEARBY:** Horse riding (4km) Sea (6km) Swimming pool (10km) Hiking (5km) Tennis (5km) Sailing (8km) Railway station (10km) Shops (5km) **NOTES:** Pets admitted

VILLEDIEU-LES-POELES

♦♦♦♦ Fontaine Minérale Jean et Nicole COTTAIS
1, Fontaine Minérale, route de Granville,
50800 VILLEDIEU-LES-POELES
☎ 02 33 61 06 00
Mont Saint-Michel 35 km. This modern house surrounded by gardens has three first floor rooms (total seven people). One shower per room, three wcs. Central heating. Picnicking. Restaurant 1km. Forest 10km. Open all year.
PRICES: s €30; d €35-€36; t €41; extra person €8 **ON SITE:** Hiking **NEARBY:** Horse riding (10km) Golf (35km) Sea (30km) Fishing (1km) Swimming pool (1km) Tennis (1km) Sailing (30km) Railway station (2km) Shops (1km) **NOTES:** Pets admitted

YVETOT-BOCAGE

♦♦♦♦ Fenard Elisabeth BAUDRY
route de Bricquebec, 50700 YVETOT-BOCAGE
☎ 02 33 40 19 81 ▤ 02 33 21 19 84
Valognes 5 km. This countryside establishment has three first floor rooms including two triples and a family room for four, all with own bath and wc. Central heating. Sitting room. Guests touring on horseback welcome. Restaurant and creperie 1.5km. Open all year.
PRICES: s €27; d €33; t €43; extra person €10 **NEARBY:** Horse riding (9km) Golf (20km) Sea (14km) Fishing (2km) Swimming pool (6km) Hiking (11km) Tennis (5km) Sailing (14km) Railway station (4km) Shops (5km) **NOTES:** No pets

Prices are given in Euros €1 = £0.62
at the time of going to press

❦Places with this symbol are farmhouses

ARGENTAN

♦♦♦♦ ❦ Chambre d'hôtes Claude et Odile SINEUX
La Gravelle, 61200 SARCEAUX
☎ 02 33 67 04 47 ▤ 02 33 67 04 47
In the Région des Haras, the Sineux family offer accommodation in their large country house. Ground floor: double room, with shower and wc, kitchenette, open fire and TV. Upstairs: double room with private bath and wc; room for three with private bath and wc; double room with shower and wc. Living room with cooking area reserved for guests. Mountain bike circuit. Open all year.
PRICES: s €30; d €38; t €41 **ON SITE:** Fishing **NEARBY:** Horse riding (2km) Forest (2km) Golf (40km) Sea (80km) Swimming pool (2km) Stretch of water (2km) Hiking (2km) Tennis (2km) Spa (40km) Railway station (2km) Shops (2km) ARGENTAN (3km) **NOTES:** No pets English spoken

ARGENTAN-OCCAGNES

♦♦♦♦ ❦ Le Mesnil Rémy LAIGNEL
61200 OCCAGNES
☎ 02 33 67 11 12
M and Mme Laignel invite guests to their farm in the Haras region. In a separate building, two bedrooms (double bed and possible extra single) with shower room, wc and mini-kitchenette. In the owners' house, upstairs: a double room with possible extra single, bath, wc and TV. Electric and central heating. For trail bike fans: a circuit pass for two or more days. Open all year.
PRICES: s €24-€26; d €35-€37; t €41; extra person €6 **NEARBY:** Horse riding (5km) Forest (7km) Golf (30km) Sea (60km) Fishing (2km) Swimming pool (5km) Stretch of water (5km) Hiking (2km) Tennis (5km) Spa (50km) Railway station (5km) Shops (5km) ARGENTAN (3km) **NOTES:** Pets admitted

AUBRY-EN-EXMES

♦♦♦♦ ❦ ⦿¡ La Grande Ferme Pierre MAURICE
Ste-Eugénie, 61160 AUBRY-EN-EXMES
☎ 02 33 36 82 36 ▤ 02 33 36 99 52
e-mail: GHIS.P.MAURICE@wanadoo.fr
Argentan 10 km. A large house belonging to the Maurice family, on the edge of the forest, on farmland with a park and stream behind. Three rooms with own access. First floor: one double and one triple room, each with en suite shower and wc. Central heating and electric heating. Lounge for guests. Small kitchen (€2.5/day). Cycle hire and lock-up. Meals (if booked) Thursday and Saturday. Trail bike circuit offer. Open all year.
PRICES: s €27; d €37; t €44; extra person €8; dinner €14
ON SITE: Horse riding Forest Hiking **NEARBY:** Golf (50km) Sea (70km) Fishing (4km) Swimming pool (10km) Stretch of water (6km) Tennis (4km) Spa (50km) Railway station (10km) Shops (4km) TRUN (7km) **NOTES:** Pets admitted English spoken

BANVOU

♦♦♦♦ ⦿¡ La Vieille Maison Brigitte et Didier JEUSSET
Le Pont, 61450 BANVOU
☎ 02 33 96 44 02 ▤ 02 33 96 44 02
Flers 12 km. An old building, full of character close to the Forest of Andaine, Bagnoles-de-l'Orne, and the surrounding *bocage*. Guest rooms are in outbuildings of the owners' home. First floor: room with one double bed, one single and possibly a cot, with bathroom and wc; a double room with bath and wc; double room with shower and wc. Electric heating. Lounge with TV and fire. Stables available. Open March to September.
PRICES: s €30; d €44; t €53; extra person €11; dinner €13

continued

ON SITE: Hiking **NEARBY:** Horse riding (12km) Forest (18km) Golf (18km) Sea (80km) Fishing (2km) Swimming pool (12km) Stretch of water (2km) Tennis (2km) Spa (18km) Railway station (12km) Shops (1km) MESSEI (12km) **NOTES:** Pets admitted

CETON

⠀⠀ 〇〇 L'Aître Thérèse PINOCHE
61260 CETON
☎ 02 37 29 78 02

Upstairs in the owner's house in the heart of the Regional Natural Park of Perche: a suite (three single beds and a cot), shower room and wc. In separate buildings, upstairs: one twin room with shower/wc; one suite for three with a cot, therapy bath and wc. Living room reserved for guests. Central heating. Madame Pinoche's house is pleasant and full of character. Vegetarian meals available. Garden produce. Open all year.
PRICES: s €39; d €43-€50; t €53-€64; extra person €9; dinner €16
ON SITE: Fishing Hiking **NEARBY:** Horse riding (7km) Forest (20km) Golf (12km) Sea (150km) Swimming pool (1km) Stretch of water (1km) Tennis (1km) Railway station (7km) Shops (1km) LE THEIL-SUR-HUISNE (10km) **NOTES:** No pets English spoken

CHAMBOIS

⠀⠀ Le Château Micheline CLAPEAU
4 rue des Polonais, 61160 CHAMBOIS
☎ 02 33 36 71 34
e-mail: chambois@clapeau.com http://www.clapeau.com

An Empire-style château near the famous Haras du Pin not far from the Pays d'Auge. Madame Clapeau's comfortable house at the foot of the Donjon of Chambois offers two double rooms and a triple (with showers or bath and wc) on the ground floor. The first floor has one double room and a triple (each with shower or bath and wc). Central heating. Open all year.
PRICES: s €39; d €45; extra person €11 **NEARBY:** Horse riding (6km) Forest (6km) Sea (70km) Fishing (1km) Swimming pool (12km) Stretch of water (6km) Hiking (1km) Tennis (1km) Spa (45km) Railway station (12km) Shops (7km) TRUN (7km) **NOTES:** No pets English spoken

CONDE-SUR-SARTHE

⠀⠀ Le Clos des Roses Simone et Pierre PELLEGRINI
10 rue de la jardinière, 61250 CONDE-SUR-SARTHE
☎ 02 33 27 70 68

This renovated house stands at the gateway to the Alpes Mancelles, overlooking the Sarthe. The garden has a collection of roses, a summerhouse, fancy ironwork, and a fountain. On the ground floor, with separate access, a room for three with cot if required. Upstairs, two double rooms (one grade 2). Each room has private shower or bath and wc. Central heating. Lounge. Veranda. Open all year.
PRICES: s €27; d €38; t €49; extra person €11 **ON SITE:** Fishing Hiking Tennis **NEARBY:** Horse riding (4km) Forest (10km) Golf (5km) Sea (120km) Swimming pool (1km) Stretch of water (24km) Spa (42km) Railway station (5km) Shops (1km) ALENCON (3km) **NOTES:** No pets

COURGEON

⠀⠀ 🐓 〇〇 Ferme de l'Hôtel Neveu
Marie-Claire & Gilbert SIMOEN
61400 COURGEON
☎ 02 33 25 10 67 📠 02 33 83 39 57

L'Hôtel Neveu is a typical Percheron farmhouse, inside the Regional Natural Park. M and Mme Simoen invite you to sample the dairy products made on the farm. On the ground floor is the large sitting room with fireplace and TV. Upstairs (in the mansard roof): a room for four (one double bed, two singles and a cot); and a room for three. Downstairs: a double room. All rooms have

shower and wc. Electric and central heating. Table tennis and children's games. Open all year.
PRICES: s €29; d €37-€40; t €44; extra person €8; dinner €13
ON SITE: Hiking **NEARBY:** Horse riding (4km) Forest (4km) Golf (15km) Sea (120km) Fishing (6km) Swimming pool (8km) Stretch of water (4km) Tennis (4km) Spa (100km) Railway station (25km) Shops (4km) MORTAGNE-AU-PERCHE (8km) **NOTES:** Pets admitted English spoken

DOMFRONT

⠀⠀ La Demeure d'Olwenn Sylvia TAILHANDIER
1 rue de Godras, 61700 DOMFRONT
☎ 02 33 37 10 03 📠 02 33 37 10 03
e-mail: sylviatchd@aol.com

In the heart of the medieval city of Domfront, Sylvia Tailhandier's old house is full of charm. Upstairs: one triple room, one double, and one room with a double bed plus two singles in a mansard mezzanine. Shower, wc and TV if needed in each room. Central heating. Lounge and living room with fireplace for guests' use. Large garden overlooking the ramparts. All year except October.
PRICES: s €46; d €46; t €57; extra person €11 **ON SITE:** Hiking **NEARBY:** Horse riding (19km) Forest (3km) Golf (19km) Sea (80km) Fishing (1km) Swimming pool (19km) Stretch of water (19km) Tennis (1km) Spa (19km) Railway station (16km) DOMFRONT **NOTES:** No pets English spoken

FAVEROLLES

⠀⠀ 🦃 〇〇 Le Mont Rôti Sylviane et Bernard FORTIN
61600 FAVEROLLES
☎ 02 33 37 34 72 📠 02 33 37 34 72

Bagnoles de l'Orne 15 km. Le Mont Rôti is a farmhouse in open country between the *bocage* and Suisse Normande. Bernard and Sylviane Fortin welcome guests to their charming accommodation situated in the mansard roof. One room for three people; one suite for three; and one double with separate access. All have private shower or bath and wc. Central heating. Veranda for guests. Many sites to discover in the neighbourhood. Open all year. Half board: €56/two people.
PRICES: s €26; d €32; t €41; extra person €9; HB €56; dinner €12
ON SITE: Hiking **NEARBY:** Horse riding (10km) Forest (13km) Golf (13km) Sea (100km) Fishing (3km) Swimming pool (13km) Stretch of water (13km) Tennis (13km) Spa (18km) Railway station (8km) Shops (8km) BRIOUZE (8km) **NOTES:** No pets English spoken

GEMAGES

⠀⠀ 〇〇 Le Moulin de Gémages Anna IANNACCONE
61130 GEMAGES
☎ 02 33 25 15 72 📠 02 33 25 18 88
e-mail: annieriv.iann@wanadoo.fr

Bellême 12 km. Old hay lofts at a renovated mill house. Three separate guest rooms at garden level. Each room has a double and a single bed, shower or bathroom and wc. Electric heating. Garden with accessible river and pond. Le Moulin de Gémages lies in the hollow of a green valley in the Regional Natural Park of Perche, and has a millrace, lockgates, wheel and river. Open all year.
PRICES: s €40-€50; d €50-€60; t €60-€70; dinner €20 **ON SITE:** Fishing **NEARBY:** Horse riding (1km) Forest (1km) Golf (12km) Swimming pool (10km) Stretch of water (15km) Hiking (1km) Tennis (5km) Spa (120km) Railway station (15km) Shops (1km) LE THEIL-SUR-HUISNE (10km) **NOTES:** No pets English spoken

continued

NORMANDY

LA CHAPELLE-PRES-SEES

♏♏♏ 🐎 ⫫◎⫫ Les Tertres
Odile et Jean-Claude BESNIARD
61500 LA-CHAPELLE-PRES-SEES
☎ 02 33 27 74 67 & 06 88 08 94 47 📠 02 33 27 74 67
This farm, near the Forest d'Ecouves, gives visitors the chance to explore the country by horse or pony. One ground floor double room. Upstairs there are three doubles, and a double with a sofa bed. All rooms have bath or shower and wc. Guests' lounge. Central heating. Garden. A few kilometres away is the cathedral at Sées. Open all year.
PRICES: s €30; d €37; t €44; extra person €8; HB €42; dinner €12
ON SITE: Horse riding Forest Hiking **NEARBY:** Golf (15km) Sea (100km) Fishing (10km) Swimming pool (20km) Stretch of water (18km) Tennis (5km) Spa (50km) Railway station (5km) Shops (5km) SEES (5km) **NOTES:** Pets admitted English spoken

LA FERTE-MACE

♏♏♏ 🐎 La Péleras Christine VOLCLAIR
61600 LA FERTE-MACE
☎ 02 33 37 28 23 📠 02 33 38 78 83
Large Norman-style half-timbered house near Bagnoles de l'Orne, built by the owners, and furnished with antiques. Upstairs: one room for three (three single beds); two rooms for three (one double, one single bed); one double room; one room for four. All have private bathroom and wc. Lounge; central heating; garden; terrace. From the rooms the view extends over the lake and meadows to the little village of La Ferté-Macé. Open all year.
PRICES: s €38; d €46; t €61; extra person €15 **ON SITE:** Horse riding Golf Fishing Stretch of water Hiking Tennis **NEARBY:** Forest (2km) Sea (80km) Swimming pool (2km) Spa (5km) Railway station (11km) Restaurant nearby LA FERTE-MACE **NOTES:** No pets English spoken

LA FORET-AUVRAY

♏♏♏ L'Orangerie Philippe GUYARD
61210 LA-FORET-AUVRAY
☎ 02 33 64 29 48 & 06 08 26 80 20
e-mail: phguyard@club internet.fr

Briouze 15 km. In a little valley in Suisse Normande, is this 19th-century orangery that offers comfortable guest rooms. Three ground floor bedrooms: one double, with cot; one double with possible extra single; one triple, with cot. All have shower or bath and wc. Sitting room; lounge with open fire; central heating; garden. Open all year.
PRICES: s €30; d €38; t €53; extra person €15 **ON SITE:** Forest Fishing Hiking **NEARBY:** Horse riding (7km) Golf (15km) Sea (60km) Swimming pool (7km) Stretch of water (7km) Tennis (7km) Spa (40km) Railway station (15km) Shops (17km) PUTANGES-PONT-ECREPIN **NOTES:** No pets English spoken

LA HAUTE-CHAPELLE

♏♏♏ La Fontaine des Etoiles Jill ARMSTRONG
Le Bourg, 61700 LA HAUTE-CHAPELLE
☎ 02 33 38 37 16 📠 02 33 38 03 95
e-mail: fontetoil@aol.com
Built in 1730, this presbytery was restored a few years ago. Ground floor: visitors' lounge (TV, fireplace), plus use of kitchen. Upstairs: two double rooms (one grade 2) with shower or bath and wc, and a suite with two rooms containing five single beds, with shower room and wc. Central heating, garden. Amble through the alleys of Domfront, stroll the walking trails, and visit the many antique shops. Open all year.
PRICES: s €30; d €46; t €61; extra person €15 **ON SITE:** Hiking Tennis **NEARBY:** Horse riding (15km) Forest (5km) Golf (15km) Sea (60km) Fishing (2km) Swimming pool (30km) Stretch of water (10km) Spa (15km) Railway station (22km) Shops (3km) DOMFRONT (2km) **NOTES:** No pets English spoken

See advert on opposite page

LONGNY-AU-PERCHE

♏♏♏ ⫫◎⫫ L'Orangerie Edith et Marc DESAILLY
9 rue des Prés, 61290 LONGNY-AU-PERCHE
☎ 02 33 25 11 78
e-mail: Desailly@net-up.com
Mortagne-au-perche 18 km. An old orangery with its own entrance. Edith, Marc and their family offer comfortable rooms in the colours of meadow flowers. On the ground floor is an enormous guest lounge with open fire. Upstairs are three bedrooms: one for three (double plus single) and two double rooms. All have shower or bath and wc. Electric heating. Garden. Meals only if booked. Longny-au-Perche is in a region of forests, manor houses and horses, in the Regional Nature Park. Open all year.
PRICES: s €29; d €39; t €49; extra person €10; dinner €12 **ON SITE:** Fishing Swimming pool **NEARBY:** Horse riding (7km) Forest (2km) Golf (34km) Sea (130km) Stretch of water (2km) Hiking (1km) Tennis (1km) Spa (110km) Railway station (28km) Shops (1km) LONGNY-AU-PERCHE **NOTES:** No pets English spoken

MAISON-MAUGIS

♏♏♏ 🐎 Domaine de l'Emière
Edith et Jean-Louis GRANDJEAN
61110 MAISON-MAUGIS
☎ 02 33 73 74 19 📠 02 33 73 69 80
Mortagne-au-perche 18 km. Bellême 23 km. The 17th-century Domaine de l'Emière is run by Edith and Jean-Louis who welcome guests to their home. On the first floor: two double rooms, with bath or shower and wc. Lounge with open fire. In a separate building, with its own access: ground floor living room and upstairs double room (150cm bed) with shower and wc. Electric and central heating. Large park, terrace with ornamental lake. Open all year.
PRICES: s €75-€90; d €85-€100; extra person €15 **ON SITE:** Forest Hiking **NEARBY:** Horse riding (8km) Golf (20km) Sea (180km) Fishing (8km) Swimming pool (10km) Stretch of water (10km) Tennis (8km) Spa (150km) Railway station (18km) Shops (10km) REMALARD (10km) **NOTES:** No pets English spoken

> Ask the proprietor for directions when booking

MARCHEMAISONS

♯♯♯ ⍥ Boisaubert M. Antonio GIULIVO
61170 MARCHEMAISONS
☎ 02 33 31 91 29 📠 02 33 31 91 31
In separate outbuildings of the proprietor's house, set out in the arc of a circle, at ground level, two double rooms, one twin room and one triple room, each with shower room and wc. Lounge with open fire. Central heating. Garden with two ponds. Possibility of stables for horses. Open 1st February to 15th October.
PRICES: s €38; d €43; extra person €15; dinner €15 **NEARBY:** Horse riding (1km) Forest (1km) Golf (18km) Sea (100km) Fishing (3km) Swimming pool (18km) Stretch of water (3km) Hiking (1km) Tennis (3km) Spa (60km) Railway station (18km) Shops (3km) LE MELE-SUR-SARTHE (3km) **NOTES:** Pets admitted

MOULICENT

♯♯♯♯ La Grande Noë
Pascale et Jacques DE LONGCAMP
61290 MOULICENT
☎ 02 33 73 63 30 📠 02 33 83 62 92
e-mail: grandenoe@wanadoo.fr
In the calm of the open countryside of Perche, guests are welcome in the family home (a château dating from the 15th century) of M and Mme Longcamp. Upstairs: a double room, a twin room and a room for three, each with bathroom and wc. Central heating. Large park, table tennis, bikes, stables for horses, harness. Open 1st March to 30th November.
PRICES: s €85-€95; d €92-€105; extra person €15 **NEARBY:** Horse riding (12km) Forest (2km) Golf (25km) Sea (110km) Swimming pool (8km) Stretch of water (15km) Hiking (2km) Tennis (5km) Railway station (25km) Shops (5km) LONGNY-AU-PERCHE (6km) **NOTES:** No pets English spoken

NEUILLY-SUR-EURE

♯♯♯ Les Hautes Bruyères Monique et André DI GIOVANNI
61290 NEUILLY-SUR-EURE
☎ 02 33 73 92 23
This is a famous hunting estate in the Perche, and the décor of the house is reminiscent of big game hunting. Upstairs: two rooms for three (single beds); a double (plus cot) and a double. Each room has shower and wc. Two extra beds available. Central heating. Enormous lounge with open fire. Hunting available on the estate. Open all year.
PRICES: s €34; d €38; t €53 **ON SITE:** Forest Fishing Hiking **NEARBY:** Horse riding (1km) Golf (10km) Swimming pool (8km) Stretch of water (1km) Tennis (1km) Railway station (10km) Shops (1km) LONGNY-AU-PERCHE (16km) **NOTES:** Pets admitted

NEUVILLE-PRES-SEES

♯♯♯ 🐓 Le Lion du Haut Montrond
David et Véronique SCHNEIDER
Le Haut Montrond, 61500 NEUVILLE-PRES-SEES
☎ 02 33 35 41 58 📠 02 33 35 41 58
David Schneider is happy to share his passion for working horses and owns a pair of Percherons. His house is old but renovated. Upstairs, three double rooms, and two rooms for four (one double, two single beds). Each with shower and wc. Electric heating. Vast lounge with TV corner. Stables for horses. Le Haut Montrond is a hamlet a few kilometres from Sées with its famous cathedral. Open all year.
PRICES: s €30; d €40; t €49; extra person €9 **ON SITE:** Fishing Hiking **NEARBY:** Horse riding (12km) Forest (16km) Golf (6km) Sea (100km) Swimming pool (30km) Stretch of water (17km) Tennis (12km) Spa (60km) Railway station (10km) Shops (8km) SEES (12km) **NOTES:** No pets English spoken

La Fontaine des Etoiles

61700 La Haute Chapelle, Normandy
Tel: 02 33 38 37 16 or 02 33 38 03 95
E-mail: fontetoil@aol.com
Web site: www.la-fontaine-des-etoiles.co.uk

La Fontaine comprises a newly restored and converted Priests house and cottage. The Priests house was built in 1830 of local stone and the cottage is the oldest building in the village.
A large east facing terrace looks out over open meadows.
The bedrooms are centrally heated and have spectacular views.
There are tennis courts and Boules opposite and a pool with slides just 25 minutes away. At La Ferte Mace there is a large reservoir with water sports activities and golf, it takes 20 minutes drive on a beautiful road through the Forest d'Andaine.

REMALARD

♯♯♯ ⍥ Domaine de Launay John BAKKER
Launay, 61110 REMALARD
☎ 02 33 83 61 33 📠 02 33 73 66 18
e-mail: Domainedelaunay@wanadoo.fr
The 16th-century farmhouse of the Domaine de Launay stands on 15ha of wood and meadows. In an outbuilding, three suites and one twin room with shower and wc, two of which have lounge or sitting area, and two of which have a cooking area. Sitting room with TV. Central heating. Garden with outdoor furniture, pond and woods. Four stables. Open 1st March to 30th October.
PRICES: s €99; d €130; dinner €23 **ON SITE:** Forest Hiking **NEARBY:** Horse riding (20km) Golf (20km) Sea (150km) Fishing (20km) Swimming pool (4km) Stretch of water (20km) Tennis (4km) Spa (110km) Railway station (10km) Shops (4km) REMALARD (3km) **NOTES:** No pets English spoken

SAINT-AUBIN-D'APPENAI

♯♯♯ 🐓 ⍥ Le Gué Falot Marie-Annick FLOCHLAY
61170 ST-AUBIN-D'APPENAI
☎ 02 33 28 68 12 📠 02 33 28 68 12
In the Pays Mêlois region, a stone's throw from the Forest of Bourse, Mme Flochlay's restored house is in the local style. On the ground floor are a twin room and a room for three (double bed and single). Each has private shower room and wc. Upstairs is a room with four single beds, with shower room and wc. Central heating, games room, library. Open 1st February to 30th November. Half board €33.5 each.
PRICES: s €24; d €37; t €50; extra person €14; dinner €15 **ON SITE:** Children's play area Fishing Hiking **NEARBY:** Horse riding (1km) Forest (1km) Golf (20km) Sea (120km) Swimming pool (18km) Stretch of water (5km) Tennis (5km) Railway station (15km) Shops (5km) LE MELE-SUR-SARTHE (5km) **NOTES:** Pets admitted English spoken

NORMANDY

SAINT-BOMER-LES-FORGES

🍴 🍽 La Roculière Pierre ROUSSEL
61700 ST-BOMER-LES-FORGES
☎ 02 33 37 60 60 📠 02 33 37 60 60
In the *bocage* between Domfront and Flers, the hosts welcome guests to their farm with its comfortable and cosy rooms. Two double rooms on the first floor, one with bath and wc, the other with shower and wc. Cot available. Old bread oven available for guests' use. Botanic trail. Meals if booked (except Sunday evening). Charming countryside. Mont St Michel 80km. Open 5th May to 20th December.
PRICES: s €30; d €37; t €47; dinner €15 **ON SITE:** Fishing Hiking **NEARBY:** Horse riding (3km) Forest (10km) Golf (25km) Sea (80km) Swimming pool (10km) Stretch of water (10km) Tennis (3km) Spa (25km) Railway station (10km) Shops (3km) DOMFRONT (8km) **NOTES:** No pets English spoken

SAINT-DENIS-DE-VILLENETTE

🍴 🍽 La Prémoudière Marie et Pascal BRUNET
La Premoudière, 61330 ST-DENIS-DE-VILLENETTE
☎ 02 33 37 23 27 📠 02-33-37-23-27
Domfront 10 km. Old restored house in the forests and *bocage* country. On the ground floor are the lounge (TV and fireplace) and two double bedrooms, one of which contains a kitchenette. Upstairs are a room for two (with a cot), a double, a room for three and a room for four. All have bath or shower and wc. Electric heating. Open fire and beams, apple and pear trees in the garden. Marie and Pascal invite guests to sample their farm produce. Open all year.
PRICES: s €28; d €36; t €43; extra person €8; dinner €14
ON SITE: Wine tasting **NEARBY:** Horse riding (15km) Forest (6km) Golf (15km) Sea (76km) Fishing (15km) Swimming pool (10km) Stretch of water (20km) Hiking (6km) Tennis (6km) Spa (15km) Railway station (30km) Shops (5km) JUVIGNY-SOUS-ANDAINE (5km) **NOTES:** Pets admitted English spoken

SAINT-HILAIRE-DE-BRIOUZE

🍴 🍽 La Grande Bêche Denis SAUQUET
61220 ST-HILAIRE-DE-BRIOUZE
☎ 02 33 66 02 17 & 06 03 74 33 30 📠 02 33 66 02 17
La Ferté Macé 16 km. Between the Forest of Andaine and Suisse Normande, is Le Houlme, a green and peaceful landscape. At La Grande Bêche there are three upstairs double rooms (one with separate access), each with shower room and wc. Possible extra couch. Guests' lounge with fireplace and TV. Central heating. Open all year.
PRICES: s €28; d €35; t €43; extra person €9; dinner €15
ON SITE: Fishing **NEARBY:** Horse riding (7km) Forest (20km) Golf (21km) Sea (90km) Swimming pool (25km) Stretch of water (16km) Tennis (5km) Spa (21km) Railway station (5km) Shops (5km) BRIOUZE (4km) **NOTES:** No pets English spoken

SURVIE

🍴 🍽 Les Gains
Diana & Christopher WORDSWORTH
61310 SURVIE
☎ 02 33 36 05 56 📠 02 33 35 03 65
e-mail: christopher.wordsworth@libertysurf.fr
Vimoutiers 10 km. Between the Region of Haras and the Pays d'Auge, a wing of the owners' house provides one double, one twin and a room for three, all with bath or shower and wc. Electric heating. Guests' lounge. Near the sites of the Battle of Normandy and the charming village of Camembert. Open March to November.
PRICES: s €35; d €46-€50; t €58; extra person €12; dinner €20

ON SITE: Hiking **NEARBY:** Horse riding (5km) Forest (20km) Golf (20km) Sea (80km) Fishing (1km) Swimming pool (10km) Stretch of water (10km) Tennis (10km) Spa (70km) Railway station (20km) Shops (10km) EXMES (10km) **NOTES:** No pets English spoken

TOUROUVRE

🍴 Moulin de la Fonte Daniel MONDAIN
61190 TOUROUVRE
☎ 02 33 25 28 53 & 02 33 83 08 30 📠 02 33 25 23 33
e-mail: mondaind@aol.com www.moulin-de-la-fonte.com
This old mill nestles in the green countryside at the heart of Perche. On the ground floor: one double room. Upstairs: three double rooms and a suite (one double bed and a fold-up bed). Rooms have bath or shower and wc. Possible extra room with two single beds. TV and video recorder in each room. Electric and central heating. Living room. Lounge. 2.7ha pond with trout fishing. Children's games. Open all year.
PRICES: s €32-€64; d €37-€69; t €73; extra person €5 **ON SITE:** Forest Fishing Stretch of water Hiking **NEARBY:** Horse riding (6km) Golf (4km) Sea (90km) Swimming pool (10km) Tennis (4km) Spa (100km) Railway station (23km) Shops (4km) TOUROUVRE (4km) **NOTES:** No pets English spoken

ANCEAUMEVILLE

🍴 🍽 Chambre d'hôtes
Roger et Ginette ALEXANDRE
95 route de Sierville, 76710 ANCEAUMEVILLE
☎ 02 35 32 50 22 📠 02 35 32 50 22
e-mail: gites.76@wanadoo.fr www.gites-normandie-76.com
Montville 4 km. Ginette and Roger Alexandre invite guests to their farm in the middle of the village. Their Norman-style farmhouse is surrounded by a garden and has three guest rooms with their own entrance. There is a ground floor triple, and a first floor double and triple, all with own bath and wc. Sitting room, living room, TV. Meals during the week by arrangement. Restaurant 3km. Open all year.
PRICES: s €30; d €37; t €50; extra person €9; dinner €15
ON SITE: Hiking **NEARBY:** Bathing (40km) Horse riding (6km) Golf (6km) Fishing (4km) Swimming pool (4km) Tennis (4km) Railway station (4km) Shops (4km) CLERES (6km) **NOTES:** No pets

ANGERVILLE-BAILLEUL

🍴 🍽 Ferme de l'Etang
Jacques et Gilberte MADIOT
76110 ANGERVILLE-BAILLEUL
☎ 02 35 27 74 89 📠 02 35 27 74 89
Fécamp 10 km. Close to the sea, this farm belonging to Gilberte and Jacques Madiot has a fine half-timbered farmhouse with four guest rooms with their own entrance. There is a ground floor triple with own shower and wc, and on the first floor two doubles with own shower and wc and a five-bed family room with own bath

continued

continued

and wc. First floor sitting room, large living room with traditional open fireplace. Baby equipment. Meals featuring farm produce by arrangement. Farm produce for sale. Restaurant 8km. Open all year.
PRICES: s €43; d €46-€52; t €69-€78; extra person €19; dinner €16-€22
ON SITE: Canoeing Stretch of water Hiking **NEARBY:** Bathing (10km) Horse riding (10km) Golf (20km) Fishing (5km) Swimming pool (5km) Tennis (1km) Railway station (7km) Shops (5km) GODERVILLE (8km)
NOTES: No pets

ANGERVILLE-LA-MARTEL

♦♦♦ ⟨◯⟩ Les Hates Gilbert et Michèle LEDOULT
Les Hates No 229, Miquetot,
76540 ANGERVILLE-LA-MARTEL
☎ 02 35 29 80 82
Fécamp 8 km. Michèle and Gilbert Ledoult welcome guests to their large house with extensive landscaped garden in the middle of peaceful countryside. There is a ground floor double with own bath and wc, and in a separate building, a double with kitchenette and own shower and wc, plus a twin with kitchenette and own shower and wc. Extra beds available. €61 per four persons. Parking. Pétanque. 8km from Fécamp. Restaurant 1km. Open all year.
PRICES: ; d €38; t €46; extra person €15; dinner €16
ON SITE: Children's play area Hiking **NEARBY:** Bathing (6km) Horse riding (9km) Golf (25km) Fishing (3km) Swimming pool (9km) Stretch of water (12km) Tennis (2km) Railway station (9km) Shops (3km) VALMONT (4km) **NOTES:** No pets

ARGUEIL

♦♦♦ Ferme du Claireval Brigitte GOIK
CD41, 76780 ARGUEIL
☎ 02 35 09 00 72
Forges-les-Eaux 10 km. Set in well-preserved surroundings in the Bray countryside, Brigitte Goïk's old farmhouse has been tastefully restored. The three first floor guest rooms have their own entrance and include three doubles, one with own bath and wc, one with own bath and wc, and one with own shower and wc. Quiet reading area. Garden furniture. Restaurant 9km.
PRICES: s €38; d €46; extra person €8 **NEARBY:** Bathing (49km) Horse riding (7km) Golf (25km) Fishing (3km) Swimming pool (9km) Tennis (9km) Railway station (11km) Shops (1km) ARGUEIL
NOTES: No pets

AUBERVILLE-LA-MANUEL

♦♦♦ ⟨◯⟩ Au Repos Cauchois Evelyne GUILLOT
rue de Yaume, 76450 AUBERVILLE-LA-MANUEL
☎ 02 35 57 24 17 📠 02 35 57 24 17
Veulettes-sur-Mer 2 km. In a quiet village on the coast, five guest rooms are on offer in this large brick-built house with a courtyard garden. There is a ground floor twin with own shower, and on the first floor a family room for four with own shower, two doubles with own shower, a Grade 2 double with separate shower, and a triple with own shower. All rooms have own wc. Sitting room with TV and open fireplace. Table football, pétanque, archery, mountain bikes. Meals by arrangement. Restaurant 2km. Open all year.
PRICES: s €34; d €43; extra person €15; dinner €18 **ON SITE:** Hiking Tennis **NEARBY:** Bathing (2km) Canoeing (2km) Horse riding (12km) Golf (40km) Fishing (2km) Swimming pool (8km) Stretch of water (8km) Railway station (12km) Shops (8km) CANY-BARVILLE (8km) **NOTES:** No pets

> Prices are given in Euros €1 = £0.62
> at the time of going to press

AUTIGNY

♦♦♦ ♥ Chambre d'hôtes René et Yvette HELUIN
Centre du Bourg, Le Village, 76740 AUTIGNY
☎ 02 35 97 42 55
Veules-les-Roses 10 km. Yvette and René Heluin invite guests to stay in a traditional brick and flint building close to their 19th-century home in its landscaped garden. On the ground floor there is a double and a twin both with own shower and wc, and on the first floor a double and two family rooms (one four-bed, one five-bed), all with own shower and wc. Cot and high chair. Kitchen and sitting area with open fireplace. Horse-feed available. Table tennis, climbing frame. Restaurant 2.5km. St-Valéry-en-Caux 16km. Open all year.
PRICES: s €27; d €35; t €47; extra person €12 **ON SITE:** Tennis **NEARBY:** Bathing (1km) Horse riding (8km) Golf (25km) Fishing (10km) Swimming pool (16km) Hiking (10km) Railway station (25km) Shops (3km) FONTAINE-LE-DUN (2km) **NOTES:** No pets English spoken

BARDOUVILLE

♦♦♦ Le Val Sarah Jean et Micheline LEFEBVRE
Beaulieu, 76480 BARDOUVILLE
☎ 02 35 37 08 07 📠 02 35 37 11 33
In an attractively landscaped setting close to the River Seine, this detached house belonging to Jean and Micheline Lefebvre has three ground floor guest rooms including two doubles and a triple, all with own shower and wc. Well-equipped kitchen (washing machine, dishwasher), sitting room, living room with open fireplace, TV. Enclosed garden, outdoor furniture. Children's games, tennis, table tennis, pétanque. Banqueting hall (150 guests, parking for 90 cars) for hire. Restaurant at La Bouille 6km. Open all year.
PRICES: s €30; d €33; t €43 **ON SITE:** Children's play area Hiking Tennis **NEARBY:** Bathing (50km) Horse riding (5km) Golf (20km) Swimming pool (10km) Railway station (25km) Shops (6km) DUCLAIR (6km) **NOTES:** No pets CC

BEC-DE-MORTAGNE

♦♦♦ La Vallée J-Pierre & Arlette MOREL
1 rue de la Chenaie, 76110 BEC-DE-MORTAGNE
☎ 02 35 28 00 81
Fécamp 9 km Close to a river in the middle of the village, this half-timbered residence belonging to Arlette and Jean-Pierre Morel has a large and attractive garden. The three first floor rooms include two doubles and a triple, all with own shower and wc. Extra bed available. Garden furniture. Small pets welcome by prior agreement. Restaurant 2km. Open between Easter and 1 November.
PRICES: ; d €38; t €49; extra person €12 **ON SITE:** Hiking **NEARBY:** Bathing (10km) Horse riding (9km) Golf (18km) Fishing (6km) Swimming pool (9km) Tennis (9km) Railway station (12km) Shops (9km) GODERVILLE (10km) **NOTES:** No pets

BERVILLE-EN-CAUX

♦♦♦ ♥ ⟨◯⟩ La Ferme Pillet
J-P et M VANDECANDELAERE
76560 BERVILLE-EN-CAUX
☎ 02 35 96 17 36
Saint-Valéry-en-Caux 20 km. A farm in a quiet little village in the Caux countryside. The brick-built farmhouse in the courtyard has four guest rooms including a ground floor twin and on the first floor a family room for four (double bed and bunk), two doubles and another family room (double and single), all with own bath or shower and wc. Baby equipment. Sitting room with open fireplace and kitchenette. Meals featuring farm bred rabbits and poultry. Own fishing lake. Restaurant 4km. Open all year.

continued

PRICES: s €30; d €40; t €52; extra person €12; dinner €14
ON SITE: Wine tasting Fishing **NEARBY:** Bathing (20km) Canoeing (20km) Horse riding (10km) Golf (32km) Swimming pool (12km) Stretch of water (20km) Hiking (2km) Tennis (1km) Railway station (7km) Shops (1km) DOUDEVILLE (3km) **NOTES:** No pets

BUTOT-VENESVILLE

Chambre d'hôtes Marc et Marie-France MOSER
1 Sente du Gite, Hameau de Vaudreville,
76450 BUTOT-VENESVILLE
☎ 02 35 97 52 86
Only 5km from Petites Dalles beach, this fine 17th-century house belonging to M and Mme Moser stands in an attractively landscaped park, and has a Grade 3 triple on the first floor with separate entrance and own bath and shower. A separate 19th-century building has three first floor guest rooms with their own entrance including a Grade 2 double with own shower, a Grade 2 double with separate shower, and a Grade 3 twin with own shower. All have own wc. Restaurants 4km. Open all year.
PRICES: s €27; d €34-€38; t €53; extra person €12 **ON SITE:** Hiking
NEARBY: Bathing (5km) Horse riding (8km) Golf (30km) Fishing (5km) Swimming pool (8km) Stretch of water (8km) Tennis (2km) Railway station (29km) Shops (4km) CANY-BARVILLE (5km) **NOTES:** Pets admitted English spoken

CANEHAN

Les Terres du Thil Marie-Claire BLANGEZ
rue de la Laiterie, 76260 CANEHAN
☎ 02 35 86 72 56
Le Tréport 10 km. This establishment is situated in a peaceful countryside setting on the banks of the River Yères. On the ground floor there is a family suite for four or five with terrace, separate entrance through the garden, and own luxury bathroom and wc. On the first floor are four doubles with own shower and wc. Lovely views. Meals by arrangement. Garden furniture, barbecue, seating. Parking. Private fishing lake. Close to beaches at Criel and Le Tréport and to the Eu Forest. Open all year.
PRICES: s €37; d €40; extra person €15; dinner €17 **ON SITE:** Fishing
NEARBY: Bathing (4km) Canoeing (10km) Horse riding (5km) Golf (25km) Swimming pool (10km) Stretch of water (12km) Hiking (1km) Tennis (10km) Railway station (10km) Shops (5km) EU (8km)
NOTES: No pets English spoken

CANOUVILLE

Chambre d'hôtes Jean et Monique DOURY
24, rue du Bas, 76450 CANOUVILLE
☎ 02 35 97 50 41
Fécamp 25 km. This spacious residence belonging to Monique and Jean Doury stands in landscaped gardens and has five guest rooms. On the first floor are two triples and a family room for four with own shower and wc, and on the second floor a double and a triple with own shower and wc. Sitting room. Restaurants in Cany-Barville 5km. Open all year.
PRICES: s €34; d €41-€46; t €53; extra person €12 **NEARBY:** Bathing (4km) Horse riding (5km) Golf (30km) Fishing (4km) Swimming pool (4km) Hiking (4km) Tennis (4km) Railway station (15km) Shops (5km) CANY-BARVILLE (5km) **NOTES:** No pets

CAUDEBEC-EN-CAUX

Les Poules Vertes Hubert et Christine VILLAMAUX
68 rue de la République, No 1 Cavée Saint-Léger,
76490 CAUDEBEC-EN-CAUX
☎ 02 35 96 10 15 ▤ 02 35 96 75 25
e-mail: christiane.villamaux@libertysurf.fr
http://villamaux.ifrance.com

Le Havre 50 km / Rouen 35 km. On the 'Route des Abbayes', 3km from Saint-Wandrille and only 500m from the River Seine, this old house has a garden and orchard. There is a ground floor double and on the first floor a double, a triple and a four-bed room, all with own shower and wc. Sitting room with fridge and microwave. Breakfast in family dining room. Garden furniture. Shops and restaurants 500m. Open all year.
PRICES: s €39; d €45; t €57; extra person €12 **ON SITE:** Canoeing Fishing Stretch of water Hiking **NEARBY:** Bathing (40km) Horse riding (2km) Golf (20km) Swimming pool (4km) Tennis (2km) Railway station (10km) CAUDEBEC-EN-CAUX **NOTES:** Pets admitted English spoken

CLIPONVILLE

Rucquemare J-Pierre et Béatrice LEVEQUE
Hameau de Rucquemare, 76640 CLIPONVILLE
☎ 02 35 96 72 21 ▤ 02 35 96 72 21

Yvetot 10 km. Béatrice and Jean-Pierre welcome guests to their farm with dovecote, courtyard, and 17th-century Norman-style residence. The individually decorated guest rooms include a ground floor triple and a double, and on the first floor there are two triple rooms, all with shower and wc. Child's bed available. Sitting room, kitchen, telephone, TV, garden furniture, table tennis, badminton, mountain bikes. Parking. Reduced rates for stays of more than two days except in July and August. Restaurant 4km. Open all year.
PRICES: s €29; d €37; t €47; extra person €11 **ON SITE:** Fishing Stretch of water **NEARBY:** Bathing (25km) Horse riding (7km) Golf (30km) Swimming pool (5km) Hiking (7km) Tennis (5km) Railway station (10km) Shops (5km) FAUVILLE-EN-CAUX (5km) **NOTES:** Pets admitted English spoken

CRIQUEBEUF-EN-CAUX

Chambre d'hôtes Véronique et Thierry BAUDRY
52 rue de l'Eglise, 76111 CRIQUEBEUF-EN-CAUX
☎ 02 35 28 70 15
Etretat 14 km. Véronique and Thierry look forward to greeting guests at their spacious brick and flint home in seaside style standing in its attractive and tree-lined grounds. The five first floor rooms include a large double and another double with separate bath and wc, a family suite for four with own shower and wc, a double and a family room for three, both with own facilities. Dining room, billiard, games and TV room. Meals provided. Restaurant 2km. Open all year.
PRICES: s €37; d €43; t €69; extra person €12; dinner €15
ON SITE: Hiking **NEARBY:** Bathing (2km) Canoeing (26km) Horse riding (7km) Golf (14km) Fishing (2km) Swimming pool (5km) Stretch of water (26km) Tennis (1km) Railway station (5km) Shops (2km) Restaurant nearby FECAMP (5km) **NOTES:** No pets

continued

CRIQUETOT-L'ESNEVAL

⚓ Le Prêche Thierry et Isabelle REAL
33 route d'Etretat, 76280 CRIQUETOT-L'ESNEVAL
☎ 02 35 27 47 84
Etretat 9 km. In a peaceful setting on the Etretat road close to the centre of Criquetot, this large 19th-century house belonging to Thierry and Isabelle stands in a landscaped park. On the first floor are two doubles, including one Grade 2 with separate shower and wc, and on the second floor a family suite for four with own shower and wc. Sitting room. Well located for exploring the Alabaster Coast along long-distance footpaths. Bike-carrying tourist train 5km. Open all year.
PRICES: s €30; d €35-€40; t €52; extra person €12 **NEARBY:** Bathing (9km) Canoeing (36km) Horse riding (9km) Golf (9km) Fishing (9km) Swimming pool (9km) Stretch of water (36km) Hiking (1km) Tennis (9km) Railway station (10km) Shops (1km) CRIQUETOT-L'ESNEVAL
NOTES: Pets admitted

DIEPPE

⚓ Villa Florida Danièle NOEL
24 Chemin du golf, 76200 DIEPPE
☎ 02 35 84 40 37 📠 02 35 84 32 51
e-mail: villa-florida@wanadoo.fr 🖳 dieppefloridagolf.free.fr
Close to the sea in the exclusive surroundings of Dieppe-Pourville golf course, this is a fine example of contemporary domestic architecture, with well-proportioned and sunny rooms. The first floor guest rooms include a twin with own shower and wc, a twin with own bath and wc, and a triple (single bed on mezzanine) with own shower and wc. All rooms have a terrace with golf course views. Restaurant 500m. Open all year.
PRICES: d €54-€58; t €69; extra person €15 **ON SITE:** Golf
NEARBY: Bathing (2km) Horse riding (4km) Fishing (7km) Swimming pool (1km) Hiking (3km) Tennis (2km) Railway station (2km) Shops (1km) DIEPPE **NOTES:** Pets admitted English spoken
See advert on this page

DUCLAIR

⚓ Chambre d'hôtes Bernard et Renée LEMERCIER
282 Chemin du Panorama, Le Catel, 76480 DUCLAIR
☎ 02 35 37 68 84 & 06 70 57 87 28

Rouen 18 km. Built in 1930, this property by the River Seine is on a long-distance footpath and the 'Route des Abbayes'. The three first floor rooms include a triple with own bath and wc, a double with own shower and wc, and a family suite for five with own bath and wc. South-facing terrace and garden furniture. Courtyard parking. Restaurants 500m. Recreation centre 8km. Open all year.
PRICES: s €34; d €46; t €53; extra person €8 **ON SITE:** Hiking
NEARBY: Bathing (80km) Horse riding (8km) Golf (8km) Fishing (1km) Swimming pool (10km) Stretch of water (8km) Tennis (1km) Railway station (20km) Shops (1km) DUCLAIR (1km) **NOTES:** No pets CC

La Villa Florida

24, chemin du Golf, 76 200 Dieppe

Tél: 33 (0)235 84 40 37 – Fax: 33 (0)235 84 32 51
EMail: adn@lavillaflorida.com
Web: http://www.lavillaflorida.com

The Villa Florida is wonderfully appealing in its brightness and charm. Situated near the sea in an exclusive suburb, far from the noise of the town, *The Villa Florida* is an architecturally interesting house where the garden opens onto an 18 hole golf course. The house has three elegant guest bedrooms, each with en-suite. Parking in the property

⚓ Les Tamayas Elisabeth NONCLE
61 rue Clarin Mustad, 76480 DUCLAIR
☎ 02 35 37 12 93 & 06 10 75 92 27
e-mail: noncle@wanadoo.fr
http://perso.wanadoo.fr/chambreshotes.noncle
A 19th-century residence standing in a well-wooded park and with three individually named rooms. There is a large ground floor triple (Pommiers) with own shower and wc and kitchen, and on the first floor a large triple (Nympheas) with own spacious bath, shower and wc, and another triple (Armada) with own shower and wc. Extra bed available. Baby-sitting. Sitting room. River Seine nearby. Restaurant 300m.
PRICES: s €38; d €41-€46; t €56; extra person €11 **ON SITE:** Hiking
NEARBY: Bathing (70km) Horse riding (2km) Golf (5km) Fishing (1km) Swimming pool (8km) Stretch of water (5km) Tennis (1km) Railway station (22km) DUCLAIR **NOTES:** Pets admitted English spoken

ECTOT-L'AUBER

⚓ ✿ ⏃ Chambre d'hôtes J-Pierre & Bénédicte VIN
Le Village, 76760 ECTOT L'AUBER
☎ 02 35 96 84 14 & 06 20 43 20 55 📠 02 35 96 81 32
e-mail: jp.vin@free.fr http://www.agri76.fr/hetraie
Surrounded by beech trees, and complete with dovecote, barn and cart-shed, this fine old 18th-century farmhouse has been converted to house three charming and attractively decorated rooms, all with own shower and wc. Kitchenette, barbecue, table tennis, bikes. Meals by arrangement. Hosts are a good source of information on nearby attractions. Restaurant 3km. Open all year.
PRICES: s €41; d €47; dinner €18 **ON SITE:** Hiking **NEARBY:** Bathing (27km) Canoeing (32km) Horse riding (5km) Golf (25km) Fishing (6km) Swimming pool (10km) Stretch of water (32km) Tennis (2km) Railway station (10km) Shops (3km) YERVILLE (3km) **NOTES:** No pets English spoken

EPOUVILLE

Le Moulin d'Epouville Martine LEBOURGEOIS
28 rue Aristide Briand, 76133 EPOUVILLE
☎ 02 35 30 84 46 🖷 02 35 30 99 64
e-mail: ml.lemoulin@wanadoo.fr
http://www.lemoulindepouville.com

Le Havre 7 km. In wooded surroundings close to the town centre, this watermill with its two streams has three guest rooms, all doubles, one with own bath and wc, the others with own shower and wc. Sitting room, TV. River fishing. Open all year.
PRICES: s €51; d €55; extra person €11 **ON SITE:** Fishing
NEARBY: Bathing (10km) Horse riding (3km) Golf (9km) Swimming pool (3km) Hiking (2km) Tennis (1km) Railway station (12km) MONTIVILLIERS **NOTES:** No pets Minimum 2 night stay English spoken

EU

Manoir De Beaumont Jean-Marie DEMARQUET
76260 EU
☎ 02 35 50 91 91 & 06 72 80 01 04
e-mail: CD@fnac.net www.chez.com/demarquet

Le Tréport 5 km. Set in a peaceful park overlooking the valley, this Anglo-Norman manor house and its 18th-century hunting lodge offers four guest rooms. In the house is a first floor triple with own shower and wc and on the first floor of the lodge a double with own shower and wc and a family suite for five with kitchenette and own shower and wc. TV in all rooms. Mountain bikes. On the edge of the Eu Forest. Open all year.
PRICES: s €32; d €45; t €55; extra person €11 **ON SITE:** Hiking
NEARBY: Bathing (4km) Horse riding (4km) Golf (37km) Fishing (7km) Swimming pool (5km) Tennis (2km) Railway station (3km) Shops (2km) EU **NOTES:** Pets admitted English spoken

> For further information on these and other chambres d'hôtes, consult the Gîtes de France website
> *www.gites-de-france.fr*

FLAMETS-FRETILS

La Dranvillaise Claudie PETIT
Dranville, Route de la Chapelle, 76270 FLAMETS-FRETILS
☎ & 06 81 73 70 80
Forges-les-Eaux 17 km, Dieppe 40 km. This restored farmhouse in the middle of the Bray countryside offers a traditional Norman atmosphere. With their own entrance, the three rooms include a pink family suite (three beds) in a separate building with cot and own shower and wc, a green room (double) with own shower and wc, and a yellow room (triple) with own shower and wc. Sitting room. Restaurant 10km. Open all year.
PRICES: s €22; d €39; t €46; extra person €13; dinner €15
ON SITE: Children's play area **NEARBY:** Bathing (40km) Canoeing (10km) Horse riding (8km) Golf (25km) Fishing (15km) Swimming pool (10km) Stretch of water (17km) Hiking (2km) Tennis (10km) Railway station (12km) Shops (10km) NEUFCHATEL-EN-BRAY (10km)
NOTES: Pets admitted English spoken

HAUDRICOURT

Ferme de la Mare du Bois
Stéphane et Florence NUTTENS
route de Neufchâtel-Aumale, 76390 HAUDRICOURT
☎ 02 35 94 44 56 🖷 02 35 93 38 52
e-mail: la.mare.du.bois@libertysurf.fr www.lamaredubois.com
Stéphane and Florence Nuttens welcome guests to their farm with its spacious gentleman's residence which has three first floor doubles, all with own shower and wc. Meals. Reduced rates for longer stays out of season. Gîte. Camping. Small dogs accepted with previous agreement of proprietor. Open all year.
PRICES: s €35; d €35 **ON SITE:** Horse riding Hiking **NEARBY:** Bathing (54km) Fishing (6km) Swimming pool (6km) Tennis (6km) Railway station (6km) Shops (6km) Restaurant nearby AUMALE (6km)
NOTES: No pets

ISNEAUVILLE

La Muette Jacques et Danielle AUFFRET
1057 rue des Bosquets, 76230 ISNEAUVILLE
☎ 02 35 60 57 69 & 06 86 78 43 91 🖷 02 35 61 56 64
e-mail: JDFTM.AUFFRET@wanadoo.fr http://lamuette.free.fr

Rouen 8 km. On the very edge of the forest, this charming, fully restored Norman-style house belongs to Jacques and Danielle Auffret. The four guest rooms in an adjacent 18th-century cider press building with separate entrance include a double (with small adjacent room with single bed), a triple (single bed on mezzanine), a double and a triple, all with TV point, own shower and wc. Ground floor sitting room with open fireplace. Meals two evenings a week by arrangement. Open February to 23 December.
PRICES: s €45; d €55; t €67-€70; dinner €23 **ON SITE:** Wine tasting
NEARBY: Horse riding (4km) Golf (3km) Swimming pool (5km) Tennis (2km) Railway station (8km) Shops (2km) BOIS-GUILLAUME (4km)
NOTES: No pets English spoken

JUMIEGES

♦♦♦ Le Relais de l'Abbaye Patrick et Brigitte CHATEL
798 rue du Quesney, 76480 JUMIEGES
☎ 02 35 37 24 98 📠 02 35 37 24 98
In a quiet location on the edge of a wooded park, this Norman-style house belongs to Brigitte and Patrick Chatel and has a garden with terrace. There is a ground floor twin plus a double, while on the first floor is a double and a triple. All rooms have own wc and shower. Separate entrance. Plenty of brochures and other material about the area. Six mini-gîtes. Country inn and restaurant 1km. Rouen 25km. Open all year.
PRICES: s €32; d €37; t €46 **ON SITE:** Hiking **NEARBY:** Bathing (60km) Horse riding (3km) Golf (3km) Fishing (3km) Swimming pool (15km) Tennis (3km) Railway station (25km) Shops (1km) DUCLAIR (12km) **NOTES:** Pets admitted

LA CHAPELLE-SUR-DUN

♦♦♦ Chalet du Bel Event Daniel et Virginie WESTHEAD
Chemin de Bel Event, 76740 LA CHAPELLE-SUR-DUN
☎ 02 35 57 08 44
e-mail: dwesthead@yahoo.com www.chaletdubelevent.com
Veules-les-Roses 3 km, Dieppe 20 km. In a parkland setting midway between coast and countryside, the house belonging to Daniel and Virginie has a traditional 19th-century seaside character. A nearby brick building has a first floor double and three second floor doubles, all with own bath or shower and wc. Ground floor entrance, sitting room, living rooms, piano. Tennis. Colourful restaurant 200m. Open all year.
PRICES: s €46; d €46-€53; extra person €12 **ON SITE:** Tennis **NEARBY:** Bathing (3km) Canoeing (25km) Horse riding (15km) Golf (15km) Fishing (4km) Swimming pool (12km) Stretch of water (25km) Hiking (3km) Railway station (25km) Shops (1km) FONTAINE-LE-DUN (7km) **NOTES:** Pets admitted English spoken

♦♦♦ ⁙◎⁙ La Hosannière Tan et Martine DO PHAT-LATOUR
Chemin du Simplon, 76740 LA CHAPELLE-SUR-DUN
☎ 02 35 97 44 59 📠 02 35 97 43 87
e-mail: lahosanniere@fnac.net

Veules-les-Roses 3 km. Tan and Martine welcome guests to their typical Norman long and low farmhouse dating from the 16th-century. There is a ground floor twin with own shower and wc, and on the first floor a twin and a four-bed room, both with bath and wc. Children's beds available. Comfortable first floor sitting room, ground floor sitting room with open fireplace, breakfast room with open fireplace. Quality meals (vegetarian if required). Sauna €8 per person. Bike hire. Golfing and aerobics instruction. Restaurants 3km. Open all year.
PRICES: s €47; d €55-€59; t €70; extra person €15; dinner €17 **NEARBY:** Bathing (4km) Canoeing (23km) Horse riding (3km) Golf (23km) Fishing (4km) Swimming pool (11km) Stretch of water (23km) Hiking (3km) Tennis (4km) Railway station (11km) FONTAINE-LE-DUN (7km) **NOTES:** No pets English spoken

LA MAILLERAYE-SUR-SEINE

♦♦♦ La Renardière Michel LEFRANCOIS
Route de Brotonne, 76940 LA MAILLERAYE SURSEINE
☎ 02 35 37 13 25 📠 02 35 37 02 69

This half-timbered house stands among attractive gardens in a four hectare estate in the Normandy Seine Regional Park. There are two first floor rooms, both with twin beds convertible into doubles, one of them with an additional single bed, both with own shower and wc. Sitting room with open fireplace. Another room in a separate annexe with three single beds (two convertible into double), own shower and wc, sitting area and kitchenette. Extra beds available. Open all year.
PRICES: s €30; d €40-€43; t €53; extra person €11 **ON SITE:** Swimming pool Hiking **NEARBY:** Bathing (50km) Horse riding (7km) Golf (7km) Fishing (7km) Stretch of water (7km) Tennis (1km) Railway station (20km) Shops (1km) CAUDEBEC-EN-CAUX (7km) **NOTES:** Pets admitted English spoken

LA VIEUX-RUE

♦♦♦ ❦ La Clé des Champs Roselyne FLEUTRY
257 rue du 8 Mai 1945, 76160 LA VIEUX RUE
☎ 02 35 59 92 71
Darnétal 8 km. A Normandy home in peaceful countryside only 12km from Rouen. The first floor rooms with separate entrance include a family suite for four with own shower and wc and two doubles with own shower and wc. Attractive garden with outdoor furniture, seesaw, toboggan, sandpit and barbecue. Reduced rates for stays of more than three days. Restaurant 4km. Open all year.
PRICES: s €30; d €38; t €46; extra person €8 **ON SITE:** Hiking **NEARBY:** Bathing (50km) Horse riding (5km) Golf (12km) Fishing (8km) Swimming pool (7km) Tennis (1km) Railway station (4km) Shops (2km) DARNETAL (8km) **NOTES:** No pets CC

LE TREPORT

♦♦♦ ❦ Prieuré Sainte-Croix Romain et Nicole CARTON
76470 LE TREPORT
☎ 02 35 86 14 77
Le Tréport 2 km. This building of character on the old farm of the Eu Château has a ground floor suite (double and sofa bed in sitting room) with kitchenette, private garden, own bath and wc, and four first floor rooms including three doubles and a twin, all with own shower and wc. Two of the rooms can be linked. Sitting room. Garden and outdoor furniture, courtyard parking. Restaurant 2km. Open all year.
PRICES: ; d €42-€54; extra person €12 **ON SITE:** Hiking **NEARBY:** Bathing (3km) Horse riding (2km) Golf (30km) Fishing (2km) Swimming pool (3km) Tennis (1km) Railway station (2km) Shops (1km) EU (2km) **NOTES:** No pets English spoken

LES LANDES-VIEILLES-ET-NEUVES

♥♥♥ Château des Landes J et G SIMON-LEMETTRE
76390 LES LANDES-VIEILLES-ET-NEUVES
☎ 02 35 94 03 79 ▤ 02 35 94 03 79
e-mail: jgsimon@chateaudeslandes.com
www.chateaudeslandes.com

A 19th-century chateau just a step from the Eu Forest. The five spacious rooms include a first floor double room and a four-bed suite, and on the second floor a double, a triple (double plus single bed) and another triple (three single beds), all with own shower and wc. Luxury four-person suite: €100. No charge for child's bed. Dining room, sitting room/library. Breakfast served on veranda. Open all year.
PRICES: s €41-€47; d €47-€56; t €73; extra person €17 **ON SITE:** Hiking
NEARBY: Bathing (42km) Horse riding (12km) Golf (30km) Fishing (14km) Swimming pool (12km) Tennis (12km) Railway station (12km) Shops (12km) AUMALE (12km) **NOTES:** No pets English spoken

MELLEVILLE

♥♥♥ ♥ La Marette Etienne et Nelly GARCONNET
76260 MELLEVILLE
☎ 02 35 50 81 65 ▤ 02 35 50 81 65
Le Tréport 13 km. Dating from 1900, this house is on the edge of the Eu Forest. There are two family suites, one with two double beds (extra single available) and own bath, the other with two double beds (extra single available) has a shared shower. A third room is a double (extra single available €15) with shared shower. All have own wc. Sitting room, games room, garden furniture and kitchen for use of guests in summer. €61/86 per suite. Restaurant 7km. Open all year.
PRICES: d €31-€43; t €61-€86; extra person €15 **ON SITE:** Hiking
NEARBY: Bathing (14km) Horse riding (7km) Golf (14km) Fishing (7km) Swimming pool (12km) Tennis (4km) Railway station (7km) Shops (7km) EU (11km) **NOTES:** No pets English spoken

NESLE-NORMANDEUSE

♥♥♥ Chambre d'hôtes Jacqueline DUJARDIN
7 route de Campneuseville, 76340 NESLE-NORMANDEUSE
☎ 02 35 93 54 96
Le Tréport 25 km. Jacqueline Dujardin welcomes guests to her 18th-century property 3 km from the Eu Forest. On the ground floor of the annexe to the house are two doubles and two triples, all with TV, own bath and wc. Breakfast served in the house. Garden with loungers. Fishing lake €7.6 per person per day. Restaurant at Blangy-sur-Bresle 4km. Open all year.
PRICES: s €38; d €46; t €64; extra person €15 **ON SITE:** Children's play area **NEARBY:** Bathing (28km) Fishing (3km) Swimming pool (30km) Hiking (3km) Tennis (4km) Railway station (4km) Shops (4km) BLANGY-SUR-BRESLE (4km) **NOTES:** Pets admitted

NEUFCHATEL-EN-BRAY

♥♥♥ ♥ Le Val Boury Xavier et Valérie LEFRANCOIS
76270 NEUFCHATEL EN BRAY
☎ 02 35 93 26 95 ▤ 02 35 97 12 30
e-mail: xavier.lefrancois@wanadoo.fr www.cellier-val-boury.com
Dieppe 25 km. In a peaceful setting just a few steps from the town centre, this old storehouse dating from the 17th-century stands at the start of a footpath leading along the valley. There are three doubles with own shower and wc and a suite with three double beds (extra bed available), cot, and sitting area. Garden with furniture, barbecue, play area. Baby-sitting. Gîte. Restaurant 500m. Open all year.
PRICES: s €37; d €40; t €50; extra person €14 **ON SITE:** Hiking
NEARBY: Bathing (30km) Canoeing (15km) Horse riding (15km) Golf (10km) Fishing (10km) Swimming pool (1km) Stretch of water (1km) Tennis (1km) Railway station (1km) NEUFCHATEL-EN-BRAY **NOTES:** No pets English spoken

OMONVILLE

♥♥♥ ♥ Les Ecureuils Jérome et Nicole LEMARCHAND
542 rue Jacob Bontemps, 76730 OMONVILLE
☎ 02 35 83 21 69 ▤ 02 35 83 21 69
Dieppe 15 km / Varengeville 10 km. In a quiet and leafy setting between the château and the church, this is the working farm with a 17th-century house with exposed timbers and open fireplace. On the first floor are two doubles, a twin and a triple, all with own shower and wc. Children's bed and games. Kitchen available. Garden. Sea-fishing 6km. Horticultural hints. Restaurant 3km. Open all year.
PRICES: s €28; d €34-€35; t €45; extra person €10 **NEARBY:** Bathing (15km) Canoeing (12km) Horse riding (8km) Golf (8km) Fishing (3km) Swimming pool (15km) Stretch of water (15km) Hiking (3km) Tennis (8km) Railway station (8km) Shops (3km) BACQUEVILLE-EN-CAUX (4km) **NOTES:** No pets

OUAINVILLE

♥♥♥ ⦿ Chambre d'hôtes Liliane DETOLLENAERE
Hameau de Bardeville, 76450 OUAINVILLE
☎ 02 35 97 86 88 ▤ 02 35 97 86 88
e-mail: maisondebardeville@wanadoo.fr
www.maisondebardeville.com
Saint-Valéry 12 km, Fécamp 18 km. In a rustic setting close to beaches and cliffs, this brick and flint house in landscaped garden. The three ground floor rooms include a family suite for five with separate entrance, shared bath and wc, and two doubles, one with disabled access, both with own spacious shower room and wc. Baby equipment. Sitting room with traditional open fireplace. Swimming pool. Restaurant 1km. Open all year.
PRICES: s €61; d €61; t €114; extra person €23; dinner €27
ON SITE: Children's play area Swimming pool **NEARBY:** Bathing (7km) Canoeing (2km) Horse riding (3km) Golf (37km) Fishing (2km) Stretch of water (2km) Hiking (1km) Tennis (2km) Railway station (20km) Shops (1km) CANY-BARVILLE (1km) **NOTES:** No pets CC English spoken

PONTS-ET-MARAIS

♥♥♥ Chambre d'hôtes Christian LEPAN
Chemin de Jérusalem, 76260 PONTS-ET-MARAIS
☎ 02 35 86 50 67 ▤ 03 22 30 35 65
This large house stands in luxuriant gardens close to the sea and has lovely views over the valley of the River Bresle. The three cheerfully decorated rooms include a blue ground floor double, and on the first floor a yellow double, and a green triple (extra bed available), all with own shower and wc. Kitchenette. Restaurant 3km. Open all year.
PRICES: s €39; d €39; t €47; extra person €9 **ON SITE:** Hiking

continued

NEARBY: Bathing (5km) Canoeing (10km) Horse riding (3km) Golf (30km) Fishing (3km) Swimming pool (5km) Stretch of water (3km) Tennis (1km) Railway station (3km) Shops (3km) EU (3km)
NOTES: Pets admitted

QUIBERVILLE-SUR-MER

♦♦♦ Les Vergers Christian & M-France AUCLERT
Rue des Vergers, 76860 QUIBERVILLE-SUR-MER
☎ 02 35 83 16 10 🖷 02 35 83 36 46
e-mail: chauclert@aol.com
Dieppe 15 km. Marie-France and Christian Auclert welcome guests to their quiet and comfortable château in landscaped gardens. The rooms include a first floor double and a twin, both with own bath, and on the second floor, a double with own shower. All have own wc. €78 per four. Restaurants at Quiberville-sur-Mer 1km and Dieppe 15km. Open all year.
PRICES: s €40; d €52-€55; t €64; extra person €14 **NEARBY:** Bathing (1km) Canoeing (1km) Horse riding (12km) Golf (10km) Fishing (1km) Swimming pool (15km) Stretch of water (1km) Hiking (1km) Tennis (1km) Railway station (15km) Shops (8km) OFFRANVILLE (12km)
NOTES: No pets CC English spoken

ROUEN

♦♦♦ Chambre d'hôtes Philippe AUNAY
45 rue aux Ours, 76000 ROUEN
☎ 02 35 70 99 68
With an unparalleled knowledge of Rouen, Philippe Aunay welcomes guests to this 15th and 16th-century house which has been in his family since the 19th-century and is completely furnished in Norman style. There is a first floor double with own bath and wc, a second floor twin with own bath and wc, and a third floor family suite for three with own bath and wc. Two rooms with cooking facilities. Sitting room. Open all year.
PRICES: s €35; d €50; extra person €25 **NEARBY:** Bathing (60km) Horse riding (11km) Golf (5km) Fishing (25km) Swimming pool (1km) Hiking (11km) Tennis (3km) Railway station (1km) ROUEN **NOTES:** Pets admitted English spoken

ROUVILLE

♦♦♦ ♥ ⊙ Ferme du Château
J-Cl. et M-Madeleine HERVIEUX
76210 ROUVILLE
☎ 02 35 31 13 98 🖷 02 35 39 00 77
e-mail: hervieux@libertysurf.fr

Honfleur 30 mins. This historic house belongs to Marie-Madeleine and Jean-Claude and stands in its attractive garden outside the village. The three first floor rooms include a family suite for four and two family suites for three, all with own shower and wc. Good range of baby equipment. Sitting room, TV, garden furniture, barbecue. €62 for four. Reduced rates for stays of more than one night. Special business rate €74. Restaurants at Fauville and Bolbec 6km. Open all year.

PRICES: s €34; d €38; t €58; dinner €13 **ON SITE:** Hiking
NEARBY: Bathing (18km) Horse riding (6km) Golf (20km) Fishing (18km) Swimming pool (5km) Tennis (1km) Railway station (10km) Shops (2km) BOLBEC (6km) **NOTES:** No pets

SAINNEVILLE-SUR-SEINE

♦♦♦ ♥ Ferme Drumare Bruno et Christine DERREY
route de Montivilliers - CD39,
76430 SAINNEVILLE-SUR-SEINE
☎ 02 35 20 59 29 & 06 07 70 01 01 🖷 02 35 30 68 59
e-mail: derrey.christine@libertysurf.fr

Etretat 15 km. Guests will enjoy the peace and quiet on this farm with Christine and Bruno in their 16th-century family home. The three first floor rooms with own entrance include a double with own bath, a triple with own shower, and a family room for four with own shower. All have own wc and TV point. Kitchenette. Baby equipment. Garden furniture, barbecue, children's games. Restaurant and country inn 7km. 15 minutes from Honfleur, 20 minutes from Etretat and 10 minutes from Le Havre. Open all year.
PRICES: s €34; d €41; t €50; extra person €9 **ON SITE:** Hiking
NEARBY: Bathing (15km) Horse riding (6km) Golf (12km) Swimming pool (6km) Tennis (1km) Railway station (7km) Shops (1km) SAINT-ROMAIN-DE-COLBOSC (7km) **NOTES:** Pets admitted

SASSETOT-LE-MAUCONDUIT

♦♦♦ ♥ Chambre d'hôtes
Michel et Danièle SOUDRY
Hameau de Criquemanville,
76540 SASSETOT-LE-MAUCONDUIT
☎ 02 35 27 45 64
Cany-Barville 6 km. Danièle and Michel Soudry welcome guests to their lovely Norman-style house dating from the 18th-century. The first floor rooms include two doubles, a triple, and a family room for four with balcony, all with own shower and wc. Kitchenette, sitting room with TV, garden furniture, garage. €52 for four. Restaurants at Sassetot-le-Mauconduit 2km and Cany-Barville 6km. Open all year.
PRICES: s €31; d €36; t €42; extra person €10 **ON SITE:** Hiking
NEARBY: Bathing (3km) Horse riding (2km) Golf (10km) Fishing (6km) Swimming pool (6km) Tennis (2km) Railway station (10km) Shops (2km) VALMONT (7km) **NOTES:** No pets

SAUSSEUZEMARE-EN-CAUX

♦♦♦ ⊙ La Mare du Montier Josette COISY
D72, 76110 SAUSSEUZEMARE
☎ 02 35 27 93 55 🖷 02 35 27 93 55
e-mail: nicole.coisy@wanadoo.fr www.chez.com/cqf/nicole
Fécamp 8 km. Between Etretat and Fécamp, this 18th-century Norman-style house stands in peaceful countryside. There are three attractive first floor doubles with their own entrance, all with own shower and wc. Spacious living room with open fireplace.

continued

continued

NORMANDY

Meals by arrangement; refined cuisine featuring produce from the garden. Half-board: €70/75 for two. Open all year.
PRICES: s €35; d €40-€45; HB €70-€75; dinner €20 **ON SITE:** Hiking **NEARBY:** Bathing (10km) Horse riding (10km) Golf (10km) Fishing (10km) Swimming pool (2km) Tennis (2km) Railway station (8km) Shops (3km) GODERVILLE (2km) **NOTES:** No pets

SENNEVILLE-SUR-FECAMP

₩₩ **Val de la Mer** André et Mireille LETHUILLIER
76400 SENNEVILLE-SUR-FECAMP
☎ 02 35 28 41 93

Mireille and André Lethuillier look forward to welcoming guests to their fine example of a Norman-style home. There is a ground floor twin with own bath and wc, and a first floor triple with own shower and wc and a double with own bath and wc. Restaurant at Fécamp 3km. Open all year except August.
PRICES: s €39; d €50; t €61 **ON SITE:** Hiking **NEARBY:** Bathing (1km) Horse riding (3km) Golf (18km) Fishing (4km) Swimming pool (4km) Tennis (4km) Railway station (4km) Shops (4km) FECAMP (4km) **NOTES:** No pets

SOMMERY

₩₩ 🍂 **Ferme de Bray** Patrice et Liliane PERRIER
76440 SOMMERY
☎ 02 35 90 57 27
e-mail: ferme.de.bray@wanadoo.fr ferme.de.bray.free.fr
Forges-les-Eaux 10 km. Liliane and Patrice Perrier welcome guests to their large and splendid 16th and 17th-century brick residence in an attractive park. The five first floor rooms include a double, three triples, and a family room for four, all with own bath and wc. Sitting room. Countryside activities offered include farm tours (mill, press, dovecote, dairy) and fishing. 100-seat hall and kitchen for hire. €58 for four. Children's bed €8. Restaurant 800m. Forges-les-Eaux 7km. Open all year.
PRICES: s €34; d €41; t €49; extra person €9 **ON SITE:** Fishing Hiking **NEARBY:** Bathing (40km) Horse riding (7km) Golf (15km) Swimming pool (7km) Tennis (2km) Railway station (3km) Shops (2km) SAINT-SAENS (15km) **NOTES:** No pets

SOTTEVILLE-SUR-MER

₩₩ 🍂 🍽 **Le Bout du Haut**
François et Denise LEFEBVRE
Rue du Bout du Haut, 76740 SOTTEVILLE-SUR-MER
☎ 02 35 97 61 05 📠 02 35 97 61 05
Saint-Valéry-en-Caux 10 km. Denise and François Lefebvre are a farming couple who live in peaceful surroundings only 800m from the sea. Guests are welcomed to a modern building in traditional style close to their old residence, a weavers' house. The three first floor rooms include two doubles and a triple, all with own shower and wc. Sitting and living room. TV. Parking. Attractive garden. Stabling for horses. Restaurant 400m. Veules-les-Roses 2.5km, Dieppe 20km. Open all year.

PRICES: s €35; d €35; t €47; extra person €12; dinner €14
ON SITE: Hiking **NEARBY:** Bathing (1km) Horse riding (3km) Golf (15km) Fishing (1km) Swimming pool (9km) Tennis (1km) Railway station (10km) Shops (1km) FONTAINE-LE-DUN (11km) **NOTES:** No pets English spoken

ST-AUBIN-LE-CAUF

₩₩₩ **La Châtellenie** Agnès BOSSELIN
76510 SAINT-AUBIN-LE-CAUF
☎ 02 35 85 88 69 📠 02 35 85 84 21
e-mail: lachatellenie@wanadoo.fr
www.planete-b.fr/la-chatellenie

Dieppe 10 km. This château belonging to Agnès Bosselin stands in an extensive park with a river in a lovely valley. There are three doubles (one on the ground floor), a triple and a twin, all with own shower and wc. Ground and first floor sitting rooms. Reception room. River and lake fishing, table tennis, pétanque, secure bike shed, garden furniture and arbour. Restaurant 3km. Open 15 March to 1 November.
PRICES: s €45; d €49-€60; t €70; extra person €16 **ON SITE:** Fishing Stretch of water Hiking **NEARBY:** Bathing (12km) Canoeing (4km) Horse riding (3km) Golf (12km) Swimming pool (4km) Tennis (10km) Railway station (11km) Shops (1km) ENVERMEU (7km) **NOTES:** No pets CC

ST-AUBIN-SUR-MER

₩₩₩ **Ramouville** Gisèle GENTY
Route de Quiberville,
76740 SAINT-AUBIN-SUR-MER
☎ 02 35 83 47 05

Dieppe 18 km. Guests can expect a warm welcome here. Two rooms with separate entrance include a ground floor triple with own shower and wc and a first floor double with own bath and wc. An annexe has a ground floor family room for four with separate entrance, and on the first floor a twin and a triple, all with own shower and wc. Ground floor sitting and kitchen area, TV. Baby equipment. Stabling for horses. 18th-century bread oven. Upholstery instruction by arrangement. Restaurant 1.5km. Open all year.

continued

continued

PRICES: s €32; d €41; t €54; extra person €13　**ON SITE:** Hiking
NEARBY: Bathing (1km)　Canoeing (27km)　Horse riding (6km)　Golf (18km)　Fishing (1km)　Swimming pool (14km)　Stretch of water (27km)　Tennis (1km)　Railway station (18km)　Shops (4km)　FONTAINE-LE-DUN (8km)　**NOTES:** Pets admitted

ST-AUBIN-SUR-SCIE

¶¶¶ ❦ Rouxmesnil-le-Haut Gérard et Viviane LULAGUE
route de Paris D915, 76550 SAINT-AUBIN-SUR-SCIE
☎ 02 35 84 14 89 & 06 67 36 40 92　🖹 02 35 84 59 11
Dieppe 3 km. Separate from the owners' house, this fine old brick and flint house dates from the 17th-century. The first floor rooms include a family room for four, two triples and two doubles, all with own shower and wc. Ground floor sitting room. Use of kitchen. Landscaped garden, climbing frame, table tennis. Phone point in rooms. Restaurant 500m and country inn at Eawy 20km. Open all year.
PRICES: s €28; d €39; t €47; extra person €12　**NEARBY:** Bathing (3km)　Horse riding (1km)　Golf (3km)　Fishing (3km)　Swimming pool (1km)　Hiking (1km)　Tennis (1km)　Railway station (3km)　Shops (1km)　OFFRANVILLE (2km)　**NOTES:** No pets　English spoken

ST-EUSTACHE-LA-FORET

¶¶¶ ♿ La Petite Rue Agnès SAILLARD
65 A La Petite Rue, 76210 SAINT EUSTACHE LA FORET
☎ 02 35 38 34 36　🖹 02 35 38 33 67
This old lodge close to the owners' house has been restored to provide two ground floor doubles and a triple with access for the less mobile, and a first floor twin, all with own shower and wc. Sitting room, well-equipped kitchen, TV. The landscaped garden has a pool with black swans. Garden furniture, barbecue. Nearby: Etretat, Fécamp, Notre-Dame-de-Gravenchon and Gruchet-le-Valasse Abbey. Leisure park 5 minutes. Covered swimming pool with wave machine 11km. Open all year.
PRICES: s €36; d €46; t €66; extra person €10　**ON SITE:** Stretch of water　Hiking　**NEARBY:** Bathing (20km)　Horse riding (20km)　Golf (22km)　Fishing (11km)　Swimming pool (11km)　Tennis (1km)　Railway station (10km)　Shops (4km)　BOLBEC (4km)　**NOTES:** No pets

ST-JEAN-DU-CARDONNAY

¶¶¶ ❦ ♿ La Ferme du Vivier
J-Claude et M-Cécile LAMBERT
88 route de Duclair, 76150 SAINT-JEAN-DU-CARDONNAY
☎ 02 35 33 80 42
e-mail: chambre-dhotes.lambert@libertysurf.fr
Rouen 7 km. Marie-Cécile and Jean-Claude welcome guests to their 17th-century Norman home on the farm. The ground floor rooms with separate entrance include a twin and a double, both with own shower and wc, one suitable for less mobile (if assisted), and on the first floor is a family room for four, a triple and a double, all with own bath or shower and wc. Children's bed €14. Sitting and living room, TV, kitchenette, washing-machine. Garden with furniture. Restaurant 4.5km, Jumièges 15km. Open all year.
PRICES: s €28; d €36; t €53; extra person €14　**NEARBY:** Bathing (45km)　Horse riding (5km)　Golf (15km)　Fishing (15km)　Swimming pool (4km)　Hiking (1km)　Tennis (1km)　Railway station (4km)　Shops (4km)　NOTRE-DAME-DE-BONDEVILLE (4km)　**NOTES:** No pets

ST-JOUIN-BRUNEVAL

¶¶¶ Manoir de Guetteville Fabienne et Serge PREVOST
rue legros, Hameau de Guetteville,
76280 SAINT-JOUIN-BRUNEVAL
☎ 02 35 29 44 19 & 02 32 96 96 43
e-mail: haroldprevost@aol.com　www.planete-b.fr/prevost
Etretat 9 km. Fabienne and Serge welcome guests to this peaceful

17th-century flint-built Guetteville manor house, surrounded by extensive gardens and shady fruit trees. The four second floor rooms with separate entrance include three doubles and a triple, all with own shower and wc. Sitting area with TV and games. Fine walk to the coastal coombe at Bruneval. Restaurant 3km. Open all year.
PRICES: s €34; d €41; t €53　**ON SITE:** Hiking　**NEARBY:** Bathing (3km)　Horse riding (3km)　Golf (5km)　Swimming pool (15km)　Tennis (2km)　Railway station (12km)　Shops (2km)　CRIQUETOT-L'ESNEVAL (7km)　**NOTES:** No pets　English spoken

ST-SAENS

¶¶¶ Le Logis d'Eawy Françoise BENKOVSKY
1 rue du 31 Août 1944, 76680 SAINT-SAENS
☎ 06 19 15 52 04　🖹 02 35 34 60 29
e-mail: bernard.benkovsky@freesbee.fr　www.lelogisdeawy.com
Rouen 30 km, Dieppe 35 km. Françoise welcomes guests to this charming residence in the middle of a town in the Bray countryside close to the Eawy Forest. The ground floor has a double/twin with separate entrance and disabled access and on the first floor there is a double and a family suite for four, all with own shower and wc. Internal courtyard and garden. Wonderful walking area. Open all year.
PRICES: s €43-€46; d €49-€53; t €64-€69; extra person €15　**ON SITE:** Fishing　**NEARBY:** Bathing (35km)　Canoeing (1km)　Horse riding (1km)　Golf (1km)　Swimming pool (15km)　Stretch of water (30km)　Hiking (1km)　Tennis (1km)　Railway station (7km)　SAINT-SAENS　**NOTES:** No pets　English spoken

ST-VALERY-EN-CAUX

¶¶¶ Chambre d'hôtes Annie PORCHER
Hameau d'Ectot, 76460 SAINT-VALERY-EN-CAUX
☎ 02 35 97 88 05
e-mail: lma.thomas@wanadoo.fr
Annie welcomes guests to this peaceful hamlet between coast and countryside on the approach to the resort of Saint-Valéry-en-Caux. The converted farm building was fully restored in 1997 and has three first floor guest rooms including two doubles and a triple, all with own shower and wc. Large ground floor sitting and breakfast room. Extensive garden with parking. Restaurant 800m. Open all year.
PRICES: s €31; d €42; t €51　**ON SITE:** Wine tasting　Hiking　**NEARBY:** Bathing (2km)　Horse riding (15km)　Golf (27km)　Fishing (20km)　Swimming pool (2km)　Tennis (2km)　Railway station (2km)　Shops (2km)　SAINT-VALERY-EN-CAUX (2km)　**NOTES:** No pets　English spoken

TOURVILLE-SUR-ARQUES

¶¶¶ Chambre d'hôtes Francine LAMIRAND
54 route des Coteaux, 76550 TOURVILLE-SUR-ARQUES
☎ 02 35 04 10 63
Dieppe 8 km. Francine's lovely traditional residence stands in a large landscaped garden with a pool, and has two doubles plus a family suite with two double beds and a child's bed, all with own shower and wc. Separate entrance, kitchenette, TV. Secure parking. Garden furniture. Lake and river fishing nearby. €61 per four. Open all year.
PRICES: s €30-€38; d €38-€46; t €56　**ON SITE:** Hiking　**NEARBY:** Bathing (8km)　Horse riding (4km)　Golf (8km)　Fishing (6km)　Swimming pool (6km)　Stretch of water (6km)　Tennis (4km)　Railway station (8km)　Shops (2km)　OFFRANVILLE (4km)　**NOTES:** No pets　English spoken

continued

NORMANDY

TURRETOT

♯♯♯ Ecuquetot Jean et Cécile LHOMMET
76280 TURRETOT
☎ 02 35 20 20 76

Etretat 10 km. This Norman-style house with separate entrance giving on to a lovely garden belongs to Cécile and Jean Lhommet and has an interior with exposed timbers and an open fireplace. The first floor rooms include a triple and two doubles, all with own shower and wc. Dining and sitting area on first floor. Reduced rates for stays of more than two days. 18km from the Pont de Normandie, and 1km from the Fécamp-Le Havre expressway. Restaurant 5km.

PRICES: s €28; d €37; t €50; extra person €11 **ON SITE:** Hiking
NEARBY: Bathing (10km) Horse riding (8km) Golf (10km) Fishing (7km) Swimming pool (12km) Tennis (1km) Railway station (3km) Shops (1km) CRIQUETOT-L'ESNEVAL (4km) **NOTES:** No pets

♯♯♯ 🐔 |Ô| Les Quatre Brouettes Alain et Claudine RAS
76280 TURRETOT
☎ 02 35 20 23 73 📠 02 35 20 23 73

continued

Etretat 10 km. This traditional Norman-style house is 20 minutes from the Pont de Normandie. The rooms have individual names. There is a ground floor 'Poppy' suite with double bed and sofa-bed, sitting area/kitchenette and TV, and on the first floor a 'Camellia' triple and a 'Periwinkle' double plus cot, share a sitting room and kitchenette. Also on first floor a 'Forget-Me-Not' triple with own shower and wc. Meals by arrangement. Garden. Bike hire. Open all year.

PRICES: s €28; d €35-€40; extra person €10; dinner €16
ON SITE: Hiking **NEARBY:** Bathing (7km) Horse riding (10km) Golf (10km) Fishing (7km) Swimming pool (10km) Tennis (1km) Railway station (4km) Shops (1km) CRIQUETOT-L'ESNEVAL (5km) **NOTES:** Pets admitted

VILLERS-ECALLES

♯♯♯ Les Florimanes Marie-Claire LEREVERT
850 rue gadeau de Kerville, 76360 VILLERS-ECALLES
☎ 02 35 91 98 59 📠 02 35 91 98 59

Rouen 20 km. In quiet countryside only 15 minutes from Rouen, this manor house dates from the 17th century and stands in its own landscaped grounds. The three spacious first floor rooms (non-smoking) include two triples and a double, all with own shower and wc. Separate entrance. Sitting room, music room and library. Unfenced lake. A well-known watercolour painter, Marie-Claire gives courses in framing and book-binding. Restaurant 2km. 30 minutes from Saint-Valéry-en-Caux. Open all year.

PRICES: s €52-€55; d €59-€63; t €78 **ON SITE:** Hiking
NEARBY: Bathing (35km) Horse riding (8km) Golf (10km) Fishing (3km) Swimming pool (3km) Stretch of water (10km) Tennis (1km) Railway station (3km) Shops (1km) PAVILLY (4km) **NOTES:** No pets English spoken

PAYS DE LA LOIRE

LOIRE-ATLANTIQUE

ABBARETZ

♯♯♯ La Jahotière Jean-François NODINOT
44170 ABBARETZ
☎ 02 40 55 23 34 & 06 81 78 92 30

Set in 100 hectares with a lake, hunting reserve and the ruins of a French smelting furnace. The house has four en suite bedrooms and two lounges for TV or reading. Guests can use the garden furniture and enjoy the enclosed grounds. Nantes 40km. La Baule 60km. Open all year.

PRICES: d €56; t €69; extra person €12 **ON SITE:** Hiking
NEARBY: Bathing (3km) Golf (40km) Sea (60km) Fishing (3km) Water sports (3km) Shops (3km) CHATEAUBRIANT (22km)
NOTES: No pets English spoken

ARTHON-EN-RETZ

♯♯♯ 🔥 Chambre d'hôtes Marie Claire MALARD
Route de Chauvé, 44320 ARTHON-EN-RETZ
☎ 02 40 64 85 81

Pornic 10 km. Noirmoutier 50 km. Close to the sea in peaceful countryside, the house has four en suite guest rooms with shower
continued

---

and wc, one room is accessible for the less mobile. Electric heating. Breakfast room with kitchenette. Separate entrance. The garden has childrens' games, BBQ and furniture. Private parking. Easy access. Open all year.

PRICES: s €29; d €34; t €39; extra person €5 **ON SITE:** Hiking
NEARBY: Golf (10km) Sea (7km) Fishing (7km) Swimming pool (10km) Water sports (7km) Tennis (1km) Shops (1km) Railway Station (12km) PORNIC (10km) **NOTES:** Pets admitted

ASSERAC

♯♯♯ Chambre d'hôtes Marie PHILIPPE-PAUVERT
15 rue du Calvaire, 44410 ASSERAC
☎ 02 51 10 28 68 · e-mail: le.marquisat@caramail.com

An early 18th-century manor house situated between the Parc de Brière and the saltern marshes. Three en suite double rooms with shower and wc. Guests can use the main lounge with open fireplace, the attractive garden, furnished terrace, BBQ and private parking. Open all year.

PRICES: d €54-€60; t €72-€78; extra person €18 **NEARBY:** Bathing (25km) Golf (10km) Sea (6km) Fishing (16km) Swimming pool (6km) Hiking (6km) Tennis (6km) Railway Station (25km) LA BAULE (25km)
NOTES: No pets

Chambre d'hôtes Christine JOSSO
Pen Bé, La Baie des Dames, 44410 ASSERAC
☎ 02 40 01 72 45
Uninterrupted views of the sea are a feature here. There are three first-floor bedrooms for two or three guests, each has TV, shower and wc. There is a library and lounge/games room on the ground floor. The large enclosed garden has a terrace and garden furniture. Friendly dinner-time atmosphere. Medieval city nearby. Open Easter to 1st November.
PRICES: s €46; d €50; t €66; extra person €15; dinner €18 **ON SITE:** Sea Fishing Hiking Water sports **NEARBY:** Golf (20km) Swimming pool (20km) Tennis (6km) Shops (6km) Railway station (20km) LA BAULE (20km) **NOTES:** No pets

CHATEAU-THEBAUD

La Pennissière Gérard et Annick BOUSSEAU
44690 CHATEAU-THEBAUD
☎ 02 40 06 51 22 📠 02 40 06 51 22
Guests are warmly welcomed to this wine-growing estate in the heart of Muscadet. There are three individually appointed first-floor bedrooms, tastefully decorated with antique furniture and enjoying views of the vineyards. These peaceful bedrooms have private bathrooms and wcs. There is a separate guest entrance, a large warm reception room with exposed stonework and a mezzanine (with optional extra bed). Peaceful lounge area, fireplace and TV. Meals by arrangement. Open all year. Fishing on a private lake 400m away.
PRICES: s €32; d €38; extra person €11 **ON SITE:** Water sports **NEARBY:** Fishing (1km) Swimming pool (6km) Hiking (1km) Tennis (2km) Shops (2km) Railway station (15km) NANTES (15km) **NOTES:** Pets admitted

Le Petit Douet Thérèse MECHINEAU
44690 CHATEAU-THEBAUD
☎ 02 40 06 53 59 📠 02 40 06 57 42
This house has three ground floor guest bedrooms with private showers & wc. These comprise a twin, large double and standard double. The shared lounge has an open fireplace. Private shady garden. Cellar tours. Evening meals by arrangement, (except Sundays or public holidays). Meals are taken with your hosts in a friendly atmosphere. Open February to end of October.
PRICES: s €36; d €38-€40; t €49; dinner €18 **ON SITE:** Hiking **NEARBY:** Sea (60km) Fishing (1km) Swimming pool (6km) Water sports (3km) Tennis (2km) Shops (2km) Railway station (15km) CLISSON (13km) **NOTES:** Pets admitted

CHAUVE

La Caillerie Colette LESUEUR
44320 CHAUVE
☎ 02 40 21 16 18 & 06 60 84 77 97 📠 02 40 21 16 18
e-mail: lesueurcolette@yahoo.fr
A peaceful rural setting in the heart of the Pays de Retz, south of the Loire and 12km from Pornic and the Côte de Jade beaches. Four ground-floor guest bedrooms are available for two to four people, all with private bathroom, TV and separate entrance. Large shady garden, private parking. Evening meals can be booked according to availability. Open all year.
PRICES: d €43-€48; t €58; extra person €10; dinner €17 **ON SITE:** Hiking **NEARBY:** Bathing (10km) Golf (12km) Sea (12km) Fishing (4km) Swimming pool (12km) Water sports (12km) Tennis (3km) Shops (4km) Railway station (25km) PORNIC (15km) **NOTES:** No pets English spoken

---

Ask the proprietor for directions
when booking

CHEMERE

Prince Neuf Hubert HARDY
44680 CHEMERE
☎ 02 40 21 30 35 📠 02 40 21 30 35
A former hunting lodge dating from the 19th century, at the edge of the Princé forest. The estate has direct access to long forest walks and adjoining grounds. There are four first-floor en suite double bedrooms. Central heating. Pornic 18km. Open all year.
PRICES: s €38; d €43 **ON SITE:** Hiking Tennis **NEARBY:** Golf (18km) Sea (15km) Swimming pool (18km) Water sports (15km) Shops (4km) Railway station (12km) PORNIC (12km) **NOTES:** No pets

CROSSAC

La Cossonnais Yvette HOUIS
44160 CROSSAC
☎ 02 40 01 05 21 & 06 81 43 11 62
On the first floor of the owner's house there are three guest bedrooms for two to three people (one has a separate entrance and one is grade 2). Private bathroom for each bedroom. Telephone, TV, lounge with fireplace. Peaceful garden, grounds, terrace, garden furniture. Open all year.
PRICES: s €35; d €40; t €50; extra person €10 **NEARBY:** Golf (6km) Sea (25km) Fishing (6km) Swimming pool (6km) Hiking (2km) Water sports (6km) Tennis (6km) Shops (2km) Railway station (6km) SAINT NAZAIRE (22km) **NOTES:** Pets admitted

FAY-DE-BRETAGNE

Le Pâtureau Robert MOULLEC
44130 FAY-DE-BRETAGNE
☎ 02 40 79 92 29
Peace and quiet are guaranteed at Le Patureau. On the first floor of the host's house there are three en suite guest rooms for two to four people, with a suite or mezzanine. Lounge area and shared TV. Large shady garden (one hectare). Open all year.
PRICES: s €46; d €46; t €53 **NEARBY:** Golf (14km) Sea (40km) Fishing (5km) Swimming pool (5km) Hiking (5km) Water sports (10km) Tennis (3km) Shops (3km) Railway station (14km) BLAIN (5km) **NOTES:** No pets

FROSSAY

Château de La Rousselière Catherine SCHERER
44320 FROSSAY
☎ 02 40 39 79 59 📠 02 40 39 77 78
e-mail: larouss@club-internet.fr

An 18th-century château in beautiful grounds in the Pays de Retz, just 3km from the Canal de la Martinière. Three spacious en suite bedrooms with separate entrances. Lounge and dining room for guests. Billiards, swimming pool, horses accepted. Forest 10km. Pornic 20km. St Brévin 18km. Open May to September.
PRICES: d €70; extra person €16 **NEARBY:** Bathing (8km) Golf (20 Sea (20km) Fishing (3km) Swimming pool (18km) Hiking (3 sports (3km) Tennis (1km) Shops (10km) Railway stat PORNIC (20km) **NOTES:** Pets admitted Englis

HERBIGNAC

♯♯♯ Château de Coëtcaret Cécile DE LA MONNERAYE
Coëtcaret, 44410 HERBIGNAC
☎ 02 40 91 41 20 📄 02 40 91 37 46
e-mail: coetcaret@multimania.com
http://welcome.to/coetcaret.com

This small 19th-century château enjoys an exceptional setting on a large wooded estate between the ocean and the Parc Régional de Brière. There are three quiet, comfortable en suite bedrooms, one is suitable for a family of three with one child under 12. Heating, table tennis, garden furniture, nature trail in the grounds. The knowledgeable hosts are happy to help guests plan day trips. Payphone. Open all year.
PRICES: d €85-€95; extra person €23 **ON SITE:** Hiking
NEARBY: Golf (12km) Sea (14km) Fishing (2km) Swimming pool (12km) Water sports (2km) Tennis (4km) Shops (3km) Railway station (20km) SAINT NAZAIRE (25km) **NOTES:** No pets English spoken

LA CHAPELLE-SUR-ERDRE

♯♯♯ La Gandonnière Françoise GIRARD
44240 LA-CHAPELLE-SUR-ERDRE
☎ 02 40 72 53 45 📄 02 40 72 53 45
http://www.web-de-loire.com/C/44H891433.htm

Dating from the 18th century, La Gandonnière stands at the entrance to Nantes in an area of outstanding beauty. Guests can take advantage of the quiet terraced gardens overlooking the lake. The three restored bedrooms look towards l'Erdre, each has a private bathroom. The first-floor double has an additional bed for a child, the second-floor rooms are a twin, and a double suite with one double bed and twin beds. Restaurant 1.5km. Open 1 May to 30 September and by prior booking at other times.
PRICES: s €57; d €62; t €92; extra person €15 **ON SITE:** Fishing Hiking Water sports **NEARBY:** Golf (5km) Sea (50km) Swimming pool (5km) Tennis (2km) Shops (2km) Railway station (12km) NANTES (12km)
NOTES: No pets

🐓Places with this symbol are farmhouses

LA CHEVROLIERE

♯♯♯ 🐓 Chambre d'hôtes Joseph et Danielle CHEVALIER
26 Thubert, 44118 LA CHEVROLIERE ☎ 02 40 31 31 26
Set in the country, four ground-floor rooms with bathrooms and separate entrances. Two rooms have kitchenettes. Guest lounge, dining room with kitchen and TV. Terrace, lawn, garden furniture for each guest room. Restaurant 2km. Nantes, station, airport 10km. Lake, leisure centre and attractions nearby. Open all year.
PRICES: s €29; d €38; t €46; extra person €9 **NEARBY:** Golf (35km) Sea (35km) Fishing (10km) Swimming pool (10km) Hiking (5km) Water sports (10km) Tennis (4km) Shops (4km) Railway station (10km) NANTES (12km) **NOTES:** No pets

LE LANDREAU

♯♯♯ Le Relais de la Rinière Françoise LEBARILLIER
44430 LE LANDREAU
☎ 02 40 06 41 44 📄 02 51 13 10 52
e-mail: lariniere@chez.com http://www.chez.com/lariniere
This charming house with large flower-filled gardens is in the heart of wine country and an ideal base for exploring the Loire. Three en suite bedrooms. Picnics can be enjoyed in the garden and there are games for children. Pony trekkers welcome. Open all year.
PRICES: s €36; d €40; extra person €11 **NEARBY:** Sea (60km) Fishing (4km) Swimming pool (6km) Hiking (3km) Water sports (15km) Tennis (6km) Shops (3km) Railway station (25km) CLISSON (15km)
NOTES: Pets admitted English spoken

LE LOROUX BOTTEREAU

♯♯♯ 🍽 La Roche Marie Christine PINEAU
44430 LE-LOROUX-BOTTEREAU
☎ 02 40 03 74 69 & 06 10 94 24 50 📄 02 40 33 89 96
A warm welcome is offered from the friendly owners of this vineyard. From the veranda you can enjoy panoramic views of the vines and your hosts will encourage you to appreciate their wine and local produce, cellar tours can be arranged. There is a large garden and terrace with garden furniture and loungers. Three en suite bedrooms for two or four people. TV, evening meals by arrangement, except for Sunday. Open all year.
PRICES: s €36; d €40; t €50; extra person €10; dinner €18
ON SITE: Hiking **NEARBY:** Golf (15km) Sea (70km) Fishing (5km) Swimming pool (3km) Water sports (5km) Tennis (3km) Shops (3km) Railway station (18km) CLISSON (17km) **NOTES:** Pets admitted

LE TEMPLE-DE-BRETAGNE

♯♯♯ 🍽 ♿ Chambre d'hôtes Marguerite DE SARIAC
52 Rue Georges Bonnet, La Mariaudais,
44360 LE TEMPLE-DE-BRETAGNE
☎ 02 40 57 09 38 & 06 10 71 50 50
e-mail: margotds@hotmail.com

Nantes 20 km. La Baule 50 km. At the exit of the village. Former stables have been renovated to offer three spacious triple

continued

bedrooms with showers and wcs. Dining room with TV and kitchen area for guests. Separate entrance. Evening meals by arrangement (crêpes or alternatives). Adjoining courtyard, orchard and vegetable garden. Open all year.
PRICES: s €35; d €43; t €52; extra person €9; dinner €12 **NEARBY:** Golf (10km) Sea (40km) Swimming pool (11km) Hiking (1km) Water sports (40km) Tennis (8km) Railway station (10km) BLAIN (15km) **NOTES:** No pets English spoken

MARSAC-SUR-DON

♦ La Mérais Patrick EISELE
44170 MARSAC-SUR-DON ☎ 02 40 87 53 29
This longbarn has been lovingly restored by the owners and offers two en suite first-floor bedrooms for two or three guests with independent entrances. A further ground floor room and mezzanine will sleep four and also has a separate entrance. A large reception room has a kitchen and dining area, and there are terraces with garden furniture for guests. Open all year.
PRICES: s €31; d €40; t €46; extra person €10 **NEARBY:** Bathing (5km) Golf (20km) Sea (60km) Fishing (1km) Swimming pool (5km) Hiking (3km) Water sports (5km) Tennis (5km) Shops (1km) Railway station (30km) BLAIN (12km) **NOTES:** Pets admitted English spoken

MESQUER

♦ Clos de Botelo Liliane LEDUC
249 Rue des Caps Horniers, Clos de Botelo Kercabellec, 44420 MESQUER ☎ 02 40 42 50 20 & 06 22 61 11 06

A peaceful, character house with marsh views. Furnished with antiques, a fireplace and a collection of paintings and works of art belonging to your hostess. Two of the five upstairs rooms are independent. The rooms sleep four, three, or two people and each has private shower and wc. TV on the mezzanine. Terrace, orchard, lawns. Parking for cars, storage for bikes and windsurfs. Restaurants nearby. Guérande 10km. Open all year.
PRICES: s €40; d €46; t €60; extra person €14 **ON SITE:** Sea Fishing Hiking Water sports **NEARBY:** Golf (14km) Swimming pool (8km) Tennis (3km) Shops (1km) Railway station (14km) SAINT NAZAIRE (28km) **NOTES:** No pets

MISSILLAC

♦ IOI Morican Olivier COJEAN
44780 MISSILLAC ☎ 02 40 88 38 82 ▤ 02 40 88 38 82
e-mail: cojean.morican@wanadoo.fr
Stay in the Parc Naturel Régional de Brière where you can join your hosts in their longbarn for breakfast, and evening meals by arrangement. The five guest bedrooms are as follows; "Cavalière", "Océane (with shower & wc)", "Royale", "Nuptiale", "Campagnarde" (with bath & wc). Horse-drawn carriage outings and driving classes available. Stabling, loose-box, paddock. Reduced price golf at Bretesche (5 mins). La Baule 30 mins. Open all year.
PRICES: s €32-€37; d €40-€44; t €53; dinner €21 **ON SITE:** Fishing

NEARBY: Bathing (12km) Golf (6km) Sea (30km) Swimming pool (12km) Hiking (6km) Water sports (12km) Tennis (6km) Railway station (15km) LA BAULE (25km) **NOTES:** No pets English spoken

MONNIERES

♦♦♦ Château Plessis-Brezot Annick et Didier CALONNE
44690 MONNIERES ☎ 02 40 54 63 24 ▤ 02 40 54 66 07
e-mail: a.calonne@online.fr
Dating from the 17th century, this charming chambre d'hôtes is in the heart of the Nantais vineyards producing Muscadet Sèvre et Maine. Wine tasting, cellar tours, local visits and walks can be arranged. The five restored en suite bedrooms have period furnishings and private bathrooms. Covered swimming pool. Guests may bring horses. Several restaurants nearby. Open 1 April to 31 October, other dates by arrangement.
PRICES: d €74-€104; extra person €16 **ON SITE:** Fishing Swimming pool Hiking Water sports **NEARBY:** Golf (25km) Tennis (1km) Shops (5km) Railway station (2km) CLISSON (5km) **NOTES:** Pets admitted English spoken

NOZAY

♦♦♦ Grand Jouan Pierre et Monique MARZELIERE
44170 NOZAY
☎ 02 40 79 45 85 & 06 80 84 18 63 ▤ 02 40 79 45 85
This former agricultural school is situated between Nantes and Rennes. Four en suite bedrooms for two or three people. Guest TV lounge area, games room and dining room. Shady grounds, horse boxes, lakes, mini-golf. Creperie. Restaurants 2.5km. Open all year.
PRICES: s €31; d €39; t €47; extra person €8 **NEARBY:** Sea (70km) Fishing (1km) Swimming pool (3km) Hiking (1km) Water sports (1km) Tennis (3km) Shops (3km) Railway station (25km) BLAIN (12km) **NOTES:** Pets admitted

PONT-SAINT-MARTIN

♦♦♦♦ IOI Le Château du Plessis Josiane BELORDE
44860 PONT-SAINT-MARTIN
☎ 02 40 26 81 72 ▤ 02 40 32 76 67
e-mail: josiane.belorde@wanadoo.fr
In a peaceful setting 11km south of Nantes and only 5km from the airport (although not disturbed by its proximity). The chateau is a historic monument dating from the 14th and 15th centuries with three guest bedrooms. Exquisite cuisine and fine wines are complemented by beautiful grounds and rose gardens. Bikes, mountain bikes, children's games. Prices reduced after two nights. Honeymoon package with champagne. Special half board rates and half-price for children under 12. Open all year.
PRICES: s €70-€95; d €95-€140; t €155-€170; extra person €25-€30; HB €90-€105; dinner €25-€70 **NEARBY:** Bathing (10km) Golf (15km) Sea (30km) Fishing (1km) Swimming pool (7km) Hiking (1km) Water sports (10km) Tennis (2km) Shops (1km) Railway station (11km) NANTES (11km) **NOTES:** No pets English spoken

PORNIC

♦♦♦ Le Jardin de Retz
M/J BLONDEAU-RAEDERSTOERFFER
Avenue du Général de Gaulle, 44210 PORNIC
☎ 02 40 82 02 29 & 02 40 82 22 69 ▤ 02 40 82 02 29
Relax for a night, a weekend or longer break in the lush surroundings of a large botanic park and peaceful gardens. Three double guest bedrooms are available with independent access and private bathrooms. Private parking. Sea-water therapy 1km. Many leisure activities nearby. Open all year.
PRICES: s €45-€55; d €50-€55 **ON SITE:** Sea Fishing Hiking Water sports Tennis **NEARBY:** Golf (1km) Swimming pool (1km) Railway station (25km) PORNIC **NOTES:** No pets

♦♦♦ Cupidon Françoise GAGNOT & Gerard CATU
Plage de Portmain, 44210 PORNIC
☎ 02 51 74 19 61 ◻ 02 51 74 19 20
e-mail: gagnot-catu@club-internet.fr
Cupidon is on Portmain beach, just off a small country road in the heart of the Côte Sauvage. The prettily decorated rooms benefit from sea views. Large breakfasts are served on the terrace looking out to sea or in the lounge area by the fireplace. Guests can use a heated swimming pool, a terrace, cycles, mountain and trail bikes. You can enjoy the beach, coastal walks or fishing amongst the rocks. On-site parking. Open all year.
PRICES: s €37-€45; d €42-€50; t €60 **ON SITE:** Bathing Sea Fishing Swimming pool Hiking Water sports **NEARBY:** Golf (3km) Tennis (3km) Shops (2km) Railway station (6km) PORNIC (6km) **NOTES:** Pets admitted

♦♦♦ Villa Delphine Chantal GUENON
55 Rue de la Source, 44210 PORNIC
☎ 02 40 82 67 79 & 06 62 36 67 79 ◻ 02 40 82 67 79
e-mail: VILLA-DELPHINE2@wanadoo.fr
A *fin de siècle* villa conveniently situated in the centre of Pornic, near to the sea-water therapy centre. Upstairs there is a basic room with a large single bed and two further double bedrooms with TV. All rooms have a private bathroom. Private garden. Tourist tax payable. Train 400m. Open all year.
PRICES: s €35-€42; d €41-€50 **NEARBY:** Golf (2km) Sea (1km) Fishing (1km) Swimming pool (1km) Hiking (1km) Water sports (1km) Tennis (2km) Railway station (50km) **NOTES:** No pets

PORT-SAINT-PERE

♦♦♦ La Petite Pelletanche Louis et Simone CHAUVET
44710 PORT-SAINT-PERE
☎ 02 40 31 52 44 ◻ 02 40 31 52 44
A family house and separate accommodation at the centre of a farm, offering three guest bedrooms, each with shower and wc. Shared lounge with fireplace and kitchen area. Breakfast is served in your hosts' house, comprising Pays de Retz honey, jam, fruit juices, brioche or pastries and local bread. Garden furniture and BBQ. Canoeing on the river, 8km. Planète Sauvage 4km. Grand Lieu lake 16km. Open all year.
PRICES: s €30; d €37; t €46; extra person €10 **ON SITE:** Fishing Hiking **NEARBY:** Bathing (25km) Sea (25km) Swimming pool (15km) Water sports (7km) Shops (3km) Railway station (6km) NANTES (23km) **NOTES:** No pets

RIAILLE

♦♦♦ ☙ ΙΟΙ La Meilleraie J Paul & Madeleine HAREL
44440 RIAILLE
☎ 02 40 97 89 52 & 06 83 57 95 07 ◻ 02 40 97 89 52
e-mail: mjp.harel@free.fr
A character house near Meilleraye Abbey and Provostière lake where you can fish and walk. The area between Ancenis and Chateaubriant is covered with forests and ponds, inviting walking, relaxation and discovery. Three en suite bedrooms with TV. Breakfast and meals can be taken on the terrace or in the large reception room with fireplace. Swimming pool, lawn, garden furniture, BBQ, picnic area, evening meals by arrangement. No smoking inside. Open 1 April to 1 November.
PRICES: s €35; d €40; t €47; dinner €14 **ON SITE:** Swimming pool Hiking **NEARBY:** Bathing (9km) Golf (37km) Fishing (1km) Water sports (9km) Tennis (5km) Shops (5km) Railway station (25km) ANCENIS (25km) **NOTES:** No pets

SAINT MOLF

♦♦♦ Kervenel Jeannine BRASSELET
44350 SAINT-MOLF
☎ 02 40 42 50 38 & 06 17 73 31 75 ◻ 02 40 42 50 55
e-mail: ybrasselet@AOL.COM

A peaceful country setting just 3km from the sea. Three en suite bedrooms with separate entrances, an extra child bed can be added. Lounge with TV and library. Garden furniture, private parking, cycle hire. Activities within 10km: La Baule, Parc Naturel de Brière. Boating and carriage driving, hunting. Tours to medieval city of Guérande 5km, La Turballe fishing port 5km. Open 1 April to 1 October.
PRICES: s €46; d €54; t €81; extra person €18 **NEARBY:** Golf (10km) Sea (3km) Fishing (5km) Swimming pool (12km) Hiking (5km) Water sports (5km) Tennis (3km) Shops (3km) Railway station (12km) SAINT NAZAIRE (25km) **NOTES:** No pets English spoken

SAINTE-REINE-DE-BRETAGNE

♦♦♦ La Thorelle Françoise et Michel PINTUREAU
27 rue René Guy Cadou,
44160 SAINTE-REINE-DE-BRETAGNE
☎ 02 40 01 03 50 & 06 03 52 33 02 ◻ 02 40 01 03 50
This early 20th-century house in spacious grounds has been completely renovated. Bedrooms, on the first floor, are bright, spacious and equipped with bathrooms. This is an ideal base for trips to the Brière park, the côte d'Amour, Guérande, La Roche Bernard and the Pays des 3 Rivières. Open all year.
PRICES: s €41-€49; d €45-€53; t €61; extra person €8 **NEARBY:** Bathing (10km) Golf (8km) Sea (25km) Fishing (2km) Swimming pool (8km) Hiking (1km) Water sports (20km) Tennis (2km) Shops (5km) Railway station (8km) SAINT NAZAIRE (25km) **NOTES:** No pets English spoken

SAINT-MALO-DE-GUERSAC

♦♦♦ ΙΟΙ Chambre d'hôtes Alain COLLARD
25 Errand, Ty Gween, 44550 SAINT-MALO-DE-GUERSAC
☎ 02 40 91 15 04
A lovely old cottage found on an island in the Brière marshes. The four spacious bedrooms all have shower and wc and are as follows: "L'Ecossaise" double, "La Verte", twin, "La Bleue" double and single, "La Rose" double and single. The rustic dining room has a fireplace, there is central heating. Private parking, enclosed garden. Separate entrance. Local attractions include a wildlife park 3km, walking routes, barge trips, cycling. Evening meals by arrangement. Open 1 April to 1 October.
PRICES: s €38; d €47; t €54; dinner €19 **ON SITE:** Hiking **NEARBY:** Golf (25km) Sea (14km) Fishing (1km) Water sports (22km) Tennis (2km) Shops (2km) Railway station (14km) SAINT NAZAIRE (14km) **NOTES:** No pets

SAINT-MARS-DU-DESERT

♥♥♥ Longrais Dominique MORISSEAU
44850 SAINT-MARS-DU-DESERT
☎ 02 40 77 48 25 & 06 80 62 95 63
www.web-de-loire.com/C/44_891152.htm

An 18th-century character property deep in the countryside yet 15 minutes from Nantes and 10 minutes from Beaujoire. Relax and enjoy the enclosed landscaped gardens. Three separate en suite bedrooms comprise two ground floor rooms for three people and a first-floor room for two people, with antique furnishings. Satellite TV and guest kitchen. Garden furniture, private parking. Boat trips nearby on the river Erdre and the Loire. Station 17km. Restaurants 4km. Extra beds can be added. Arrangements for long stays and low season. Open all year.

PRICES: s €35-€43; d €42-€50; t €56-€60; extra person €11
NEARBY: Bathing (23km) Golf (9km) Sea (65km) Fishing (6km) Swimming pool (6km) Hiking (1km) Water sports (8km) Tennis (4km) Shops (4km) Railway station (17km) NANTES (17km) **NOTES:** No pets

SOUDAN

♥♥♥ ⚬⚬⚬ La Boissière Jacqueline NICOL
44110 SOUDAN
☎ 02 40 28 60 00 & 06 87 44 75 51 ▤ 02 40 28 60 00
e-mail: les-marches-de-bretagne@wanadoo.fr
http://www.lesmarchesdebretagne.com

This 17th-century longbarn is in a typical hamlet featuring local shale stone. Guest accommodation comprises a lounge with TV, fireplace and library, two ground floor bedrooms with private terraces and two first-floor bedrooms with mezzanines. All bedrooms have private bathrooms. For gourmets, a daily changing menu can be enjoyed in a warm and friendly atmosphere. Kitchenette also available. Leisure facilities include private swimming pool, nature trail and astronomy evenings. Open all year.

PRICES: s €33; d €43-€51; t €57; extra person €13; dinner €13
ON SITE: Swimming pool **NEARBY:** Bathing (16km) Golf (24km) Sea (110km) Fishing (9km) Hiking (1km) Water sports (16km) Tennis (13km) Shops (6km) Railway station (13km) CHATEAUBRIANT (13km)
NOTES: No pets English spoken

VARADES

♥♥♥ Le Grand Patis Jacques ROY
44370 VARADES
☎ 02 40 83 42 28

This small renovated château is set in a large park. There are four guest bedrooms available for two, three and five people respectively. All bedrooms have a shower and wc. Lounge, parking. Open all year. Varades 2.5km. Ancenis 8km. Nantes 50km. Angers 45km.

PRICES: s €28-€31; d €37-€44; t €55; extra person €11
NEARBY: Bathing (40km) Golf (25km) Sea (100km) Fishing (5km) Swimming pool (10km) Hiking (1km) Water sports (10km) Tennis (3km) Shops (3km) Railway station (5km) ANCENIS (10km) **NOTES:** No pets

ANDARD

♥♥♥ ⚬⚬⚬ Château de Rezeau
Christian et Catherine BEZIAU
49800 ANDARD
☎ 02 41 74 09 21 ▤ 02 41 74 09 21

Close to Angers. Catherine and Christian welcome you to their 16th-century residence, overlooking a courtyard shaded by old sequoias. On the first floor, 'Lavande', 'Granny' and 'Jonquille' are all double rooms, while 'Sable' is a twin room. Each has a private shower or bathroom and wc. Tree and flower-filled garden with outdoor furniture. Breakfast and table d'hôtes meals are served in front of the fireplace in the beamed lounge. Ask proprietors for directions. Open all year.

PRICES: s €46; d €50; extra person €10; dinner €20 **NEARBY:** Horse riding (5km) Fishing (2km) Swimming pool (7km) Tennis (5km) Shops (2km) **NOTES:** No pets

♥♥♥ Le Grand Talon Annie GUERVILLY
3, route des Chapelles   RN147, 49800 ANDARD
☎ 02 41 80 42 85 ▤ 02 41 80 42 85

Close to Angers. This elegant 18th-century vine-covered residence offers prettily decorated guest rooms: one double, one with a 130 cm bed and a single bed, and one with two double beds. All rooms have bathroom and wc. You can picnic in the park or relax in the beautiful tiled courtyard. Garden to the rear of the house with sunloungers and parasols. Ask proprietor for directions.

PRICES: s €38; d €49-€57; extra person €11 **NEARBY:** Horse riding (20km) Fishing (3km) Swimming pool (8km) Tennis (2km) Shops (2km) **NOTES:** Pets admitted

AUVERSE

♥♥♥ Domaine de la Bregellerie Isabelle SOHN
49490 AUVERSE
☎ 02 41 82 11 69 ▤ 02 41 82 11 87
e-mail: isabelle.sohn@wanadoo.fr
http://www.multimania.com/nambreg/

Angers 55 km. Isabelle and Alain welcome you to their five themed guest rooms 'Loire', 'Forest', 'Vine', 'Fields' and 'Pond'. All rooms have private bathrooms and 140cm beds except 'Forest', which has an additional single bed. Small animals admitted. Lounge with billiard table and TV available. Pond, fishing. Close to the Loire and its marvellous châteaux, the location will delight guests who love peace and nature. Reduced rates from the third night. Open all year.

PRICES: s €46-€61; d €53-€69 **ON SITE:** Fishing Swimming pool Hiking **NEARBY:** Horse riding (7km) Tennis (4km) Shops (4km) **NOTES:** Pets admitted English spoken

BEAUFORT-EN-VALLEE

♥♥♥ |○| Relais de Beaufort Arnauld KINDT
16, avenue du Général Leclerc, 49250 BEAUFORT-EN-VALLEE
☎ 02 41 57 26 72 📠 02 41 57 26 72
An attractive 18th-century coaching inn. First floor: two rooms with
150 x 200 cm beds, private bathrooms, and one room with 100 x
200 cm bed. Lounge with TV. One-hectare park with terrace. Table
d'hôte meals on reservation. Special rates out of season. Ask
proprietor for directions. Open all year except 25 January to 12
February.
PRICES: s €58; d €64; extra person €11; dinner €18 **ON SITE:** Swimming
pool Tennis **NEARBY:** Fishing (3km) Railway station (25km)
NOTES: Pets admitted English spoken

BOCE

♥♥♥ |○| Chant d'oiseau Jannick et J.Pierre GALLET
Les Rues, 49150 BOCE
☎ 02 41 82 73 14 📠 02 41 82 73 14
Jannick, Jean-Pierre and Claire welcome you to their home 'Chant
d'oiseau', which has been restored in local style, and is close to
the forest of Chandelais. There are three bedrooms on the ground
floor of an annexe building: 'Alouette' has twin beds; 'Rossignol' is
a family room with one double bed and two singles on a
mezzanine floor; and 'Mésange' is a double room accessed by an
exterior staircase. Each room has a private bathroom. Reception
room with kitchenette. Enclosed landscaped garden with barbecue
and bikes. Ask proprietor for directions. Open all year.
PRICES: s €37; d €43; t €53; extra person €10; dinner €16
NEARBY: Horse riding (2km) Fishing (2km) Swimming pool (5km)
Hiking (2km) Tennis (1km) Shops (5km) **NOTES:** No pets

BRION

♥♥♥ |○| Domaine des Hayes Patricia et Gilles PATRICE
La Chouannière, 49250 BRION
☎ 02 41 80 21 74
In the grounds of a castle, Patricia and Gilles have converted three
rooms in an annexe of their 16th-century house. Situated on the
edge of the forest, this location will seduce you with its peace and
greenery. On the ground floor, 'Cannelle' offers two beds, one
160 cm and one 120 cm, private shower and wc. 'Muscade' has
one 120 cm bed and one 90 cm bed, private shower room and wc.
TV in each room. One hectare of landscaped garden with outdoor
furniture. Bikes may be borrowed. Ask proprietor for directions.
Open all year.
PRICES: d €44–€69; t €61; extra person €13; dinner €18
ON SITE: Hiking **NEARBY:** Horse riding (7km) Fishing (6km)
Swimming pool (6km) Tennis (6km) Shops (6km) **NOTES:** No pets

♥♥♥ |○| Logis du Pressoir J-Marc et Anne LE FOULGOCQ
Villeneuve, 49250 BRION
☎ 02 41 57 27 33 📠 02 41 57 27 33
e-mail: lepressoir@wanadoo.fr http://www.lepressoir.fr.st
Anne and Jean-Marc welcome you to their five guest rooms in a
tranquil, green setting. Two of the rooms have a mezzanine floor
and sleep four people. One has a kitchenette. There is also a
three-person room, a first-floor double room, and a ground-floor
double. Each room has a private bathroom and TV. Games room
with billiard table and table tennis. Private swimming pool, 1.6
hectare park. Old restored winepress with viewpoint and cellar.
Ask proprietor for directions.
PRICES: d €46–€53; extra person €13; dinner €18 **ON SITE:** Hiking
NEARBY: Horse riding (2km) Forest (4km) Fishing (5km) Tennis (4km)
Shops (4km) Railway station (30km) **NOTES:** No pets

CHANZEAUX

♥♥♥ |○| Moulin du Chapitre Didier et Rose LELIEVRE
49750 CHANZEAUX
☎ 02 41 74 01 42 📠 02 41 74 01 42
Crossed by the River Hydrôme, which feeds the mill race, the
Moulin du Chapitre stands amidst the tranquillity of the Angers
countryside. Rose and Didier offer two first-floor rooms with
shower and wc: 'Chaume' has a double bed and an adjoining
room with a double bed; 'A l'Iris' is a grade 2 room with a double
bed. Both rooms share a kitchenette. 'Bonnezeaux' is a twin room
with a private bathroom. Table d'hôte meals on reservation. Two
self-catering gîtes on site. Six-hectare park. Open all year.
PRICES: s €33; d €47; t €61; extra person €8; dinner €14
ON SITE: Fishing Hiking **NEARBY:** Horse riding (5km) Swimming pool
(8km) Tennis (1km) Shops (4km) Railway station (32km) **NOTES:** No
pets

CHARCE-SAINT-ELLIER

♥♥♥ La Pichonnière COLIBET-MARTIN
49320 CHARCE-SAINT-ELLIER
☎ 02 41 91 29 37 📠 02 41 91 96 85
e-mail: gite-brissac@wanadoo.fr
20 km south of d'Angers. Brissac 3 km. Jean-Claude and Martine
welcome you to the Ferme de la Pichonnière, a group of buildings
of some character. The four individual rooms comprise:
'Mesanges', a large grade 3 double room with lounge area and
direct access to the garden; 'Garenne', a double room with an
independent entrance, wash basin, shower and wc; 'Ecureuil',
another double and 'Hérisson', which is a twin room. The last two
rooms have private showers and share a wc. Electric heating.
Information available on visit and walks. Breakfast served in your
hosts' dining room. Ask proprietor for directions. Open all year,
winter on reservation.
PRICES: d €38–€46 **NEARBY:** Forest (3km) Fishing (3km) Swimming
pool (3km) Stretch of water (7km) Hiking (3km) Tennis (3km) Shops
(3km) Railway station (20km) **NOTES:** No pets English spoken

CHAZE-SUR-ARGOS

♥♥♥ |○| La Chaufournaie Susan SCARBORO
49500 CHAZE-SUR-ARGOS
☎ 02 41 61 49 05 📠 02 41 61 49 05
e-mail: susan@libertysurf.fr
This welcoming house is on the D770 between Vern d'Anjou and
Candé, in a peaceful countryside setting. On the first floor there
are two double rooms, two twin rooms, and one room with a
double and a single bed. Each has a private shower and wc, and
tea and coffee-making facilities. Lounge with TV and fireplace
shared with proprietors. Games room with large snooker table.
Library. Electric heating. Garden furniture, pétanque. Ask
proprietor for directions. Table d'hôte meals in summer, on
reservation. Open all year.
PRICES: s €30; d €35; t €47; extra person €12; dinner €18
NEARBY: Horse riding (14km) Forest (15km) Fishing (3km) Swimming
pool (3km) Stretch of water (30km) Hiking (3km) Tennis (3km) Shops
(3km) Railway station (14km) **NOTES:** No pets English spoken

CHEMELLIER

♥♥♥ La Gaignardière Chantal ARCHAUX
49320 CHEMELLIER
☎ 02 41 45 52 75 📠 02 41 45 52 75
e-mail: chantal.archaux@libertysurf.fr
http://perso.libertysurf.fr/archaux
Angers 25 km. Chantal welcomes you to the heart of the Aubance
region. There are three en suite rooms in her typical tuffeau
house, all spacious, comfortable and delightfully decorated.

continued

'Romantique' and 'Clair de Lune' are large double rooms with large lounge areas. 'Alizé' is a double with an adjoining suite ('Parfum d'Orient') of three single beds. Games room, outdoor leisure area. Cost for four people: €79. Open all year.
PRICES: d €58; extra person €15 **ON SITE:** Hiking **NEARBY:** Horse riding (8km) Swimming pool (7km) Tennis (2km) Shops (1km)
NOTES: No pets English spoken

♦♦♦ ⏸ **Maunit** Eliette EDON
49320 CHEMELLIER
☎ 02 41 45 59 50 📠 02 41 45 01 44
e-mail: daniel.edon@wanadoo.fr

Three rooms in a house built in typical local style. On the ground floor one room has three single beds and a separate shower room and wc. On the first floor, the yellow room is a double with separate shower and wc, while the green room is a double with en suite shower and wc. Electric heating. Lounge with fireplace, colour TV and billiard table. Bikes available, table tennis and porch. Board games. Table d'hôte meals on reservation. Swimming 2 km. Ask proprietor for directions to property.
PRICES: s €34; d €41; t €53; dinner €18 **ON SITE:** Children's play area **NEARBY:** Horse riding (4km) Fishing (1km) Swimming pool (6km) Stretch of water (2km) Hiking (4km) Tennis (2km) Sailing (8km) Shops (2km) Railway station (25km) **NOTES:** No pets

CHIGNE

♦♦♦ 🐓 **Le Grand Clairay** Christian GRIPPON
49490 CHIGNE
☎ 02 41 82 10 30 & 06 83 30 48 38 📠 02 41 82 10 30
http://grandclairay.free.fr
Le Lude 7 km. Nicole and Christian welcome you the heart of the countryside, in the Baugeois region, close to the valley of the Loir, and their three characterful guest rooms with private swimming pool. The bedrooms are situated in an annexe, where there is also a dining room, lounge and a small kitchen. One ground-floor room with a double and a single bed; two first-floor rooms, one with two double beds and one with a double bed and a lounge area. Each has its own shower room and wc. Child's bed or cot on request. Reduced rates after the second day. Porch, garden furniture, barbecue. Bikes available. Zoo 18 km. Fishing lake on site. Open all year.
PRICES: s €35; d €43; t €51 **ON SITE:** Children's play area Fishing Hiking **NEARBY:** Horse riding (2km) Tennis (7km) Shops (3km) Railway station (20km) **NOTES:** Pets admitted

CORNE

♦♦♦ **Les Genets** Michel et Nadeige BRIAND
63, Route de Baune, 49630 CORNE
☎ 02 41 45 05 21 📠 02 41 45 05 21
Three very comfortable guest rooms in a 19th-century country house, on a peaceful one-hectare estate. 'Matisse' and 'Monet' are doubles, while 'Lurçat' is a twin room; each has a private shower

room and wc. An extra bed can be installed in each room. Garden, terrace, outdoor furniture. Reduced prices for longer stays.
Directions: Angers-Saumur (N147), at Corné take the D82 in the direction of Bauné. Open all year.
PRICES: s €32; d €43; extra person €12 **NEARBY:** Horse riding (2km) Forest (2km) Fishing (4km) Swimming pool (15km) Hiking (2km) Tennis (2km) Shops (2km) Railway station (15km) **NOTES:** No pets English spoken

CUNAULT

♦♦♦ ⏸ **Les Bateliers** Marie-Noëlle VOLEAU
28, rue de Beauregard,
49350 CHENEHUTTE-TREVES-CUNAULT
☎ 02 41 67 94 49 & 06 78 27 94 07 📠 02 41 67 94 49
e-mail: m.voleau1@libertysurf.fr
http://perso.libertysurf.fr/bateliers/
Saumur 12 km. Cunault church 100 m. Angers 35 km. Marie-Noëlle welcomes you to her mid-19th-century boatman's house on the banks of the Loire. The accommodation includes a cave suite, accessed by a staircase in the garden, comprising one double bedroom, shower room and wc, and an adjoining room with dining area, bench and private terrace. In the main house, there is independent access to two double rooms, one of which has an exterior staircase, and a separate twin room. Each has a private bathroom. Table d'hôte on reservation. Dining room. Ask proprietor for directions.
PRICES: s €40-€50; d €45-€55; extra person €15; dinner €15 **ON SITE:** Fishing Hiking **NEARBY:** Horse riding (2km) Swimming pool (3km) Tennis (3km) Shops (3km) Railway station (15km) **NOTES:** No pets

DENEE

♦♦♦ **La Noue** O et Catherine DE CENIVAL
49190 DENEE
☎ 02 41 78 79 80 📠 02 41 68 05 61
e-mail: odecenival@aol.com
Angers 18 km. At the entrance to Angers, winegrowers Olivier and Catherine have restored the outbuildings of a 16th-century walled house. Four spacious rooms open onto a romantic 19th-century listed garden. The Green Room and the Yellow Room have twin beds, while the Raspberry Room and the Blue Room have large double beds. Each room has a private bathroom. Sample wines from the estate or homemade jam in the breakfast room, in front of the fireplace in the lounge, or even in the garden. Open all year.
PRICES: d €61; extra person €15 **NEARBY:** Fishing (1km) Swimming pool (5km) Hiking (1km) Tennis (1km) Shops (6km) **NOTES:** No pets

DOUE LA FONTAINE

♦♦♦ ⏸ **Les Roses Roses** Françoise DOUET
34 rue de Soulanges, 49700 DOUE LA FONTAINE
☎ 02 41 59 21 43 & 06 71 63 02 03
e-mail: douet.françoise@wanadoo.fr
Angers 40 km. Saumur 15 km. Françoise welcomes you to her house on an old winegrowing estate next to the Jardin des Roses and close to Doué zoo. There are three first-floor rooms: the Green Room with a large double bed, a large bathroom and a wc; 'Le Pavillon' with a double bed, a single bed, sink, shower and wc; and the Pink Room with two single beds, shower room and wc. Parking in the lockable courtyard. Open all year.
PRICES: d €45; extra person €15; dinner €14 **NEARBY:** Swimming pool (1km) Tennis (1km) Shops (1km) **NOTES:** No pets

continued

DRAIN

▥▥▥ ⫶◎⫶ Le Mesangeau Brigitte et Gérard MIGON
49530 DRAIN
☎ 02 40 98 21 57 🖷 02 40 98 28 62
e-mail: le.mesangeau@wanadoo.fr
www.anjou-et-loire.com/mesangeau
Loire 5 km. Joachim du Bellay museum at Liré 7 km. This
welcoming 19th-century manor house has lovely fireplaces,
old beams and a six-hectare park with lake and chapel. The
carefully-decorated bedrooms (four doubles and one twin)
have a rustic charm, and each has its own bath or shower
room and wc. Piano, billiards. Bikes, table tennis, small driving
range, outdoor furniture, summerhouse beside the lake.
Tables d'hôte meals by prior reservation only. Numerous
restaurants between 4 and 12 km. Winetasting in the village.
Reduced rates after the third night. Open all year.
PRICES: s €60-€70; d €70-€80; dinner €25 **ON SITE:** Fishing
Hiking **NEARBY:** Horse riding (9km) Swimming pool (8km) Tennis
(8km) Shops (5km) Railway station (12km) **NOTES:** No pets
English spoken

DURTAL

▥▥▥ Château de Gouis Monique LINOSSIER
49430 DURTAL
☎ 02 41 76 03 40 🖷 02 41 76 03 40
Nineteenth-century château peacefully set in a shady, flower-filled
park. The elegant en suite bedrooms include three on the first
floor: 'Louis XV' (double), 'Louis XVI' (twin) and the Beige Room
(double). On the second floor, the Blue Room and 'Fushia' are
both doubles with adjoining double rooms. Parking. Ask proprietor
for directions.
PRICES: d €53-€69; extra person €23 **ON SITE:** Fishing Stretch of water
Hiking **NEARBY:** Horse riding (10km) Forest (3km) Swimming pool
(1km) Tennis (1km) Shops (1km) Railway station (36km)
NOTES: No pets

▥▥▥ ⫶◎⫶ Le Chaudron Rogine DORE
103 rue St Pierre, 49430 DURTAL
☎ 02 41 76 39 09 🖷 02 41 76 39 09
River Loir 100 m. This attractive 15th-century Anjou house is
situated at the gateway to a region with a wonderful natural and
historical heritage. On the ground floor a double room offers
either a king-size or twin beds, en suite shower room and wc. On
the first floor, there is a double room with a king-size bed, en suite
shower room and wc; a suite with a double bed and three singles,
en suite shower room and wc; and a twin room with private
shower room and wc. Terrace with outdoor furniture. Independent
entrance for guests. Open all year.
PRICES: s €43; d €47; extra person €15; dinner €17 **NEARBY:** Horse
riding (6km) Fishing (1km) Swimming pool (1km) Hiking (1km) Tennis
(1km) Shops (1km) **NOTES:** No pets English spoken

FAYE-D'ANJOU

▥▥▥ Le Logis de la Brunetière
François et Isabelle BILLEROT
49380 FAYE-D'ANJOU
☎ 02 41 54 16 24 🖷 02 41 54 16 24
Isabelle and François welcome you to the Logis de la Brunetière,
which dates back to 1489. The three double guest rooms comprise
'Aubance' on the ground floor, and 'Layon' and 'Lys' on the first
floor. Each room has a private bathroom and separate wc. Lounge
room with kitchenette. Self-catering gîte on site. 500 m from the
town centre. Ask proprietors for directions to the property.

PRICES: s €43; d €46; extra person €12 **ON SITE:** Hiking
NEARBY: Horse riding (8km) Fishing (3km) Swimming pool (4km)
Tennis (1km) Shops (4km) **NOTES:** No pets English spoken

FORGES

▥▥▥ ⫶◎⫶ La Fosse M et C TRIBONDEAU-BERREHAR
49700 FORGES
☎ 02 41 50 90 09 & 06 85 65 58 10
e-mail: info@chambrehote.com www.chambrehote.com
Doué-la-Fontaine 4 km. Caves nearby. Close to Doué-la-Fontaine
and Saumur, Carole and Michel offer two guest rooms in the main
house, one of which is suitable for a family, and three poolside
rooms. Each room has a private bathroom. Dining room, lounge
room opposite the heated pool. Kitchen available. Exhibition of
glassworks. Specialists in wines of the Loire. Open all year.
PRICES: s €40; d €44-€58; extra person €12; dinner €20
NEARBY: Horse riding (4km) Tennis (4km) Shops (4km) **NOTES:** Pets
admitted English spoken

GREZILLE

▥▥▥ ⫶◎⫶ La Cotinière Marie-Hélène de ROCQUIGNY
Le Clos d'Aligny, 49320 GREZILLE
☎ 02 41 59 72 21 & 06 88 28 99 28 🖷 02 41 59 72 21
e-mail: la.cotiniere@anjou-et-loire.com
www.anjou-et-loire.com/cotiniere

Saumur 20 km. In the centre of a hamlet, this 18th-century house
offers three guest rooms. On the ground floor of the main house,
'Tournesol' has a double and a single bed, shower room and wc.
'Coquelicot' is on the first floor and also has a double and a single
bed, shower room and wc. In a separate annexe building, 'Pivoine'
is a double room with twin beds on a mezzanine floor, bathroom
and wc. Table d'hôte meals on reservation. Garden with outdoor
furniture. Many troglodyte dwellings and 15th-century chapel
nearby. Ask proprietor for directions.
PRICES: d €55; extra person €15; dinner €23 **ON SITE:** Hiking
NEARBY: Swimming pool (10km) Tennis (2km) Shops (2km) Railway
station (20km) **NOTES:** No pets English spoken

continued

GREZ-NEUVILLE

¶¶¶¶ La Croix d'Etain Auguste BAHUAUD
2, rue de l'Ecluse, 49220 GREZ-NEUVILLE
☎ 02 41 95 68 49   📠 02 41 18 02 72
e-mail: croix.etain@anjou-et-loire.com
www.anjou-et-loire.com/croix

In the middle of a tree-lined park beside the Mayenne, this 18th-century mansion offers four stylish guest rooms - two doubles and two twins - each with private bathroom and wc. Lounge with TV. Furnished terrace. Table d'hôte meals possible (drinks not included in the price). Nearby: golf, fishing, marina, boat hire, museums and chateaux. Ask proprietor for directions.
PRICES: s €48; d €61-€74; extra person €15   **ON SITE:** Fishing Stretch of water Hiking Sailing   **NEARBY:** Horse riding (4km) Forest (7km) Swimming pool (4km) Tennis (2km) Shops (4km) Railway station (20km)   **NOTES:** Pets admitted CC

JARZE

¶¶¶ 🌿 Le Point du Jour Vincent et Véronique PAPIAU
49140 JARZE
☎ 02 41 95 46 04   📠 02 41 95 46 04
Véronique and Vincent, organic farmers who rear cattle, are delighted to welcome you to 'Le Point du Jour'. There is independent access to the three comfortable guest rooms, each decorated in period style: 'Saumon' has a double and a single bed; 'A Rayures' is a double and 'Verte' is a twin room. Each has a private shower room and wc. Kitchenette available. Reduced rated after three nights. Extra bed and cot available. Barbecue. Outdoor furniture. Open all year.
PRICES: s €30; d €38; t €50; extra person €12   **ON SITE:** Children's play area   **NEARBY:** Horse riding (12km) Forest (2km) Swimming pool (10km) Stretch of water (5km) Hiking (5km) Tennis (1km) Shops (1km) Railway station (30km)   **NOTES:** No pets English spoken

LA POSSONNIERE

¶¶¶ 🍴 La Rousselière Jeanne CHARPENTIER
49170 LA POSSONNIERE
☎ 02 41 39 13 21   📠 02 41 39 13 21
e-mail: larousseliere@unimedia.fr
http://unimedia.fr/homepage/larousseliere
Jeanne welcomes you to her 18th-century family home and five spacious guest rooms with views of the park. On the first floor, there are three rooms with private bathrooms and windows over the garden and two rooms with shower. Mini-bar. TV. Central heating. Lounge. Billiard table. Dining room with fireplace. Canopied veranda. Four-hectare park, walled courtyard, private swimming pool, porch, table tennis, pétanque, garden furniture. 17th-century chapel. Private parking. Table d'hôte meals on reservation. Seventh night free. Ask proprietor for directions.
PRICES: d €48-€66; t €63-€81; extra person €15; dinner €23-€14
ON SITE: Children's play area Fishing Hiking   **NEARBY:** Horse riding

(5km) Tennis (5km) Shops (4km) Railway station (20km) **NOTES:** No pets

LE LION-D'ANGERS

¶¶¶ Les Travailleres François et Jocelyne VIVIER
49220 LE LION-D'ANGERS
☎ 02 41 61 33 56 & 06 77 86 24 33
This renovated farmhouse is in a peaceful countryside setting, 20 minutes from Angers. There are two guest rooms on the first floor, one double with shower room and wc, and one double with bathroom, wc and adjoining twin room. On the ground floor there is a double room with shower room and wc and an adjoining twin room. Independent access to rooms. Central heating. Lounge with fireplace. Library, board games. Shady, relaxing garden, courtyard, outdoor furniture, barbecue. Bikes available. Terrace for picnics. Peace and quiet guaranteed. Ask proprietor for directions. Open all year.
PRICES: s €26; d €34-€36; t €48; extra person €12   **NEARBY:** Horse riding (5km) Fishing (2km) Swimming pool (5km) Hiking (5km) Tennis (2km) Shops (5km) Railway station (31km)   **NOTES:** Pets admitted English spoken

LE MAY-SUR-EVRE

¶¶¶ Le Petit Cazeau DAVOUST
49122 LE MAY-SUR-EVRE
☎ 02 41 63 16 88   📠 02 41 63 16 88
Twenty mintues from Puy-du-Fou, this old farmhouse offers three themed guest rooms, each with private shower room and wc. 'L'Africaine' is a double room with exotic décor, 'la Romantique' is also a double, while twin-bedded 'la Provençale' will warm your heart with its sunny colour scheme. The garden, which is full of flowers in the summer, has outdoor furniture so you can sit and admire the surrounding countryside. Central heating. Ask proprietor for directions. Open all year.
PRICES: s €38; d €44; extra person €12   **ON SITE:** Hiking
NEARBY: Horse riding (10km) Forest (1km) Fishing (1km) Swimming pool (7km) Tennis (3km) Sailing (10km) Shops (3km) Railway station (7km) Golf (3km)   **NOTES:** No pets English spoken

LE PUY-NOTRE-DAME

¶¶¶ Château la Paleine Philippe et Caroline WADOUX
10, place Jules Raimbault, 49260 LE PUY-NOTRE-DAME
☎ 02 41 38 28 25
e-mail: p.wadou@libertysurf.fr
www.france-bonjour.com/chateau-la-paleine/
In a charming village, with views over the vine-covered hills, Caroline and Philippe welcome you to their 19th-century house, the seat of an old winegrowing estate. On the second floor of the main house, 'Collégiale' has a double bed, while 'Raimbault' is a family room with a double bed and a separate twin room. There are three further rooms on the first floor of the old storehouse: 'Pressoir' has a double and a single bed; 'Cerisaie' and 'Noyer' each have a king-size bed. Each room has a private bath or shower

continued   *continued*

room and wc. Equipped kitchen available. Open all year.
PRICES: s €38; d €42; t €53; extra person €11 **ON SITE:** Hiking
NEARBY: Fishing (6km) Swimming pool (8km) Tennis (1km)
NOTES: No pets English spoken

LE VIEIL-BAUGE

⚜ 🐾 🍽 La Guitoisière Chantal REVEAU
49150 LE VIEIL-BAUGE
☎ 02 41 89 25 59 ▤ 02 41 89 06 04
Three first-floor guest rooms in an annexe building of a 13th-
century farm. 'Echigné' and 'Montivert' are doubles, and 'Sensé' is
a twin room. Each has its own shower room and wc. Heating,
lounge with fireplace, library, dining room. Table d'hôtes on
reservations. Large landscaped garden with terrace, outdoor
furniture and children's games. Farm produce.
PRICES: s €35; d €40; extra person €12; dinner €14 **ON SITE:** Children's
play area Forest **NEARBY:** Horse riding (8km) Fishing (3km) Swimming
pool (6km) Stretch of water (3km) Hiking (5km) Tennis (3km) Sailing
(25km) Shops (5km) Railway station (35km) **NOTES:** Pets admitted

⚜ 🍽 Landifer J.Claude et C LEGENDRE
49150 LE VIEIL-BAUGE
☎ 02 41 82 85 72
Chandelais forest 2 km. La Flèche zoo 15 km. Situated in a large
park, Christiane and Jean-Claude's house offers five first-floor
guest rooms. 'Chandelais', 'Les Prats' and 'Fleur de Lampaul' are
all double rooms, while 'Romantique' is a double with an
additional single bed. 'Antillaise' is a double with an adjoining twin
room. Each room has a private shower room and wc. Dining room
with fireplace. Terrace, outdoor furniture, pétanque, barbecue.
Reduced rates from the third night. Open all year.
PRICES: s €40; d €46; t €58; extra person €17; dinner €15
ON SITE: Children's play area Forest Hiking **NEARBY:** Horse riding
(2km) Fishing (1km) Swimming pool (2km) Tennis (2km) Shops (2km)
NOTES: No pets

⚜ 🍽 Le Logis de Poellier
49150 LE VIEIL-BAUGE
☎ 02 41 89 20 56 ▤ 02 41 89 20 56
e-mail: Le.Logis.de.Poellier@wanadoo.fr
http://www.poellier.free.fr
Baugé 6 km. A 16th-century tufa stone building, tranquilly set amid
protected countryside. Marie-Françoise Jourdrin offers three
character guest rooms: on the first floor, 'Concerto' is a family
room with a double and twin beds; ground-floor 'Sonate' is a twin
room; and 'Prélude' is accessed from the outside and has a double
bed and one single. Each room has a private bathroom. Lounge,
TV and kitchenette available. Two bikes may be borrowed. Table
d'hôtes by reservation. Open all year.
PRICES: s €35-€46; d €43-€55; extra person €15; dinner €18
ON SITE: Hiking **NEARBY:** Horse riding (6km) Fishing (5km)
Swimming pool (6km) Tennis (6km) Shops (6km) Railway station (6km)
NOTES: Pets admitted English spoken

MARTIGNE-BRIAND

⚜ Domaine de l'Etang Gilles TENAILLON
49540 MARTIGNE-BRIAND
☎ 02 41 59 92 31 ▤ 02 41 59 92 30
e-mail: domaine.etang@ifrance.com www.domaine-etang.com
These guest rooms are on the first floor of an annexe building: the
Blue Room and the Red Room each offer a double and a single
bed, the Green Room twin beds and the Yellow Room a double
bed. Each has a private bath or shower room and wc. Highchair
available. Lounge room. Central heating. Two-hectare park
including private tennis court, table football, outdoor furniture,
winter garden. Numerous walks possible. Ask proprietor for
directions. Open all year.

continued

PRICES: s €39-€46; d €54; t €61 **ON SITE:** Forest Hiking Tennis
NEARBY: Horse riding (5km) Swimming pool (3km) Shops (3km)
Railway station (40km) **NOTES:** Pets admitted English spoken

MONTJEAN-SUR-LOIRE

⚜ Les Cèdres Danielle WITTEVERT
17, rue du Prieuré, 49570 MONTJEAN-SUR-LOIRE
☎ 02 41 39 39 25 & 06 62 17 39 25 ▤ 02 41 39 64 36
e-mail: les.cedres@wanadoo.fr

Danielle and Bernard welcome you to their family home, an old
building in a pretty village beside the Loire. The individual guest
rooms have private bathrooms. On the first floor 'Mozart' has a
queen-size bed, while 'Bartok' has a double. Lounge available.
'Mahler' is on the second floor and has a queen-size bed.
Breakfast is served in the ground-floor dining room. Music room.
One-hectare garden with outdoor furniture. Marked walking
routes, boat trips. In summer: exhibition of giant sculptures in the
village, hemp festival. Open Easter to 1 November.
PRICES: d €55-€58; extra person €16 **ON SITE:** Fishing Swimming pool
Hiking Tennis **NEARBY:** Horse riding (3km) **NOTES:** No pets English
spoken

MONTREUIL-BELLAY

⚜ Chambre d'hôtes Jacques GUEZENEC
Place des Augustins, 49260 MONTREUIL-BELLAY
☎ 02 41 52 33 88 ▤ 02 41 52 33 88
e-mail: moniqueguezenecbb@minitel.net
Monique and Jacques Guézenec welcome you to their peaceful
17th-century home. On the ground floor there is a bedroom with a
double and a single bed, while on the first floor one room has a
double and twin beds and the other has a double and a single.
Each has a private bath or shower room and wc. Guest lounge.
Electric heating. Village 500 m. Chemist close by. Ask proprietor for
directions.
PRICES: s €40; d €55; t €70; extra person €10 **NEARBY:** Horse riding
(16km) Forest (5km) Fishing (1km) Swimming pool (1km) Hiking (1km)
Tennis (1km) Sailing (1km) **NOTES:** Pets admitted English spoken

MONTREUIL-JUIGNE

⚜ Chambre d'hôtes Jean-Louis HUEZ
Le Plateau, Rue Espéranto, 49460 MONTREUIL-JUIGNE
☎ 02 41 42 32 35
This large family house offers four guest rooms, each with
independent access, private bath or shower room and wc. On the
first floor 'Jacques' has a double and a single bed, 'Bernard' is a
twin room, 'Geneviève' is a double and 'Antoinette' has three
single beds. Mezzanine floor for breakfast and TV. Lounge. Terrace,
grounds, outdoor furniture. Restaurant 2 km. Bus 50 m. Ask
proprietor for directions.
PRICES: s €27; d €40; extra person €12 **ON SITE:** Fishing
NEARBY: Horse riding (3km) Swimming pool (2km) Tennis (2km)
Sailing (2km) Shops (2km) Railway station (7km) **NOTES:** Pets admitted

MONTREUIL-SUR-LOIR

♯♯♯ IOI Château de Montreuil Jacques BAILLIOU
Mantreuil sur Loir, 49140 SEICHES-SUR-LOIR
☎ 02 41 76 21 03
e-mail: chateau.montreuil@anjou-et-loire.com

This château has panoramic views of the Loir Valley and the Forest of Boudre. There are two double guest rooms, one twin room, and one room with a double and a single bed; each room has private bathroom facilities. Ground-floor dining room and lounge. Terrace overhanging the Loir. Garden and large wooded park alongside the river. Village 200 m. Canoeing on site. Five golf courses in a 30 km radius. Ask proprietors for directions. Open 15 March to 15 November.
PRICES: s €57; d €61-€65; extra person €15-€30; dinner €23
ON SITE: Horse riding Forest Fishing Hiking **NEARBY:** Swimming pool (5km) Tennis (5km) Shops (5km) **NOTES:** No pets

MOULIHERME

♯♯♯ La Verrie Marguerite DELVAL
49390 MOULIHERNE
☎ 02 41 67 09 27
e-mail: bernard.delval@libertysurf.fr
Angers 60 km. Saumur 30 km. In the heart of the Monnaie Forest, this splendid 17th-century farmhouse offers the warmest of welcomes. Three guest rooms (one double and two triple) with private bathroom and wc. Vast lounge with fireplace, beams and half-timbering. Private terrace opening onto the park with its majestic cedar tree. Open all year.
PRICES: d €46; extra person €15 **ON SITE:** Hiking **NEARBY:** Horse riding (7km) Fishing (4km) Tennis (4km) Shops (4km)
NOTES: No pets English spoken

MOZE-SUR-LOUET

♯♯♯ Les Roches Philippe CATROUILLET
49610 MOZE-SUR-LOUET
☎ 02 41 78 84 29
This restored 18th-century house, with exposed stone and beams is situated overhanging a river amid a vineyard, in a peaceful hamlet at the entrance to Angers. On the first floor there are two spacious rooms for three people, each with private bath or shower room. The Green Room and the White Room both have a queen-size bed and a single bed. On the ground floor of a converted outbuilding, there is a kitchenette and lounge area, with twin beds, shower room and wc on a mezzanine level. Outdoor furniture.
PRICES: s €38; d €45-€50; extra person €14 **ON SITE:** Fishing Hiking
NEARBY: Horse riding (10km) Forest (10km) Swimming pool (6km) Stretch of water (8km) Tennis (2km) Shops (2km) Railway station (12km)
NOTES: No pets English spoken

MURS-ERIGNE

♯♯♯ IOI Le Jau Françoise TERRIERE
49610 MURS-ERIGNE
☎ 02 41 57 70 13 & 06 83 26 38 80
e-mail: le.jau@anjou-et-loire www.anjou-et-loire.com/jau

Amidst châteaux and vineyards, this attractive, romantic house is in a verdant setting. There are three quiet, comfortable guest rooms with views over the park, each with private bathroom and wc. TV in two bedrooms. Large, welcoming kitchen. Lounge with fireplace and TV. Evening meals on reservation. Terrace, outdoor furniture, barbecue. Your hostess, Françoise Terrière, offers a simple, friendly welcome. Bathing 500 m. Special weekend rates. Ask proprietor for directions. Open all year (by reservation between November and Easter).
PRICES: s €37-€57; d €40-€60; t €65-€75; extra person €15; dinner €23
ON SITE: Hiking **NEARBY:** Fishing (1km) Swimming pool (8km) Stretch of water (8km) Railway station (8km) **NOTES:** No pets

NEUILLE

♯♯♯ Château le Goupillon Monique CALOT
Neuille, 49680 VIVY
☎ 02 41 52 51 89 ▤ 02 41 52 51 89
Comfortable, quiet château in a lush four-hectare park. The three individually decorated bedrooms have antique furnishings. One room has a double and a single bed, adjoining twin room, bathroom and wc. Another room has a double and a single bed, bathroom and wc. The last room has a four-poster bed, shower room and wc. Beamed lounge with fireplace. Central heating. Outdoor furniture. A timeless place, ideal for discovering the Saumur vineyards and visiting the châteaux of the Loire. Ask proprietor for directions. Open all year (by reservation in winter).
PRICES: d €55-€76; extra person €15 **ON SITE:** Hiking
NEARBY: Horse riding (6km) Forest (1km) Fishing (2km) Swimming pool (7km) Tennis (10km) Shops (2km) **NOTES:** Pets admitted

NOYANT

♯♯♯ Galmer Guy COURAULT
49490 NOYANT
☎ 02 41 89 50 17
Between Anjou and Touraine, M. Courault welcomes you to the peace of the countryside. One double room in the proprietor's house has a bathroom and wc. On the first floor of an annexe building, there is a room with a queen-size bed, bathroom and wc, and a twin room with shower room and wc. Cot available. Kitchen, lounge. Electric heating. Directions: from Noyant, follow signs to Bourgueil.
PRICES: s €30; d €38; extra person €8 **NEARBY:** Horse riding (15km) Forest (7km) Fishing (7km) Swimming pool (3km) Stretch of water (15km) Hiking (7km) Tennis (3km) Shops (3km) **NOTES:** No pets

PONTIGNE

♥♥♥ ❤ ◯ Chambre d'hôtes Laéticia et Hugo SALLE
Les Hautes Roches, 49150 PONTIGNE
☎ 02 41 89 19 63 🖨 02 41 89 19 63
With views of the Couasnon valley and the Forest of Chandelais, this organic farm offers four peaceful guest rooms on the first floor. There are two twin rooms and two doubles, one of which also contains a child's bed. Each room has its own shower room and wc. Lounge with kitchenette. Central heating. Table d'hôte meals on reservation. Pétanque, table tennis, large courtyard. Garden furniture, swings, barbecue. Walks nearby, fishing in the lake on the farm. Donkey rides for children. Nearby places of interest include a church with a twisted steeple, dolmen, the château of King René XV and the Vraie Croix d'Anjou. Open all year.
PRICES: s €34; d €38; dinner €14 **ON SITE:** Children's play area Fishing Hiking **NEARBY:** Horse riding (4km) Swimming pool (4km) Stretch of water (6km) Tennis (4km) Shops (4km) Railway station (35km) Golf (3.7km) **NOTES:** No pets

POUANCE

♥♥♥ Le Pigeonnier Yannick et Marie-Jo BROUSSE
La Saulnerie, 49420 POUANCE
☎ 02 41 92 62 66 🖨 02 41 92 62 66
e-mail: brousse.gite@wanadoo.fr
On the Anjou-Brittany border, Marie-Jo and Yannick welcome you to the Pigeonnier, which stands opposite the fortified castle. Ground floor: reception hall with kitchenette, living room, lounge and one bedroom with a double and a single bed (accessible to the less mobile). First floor: two double rooms and a family suite of four single beds; each room has a TV and private bathroom. Covered swimming pool at La Saulnerie, the propriators' house. Two self-catering gîtes available. Ask proprietors for directions. Open all year.
PRICES: s €31; d €41; extra person €13 **ON SITE:** Hiking
NEARBY: Horse riding (13km) Forest (5km) Fishing (1km) Stretch of water (2km) Tennis (2km) Sailing (2km) **NOTES:** Pets admitted

RABLAY-SUR-LAYON

♥♥♥ Chambre d'hôtes Luc et Sylvaine ARENOU-BIDET
66, Grande Rue, 49750 RABLAY-SUR-LAYON
☎ 02 41 78 60 69 🖨 02 41 78 62 58
Welcome to the Domaine des Quarres, a peaceful spot amid gardens and vineyards. This late 19th-century winegrower's house offers four first-floor guest rooms with private bathrooms. There are two double rooms, a family room with a double and a single bed, and a twin-bedded room. Taste wines from the estate (Anjou, Coteaux du Layon). Open April to mid-September.
PRICES: s €36; d €40; extra person €11 **ON SITE:** Wine tasting Fishing Hiking **NEARBY:** Horse riding (7km) Swimming pool (10km) Tennis (7km) Railway station (27km) **NOTES:** No pets

♥♥♥ La Girardière Eliette PHELIX
49750 RABLAY-SUR-LAYON
☎ 02 41 78 65 51
In the peace of the Anjou countryside, amid the Layon vineyards, choose from three comfortable en suite rooms, one of which has a little kitchen. You can swim in the pool or ask Eliette to recommend numerous activities, which can be enjoyed nearby. Visit the châteaux of the Loire, Angers' famous Apocalypse Tapestry or the Puy-du-Fou. Taste the famous Layon wines at one of several vineyards. Bikes may be borrowed. Private parking. Reduced rates for longer stays.
PRICES: s €30-€35; d €38-€44; extra person €15 **ON SITE:** Hiking **NEARBY:** Horse riding (4km) Forest (4km) Fishing (1km) Sailing (1km) Shops (1km) Railway station (26km) **NOTES:** No pets

SAINT-MARTIN-DU-FOUILLOUX

♥♥♥ ◯ La Rabinelaie Dominique DUCHENE
49170 SAINT-MARTIN-DE-FOUILLOUX
☎ 02 41 39 72 61
Dominique welcomes you to her home, which offers three guest rooms, two on the ground floor and one on the first. The Blue Room and the Green Room both have a double bed and twin beds on a mezzanine. Each has a TV and an en suite bathroom. The first-floor room offers a queen-size bed and a single bed. Lounge area with kitchenette and TV. Enclosed grounds of 800 m². Winter garden. Table d'hôte on reservation. Open all year.
PRICES: s €34-€42; d €38-€46; extra person €12; dinner €13 **NEARBY:** Horse riding (8km) Fishing (12km) Swimming pool (10km) Hiking (2km) Tennis (2km) Shops (8km) **NOTES:** Pets admitted

SAUMUR

♥♥♥ Chambre d'hôtes KEMPCZYNSKI
Ile du Saule, 49400 SAUMUR ☎ 02 41 51 38 71
Christiane welcomes you to her three guest rooms at l'Ile du-Saule, in a green and pleasant setting. One room has a double bed, shower room and wc and an adjoining twin room. There is also a twin room and a double room, each with their own shower and wc. Central heating. Parking. Garden with outdoor furniture. Open all year.
PRICES: s €30; d €39; t €50; extra person €12 **NEARBY:** Horse riding (5km) Forest (5km) Fishing (5km) Swimming pool (5km) Hiking (5km) Tennis (5km) Shops (2km) Railway station (5km) **NOTES:** No pets English spoken

SEGRE-SAINT-AUBIN-DU-PAVOIL

♥♥♥ ◯ La Grange du Plessis Janette KRONNEBERG
Place de l'Eglise, 49500 SEGRE
☎ 02 41 92 85 03 🖨 02 41 92 85 03
Three kilometres from the town centre, a charming village, an authentic former barn, an historic 17th-century presbytery and Janette Kronneberg's friendly welcome all combine to offer guests a memorable stay. There are four individual guest rooms: on the first floor there is a double room with a king-size bed and three twin rooms, one of which also contains a sofa. Each room has a TV, phone, private bath or shower room and wc. Wooded park. Direct access to the river, boat available. Bike hire on site. Open all year.
PRICES: s €43; d €55; extra person €12; dinner €20 **ON SITE:** Hiking **NEARBY:** Horse riding (3km) Swimming pool (3km) Tennis (3km) Shops (2km) **NOTES:** No pets English spoken

SEICHES-SUR-LOIR

♥♥♥ ◯ Domaine de Bré Brigitte et Eric DONON
49333 SEICHES-SUR-LOIR
☎ 02 41 76 18 61 e-mail: dononbre@aol.com

Dating from 1850, Brigitte and Eric's attractive house is at the heart of a 400-hectare forest. A calm, relaxing spot, the grounds are

continued

crossed by a canalised river. The three very comfortable, individual guest rooms have private bathrooms. Activities include walking, mountain-biking, fishing, canoeing and swimming on site. Many places of touristic, cultural and gastronomic interest nearby. Marcé airport and nearest motorway junction 8 km. TGV station 25 km. Ask proprietor for directions to property. Reservations necessary out of season.

PRICES: s €50; d €60; extra person €15; dinner €20 **ON SITE:** Fishing Hiking **NEARBY:** Swimming pool (5km) Tennis (5km) Shops (6km) **NOTES:** No pets English spoken

ST-GEORGES-DES-SEPT-VOIES

♦♦♦ iOi La Gauvenière Philippe et Jocelyne VOLLET
49350 ST-GEORGES-DES-SEPT-VOIES
☎ 02 41 57 91 51 📠 02 41 57 91 51

La Gauvenière offers three en suite rooms in an annexe building. 'Tilleul' is a ground-floor double room, while on the first floor 'Cèdre' is a twin room and 'Abbyzzia' is a double with an extra single bed. Ground-floor reception room. Table d'hôte meals feature organic produce. Sauna (€8 a session). Self-catering gîte on site. Private covered swimming pool heated all year round. Ask proprietor for directions.

PRICES: s €34; d €40; extra person €13; dinner €16 **NEARBY:** Horse riding (5km) Fishing (2km) Hiking (1km) Tennis (3km) Shops (4km) **NOTES:** No pets

♦♦♦ Le Sale Village Marcelle PAUMIER
49350 ST-GEORGES-DES-SEPT-VOIES
☎ 02 41 57 91 83

This house offers one ground floor room with a king-size bed, private bathroom and wc. On the first floor there is a double room with private shower room and wc. The TV, garden and garden furniture are shared with the proprietors.

PRICES: d €41; t €53; extra person €15 **ON SITE:** Forest **NEARBY:** Horse riding (9km) Fishing (2km) Swimming pool (3km) Hiking (1km) Tennis (3km) Sailing (3km) Shops (3km) Railway station (16km) **NOTES:** No pets

ST-GEORGES-SUR-LOIRE

♦♦♦ iOi Prieuré de l'Epinay
Bernard et Geneviève GAULTIER
49170 ST-GEORGES-SUR-LOIRE
☎ 02 41 39 14 44 📠 02 41 39 14 44

Bernard and Geneviève welcome you to Jean Racine's priory, founded in the 13th century. There are three very large suites in the converted outbuildings, each with a lounge, bedroom and private bathroom. There is a communal lounge in the chapel, a TV and books of local interest. Bike hire on site. One-hectare park with private swimming pool. This quiet location makes an ideal base for exploring Augers (15 min) and the Layon hills and vineyards (5 min). Open 1 May to 30 September.

PRICES: s €55; d €65; extra person €15; dinner €25 **NEARBY:** Horse riding (7km) Tennis (3km) Sailing (15km) Shops (3km) Railway station (18km) **NOTES:** No pets English spoken

ST-JUST-SUR-DIVE

♦♦♦ iOi Les Gastines Friederike HAGEDORN
49260 ST-JUST-SUR-DIVE
☎ 02 41 67 39 39 📠 02 41 67 19 79

Saumur 10 km. Situated on the banks of the Thouet, in the heart of the Sancerrois region, Friederike's welcoming house is full of character. The five very spacious and comfortable bedrooms all have private bathrooms and wcs. Additional bed and cot available. Private heated swimming pool. Bikes available.

PRICES: s €40-€53; d €45-€58; extra person €14; dinner €20 **ON SITE:** Fishing Swimming pool Hiking **NEARBY:** Horse riding (10km) Tennis (10km) Shops (7km) **NOTES:** Pets admitted English spoken

ST-MATHURIN-SUR-LOIRE

♦♦♦ Chambre d'hôtes Marie et Gérard BRIOLON
4, Grande Rue, Les Muriers,
49250 ST-MATHURIN-SUR-LOIRE
☎ 02 41 57 04 15

Saumur 25 km. Angers 20 km. Close to the Loire, Marie and Gérard offer a warm welcome to their three guest rooms. The ground-floor Blue Room and the first-floor Green Room are both doubles, while the White Room, also on the first floor, has a double and a single bed. All rooms have private shower rooms and wcs. Dining room available for guests. Large garden.

PRICES: s €35; d €43; extra person €12 **ON SITE:** Fishing **NEARBY:** Horse riding (1km) Swimming pool (1km) Hiking (3km) Tennis (1km) Shops (1km) Railway station (20km) **NOTES:** No pets

♦♦♦ iOi La Bouquetterie Claudine PINIER
118, rue du Roi René, 49250 ST-MATHURIN-SUR-LOIRE
☎ 02 41 57 02 00 📠 02 41 57 31 90
e-mail: cpinier@aol.com www.anjou-et-loire.com/bouquetterie

This 19th-century house, situated on the banks of the Loire, has stacks of character. Four of the six spacious guest rooms are on the first floor of a pretty 18th-century outbuilding. Five rooms sleep

continued　　　　　　　　　　　　　　　　　*continued*

2-3 people and the family suite (with kitchenette) sleeps four. Each room is furnished with antiques and has a private shower room and wc. Lounge. Garden, summer house with kitchenette, outdoor furniture, courtyard. Reduced rates from the third night. Bike and canoe hire 5 km. Themed weekends, dinners with entertainment. Open all year (on reservation during winter).
PRICES: s €38-€44; d €51-€59; t €67-€74; extra person €11; dinner €22
ON SITE: Children's play area Fishing Hiking **NEARBY:** Horse riding (6km) Swimming pool (1km) Stretch of water (8km) Tennis (1km) Sailing (4km) Shops (1km) **NOTES:** No pets English spoken

ST-SAUVEUR-DE-FLEE

♦♦♦ Château du Teilleul Brigitte DE VITTON
49500 ST-SAUVEUR-DE-FLEE
☎ 02 41 61 39 55 & 06 80 74 28 97 📠 02 41 61 37 61
Brigitte and Emmanuel de Vitton welcome guests at their charming residence with its largely 18th-century façade. The three first-floor guest rooms comprise the twin Yellow Room, the double Blue Room and the adjoining Pink Room, which is a single. Each room has its own bathroom and wc. Three-hectare park with lake. Open from July to September.
PRICES: d €61-€91; extra person €15 **ON SITE:** Fishing Hiking
NEARBY: Horse riding (2km) Swimming pool (10km) Shops (5km)
NOTES: No pets

VARENNES-SUR-LOIRE

♦♦♦ Chambre d'hôtes Gérard DENOZI
18, rue du Bas Chavigny, 49730 VARENNES-SUR-LOIRE
☎ 02 41 38 18 06
Three guest rooms in an annexe wing of the proprietors' house. One double bedroom is on the ground floor, as is the dining room and guests' kitchen. There are two further doubles on the first floor, one of which has an additional single bed. Each room has a private shower room and wc. Garden with outdoor furniture. The Loire is 200 m away. Open all year.
PRICES: s €35; d €40; t €50 **NEARBY:** Horse riding (10km) Swimming pool (10km) Tennis (2km) Sailing (15km) Shops (2km) Railway station (15km) **NOTES:** Pets admitted

♦♦♦ Les Marronniers France BODINEAU
49730 VARENNES-SUR-LOIRE
☎ 02 41 38 10 13
This 19th-century house with panoramic views of the Loire offers five en suite guest rooms, three on the first floor and two on the second. There are two double rooms, one room with a double and two single beds, one room with three single beds, and one room with a double and a single bedroom. Landscaped garden. Peace and relaxation assured. Doctor and chemist 1 km. Open all year.
PRICES: d €41; t €53; extra person €14 **ON SITE:** Fishing Hiking
NEARBY: Horse riding (8km) Swimming pool (8km) Tennis (1km) Sailing (2km) Shops (1km) Railway station (10km) **NOTES:** Pets admitted

VAUCHRETIEN

♦♦♦ Le Moulin de Clabeau François et Nelly DAVIAU
49320 VAUCHRETIEN
☎ 02 41 91 22 09
Angers 16 km. In a verdant setting alongside the Aubance, close to Brissac Quincé, Nelly and François welcome you to their old water mill offering three first-floor guest rooms. 'Agathe' is a family room with a double and twin beds, while 'Jeanne' and 'Valentine' both have queen-size beds. Each room has a private bathroom. Lounge area with kitchenette. Price for four people: €79. Open all year.
PRICES: d €47 **ON SITE:** Fishing Hiking **NEARBY:** Horse riding (7km) Swimming pool (3km) Tennis (3km) Shops (3km) **NOTES:** No pets

CHANGE

♦♦♦ La Verrerie Odile GUYON
53810 CHANGE LES LAVAL
☎ 02 43 56 10 50 📠 02 43 56 10 50
Character house in a haven of greenery, close to Laval. This welcoming building has been equipped entirely with guests in mind, and is home to four bedrooms with private bathrooms, all of which are individually decorated, spacious and very comfortable. Living room, lounge, kitchenette. Relaxation and well-being are assured. Open all year.
PRICES: s €27; d €35; t €46; extra person €8 **NEARBY:** Bathing (15km) Horse riding (8km) Rock climbing (10km) Forest (10km) Golf (8km) Fishing (8km) Swimming pool (10km) Hiking (5km) Tennis (8km) Sailing (10km) Shops (5km) Railway station (10km) LAVAL (8km) **NOTES:** No pets

CHATEAU-GONTIER-BAZOUGES

♦♦♦ Chambre d'hôtes André DUPRE
la Coudre, 53200 CHATEAU GONTIER
☎ 02 43 70 36 03
Three en suite guest rooms in a completely renovated farmhouse. One room is a twin, while the other two each contain a double and a single bed. Electric heating and TV in each room. Kitchenette available. Delightful garden, porch, outdoor furniture and barbecue available. Private stretch of water 200m, boules pitch. Restaurants 1 km. Mini-golf, animal shelter and racecourse nearby. Open all year.
PRICES: s €24; d €34; t €43; extra person €9 **ON SITE:** Fishing Hiking
NEARBY: Bathing (6km) Horse riding (4km) Rock climbing (10km) Forest (15km) Golf (30km) Swimming pool (4km) Tennis (1km) Sailing (3km) Shops (1km) Railway station (30km) CHATEAU GONTIER BAZOUGES (3km) **NOTES:** No pets

CRAON

♦♦♦ ❤ 🍴 Le David René et Marie Claude GANDON
53800 BOUCHAMPS LES CRAON
☎ 02 43 06 21 36 📠 02 43 06 21 36
Two guest rooms on the first floor of your hosts' house (double bed, twin beds and a child's bed), each with TV, private shower room and wc. There are two further rooms on the first floor of a neighbouring building (three double beds and one single), also with private shower room and wc. The ground floor room has a double and a single bed, and separate shower and wc. Lounge available. Table d'hôte meals served. Fishing on a 5000m² stretch of water. Open all year.
PRICES: s €29; d €37; t €46; extra person €15; dinner €15
ON SITE: Fishing **NEARBY:** Bathing (3km) Horse riding (1km) Rock climbing (3km) Forest (20km) Golf (2km) Swimming pool (3km) Hiking (1km) Tennis (3km) Sailing (2km) Shops (2km) Railway station (30km) CRAON **NOTES:** No pets

ERNEE

♦♦♦ ❤ La Gasselinais Florent et Catherine GENDRON
53500 ERNEE
☎ 02 43 05 70 80 & 02 43 05 69 61 📠 02 43 05 70 80
e-mail: famillegendron@wanadoo.fr www.bienvenuealaferme.net
Catherine, Florent and their children welcome you to their restored farmhouse in the Ernée Valley. Discover life on the farm, see the animals and taste the organic produce, including apple juice, jam and milk. The three guest rooms have private shower rooms and wcs. One room has a kitchenette and mezzanine floor for a family. Lounge with fireplace and kitchenette. Reduced rates from the third night. Open all year.
PRICES: s €25; d €33; t €41; extra person €8 **ON SITE:** Fishing Hiking

continued

NEARBY: Bathing (2km) Horse riding (9km) Rock climbing (20km) Forest (10km) Golf (25km) Swimming pool (2km) Tennis (2km) Sailing (23km) Shops (2km) Railway station (25km) ERNEE (2km) **NOTES:** No pets English spoken

ERNEE-MEGAUDAIS

▦ ❦ ◎ La Rouaudière Maurice TRIHAN
53500 ERNEE/MEGAUDAIS
☎ 02 43 05 13 57 ▤ 02 43 05 71 15
15 minutes from Fougères. Thérèse and Maurice and their son Damien welcome you to their house on a smallholding. Guests can enjoy the relaxing garden, which is full of perennial plants, rose bushes and shrubs. The three guest rooms each sleep 2-3 people and benefit from a lounge, private bath or shower room and wc. Lounge with fireplace. Independent guest entrance. Garden furniture, terrace. Supplement of €3 payable for pets. Choice of restaurants nearby, one of which is fine dining and only five minutes away.
PRICES: s €28; d €43; extra person €12 **ON SITE:** Hiking
NEARBY: Bathing (18km) Horse riding (15km) Rock climbing (30km) Forest (15km) Golf (30km) Fishing (10km) Swimming pool (5km) Tennis (5km) Sailing (18km) Shops (5km) Railway station (35km) ERNEE (5km) **NOTES:** Pets admitted English spoken

GORRON

▦ ❦ Maison-Neuve des 4 Epines Gilbert LEDEME
53120 GORRON
☎ 02 43 08 63 93 & 06 07 65 29 63
Gorron 1 km. Three en suite guest rooms on the first floor of your hosts' home, in the north of Mayenne, at the heart of the Mayennais *bocage.* Independent guest entrance. Reception room, lounge with fireplace and dining room all available for guests to enjoy. Outdoor furniture. Open all year.
PRICES: s €23; d €30; t €46 **NEARBY:** Bathing (35km) Horse riding (1km) Rock climbing (1km) Forest (30km) Golf (35km) Fishing (1km) Swimming pool (1km) Hiking (1km) Tennis (1km) Sailing (15km) Shops (1km) Railway station (50km) **NOTES:** No pets

MONTSURS

▦ ◎ Le Logis d'Eritel Bernard VALLEE
13 avenue de la Libération, 53150 MONTSURS
☎ 02 43 37 33 01 & SR : 02 43 53 58 78 ▤ 02 43 37 43 05
Bernard and Annick will be delighted to welcome you to their superb 19th-century house and its three guest rooms, each with private wc and bath or shower room. You will find the 'royal' room particularly appealing and the excellent breakfasts will ensure you don't go hungry.
PRICES: s €30; d €38-€46; extra person €14; dinner €13
ON SITE: Bathing Hiking **NEARBY:** Horse riding (10km) Rock climbing (20km) Forest (10km) Golf (20km) Swimming pool (10km) Sailing (20km) Railway station (10km) EVRON (10km) **NOTES:** Pets admitted

RUILLE-FROID-FONDS

▦ ❦ ◎ Logis de Villeprouvé Christophe DAVENEL
Villeprouve, 53170 RUILLE FROID FONDS
☎ 02 43 07 71 62 & 06 89 81 50 13 ▤ 02 43 07 71 62
This 17th-century character house offers large, comfortable guest rooms with rustic furnishings: four-poster beds, hexagonal floor tiling, tufa stone fireplaces and half-timbering. There are two double rooms, one three-person room, and one four-person room, each with private bathroom and wc. Lounge available. Garden, stretch of water. Table d'hôte meals feature farm produce. From your third night in a double room, a 10% discount will be deducted from the cost of your stay. Open all year.
PRICES: s €32; d €38; t €47; extra person €9; dinner €12
ON SITE: Forest Fishing Hiking **NEARBY:** Bathing (9km) Horse riding (1km) Rock climbing (23km) Golf (25km) Swimming pool (9km) Tennis (9km) Sailing (9km) Shops (10km) Railway station (25km) MESLAY DU MAINE (10km) **NOTES:** Pets admitted English spoken

ST-DENIS-D'ANJOU

▦ Le Logis du Ray Martine LEFEBVRE
le Ray, 53290 ST DENIS D'ANJOU
☎ 02 43 70 64 10 ▤ 02 43 70 65 53
This house dates back to 1830 and has been furnished in period style. There are three first-floor guest rooms with private shower and wc, one of which has a four-poster bed. Additional child's bed: €23. Cycles and mountain bikes may be borrowed. English-style garden. Loose-box for horses. Private garage. Wagon rides with qualified carriage driver. Two restaurants 800m. Reduced rates: 3-4 nights -10%; 5-7 nights -15%. Carriage driving school, courses available at all levels. Tourist tax payable from 1 June to 31 August. Open all year.
PRICES: s €50-€57; d €58-€65; t €90; extra person €25 **ON SITE:** Hiking
NEARBY: Bathing (6km) Horse riding (9km) Forest (12km) Golf (12km) Fishing (1km) Swimming pool (9km) Tennis (1km) Sailing (9km) Shops (1km) Railway station (9km) **NOTES:** No pets English spoken

ST-GERMAIN-LE-FOUILLOUX

▦ ❦ ◎ L'Hommeau - Fleurs des Champs
Thérèse GEHANNIN
53240 ST GERMAIN LE FOUILLOUX
☎ 02 43 01 18 41 ▤ 02 43 37 68 11
e-mail: fleurs.des.champs.online.fr
Thérèse and Jean-Claude offer guests a quiet, restful stay at their farm in the middle of the Mayennais *bocage,* 10 km from Laval. Each of the renovated guest rooms has been individually decorated on the theme of wildflowers. There are two doubles with balcony and a larger room for four people; each has a TV and private bathroom. Copious breakfasts are served in the bright lounge, or outside in summer. Table d'hôte meals can be arranged. The varied flora and fauna together with the quiet, comfortable rooms make this a delightful stop. Open all year.
PRICES: s €33; d €40; extra person €10; dinner €13 **ON SITE:** Hiking
NEARBY: Bathing (8km) Horse riding (8km) Rock climbing (15km) Forest (15km) Golf (10km) Fishing (4km) Swimming pool (10km) Tennis (8km) Sailing (10km) Shops (3km) Railway station (10km) LAVAL (10km) **NOTES:** No pets

ST-JEAN-SUR-ERVE

▦ Clos de Launay Pierre BIGOT
53270 ST JEAN SUR ERVE
☎ 02 43 90 26 19 & 06 03 20 05 87
This renovated house is situated in a village, close to the N157. Your hosts Pierre and Aline offer a warm welcome to this leafy location. Four guest rooms - two doubles and two twins - each have a TV point, private wc and bath or shower room. Children €8

continued

per night. A river runs alongside the property, which is situated between the medieval city of Ste-Suzanne and Saulges with its prehistoric caves. From 1 April to 15 December.
PRICES: s €38; d €43; extra person €12 **ON SITE:** Forest Fishing Hiking Tennis **NEARBY:** Bathing (20km) Horse riding (11km) Rock climbing (7km) Golf (30km) Swimming pool (9km) Sailing (20km) Railway station (30km) EVRON (15km) **NOTES:** No pets

SARTHE

ASNIERES-SUR-VEGRE

♦♦♦ ✿ ⊙ La Tuffière Mauricette et Yves DAVID
72430 ASNIERES-SUR-VEGRE
☎ 02 43 95 12 16 🖷 02 43 92 43 05
e-mail: www.tuffiere.com
Situated on the banks of the River Vègre, this house offers two first floor guest rooms with a double and a room with a double and two single beds. All rooms have en suite shower-room/wc and electric heating. Fishing and boating on site. Tourist tax applied. Table d'hôte meals. Open all year.
PRICES: s €28; d €34-€38; t €40-€45; extra person €9; dinner €14
ON SITE: Fishing Stretch of water Bicycle hire **NEARBY:** Horse riding (18km) Swimming pool (12km) Tennis (5km) Shops (3km) Railway station (13km) SABLE-SUR-SARTHE (13km) **NOTES:** No pets

AUBIGNE-RACAN

♦♦♦ ⊙ Le Gravier Mme GUIDOIN
Le Relais du Gravier, 72800 AUBIGNE-RACAN
☎ 02 43 46 20 61
This old coaching inn enjoys a very rural position close to the River Loir. It offers four first floor guest rooms, two doubles and one twin, and one room sleeping three. Large dining room with French billiards, lounge area, open fireplace, reading room with piano, lounge with TV/video. Lake for fishing/ walks. Packed lunch available. Open all year.
PRICES: d €38; dinner €12 **ON SITE:** Fishing Stretch of water Bicycle hire **NEARBY:** Horse riding (8km) Swimming pool (8km) Tennis (8km) Shops (2km) **NOTES:** No pets English spoken

BAZOUGES-SUR-LE-LOIR

♦♦♦ ⊙ La Maison Neuve Marie et Jean VIEILLEROBE
Chemin de la Galopière, 72200 BAZOUGES-SUR-LE-LOIR
☎ 02 43 45 30 08 🖷 02 43 45 30 08
www.chez.com/bandb
Marie and Jean extend a warm welcome at their restful home situated in landscaped grounds beside a lake and they offer the following accommodation: one double guest room, one room with a kitchenette and a double and a single bed, one double room with a kitchenette and one first floor twin room with an external staircase. All rooms have en suite shower-room/wc. Table d'hôte meals. Open all year.
PRICES: s €38; d €43-€46; t €58; extra person €12; dinner €14
ON SITE: Bicycle hire **NEARBY:** Horse riding (5km) Forest (1km) Fishing (1km) Swimming pool (10km) Stretch of water (10km) Tennis (2km) Sailing (10km) Shops (3km) Railway station (25km) LA FLECHE (10km) **NOTES:** No pets

BOULOIRE

♦♦♦ La Jonquière Danielle GAUCHER
72440 BOULOIRE
☎ 02 43 35 43 34 🖷 02 43 35 97 12
In her large house situated in woodland on the N157 between Bouloire and St. Calais (direction Maisoncelles), Danielle offers the following first-floor accommodation: three double guest rooms with en suite shower-room/wc, one grade1 double and one grade

1 twin room, sharing bathroom/wc. Cot available. On site: lake, boat, bicycles. Nearby: safari park, mini-golf (8 km), archery (2 km), microlighting (7 km), restaurant (4 km). Open all year.
PRICES: s €29-€33; d €33-€40; extra person €11 **ON SITE:** Forest Fishing Stretch of water Bicycle hire **NEARBY:** Horse riding (20km) Swimming pool (11km) Tennis (4km) Sailing (11km) Shops (4km) Railway station (34km) BOULOIRE (4km) **NOTES:** Pets admitted

BRAINS-SUR-GEE

♦♦♦ ⊙ La Sablière BRIAND
72550 BRAINS-SUR-GEE
☎ 02 43 88 75 19 🖷 02 43 88 75 19
Close to Le Mans, yet in a peaceful, rural setting, this property offers the following accommodation: one ground floor double room with en suite shower-room/wc, one first floor double room and a room sleeping three. All rooms have en suite shower-room/wc. Guest lounge with TV; electric heating; simple, tasty meals; patinated furniture; objects chosen with loving care. Close to RN 157 (direction Brittany, easy access). Open all year.
PRICES: s €32; d €38; t €46; extra person €11; dinner €7-€12
ON SITE: Bicycle hire **NEARBY:** Horse riding (20km) Forest (20km) Fishing (15km) Swimming pool (15km) Stretch of water (12km) Tennis (3km) Sailing (20km) Shops (3km) Railway station (17km) LE MANS (17km) **NOTES:** No pets

CHAMPFLEUR

♦♦♦ ✿ ⊙ La Garencière Christine et Denis LANGLAIS
72610 CHAMPFLEUR
☎ 02 33 31 75 84

This typical 19th-century farm enjoys a rural setting, where Monsieur and Madame Langlais offer the following accommodation: five guest rooms, sleeping two, three or four people, all with en suite shower-room/wc. Lounge with TV, central heating, table d'hôte (farm/regional specialities), covered swimming pool. Open all year.
PRICES: s €33; d €42-€45; extra person €11; dinner €18
ON SITE: Swimming pool **NEARBY:** Horse riding (1km) Forest (1km) Fishing (2km) Tennis (1km) Shops (1km) Railway station (6km) ALENCON (6km) **NOTES:** Pets admitted English spoken

CHANTENAY-VILLEDIEU

♦♦♦ ✿ ⊙ Chauvet Marylise VOVARD
72430 CHANTENAY-VILLEDIEU
☎ 02 43 95 77 57 🖷 02 43 92 54 88
e-mail: marylise.vovard@wanadoo.fr
http://perso.wanadoo.fr/chauvet.hotes
Marylise and Jean-Noël will gladly show their guests around their farm, which breeds pigs and poultry. At their farmhouse they offer the following accommodation: one ground floor double room with en suite bathroom/wc and two first floor double rooms, each with en suite bathroom/wc. Living room, lounge with TV, cot/baby requirements, central heating, garden furniture, evening meals

continued

continued

with the family (by arrangement, children's meals €8). Nearby: mini-golf (2 km). Tourist tax applied. Open all year.

PRICES: s €30; d €40; extra person €12; dinner €15 **NEARBY:** Horse riding (17km) Forest (35km) Fishing (2km) Swimming pool (2km) Stretch of water (2km) Tennis (2km) Sailing (10km) Bicycle hire (9km) Shops (2km) Railway station (17km) BRULON (9km) **NOTES:** No pets English spoken

CHATEAU-DU-LOIR

🍴🍴🍴 **Chambre d'hôtes** Dianne LE GOFF
22 rue de l'Hôtel de Ville, 72500 CHATEAU-DU-LOIR
☎ 02 43 44 03 38
Monsieur and Madame Le Goff extend a warm welcome at their old house behind the main square in the centre of town. They provide three first floor double guest rooms, all with en suite shower-room/wc. Nearby: parking and restaurants. Reductions available on longer bookings. Open all year, except between October and the end of March.
PRICES: s €35; d €43 **NEARBY:** Horse riding (4km) Forest (6km) Fishing (4km) Swimming pool (1km) Stretch of water (6km) Tennis (1km) Sailing (6km) Bicycle hire (1km) Railway station (1km) CHATEAU DU LOIR **NOTES:** No pets English spoken

See advert on this page

CHEMIRE-LE-GAUDIN

🍴🍴🍴 🍽 **Théval** Anne-Marie FORNELL
72210 CHEMIRE-LE-GAUDIN
☎ 02 43 88 14 92
e-mail: ATHEVAL@aol.com
Guests will appreciate not only the comfort and the conviviality provided by the hosts, but also the peace and the natural setting beside the River Sarthe. They offer four elegant, comfortable and spacious rooms accommodating two or three guests, all with en suite bathroom/wc. Sumptuous table d'hôte meals prepared by the lady of the house, followed by siestas beneath the 100-year-old plane trees or a game of boules. Nearby: boating, fishing, walking along the banks or exploring the islands of the River Sarthe. Tourist tax applied. Open all year.
PRICES: s €40; d €45-€50; t €60; extra person €20; dinner €20
ON SITE: Fishing Bicycle hire **NEARBY:** Horse riding (5km) Forest (30km) Swimming pool (5km) Stretch of water (18km) Tennis (5km) Sailing (18km) Shops (2km) Railway station (5km) Restaurant nearby LA SUZE-SUR-SARTHE (5km) **NOTES:** No pets English spoken

Places with this symbol are farmhouses

CLERMONT-CREANS

🍴🍴🍴 **Château d'Oyre** Danièle et François HALLIER
72200 CLERMONT-CREANS
☎ 02 43 48 00 48 📠 02 43 48 00 41
Peace and quiet is guaranteed in this 15th-century château with its parkland and French-style garden. Six double guest rooms are offered, all with en suite shower-room/wc. Open all year.
PRICES: d €60 **ON SITE:** Forest **NEARBY:** Horse riding (3km) Fishing (2km) Swimming pool (5km) Stretch of water (5km) Tennis (1km) Sailing (5km) Bicycle hire (5km) Shops (1km) Railway station (30km) **NOTES:** Pets admitted English spoken

CORMES

🍴🍴🍴 🐓 **Chambre d'hôtes** Odette et Désiré CHERRIER
Planchettes, 72400 CORMES
☎ 02 43 93 24 75 & 06 80 33 97 61 📠 02 43 93 24 75
La Ferté Bernard 7 km. Le Mans 40 km. Odette and Désiré are always happy to welcome guests at their lovingly restored 13th-century manor, which is situated in quiet, rural surroundings. First floor accommodation comprises: one double room with en suite facilities and two rooms with two beds, accommodating up to four people, with lounge, open fireplace, en suite and separate bathroom facilities. All rooms have central heating, heated towel rail and TV. The Yellow Room carries a supplement of €8. Large garden, children's games, walks, fishing lake. Open all year.
PRICES: s €39; d €46-€54; t €69; extra person €16 **ON SITE:** Children's play area Fishing Bicycle hire **NEARBY:** Horse riding (4km) Forest (10km) Swimming pool (4km) Stretch of water (7km) Tennis (3km) Sailing (7km) Shops (3km) Railway station (7km) **NOTES:** Pets admitted

COULAINES

₩₩ Le Monet Lucette BORDEAU
72190 COULAINES
☎ 02 43 82 25 50
Le Mans 8 km. In a detached property close to their own home, Monsieur and Madame Bordeau provide two ground floor double rooms and two first floor double rooms, all with en suite shower-room/wc The house enjoys a rural location and is situated in wooded grounds. Facilities include central heating, living room, lounge, kitchen area, parking, covered terrace, picnic area. Nearby: restaurant (3 km), golf (3 km), 24 hour racing circuit (3 km). Open all year.
PRICES: s €32; d €42 **NEARBY:** Fishing (3km) Swimming pool (1km) Tennis (1km) Sailing (25km) Shops (1km) Railway station (4km) LE MANS (3km) **NOTES:** No pets

DISSAY-SOUS-COURCILLON

₩₩ Le Moulin du Prieuré
M-Claire et Martin BRETONNEAU
3 rue de la Gare, 72500 DISSAY-SOUS-COURCILLON
☎ 02 43 44 59 79

Château du Loir 5 km. This 18th-century watermill is situated in the heart of the village and offers two ground floor guest rooms accommodating three, and one first floor family room. All rooms have en suite facilities and children are catered for. Breakfast is served in the mill. Other facilities include an enclosed garden, secure parking, French/English books, packed lunch. Tourist tax applied. Open all year.
PRICES: s €31; d €43; extra person €16 **ON SITE:** Fishing Tennis Bicycle hire **NEARBY:** Horse riding (3km) Forest (7km) Swimming pool (5km) Stretch of water (5km) Railway station (5km) **NOTES:** Pets admitted

GUECELARD

₩₩ ΙΟΙ Château de Mondan Catherine BABAULT
Route de la Suze, 72230 GUECELARD
☎ 02 43 87 92 16 📠 02 43 77 13 85
e-mail: chateau.mondan@wanadoo.fr
http://perso.wanadoo.fr/chateau.mondan

Relax in a peaceful, lush setting on the banks of the River Sarthe, either in the château, which offers four double guest rooms with en suite facilities, or in the adjoining farmhouse, which has two grade 2 family rooms accommodating three and four guests, also with en suite facilities. On site: golf driving range to suit all levels, two tennis courts, river walks, river fishing, table d'hôte meals on request. Reduced rates, depending on number of nights.
PRICES: s €47; d €55; t €61; extra person €11; dinner €18
ON SITE: Fishing Tennis **NEARBY:** Horse riding (5km) Forest (10km) Swimming pool (5km) Stretch of water (8km) Sailing (8km) Shops (1km) Railway station (15km) **NOTES:** Pets admitted

LAVENAY

₩₩ ΙΟΙ Le Patis du Vergas Monique et Jacques DEAGE
72310 LAVENAY
☎ 02 43 35 38 18 📠 02 43 35 38 18
In a verdant setting beside a very large, well-stocked fishing lake and a river, Monique and Jacques provide accommodation in an annexe on their six-acre estate. Five guest rooms comprising three double rooms and two rooms with one double and one single bed, each with separate entrance and en suite shower room/wc. Lounge, TV, kitchenette, billiards, table football, sauna (at extra cost), volleyball, croquet, boules, table tennis, boat, barbecue, free fishing, picnic area. Breakfast and evening meals served on the veranda. 10% reduction on two or more nights. Open 15 March to 1 November, otherwise by arrangement only.
PRICES: d €43; t €52; dinner €14 **ON SITE:** Fishing Stretch of water Bicycle hire **NEARBY:** Horse riding (18km) Forest (8km) Swimming pool (8km) Tennis (8km) Sailing (15km) Shops (1km) Railway station (23km) LA CHARTRE-SUR-LE-LOIR (10km) **NOTES:** Pets admitted
See advert on opposite page

LE LUDE

₩₩ Chambre d'hôtes M. et Mme PEAN
5 Grande Rue, 72800 LE LUDE
☎ 02 43 94 63 36

The accommodation is in an old house near the château in the centre of town and comprises three first floor double guest rooms, two with en suite bathroom/wc and one with en suite shower-room/wc. Facilities include central heating and a garden. Open from 1 April to 30 September.
PRICES: d €46 **ON SITE:** Forest Bicycle hire **NEARBY:** Horse riding (3km) Fishing (1km) Swimming pool (1km) Stretch of water (12km) Tennis (1km) Sailing (12km) Railway station (21km) **NOTES:** Pets admitted

LOUE

₩₩ Chambre d'hôtes Suzanne et Gary PLEDGER
2 rue de la Libération, 72540 LOUE
☎ 02 43 88 07 83
Le Mans 30 km. Suzanne and Gary Pledger fell in love with the village of Loué and now live in the oldest house in the district,

continued   *continued*

which they enjoy sharing with guests. All four guest rooms are spacious and furnished in keeping with the style of the house, and each is equipped with shower or bath and wc, also tea/coffee making facilities. Children up to ten free. Generous breakfasts, either continental or full English (€8 supplement), served at the large dining table or on the terrace. Open all year.
PRICES: d €53; t €61; extra person €8 **ON SITE:** Fishing Swimming pool Tennis Bicycle hire **NEARBY:** Horse riding (12km) Forest (8km) Stretch of water (7km) Sailing (7km) Railway station (30km) **NOTES:** No pets

LUCEAU

♦♦♦ ⦿ Le Moulin Calme Michel SUEUR
Gascheau, 72500 LUCEAU
☎ 02 43 46 39 75 📠 02 43 46 49 96
Tours 40 km. Le Lude 15 km. Le Mans 40 km. Michel extends a warm welcome at his tranquil mill, situated in the Loir Valley five minutes from Château du Loir. It offers three completely renovated guest rooms and a family suite for four. All rooms have en suite bathroom/wc, new mattresses and bed linen, and views of the lake. Breakfast is served on the veranda or on the terrace by the lake. Table d'hôte meals on request. Two fishing lakes, secure parking, free swimming, pedalos and bicycles. All-inclusive weekly/weekend rates available. Open March to end November (January to March by arrangement only).
PRICES: s €43-€50; d €50-€58; t €70-€84; extra person €23; dinner €15 **ON SITE:** Fishing **NEARBY:** Horse riding (5km) Forest (2km) Swimming pool (5km) Stretch of water (10km) Tennis (5km) Sailing (10km) Bicycle hire (3km) Shops (2km) Railway station (5km) **NOTES:** Pets admitted

MANSIGNE

♦♦♦ La Maridaumière M-D HAMANDJIAN-BLANCHARD
Route de Tulièvre, 72510 MANSIGNE
☎ 02 43 46 58 52 📠 02 43 46 58 52
Situated on the D77 between Requeil and Mansigné, La Maridaumière's floral décor, beeswaxed furniture, warm brioches and homemade jam enable guests to rediscover all the pleasures of the grand country house and holidays in the heart of the countryside. The four first floor rooms have every modern comfort, including en suite bathroom/wc. Facilities include lounge, TV, books, brunch at 11a.m. on request (€12 per person), garden with flowers. Nearby: lake with watersports. Open all year (between October and March by arrangement only).
PRICES: s €38; d €43-€58; t €50-€66; extra person €9 **NEARBY:** Horse riding (5km) Forest (15km) Fishing (3km) Swimming pool (3km) Stretch of water (3km) Tennis (3km) Sailing (3km) Shops (3km) Railway station (12km) MANSIGNE (3km) **NOTES:** No pets English spoken

MONCE-EN-BELIN

♦♦♦ ♥ ⦿ Le Petit Pont Bernard BROU
72230 MONCE-EN-BELIN ☎ 02 43 42 03 32

This working cattle farm offers one grade 3 double guest room

Les Patis du Vergas
72310 Lavenay
Tel & Fax: 00 33 2 43 35 28 18

Set in its own park Les Patis du Vergas is the ideal location for fishing holidays. The hotel is attractively furnished; all guest rooms have en-suite facilities. Within the grounds, you can enjoy various sporting activities. Visit the many beautiful castles and medieval towns within the surrounding area with Le Mans the nearest town, well worth a visit. Tours. The hotel has its own restaurant and open parking.

and four grade 2 double rooms, all with en suite shower-room/wc, located in the owners' house, which also has a living room and a lounge with TV. Outside: garage, garden, parking, stabling facilities. Nearby: restaurant (1 km) Open all year.
PRICES: s €32; d €40; extra person €13; dinner €13-€16
NEARBY: Horse riding (1km) Fishing (1km) Swimming pool (10km) Tennis (2km) Railway station (15km) LE MANS (15km) **NOTES:** Pets admitted

MONHOUDOU

♦♦♦ ♥ ⦿ Château de Monhoudou
Michel DE MONHOUDOU, 72260 MONHOUDOU
☎ 02 43 97 40 05 📠 02 43 33 11 58
This 18th-century château set in fifty acres of English-style parkland offers five double guest rooms, each with en suite bathroom or shower-room and wc. Two lounges and a library are also available. On site: horses, bicycles, tandem, candlelit dinners with the owners by arrangement. Open all year.
PRICES: d €75-€100; t €114; extra person €15; HB €74-€86; dinner €37 **ON SITE:** Horse riding Fishing Bicycle hire **NEARBY:** Forest (10km) Swimming pool (10km) Tennis (3km) Sailing (20km) Shops (3km) Railway station (40km) MAROLLES-LES-BRAULTS (3km) **NOTES:** Pets admitted English spoken CC

OISSEAU-LE-PETIT

♦♦♦ Chambre d'hôtes Jean PERCHERON
17 rue la Fontaine, 72610 OISSEAU-LE-PETIT
☎ 02 33 26 80 09 📠 02 33 26 82 62
Marie-Odile and Jean provide a convivial atmosphere and generous breakfasts in a setting of flowers, meadows, greenery and old stone. The accommodation comprises four self-contained double rooms, all with en suite shower-room/wc and a spare bed,

continued

continued

and one with a TV. Other facilities include: TV lounge; private, covered swimming pool from 15/03-15/11. Open all year
PRICES: s €33-€37; d €42-€46; extra person €14 **ON SITE:** Swimming pool **NEARBY:** Forest (10km) Fishing (10km) Tennis (10km) Shops (10km) Railway station (10km) ALENCON (10km) **NOTES:** Pets admitted

PONTVALLAIN

♦♦♦♦ Chambre d'hôtes Guy VIEILLET
Place Jean Graffin, 72510 PONTVALLAIN
☎ 02 43 46 36 70
This large, impressive 17th-century house offers three guest rooms in two adjacent buildings, with a private entrance and their own garden. The accommodation comprises one room sleeping four people in one double and two single beds, with TV, old fireplace, kitchen area, lounge, shower-room and wc, one double room with en suite shower-room/wc and one room with three single beds, TV and en suite shower-room/wc. A cot is also available. Facilities include large, landscaped grounds, mountain bike hire, table tennis, barbecue, swimming pool, dining room in the main house, well-prepared breakfasts. Open all year.
PRICES: d €48-€60; t €71-€79; extra person €19 **ON SITE:** Forest Fishing Swimming pool Tennis Bicycle hire **NEARBY:** Horse riding (5km) Stretch of water (5km) Sailing (5km) Railway station (6km) LE LUDE (14km) **NOTES:** No pets English spoken

ROUEZ-EN-CHAMPAGNE

♦♦♦ 🐓 L'Abbaye de Champagne
M-Annick et Pierre LUZU
72140 ROUEZ-EN-CHAMPAGNE
☎ 02 43 20 15 74 📠 02 43 20 74 61

Eighteenth-century guest rooms are available in Marie-Annick and Pierre's 12th-century abbey, all with en suite bathroom/wc and electric heating. Art courses on request. On site: gîte, two fishing lakes, hunting (by the day/weekend), pedalos, swimming pool. Tourist tax applied. Open all year.
PRICES: d €46-€64; extra person €12; dinner €14-€23
ON SITE: Fishing Swimming pool **NEARBY:** Horse riding (10km) Forest (10km) Stretch of water (10km) Tennis (4km) Sailing (10km) Shops (4km) Railway station (10km) Restaurant nearby SILLE-LE-GUILLAUME (10km) **NOTES:** No pets

SILLE-LE-PHILIPPE

♦♦♦ Château de Chanteloup Michel SOUFFRONT
72460 SILLE-LE-PHILIPPE
☎ 02 43 27 51 07 & 02 43 81 72 56
The five guest rooms accommodating two, three or four people, are situated in an old building adjoining the Château de Chanteloup. All rooms have en suite shower-room/wc. Guests may avail themselves of the following campsite facilities within the grounds: swimming pool, tennis, billiard room, fishing, boating. Open 1 May to 30 September.
PRICES: s €61; d €69; t €76 **ON SITE:** Fishing Swimming pool Tennis

NEARBY: Horse riding (4km) Stretch of water (12km) Sailing (12km) Shops (1km) Railway station (18km) MONTFORT-LE-GESNOIS (9km) **NOTES:** No pets English spoken

SOLESMES

♦♦♦ 🐓 🍽 Le Fresne M-Armelle et Pascal LELIEVRE
72300 SOLESMES
☎ 02 43 95 92 55 📠 02 43 95 92 55
Marie-Armelle and Pascal extend a warm welcome at their home near Solesmes in the Sarthe valley. The self-contained, ground floor accommodation is located in a building adjoining their own house. One room with a double and two single beds and en suite bathroom/wc, one twin-bedded room with en suite shower-room/wc and one room sleeping four in a double and two single beds, with mezzanine and en suite shower room/wc. Electric heating. Pets accepted (€5 per night). Table d'hôte meals on request. Reduced rates on bookings of four nights and over. Tourist tax applied. Open all year.
PRICES: s €33; d €42; t €53; extra person €11; dinner €19
ON SITE: Fishing **NEARBY:** Horse riding (5km) Forest (15km) Swimming pool (6km) Stretch of water (15km) Tennis (3km) Sailing (25km) Bicycle hire (6km) Shops (3km) Railway station (7km) SABLE-SUR-SARTHE (7km) **NOTES:** Pets admitted English spoken

ST-COSME-EN-VAIRAIS

♦♦♦ Les Hautes Grouas Evelyne COUPE
72580 ST-COSME-EN-VAIRAIS
☎ 02 43 33 90 40
The three double guest rooms, each with en suite shower-room/wc, are located in rural, wooded surroundings on the first floor of a building belonging to an old farmhouse. On the ground floor there is an 80m² guest lounge with TV and books. Other facilities include: central heating, terrace, garden furniture. Stabling/grazing for horses is available. Fifth night free. Restaurant (2 km). Open all year.
PRICES: d €40 **NEARBY:** Horse riding (12km) Forest (15km) Fishing (3km) Swimming pool (12km) Stretch of water (12km) Tennis (1km) Sailing (12km) Bicycle hire (2km) Shops (2km) Railway station (17km) MAMERS (12km) **NOTES:** No pets

ST-JEAN-DE-LA-MOTTE

♦♦♦ 🍽 Château de la Vivantière Margaret ALLENET
72510 ST-JEAN-DE-LA-MOTTE
☎ 02 43 45 29 15 📠 02 43 45 29 15
e-mail: oallenet@aol.com
http://members.aol.com/vivantiere/chateau.html/

Saint-Jean-de-la-Motte 3 km. La Flèche 15 km. This 17th-century château was restored during the Napoléon III era and is surrounded by one hundred-year-old trees. Guests will appreciate the quiet rooms and the home-produced honey, goat's cheese and poultry on offer at the table d'hôte meals. Accommodation comprises: one guest room 'Summer' with shower-room/wc, and

continued

continued

three suites, 'Spring' with bathroom/wc, 'Autumn' with bathroom/wc and 'Winter' with shower room/wc. Open all year.
PRICES: s €27; d €53; dinner €27 **NEARBY:** Horse riding (5km) Fishing (3km) Swimming pool (3km) Tennis (3km) Sailing (3km) Bicycle hire (3km) Shops (3km) Railway station (30km) **NOTES:** Pets admitted English spoken

ST-LEONARD-DES-BOIS

▦ Le Moulin de l'Inthe Claude ROLLINI
72590 ST-LEONARD-DES-BOIS
☎ 02 43 33 79 22
On the banks of the River Sarthe and in the heart of the Alpes Mancelles, the Moulin de l'Inthe offers three double rooms, one room sleeping three and one accommodating up to four people, all with en suite bathroom/wc. Facilities include: guest lounges with TV, mountain bike hire, fishing and helipad. Open all year (except 1 January to 30 March).
PRICES: s €44; d €58; t €73; extra person €19 **ON SITE:** Horse riding Forest Fishing Tennis Bicycle hire **NEARBY:** Swimming pool (12km) Stretch of water (25km) Sailing (25km) Railway station (18km)
NOTES: No pets English spoken

ST-SYMPHORIEN

▦ ▯ Manoir Le Mont Porcher
C et B MEYER-DE LA BRETONNIERE
72240 ST-SYMPHORIEN
☎ 02 43 20 75 61
Mont Porcher Manor enjoys a prime location on a promontory close to the edge of Charnie Forest. Without detracting from the authenticity of the surroundings, expert renovation has made it possible to incorporate four very comfortable guest rooms. Guests are assured a warm welcome from the young owners. Exclusively for guests: a consecrated chapel, a lounge/library opening on to the French-style garden, candlelit dinners on request. Nearby: restaurant (2.5 km). Open 1 May to 30 September.
PRICES: s €80; d €90; extra person €30; dinner €40 **ON SITE:** Forest **NEARBY:** Horse riding (2km) Fishing (5km) Swimming pool (5km) Stretch of water (15km) Tennis (2km) Sailing (15km) Bicycle hire (2km) Shops (2km) Railway station (10km) CONLIE (10km) **NOTES:** No pets English spoken

THOIRE-SUR-DINAN

▦ ▯ ▯ Le Saut du Loup Claudine et Jacques CISSE
72500 THOIRE-SUR-DINAN
☎ 02 43 79 12 36

Claudine and Jacques extend a warm welcome at their dairy farm bordering Bercé Forest (5500 hectares) in the Loir Valley. They provide the following first-floor accommodation: one double guest room; one room with three single beds; two adjoining rooms with four single beds. All rooms have en suite bathroom or shower-room and wc, TV point and electric heating. On the ground floor: books, billiard room, refrigerator, TV point, terrace with garden

furniture, boules area, large garden. Nearby: public footpaths, mountain biking in Bercé Forest. Free tourist tax. Table d'hôte meals with the family by arrangement. Open all year.
PRICES: s €35; d €43; t €61; dinner €14 **ON SITE:** Forest **NEARBY:** Horse riding (5km) Fishing (3km) Swimming pool (9km) Stretch of water (5km) Tennis (3km) Sailing (5km) Bicycle hire (3km) Shops (3km) Railway station (9km) CHATEAU-DU-LOIR (9km) **NOTES:** No pets

VENDÉE

ANGLES

▦ ▯ Chambre d'hôtes Roger & Chantal GUIET
4 route du Port, Moricq, 85750 ANGLES
☎ 02 51 97 56 20 ▤ 02 51 28 98 25
e-mail: roger.guiet@freesbee.fr
Luçon 18 km. St-Vincent-sur-Jard 10 km. At the gateway into the Marais-Poitevin and 8km from the sea, this old working farm has four guest rooms: two doubles and one double with single in an annexe and a double and single room in the farmhouse. All rooms are recently refurbished, have private shower room, wc, and TV. Communal room with equipped kitchen, library and games, conservatory, terrace, play area and well-kept grounds. Animals allowed by reservation. Open all year.
PRICES: s €35; d €37-€40; t €47-€50 **ON SITE:** Fishing Hiking **NEARBY:** Bathing (18km) Horse riding (5km) Golf (20km) Sea (8km) Swimming pool (25km) Stretch of water (10km) Tennis (1km) Shops (1km) Railway station (25km) LUCON (18km) **NOTES:** Pets admitted

CHATEAUNEUF

▦ ▯ ▯ Les Boulinières
Bernard & Martine BOCQUIER
85710 CHATEAUNEUF
☎ 02 51 49 30 81
Challans 8 km. Beauvoir-sur-Mer 10 km. The whole upstairs of this fully renovated and refurbished farmhouse is given over to the guest rooms of which there are four: one with two doubles and one single, one with double and single, and one double, all with shower room and wc. The other has two doubles, a private bathroom and own entrance. Living room, garden, games area, parking. Nearby: fishing, working windmill, riding, Marais Discovery Centre. Bikes available. Open all year.
PRICES: s €35; d €39; t €48; extra person €9; dinner €13 **ON SITE:** Children's play area Fishing Hiking Tennis **NEARBY:** Horse riding (5km) Golf (20km) Sea (15km) Swimming pool (10km) Railway station (10km) CHALLANS (8km) **NOTES:** No pets

CHAVAGNES-EN-PAILLERS

▦ Bénaston Pierre & Guiguitte DAVID
85250 CHAVAGNES-EN-PAILLERS
☎ 02 51 42 22 63 & 06 87 98 62 45
Montaigu 10 km. Le Puy-du-Fou 30 km. Surrounded by leafy woodlands, the owners welcome guests to four rooms, situated on the first floor of their home. There is a communal entrance, reception room, and use of kitchen and telephone can be arranged. Two doubles and one double with twin beds have TV. Another double with single bed available. All rooms have private shower rooms and wc. Open all year.
PRICES: s €27; d €35; t €43; extra person €11 **NEARBY:** Bathing (15km) Golf (40km) Sea (65km) Fishing (2km) Swimming pool (13km) Stretch of water (4km) Hiking (4km) Tennis (2km) Shops (2km) Railway station (12km) MONTAIGU (10km) **NOTES:** No pets

Use the atlas at the back of the guide to locate your chambre d'hôtes

continued

♦♦♦ IOI La Déderie Marie GAUVIN
85250 CHAVAGNES-EN-PAILLERS
☎ 02 51 42 22 59 📠 02 51 42 22 59
e-mail: mariegauvin@wanadoo.fr
Montaigu 10 km. Le Puy-du-Fou 30 km. This 18th-century manor house, fully renovated earlier this year, offers four guest rooms: one with two doubles, one double, and one double with single beds, all with private shower rooms and wc. Another double with single beds has its own bathroom. Living room with TV for guests' use. Walled garden, garage, parking. Restaurant, shops nearby. Several chateaux within 20 km. Open all year.
PRICES: s €33-€40; d €39-€46; t €52-€62; extra person €13-€16; dinner €16 **ON SITE:** Fishing Hiking **NEARBY:** Bathing (6km) Horse riding (5km) Golf (35km) Sea (65km) Swimming pool (5km) Stretch of water (3km) Tennis (2km) Shops (1km) Railway station (12km) MONTAIGU (10km) **NOTES:** No pets

COEX

♦♦♦ 🐓 IOI Ferme du Latoi CRAPPE-LEMEY
Le Latoi, 85220 COEX
☎ 02 51 54 67 30 📠 02 51 60 02 14
e-mail: camping@ferme-du-latoi.fr
St-Gilles-Croix-de-Vie 13 km. Challans 25 km. Le Puy-du-Fou 70 km. Only 10 minutes from the ocean, in flowery surroundings, this typical 19th-century Vendeen farmhouse has five guest rooms: one double room on the ground floor and one double, and three doubles with singles one the first floor. All rooms have private shower rooms. Comfortable living room with kitchen area and TV. Available on site: fishing pond, tennis and swimming pool (open 1 June to 15 September). Also camping. Nearby: cycling, riding, golf. Animals permitted with supplement. Meals on request. Open all year.
PRICES: s €34; d €42; t €51; dinner €17 **ON SITE:** Fishing Swimming pool Hiking Tennis **NEARBY:** Horse riding (3km) Golf (3km) Sea (12km) Stretch of water (2km) Shops (2km) Railway station (15km) ST GILLES CROIX DE VIE (12km) **NOTES:** Pets admitted

DOIX

♦♦♦ Logis de Chalusseau Marie-Thérèse BAUDRY
111 rue de Chalusseau, 85200 DOIX
☎ 02 51 51 81 12 📠 02 51 51 81 12
e-mail: chaluss@wanadoo.fr
Fontenay-le-Comte 9 km. L'Abbaye St-Pierre de Maillezais 6 km. Close to the Marais fen-lands, the 17th-century Logis de Chalusseau offers three guest rooms, all full of character with original features: one double with single with private bathroom and wc and one double with shower room wc. There is also a suite with its own entrance, with double and twin beds, both with en suite shower rooms and wc. Guests' own living room, salon and kitchen, outdoor seating area. Open from 1 April to 15 November.
PRICES: s €31-€41; d €41-€47; t €51-€57; extra person €10
NEARBY: Bathing (15km) Horse riding (9km) Golf (30km) Sea (40km) Fishing (6km) Swimming pool (9km) Stretch of water (15km) Hiking (2km) Tennis (6km) Shops (1km) Railway station (9km) FONTENAY LE COMTE (9km) **NOTES:** No pets

FEOLE-LA-REORTHE

♦♦♦ IOI Chambre d'hôtes Geneviève ROUAULT
36 rue Georges Clémenceau, 85210 FEOLE-LA-REORTHE
☎ 02 51 27 83 33 📠 02 51 27 82 27
Chantonnay 10 km. Le Puy-du-Fou 40 km. Situated in a market town just off the RN137, this 15th-century coaching-house has four guestrooms. These are all upstairs, individually decorated with double beds, and have en suite shower rooms and wc. Downstairs, there is a kitchen and a grand sitting room with a monumental

fireplace and TV. Dinner available on reservation and restaurant nearby. Parking in interior courtyard. Marais-Poitevin 35km. Open all year.
PRICES: s €26; d €35; dinner €11 **NEARBY:** Bathing (8km) Horse riding (14km) Sea (40km) Fishing (3km) Swimming pool (4km) Stretch of water (2km) Hiking (1km) Tennis (2km) Shops (4km) Railway station (10km) CHANTONNAY (10km) **NOTES:** Pets admitted

ILE-D'YEU

♦♦♦ Chambre d'hôtes Pierre & Monique CADOU
10 Ker Guérin, St-Sauveur, 85350 ILE-D'YEU
☎ 02 51 58 55 13
Challans 52 km. Port-Joinville 2.5 km. Set sail for the Island of Yeu and make Pierre and Monique's guest house your port-of-call. Situated in a pretty little village on the interior of the island, it has three charming guest rooms, all on the ground floor with their own entrance. Each has one double bed and shower room with wc, and twin beds on a mezzanine. Flowery walled courtyard, with seating area for each room. Communal garage with bikes. Port 2.5km. Open all year.
PRICES: s €30; d €49; t €69; extra person €14 **NEARBY:** Horse riding (2km) Sea (3km) Fishing (3km) Hiking (2km) Tennis (2km) CHALLANS (52km) **NOTES:** No pets

♦♦♦ IOI Villa Monaco Moïsette DUPONT
Pointe des Corbeaux, 85350 ILE-D'YEU
☎ 02 51 58 76 56 📠 02 51 58 52 98
Challons 80 km. Port-Joinville 8 km. Situated on the tip of the island, in an area of protected natural beauty and only 100m from the beach, this modern guesthouse boasts exceptional views of the ocean. There are three guest rooms in the main house and another in an annexe, each with private bath or shower room and wc. Living room with TV and telescope, sitting room with fireplace, calm and pleasant garden. 8km from port. Open April to September.
PRICES: d €83-€120; dinner €21 **ON SITE:** Sea Fishing Hiking **NEARBY:** Horse riding (6km) Tennis (4km) Shops (3km) CHALLANS (80km) **NOTES:** Pets admitted

LA CHAIZE-LE-VICOMTE

♦♦♦ Demeure du Marillet Laurent FAGOT
59 rue des Frères Payraudeau,
85310 LA CHAIZE-LE-VICOMTE
☎ 02 51 40 11 62 & 06 87 08 15 73 📠 02 51 40 11 62
La Roche-sur-Yon 9 km. Le Puy-du-Fou 45 km. Situated in the centre of a small market town, this 100-year-old manor house offers five guest rooms, all recently renovated: two doubles, one double with twin beds, one with two doubles, one double with single. All rooms have private bath or shower room and wc. Kitchen, living room, billiard room, park with private pool (open 1 June to 30 September). Bikes available in summer.
PRICES: s €37; d €42; t €54; extra person €13 **ON SITE:** Swimming pool Hiking Tennis **NEARBY:** Bathing (20km) Horse riding (3km) Golf (18km) Sea (40km) Fishing (15km) Stretch of water (10km) Railway station (15km) LA ROCHE SUR YON (9km) **NOTES:** No pets

LA CHAPELLE-ACHARD

♦♦♦ 🐓 Le Plessis Jousselin
Dominique & Maïté CHIFFOLEAU
85150 LA CHAPELLE-ACHARD
☎ 02 51 05 91 08
Les Sables-d'Olonne 12 km. St-Vincent-sur-Jard 25 km. In the heart of the countryside, near the sea, this recently renovated farmhouse has four double-bedded guest rooms: two on the ground floor and two upstairs with their own entrance. All rooms have private

continued   *continued*

shower rooms and wc. Cot and folding bed available. Communal living room with equipped kitchen area, TV, washing machine, terrace with outdoor seating. Animals by reservation. Open all year. **PRICES:** s €31; d €37 **NEARBY:** Bathing (8km) Horse riding (8km) Golf (10km) Sea (12km) Fishing (8km) Swimming pool (15km) Stretch of water (8km) Hiking (1km) Tennis (2km) Shops (2km) Railway station (2km) LES SABLES D'OLONNE (15km) **NOTES:** Pets admitted

LA FAUTE-SUR-MER

††† ı◎ı L'ESTEREL André & Madeleine HERVE
12 bis rue des Oeillets, 85460 LA FAUTE-SUR-MER
☎ 02 51 97 02 14 ▤ 02 51 97 02 14
Luçon 25 km. La Rochelle 45 km. Surrounded by a shady, walled garden, filled with flowers, this guesthouse offers four rooms, each with double and single beds, their own entrances, shower rooms and wc, as well as individual terraces and outdoor seating areas. Kitchenettes, TV, washing machine and bikes available. Fine sandy beaches only 8km. Home-made baking and jam for breakfast. Evening meals offer local seafood. Open 15 February to 15 November.
PRICES: s €31-€39; d €39-€46; t €46-€59; dinner €15 **ON SITE:** Sea Fishing Hiking Tennis **NEARBY:** Bathing (1km) Horse riding (1km) Golf (30km) Swimming pool (20km) Stretch of water (1km) Shops (1km) Railway station (20km) LUCON (25km) **NOTES:** No pets

LANDEVIEILLE

††† ✿ La Jarrie Jacky & M-Thérèse ROBIN
85220 LANDEVIEILLE
☎ 02 51 22 90 92 ▤ 02 51 22 90 92
St-Gilles-Croix-de-Vie 15 km. Les Sables-d'Olonne 20 km. Savour the peace of the country, only 10 minutes from the ocean, at this renovated 19th-century farmhouse with four guest rooms: two twin rooms on the ground floor; one double, and one double with single upstairs. All rooms have private bath or shower room and wc and have independent access. Communal room with cooking and washing equipment. Seating area in garden and bikes available to explore surrounding lakes and forests. Open 1 April to 1 November.
PRICES: s €30; d €40; t €50 **NEARBY:** Horse riding (10km) Golf (10km) Sea (10km) Fishing (5km) Swimming pool (15km) Stretch of water (5km) Tennis (5km) Shops (4km) Railway station (20km) ST GILLES CROIX DE VIE (15km) **NOTES:** No pets

LE BOUPERE

††† Manoir de la Baussonnière Pierre & Yvette SOULARD
85510 LE BOUPERE
☎ 02 51 91 91 48
Les Herbiers 12 km. Le Puy-du-Fou 12 km. In the Vendée forest, this 16th-century manor house has 5 guest rooms, fully refurbished in 1998: four doubles and one with a double and a single. All rooms have private shower room and wc. Guests have use of small kitchen and living room with TV. Pleasant gardens with outdoor seating areas. Private parking. Restaurant 3km. Open all year.
PRICES: s €37; d €43; t €57 **NEARBY:** Bathing (2km) Horse riding (3km) Golf (35km) Sea (65km) Fishing (2km) Swimming pool (3km) Stretch of water (2km) Hiking (2km) Tennis (2km) Shops (3km) Railway station (6km) LES HERBIERS (12km) **NOTES:** Pets admitted

LE CHATEAU-D'OLONNE

††† ✿ La Châtaigneraie Didier & Martine BOULINEAU
85180 LE CHATEAU-D'OLONNE
☎ 02 51 96 47 52
Les Sables-d'Olonne 5 km. St-Vincent-sur-Jard 20 km. Enjoy the calm of the countryside at this farmhouse, close to the Sables

d'Olonne. Three guest rooms above the main house with their own entrance: one with double and twin beds, one double, one double with large single. Each room has a private bathroom. Folding bed and cot available. Communal living room with kitchen area, well-kept terrace with tables and chairs. Take the D36 for 3km out of town. Open 1 February to 15 November.
PRICES: s €32; d €40; t €50; extra person €10 **NEARBY:** Horse riding (3km) Golf (5km) Sea (5km) Fishing (15km) Swimming pool (7km) Stretch of water (15km) Hiking (3km) Tennis (3km) Shops (4km) Railway station (7km) LES SABLES D'OLONNE (5km) **NOTES:** No pets

LE GUE-DE-VELLUIRE

††† ı◎ı Le Logis d'Elpenor Thierry & Martine BERTIN
5 rue de la Rivière, 85770 LE GUE-DE-VELLUIRE
☎ 02 51 52 59 10 ▤ 02 51 52 57 21
Fontenay-le-Comte 15 km. La Rochelle 35 km. This charming house is situated in a quiet little market town on the banks of the Vendée river. It houses five guest rooms: two doubles with single; one with two doubles (each of which has a private shower room and wc); one with two doubles; and one double with single (each with private bathroom and wc). Guests' living room with TV and library. Use of garden with table, chairs, barbecue and river terrace. Dinner available on reservation (except Saturdays). Open February to November.
PRICES: s €44; d €50; t €61; extra person €11; dinner €19 **ON SITE:** Fishing Hiking **NEARBY:** Bathing (30km) Horse riding (30km) Golf (30km) Sea (25km) Swimming pool (10km) Stretch of water (5km) Tennis (10km) Railway station (35km) FONTENAY LE COMTE (15km) **NOTES:** Pets admitted CC English spoken

LE MAZEAU

††† Chambre d'hôtes Chantal FRERE
12 rue du Port, 85420 LE MAZEAU
☎ 02 51 52 95 49
Fontenay-le-Comte 20 km. L'abbaye St-Pierre de Maillezais 7 km. This is a traditional townhouse in Mazeau, in the heart of France's 'Green Venice'. It has three guest rooms: one with twin beds and two doubles, all with en suite bath or shower and wc. Use of communal room, part sitting room, part kitchen and walled garden. Parking. Restaurant, boat trips 150m. Nearby: La Rochelle, Puy de Fou, Futuroscope. Open all year.
PRICES: s €33; d €37; t €49 **ON SITE:** Fishing Hiking Tennis **NEARBY:** Bathing (25km) Horse riding (5km) Golf (20km) Sea (50km) Swimming pool (15km) Stretch of water (12km) Railway station (20km) FONTENAY LE COMTE (20km) **NOTES:** No pets

LES CHATELLIERS-CHATEAUMUR

††† Le Bas Chatellier Romain & Pierrette BETTOLI
85700 LES CHATELLIERS-CHATEAUMUR
☎ 02 51 57 23 86
e-mail: romain.bettoli@wanadoo.fr
Les Herbiers 14 km. Le Puy-du-Fou 7 km. Romain and Pierrette welcome guests to their fully restored 18th-century farmhouse, situated in the 'Haut-Bocage'. It has four guest rooms: three with double and single (all with shower and wc), two of which are in the main house and the other in the annex. Also in the annex is another room with two doubles, a living room and bathroom. Country garden and outdoor seating area. Open all year.
PRICES: s €31; d €40; t €51; extra person €11 **NEARBY:** Horse riding (9km) Golf (20km) Sea (80km) Fishing (2km) Swimming pool (12km) Stretch of water (9km) Tennis (6km) Shops (6km) Railway station (9km) LES HERBIERS (14km) **NOTES:** Pets admitted

continued

LES EPESSES

♦♦♦ ♥○♥ La Trainelière J-François & Soizic YOU
85590 LES EPESSES
☎ 02 51 57 41 20 📠 02 51 57 41 20
e-mail: syou@net-up.com
Les Herbiers 10 km. Le Puy-du-Fou 1 km. Surrounded by open countryside, these five guest rooms are situated in a former farmhouse, which has been completely renovated. Four rooms (two doubles and two doubles with single) are on the ground floor with separate entrances. Another double with single (and possible extra bed) upstairs. All rooms en suite shower rooms and wc. Use of terrace with tables and chairs. Dinner available on reservation. Organised tourist trips on request. Open all year.
PRICES: d €49; t €64; dinner €15 **ON SITE:** Hiking **NEARBY:** Bathing (16km) Horse riding (10km) Golf (25km) Sea (80km) Fishing (4km) Swimming pool (4km) Stretch of water (4km) Tennis (4km) Shops (4km) Railway station (25km) LES HERBIERS (10km) **NOTES:** No pets English spoken

♦♦♦ Le Petit Bignon Brigitte BRIDONNEAU
85590 LES EPESSES
☎ 02 51 57 45 57 📠 02 51 57 45 57
Les Herbiers 10 km. Le Puy-du-Fou 1 km. This old, converted barn was totally redecorated last year and has three guest rooms, each with their own entrance. There are two doubles and one room with double and single. Each has private shower room, wc, TV, terrace and outdoor seating area. Use of living room and dinner available on reservation. Open all year.
PRICES: d €50; t €65 **ON SITE:** Hiking **NEARBY:** Bathing (16km) Horse riding (10km) Golf (25km) Sea (80km) Fishing (4km) Swimming pool (4km) Stretch of water (4km) Tennis (4km) Shops (4km) Railway station (25km) LES HERBIERS (10km) **NOTES:** No pets English spoken

LES HERBIERS

♦♦♦ ARDELAY Joël MARCHAIS
57 rue Monseigneur Massé, 85500 LES HERBIERS
☎ 02 51 64 95 10 & 06 10 26 27 75
e-mail: joel.marchais@wanodoo.fr
http://perso.worldonline.fr/famille-marchais/
Le Puy-du-Fou 6 km. This delightful house is located five minutes from Puy-de-Fou. Joël, Odile and their children welcome you to their three spacious guest rooms: all double bedrooms with private bathrooms and wc. Folding beds available on request. Use of charming garden with seating area, table tennis, billiard room and swimming pool. Open 1 June to 30 August.
PRICES: d €40-€50 **ON SITE:** Children's play area Swimming pool **NEARBY:** Bathing (4km) Horse riding (2km) Sea (70km) Fishing (5km) Stretch of water (15km) Hiking (2km) Tennis (2km) Railway station (25km) LES HERBIERS **NOTES:** No pets English spoken

♦♦♦ ♥ La Métairie du Bourg
Bernard & Janine RETAILLEAU
85500 LES HERBIERS
☎ 02 51 67 23 97
Les Herbiers 5 km. Le Puy-du-Fou 5 km. Deep in the countryside, at the gateway to Puy-de-Fou, lies this welcoming family farm. There are three recently redecorated guest rooms: one yellow room with two doubles, one blue and pink room with double and single, and another with two doubles. All have shower room and wc. Independent access. A generous, gourmet breakfast is provided and light meals are available. Well-kept garden with seating area. Kennel for dogs. Open all year.
PRICES: d €38-€46; extra person €15 **NEARBY:** Bathing (14km) Horse riding (5km) Sea (80km) Fishing (5km) Swimming pool (5km) Stretch of water (5km) Hiking (5km) Tennis (5km) Shops (5km) Railway station (25km) LES HERBIERS (5km) **NOTES:** Pets admitted

♦♦♦ ♥ L'Abri des Alouettes Marie-Jeanne PINEAU
La Cossonnière, 85500 LES HERBIERS
☎ 02 51 67 11 42 📠 02 51 66 90 27
Le Puy-du-Fou 6 km. The owners of L'Abri des Alouettes welcome guests to their organic farm. There are four guest rooms, all in the modern farmhouse with individual entrances: two with double and single, and two with twin beds. All have private shower room, wc and fitted kitchen area. Use of owner's living room with TV, library and telephone, open-air games, arranged visits around farm. Reduced rates for stays over three nights. Open all year.
PRICES: s €33; d €40; t €50 **ON SITE:** Children's play area **NEARBY:** Bathing (12km) Horse riding (16km) Sea (80km) Fishing (3km) Swimming pool (3km) Stretch of water (3km) Tennis (3km) Shops (3km) Railway station (25km) LES HERBIERS (3km) **NOTES:** No pets

LUCON

♦♦♦ Chambre d'hôtes Henri & Elisabeth LUGAND
1 rue des Chanoines, 85400 LUCON
☎ 02 51 56 34 97 & 02 51 56 08 97
Marais-Poitevin 20 km. La Rochelle 50 km. An oasis in the middle of the town, this 18th-century dwelling is situated in a spacious, leafy park. It offers three double bedrooms with private shower rooms and wc and a suite with double and single, bathroom and wc. Use of sitting room/library, terrace and outdoor seating area. Open 10 January to 15 December.
PRICES: s €34; d €43-€53; t €61 **NEARBY:** Bathing (2km) Horse riding (5km) Golf (25km) Sea (20km) Fishing (2km) Swimming pool (1km) Stretch of water (2km) Hiking (5km) Tennis (1km) Railway station (1km) LUCON **NOTES:** No pets

MAILLEZAIS

♦♦♦ Chambre d'hôtes Liliane BONNET
69 rue de l'Abbaye, 85420 MAILLEZAIS
☎ 02 51 87 23 00 📠 02 51 00 72 44
e-mail: liliane.bonnet@wanadoo.fr
La Rochelle 48 km. In the centre of a fen-land village, right next to the abbey, stands this 19th-century mansion. It has five guest rooms, fully renovated to include all modern comforts. One double with direct access to the park, three doubles upstairs, and one with double and single beds. All rooms have private shower room and wc, one with private bathroom. Use of sitting room with library and TV, tennis court, private fishing. Boat, bikes, available. Parking. Open all year.
PRICES: s €53; d €58-€61; t €69 **ON SITE:** Fishing Tennis **NEARBY:** Bathing (8km) Horse riding (7km) Sea (48km) Swimming pool (15km) Stretch of water (8km) Railway station (25km) FONTENAY LE COMTE (13km) **NOTES:** No pets English spoken

♦♦♦ ♥ La Genîte Paul QUILLET
85420 MAILLEZAIS
☎ 02 51 00 71 17 📠 02 51 00 71 17
L'abbaye St-Pierre de Maillezais 3 km. Yvette and Paul completely renovated this ancient shell of a farmhouse 10 years ago and have since made four guest rooms available: one family room for four upstairs, complete with bathroom and wc; two doubles with single and two doubles, all with en suite shower rooms and wc on the ground floor. Use of sitting room with fireplace, living room, garden and outdoor seating area. Barge trips through the Marais-Poitevin available on site. Open all year.
PRICES: s €35; d €38; t €47; extra person €10 **ON SITE:** Fishing **NEARBY:** Bathing (18km) Horse riding (3km) Sea (50km) Swimming pool (7km) Stretch of water (18km) Tennis (3km) Shops (3km) Railway station (25km) FONTENAY LE COMTE (15km) **NOTES:** No pets

♦♦♦ ✿ Le Censif Gabriel ROBIN
85420 MAILLEZAIS
☎ 02 51 00 71 50 📠 02 51 00 71 50

L'abbaye St-Pierre de Maillezais 2 km. Discover the beauty and peace of the Marais-Poitevin in this authentic 17th-century farmhouse. Owners Jeanette and Gaby offer three very comfortable guest rooms, all furnished with antiques: one double, two doubles and single, one with mezzanine. All have private bathroom and wc, and have independent access. Folding bed available. Communal living room with TV, kitchen and washing area. Use of garden, terrace, surrounded by meadows and a working farm. Open all year.

PRICES: s €30; d €32-€38; t €40-€47; extra person €9

ON SITE: Children's play area Fishing **NEARBY:** Bathing (15km) Horse riding (5km) Sea (45km) Swimming pool (5km) Stretch of water (15km) Hiking (1km) Tennis (2km) Shops (2km) Railway station (25km) FONTENAY LE COMTE (12km) **NOTES:** No pets

---

MARTINET

♦♦♦ ✿ ⦿ Montmarin
Martial & Françoise FORTINEAU
85150 MARTINET
☎ 02 51 34 62 88 📠 02 51 34 65 52

Les Sables-d'Olonne 20 km. Situated in a leafy spot near the sea, this is a working farm. The four guest rooms are in the recently renovated 19th-century farmhouse, above the owner's home. Two doubles, one double with single and one with two doubles, all with private shower room and wc. Guests' living room with kitchen and washing area available. Dinner on reservation (except Fridays). Pond, outdoor seating area, parking. Animals allowed. Open 1 April to 1 November.

PRICES: s €31; d €37; t €46; extra person €9; dinner €13

ON SITE: Fishing Stretch of water **NEARBY:** Horse riding (4km) Golf (15km) Sea (20km) Swimming pool (10km) Tennis (4km) Shops (4km) Railway station (5km) LES SABLES D'OLONNE (20km) **NOTES:** Pets admitted

---

MONSIREIGNE

♦♦♦ ✿ La Baudonnière John COLLINSON
85110 MONSIREIGNE
☎ 02 51 66 43 79 📠 02 51 66 43 79
e-mail: wjsjfrance@aol.com

Chantonnay 20 km. Le Puy-du-Fou 20 km. Lac de Rochereau 3 km. This elegant 16th-century manor house is located on a farm in the heart of the Vendée forests and has four guest rooms, all with independent entrance. Two doubles with extra single and two double with twin beds, all with en suite bath or shower rooms and wc. One with kitchen area. Use of dining room and sitting room with TV and fireplace. Shops 1 km, restaurants 2-4km. Open all year.

PRICES: s €34; d €38-€42; t €51-€54; extra person €12

ON SITE: Fishing Hiking **NEARBY:** Bathing (5km) Horse riding (6km)

Golf (30km) Sea (60km) Swimming pool (2km) Stretch of water (5km) Tennis (1km) Shops (12km) Railway station (12km) CHANTONNAY (12km) **NOTES:** No pets English spoken

---

MOUZEUIL-ST-MARTIN

♦♦♦ ✿ La Verronnerie Jocelyne DIBOT
85370 MOUZEUIL-ST-MARTIN
☎ 02 51 28 71 98 & 06 14 58 65 37 📠 02 51 28 71 98
e-mail: dibot.jocelyne@terre-net.fr

L'abbaye St-Pierre de Maillezais 20 km. Enjoy the peace of the country in this turn-of-the-last-century house surrounded by an arable farm. Owner Jocelyne welcomes guests to her three recently decorated guest rooms: one double, one with double and twin beds, and one with double and single, all with private shower rooms and wc and independent access. Use of guests' own living room with TV and kitchen area, garden with seating area. Animals accepted on reservation. Open all year.

PRICES: s €24-€28; d €28-€31; t €39-€45; extra person €8

NEARBY: Bathing (15km) Horse riding (10km) Sea (30km) Fishing (5km) Swimming pool (10km) Stretch of water (10km) Hiking (2km) Tennis (2km) Shops (2km) Railway station (15km) FONTENAY LE COMTE (14km) **NOTES:** Pets admitted

---

NIEUL-LE-DOLENT

♦♦♦ ✿ Les Sorinières Patrick & Françoise BOURON
85430 NIEUL-LE-DOLENT
☎ 02 51 07 91 58 & 02 51 07 93 46 📠 02 51 07 94 78
e-mail: bouronp@club-internet.fr

Les Sables-d'Olonne 20 km. Le Puy-du-Fou 75 km. Only 15 minutes from the Sables d'Olonne, this distinctive 1920s farmhouse offers a relaxed and simple atmosphere. It has four guest rooms: one with two doubles, one double with single and two doubles. All rooms have private shower rooms and wc. Use of reception room, sitting room with TV and kitchen. Camping and holiday cottages also on site. Private pool (open 1 June to 30 September). Restaurant 2km. Open all year.

PRICES: s €30; d €39; t €48; extra person €10 **ON SITE:** Swimming pool **NEARBY:** Horse riding (5km) Golf (20km) Sea (20km) Fishing (3km) Stretch of water (8km) Tennis (2km) Shops (2km) Railway station (17km) LA ROCHE SUR YON (18km) **NOTES:** No pets

continued

NIEUL-SUR-L'AUTIZE

Le Rosier Sauvage Christine CHASTAIN-POUPIN
1 rue de l'Abbaye, 85240 NIEUL-SUR-L'AUTIZE
☎ 02 51 52 49 39 ▤ 02 51 52 49 46
At the entrance to the Marais-Poitevin, opposite the Royal Abbey, stands this delightful 18th-century townhouse, with four comfortable and charmingly decorated guest rooms: two double and two with double and single, all with private shower rooms and wc. Guest sitting room with library, TV and fireplace. Garden with table and chairs. Breakfast in a superbly renovated former stable. Restaurants nearby. Open all year.
PRICES: s €32-€35; d €41-€44; t €50-€53 **ON SITE:** Hiking Tennis **NEARBY:** Bathing (10km) Horse riding (11km) Golf (60km) Sea (60km) Fishing (15km) Swimming pool (11km) Stretch of water (10km) Railway station (25km) FONTENAY LE COMTE (10km) **NOTES:** No pets English spoken

NOIRMOUTIER

Chambre d'hôtes Mauricette BARANGER
8 rue de la Mougendrie, 85330 NOIRMOUTIER-EN-L'ILE
☎ 02 51 39 12 59 ▤ 02 51 39 12 59
Challans 40 km. This turn-of-the-last-century house is situated near the old castle and the port. It has five guest rooms: the four upstairs are doubles with balcony; the ground-floor room is also a double. All rooms have en suite bath or shower room and wc. Use of living room, sitting room with fireplace, small garden, terrace with seating area. Get to the island by bridge or barge. Free parking 50m. Restaurants nearby. Open 1 April to 15 September.
PRICES: s €38; d €44 **NEARBY:** Horse riding (1km) Golf (30km) Sea (1km) Fishing (1km) Hiking (1km) Tennis (1km) Railway station (40km) CHALLANS (40km) **NOTES:** No pets

REAUMUR

La Pillaudière Alphonse & Augusta SACHOT
85700 REAUMUR
☎ 02 51 65 88 69
Le Puy-du-Fou 25 km. Marais-Poitevin 60 km. In the midst of peaceful countryside, this stylish house offers three guest rooms: one double, one with double and single, one with double and folding bed. Each has private shower room and wc. Use of outdoor seating area, parking. Animals accepted on reservation. Nearby: Vouvant-Mervent and Futuroscope. Open all year.
PRICES: s €33; d €36; t €48; dinner €13 **ON SITE:** Hiking **NEARBY:** Bathing (7km) Horse riding (8km) Golf (30km) Sea (80km) Fishing (2km) Swimming pool (7km) Stretch of water (7km) Tennis (8km) Shops (2km) Railway station (5km) LES HERBIERS (25km) **NOTES:** Pets admitted

ST-CHRISTOPHE-DU-LIGNERON

La Vergne Neuve Marylène BOURMAUD
85670 ST-CHRISTOPHE-DU-LIGNERON
☎ 02 51 93 32 52 ▤ 02 51 93 17 08
St-Gilles-Croix-de-Vie 15 km. Dating from 1880, this farmhouse is close to the sea and surrounded by peaceful countryside. The four guest rooms have been carefully restored, leaving the original walls and beams exposed and are furnished with antiques. All rooms have double and single beds, private shower room and wc. Folding bed available. Use of guest living room/kitchen, outdoor seating, fish pond. Open all year.
PRICES: s €35; d €39; t €48 **ON SITE:** Children's play area Fishing **NEARBY:** Bathing (5km) Horse riding (1km) Golf (15km) Sea (18km) Swimming pool (5km) Stretch of water (5km) Tennis (4km) Shops (4km) Railway station (10km) CHALLANS (9km) **NOTES:** No pets

L'Hubertière Gérard & Michelle LOIZEAU
85670 ST-CHRISTOPHE-DU-LIGNERON
☎ 02 51 35 06 41 ▤ 02 51 49 87 43
e-mail: michelle.loizeau@terre-net.fr
Le Puy-du-Fou 70 km. Only 20 minutes from the ocean and in the heart of the Vendée, Gérard and Michelle welcome you to their friendly 18th-century home. This working farm has four guest rooms: two with double and single, and one with two doubles and a single, are in the main farmhouse. Double with kitchen located in converted stable. All rooms have en suite shower rooms and wc. TV available. Open 15 March to 15 November.
PRICES: s €34; d €42; t €52; extra person €11; dinner €15 **ON SITE:** Children's play area **NEARBY:** Bathing (15km) Horse riding (7km) Golf (15km) Sea (20km) Fishing (7km) Swimming pool (7km) Stretch of water (5km) Hiking (1km) Tennis (7km) Shops (7km) Railway station (15km) CHALLANS (15km) **NOTES:** Pets admitted

ST-CYR-EN-TALMONDAIS

La Maison Neuve
Gérard & Marie-Renée MASSON
85540 ST-CYR-EN-TALMONDAIS
☎ 02 51 30 80 13 ▤ 02 51 30 89 37
e-mail: massong@85.cernet.fr
St-Vincent-sur-Jard 18 km. Located on the borders of the Marrais fen-lands, in a protected area, this farmhouse has four guest rooms: on the ground floor is a double with single and own entrance. Upstairs, two more with double and single and one double. All rooms have private shower, wc and TV. Use of reception room with TV, meadow, children's games. Open all year. 2.5km from town along D949.
PRICES: s €34; d €39-€42; t €47; dinner €13 **ON SITE:** Children's play area Hiking **NEARBY:** Golf (25km) Sea (12km) Fishing (3km) Swimming pool (16km) Stretch of water (8km) Tennis (3km) Shops (3km) Railway station (16km) LUCON (15km) **NOTES:** No pets

STE-HERMINE

La Barre Marie-Elisabeth CAREIL
Route de St-Juire Champgillon, 85210 STE-HERMINE
☎ 02 51 27 85 18
Le Puy-du-Fou 45 km. This picturesque 16th-century country house stands at the entrance of a hunting lodge, near the traditional market town of St-Juire-Champgillon. It offers three guest rooms, all with double beds, showers and wcs. One with own kitchenette. Use of sitting room with TV, library, games, well-kept grounds with seating area, table tennis, and bikes. Dinner by reservation. Reduced rates after three nights. Open all year.
PRICES: s €26; d €32; dinner €11 **NEARBY:** Bathing (15km) Horse riding (10km) Sea (40km) Fishing (3km) Swimming pool (4km) Stretch of water (15km) Hiking (4km) Tennis (4km) Shops (4km) Railway station (15km) LUCON (15km) **NOTES:** No pets

ST-FLORENT-DES-BOIS

Le Plessis Tesselin J-Pierre & M-Alice ROUX
85310 ST-FLORENT-DES-BOIS
☎ 02 51 31 91 12 & 02 51 46 72 22 ▤ 02 51 46 72 22
Le Puy-du-Fou 50 km. In a rural setting, near La Roche sur Yon, this guest house has three rooms, as well as six camping places. Each room has a double bed, shower room and wc. Folding bed available. Use of cosy sitting room with TV, living room, outdoor seating area, fishing lake, play area. Dinner available on reservation. Open all year.
PRICES: s €30; d €36; dinner €13 **ON SITE:** Children's play area Fishing Stretch of water Hiking **NEARBY:** Horse riding (4km) Golf (6km) Sea (35km) Swimming pool (10km) Tennis (3km) Shops (3km) Railway station (10km) LA ROCHE SUR YON (10km) **NOTES:** No pets

ST-GERVAIS

🏠 🐦 Le Pas de l'Ile Henri & M-Thérèse PITAUD
85230 ST-GERVAIS

☎ 02 51 68 78 51 📠 02 51 68 42 01

Ile de Noirmoutier 12 km. This ancient house, surrounded by open countryside, is right of the edge of the Breton Marais. The owners, Marie-Thérèse and Henri, offer a warm welcome to their three guest rooms, each of which has double and single beds, shower room and wc, and are furnished with local antiques. Use of living room with kitchen area and TV, well-kept grounds, lake, boats and bikes. Farm produce available. Open Easter to 1 November.

PRICES: s €35; d €40; t €50 **ON SITE:** Fishing Hiking **NEARBY:** Horse riding (4km) Golf (10km) Sea (6km) Swimming pool (3km) Tennis (3km) Shops (3km) Railway station (15km) CHALLANS (12km) **NOTES:** No pets

ST-JEAN-DE-MONTS

🏠 La Bourrine Isabelle BERNARD
184 avenue d'Orouet, 85160 ST-JEAN-DE-MONTS

☎ 02 51 59 55 31

Ile de Noirmoutier 15 km. This traditional house, situated between St Jean de Monts and St Gilles Croix de Vie, was recently fully renovated. It has three guest rooms, all provided with antique furniture, with views over the Marais. One room with double and single beds, disabled access; one double; one twin. All have shower room and wc. Walled garden with outdoor seating. Private parking. Restaurants nearby. Open 25 March to 6 October.

PRICES: s €38-€41; d €38-€41; t €46-€50 **NEARBY:** Horse riding (4km) Golf (10km) Sea (3km) Fishing (3km) Swimming pool (8km) Stretch of water (20km) Hiking (8km) Tennis (11km) Shops (1km) Railway station (8km) ST GILLES CROIX DE VIE (8km) **NOTES:** No pets

ST-JULIEN-DES-LANDES

🏠 🐦 🍴 Les Suries Alain & Monique GROSSIN
85150 ST-JULIEN-DES-LANDES

☎ 02 51 46 64 02 & 06 86 67 35 20 📠 02 51 46 64 02

e-mail: monique-et-alain.grossin@wanadoo.fr

Le Puy-du-Fou 80 km. Only a few minutes from the ocean, this farmhouse enjoys a beautiful wooded location. It offers three guest rooms, recently decorated: one with double and one with double and single in the main house, and one with two doubles in a converted barn. All have private shower room, wc and TV. Dinner by reservation. Holiday cottage and fishing pond also on site. Open all year.

PRICES: s €31; d €39; t €47; extra person €8; dinner €13

ON SITE: Fishing Hiking **NEARBY:** Bathing (15km) Horse riding (5km) Golf (20km) Sea (15km) Swimming pool (15km) Stretch of water (5km) Tennis (2km) Shops (2km) Railway station (5km) LES SABLES D'OLONNE (20km) **NOTES:** Pets admitted

ST-MALO-DU-BOIS

🏠 🐦 🍴 Les Montys André & Régina FRUCHET
85590 ST-MALO-DU-BOIS

☎ 02 51 92 34 12 📠 02 51 64 62 45

Le Puy-du-Fou 7 km. Situated in the heart of a fascinating rural tourist region, this 19th-century guest house offers a warm welcome and pleasant atmosphere. Les Montys has five rooms, all with en suite shower room and wc: one with two doubles, two with double and single, two doubles. Two have their own entrance. Use of upstairs sitting room with TV and kitchen area, shared living room with old fireplace, TV, kitchen and washing area. Dinner by reservation (except Sunday, Monday and Tuesday). Open all year.

PRICES: s €27; d €37; t €47; extra person €8; dinner €14

ON SITE: Fishing Hiking **NEARBY:** Horse riding (4km) Golf (15km) Sea (90km) Swimming pool (8km) Tennis (2km) Shops (2km) Railway station (15km) LES HERBIERS (16km) **NOTES:** No pets

ST-MATHURIN

🏠 Château de la Millière
Claude & Danielle HUNEAULT
85150 ST-MATHURIN

☎ 02 51 22 73 29 📠 02 51 22 73 29

This elegant 19th-century building houses five guest rooms: four double rooms and one suite of two double rooms. All have private bathroom and wc. Guests are welcome to use library, billiard room, TV, telephone and swimming pool. Terrace with outdoor seating, fishing pond, bikes, barbecue, table tennis all on site. Restaurants nearby. Open 1 May to 30 September.

PRICES: s €87; d €95; t €110; extra person €15 **ON SITE:** Fishing Swimming pool **NEARBY:** Horse riding (8km) Golf (3km) Sea (10km) Tennis (1km) Shops (1km) Railway station (10km) LES SABLES D'OLONNE (8km) **NOTES:** No pets English spoken

ST-MICHEL-EN-L'HERM

🏠 🐦 Basse Brenée Michel & M-Noëlle ARDOUIN
85580 ST-MICHEL-EN-L'HERM

☎ 02 51 30 24 09 📠 02 51 30 24 09

e-mail: michel.ardouin@free.fr

La Rochelle 45 km. Marie-Noëlle and Michel offer a warm welcome to their 18th-century Marais farmhouse in its tranquil, rural setting. There are three guest rooms, all with private shower rooms and wc: one with double, one with two doubles and a single, and a completely separate double room with kitchen and sofa. Use of sitting room with equipped kitchen area, games room. Camping on site. Restaurants nearby. Open all year.

PRICES: s €27-€34; d €32-€38; t €41-€47; extra person €9

ON SITE: Hiking **NEARBY:** Bathing (7km) Horse riding (7km) Golf (35km) Sea (8km) Fishing (2km) Swimming pool (15km) Stretch of water (2km) Tennis (3km) Shops (3km) Railway station (15km) LUCON (15km) **NOTES:** Pets admitted

ST-MICHEL-LE-CLOUCQ

🏠 🐦 Bel Air J-Christian & M-Jo BOURDIN
78 rue de la Mairie, 85200 ST-MICHEL-LE-CLOUCQ

☎ 02 51 69 24 24 & 06 82 71 95 40 📠 02 51 69 24 24

Marais-Poitevin 15 km. Located in a small market town between the Marais-Poitevin and the great forest of Mervent, this 1850 farmhouse has recently been fully renovated, but is still full of character. It offers three guest rooms: two doubles and one double with extra single bed, all with private shower room and wc. Use of shared living room, outdoor seating area. Holiday cottage also on site. Rates decrease for longer stays. Open all year.

PRICES: s €33; d €40; t €50 **NEARBY:** Bathing (5km) Horse riding (5km) Sea (60km) Fishing (3km) Swimming pool (5km) Stretch of water (5km) Tennis (1km) Shops (5km) Railway station (30km) FONTENAY LE COMTE (5km) **NOTES:** No pets

ST-PAUL-EN-PAREDS

⬗⬗⬗ 🐓 La Gelletière Charly MERLET
85500 ST-PAUL-EN-PAREDS
☎ 02 51 92 00 43 & 02 51 92 00 25 📠 02 51 92 00 43

Le Puy-du-Fou 15 km. This former barn, converted in 1999 to include the owner's home, a holiday cottage and five guestrooms, is located on a working farm. There is one double room and four double with extra single, all with en suite shower room and wc and their own entrance. Use of shared living room with kitchen area, private pool (open June to October), and leafy picnic area beside river. Restaurant 3km. Open May to September.
PRICES: s €30; d €41; t €53 **ON SITE:** Fishing Swimming pool Hiking
NEARBY: Bathing (10km) Horse riding (8km) Golf (30km) Sea (70km) Stretch of water (10km) Tennis (2km) Shops (8km) Railway station (30km) LES HERBIERS (6km) **NOTES:** No pets

ST-PIERRE-LE-VIEUX

⬗⬗⬗ 🐓 Les Ecluseaux Chrystèle PEPIN
Les Bas, 85420 ST-PIERRE-LE-VIEUX
☎ 02 51 00 76 14 📠 02 51 00 76 14
e-mail: pepin.eric.christelle@wanadoo.fr
www.ferme-ecluzeaux.com
L'abbaye St-Pierre de Maillezais 3 km. You'll find peace and relaxation on this organic farm in the heart of the Marais-Poitevin fen-lands. There are three guest rooms, all with independent entrance, shower room and wc: two doubles with extra single and another double. Use of living room with kitchen area. Homemade breakfast with produce from farm. Camping and boat trips on site. Restaurants 3km. Open all year.
PRICES: s €27; d €38; t €49 **ON SITE:** Fishing Hiking
NEARBY: Bathing (15km) Horse riding (10km) Sea (50km) Swimming pool (10km) Stretch of water (15km) Tennis (3km) Shops (3km) Railway station (22km) FONTENAY LE COMTE (12km) **NOTES:** No pets

ST-VINCENT-SUR-JARD

⬗⬗⬗ 🐓 Les Chabosselières Bernadette FIROME
24 route de Jard, 85520 ST-VINCENT-SUR-JARD
☎ 02 51 33 43 32
St-Vincent-sur-Jard 1.5 km. This modern house, surrounded by a spacious, well-tended park, is situated in a little hamlet on the Vendée coast. It offers three double-bedded rooms, all recently redecorated. All rooms have private bath or shower rooms and wc. Folding bed available. Use of sitting room with TV and kitchenette, terrace with seating, shaded parking. Open 15 November to 30 September.
PRICES: s €35-€38; d €40-€44; extra person €10 **ON SITE:** Hiking
NEARBY: Bathing (14km) Horse riding (1km) Golf (12km) Sea (2km) Fishing (2km) Swimming pool (2km) Stretch of water (3km) Tennis (1km) Shops (1km) Railway station (20km) LES SABLES D'OLONNE (20km)
NOTES: No pets

TALMONT-ST-HILAIRE

⬗⬗⬗ 🐓 La Pinière Bertrand CARAYOL
85440 TALMONT-ST-HILAIRE
☎ 02 51 22 25 66 & 06 70 30 55 16
St-Vincent-sur-Jard 15 km. This renovated farmhouse is surrounded by an organic farm in a beautiful wooded valley. It houses four guest rooms; two doubles and two doubles with extra single. All have their own entrance and en suite shower room and wc. Use of a shared sitting room with fireplace. Holiday cottage, riding courses and fishing available on site. Rabbit hunts available by reservation from October to January. Open all year.
PRICES: s €32; d €40; t €54 **NEARBY:** Horse riding (5km) Golf (3km) Sea (3km) Fishing (2km) Swimming pool (2km) Tennis (1km) Shops (1km) Railway station (12km) LES SABLES D'OLONNE (12km)
NOTES: Pets admitted

⬗⬗⬗ 🐓 🍴 Les Touillères Gilles & Annie PAPON
85440 TALMONT-ST-HILAIRE
☎ 02 51 90 24 02
St-Vincent-sur-Jard 8 km. Annie and Gilles welcome you to their farmhouse in the heart of the countryside, near the sea. They offer four guest rooms: one double, one double with extra single and two superb family rooms. One in the ancient farmhouse, with double and twin beds. The other, in a converted barn, also with double and twin beds. All have private shower rooms and wc. Cot available. Leafy grounds with seating area. Two holiday cottages also on site. Dinner by reservation (except Sundays). Open all year.
PRICES: s €30; d €35; t €42; extra person €8; dinner €13
ON SITE: Fishing **NEARBY:** Horse riding (10km) Golf (8km) Sea (6km) Swimming pool (10km) Stretch of water (4km) Tennis (4km) Shops (4km) Railway station (16km) LES SABLES D'OLONNE (16km)
NOTES: Pets admitted

PICARDY

PICARDY

AISNE

BERRIEUX

🎏 🐓 🍽 Ferme du Jardin Monsieur Gilles PAYEN
12, rue de la Fontaine, 02820 BERRIEUX
☎ 03 23 22 42 41 📠 03 23 22 42 41

Laon 20 km. Reims 35 km. Three spacious, comfortable first-floor rooms in an old stable block on a farm, in a little village between Laon and Reims with a forest nearby. One room with a double and a single bed, a family room for five people with one double bed and three singles, additional bed available, one double room with a sitting area. Each has a private shower room and wc. Lounge with television, dining room, garden with furniture and barbecue and enclosed courtyard with parking. Children up to 10 years €12.20. Five people €76.22. Table d'hotes with drinks included, reservations necessary. Open 15 January to 15 December.
PRICES: s €29; d €38; extra person €15; dinner €14 **ON SITE:** Children's play area Hiking **NEARBY:** Horse riding (1km) Golf (15km) Fishing (15km) Swimming pool (10km) Stretch of water (15km) Tennis (15km) Sailing (15km) Railway station (4km) Shops (4km) **NOTES:** No pets CC

BONY

🎏 Ferme du Vieux Puits Philippe GYSELINCK
5 bis, rue de l'Abbaye, 02420 BONY
☎ 03 23 66 22 33 📠 03 23 66 25 27

Three spacious and comfortable rooms above a farm hotel, all with private facilities, hairdryers, telephone and satellite television. Two rooms with a double and a single bed, one twin room. Lounge and kitchenette for guest use with independent access. Other facilities include a heated swimming pool (open 1 May-30 September), garden furniture, a terrace, five mountain bikes, table tennis, volley ball and mini basketball court. Open all year.
PRICES: s €35; d €50; t €67; extra person €14; dinner €16; HB €46; FB €59 **ON SITE:** Wine tasting Children's play area Swimming pool Hiking Tennis **NEARBY:** Horse riding (10km) Golf (15km) Fishing (6km) Railway station (15km) Shops (2km) Restaurant nearby **NOTES:** Pets admitted

BRAYE-EN-LAONNOIS

🎏 🍽 Chambre d'hôtes David KAZMAREK
2, rue de l'Eglise, 02000 BRAYE-EN-LAONNOIS
☎ 03 23 25 68 55

Laon 20 km, Chemin des Dames. A peaceful location, surrounded by greenery, this establishment offers four spacious rooms on an old Picardy village farm, each with a private shower room and wc. Two double rooms, one room for three people with a double and a single bed, one room for four people with one double and two single beds. A free child bed is available on request. The facilities include a large communal lounge with fireplace, a cooker, enclosed parking, private courtyard and garden and generous breakfasts. Open all year.
PRICES: s €200; d €250; t €350; extra person €60; dinner €95 **NEARBY:** Golf (6km) Fishing (6km) Swimming pool (20km) Stretch of water (6km) Tennis (6km) Sailing (6km) Railway station (20km) Shops (10km) **NOTES:** No pets

BRUYERES-SUR-FERE

🎏 🍽 Val Chrétien Jean et Nariko SION
02130 BRUYERES-SUR-FERE
☎ 03 23 71 66 71 📠 03 23 71 66 71
e-mail: val.chretien@wanadoo.fr

Reims 50 km. Eurodisney 80 km. Roissy 90 km. Paris 110 km. Peaceful surroundings in the remains of an abbey. Three twin rooms and one double room each with their own shower room and wc. One large double room with bathroom and private wc. Lounge with fireplace, two dining rooms with television. Table d'hôtes by reservation using local produce with Japanese food a speciality. Near to scenic and historic routes with Fére-en-Tardenois at 7 km and Château-Thierry 15 km. Open all year.
PRICES: s €40; d €50-€59; extra person €25; dinner €20 **ON SITE:** Children's play area Fishing Stretch of water Hiking Tennis **NEARBY:** Horse riding (7km) Golf (15km) Swimming pool (15km) Railway station (7km) Shops (6km) **NOTES:** No pets English spoken

BURELLES

🎏 ♿ Chambre d'hôtes Georges LOUVET
4, rue de la Fontaine, 02140 BURELLES
☎ 03 23 90 03 03 📠 03 23 90 03 03

Reims 75 km. Set in the middle of the village, in the heart of Thiérache, with its fortified churches, are three rooms with two double beds and two single beds each with their own shower room and wc. There is a day room with television. An additional bed is available for children up to 10 years. Children €10.67, adults €15.25. Inn 200 m away. Open all year.
PRICES: s €29; d €40; t €16; extra person €11-€16 **NEARBY:** Golf (15km) Fishing (7km) Swimming pool (20km) Hiking (6km) Tennis (6km) Railway station (5km) Shops (5km) **NOTES:** Pets admitted

CHERET

🎏 🍽 Le Clos Cheret Monique SIMONNOT
02860 CHERET
☎ 03 23 24 80 64

An 18th-century winery surrounded by a large park. Two grade 2 rooms with a double and twin beds, each with a washbasin, sharing a shower room and wc. Cot available. One room for three to five people with own bathroom and wc. One double room with shower room and wc. One twin room on the ground floor with private shower room and wc. Day room, lounge, library, parking, table tennis. Family table d'hôte by prior arrangement with wine included - except for Sunday evenings. Open 15 March to 15 October. Other times by reservation only (no table d'hôte).
PRICES: s €30-€38; d €34-€46; extra person €15; dinner €15 **ON SITE:** Children's play area Hiking **NEARBY:** Golf (8km) Fishing (8km) Swimming pool (8km) Stretch of water (7km) Tennis (8km) Sailing (8km) Railway station (7km) Shops (2km) **NOTES:** No pets

CONNIGIS

🎏 🍽 Ferme du Château Pierre et Jeanine LECLERE
02330 CONNIGIS
☎ 03 23 71 90 51 📠 03 23 71 48 57

Expect a friendly winegrower's welcome to the ancient château's farm in the village. Five spacious rooms, two doubles, two for three people, and each with their own bathroom and wc. One en

continued

suite double room with a lounge is in a tower. Table d'hote meals available if reserved, including drinks with a champagne aperitif. On site - a billiard room, a large wooded park, bicycles to hire, footpaths (GR14, PR), top quality fishing, local produce for sale. There is a €3.05 heating supplement per room between 1 October and 31 March. On the Champagne tourist route and 50 minutes from Disneyland Paris. Open all year.
PRICES: s €30-€37; d €37-€46; t €52; extra person €15-€18; dinner €14 **ON SITE:** Children's play area Fishing **NEARBY:** Horse riding (10km) Golf (15km) Swimming pool (10km) Stretch of water (15km) Tennis (3km) Sailing (10km) **NOTES:** No pets CC

CUIRY-HOUSSE

ﾙﾙﾙ ⏀ Chambre d'hôtes Jean-Louis MASSUE
6 rue de Soissons, 02220 CUIRY-HOUSSE
☎ 03 23 55 01 06 & 06 08 84 37 87 ▤ 03 23 55 01 06
e-mail: http://perso.wanadoo.fr/Cuiry-housse
Soissons 16 km. Reims 48 km. Paris 100 km. A tranquil, pastoral environment 25 km from the Paris-Strasbourg, Calais-Lyon-Paris-Lille motorways and one hour from Disneyland Paris. Four rooms with their own facilities, wc and television in a huge, completely renovated house built in 1874. Three double rooms, one family room with double bed and two singles. Large communal room, covered garage, terrace, summer kitchen, large park and bicycles. Evening table d'hôte meals can be reserved. Open all year.
PRICES: d €46; extra person €15; dinner €15 **ON SITE:** Wine tasting Children's play area Hiking **NEARBY:** Horse riding (15km) Golf (20km) Fishing (8km) Swimming pool (15km) Stretch of water (15km) Tennis (8km) Sailing (8km) Railway station (18km) Shops (6km)
NOTES: No pets

EPARCY

ﾙﾙﾙ ⏀ Chambre d'hôtes Nathalie POINTIER
7, route de Landouzy, 02500 EPARCY
☎ 03 23 98 46 17
Eparcy is a typical small village in the heart of the Thiérarche, halfway between Paris and Brussels. Five rooms in a large mansion set in peaceful, wooded parkland that stretches to the banks of the River Thon, where you can fish. There are three double rooms - one with twin beds - each has a private shower, the wc is shared. An extra bed and child's bed is available. Two further double rooms each with their own bathroom and wc. Set price table d'hôte meals by reservation, 32 euros for two adults and one child. Full facilities in Hirson, 5 km away, and the Tilleul 18-hole golf course 3 km away. Open all year.
PRICES: s €24; d €35-€38; extra person €12; dinner €12
ON SITE: Fishing Hiking **NEARBY:** Horse riding (5km) Golf (3km) Swimming pool (5km) Tennis (5km) Sailing (35km) Railway station (5km) Shops (5km) **NOTES:** No pets

ETOUVELLES

ﾙﾙﾙ ⏀ Chambre d'hôtes Isabelle TRICHET
24, route de Paris, 02000 ETOUVELLES
☎ 03 23 20 15 72
e-mail: www.multimania.com/aubonaccueil/
Laon 2 km. Chemin des dames 10 km. Reims 50 km. Five spacious, themed, ground-floor rooms with an independent entrance in a house with character. The accommodation ranges from a simple twin room, a double room with a canopied bed and two-person spa bath, a room with a double bed and open fire and two double-bedded rooms with sitting area and space for an extra bed. All rooms have private facilities. Large games room with billiards, pinball machine, table football and darts. Table d'hôte meals may be reserved, drinks not included. Large park with pond, a river, children's games and parking. Open all year.

PRICES: s €42-€48; d €46-€52; extra person €15; dinner €16 **ON SITE:** Children's play area Fishing Hiking **NEARBY:** Horse riding (2km) Golf (17km) Swimming pool (3km) Stretch of water (8km) Tennis (2km) Sailing (17km) Railway station (3km) Shops (2km) **NOTES:** No pets

FERE-EN-TARDENOIS

ﾙﾙﾙ ⏀ Chambre d'hôtes Martine DESRUELLE
13, rue du Château, 02130 FERE-EN-TARDENOIS
☎ 03 23 82 30 39

Château-Thierry 25 km. Reims 50 km. Just 1¼ hours from Paris and 45 minutes from Disneyland Paris this beautiful house is set in a large park with a lake near the town centre. There are two double rooms, one twin room and one room with three single beds. A child's bed is available for 11 euros. Each room has private facilities - three with shower rooms, one with a bathroom. Meals are available though drinks are not included. There is a lounge with fireplace, an enclosed flower garden and a swimming pool open from June to September. Open all year except January.
PRICES: s €30; d €41; t €56; extra person €15; dinner €14
ON SITE: Children's play area Fishing Swimming pool Hiking
NEARBY: Horse riding (1km) Golf (15km) Stretch of water (2km) Tennis (2km) Sailing (2km) Railway station (1km) **NOTES:** No pets English spoken

ﾙﾙﾙ Clairbois François CHAUVIN
02130 FERE-EN-TARDENOIS
☎ 03 23 82 21 72 ▤ 03 23 82 62 84
Paris 90 km. Disneyland Paris 75 km. Reims 45 km. Epernay 45 km. This beautifully situated property is just off the Champagne trail near the Château de Fere-en-Tardenois. There is a large lake on-site to walk around or to boat on and a tennis court for guest use. The three rooms all have private bathrooms, one room is a double, one a twin and one a family room. There is a lounge for guests and meals are available if reserved - minimum 4/5 people at 16 euros per person. Open all year.
PRICES: s €40-€46; d €46-€55; t €69-€77; extra person €23
ON SITE: Children's play area Fishing Stretch of water Tennis
NEARBY: Horse riding (3km) Golf (23km) Swimming pool (23km) Railway station (3km) Shops (1km) **NOTES:** No pets English spoken

LA CHAPELLE-MONTHODON

ﾙﾙﾙ Hameau de Chezy Christian DOUARD
02330 LA CHAPELLE-MONTHODON
☎ 03 23 82 47 66 ▤ 03 23 82 72 96
Peaceful surroundings with a countryside view. Four double rooms with their own bathroom and wc. One family room with one double and two single beds with own bathroom and wc. There is independent access and safe parking at the farm. Other facilities are a charming lounge for guest use, a games room, a television, and mountain bike hire. Champagne tasting possible, and a glass is offered as an aperitif. Drinks not included in the meal price. Available for meetings and conferences. Golf and archery 2 km.

continued　　　　　　　　　　　　　　*continued*

Mini-golf 5 km. Open all year except January and February.
PRICES: s €35; d €43; t €61; extra person €9; dinner €13
ON SITE: Wine tasting **NEARBY:** Horse riding (5km) Golf (2km)
Swimming pool (5km) Hiking (2km) Tennis (5km) Railway station (5km)
Shops (5km) **NOTES:** No pets CC

LE CHARMEL

⁙ Chambre d'hôtes Gaston ASSAILLY
6, route du Moulin, 02850 LE CHARMEL
☎ 03 23 70 31 27 🖷 03 23 70 15 08

Rooms in a little village near the Marne Valley. Two double rooms,
two twin rooms, one triple room for adults with own shower room
and wc. Telephone in each room, television, kitchen for guest use,
secure parking, large well-kept garden with furniture and trail
bikes for hire. Exit A4 16 km. Places to eat nearby. Open all year.
PRICES: s €38; d €43-€46; t €73.50 **ON SITE:** Tennis
NEARBY: Golf (12km) Fishing (3km) Railway station (16km) Shops
(3km) **NOTES:** No pets

L'EPINE-AUX-BOIS

⁙ 🍽 Les Patrus Marc et Mary-Ann ROYOL
Domaine des Patrus, La Haute Epine,
02540 L'EPINE-AUX-BOIS
☎ 03 23 69 85 85 🖷 03 23 69 98 49
e-mail: contact@domainedespatrus.com
Disneyland Paris 45 km. A large farm dating back to the 17th
century, deep in the countryside of Brie-Champenoise, between
Ferté-sous-Jouarre and Montmirail, and just one hour from Paris.
Five large, comfortable and quiet rooms each with their own
facilities. The house has a reading/music room, a large enclosed
courtyard and stables. Surrounded by walks through beautiful
fields, meadows, woods and ponds. Table d'hôte meals can be
reserved. An on-site exhibition of the Fables of La Fontaine is open
between April and October (closed Tuesdays). Visa and Mastercard
accepted. Open all year.
PRICES: d €65-€80; extra person €21; dinner €28 **ON SITE:** Wine
tasting Fishing **NEARBY:** Horse riding (15km) Golf (18km) Swimming
pool (20km) Tennis (3km) **NOTES:** No pets CC

MONDREPUIS

⁙ 🍽 L'Arbre Vert Réjane DUGAUQUIER
70 route de Fourmies, 02500 MONDREPUIS
☎ 03 23 58 14 25
Chimay, trappist beer 25 km. Race-course de la Capelle 10 km.
In the heart of the Thiérache, a 19th-century house in typical local
style with five well-appointed rooms. There is a room for three
with a double and a single bed and a family room with a double
and two single beds, each with a private bathroom and wc. Three
double rooms each with a private shower room and wc. Other
facilities include a lounge, a dining room, an enclosed courtyard,
parking and a garage. 67 euros. It is close to the tourist route for
fortified churches and near Belgium. Open all year.

PRICES: s €30; d €43; t €55; extra person €12; dinner €15
NEARBY: Horse riding (9km) Golf (15km) Fishing (4km) Swimming
pool (4km) Stretch of water (22km) Hiking (5km) Tennis (5km) Sailing
(22km) Railway station (4km) Shops (4km) **NOTES:** No pets

RESSONS-LE-LONG

⁙ 🐓 Ferme de la Montagne Patrick FERTE
02290 RESSONS-LE-LONG
☎ 03 23 74 23 71 🖷 03 23 74 24 82
Paris 95 km. Soissons 15 km. Compiègne 25 km. A 14th-century
mountain farm that dominates the Aisne Valley, described in
historical documents and part of the lands of the royal abbey of
Notre-Dame de Soissons. There are five spacious rooms for two
or three people with private shower room and wc. One room is
on the ground floor, three rooms are grade 3, two rooms are
awaiting classification. Two rooms have a double and a single
bed, one has three singles, one a double and one twin beds.
There is a large garden with paths and a tennis court and a
restaurant in the village 500m away. Open all year except January
and February.
PRICES: s €38; d €46; t €60; extra person €15 **ON SITE:** Hiking Tennis
NEARBY: Horse riding (4km) Golf (25km) Swimming pool (10km)
Stretch of water (40km) Sailing (40km) Railway station (15km) Shops
(3km) **NOTES:** No pets English spoken

REUILLY-SAUVIGNY

⁙ 🍽 Chambre d'hôtes
Bill et Mérédith GRAHAM-SYKES
Rue des Vaches, 02850 REUILLY-SAUVIGNY
☎ 03 23 70 68 62 & 06 13 24 46 16 🖷 03 23 70 68 63
e-mail: bg@mail.dotcom.fr www.marneweb.com/bnb
This American couple invite you to share the calm of their ancient
Champagne farm, charmingly restored and surrounded by the
vines of the Marne Valley. Three rooms with character overlooking
the private courtyard and the forest - two doubles and one twin
with private shower rooms. There is a lounge with fireplace, library
and television for guests. There is a large, double-glazed veranda
next to an indoor jacuzzi kept at 30° throughout the year. Guests
can dine with their hosts, Mérédith and Bill, or visit the nearby
gourmet restaurant. Discounts available. Champagne tourist trail
nearby. Open all year. Prices vary for longer stays.
PRICES: s €55; d €65; extra person €15; dinner €15-€25
ON SITE: Fishing Swimming pool Hiking **NEARBY:** Horse riding (3km)
Golf (10km) Tennis (6km) Railway station (6km) Shops (6km)
NOTES: No pets English spoken

SORBAIS

⁙ 🍽 Chambre d'hôtes Blandine DOUNIAUX
10, rue du Gué, 02580 SORBAIS
☎ 03 23 97 49 83 🖷 03 23 97 39 42

Race-course de la Capelle 7km. Tranquil riverside spot with
canoeing, kayaking and mountain biking available on-site and a

continued   continued

climbing wall 1 km away. Axe Vert in the village and close to the fortified church tourist route. There are rooms on the ground floor with their own entrance. One room with a double and a single bed with shower room and wc, and two rooms for two people with a shower room, wc and kitchenette. The three rooms on the first floor also have private shower rooms and wcs. One room with a double and a single bed, one room with a double, a single and a cot and one room with three single beds. There is a lounge, a seating area with fireplace, television, secure parking and baby equipment. Table d'hôte meals in the evenings only with children's meals (to 10 years) 8 euros. Open all year.

PRICES: s €30; d €43; t €53; extra person €11; dinner €12-€18
ON SITE: Fishing Hiking **NEARBY:** Horse riding (8km) Swimming pool (20km) Railway station (16km) **NOTES:** No pets

STE-CROIX

♦♦♦ La Besace Jean LECAT
21, rue Haute, 02820 STE-CROIX
☎ 03 23 22 48 74 ▤ 03 23 22 48 74
A small, ancient village farmhouse with stabling on site. Three double rooms, one twin room and one room with a double bed and bunks. Each room has a private shower room and wc. Other facilities include a lounge, television, fireplace, garden, playground, table tennis, volley ball and parking. Table d'hôte meals available, drinks not included. There is a river, a restaurant and the Vauclair forest 3 km away. Open from beginning March to end September; other times by reservation only.

PRICES: s €34; d €40; extra person €13; dinner €15 **ON SITE:** Children's play area **NEARBY:** Horse riding (3km) Golf (6km) Swimming pool (18km) Stretch of water (6km) Sailing (6km) **NOTES:** Pets admitted

VILLERS-AGRON-AIGUIZY

♦♦♦♦ ❤ ï⊙ï Ferme du Château
Xavier et Christine FERRY
02130 VILLERS-AGRON-AIGUIZY
☎ 03 23 71 60 67 ▤ 03 23 69 36 54
e-mail: xavferry@club-internet.fr
A beautiful 15th-century manor and farm on the edges of Picardy and Champagne in a typical Tardenois village. Set in a peaceful park overlooking a golf course. Four rooms with private shower and wc - two grade 3 rooms and two grade 4. Children up to 4 years 13 euros. Table d'hôte meals available - except for weekends - set price includes a glass of champagne, entrée, main course, cheese, dessert, wine, coffee or tisane. Open all year.

PRICES: s €53-€70; d €57-€70; t €95; extra person €24; dinner €30
ON SITE: Golf Tennis **NOTES:** No pets English spoken

OISE

ANSERVILLE

♦♦♦ ï⊙ï Chambre d'hôtes
Jean et Marie-Louise COUBRICHE
4 Grande Rue, 60540 ANSERVILLE
☎ 03 44 08 38 90
Situated in a village, this farmhouse has six guest bedrooms; three double, two twin and one single, all with telephone and en suite facilities. A guest lounge and television room are available. Guests also have access to a garden with a covered seating area and a playing field. The hotel offers parking and the nearest restaurant is only 500m away.

PRICES: s €39; d €42; t €55; HB €55; dinner €13 **NEARBY:** Horse riding (5km) Golf (20km) Fishing (3km) Swimming pool (7km) Tennis (3km) Railway station (8km) Shops (8km) Restaurant nearby
NOTES: No pets

ATTICHY

♦♦♦ Chambre d'hôtes M. FENARD
13 rue Tondu de Metz, 60350 ATTICHY
☎ 03 44 42 15 37 ▤ 03 44 42 15 37
This chambre d'hôtes boasts five double rooms, all on the ground floor, each with private bathroom facilities. A lounge is available for guests. Open all year round.

PRICES: s €32; d €38; t €46 **ON SITE:** Horse riding Forest Fishing Swimming pool Tennis **NEARBY:** Railway station (15km) Restaurant nearby **NOTES:** Pets admitted

BERNEUIL SUR AISNE

♦♦♦ Manoir du Rochefort Estelle ABADIE
60350 BERNEUIL SUR AISNE
☎ 03 44 85 81 78 & 06 87 08 90 63
Guest rooms at the 17th-18th century Manoir du Rochfort are located in the old chapel. There are four double rooms situated on the ground floor, each with en suite facilities. Its location dominates the village of Berneuil-sur-Aisne. Open all year.

PRICES: s €61; d €69 **ON SITE:** Forest **NEARBY:** Horse riding (8km) Golf (12km) Swimming pool (4km) Tennis (4km) Railway station (16km) **NOTES:** No pets English spoken

CAMBRONNE-LES-RIBECOURT

♦♦♦ ï⊙ï Chambre d'hôtes Pauline BRUNGER
492 rue de Bellerive, 60170 CAMBRONNE-LES-RIBECOURT
☎ 03 44 75 02 13 ▤ 03 44 76 10 34
e-mail: bellerive@minitel.net
Of English origin, Pauline Brunger welcomes guests to this lovely chambre d'hôtes on the banks of the Oise Canal. There are two rooms on the ground floor, one single and one double, and two double rooms on the first floor. All rooms have en suite facilities. The location offers the chance to explore the Forest of Compiègne, which is on the doorstep. Food and drink not included in prices. Open all year round.

PRICES: s €30; d €45; dinner €14 **NEARBY:** Horse riding (6km) Forest (12km) Golf (12km) Fishing (12km) Swimming pool (12km) Tennis (12km) Railway station (12km) **NOTES:** No pets English spoken

ESQUENNOY

♦♦♦ ï⊙ï Chambre d'hôtes Françoise RIVIERE
37 Grande Rue, 60120 ESQUENNOY
☎ 03 44 80 64 01 & 03 44 07 13 41
Situated in a village, this property has four double rooms, one with self-catering facilities, and two three-bedded rooms. All rooms have private bathrooms. A lounge is available to guests and television can be viewed on request. The garden boasts a covered seating area and local produce is available in the area. A car is an essential for this location. Reductions are available for stays of two nights or more. Children under 10 years half price.

PRICES: s €30; d €43; t €55; extra person €12; HB €41; FB €53; dinner €13 **ON SITE:** Horse riding **NEARBY:** Fishing (5km) Tennis (5km) Railway station (5km) Shops (5km)
NOTES: Pets admitted

> For further information on these and other chambres d'hôtes, consult the Gîtes de France website
> *www.gites-de-france.fr*

FLAVACOURT

♦♦♦ ❧ Chambre d'hôtes Pascal VANHESTE
Ferme de la Folie, 60590 FLAVACOURT
☎ 03 44 84 80 28
Gisors 6 km. Beauvais 20 km. With three guest rooms, this renovated farmhouse building has a double room with additional single bed located on the ground floor, and two double rooms on the first floor. All rooms have en suite shower rooms, and a guest lounge is provided with self-catering facilities available on request. Open all year round.
PRICES: s €35; d €38; t €49 **NEARBY:** Golf (13km) Fishing (5km) Swimming pool (13km) Tennis (2km) Railway station (6km) Shops (2km)
NOTES: No pets

FONTAINE-CHAALIS

♦♦♦ La Bultée Annie ANCEL
60300 FONTAINE-CHAALIS
☎ 03 44 54 20 63 ▤ 03 44 54 08 28
Parc Asterix 7 km. Roissy 25 km. Situated on a typical Valois farm, this chambre d'hôtes has five guest rooms in an annexe. The ground floor has one twin room, with three double rooms located on the first floor. The first floor also offers a six-bedded room. Each of the rooms has private bathroom facilities. There is a guest lounge with an open fire, and television. The nearest restaurant can be found 2 km away.
PRICES: s €35; d €50; extra person €15 **NEARBY:** Horse riding (2km) Golf (7km) Swimming pool (8km) **NOTES:** No pets

HANNACHES

♦♦♦ ❧❍❧ Bellefontaine Pascal BRUANDET
13 Bellefontaine, 60650 HANNACHES
☎ 03 44 82 46 63 ▤ 03 44 82 46 63
e-mail: bruandet@club-internet.fr
Beauvais 25 km. Gerberoy (medieval town) 2 km. Based on an old farm, Monsieur Bruandet is a sculptor and uses the traditional agricultural tools of the farm to make works of art filled with colour and humour. His chambre d'hôtes offers three guest rooms situated in a converted farm building. Two double rooms can be found on the ground floor, one with an additional single bed. The third room is located on the mezzanine floor and has both a double and twin beds. Courses on the 'art of plastic' are available by arrangement.
PRICES: s €34; d €41; t €49; extra person €7; dinner €14
NEARBY: Horse riding (7km) Golf (20km) Fishing (10km) Swimming pool (7km) Tennis (7km) Railway station (7km) Shops (3km)
NOTES: No pets English spoken

LAVERRIERE

♦♦♦ ❍❧ Auberge de la Ferme Monsieur SWIERZ
1 rue Saint-Pierre, 60210 LAVERRIERE
☎ 03 44 46 73 62
This chambre d'hôtes has four guest rooms located in an annexe building. These double rooms all have television and en suite facilities, and one room offers an additional single bed in order to sleep three guests. The price of food and drinks is not included.
PRICES: s €34; d €41; t €55; extra person €8; HB €45; dinner €20
ON SITE: Tennis **NEARBY:** Horse riding (5km) Swimming pool (5km) Railway station (5km) Shops (5km) Restaurant nearby **NOTES:** No pets
See advert on opposite page

MONTREUIL-SUR-BRECHE

♦♦♦ ❧ ❍❧ Chambre d'hôtes Annie FREMAUX
La Ferme des 3 Bouleaux, 154 rue de Clermont, 60480 MONTREUIL-SUR-BRECHE
☎ 03 44 80 44 85 ▤ 03 44 80 08 52
A 19th-century, timbered barn, recently restored to its original

condition houses four guest rooms. The ground-floor room is a double, and has disabled access, while the first floor has one double and two twin rooms. The double room has an additional fold-down bed if required. All rooms have television and en suite shower rooms. A lounge, barbecue and self-catering facilities are available to guests. The proprietor offers good food made from local produce. Reservations for dinner are required. Reductions are available for stays of two or more nights. Open all year round.
PRICES: s €29; d €35; t €43; extra person €8; dinner €12
NEARBY: Fishing (15km) Tennis (2km) Railway station (10km) Shops (2km) **NOTES:** No pets

ORROUY

♦♦♦ ❧ ❍❧ Chambre d'hôtes Daniel et Germaine GAGE
64 rue de la Forêt, 60129 ORROUY
☎ 03 44 88 60 41 ▤ 03 44 88 92 09
This property offers four double rooms. One room has disabled access and another an additional single bed. All rooms have en suite facilities. A vegetarian menu is available on request. Drinks not included. Open all year round.
PRICES: s €38; d €45; t €52; extra person €95; dinner €13
ON SITE: Forest **NEARBY:** Golf (10km) Swimming pool (13km) Tennis (7km) Railway station (7km) Shops (7km) **NOTES:** No pets

PLAILLY

♦♦♦ Chambre d'hôtes Evelyne et Patrice GUERIN
19 rue du Docteur Laporte, 60128 PLAILLY
☎ 03 44 54 72 77 ▤ 03 44 54 39 75
e-mail: gercom@wanadoo.fr
Situated in its own grounds, this charming 19th-century house has three well-furnished double rooms, one with an additional single bed. In addition there are two communicating rooms, one double and one twin. The panelled dining room has an open fire, and proprietors Evelyne and Patrice offer a warm welcome. Local attractions include the Parc Asterix. Open all year round.
PRICES: s €40; d €50; t €60; extra person €10 **ON SITE:** Horse riding Forest Fishing Tennis **NEARBY:** Golf (10km) Swimming pool (10km) Railway station (10km) **NOTES:** Pets admitted

PUITS-LA-VALLEE

♦♦♦ ❍❧ Chambre d'hôtes Catherine & Philippe DUMETZ
8 rue du Château, 60480 PUITS-LA-VALLEE
☎ 03 44 80 70 29 ▤ 03 44 80 55 52

With its own grounds and pheasantry, this beautiful house has three double guest rooms, two with bed settee if required. All three rooms have private bathrooms. There is a large guest lounge and television is also available. Reservations can be made for dinner, and visits to the pheasantry are by arrangement. Open all year round.
PRICES: d €42.70; t €58; extra person €8; dinner €16 **NEARBY:** Horse riding (10km) Swimming pool (25km) Tennis (5km) Railway station (25km) Shops (5km) **NOTES:** No pets

continued

REILLY

♦♦♦♦ ⅠОⅠ Chambre d'hôtes
D et H GAUTHIER ET PEARSON
Château, 60240 REILLY
☎ 03 44 49 03 05 📠 03 44 49 39 89
In the heart of a medieval village, recently awarded the title 'village que j'aime', proprietors Hilary and David welcome you to the elegant sophistication of their 19th-century castle. With grounds of twelve hectares, there is much to see. There are three double bedrooms, and one suite with both double and twin beds. All rooms are en suite, and there is a television lounge. Hunting can be arranged for guests. A supplement for animals of €4.57 per night is payable. Open all year round.
PRICES: s €49; d €59-€75; t €67; extra person €7; dinner €18
ON SITE: Horse riding Fishing Tennis **NEARBY:** Golf (4km) Swimming pool (4km) Railway station (5km) Shops (5km) **NOTES:** Pets admitted English spoken

SAINT CREPIN IBOUVILLERS

♦♦♦ ⅠОⅠ Haillancourt Marianne ROUSSEL GALL
31, rue Gaston Hebert, 60149 SAINT CREPIN IBOUVILLERS
☎ 03 44 08 82 21
Paris 50 km. Five attractive and well-furnished guest rooms form part of the extension of the proprietors' home. The ground floor houses two twin rooms, while the first floor has three double rooms. Each room has television and en suite facilities. The chambre d'hôtes also offers breakfast served on the verandah, and a heated and covered swimming pool as well as a Turkish bath! Internet access is available. Open all year round.
PRICES: s €58; d €65; dinner €18 **ON SITE:** Swimming pool
NEARBY: Horse riding (5km) Golf (2km) Fishing (5km) Tennis (5km) Shops (3km) **NOTES:** No pets English spoken

SAVIGNIES

♦♦♦ 🌱 ⅠОⅠ Chambre d'hôtes
Annick et J-Claude LETURQUE
14 rue du Four Jean Legros, 60650 SAVIGNIES
☎ 03 44 82 18 49 📠 03 44 82 53 70
e-mail: ferme.Colombier@wanadoo.fr
This chambre d'hôtes offers four guest rooms housed in a converted farm building. The ground floor has a double room, while the first floor has one double room with a child's bed, and two rooms sleeping three, each with a double and a single bed. All rooms are en suite, and additional children's beds are available on request. Food and drink is included, and reductions are available for stays of three nights or more. Open all year round.
PRICES: s €30; d €38; t €39; extra person €9; HB €32; dinner €13
ON SITE: Forest Swimming pool Tennis **NEARBY:** Golf (3km) Fishing (10km) Railway station (10km) Shops (10km) **NOTES:** No pets English spoken

ST-JEAN-AUX-BOIS

♦♦♦ Chambre d'hôtes Soizick LANGEVIN
2 rue Parquet, 60350 ST-JEAN-AUX-BOIS
☎ 03 44 42 84 48
Situated on a charming property in the Compiègne Forest, this annexe has one double and one twin room, both en suite. In addition, a family room is available, and is made up of two communicating rooms, one with a double and one with twin beds. These two rooms share a bathroom. Open all year round.
PRICES: s €45; d €54; t €69 **ON SITE:** Forest **NEARBY:** Horse riding (10km) Golf (10km) Swimming pool (10km) Tennis (6km) Railway station (10km) Shops (6km) **NOTES:** No pets

Auberge de la Ferme
Domaine de Laverriere
Grandvilliers

Situated in a little village of green picardie, the Auberge offer quality products. We will welcome you throughout the year, booking essential. You will taste regional products and will receive a very warm welcome. We cater for business meetings, receptions & banquets. If you are looking for a relaxing stay, you will be able to stroll in the countryside or in the park.

Prices: **Bedroom 1 pers: €34**
Bedroom 2 pers: €41
Bedroom 3 pers: €55 (2 beds)
Bedroom 4 pers: €58 (2 beds)

ST-LEGER-EN-BRAY

♦♦♦ Domaine du Colombier Aude MENARD
D981, 60155 ST-LEGER-EN-BRAY
☎ 03 44 47 67 17 📠 03 44 47 72 63
e-mail: docolomb@club-internet.fr www.cci.oise.fr/domaine
Situated in four hectares of land, this chambre d'hôtes has a lake, a dovecote and a river of its own. The double room, with extra single bed, and three single rooms are to be found on the first floor of a renovated barn. All rooms have en suite facilities. Breakfast is served on the ground floor, in front of the period fireplace. Tastings of the local produce can be arranged, and picnic baskets can be prepared for your visits to such places as Beauvais and the Pays de Bray. There is private parking. Open all year.
PRICES: s €41; d €60; t €80 **ON SITE:** Fishing **NEARBY:** Horse riding (12km) Forest (1km) Golf (12km) Swimming pool (8km) Tennis (3km) Railway station (8km) Shops (3km) **NOTES:** No pets

ST-QUENTIN-DES-PRES

♦♦♦ ⅠОⅠ Chambre d'hôtes Dominique SIMON
1 rue des Cressonières, 60380 ST-QUENTIN-DES-PRES
☎ 03 44 82 41 18
Casino at Forges-les-Eaux 15 km. Beauvais 30 km. Once a traditional farm, this chambre d'hôtes has five guest bedrooms. There is a single and two double rooms as well as two rooms which can sleep three. All have en suite facilities. The building has private parking and independent access for guests. There is also a guest lounge with television available. Reductions are available for stays of two nights or more. Open all year round.
PRICES: s €38; d €46; t €54; HB €39; FB €52; dinner €16
NEARBY: Horse riding (6km) Forest (7km) Golf (15km) Fishing (4km) Swimming pool (4km) Tennis (4km) Railway station (4km) Shops (4km) **NOTES:** No pets English spoken

THIERS-SUR-THEVE

▦▦▦ Chambre d'hôtes Sophie TREVAUX
2 rue Mortefontaine, 60520 THIERS-SUR-THEVE
☎ 03 44 54 98 43 📠 03 44 54 14 38
Chantilly 10 km. Senlis 6 km. This 19th-century hunting lodge sits on the edge of the Forest of Chantilly. There are four rooms, each offering two double beds, in addition to the one three-person and two double rooms. All rooms have television and en suite facilities. There is a guest lounge, which offers an open fire and a library. Open all year round.
PRICES: s €43; d €54; t €65; extra person €12 **ON SITE:** Forest **NEARBY:** Horse riding (10km) Golf (10km) Fishing (2km) Swimming pool (6km) Tennis (6km) Shops (6km) **NOTES:** No pets

TRIE-LA-VILLE

▦▦▦ ⑩ Ferme des 4 Vents Monique PIHAN
14 rue des Hirondelles, 60240 TRIE-LA-VILLE
☎ 03 44 49 74 41 📠 03 44 49 62 07
This property has one twin room on the ground floor, and two double rooms on the first floor, with two additional rooms, one double and one three-bedded, located in an annexe. All rooms have en suite facilities and a guest lounge offers television and the chance to relax. Open all year round.
PRICES: s €34; d €37; t €55; dinner €14 **NEARBY:** Horse riding (5km) Golf (5km) Swimming pool (5km) Tennis (5km) Railway station (5km) Shops (5km) **NOTES:** Pets admitted

SOMME

ARGOULES

▦▦▦ La Vallée Saint-Pierre Michelle HARFAUX
Chemin des Moines-Valloires,
80120 ARGOULES
☎ 03 22 29 86 41 📠 03 22 29 86 48
e-mail: michele@vallee-st-pierre.com www.vallee-st-pierre.com
Opposite the Abbaye de Valloires, this property is located in the centre of a 15-hectare wooded park with opportunities for walking or to fish in the pond or river. Arranged around a central patio, there are three first-floor rooms and one suite, each with its own seating area. One room has a double bed on the ground floor and twin beds on a mezzanine level; there is also a further double room and a twin room. The suite comprises two rooms with an electric, adjustable double bed, two single beds and a fridge. All rooms have private bathroom facilities. Breakfast alfresco or by the fire. Private parking is provided and the garage can be locked on request. Stabling of horses is possible, either in a box or in the pasture. Bicycles available. Open all year.
PRICES: s €60; d €74; t €86; extra person €14 **ON SITE:** Horse riding Fishing Hiking **NEARBY:** Forest (10km) Golf (5km) Sea (25km) Swimming pool (20km) Tennis (7km) Railway station (20km) Shops (5km) **NOTES:** Pets admitted English spoken

See advert on opposite page

BEHEN

▦▦▦ Château de Béhen Famille CUVELIER
8 rue du Château, 80870 BEHEN
☎ 03 22 31 58 30 📠 03 22 31 58 39
e-mail: norbert-andre@cuvelier.com www.cuvelier.com
Baie de Somme, Saint-Valery-sur-Somme 19 km. Abbeville 10 km. Near the D928, in the Vimeu Vert region, the Château de Béhen dates back to the 18th and 19th centuries. Set within a five-hectare park, this family home offers four bedrooms and two suites, each with TV, telephone, bathroom and wc. There is an 18th-century sitting room and hall, and meals are available on request. Table tennis, horse riding and mountain biking are all available within the grounds and horses can be stabled on request. The GR125

walking route borders the property. Open all year.
PRICES: s €74-€104; d €84-€114; t €99-€134; extra person €20; dinner €16 **ON SITE:** Horse riding Hiking **NEARBY:** Golf (12km) Sea (20km) Tennis (12km) Railway station (10km) Shops (10km) **NOTES:** No pets CC English spoken

See advert on opposite page

BELLOY-SUR-SOMME

▦▦▦ Chambre d'hôtes M & Mme WILBERT
29, rue Ch. de Gaulle, 80310 BELLOY SUR SOMME
☎ 03 22 51 41 05 📠 03 22 51 25 14
Amiens 16 km. On the outskirts of the village, off the main road, this house offers three first-floor guest rooms. One single room has a shower room and wc, and the other room has one double bed, bathroom and wc. There is also a suite with double bed and lounge, shower room and wc. The lounge/dining room is available to guests and has a billiard table. A conservatory leads onto an enclosed garden with terrace area with deckchairs for relaxation. Private parking, pets admitted on request. Open all year.
PRICES: s €41; d €49; extra person €13 **ON SITE:** Horse riding Tennis Fishing **NEARBY:** Forest (20km) Sea (20km) Swimming pool (20km) Railway station (2km) Shops (2km) **NOTES:** Pets admitted English spoken

BERNAY-EN-PONTHIEU

▦▦▦ 🐓 La Bucaille Julie CHUFFART SARL BELLEVUE
121, rue de Bellevue, 80120 BERNAY EN PONTHIEU
☎ 03 22 29 92 55 📠 03 22 29 44 68
e-mail: julie.chuffart@ferme-bellevue.fr www.ferme.bellevue.fr
Crécy-en-Ponthieu forest 1 km. In the vicinity of La Bucaille, close to the A16, this smallholding offers four double rooms and two mezzanine beds on the first floor of a brick and white stone building, close to the owners' house. Two rooms have a private bathroom and wc, and two have a private shower room and wc. A ground-floor lounge with kitchenette and bathroom is available. Terrace with garden furniture and barbecue. The gîte can also be hired on a self-catering basis. Open all year.
PRICES: s €52; d €52; t €67 **NEARBY:** Horse riding (6km) Forest (1km) Golf (9km) Sea (15km) Fishing (10km) Swimming pool (21km) Hiking (1km) Tennis (6km) Railway station (6km) Shops (6km) **NOTES:** Pets admitted English spoken

BUSSY-LES-POIX

▦▦▦ ⑩ Chambre d'hôtes Françoise GUERIN
1 rue de l'Eglise, 80290 BUSSY-LES-POIX
☎ 03 22 90 06 73

Poix-de-Picardie 6 km. In a village, not far from the N29 (Amiens-Rouen), this old farmhouse has been restored to provide accommodation in the form of one double bedroom (grade 2) with shower room and wc on the ground floor and three grade 3 bedrooms on the first floor. One first-floor bedroom has one single bed and one double bed, a second is a twin bedroom and the

continued

continued

third contains one double bed and one single bed. All of these come with a shower room and wc with extra beds available on request. The lounge/ library is available for guests and a conservatory leads onto a beautiful garden. Meals can be provided and pets are permitted by prior arrangement. Private parking is available. €52 for 4 people. Open all year.

PRICES: s €35; d €40; t €46; dinner €13 **ON SITE:** Forest Hiking
NEARBY: Horse riding (10km) Golf (28km) Fishing (6km) Swimming pool (6km) Tennis (6km) Railway station (6km) Shops (6km)
NOTES: Pets admitted English spoken

CAOURS

⫻ ❤ Chambre d'hôtes
Marc et Hélène DE LAMARLIERE
2 rue de la Ferme, La Rivièrette, 80132 CAOURS
☎ 03 22 24 77 49 🖹 03 22 24 76 97
e-mail: de.lamarlierem@wanadoo.fr

Abbaye de Saint-Riquier 4 km. Opposite the owners' home, this renovated building offers five guest rooms. Situated on the ground floor, the rooms have access straight into the garden that runs down to a river. There are three double bedrooms with an extra single bed in each, and one twin with an extra single bed; each has either a bathroom or shower room with wc. The fifth double room has a bathroom and wc. Another room contains a kitchenette that can be used as a studio (8 euros per night supplement). There is also a lounge with kitchen area available to guests. Pets are charged 3 euros per night. Mountain bikes can be hired and horses can be stabled in the grounds. Croquet, table tennis, basketball and an indoor swimming pool are also available to guests. There are restaurants and tennis courts in the village. Open all year.

PRICES: s €39; d €54; t €69; extra person €15 **ON SITE:** Fishing Swimming pool Hiking Tennis **NEARBY:** Horse riding (5km) Forest (18km) Golf (12km) Sea (20km) Railway station (5km) Shops (4km)
NOTES: Pets admitted English spoken

CARREPUIS

⫻ ◯ Le Manoir Roses de Picardie France MATHIEU
16 Grande Rue, 80700 CARREPUIS
☎ 03 22 87 84 84 🖹 03 22 87 83 83

Roye 2 km. This manor house is situated within a lovely 2.5 hectare park with woodland, pond and flowerbeds. The first double bedroom has a bathroom and wc, whilst the second double bedroom has a power shower and wc; this bedroom forms part of a suite with a lounge area with sofabed. On the first floor of an adjoining building, there are a further two bedrooms; one double and one room with two double beds (one on a mezzanine level). Each of these rooms has a shower room and wc. Breakfast is served in the owners' house. Boule pitch, children's play area, garden furniture, barbecues and private garage. Horses and ponies can be hired for trekking and fencing lessons can also be arranged. Table d'hôte meals by prior arrangement. Open all year. €71 for 4 people.

Continued on next page

PRICES: s €40; d €46; t €55; extra person €13 **ON SITE:** Children's play area Horse riding Tennis **NEARBY:** Forest (20km) Fishing (2km) Swimming pool (1km) Hiking (4km) Railway station (13km) Shops (2km) **NOTES:** Pets admitted English spoken

CITERNES

♦♦♦ Yonville Philippe DES FORTS
Hameau de Yonville, 5 rue de Yonville, 80490 CITERNES
☎ 03 22 28 61 16 📄 03 22 28 61 16
Situated in the hamlet of Yonville in the middle of a 15-hectare park, this property offers three guest rooms - two double bedrooms and one twin - on the first floor of a house. Each bedroom has a bathroom and wc, and an extra bed can be installed on request. A kitchenette, lounge area and conservatory are available for guests' use. Price for four people: 99 euros. Discount after the third night. Open all year.
PRICES: s €49; d €53 **ON SITE:** Hiking Tennis **NEARBY:** Horse riding (4km) Forest (15km) Golf (19km) Sea (35km) Fishing (10km) Swimming pool (19km) Railway station (20km) Shops (5km) **NOTES:** No pets English spoken

COCQUEREL

♦♦♦ Chambre d'hôtes Maurice CREPIN
2 rue de Francières, 80510 COCQUEREL
☎ 03 22 31 82 00 📄 03 22 31 82 00
Abbeville 10 km. This property is located in the Somme Valley, on the outskirts of a village near d'Ailly-le-Haut-Clocher. Four guest rooms, each with shower and wc, are available in a brick farm building near the owners' house. On the ground floor there is a double bedroom and another bedroom with a double and a single bed. On the first floor, there is one twin bedroom and one double bedroom with kitchen area. Another room with kitchen area is available for guests' use on the ground floor. Outside there is a gravel and plant-lined courtyard with garden furniture and private parking. Animals admitted by prior arrangement. Open all year.
PRICES: s €29; d €37; t €46 **ON SITE:** Fishing Hiking **NEARBY:** Horse riding (10km) Forest (20km) Golf (12km) Sea (27km) Swimming pool (10km) Tennis (3km) Railway station (7km) Shops (4km) **NOTES:** Pets admitted

CURLU

♦♦♦ 🐔 🍴 Chambre d'hôtes Gérard PLAQUET
Le Pré Fleuri, 11 rue de Maurepas, 80360 CURLU
☎ 03 22 84 16 16 📄 03 22 83 14 67
e-mail: leprefleuri@yahoo.fr

This property is situated in the Haute-Somme Valley. Six rooms are available in a building near the main house. On the ground floor, there is one bedroom with a double bed and a single bed. Another bedroom has two single beds. Both have a private shower room and wc. On the first floor, there is one bedroom with a double bed and two twin beds, two further double rooms and one twin room; each has a shower room and wc. Downstairs there is a lounge for

guests' use. Table d'hôte meals are available on request. Bikes can be hired and there is access to a private pond for carp fishing. There are restaurants 5 km and 10 km away and the TGV station is 17 km away (pick up possible). Open all year. Price for 4 people €74.
PRICES: s €30; d €41; t €58; dinner €13-€16 **ON SITE:** Fishing Hiking **NEARBY:** Horse riding (10km) Swimming pool (10km) Tennis (10km) Railway station (10km) Shops (10km) **NOTES:** No pets CC English spoken

DURY

♦♦♦ 🍴 Chambre d'hôtes Alain et Maryse SAGUEZ
2 rue Grimaux, 80480 DURY
☎ 03 22 95 29 52 📄 03 22 95 29 52
e-mail: alainsaguez@libertysurf.fr.htm/
http://perso.libertysurf.fr/saguez/duryhtm/

Amiens 5 km. Four bedrooms are available at this property which is full of character. On the ground floor there is a twin room with shower room and wc. On the first floor there is a suite with two adjoining rooms - one double and one twin - separated by the bathroom and wc. There are two further bedrooms, each with a bathroom and wc: one double bedroom and one bedroom with a double bed and a single bed. A cot is also available. Downstairs there is a lounge with TV and a living room. Private parking is available and there is an excellent restaurant in the village. Outings in a horse-drawn carriage are available from the property. Price for four people: 89 euros. Open all year.
PRICES: s €42; d €52; t €64; extra person €14 **ON SITE:** Horse riding Hiking Tennis **NEARBY:** Forest (1km) Golf (4km) Fishing (4km) Swimming pool (3km) Railway station (6km) Shops (2km) **NOTES:** No pets English spoken

ESTREBOEUF

♦♦♦ Chambre d'hôtes Marie-Christine HOUART
15 route de Gamaches, Ch'vrai paradis, 80230 ESTREBOEUF
☎ 03 22 26 80 61 & 06 08 98 06 29
In a village 2.5 km from La Baie de Somme, this property offers four bedrooms on the first floor of the owners' house - three doubles and one bedroom with a double and a single bed. Each has its own shower room and wc. An extra bed can be installed on request. A lounge/sitting room is available, and guests can use the furniture in the tree and flower-filled garden. Fishing is possible in the stretch of water at the bottom of the garden. Private parking is provided. Bicycles and a barbecue can be used at no extra charge. There are restaurants in nearby Saint-Valery. Holiday tax is payable but children under three can stay for free. Open all year.
PRICES: s €36; d €43; t €58; extra person €16 **ON SITE:** Fishing Hiking **NEARBY:** Horse riding (10km) Forest (2km) Golf (20km) Sea (3km) Swimming pool (11km) Tennis (3km) Railway station (7km) Shops (3km) **NOTES:** No pets English spoken

> Prices are given in Euros €1 = £0.62
> at the time of going to press

continued

FAVIERES

♨ Chambre d'hôtes M. BERTHET

La Vieille Forge, 930 rue des Forges, 80120 FAVIERES
☎ 03 22 27 75 58

Baie de Somme, Le Crotoy 5 km. Situated in a village near the
D940 (Le Crotoy-Rue), this property has five bedrooms situated in
a former forge, next to the owners' house. On the ground floor,
there is one bedroom with a double bed and a single bed and wc.
On the first floor, there are two double bedrooms. The breakfast
room on the ground floor is available to guests. In another
building, there are two bedrooms, each with a double bed and
twin beds. All bedrooms have a private bath or shower room and
wc. Parking space is in front of the house and there is a shelter for
bicycles. A good-quality restaurant is within easy reach of the
house (500m away) and the Marquenterre Bird Park is nearby. A
holiday tax is payable and the rooms are available all year round,
except January.
PRICES: s €44; d €54; t €61; extra person €8 **ON SITE:** Hiking
NEARBY: Horse riding (2km) Forest (10km) Golf (15km) Sea (5km)
Fishing (5km) Swimming pool (15km) Tennis (5km) Railway station
(6km) Shops (6km) **NOTES:** No pets

♨ Chambre d'hôtes Mme DELAUNAY

773 rue de Romaine, 80120 FAVIERES
☎ 03 22 27 21 07 📠 03 22 27 21 07
This accommodation is in a newly built wing next to the main
house. There are four guest rooms on the ground floor, each with
shower room, wc and its own entrance: three doubles and one
twin. There is a communal guests' lounge and private parking in
front of the house, as well as a bike shed. Guests may use the
barbecue provided or enjoy eating at the good quality restaurant
in the village. Small pets may be allowed. Holiday tax is payable.
Price per child: 5 euros (under 6) or 9 euros (6-15). Open all year.
PRICES: s €36; d €46 **ON SITE:** Hiking **NEARBY:** Horse riding (1km)
Forest (10km) Golf (10km) Sea (4km) Fishing (4km) Swimming pool
(10km) Tennis (4km) Railway station (6km) Shops (4km) **NOTES:** Pets
admitted

FAY

♨ ☙ ΙΟΙ Chambre d'hôtes Bruno ETEVE

12 Grande Rue, 80200 FAY
☎ 03 22 85 20 53 📠 03 22 85 91 94
This post-war house is situated on a smallholding, in a village very
near to the RN29 and the A1. The guest rooms are situated on the
first floor: a twin room and one double have private shower rooms
and wc, while the other double has a bathroom and wc. A cot is
available. Meals can be provided on request. The lounge has a
library area and a TV. Guests can relax in the garden. Private
parking. There is a restaurant 12 km away and the Museum of the
Great War at Péronne is also 12 km away.
PRICES: d €39; dinner €13 **NEARBY:** Horse riding (20km) Fishing
(5km) Hiking (5km) Railway station (2km) Shops (12km) **NOTES:** No
pets English spoken

FOREST-MONTIERS

♨ Ferme de la Mottelette Yves MANIER

80120 FOREST-MONTIERS
☎ 03 22 28 32 33 📠 03 22 28 34 97
The Ferme de la Mottelette is a secluded farmhouse, 2 km from
Rue. The first-floor accommodation has a private entrance and
consists of two grade 3 double bedrooms with TV and en suite
shower rooms with wc. Two additional bedrooms are grade 2
rated: one is a double room with shower room and wc and the
other is a double room with a shower (wc in the corridor). An
extra bed is available if required. There is a guest room with a
kitchenette available during the evening. Children's games and

garden furniture are also available. The rate for four people is 67
euros (the rate is reduced after three nights' stay). Open all year.
PRICES: s €38-€44; d €43-€49; t €61; extra person €12
ON SITE: Children's play area Hiking **NEARBY:** Horse riding (4km)
Forest (2km) Golf (10km) Sea (10km) Fishing (2km) Swimming pool
(8km) Tennis (2km) Railway station (2km) Shops (2km) **NOTES:** Pets
admitted

FRESNES-MAZANCOURT

♨ ΙΟΙ Chambre d'hôtes Martine WARLOP

1 rue Genermont, 80320 FRESNES-MAZANCOURT
☎ 03 22 85 49 49 📠 03 22 85 49 59

Péronne 6 km. This architect-designed house stands in a village,
near to the church. There are five bedrooms: one family room with
a double bed and two singles, and two bedrooms with twin beds
or a large double bed. Each room has a private bathroom and wc.
A further double bedroom, with a shower and wc, has a
communicating door with a twin room with bathroom and wc.
There is a large guest lounge. Meals can be provided and there is
a discount for more than three nights' stay. Half board is possible
(based on a double room). Cookery courses, including an
introduction to the specialities of the region, can be organised. The
TGV station and autoroute are only 6 km away. Open all year.
69 euros for 4 people.
PRICES: s €40; d €46; t €60; extra person €8; HB €41; dinner €16-€21
NEARBY: Fishing (10km) Swimming pool (10km) Tennis (10km) Railway
station (5km) Shops (10km) **NOTES:** No pets English spoken

FRISE

♨ ☙ ΙΟΙ Chambre d'hôtes Annick LEPINE-RANDJIA

La Ferme de l'Ecluse, 1 rue Mony, 80340 FRISE
☎ 03 22 84 59 70 📠 03 22 83 17 56
This property is situated in the Haute Somme Valley, on a
smallholding, on the edge of the Somme, not far from the lakes. It
is an ideal spot for fishing, with three hectares of ponds reserved
for guest fishing nearby. Three guest rooms are available on the
ground floor, with a terrace and a view over the ponds: two
double or twin bedrooms and one bedroom with a double and
single bed. Each room has a shower room and wc. An extra bed is
available on request. The lounge has a TV and library, an open
fireplace and an eating area. Meals can be supplied on request.
Open all year.
PRICES: s €34; d €43; t €60; extra person €15; dinner €17
ON SITE: Fishing **NEARBY:** Horse riding (10km) Golf (40km)
Swimming pool (10km) Tennis (10km) Railway station (12km) Shops
(7km) **NOTES:** No pets English spoken

continued

GINCHY

¶¶¶ ❤ Chambre d'hôtes Roger SAMAIN
1 Grande Rue, 80360 GINCHY
☎ 03 22 85 02 24 ▤ 03 22 85 11 60
This family home offers four comfortable guest rooms, each with its own shower room and wc. The ground-floor double room is grade 2 standard, while the three grade 3 rooms are situated on the first floor. The first of these rooms has two double beds; the second has a double and a single bed plus cot if required. The third is a twin bedroom. Extra beds are available on request. The lounge with kitchenette has a TV and books. There is a restaurant 7 km away and the Musée de Longueval is also nearby. Discounts are available after the fourth night (except July and August). Children younger than four are offered free accommodation. Open from May to mid November. Price for 4 people 63 euros.
PRICES: s €30; d €40; t €50 **ON SITE:** Hiking **NEARBY:** Horse riding (8km) Forest (1km) Fishing (6km) Swimming pool (15km) Tennis (3km) Railway station (15km) Shops (2km) **NOTES:** No pets English spoken

GRANDCOURT

¶¶¶ ❤ Chambre d'hôtes Louis et Claudine BELLENGEZ
9 rue de Beaucourt, 80300 GRANDCOURT
☎ 03 22 76 65 06 ▤ 03 22 76 60 24
This chambre d'hôte offers five bedrooms, with private access, on the first floor of the owners' house. One double bedroom has an adjoining door to a single bedroom. Another bedroom has a double and a single bed. There are two further twin bedrooms and one double bedroom. Each bedroom has a shower room and wc. A cot is available on request. There is also a guest lounge, phone, garden and play area. This is an ideal location for exploring the area of the Battle of the Somme with several French, German and British monuments and cemeteries nearby. There is a discount for stays of more than seven nights. The nearest restaurant is only 5 km away.
PRICES: s €31; d €42; t €54 **ON SITE:** Children's play area
NEARBY: Horse riding (5km) Golf (30km) Fishing (5km) Swimming pool (10km) Hiking (1km) Tennis (5km) Railway station (9km) Shops (9km) **NOTES:** Pets admitted English spoken

LE CROTOY

¶¶¶ Chambre d'hôtes Isabelle DEWASTE
14 rue du Phare, Villa Marine, 80550 LE CROTOY
☎ 03 22 27 84 56 ▤ 03 22 27 84 56
e-mail: villamarine@wanadoo.fr http://www.villamarine.com
Baie de Somme, Saint-Valery-sur-Somme 5 km. Marquenterre 10 km. In the heart of Crotoy, 100m from the sea, this 1930s villa has been totally renovated to provide comfortable guest accommodation. On the first floor there are two double bedrooms and one room with a double and a single bed; all have private shower rooms and wc. On the second floor there is a suite with one double bed, lounge, bathroom and wc. A cot is available on request. Guests can use the ground-floor lounge. Mountain bikes are available to rent and there is a restaurant nearby. Open all year.
PRICES: s €44; d €55-€66; t €63; extra person €13 **ON SITE:** Horse riding Sea Fishing Swimming pool Hiking Tennis **NEARBY:** Forest (20km) Golf (20km) Railway station (8km) **NOTES:** No pets English spoken

L'ETOILE

¶¶¶ ❌ Chambre d'hôtes Laurent MERCHAT
10 rue Saint-Martin, 80830 L'ETOILE
☎ 03 22 51 02 84
In the heart of the Somme Valley, this renovated Picardy home is in the middle of the village and contains three guest bedrooms. On the ground floor, there is one double bedroom with shower room and wc and one double bedroom with children's bunk beds, bathroom and wc. On the first floor, there is a bedroom with one double bed and one single bed, bathroom and wc. Downstairs, there is a TV and a patio area. Parking is provided in an enclosed courtyard and the house is set in 1.3 hectares of parkland with a pond and tennis court. Table d'hôte meals are possible by prior arrangement. Open all year.
PRICES: s €40; d €48; extra person €15 **ON SITE:** Fishing Hiking Tennis **NEARBY:** Horse riding (10km) Forest (25km) Golf (25km) Sea (40km) Swimming pool (25km) Railway station (5km) Shops (5km) **NOTES:** No pets English spoken

OCHANCOURT

¶¶¶ Chambre d'hôtes Jacques HUGOT
38 rue de Paris, 80210 OCHANCOURT
☎ 03 22 30 24 98
e-mail: mp.hugot@wanadoo.fr
Saint-Valery-sur-Somme 10 km. Just 10 km from the Baie de Somme, this house offers three guest rooms, each with its own shower room, wc and private entrance. On the ground floor, there is a double bedroom with direct access to the terrace with garden furniture. On the second floor, there is a twin room, and a double bedroom with a communicating door to a twin room. Breakfast is served in the owners' lounge. There is a lockable garage, enclosed garden and a barbecue. A restaurant is 5 km away. Open all year. Price for 4 people 77 euros.
PRICES: s €38; d €46; t €61; extra person €15 **ON SITE:** Hiking Tennis **NEARBY:** Horse riding (10km) Forest (20km) Golf (10km) Sea (10km) Fishing (10km) Swimming pool (10km) Railway station (5km) Shops (5km) **NOTES:** No pets English spoken

¶¶¶ ❤ Ferme du Bois d'Hantecourt M. WYNANDS
13 rue de Paris, 80210 OCHANCOURT
☎ 03 22 30 25 53 ▤ 03 22 30 25 53
e-mail: ewynands@momont.com
Baie de Somme 10 km. Four bedrooms with private access are available on the first floor of this renovated Picardy farmhouse. There are two double bedrooms, each with shower room and wc, and one twin bedroom with bathroom and wc. A further bedroom has three single beds, a shower room and a wc. A barbecue and garden furniture is available for guests' use. Private parking is available. There is a discount for holidays longer than four nights, whilst children younger than five are offered free accommodation. Open all year.
PRICES: s €31; d €46; t €61; extra person €15 **ON SITE:** Tennis **NEARBY:** Horse riding (5km) Forest (20km) Golf (10km) Sea (10km) Fishing (15km) Swimming pool (5km) Railway station (17km) Shops (4km) **NOTES:** No pets English spoken

OMIECOURT

▓▓▓ ⏲◎⏳ Château d'Omiécourt Dominique DE THEZY
Route de Chaulnes, 80320 OMIECOURT
☎ 03 22 83 01 75 🖹 03 22 83 09 56
e-mail: thezy@terre-net.fr www.isasite.net/chateau-omiecourt
Péronne 15 km. Roye 'cité gastronomique' 13 km Situated in a village with views over a 16-hectare park, this château offers four bedrooms on the first floor. The two double bedrooms and twin each has its own bathroom and wc. The two-bedroom suite comprises a double room with shower and twin room with bath; the wc is shared. There is a dining room on the ground floor and evening meals are available on request. Guests may use the garden furniture, and there are games for the children (table tennis, table football, board games). Private parking is available. Open from 2 January until 23 December (closed for Christmas).
PRICES: s €43; d €50; t €66; extra person €11; dinner €20
ON SITE: Children's play area **NEARBY:** Horse riding (3km) Fishing (10km) Swimming pool (13km) Hiking (15km) Tennis (13km) Railway station (6km) Shops (3km) **NOTES:** No pets English spoken

PORT-LE-GRAND

▓▓▓ Chambre d'hôtes Jacques et Myriam MAILLARD
Bois de Bonance, 80132 PORT-LE-GRAND
☎ 03 22 24 11 97 🖹 03 22 31 72 01
e-mail: maillard.chambrehote@bonance.com
This fine 19th-century brick house, with a family swimming pool, is situated in the middle of a beautiful landscaped garden. The ground-floor twin bedroom has a bathroom and wc, whilst on the second floor, there is a suite comprising two twin bedrooms with a bathroom and wc. Another bedroom has a large double bed, bathroom and wc. A cot is also available. A further suite of twin bedrooms, with shower room and wc is situated in a separate building, leading directly onto the garden. There is no charge for children under two and small pets are allowed. After the fourth night there is a 10% reduction. The nearest restaurant is 5 km away. Open March to mid November.
PRICES: s €46; d €65; t €77; extra person €17 **ON SITE:** Swimming pool Hiking **NEARBY:** Horse riding (5km) Golf (5km) Sea (10km) Fishing (5km) Tennis (10km) Railway station (9km) Shops (9km) **NOTES:** Pets admitted English spoken

QUEND

▓▓▓ Ferme du Château de la Motte
Mona et Dominique LIBERT
36 route de Froise Monchaux, 80120 QUEND
☎ 03 22 23 94 48 🖹 03 22 23 97 57
e-mail: dominique.libert@ifrance.com
Quend-Plage 2 km. Fort-Mahon 4 km. Set in 30 hectares of grounds in the heart of the countryside, this old farmhouse offers three first-floor bedrooms with private entrance, adjacent to the owners' home. Each bedroom has a double bed, a bathroom and a wc. A cot and extra bed are also available. There is a communal lounge room with an open fireplace and comfortable seating area. In the grounds there is a swimming pool, private tennis court and garden furniture. Fishing is possible in the private ponds. Stables are available. A reduction is possible for long stays and off-peak holidays. Secure parking is provided and the property is open all year.
PRICES: s €53-€60; d €60-€67; t €74-€82; extra person €8
ON SITE: Fishing Swimming pool Hiking Tennis **NEARBY:** Horse riding (2km) Forest (15km) Golf (2km) Sea (2km) Railway station (7km) Shops (7km) **NOTES:** No pets

RUE

▓▓▓ Fermette du Marais Brigitte BOUVET
360 route d'Abbeville Lannoy, 80120 RUE
☎ 03 22 25 06 95 🖹 03 22 25 89 45
e-mail: fermette.du.marais@wanadoo.fr

Just off the D32, the south-facing Fermette du Marais is situated next to a wood. The three guest rooms are on the ground floor, each with their own entrance off a private terrace. One bedroom has a double and a single bed, plus an extra pull-out bed. Another has a double bed, a pull-out bed and a kitchenette. There is also another double bedroom. Each has a private shower room and wc, TV and direct-dial telephone. A library is also provided. Outside there is a barbecue, pond and private parking. Bicycles can be hired and the nearest restaurant is 2 km away. A holiday tax is payable. Open all year. Price for 4 people 75-80 euros.
PRICES: s €46-€48; d €58-€61; t €65-€70 **ON SITE:** Children's play area **NEARBY:** Horse riding (6km) Forest (4km) Golf (9km) Sea (7km) Fishing (1km) Swimming pool (7km) Hiking (2km) Tennis (2km) Railway station (2km) Shops (2km) **NOTES:** Pets admitted English spoken

▓▓▓ ⏲◎⏳ Le Thurel Claudine et Patrick VAN BREE
80120 RUE
☎ 03 22 25 04 44 🖹 03 22 25 79 69
e-mail: lethurel.relais@libertysurf.fr www.lethurel.com

Baie de Somme 12 km. Marquenterre 6 km. Just off the D938 (2 km from Rue), this small 19th-century manor house is surrounded by a 2.5 hectare park. There are three double bedrooms, each with shower room and wc. One family suite has two bedrooms: one double bedroom and one twin bedroom and a shared bathroom. The lounge has an open fireplace and there is also a dining room for guest use. There is a pond for private fishing and mountain bikes can be hired. There is also an enclosed parking area. Three kennels and four stables are also available. Price for four people: 115 euros. Holiday tax is payable. Open all year.
PRICES: s €66; d €73; t €96; extra person €23; dinner €25
NEARBY: Horse riding (1km) Forest (10km) Golf (10km) Sea (12km) Fishing (3km) Swimming pool (10km) Hiking (2km) Tennis (5km) Railway station (2km) Shops (2km) **NOTES:** Pets admitted English spoken

ST-BLIMONT

♦♦♦♦ Chambre d'hôtes Gilles THIEBAULT
12 hameau Ebalet, 80960 ST-BLIMONT
☎ 03 22 30 61 41 & 06 82 22 87 24

Saint-Valery-sur-Somme 8 km. In the rural hamlet of Ebalet, this property offers five guest rooms, one of which is suitable for guests with disabilities. The rooms are in a wing of the owners' house and each has its own independent access, a shower room and wc. On the ground floor, there are two double rooms. On the first floor there are two double rooms and one bedroom with a double bed and a single bed. There is a breakfast room, garden with furniture, private parking and bike hire. Open all year. **PRICES:** s €37; d €43; t €56 **ON SITE:** Tennis **NEARBY:** Horse riding (5km) Forest (15km) Golf (17km) Sea (9km) Fishing (10km) Swimming pool (5km) Railway station (15km) Shops (5km) **NOTES:** No pets

ST-VALERY-SUR-SOMME

♦♦♦♦ Chambre d'hôtes M. et Mme SERVANT
117 rue au Feurre, 80230 ST-VALERY-SUR-SOMME
☎ 03 22 60 97 56

In a separate wing of the owners' house, this chambre d'hôte offers a double room on the ground floor with bathroom, wc and French windows leading onto the garden and a small terrace. On the first floor, there is an attic room with twin beds, shower room and wc. On the ground floor of another wing, there is a double bedroom with bathroom and wc, while on the first floor of this wing, there is a two-bedroom suite, comprising one double room and one twin room, with shower and wc. The breakfast room leads onto a terrace and has a view of the garden. A cot and extra bed are available. Restaurants nearby. Price for four people: 92 euros. Holiday tax is included in the price. Open all year. **PRICES:** s €43; d €49–€54; extra person €23 **ON SITE:** Sea Fishing Hiking Tennis **NEARBY:** Horse riding (5km) Forest (15km) Golf (15km) Swimming pool (10km) Railway station (6km) **NOTES:** No pets

♦♦♦♦ Chambre d'hôtes Michèle & J-Pierre DOUCHET
La Gribane, 297 quai Jeanne d'Arc,
80230 ST-VALERY-SUR-SOMME
☎ 03 22 60 97 55

Marquenterre 20 km. Situated on a quayside opposite the Baie de Somme, the main house of this property offers two suites. The first-floor suite comprises a double bedroom and a lounge with a double sofabed, bathroom and wc. The second-floor suite consists of a double bedroom and a twin bedroom with bathroom and wc. In a separate flat, there are two further bedrooms, both of which have a double bed, lounge area, bathroom and wc. One of these rooms has an open fireplace. Breakfast features home-made specialities and is served in the owners' house or on the terrace with a view of the garden. There is a winter garden, kitchen and dining room available for guests' use. Private parking. Kayaking in the nearby Baie de Somme is possible. Price for four people: 107 euros (holiday tax not included). Open all year, except January.

PRICES: s €54; d €60; t €88; extra person €23 **ON SITE:** Sea Fishing Hiking Tennis **NEARBY:** Horse riding (5km) Forest (15km) Golf (15km) Swimming pool (10km) Railway station (6km) **NOTES:** No pets English spoken

VAUCHELLES-LES-QUESNOY

♦♦♦♦ Chambre d'hôtes Joanna CREPELLE
121 place de l'Eglise, 80132 VAUCHELLES-LES-QUESNOY
☎ 03 22 24 18 17 🖹 03 22 24 18 17
e-mail: joanna-crepelle@yahoo.fr

Situated in the centre of a village, not far from the RN1 (Amiens-Abbeville), this property offers five bedrooms. The first grade 3 bedroom has a double bed and a large bathroom with a bath and a separate shower and wc. On the first floor, there is another grade 3 double bedroom that connects to a small single bedroom with bathroom and wc. A grade 2 twin bedroom connects with another twin room, shower room and wc. The communal lounge and drawing room are on the ground floor and contain a TV. Outside there is garden and barbecue and an enclosed courtyard for cars. There are restaurants 3 km away in Abbeville and in the village. Open all year except Christmas. Price for 4 people 72 euros. **PRICES:** s €38; d €44 **NEARBY:** Horse riding (3km) Forest (8km) Golf (8km) Sea (15km) Fishing (3km) Swimming pool (3km) Tennis (3km) Railway station (4km) Shops (3km) **NOTES:** No pets

VECQUEMONT

♦♦♦♦ Vecquemont M & Mme HEBDA
5, allée des Aubépines, 80800 VECQUEMEONT
☎ 03 22 48 29 54

Amiens 10 km. Three bedrooms are available on the first floor of this modern house. There are two double bedrooms and one twin, each with its own shower room and wc. There is a breakfast room with kitchen area; access to this room and the bedrooms is from a private corridor. There is a terrace and a garden with furniture. In the village, there is a tennis court, a boule pitch and playground. Open all year.

PRICES: s €34; d €40 **ON SITE:** Tennis **NEARBY:** Horse riding (12km) Forest (30km) Golf (10km) Fishing (1km) Swimming pool (5km) Hiking (1km) Railway station (2km) Shops (5km) **NOTES:** Pets admitted

VIRONCHAUX

♦♦♦♦ 🐓 🍽 Ferme de Mezoutre M/Mme POUPART
80150 VIRONCHAUX
☎ 03 22 23 52 33 & 06 22 10 40 85 🖹 03 22 29 22 14
e-mail: ppoupart@wanadoo.fr

Abbaye de Valloires 6 km. This Picardy farmhouse, a brick and stone building, once belonged to the Abbaye de Vallois. There are four bedrooms, each with a double bed, shower room and wc. Two of the bedrooms have private access to the garden. The lounge/breakfast room has a kitchenette, and there is a TV area on a mezzanine level. The owners live next door. Outside there is a large enclosed courtyard with a duck pond, terrace and garden. Open all year.

PRICES: s €38; d €45; dinner €18 **ON SITE:** Hiking **NEARBY:** Horse riding (12km) Forest (5km) Golf (10km) Sea (21km) Fishing (4km) Swimming pool (21km) Tennis (2km) Railway station (14km) Shops (8km) **NOTES:** No pets English spoken

🍽
Places with this symbol serve table d'hôtes
evening meals - remember to book in advance

continued

POITOU-CHARENTES

CHARENTE

AIGNES-ET-PUYPEROUX

♦♦♦ Chez Jambon Mireille LE ROY
16190 AIGNES-ET-PUYPEROUX
☎ 05 45 60 20 32
Situated on a hill in the heart of a hamlet, this house has two double rooms and a third which sleeps three. All rooms are en suite and have a separate access. The chambre d'hôtes has a lounge with an open fire and outside, a large terrace with flowers and areas of shade. Guests can also enjoy petanque and ping-pong. Bicycles are available to explore the countryside, or if you prefer you can simply take a walk along the beach. Not far from Perigord. Open all year.
PRICES: s €30; d €37; t €43 **ON SITE:** Fishing **NEARBY:** Bathing (15km) Tennis (4km) Swimming pool (4km) Hiking (3km) Horse riding (4km) Railway station (4km) Shops (4km) **NOTES:** Pets admitted

BERNEUIL

♦♦♦ ❦ ❍ Chez Marquis Pierre et Denise ARSICAUD
16480 BERNEUIL
☎ 05 45 78 59 52
Nestling in the southern hills of Charente, 14km from Barbezieux, this poultry farm has five en suite rooms. There is a single room, two double rooms, one that sleeps three and a four-person room. The chambre d'hôtes has a reading room with TV, which is available to guests. Other facilities include a washing machine and dryer, internet access and a games room with table tennis, table football and billiards. There is also a garden, with a covered area. Open all year.
PRICES: s €26; d €34; t €39; HB €160; dinner €13 **ON SITE:** Hiking **NEARBY:** Bathing (7km) Tennis (7km) Fishing (7km) Swimming pool (14km) Horse riding (7km) Shops (14km) **NOTES:** Pets admitted

BIOUSSAC

♦♦♦ ❦ Chambre d'hôtes J-Louis et Christine MOY
La Grande Métairie d'Oyer, 16700 BIOUSSAC
☎ 05 45 31 15 67 ▤ 05 45 29 07 28
Set in countryside, this typical Charentais farmhouse has two guest rooms. One sleeps two, and there is also a family suite, which can sleep four. Both have private bathroom facilities. A lounge with an open fire and a kitchen area with a fridge are available for guests. The garden has a covered seating area and a swimming pool. Local produce is available on site, and the forest is only six kilometres away. A reduction for stays of more than a week. Open from end March to beginning November.
PRICES: s €30; d €38; t €48 **ON SITE:** Swimming pool **NEARBY:** Bathing (3km) Tennis (7km) Fishing (1km) Horse riding (15km) **NOTES:** No pets English spoken

CHADURIE

♦♦♦ ❦ ❍ Logis de Puy-Fort-Haut
Marie-Claude BERGERO
16250 CHADURIE
☎ 05 45 24 80 74
Four en suite guest rooms are available on the first floor of this Charentais hostelry. Two of the rooms can sleep three and there is a single room and a family suite, which includes both a double and a single room. There is a lounge with an open fire, games and TV. The garden has a terrace, ping-pong, volleyball and a seesaw. Bicycles are also available. In season, there's plenty going on, and dinner is available with advanced booking. Open all year.
PRICES: s €35; d €40; t €50; dinner €15-€20 **ON SITE:** Children's play area Swimming pool Hiking **NEARBY:** Tennis (2km) Fishing (5km) Horse riding (10km) Railway station (20km) Shops (8km) **NOTES:** Pets admitted

CHAMPNIERS

♦♦♦ ❦ La Templerie Claudine et Jean RICHON
Denat, 16430 CHAMPNIERS
☎ 05 45 68 73 89 & 05 45 68 49 00 ▤ 05 45 68 91 18

Situated on a wine-making enterprise in the heart of a Charentais village, this chambre d'hôtes has three rooms that sleep three and one room, which sleeps two. All are en suite. In addition, a family suite offers a double and a twin room, and is also en suite. There is a dining room with an open fire and a lounge, plus a library, a games room and TV. There is a large wooded garden with a swimming pool. Located on the edge of Angoulême where there is much to see and do. Open all year. Wine tasting.
PRICES: s €35; d €40; t €49 **ON SITE:** Swimming pool **NEARBY:** Bathing (6km) Tennis (3km) Fishing (3km) Hiking (1km) Horse riding (10km) Railway station (8km) Shops (4km) Restaurant (3km) **NOTES:** Pets admitted English spoken

CHENON

♦♦♦ ❦ ❍ Les Cajets Pierre NADAUD
16460 CHENON
☎ 05 45 93 94 24 ▤ 05 45 69 25 80
Not far from Charente, in a tastefully restored farmhouse, this chambre d'hôtes offers three en suite rooms. Two are doubles and the third is a family suite made up of two rooms, each sleeping two. Guests can make use of the lounge/diner with TV and an open fire. The garden has seating and a small boat with which you can explore the Charente. Open all year.
PRICES: s €38; d €41; dinner €12 **ON SITE:** Fishing **NEARBY:** Bathing (11km) Tennis (3km) Swimming pool (12km) Hiking (5km) Horse riding (1km) Railway station (12km) Shops (4km) **NOTES:** No pets English spoken

continued

CONDEON

₩₩₩ ✿ ◎ Le Bois de Maure
Guy et Jacqueline TESTARD, 16360 CONDEON
☎ 05 45 78 53 15
Situated in the centre of town, this beautifully restored house has four guest rooms. All four rooms sleep two each, are on the ground floor and have central heating and independent access. There is an enclosed garden with a picnic area and gourmet meals are served at the family dining table. Open all year.
PRICES: s €24; d €31; t €38; dinner €11 **ON SITE:** Fishing
NEARBY: Bathing (8km) Horse riding (8km) Swimming pool (10km) Tennis (3km) **NOTES:** Pets admitted

CONFOLENS

₩₩₩ Chambre d'hôtes D et N VALEYRE ET LORIETTE
9, rue du Pont de l'Ecuyer, 16500 CONFOLENS
☎ 05 45 85 32 06
Five guest rooms can be found in this stylish house in a park in the centre of town. All five are doubles, and one can have a child's bed added if required. TV can be made available in the rooms and there is a lounge and a library. Swimming pool. Open all year.
PRICES: s €38; d €46 **ON SITE:** Tennis Fishing Swimming pool Hiking
NEARBY: Horse riding (2km) Restaurant (0.3km) **NOTES:** No pets

GUIZENGEARD

₩₩₩ ✿ Relais de Buissonnet Xavier BENOIT DU REY
16480 GUIZENGEARD
☎ 05 45 98 99 31 🗎 05 45 98 49 95
e-mail: info@buissonnet.com www.buissonnet.com
Angoulême & Bordeaux 50 km. In the heart of the Saintonge, there are six double rooms available, each with en suite facilities. Guests have access to the large lounge with its monumental fireplace! There are an animal park and fishing lakes in the grounds and you can observe the deer and the wild boar. On sunny days, trips to the park in a four-wheel drive vehicle are organized for groups of up to eight people (four minimum). Open all year.
PRICES: s €30; d €43; t €64 **ON SITE:** Fishing Hiking
NEARBY: Bathing (10km) Horse riding (1km) Swimming pool (7km) Tennis (7km) Railway station (28km) Shops (10km) **NOTES:** No pets

JARNAC

₩₩₩ Chambre d'hôtes Brigitte CARIOU
56 rue des Chabannes, 16200 JARNAC
☎ 05 45 83 38 64 & 06 03 51 52 31 🗎 05 45 83 38 38
Cognac 15km, Angoulême 25km. Proprietor Brigitte welcomes you to her 19th-century castle at Jarnac, the birthplace of François Mitterrand. Situated in the heart of a two and a half hectare park, the grounds are bordered by the Charente. There are five en suite double rooms and a cot is available on request. Tennis and a swimming pool can be found on site, and there are organized boat trips only one kilometre away. The castle also has a private art collection. Open all year.
PRICES: s €60-€90; d €73-€113 **ON SITE:** Fishing Swimming pool Tennis **NEARBY:** Bathing (1km) Horse riding (13km) Hiking (25km) Golf (6km) Restaurant (1km) Railway station (2km) Shops (1km)
NOTES: No pets CC

LESIGNAC-DURAND

₩₩₩ ✿ La Rédortière Marie-Paule MICHAUD
Château de la Rédortière, 16310 LESIGNAC-DURAND
☎ 05 45 65 07 62 🗎 05 45 65 31 79
Situated in grounds of seventeen hectares, this 19th-century castle has three double rooms, and two family suites, able to sleep three or four people. The rooms all have private bathroom facilities. The castle overlooks the lake of Mas Chaban. Open all year.

PRICES: s €39; d €46-€57; t €57; dinner €15-€21 **ON SITE:** Fishing Hiking **NEARBY:** Bathing (10km) Horse riding (10km) Swimming pool (8km) Tennis (3km) Railway station (12km) Shops (3km) Restaurant nearby **NOTES:** Pets admitted English spoken

LIGNIERES-SONNEVILLE

₩₩₩ ◎ Chambre d'hôtes Roland MATIGNON
Les Collinauds, 16130 LIGNIERES-SONNEVILLE
☎ 05 45 80 51 23 🗎 05 45 80 51 23
Furnished in period style, this 19th-century Charentais hostelry offers four guest rooms. There are two double rooms, one sleeping three, and one sleeping four. All are en suite. A dining room and a reading room with TV & video, and games, plus a small kitchen with a dining area. Bicycles are available, or a ride in a horse drawn carriage may be more your style. Free access to the local tennis courts. Visit the exhibition of carriages and agricultural tools, or perhaps the distillery, which dates from the 1870s. Open all year.
PRICES: s €31; d €38; t €46; dinner €12 **ON SITE:** Children's play area **NEARBY:** Horse riding (10km) Fishing (2km) Swimming pool (12km) Tennis (2km) Railway station (12km) Shops (2km) **NOTES:** Pets admitted Minimum 2 night stay

See advert on opposite page

LOUZAC-SAINT-ANDRE

₩₩₩ Chez Les Rois Geneviève DESRENTES
16100 LOUZAC-SAINT-ANDRE
☎ 05 45 82 16 04
Three rooms are available in a renovated Charentais house in a small village. One grade 2 room can sleep two and has a shared bathroom. There is also a double room, and a room that can sleep three, both en suite. Guests are invited to make use of the lounge with its open fire. Open 1 April - 31 October.
PRICES: s €23-€29; d €29-€35; t €41 **ON SITE:** Children's play area Hiking **NEARBY:** Horse riding (4km) Fishing (5km) Swimming pool (7km) Tennis (1km) Railway station (7km) Shops (2km)
NOTES: Pets admitted

₩₩₩ Demeure du Chapître Lucette JOUSSAUME
16100 LOUZAC-SAINT-ANDRE
☎ 05 45 82 90 34 🗎 05 45 82 45 74
Cognac 6 km. Saintes 20 km Close to Cognac, celebrated for its 'eaux de vie', this chambre d'hôtes has three guest rooms on the first floor of a renovated stable. There are two doubles, and a family suite of two rooms, each capable of sleeping two. A child's bed is available. There is independent access. The ground floor of the building has a large lounge/dining room, with TV. There is a second lounge with an open fire and a kitchen. The garden has seating and a variety of games. Parking is available in the enclosed courtyard and bicycles can be hired. Open all year.
PRICES: s €31; d €37; t €48 **ON SITE:** Bathing **NEARBY:** Horse riding (2km) Fishing (3km) Swimming pool (6km) Tennis (1km) Railway station (6km) Shops (6km) Restaurant (6km) **NOTES:** Pets admitted English spoken

LUXE

₩₩₩ ✿ ◎ Les Vignauds Christian et Lucette RICHARD
Luxe-Bourg, 16230 LUXE
☎ 05 45 39 01 47 🗎 05 45 39 01 47
In a restored farmhouse, three doubles and one three-person room can be found. All rooms are en suite, and there is a lounge, a sitting room, TV and library. For entertainment, try your hand at table tennis, English billiards or petanque, or just enjoy the swimming pool, the terrace, the portico and the charming garden. There is a small kitchen, and access to a fridge and washing machine. Internet access. Reductions for stays of four nights or more between 15 September and 15 June. Open all year.

continued

continued

PRICES: s €38; d €46; t €53; dinner €13 **ON SITE:** Children's play area Swimming pool Hiking **NEARBY:** Canoeing (2km) Horse riding (6km) Fishing (1km) Tennis (20km) Railway station (1km) Restaurant (1km) **NOTES:** Pets admitted

MAGNAC-SUR-TOUVRE

♨♨♨ ⦿l **Château de Maumont** Claudine JOLY
16600 MAGNAC-SUR-TOUVRE
☎ 05 45 90 81 10
Angoulême 5 km. Sources de la Touvre 2 km. Situated in grounds of two hectares, this 16th-century castle has four double rooms, one of which has a child's bed. All rooms are en suite. There is a dining room, a lounge with an open fire and a library. TV and telephone are available. The castle has a terrace with a 14th-century tower. Chateaubriand wrote his famous novel *René* in this very castle! Open all year.
PRICES: s €76; d €91; dinner €29 **ON SITE:** Fishing **NEARBY:** Bathing (5km) Horse riding (5km) Swimming pool (5km) Tennis (5km) Railway station (5km) Shops (5km) **NOTES:** Pets admitted CC English spoken

MANSLE

♨♨♨ **La Fontaine des Arts** Marie-France PAGANO
13 rue du Temple, 16230 MANSLE
☎ 05 45 69 13 56 & 06 12 52 39 86 🖹 05 45 69 13 56
e-mail: gerard.pagano@wanadoo.fr
Angoulême 20 km. Cognac 50 km. Marie-France and Gerard have three comfortably furnished and spacious rooms; 'Fanny' a double en suite, 'Cottage' and 'Manon', each sleeping three with an en suite spa bath. Guests are invited to make use of the lounge/TV room, with video and library and games. There is a kitchen area, with a washing machine and dryer. Outdoors, you will find a swimming pool, fishing, ping-pong and enclosed garden with a portico and a fountain. Explore the region with the help of Marie-France's carefully prepared route maps. Internet access. Open all year.
PRICES: s €42-€48; d €50-€56; t €70 €73 **ON SITE:** Fishing Swimming pool **NEARBY:** Bathing (17km) Tennis (1km) Hiking (1km) Railway station (18km) **NOTES:** No pets English spoken

MESNAC

♨♨♨ 🐓 ⦿l **Le Château**
C & C CHURLAUD MOINARDEAU
Place de l'Eglise, 16370 MESNAC
☎ 05 45 83 26 61 🖹 05 45 83 17 70

Cognac 12 km. Saintes 23 km. In the heart of the Cognac vineyards, on the banks of the River Antenne, this 18th-century castle has one family and two double rooms, all with private bathroom facilities. Dining room and lounge, with TV. The large country garden has a swimming pool. Sample the gourmet food served at the local inn, and try local cognacs on offer. Parking. Open all year. Wine tasting.

Les Collinauds
16130 Lignieres Sonneville
Tel: 05 45 80 51 23

A typical house of this region built in 1850 and situated in the heart of the cognac vineyard area. The four bedrooms have wash basin and toilet and are furnished with antiques. Fitted kitchen area with seating. Lounge with TV/video and games are available for guests to use. Within the grounds in pleasant weather, take a visit to the agricultural museum with old tools and an ancient distillery. Alternatively, have a horse and carriage ride to see the beautiful surrounding countryside.

PRICES: s €46-€61; d €54-€69; t €76; dinner €16 **ON SITE:** Fishing Swimming pool Hiking **NEARBY:** Horse riding (4km) Tennis (4km) Railway station (12km) Shops (4km) Restaurant nearby
NOTES: No pets English spoken

MOULIDARS

♨♨♨ ⦿l **Chez Quillet** Jenny et Derek FORDHAM
Les Tilleuls, 16290 MOULIDARS ☎ 05 45 21 59 00

Angoulême 18 km. Jarnac 13 km. Cognac 24 km. In a small hamlet, 3 kilometres from Charente in a typical 'maison Saintonge', this chambre d'hôtes has three double guest rooms, all with en suite facilities. Lounge and dining room with TV & video, hi-fi and an open fire. Outside there is a terrace and a garden. Located in the heart of the Cognac vineyards, with easy access to Angoulême and Jarnac. Parking. Open all year.
PRICES: s €47; d €50; extra person €16; dinner €18 **NEARBY:** Bathing (3km) Horse riding (6km) Fishing (3km) Swimming pool (6km) Hiking (6km) Tennis (6km) Railway station (6km) **NOTES:** No pets English spoken

continued

REPARSAC

♥ Domaine de la Vennerie Roger BRIDIER
16200 REPARSAC
☎ 05 45 80 97 00
Cognac 7 km. These four guest rooms are located in a Charentais home, on a wine-making enterprise. There is one double room and one room sleeping three, both en suite. The remaining two rooms form a family suite with private (although not communicating) bathroom facilities. There is a lounge with an open fire, and a kitchen with TV. Visits can be arranged to the wine storeroom and the distillery. Fishing is available on a private lake, by arrangement. Open all year.
PRICES: s €24-€41; d €35-€46; t €59 **NEARBY:** Horse riding (8km) Fishing (1km) Swimming pool (7km) Tennis (3km) Railway station (7km) Shops (7km) Restaurant (8km) **NOTES:** Pets admitted English spoken

ROULLET

⁙ ⦿ Romainville Francine QUILLET
16440 ROULLET
☎ 05 45 66 32 56 📠 05 45 66 32 56
In a Charentais residence, only two kilometres from the village, this chambre d'hôtes has one double room, one three person and one family room, which can sleep three. All rooms have private bathroom facilities. There is a lounge with an open fire, library and TV. Access is available to a washing machine. Outside is a large terrace with panoramic views, plus a barbeque and an outdoor dining area. There is also a swimming pool and a shaded garden. Bicycles are available. Children under two years are free. Dinner available with advanced booking. Open 1 April to 1 October.
PRICES: s €40; d €49; t €58; dinner €20 **ON SITE:** Swimming pool **NEARBY:** Horse riding (12km) Fishing (3km) Tennis (2km) Railway station (12km) **NOTES:** Pets admitted English spoken

SALLES-DE-VILLEFAGNAN

⁙ ⦿ Chambre d'hôtes P et S BRIGGS POTTER
La Cochere, 16700 SALLES-DE-VILLEFAGNAN
☎ 05 45 30 34 60
35 km north of Angoulême. Close to RN10, in the heart of a small village in the Charente Valley, this restored farmhouse has two double rooms and one family room which comprises one double and one single bed. The rooms are en suite and there is a lounge/dining room, a library, and access to a washing machine. The garden boasts a terrace and a swimming pool. There is an exhibition of paintings on site. Open 1 April to 15 November.
PRICES: s €29; d €37; t €47; dinner €12 **ON SITE:** Swimming pool **NEARBY:** Bathing (10km) Horse riding (9km) Fishing (8km) Hiking (8km) Tennis (5km) Railway station (10km) Shops (10km) **NOTES:** Pets admitted

SOYAUX

⁙ Montboulard Arnaud GARSIGNIES
Logis de Montboulard, 16800 SOYAUX
☎ 05 45 92 07 35 📠 05 45 92 07 35
On the edge of Angoulême, in a restored 15th-century residence in the heart of a wood, this chambre d'hôtes has four double rooms and one room which sleeps four. All rooms are en suite, and guests have access to the lounge. In the grounds there is a picnic area and a barbeque and there is also a swimming pool, which is shared with local gîtes. This is an ideal location for rambling as the area has many footpaths. Internet access available. Parking. Open all year.
PRICES: s €43-€53; d €49-€61; t €59 **ON SITE:** Children's play area Swimming pool **NEARBY:** Horse riding (5km) Fishing (5km) Tennis (5km) Railway station (5km) Shops (1km) **NOTES:** No pets

ST-GENIS-D'HIERSAC

⁙ Grosbot Les Nègres de Soie
Françoise et Pascal BAUDOT
Grosbot, 16570 ST-GENIS-D'HIERSAC
☎ 05 45 21 07 20 & 06 72 02 38 92 📠 05 45 21 92 02
Angoulême 15 km. Cognac 35 km. This renovated 18th-century farmhouse is located at the centre of a hamlet overlooking the Charente Valley. Five double rooms are available, and guests are invited to use the lounge and the dining room with its open fire. There is also a garden with a terrace, and the chambre d'hôtes has a permanent exhibition of paintings. A swimming pool is shared with other owners. There are canoeing facilities 5 km away. Internet access is available. Open all year.
PRICES: s €40; d €48 **ON SITE:** Swimming pool **NEARBY:** Bathing (4km) Horse riding (5km) Fishing (3km) Hiking (1km) Tennis (1km) Railway station (15km) Shops (2km) **NOTES:** No pets English spoken

ST-MEME-LES-CARRIERES

⁙ ⦿ Le Cul d'Anon Richard et Brigitte ALEXANDRE
16720 ST-MEME-LES-CARRIERES
☎ 05 45 32 04 50 📠 05 45 32 04 50
e-mail: Richard-Alexandre@wanadoo.fr
www.geocities.com/culdanon

Cognac 15 km. Jarnac 5 km. Three well appointed double rooms are offered at this recently built bungalow, all with en suite facilities. There is a lounge/dining room as well as a garden with a terrace. The chambre d'hôtes is within walking distance of the Cognac vineyards and in vintage champagne country. Dinner is available if booked in advance. Open all year.
PRICES: s €30; d €37; dinner €11 **ON SITE:** Stretch of water **NEARBY:** Horse riding (10km) Fishing (3km) Swimming pool (5km) Tennis (5km) Railway station (5km) Shops (2km) **NOTES:** No pets English spoken

ST-PALAIS-DU-NE

⁙ ⦿ Le Moulin-de-Breuil Nicole JACQUES
16300 ST-PALAIS-DU-NE
☎ 05 45 78 72 95 & 06 81 21 24 26 📠 05 45 79 07 41

continued

Angoulême 26 km. Cognac 18 km. This farmhouse has one family suite and two double en suite rooms. The suite comprises two rooms, each sleeping two. Bathroom facilities are private, but not communicating. A cot is available for children under two years and there is access to a washing machine and an iron. There is a dining room and a lounge with an open fire, and a library and a variety of games. Parking. Open 1 April to 31 October.
PRICES: s €35; d €40; t €50; dinner €15 **ON SITE:** Fishing Hiking **NEARBY:** Bathing (18km) Horse riding (12km) Swimming pool (2km) Tennis (2km) Railway station (20km) Shops (2km) **NOTES:** No pets

ST-PALAIS-SUR-LE-NE

¶¶¶ ◯ Chambre d'hôtes Geneviève FEITO
Le Bourg, 16300 ST-PALAIS-SUR-LE-NE
☎ 05 45 78 71 64 🖹 05 45 78 71 64
In the heart of Charente, this residence, dating from the early 19th-century now houses three guest rooms. One twin room has an en suite shower, and the double room has an en suite bath. The family suite consists of a pair of rooms, both of which can sleep two. Guests have access to the lounge with its open fire, TV, a library and a washing machine. There is also a garden with a swimming pool, a portico and a barbecue. Dinner is available with a reservation. Open all year.
PRICES: s €55; d €60; dinner €30 **ON SITE:** Children's play area Swimming pool **NEARBY:** Horse riding (13km) Fishing (1km) Tennis (3km) Railway station (20km) Shops (3km) **NOTES:** Pets admitted

ST-PREUIL

¶¶¶ 🐓 Domaine de Puyrouyer Pascaline BRISSET
16130 ST-PREUIL
☎ 05 45 83 41 93 🖹 05 45 83 42 26
e-mail: cognac.brisset@free.fr

Jarnac & Charente Valley 10 km. Cognac (Blues Passion) 15 km. Proprietor Pascaline has three well appointed guest rooms in this 18th-century house, located on a wine-making farm of forty hectares in the 'Grande Champagne' appellation. The rooms sleep two and three, with the third room a family room sleeping five. All have en suite facilities. There is a lounge and a garden with a terrace and seating. Guests will see horses grazing, have the opportunity to take woodland walks, and also see many of the abbeys, castles and windmills in the area. Open all year.
PRICES: s €46; d €54; t €61 **ON SITE:** Wine tasting Hiking **NEARBY:** Horse riding (12km) Fishing (10km) Swimming pool (10km) Tennis (5km) Railway station (10km) Shops (5km) **NOTES:** Pets admitted English spoken

ST-PROJET

¶¶¶ ◯ Logis de l'Age Baston John WADDINGTON
16110 ST-PROJET
☎ 05 45 63 53 07 🖹 05 45 63 09 03
e-mail: Lagebaston@aol.com
La Rochefoucault 2 km. Used as an inn during the 17th-19th

centuries, on grounds of nine hectares, the property overlooks the Tardoire Valley and La Rochefoucauld, a city celebrated for its castle. There are three double rooms and one three-person room, all with en suite facilities. The chambre d'hôtes has a lounge and a dining room, an open fire, TV, and guests have access to the library and washing machine. Open all year.
PRICES: s €46; d €55; t €70; dinner €21 **NEARBY:** Bathing (25km) Horse riding (4km) Fishing (1km) Swimming pool (3km) Tennis (3km) Railway station (2km) Shops (2km) **NOTES:** No pets English spoken

SUAUX

¶¶¶ Brassac Paule SAUZET
16260 SUAUX
☎ 05 45 71 12 61
Housed in an 18th-century building, this chambre d'hôtes offers two family suites, each made up of two rooms, and two double rooms, all with en suite facilities. There is a dining room with an open fire, and a library and TV available to guests. The grounds are full of old trees, and there is a portico. The views are spectacular. Bicycles are available. Open all year.
PRICES: s €30; d €52 **ON SITE:** Children's play area **NEARBY:** Fishing (10km) Swimming pool (7km) Horse riding (7km) Railway station (7km) Shops (7km) **NOTES:** Pets admitted

¶¶¶ ◯ L'Age Monsieur DUJONCQUOY
16260 SUAUX
☎ 05 45 71 19 36 🖹 05 45 71 19 36
Four guest rooms are located in an annexe of the home of the proprietor. There are three double rooms, one has access to the lounge, and another, which can sleep four, has access to the lounge and kitchen. All are en suite. A washing machine is available. The garden has a terrace, and a swimming pool shared with three gîtes. On the Limousand Road, this chambre d'hôtes has access to the water sports centre at Lavard. Open all year.
PRICES: s €34; d €41; t €50; dinner €13 **ON SITE:** Swimming pool Hiking **NEARBY:** Bathing (15km) Tennis (8km) Fishing (7km) Railway station (4km) Shops (4km) **NOTES:** No pets English spoken

VARS

¶¶¶ Logis du Portal Liliane BERTHOMME
16330 VARS
☎ 05 45 20 38 19

Angoulême 17 km. Cognac 37 km. This 17th-century residence has one single and two double rooms, each furnished in keeping with the property. There is a lounge/dining room with a kitchen area, and an open fire. The typically French garden has a swimming pool. Located on the banks of the Charente, the grounds lie behind a gate, flanked on either side by two dovecotes. Parking. Open all year.
PRICES: s €43-€49; d €61; t €76 **ON SITE:** Fishing Swimming pool Hiking **NEARBY:** Canoeing (1km) Horse riding (15km) Tennis (3km) Railway station (16km) Shops (1km) **NOTES:** No pets

continued

VERRIERES

♯♯♯ La Chambre Henri et Monique GEFFARD
16130 VERRIERES
☎ 05 45 83 02 74   🖷 05 45 83 01 82
Five guest rooms are available, located on a wine-making farm in the heart of the Cognac vineyards. There are two double, and two three-person rooms, and one room, which sleeps five. All have en suite facilities. There is a lounge with television, and a room with a kitchen area for guests. Local produce is available and includes pineau, cognac and local wines, wine tasting possible. A child's bed is available on request. Open all year.
PRICES: s €27; d €35; t €44   **NEARBY:** Horse riding (8km) Fishing (2km) Swimming pool (4km) Hiking (4km) Tennis (4km) Railway station (15km) Shops (7km)   **NOTES:** No pets English spoken

VILLEFAGNAN

♯♯♯ 🍽 Le Logis des Tours Chantal DUVIVIER
16240 VILLEFAGNAN
☎ 05 45 31 74 25
Angoulème 40 km. Cognac 50 km. Futuroscope 90 km. In a leafy and colourful setting, the 'Logis des Tours' has two double rooms, one three-person room and a family suite comprising two rooms, capable of sleeping five. All the rooms are en suite, and there is a lounge with a library, an open fire and satellite TV. In the grounds are centuries old trees, and a terrace. The hostelry gets its name from the two 15th-century towers, which stand guard over the entrance. Guided visits can be arranged (a small charge is made). Parking. Open all year.
PRICES: s €43; d €58; t €73; dinner €18   **NEARBY:** Bathing (1km) Horse riding (1km) Fishing (1km) Swimming pool (9km) Hiking (1km) Tennis (1km) Railway station (9km)   **NOTES:** No pets English spoken
See advert on opposite page

VINDELLE

♯♯♯ Grattelots Edouard-François BAZECK
Cidex 314, 16430 VINDELLE
☎ 05 45 21 42 13
Six kilometres from Angoulême, on a hill overlooking the Charente, this modern house has a family suite, made up of two rooms that sleep two, and one double room, both with en suite facilities. There is a lounge, a dining room and a kitchen area and outside a wooded park with a portico. Reduced prices are available for children under 13. Open all year.
PRICES: s €30; d €38; t €61   **ON SITE:** Children's play area Tennis Hiking   **NEARBY:** Bathing (4km) Fishing (1km) Swimming pool (6km) Horse riding (9km) Railway station (6km) Shops (5km)
NOTES: Pets admitted English spoken

CHARENTE-MARITIME

AIGREFEUILLE

♯♯♯ Chambre d'hôtes
Claude et Claudine JARROSSAY
13, rue de la Rivière, 17290 AIGREFEUILLE
☎ 05 46 35 97 84   🖷 05 46 01 98 04
Situated in a market town, this establishment offers three well-furnished rooms on its first floor. Of the three rooms, two are doubles and the third a twin, each with en suite facilities. The twin room has the option of a fold-away bed for one. A guest lounge is available, with TV and a library. The large, enclosed garden has seating and ping-pong, and bicycles are available. La Rochelle is only 20 km away, and Rochefort is 18 km away. Private parking. Open 1 April to 31 October.
PRICES: s €40; d €44; extra person €13   **NEARBY:** Golf (20km) Swimming pool (1km) Tennis (1km) Railway station (20km) Shops (1km) LA ROCHELLE (20km)   **NOTES:** No pets English spoken

ARCHINGEAY

♯♯♯ 🍽 ♿ Chambre d'hôtes
M-Thérèse/J-Pierre JACQUES
16 rue des Sablières, 17380 ARCHINGEAY
☎ 05 46 97 85 70 & 06 73 39 79 70   🖷 05 46 97 61 89
e-mail: jpmt.jacques@wanadoo.fr
Val de Saintonge, 22 km to Saint Jean d'Angély. Not far from St Savinien, Rochefort and Saintes, this chambre d'hôtes has three very comfortable rooms. The first floor has two rooms, one double, and one suite for three (one double and one single bed and a fold-away bed if required). The ground floor has a double room with disabled access. All rooms are en suite. A lounge with an open fire is available to guests. With a flower garden, a terrace and dinner available by prior arrangement, an ideal base to explore the region. Open all year.
PRICES: s €38; d €44-€49; extra person €12; dinner €15   **NEARBY:** Golf (7km) Swimming pool (3km) Tennis (3km) Railway station (7km) Shops (3km) TONNAY-BOUTONNE (3km)   **NOTES:** No pets English spoken

BERNAY-SAINT-MARTIN

♯♯♯ 🍽 Breuilles
L DUMAS et C LANDRE
5, rue de l'école, 17330 BERNAY-SAINT-MARTIN
☎ 05 46 33 88 21 & 05 46 33 92 50
Set in a quiet hamlet, this former farmhouse has two annexes housing three rooms, each with private bathroom facilities. The first has two twins on the ground floor. In the second there is a family suite with two single beds on the ground floor, and a double on the mezzanine. Guests have access to the lounge, with open fire and library, as well as the garden and its games. Bicycles are available to borrow. Dinner can be arranged except Sunday and Monday. Open 15 April to 15 October.
PRICES: s €35; d €41; t €52; extra person €7-€11; dinner €14
NEARBY: Golf (10km) Swimming pool (10km) Tennis (2km) Railway station (10km) Shops (2km) SURGERES (14km)   **NOTES:** No pets English spoken

CHAMPAGNE

♯♯♯ 🍽 L'Enclos Jacques LAURENT
L'enclos des Grands Ajeots, Les Grands Ajeots, 17620 CHAMPAGNE
☎ 05 46 97 04 97   🖷 05 46 97 04 97
Located between Anuis and Saintonge, the village of Champagne is the location of this chambre d'hôtes, situated in a wooded park. It has five guest rooms, one of which is a family room. There are two twins, one double and a two-bedded room, which sleeps three. The family room is a suite made up of two rooms, each with two double beds. All rooms are en suite. In addition, the chambre d'hôtes has large reception rooms, with open fires. There is also a library and TV available. Dinner may be reserved. Open 1 April to 30 September.
PRICES: s €31; d €42-€46; t €61; extra person €16; dinner €17
NEARBY: Golf (30km) Swimming pool (3km) Tennis (3km) Railway station (17km) Shops (3km) ROCHEFORT (20km)   **NOTES:** No pets

CHATELAILLON-PLAGE

♯♯♯ Chambre d'hôtes
Marie-Armelle SUZANNE
37, Bld Georges Clémenceau, 17340 CHATELAILLON-PLAGE
☎ 05 46 56 17 64   🖷 05 46 56 30 11
This modern property has three guest rooms in a recently built maisonette. All three are doubles and have en suite facilities. A child's bed is also available. Guests may make use of the veranda and sitting room, and there is a kitchen area, which can be used

continued

on request. The garden also has a swimming pool, a barbecue and private parking. Close by, Chatelaillon has a beach ideal for swimming. The town of La Rochelle is within easy reach, as is Rochefort. Open all year.
PRICES: s €37; d €41; t €52 **ON SITE:** Swimming pool **NEARBY:** Golf (10km) Tennis (1km) Railway station (1km) Shops (1km) LA ROCHELLE (15km) **NOTES:** No pets

CHERAC
♦♦♦ 🌿 **Chez Piché** Jean-Claude CHARBONNEAU
17610 CHERAC
☎ 05 46 96 30 84 🖳 05 46 96 30 84
In the Charente Valley, on an agricultural and wine growing smallholding, this chambre d'hôtes has three very comfortable rooms. Two are doubles, and the other is a double with an additional single bed. A foldaway bed can be provided on request. Guests may use the lounge with TV, and the garden, which has seating and children's games. Martine and Jean-Claude offer a warm welcome. Visits to the wine storehouse on site can be arranged, and the chambre d'hôtes is ideal for visits to the regions of Charente, Pineau and Cognac. The village of Cognac is 12 km away. Open all year.
PRICES: s €37; d €40-€42; t €52; extra person €10 **NEARBY:** Golf (15km) Swimming pool (10km) Tennis (2km) Railway station (12km) Shops (2km) SAINTES (12km) **NOTES:** No pets English spoken

For further information on these and other chambres d'hôtes, consult the Gîtes de France website
www.gites-de-france.fr

ECHILLAIS
♦♦♦ 🍴 **Les Hibiscus** Danièle et Sylvie COURAUD
5, rue du Champ Simon, 17620 ECHILLAIS
☎ 05 46 83 11 60
In a relaxing location, this chambre d'hôtes has four comfortable guest-rooms. They are situated in an annex next to the proprietors' home. Guests may use the lounge and library, and TV is available. There is also a garden. There are three double rooms, one with an additional single bed, and one twin, all with en suite facilities. Local attractions include the Charente River, the Bridge of Nartrou, L'Ile d'Oleron, La Rochelle and Royan. Dinner available by reservation. Open all year.
PRICES: s €30; d €38; t €49; extra person €11; dinner €14
NEARBY: Golf (40km) Swimming pool (7km) Stretch of water (7km) Tennis (1km) Railway station (7km) Shops (1km) ROCHEFORT (7km)
NOTES: No pets

FOURAS
♦♦♦ **Le Clos des Courtineurs** Pierrette LEFEBVRE
4 ter,rue des Courtineurs BP47, 17450 FOURAS
☎ 05 46 84 02 87 🖳 05 46 84 02 87
e-mail: pierrette.lefebvre@wanadoo.fr
Just 150m from the ocean, this quiet property has three double and two twin rooms, each with their own access and private bathroom facilities. There is a vast garden with a seating area, and a lounge for guests. Between Royan and La Rochelle, and opposite the Ile d'Aix and Fort Boyard, it is also convenient for the Iles de Re, Oleron, Rochefort, Saintonge Romane and the wine growing area of Cognac. Private parking. Open May to September.
PRICES: s €40; d €46-€50 **ON SITE:** Tennis **NEARBY:** Golf (6km) Swimming pool (18km) Railway station (14km) ROCHEFORT (13km)
NOTES: No pets English spoken

JARNAC-CHAMPAGNE

♦♦♦♦ ❦ ⎮◯⎮ La Feuillarde des Tonneaux
C et V SARL LASSALLE
14, Rue des Tonneaux, Domaine des Tonneaux,
17520 JARNAC-CHAMPAGNE
☎ 05 46 49 50 99 & 05 46 49 57 19 ▤ 05 46 49 57 33
e-mail: lassalle@t3a.com http://www.t3a.com/lassalle
A typical Charentais house, this chambre d'hôtes has two double rooms, one en suite and one with a separate bathroom. There is also a twin room with en suite facilities. All rooms are first floor and have a fridge. Guests may use a sitting room, TV, the internet and a library. In the garden are children's games and petanque. The chambre d'hôtes also offers visits to the distillery and wine storeroom on site. Local produce is available, including Pineau, Cognac, truffles, walnuts and hazelnuts. Dinner is available with a reservation. Jonzac and Cognac are nearby. Open from March to October, other dates available by agreement.
PRICES: s €48; d €64; extra person €9; dinner €24 NEARBY: Golf (25km) Swimming pool (10km) Stretch of water (14km) Tennis (1km) Railway station (14km) Shops (1km) JONZAC (14km)
NOTES: No pets

LES ESSARDS

♦♦♦ ❦ ⎮◯⎮ Le Pinier Francine JAMIN
10, Le Pinier, 17250 LES ESSARDS
☎ 05 46 93 91 43 ▤ 05 46 93 93 64
This chambre d'hôtes offers four comfortable and well-furnished rooms. Three doubles are located in a renovated stable, while the main building houses a suite of two rooms, one double and one twin. All rooms are en suite. A guest lounge is available, as are a games room, kitchen area, washing machine, phone point and internet access. There is also a garden, and dinner is available with a reservation. Open 1 July to 31 August, and weekends in May, June and September.
PRICES: s €30; d €42; t €61; extra person €8; dinner €13 NEARBY: Golf (10km) Swimming pool (10km) Tennis (5km) Railway station (10km) Shops (4km) SAINTES (10km) NOTES: No pets English spoken

LUCHAT

♦♦♦ ⎮◯⎮ ও La Métairie Martine TRENTESAUX
17, rue de la Métairie, 17600 LUCHAT
☎ 05 46 92 07 73 & 06 83 58 25 55
This old Charentais house has been renovated and is next door to the proprietors' home. There are three comfortable and individually furnished rooms, each with en suite facilities. On the ground floor, there is a twin room with disabled access and on the first floor there are two rooms which can sleep three, one with a double and a single bed, and the second with three singles. A lounge with open fire is available, along with TV room and library. The garden is charming and there is parking for guests. Saintes or Royan are not far off. Dinner is available by reservation. Open from March to November, other dates by agreement.
PRICES: s €30; d €40; t €50; extra person €11; dinner €13
NEARBY: Golf (12km) Swimming pool (4km) Tennis (4km) Railway station (10km) Shops (4km) SAINTES (10km) NOTES: No pets English spoken

MARANS

♦♦♦ ⎮◯⎮ La Manoire Claude BARRERIE
Le Marais Sauvage, 17230 MARANS
☎ 05 46 01 17 04 ▤ 05 46 01 17 04
http://www.marcireau.fr/marans/manoire/manoire.htm
In a corner of the Marais Poitevin region, this chambre d'hôtes offers four individual rooms, 'The Exotic', a double, 'The Rose' a

twin, 'The Rustic' with both double and single beds, and finally 'The Forget-me-not', with twin beds. There is a guest lounge, which has an open fire and TV is available. There is a covered area for parking and dinner is available with a reservation (Monday, Wednesday, Friday and Sunday only). Proprietors Marie Genevieve and Claude offer a warm welcome. Open 1 April to 31 October. Pay phone.
PRICES: s €37; d €43; t €56; extra person €13; dinner €17
NEARBY: Golf (20km) Swimming pool (6km) Tennis (6km) Railway station (30km) Shops (3km) LA ROCHELLE (30km) NOTES: No pets

MESCHERS

♦♦♦ ⎮◯⎮ Chambre d'hôtes
Mauricette et Pierre REDEUILH
202, route de Royan, 17132 MESCHERS-SUR-GIRONDE
☎ 05 46 02 72 72 ▤ 05 46 02 60 70
A modern house in a peaceful area, this chambre d'hôtes has a large flower garden, a terrace and veranda. Guests are welcome to make use of the lounge, sitting room, TV and library. There are four en suite rooms. On the first floor there are three rooms, one of which is a double. The remaining two rooms share a balcony and both of these, plus the room on the ground floor have two double beds, one of which can be split into two singles if required. An additional single bed is can be provided for the ground floor room if needed. There are five beaches and creeks in the area. The harbour at Meschers and the local caves are worth a visit. Dinner is available with a reservation, and there is shaded private parking. Open all year.
PRICES: s €33; d €41; extra person €15; dinner €14 NEARBY: Golf (15km) Swimming pool (10km) Tennis (1km) Railway station (10km) Shops (3km) ROYAN (10km) NOTES: No pets

MIGRON

♦♦♦ ❦ Logis des Bessons Ginette TESSERON
17770 MIGRON
☎ 05 46 94 91 16 ▤ 05 46 94 98 22
Located on a small wine-making enterprise, this chambre d'hôtes offers three well-furnished rooms. There is one grade 2 double room with a private shower and shared wc, and two grade 3 rooms, both double and en suite, one with an additional single bed. A lounge and a sitting room are available and guests have access to TV and a library. The garden has ping-pong and there is a swimming pool on the property as well as a private fishing lake. There are also animals, including goats, sheep and Shetland ponies. Bicycles are available for hire, and Cognac and Sainte are close by. Open all year round. Wine tasting possible.
PRICES: s €34; d €41; t €52; extra person €12 ON SITE: Swimming pool NEARBY: Golf (12km) Stretch of water (4km) Tennis (1km) Railway station (12km) Shops (1km) MATHA (9km) NOTES: Pets admitted English spoken

MIRAMBEAU

♦♦♦♦ ⎮◯⎮ Le Parc Casamène René VENTOLA
95, Avenue de la République, 17150 MIRAMBEAU
☎ 05 46 49 74 38 ▤ 05 46 49 74 38
http://www.homestead.com/mirambeau/
This chambre d'hôtes offers three rooms, each tastefully furnished, in a beautiful 19th-century castle. There are two doubles, 'The Linden', on the ground floor and 'The Cedars' on the first floor. Also on the first floor is 'The Thuya Tree' room, which has twin beds. Both a lounge and a sitting room are available and there is TV and access to a library. There are four acres of wooded parkland, ideal for walking. In the heart of the Haut-Saintonge you are well placed to explore the local vineyards. Dinner is available with a reservation. Open all year (November to March, reservations only).

continued

continued

PRICES: s €70-€80; d €75-€85; dinner €35 ON SITE: Swimming pool Tennis NEARBY: Golf (50km) Stretch of water (16km) Railway station (14km) JONZAC (14km) NOTES: No pets English spoken

MONTPELLIER DE MEDILLAN

⫫⫫ ⵔ Chambre d'hôtes
Claude/Marie-Jeanne HUBIN
17 rue de la Sauvete, 17260 MONTPELLIER DE MEDILLAN
☎ 05 46 90 92 70 🖹 05 46 90 92 70
e-mail: hubin@t3a.com
Situated in a quiet hamlet, this chambre d'hôtes offers three comfortable rooms, two double and one three-bedded room, all with en suite facilities. The rooms are located in an annexe, have separate access and look out onto the garden. A lounge is available to guests. Dinner is available by arrangement, and there is a dining room with a large open fire. Between the estuaries of the Gironde and the Charente, at the source of the Seudre, this is the home of oyster farming. Open from Easter to 1 November, other dates available by reservation.
PRICES: s €35; d €40; t €55; extra person €12; dinner €16
NEARBY: Golf (25km) Swimming pool (5km) Tennis (8km) Railway station (22km) Shops (3km) SAINTES (20km) NOTES: No pets English spoken

PUYRAVAULT

⫫⫫ ⵔ ⴺ Le Clos de la Garenne
Brigitte et Patrick FRANCOIS
9, rue de la Garenne, 17700 PUYRAVAULT
☎ 05 46 35 47 71 & 06 80 62 84 56 🖹 05 46 35 47 91
e-mail: info@closdelagarenne.com www.closdelagarenne.com
In a 17th-century building, with a great deal of character, the 'Linden' and 'Belle Epoch' rooms form a family suite, which can sleep four to six, while the 'Aunisienne' can sleep two or three. In an annex, the 'Cottage' is a family suite, which sleeps five and has disabled access. All rooms have private bathroom facilities. The chambre d'hôtes offers games, TV and billiards, and there is a kitchen area and reading room. Baby facilities are available. Set in a four-hectare park with children's games, animals, table tennis and volleyball on site, there are also local tennis courts. Only 20 minutes from La Rochelle, Rochefort and Marais Poitevin. Open all year.
PRICES: s €55; d €60; t €80-€95; extra person €20; dinner €23
NEARBY: Golf (20km) Swimming pool (5km) Tennis (1km) Railway station (5km) Shops (5km) SURGERES (5km) NOTES: Pets admitted English spoken

ROCHEFORT

⫫⫫ Ferme de Béligon Andrée et Antoine CAPELLE
route de Breuil-Magne-D116, 17300 ROCHEFORT
☎ 05 46 82 04 29
In five hectares of woodland, this restored farmhouse has two double rooms on the first floor, one with an additional single bed. Both rooms have an en suite wc but separate bathroom. A third double has an additional single bed, and is also fully en suite. A child's bed is available. A shared lounge and self-catering facilities are open to guests as well as TV, library and telephone. There is a garden and a courtyard with private parking. Close by are Rochefort, Brouage, Ile d'Oleron, Ile d'Aix and the beaches of Fouras. Open all year round.
PRICES: s €29; d €40; t €55; extra person €15 NEARBY: Golf (10km) Swimming pool (2km) Tennis (2km) Railway station (2km) Shops (1km) ROCHEFORT (2km) NOTES: No pets English spoken

SAINTES

⫫⫫ Chambre d'hôtes Nicole et Daniel BOULET
23 rue du Champverdier, Narcejac, 17100 SAINTES
☎ 05 46 92 25 77 & 06 87 71 05 71
In the heart of the countryside, in a house overlooking the Charente, are three guest rooms. The 'Wood' room is a double, and located on the ground floor. On the first floor are the 'Cascade' and the 'River' rooms, both doubles. All rooms are en suite. There is a lounge with an open fire, a day room, TV and a library available to guests. Outside in the shaded garden are a terrace, and a swimming pool. The garden also gives access to the River Charente. Saintes is an interesting town. Open all year.
PRICES: s €41; d €46 ON SITE: Swimming pool NEARBY: Golf (10km) Tennis (2km) Railway station (5km) Shops (5km) SAINTES NOTES: No pets English spoken

SAINTE-SOULLE

⫫⫫ Chambre d'hôtes Monique et Pierre GILBERT
2, route de la Rochelle, Usseau, 17220 SAINTE-SOULLE
☎ 05 46 37 50 32 🖹 05 46 37 26 11
e-mail: P-GILBERT@wanadoo.fr
The three guest rooms at this chambre d'hôtes are in a restored barn. The twin room and two double rooms are located on the first floor and all have en suite facilities. A foldaway bed or cot can be made available. A lounge is reserved for guests and TV, telephone and parking are available. A shaded garden offers a swimming pool, ping-pong and children's games. Bicycles are available for exploring the area and there are local tennis courts. La Rochelle is only five minutes' drive and has many attractions. The Ile de Re is also near enough to visit. Open all year.
PRICES: s €41; d €46; extra person €12 ON SITE: Children's play area Swimming pool NEARBY: Golf (10km) Tennis (1km) Railway station (10km) Shops (2km) LA ROCHELLE (10km) NOTES: No pets English spoken

SAINT-FORT-SUR-GIRONDE

⫫⫫ Chambre d'hôtes Michèle SCHONBECK
17, rue Maurice Chastang,
17240 SAINT-FORT-SUR-GIRONDE
☎ 05 46 49 95 63 & 06 19 16 83 55 🖹 05 46 49 95 63

Three well appointed rooms are available on the first floor of this chambre d'hôtes. 'Monseigneur', is a double, and 'Rose' is a twin room. The 'Blue' room is a family suite of a double and a twin. All rooms are en suite. There is access to a sitting room, lounge, kitchen area, TV and a library. Baby facilities are available. Outside are covered terrace and charming garden. Proprietors Michèle and Giselher can help you discover the Gironde and Saintonge. Open from 1 June to 30 September.
PRICES: s €30-€37; d €38-€44; extra person €12 ON SITE: Tennis NEARBY: Golf (25km) Swimming pool (12km) Stretch of water (25km) Railway station (24km) JONZAC (24km) NOTES: No pets English spoken

SAINT-GEORGES-DES-AGOUTS

♦♦♦ ♥◎♥ Les Hautes de Font Moure
Dinah et Claude TEULET
Font Moure, 17150 SAINT-GEORGES-DES-AGOUTS
☎ 05 46 86 04 41 📠 05 46 49 67 18
e-mail: cteulet@aol.com www.fontmoure.com

In a rural corner of France, this attractive 19th-century dwelling houses three comfortable double guest rooms, each with en suite facilities. In addition, there is a family suite of two rooms, one double and one twin. There are a lounge, library, TV and video facilities. Outside, a huge terrace and swimming pool can be found. Local attractions include Roman Saintonge, and tastings at Bordelais and Cognac. Parking and cycle hire available. Open March to November (other dates and table d'hôte by reservation).
PRICES: s €50; d €58-€66; t €76; extra person €13; dinner €21
ON SITE: Swimming pool **NEARBY:** Golf (25km) Stretch of water (25km) Tennis (4km) Railway station (25km) Shops (7km) MIRAMBEAU (7km) **NOTES:** No pets English spoken

SAINT-GEORGES-DES-COTEAUX

♦♦♦ Chambre d'hôtes Anne et Dominique TROUVE
5, rue de l'église, 17810 SAINT-GEORGES-DES-COTEAUX
☎ 05 46 92 96 66 📠 05 46 92 96 66
'Moulinsart' is a three-bedded room, and along with 'Pearl Buck' a double, and 'Agatha Christie' with both a double and a single bed, it is located on the first floor of this 18th-century house. On the ground floor, the 'Picardie' has a double bed. Guests may use the lounge, a mezzanine sitting room, and a kitchen area. Enjoy French billiards, TV and a library. Outside, in the garden are a barbecue, sand pit, ping-pong and a portico. Parking. Close to Charente and Saintes. Open 1 April to 15 November.
PRICES: s €35; d €43; t €56; extra person €14 **ON SITE:** Tennis
NEARBY: Golf (6km) Swimming pool (6km) Railway station (6km) SAINTES (6km) **NOTES:** No pets English spoken

SAINT-HILAIRE-DU-BOIS

♦♦♦ ♥ Les Robins René GUILBAUD
prox D2Royan/Jonzac,
17500 SAINT-HILAIRE-DU-BOIS
☎ 05 46 48 22 37 📠 05 46 48 29 14
This charming residence has three double rooms, one with an additional single bed, and one family room, all on the first floor. The family suite has two rooms, one double and one twin. Lounge, kitchen area, library and washing machine. In addition to the large wooded garden there is also a courtyard and a swimming pool. The nearest restaurant is only 1 km away, and it is possible to arrange a swim in the geo-thermal lake at Jonzac. Open April to September.
PRICES: s €31; d €41; t €14-€16; extra person €15 **ON SITE:** Swimming pool **NEARBY:** Golf (18km) Stretch of water (4km) Tennis (4km) Railway station (4km) Shops (4km) JONZAC (4km) **NOTES:** No pets English spoken

SAINT-PIERRE-D'OLERON

♦♦♦ ♥ ♿ Le Clos - La Menounière Micheline DENIEAU
20 rue de la légère, 17310 SAINT-PIERRE-D'OLERON
☎ 05 46 47 14 34 📠 05 46 36 03 15
e-mail: denieau.jean-pierre@wanadoo.fr
http://perso.wanadoo.fr/denieau-gites
In an annexe on a winemaking enterprise, are five en suite rooms. One twin and two doubles have an additional single bed on a mezzanine. The two remaining rooms are doubles, and one offers disabled access. A foldaway bed can also be provided. There is a lounge with TV, and a kitchen area is available by arrangement. A communal garden has garden seating, portico, children's games and table tennis. The Ile d'Oleron and Continiere are nearby. The oyster beds and bird life of the marshlands are also worth seeing. Open all year.
PRICES: s €35; d €43; t €52; extra person €9 **NEARBY:** Golf (8km) Swimming pool (4km) Tennis (1km) Railway station (40km) Shops (3km) ILE D'OLERON **NOTES:** Pets admitted English spoken

SAINT-SAVINIEN

♦♦♦ ♥ ◎♥ Forgette Jeannine et Gilbert LOIZEAU
17350 SAINT-SAVINIEN
☎ 05 46 90 21 20 & 06 08 32 20 29 📠 05 46 90 21 20
e-mail: gloizeau@wanadoo.fr
In an independent house, adjacent to that of the proprietors, are three en suite guest rooms. On the first floor is a family suite, made up of two rooms, one double and one three-bedded. There is also a double room, with an additional single bed. The ground floor has one double room. A guest lounge is available and there is also a small kitchen area. The garden has a lawn and a seating area. Bicycles can be hired, and dinner is available with advanced booking. 2 km away is a leisure centre offering tennis and swimming, small boats and pedalos. Open all year.
PRICES: s €32; d €38; t €63; extra person €11; dinner €13
NEARBY: Golf (20km) Swimming pool (2km) Tennis (2km) Railway station (2km) Shops (2km) SAINT-JEAN-D'ANGELY (15km) **NOTES:** No pets

SAINT-SORNIN

♦♦♦ ◎♥ La Cassoulière
Anne-Marie PINEL-PESCHARDIERE
10 rue du Petit Moulin, 17600 SAINT-SORNIN
☎ 05 46 85 44 62 📠 05 46 85 44 62
e-mail: caussoliere@wanadoo.fr www.caussoliere.com

Located in a beautifully restored property, these four rooms are all individually furnished and have en suite facilities. The ground floor of the proprietors' home houses one double room, while the first floor has a second double. The two other bedrooms are in a restored barn, both have a double and a single bed. There is a lounge, a TV and a library, and a garden with a swimming pool. There is private parking and cycles are available. Dinner can be arranged with a reservation. Saint-Sornin is not far from the

continued

Marennes, and Royan and Oleron are both within easy reach. Open all year.
PRICES: s €45; d €50-€60; t €75; extra person €15; dinner €23
ON SITE: Swimming pool Tennis **NEARBY:** Golf (20km) Stretch of water (2km) Railway station (10km) Shops (6km) ROCHEFORT (20km)
NOTES: No pets English spoken

SAINT-SULPICE-DE-ROYAN

♨ ❤ ⛄ & Ferme Leylandy C FORGET
Chemin de la ferme, 17200 SAINT-SULPICE-DE-ROYAN
☎ 05 46 23 05 99 ▤ 05 46 23 09 81
In a semi-detached property, which adjoins a farmhouse-cum-hostel, there are six en suite guest rooms. The ground floor has three doubles, one with disabled access. The first floor has three more doubles, one with additional single bed. There is a lounge with an open fire and TV. The garden has a lawn and trees, and a terrace with seating. Meals can be arranged. Close by are beaches at Royan, the forest of Coubre and the Gironde. Open March to October.
PRICES: d €38-€46; t €53; extra person €9; dinner €13 **NEARBY:** Golf (10km) Swimming pool (5km) Tennis (1km) Railway station (5km) Restaurant nearby ROYAN (10km) **NOTES:** No pets

SAINT-XANDRE

♨ Trente Vents Annie AUTRUSSEAU
1, rue de la Grace par hasard, 17138 SAINT-XANDRE
☎ 05 46 37 22 10
This chambre d'hôtes is in a remote location and offers a twin, a double, and a family suite. The double room has an additional single bed on a mezzanine, and the family room is on the first floor and has a double and a single bed. All the rooms are en suite. Lounge with mezzanine and sitting room with reading area. TV, fridge and microwave are all available. Outside, the enclosed garden has a lawn, a terrace, a barbecue, children's games and a portico. Open all year.
PRICES: s €32; d €40; t €59 **NEARBY:** Golf (5km) Swimming pool (4km) Tennis (1km) Railway station (8km) Shops (1km) LA ROCHELLE (8km) **NOTES:** No pets English spoken

SONNAC

♨ ⛄ Le Clos du Plantis Frédérique THILL-TOUSSAINT
Le Goulet, Sonnac, 17160 MATHA
☎ 05 46 25 07 91 & 06 81 99 07 98 ▤ 05 46 25 07 91
e-mail: AUPLANTIS@wanadoo.fr
In a beautifully restored farmhouse, situated in a leafy hamlet, this chambre d'hôtes has three rooms on the ground floor. All are spacious and comfortable, and all have en suite facilities and private terraces. There are two double rooms, one with an additional single bed, and a family room, which is made up of both a twin and a double room. There is a lounge and a library, as well as a large garden bordering the river with a swimming pool. Cognac, Jarnac and Saintes are close by. Open all year round.
PRICES: s €34; d €47; t €60; extra person €14; dinner €17
ON SITE: Swimming pool **NEARBY:** Golf (19km) Stretch of water (1km) Tennis (1km) Railway station (19km) Shops (1km) COGNAC (15km)
NOTES: No pets English spoken

THAIRE D'AUNIS

♨ Le Bourg Brigitte FONTENAY-MANIEN
2, rue de Dirac, 17290 THAIRE-D'AUNIS
☎ 05 46 56 24 21
Three rooms are located in a typical 18th-century house in the region of Charente. All three rooms are doubles and have en suite facilities. Two are located on the first floor, while the third is on the ground floor. There is a lounge, a kitchen area and a games room available to guests. The English-style garden, with its garden

furniture and children's games, surrounds the house. There is a very good restaurant only 100m away. La Rochelle, Iles de Re and Aix, Fouras and Rochefort are all within easy travelling distance. Parking. Open April to end of September.
PRICES: s €38; d €43-€46; t €61 **ON SITE:** Tennis **NEARBY:** Golf (30km) Swimming pool (7km) Railway station (7km) LA ROCHELLE (17km) **NOTES:** No pets English spoken

TRIZAY

♨ ⛄ Le Chizé Elisabeth et Roland LOPEZ
17250 TRIZAY
☎ 05 46 82 09 56 ▤ 05 46 82 16 67
e-mail: lechize@wanadoo.fr http://perso.wanadoo.fr/lechize/
Five en suite rooms with separate access can be found on this restored farm, in four hectares of land. On the ground floor is a family room with mezzanine, which has one double and one twin bed. On the first floor are three double rooms with a foldaway bed. There is a lounge with TV, a library and an open fire. A kitchen area is reserved for guests. There are horses on the property and cycles for hire. There is a leisure centre 500m away, with restaurants, a supervised beach and pedalos. The chambre d'hôtes sits between Royan, La Rochelle and Saintes. Dinner is available on the weekend by reservation. Open 1 April - 15 November.
PRICES: s €43; d €49; t €60; extra person €11; dinner €18
NEARBY: Golf (30km) Swimming pool (7km) Stretch of water (1km) Tennis (2km) Railway station (13km) Shops (2km) ROCHEFORT (13km)
NOTES: No pets English spoken

YVES

♨ ❤ La Platière Marie-Noëlle/Patrick GOUSSEAU
Le Marouillet, 17340 YVES
☎ 05 46 56 44 00 & 06 15 50 87 17 ▤ 05 46 56 44 00
Located in the marshlands of Rochefort, this remote chambre d'hôtes has three double rooms, two on the first floor and one on the ground. All the rooms are en suite and have TV on demand, and one of the first floor rooms has a sitting room. There is a communal lounge, which is shared with the proprietor, and there is use of a fridge. In the garden there is seating, a barbeque and a portico. Yves is situated between La Rochelle and Rochefort, and close to Chatelaillon. Open Easter to 1 November.
PRICES: s €30-€34; d €38-€41; extra person €11 **NEARBY:** Golf (30km) Swimming pool (7km) Tennis (7km) Railway station (7km) Shops (7km) CHATELAILLON (7km) **NOTES:** No pets English spoken

ARCAIS

♨ Chambre d'hôtes Jean-Michel DESCHAMPS
Chemin du Charret, 79210 ARCAIS
☎ 05 49 35 43 34 & 06 80 02 72 08 ▤ 05 49 35 43 35
e-mail: info@veniseverteloisirs.fr http://veniseverteloisirs.fr
Niort 22 km. La Rochelle 44 km. Futuroscope 100 km. A house typical of the area with independent access. On the ground floor there is one bedroom with a mezzanine, with one double bed, a fold-out bed, shower room and wc, cooking area and TV point. On the first floor two family rooms include one double room with mezzanine, with a double, single and TV point. In the second room, two doubles and a mezzanine with one double, one baby's bed and a TV point. Each room has a private bathroom and wc. Sitting room with cooking area, terrace and barbecue. Boat hire, canoes and bicycles on site. Restaurant 800 m. Reduced rate for stays over three days. Open all year.
PRICES: s €31; d €40; t €51; extra person €11 **ON SITE:** Fishing Hiking
NEARBY: Bathing (25km) Horse riding (4km) Forest (15km) Theme park (100km) Swimming pool (4km) Stretch of water (25km) Tennis (1km) Railway station (13km) FRONTENAY ROHAN ROHAN (13km)
NOTES: No pets English spoken

continued

♯♯♯ Chambre d'hôtes du Canal Elisabeth PLAT

10 rue de l'Ouche, 79210 ARCAIS
☎ 05 49 35 42 59 🖷 05 49 35 01 34
e-mail: chambres.dhotes@wanadoo.fr www.chambre-dhote.com

This charming house with an annexe is situated in a village near the port. On the first floor are three stylish bedrooms for two to five people, doubles or singles, with TV, private bathroom or shower room with wc. In the annexe on the ground floor one bedroom offers access for the less able. Cooking facilities, a garden running down to the water where boats and canoes are available, a private heated indoor swimming pool and solarium. Walks, boat trips and bike rental on site. Parking. Open all year.
PRICES: s €43; d €50; extra person €11-€16 **ON SITE:** Fishing Swimming pool Hiking Tennis **NEARBY:** Bathing (25km) Horse riding (4km) Forest (15km) Theme park (80km) Stretch of water (25km) Railway station (20km) MAUZE SUR LE MIGNON (13km) **NOTES:** Pets admitted English spoken

♯♯♯ ⵧⵘ Les Bourdettes Jean-Claude PEAN

14 chemin de la Foulée, 79210 ARCAIS
☎ 05 49 35 88 95
Niort 25 km. La Rochelle et l'Ile de Ré 50 km. Puy-du-Fou 90 km. On the edge of Sèvre Niortaise in the Marais Poitevin area, three rooms, one of which is a suite, at this typically traditional house. On the first floor, two doubles with private shower room and wc or private bathroom and wc. Extra beds can be provided. One suite with one double and two twins, private shower room and wc. Large covered terrace with views. The sitting room has TV and fireplace. Enclosed garden and parking. Futuroscope 90 km. Walks and cycle paths on site. Open all year.
PRICES: s €35-€43; d €40-€46; extra person €11; dinner €15 **ON SITE:** Fishing Hiking **NEARBY:** Bathing (25km) Horse riding (3km) Forest (15km) Theme park (90km) Swimming pool (1km) Stretch of water (25km) Tennis (3km) Railway station (25km) Shops (2km) FRONTENAY ROHAN ROHAN **NOTES:** No pets

BEAULIEU-SOUS-PARTHENAY

♯♯♯ ⵧ Les Ouches Jean-François CASTIN

79420 BEAULIEU-SOUS-PARTHENAY
☎ 05 49 70 22 05 🖷 05 49 70 22 05
Parthenay 10 km. Marais-Poitevin 50 km. Futuroscope 45 km. A renovated farm in the heart of the Gatinaise countryside. Three bedrooms, two on the ground floor with independent entrances. The first room has two doubles, and a kitchenette. The second room has one double. On the first floor there is one double room with two extra beds. Each room has a private bathroom and wc. Peace and quiet is guaranteed. Open all year round.
PRICES: s €32; d €38; t €51; extra person €12 **ON SITE:** Hiking **NEARBY:** Horse riding (10km) Theme park (45km) Fishing (1km) Swimming pool (10km) Stretch of water (10km) Tennis (3km) Railway station (18km) Shops (3km) MAZIERES EN GATINE (10km) **NOTES:** No pets

BRESSUIRE

♯♯♯ ⵧ La Léonière de Terves Françis BISLEAU

79300 BRESSUIRE
☎ 05 49 65 19 25
Secondigny 25 km. Cholet and Parthenay 35 km. Puy-du-Fou 40 km. Four fully furnished bedrooms in a large house full of character situated close to farmland. One ground-floor bedroom with two double beds, private shower room and wc. Two first-floor bedrooms each with a double bed and a single, private shower room and wc. One studio room on the second floor with a double bed and a single, private shower room and wc. Fridge and kitchenette in each room. A comfortable guests' sitting room with TV. The large garden has a private lake for fishing and boat trips. Restaurant 2 km. Futuroscope 80 km. Open all year except Christmas and 1 January.
PRICES: s €23; d €30; t €38; extra person €8 **ON SITE:** Hiking **NEARBY:** Bathing (25km) Horse riding (2km) Theme park (80km) Fishing (2km) Swimming pool (2km) Stretch of water (30km) Tennis (3km) Railway station (2km) Shops (2km) BRESSUIRE (2km) **NOTES:** No pets

CHAMPDENIERS

♯♯♯ ⵧⵘ La Grolerie Xavier et Corinne MASSON

79220 CHAMPDENIERS
☎ 05 49 25 66 11 & 06 60 57 35 70
http://www.la-grolerie.com
Parthenay 22 km. Marais-Poitevin 17 km. Puy-du-Fou, La Rochelle 80 km. This beautiful renovated old farmhouse has four bedrooms. Two on the ground floor with two double and two single beds, private shower room and wc. Two first-floor rooms each with two 140cm beds, one 130cm bed and one 90cm bed, private shower room and wc. The large sitting room has an open fireplace. The 1-hectare garden has a pond. Games available and garage parking. 1.5 km away an amazing underground river, open to visitors. 18 km from Niort. Open all year.
PRICES: s €29; d €37; t €48; extra person €13; dinner €14 **ON SITE:** Children's play area Hiking **NEARBY:** Bathing (5km) Horse riding (5km) Forest (5km) Theme park (80km) Fishing (1km) Swimming pool (14km) Stretch of water (5km) Tennis (2km) Railway station (20km) Shops (2km) CHAMPDENIERS SAINT DENIS **NOTES:** Pets admitted English spoken

CHENAY

♯♯♯ ⵧⵘ Chambre d'hôtes Jean & Madeleine NAU

Chenay, 79120 LEZAY
☎ 05 49 07 31 28
Lezay, Bougon 8 km. Niort, Poitiers 40 km. Marais-Poitevin 45 km. Three rooms in the owners' house 200m from the small market town. On the ground floor one double room with private shower room and wc. On the first floor there is one family room with one double bed and two singles and one double room with a cot, each have private shower room and wc. A terrace overlooking the garden. Garage parking. Futuroscope 45 km. Open all year.
PRICES: s €28; d €30; extra person €8; HB €51; dinner €10 **ON SITE:** Hiking **NEARBY:** Bathing (15km) Horse riding (10km) Theme park (45km) Fishing (2km) Swimming pool (7km) Stretch of water (15km) Tennis (7km) Railway station (20km) Shops (3km) LEZAY (8km) **NOTES:** Pets admitted

CIRIERES

♯♯♯ Le Château J-Marie & M-Claude DUGAST

18 rue Ste-Radegonde, Château de Cirières, 79140 CIRIERES
☎ 05 49 80 53 08
Puy-du-Fou 25 km. Marais-Poitevin 50 km. La Rochelle 100 km. In the heart of the Bressuirais woods, this 19th-century château is

continued

surrounded by 18 hectares of parkland with meadows, lake and river. On the first floor, there are three guest bedrooms. Two bedrooms with two double beds, one room with one double and one single, all with private bathroom and wc. Billiards, bicycles on site, lake fishing, picnic in the park. Farm Inns nearby; restaurant 300m. Open from 1 May to 30 September.

PRICES: s €47; d €55; t €70; extra person €17 **ON SITE:** Fishing Hiking **NEARBY:** Bathing (15km) Horse riding (8km) Theme park (80km) Swimming pool (4km) Stretch of water (15km) Tennis (1km) Railway station (30km) Shops (4km) CERIZAY (4km) **NOTES:** No pets

COMBRAND

♦♦♦ Logis de la Girardière Christine MOREL
79140 COMBRAND
☎ 05 49 81 04 58 ▤ 05 49 81 04 58
e-mail: morelchr@wanadoo.fr
Puy-du-Fou 25 km. Cholet 33 km. Pescalis 17 km. Bressuire 17 km. Three furnished bedrooms on the first floor of this early 18th-century lodging set in a park with private lake 300m away. One double and one twin room, a suite with one double room and one room with bunk beds, private bathroom and wc for each room. Lovely sitting room, card-phone. Restaurants 4 km. Open all year.
PRICES: s €32-€37; d €37-€41 **ON SITE:** Fishing Hiking **NEARBY:** Bathing (20km) Horse riding (2km) Theme park (90km) Swimming pool (4km) Stretch of water (20km) Tennis (4km) Shops (4km) CERIZAY (4km) **NOTES:** No pets English spoken

COULON

♦♦♦ Chambre d'hôtes Rémy DELRIEU
17 rue Elise Lucas, 79510 COULON
☎ 05 49 35 90 39 & 06 17 11 54 35
Niort 10 km. This picturesque house in Le Marais-Poitevin is situated 200m from the village. On the ground floor there are three double rooms with private shower room and wc. On the large veranda overlooking la Sevre breakfast and other meals are taken; also a barbecue in also available. This charming property offers space to relax in, quality produce, private parking and fishing on site. Restaurants nearby. Open all year round.
PRICES: d €41 **ON SITE:** Fishing Hiking **NEARBY:** Bathing (60km) Horse riding (15km) Forest (25km) Theme park (90km) Swimming pool (5km) Stretch of water (30km) Tennis (1km) Railway station (10km) NIORT (10km) **NOTES:** No pets

♦♦♦ La Rigole Sergine FABIEN
180 route des Bords de Sèvre, La Rigole BP 1, 79510 COULON
☎ 05 49 35 97 90
Niort 12 km. La Rochelle 52 km. In the heart of the Marais-Poitevin region this beautiful traditional house on the edge of the river has four guest bedrooms on the first floor. One bedroom for three people with one double and one single bed, private bathroom and wc, three bedrooms with two double beds and two single beds, sitting area on the mezzanine level and garden. Local excursions possible. Open from 1 April to 31 December.

PRICES: s €32; d €40; t €47 **ON SITE:** Fishing Hiking **NEARBY:** Bathing (60km) Horse riding (15km) Forest (25km) Theme park (90km) Swimming pool (7km) Stretch of water (30km) Tennis (2km) Railway station (12km) NIORT (12km) **NOTES:** No pets

COULONGES-SUR-L'AUTIZE

♦♦♦ Chambre d'hôtes Paulette ARSIQUAUD
13 boulevard de Niort, 79160 COULONGES-SUR-L'AUTIZE
☎ 05 49 06 25 76
Puy-du-Fou 70 km. Futuroscope 95 km. Marais-Poitevin 20 km. In the centre of the village, five independent guest bedrooms in a part of the building that joins the owners' home. There are two ground floor rooms, one double and one twin, with private shower room and wc, three double rooms on the first floor, with private shower room and wc. An enclosed courtyard and garden. Kitchen and lounge with TV for guests. Open all year.
PRICES: s €29; d €32; t €40 **ON SITE:** Hiking **NEARBY:** Bathing (10km) Horse riding (1km) Forest (20km) Theme park (95km) Fishing (4km) Swimming pool (1km) Stretch of water (10km) Tennis (1km) Railway station (21km) COULONGES SUR L'AUTIZE **NOTES:** No pets

GERMOND-ROUVRE

♦♦♦ ⚫ Breilbon Didier & Josette BLANCHARD
40 Chemin de la Minée, 79220 GERMOND-ROUVRE
☎ 05 49 04 05 01
Niort 15 km. La Rochelle 65 km. Futuroscope 80 km. Puy-du-Fou 80 km. Three guest rooms in this beautifully restored property in a small village between Parthenay and Niort. On the ground floor of an outbuilding there is a double room, and a double with a single bed on the first floor. There is independent access to a further double room on the first floor of the owners' house. Each room has private shower room and wc. There is a sitting room with TV, open fireplace and card-phone. Child's bed, cot and high chair available. Five adult bicycles and table tennis. Many walks in the area. Enclosed garden. Open all year.
PRICES: s €28; d €34; t €45; extra person €10; dinner €12 **ON SITE:** Hiking **NEARBY:** Bathing (10km) Horse riding (10km) Forest (18km) Theme park (80km) Fishing (2km) Swimming pool (15km) Stretch of water (10km) Tennis (2km) Railway station (15km) Shops (8km) CHAMPDENIERS (8km) **NOTES:** Pets admitted English spoken

GLENAY

♦♦♦ ⚫ ⚫ Le Château de Biard Gilles TEXIER
20 route du Champ Fleuri, Le Château de Biard, 79330 GLENAY
☎ 05 49 67 62 40
Thouars 18 km. Parthenay 25 km. Puy-du-Fou, Marais-Poitevin 60 km. An amazing 15th-century house surrounded by farmland that offers three guest bedrooms on the first floor. One has two doubles, another has twin beds, and the third has one double. All rooms have private bathrooms. A guests' dining room with a fridge and a large courtyard. Futuroscope 60 km. Château de la Loire 65 km. Open all year round.
PRICES: s €30; d €37; t €46; extra person €10; dinner €12
ON SITE: Hiking **NEARBY:** Horse riding (6km) Theme park (60km) Fishing (2km) Swimming pool (7km) Stretch of water (12km) Tennis (2km) SAINT VARENT (6km) **NOTES:** No pets

LA CRECHE

♦♦♦ Moulin de la Papeterie Thérèse DOAN TAN
Ruffigny, 79260 LA CRECHE
☎ 05 49 17 16 65 & 06 15 39 79 55 ▤ 05 49 28 97 11
e-mail: tdoan79@club-internet.fr
Marais-Poitevin 20 km. La Rochelle 70 km. Futuroscope 70 km. Twenty kilometres from La Crèche Therese and Pascal welcome

continued

continued

you to this delightful 17th-century paper mill, on the edge of Sèvre Niortaise. This stunning property offers calm and serenity. Three bedrooms all restored to their original 17th-century style. On the ground floor one double room with private shower and wc. On the first floor one double room with private shower room and wc. Bedroom three has one double and one single bed and a private bathroom and wc. Guided tours by boat. Open all year round.
PRICES: s €44; d €52; extra person €15 **ON SITE:** Fishing Hiking
NEARBY: Bathing (2km) Horse riding (10km) Forest (10km) Theme park (70km) Swimming pool (2km) Stretch of water (10km) Tennis (2km) Railway station (12km) Shops (2km) SAINT MAIXENT L'ECOLE (12km)
NOTES: Pets admitted

LE VANNEAU

♦♦♦ Chambre d'hôtes Philippe & Chantal ROUYER
29 Ste-Sabine, 79270 LE VANNEAU
☎ 05 49 35 33 95
www.maraispoitevinchambredhote.com
Mauzé-sur-le-Mignon 13 km. La Rochelle 45 km. Futuroscope 80 km. On the edge of Conches this traditional house sits in 5 hectares in the heart of Marais-Poitevin. Five furnished rooms are available. Two double rooms, one room for three people, one room for four people and one room for five people with extra beds if required. There is a shower and wash basin in each room. The kitchen is available for the guests, as well as a large covered terrace ideal for breakfast. On site there is a private lake with fishing and boat hire. Open from 1 April to 30 October.
PRICES: s €36; d €42; t €54; extra person €12 **ON SITE:** Fishing Hiking
NEARBY: Horse riding (7km) Forest (20km) Theme park (80km) Swimming pool (7km) Stretch of water (28km) Tennis (2km) Railway station (18km) Shops (2km) FRONTENAY ROHAN ROHAN (8km)
NOTES: No pets

MAGNE

♦♦♦ Chambre d'hôtes Alain & Cécile COUVILLERS
85 route de Jousson, 79460 MAGNE
☎ 05 49 35 28 23 & 06 73 40 97 80 ▤ 05 49 35 28 23
e-mail: a-couvillers@faxvia.net
www.marais-poitevin.com/HEBERGEMENT/COUVIL.html
Niort 6 km. La Rochelle 55 km. In the charming market town of Marais Poitevin this picturesque property offers three comfortable and quiet bedrooms. It won first prize in the 'Maisons Fleuries' competition in 2000. On the ground floor with independent access, one large double room with private shower room and wc and TV aerial. On the first floor there are two rooms with two double beds and a communal shower room and wc (for families or friends). The veranda where breakfast is taken overlooks a large garden with stunning flowers and trees. Conservatory and kitchenette. Enclosed parking. Restaurant 700m. Open all year.
PRICES: s €32; d €39; t €54; extra person €11 **ON SITE:** Fishing Hiking
NEARBY: Bathing (20km) Horse riding (2km) Forest (35km) Theme park (86km) Swimming pool (1km) Stretch of water (20km) Tennis (1km) Railway station (8km) Shops (1km) NIORT (6km) **NOTES:** No pets
English spoken

MARIGNY

♦♦♦ Le Grand Mauduit Francine GARNAUD
Le Vieux Fournil, 79360 MARIGNY
☎ 05 49 09 72 20 ▤ 05 49 09 72 20
Beauvoir-sur-Niort 5 km. Niort 17 km. Marais-Poitevin 20 km. A 15th-century house, on the edge of the Chizé Forest, situated in 5 hectares of Botanical Park, full of wild flowers. A guided tour is offered to guests, a walk around the park is a must! On the first floor, one double room with private shower room and wc. On the ground floor one double room with private shower room, wc, and one room with double bed and convertible twin beds, private

shower room and wc. One extra room has a 120cm bed and a child's bed. The patio is ablaze with flowers. Sitting room with fireplace and a cooking area for guests. Walking route GR 36 on site. Open from 1 April 1 to 1 November .
PRICES: d €47-€55; extra person €16 **ON SITE:** Forest Hiking
NEARBY: Bathing (20km) Horse riding (12km) Theme park (75km) Fishing (25km) Swimming pool (20km) Stretch of water (20km) Tennis (1km) Railway station (17km) Shops (5km) BEAUVOIR SUR NIORT (5km)
NOTES: Pets admitted

MONCOUTANT

♦♦♦ ▯◯▯ La Loge Janine ROY
79320 MONCOUTANT
☎ 05 49 72 73 36 ▤ 05 49 72 73 24
Puy-du-Fou 50 km. Marais-Poitevin 65 km. Pescalis 5 km. Three guest bedrooms on the first floor of a beautifully renovated small farm with a 2 hectare garden. The terrace has a barbecue and guests may use the owners' swimming pool. Bedroom one has a double and a single bed and a private bathroom and wc. Bedroom two is a double room with private shower room and wc. Bedroom three has one double bed and one extra bed if required, private bathroom and wc. All rooms centrally heated. The sitting room has an open fireplace. Futuroscope 80 km. Open all year.
PRICES: s €37; d €41; t €52; dinner €14 **ON SITE:** Swimming pool
NEARBY: Horse riding (7km) Forest (5km) Theme park (80km) Fishing (5km) Stretch of water (6km) Hiking (5km) Tennis (5km) Railway station (15km) Shops (5km) MONCOUTANT (5km) **NOTES:** No pets

NIORT-SCIECQ

♦♦♦ ▯▯ ▯◯▯ Chambre d'hôtes Joël & Annie GOULARD
5 rue des Loges, 79000 NIORT-SCIECQ
☎ 05 49 35 69 02
La Rochelle 70 km. Four centrally heated rooms for two families. A large, totally renovated farmhouse, with courtyard and mature garden, in a small village surrounded by Sèvre Niortaise. One double room with TV, one single room with 120cm bed, bathroom and wc. One suite on the first floor and one suite in a separate renovated building on the ground floor. One double room, a mezzanine with two single beds and shower room and wc. Guest menu available. Open all year .
PRICES: s €30; d €34; t €53; extra person €15; dinner €12
ON SITE: Fishing Hiking **NEARBY:** Bathing (20km) Horse riding (12km) Theme park (80km) Swimming pool (5km) Stretch of water (20km) Tennis (3km) Railway station (4km) Shops (3km) NIORT (4km)
NOTES: No pets

NIORT-ST-LIGUAIRE

♦♦♦ La Magnolière Lucio & M-Christine RAMBALDINI
16, Impasse de l'Abbaye, 79000 NIORT
☎ 05 49 35 36 06 ▤ 05 49 79 14 28
e-mail: marie-christine.rambaldini@wanadoo.fr
Marais-Poitevin 6 km. Puy-du-Fou 70 km. On the edge of Marais Poitevin, this large residential property dominates Sèvre Niortaise and offers guests a peaceful stay. There are three rooms all with stylish furniture, TV, computer points, and spacious bathroom or shower room. Two doubles and four singles. Breakfast is served in the dining room or in the garden. There is a large sitting room, library a private swimming pool and exhibitions of contemporary paintings. La Rochelle 1hour. Open all year.
PRICES: s €64; d €64; t €84 **ON SITE:** Fishing Swimming pool Hiking
NEARBY: Bathing (25km) Horse riding (7km) Forest (25km) Theme park (80km) Stretch of water (25km) Tennis (1km) Railway station (5km) Shops (3km) NIORT (5km) **NOTES:** No pets

continued

PRAILLES

ᵚᵚᵚ ᶦ◯ᶦ Chambre d'hôtes Michel & M-Claude DUVALLON
79370 PRAILLES
☎ 05 49 32 84 43
Marais-Poitevin 25 km. Futuroscope 45 km. La Rochelle 50 km.
Two kilometres from the Hermitain Forest in a peaceful
environment this traditional Poitevin house has three bedrooms
and a sitting room available for the guests. Bedroom one is a twin
room with private shower room and wc. In an annex there are two
independent family rooms with accommodation on two floors
looking out onto woodland; one with kitchen, dining room, one
double, two twins, bunk beds and extra beds if required, shower
room and wc. The other has a kitchen, sitting room, shower room
and wc, one double with extra beds if required. Reduced rates for
long stays. Open all year round.
PRICES: s €34; d €38; t €50; dinner €14　**ON SITE:** Hiking
NEARBY: Bathing (3km)　Horse riding (4km)　Forest (2km)　Theme park
(45km)　Fishing (2km)　Swimming pool (8km)　Stretch of water (3km)
Tennis (2km)　Railway station (10km)　CELLES SUR BELLE (8km)　**NOTES:**
No pets　English spoken

SAUZE-VAUSSAIS

ᵚᵚᵚ ᵞᵉ Le Puy d'Anché Didier RAGOT
79190 SAUZE-VAUSSAIS
☎ 05 49 07 90 69 ᐧ 05 49 07 72 09
www.mellecom.fr/puyanche
Futuroscope, Marais-Poitevin 70 km. Cognac 60 km. Melle 22 km.
Six bedrooms full of character in a restored old building situated
close to the owners' farm. One double room on the ground floor
with extra beds if required. Five rooms on the first floor, five
double beds, four single beds with the possibility of extra beds if
required. Shower room and wc, TV points in each room. Ruffec 15
km. Open all year.
PRICES: s €37; d €42; t €55　**ON SITE:** Swimming pool Hiking Tennis
NEARBY: Bathing (8km)　Horse riding (5km)　Forest (4km)　Theme park
(70km)　Fishing (2km)　Stretch of water (3km)　Railway station (12km)
Shops (1km)　SAUZE-VAUSSAIS (1km)　**NOTES:** Pets admitted　CC

ST-MARTIN-DE-BERNEGOUE

ᵚᵚᵚ ᵞᵉ ᶦ◯ᶦ Chambre d'hôtes
Pierre & Andrée SAIVRES
285 route de Brûlain,
79230 ST-MARTIN-DE-BERNEGOUE
☎ 05 49 26 47 43

*La Rochelle 70 km. Marais-Poitevin 25 km. Chizé 12 km. Niort 15
km.* Situated in a delightful little village three fully furnished rooms
in a farm building adjoining the main house. On the ground floor
one twin room with full access for the less able guest. On the first
floor bedroom two has a double bed with canopy and a single
bed, bedroom three is a family room with one double bed and
two singles; each room has a private shower room and wc. Living
room with TV and fire place. Futuroscope 80 km. Open all year.

PRICES: s €30; d €38-€49; t €49-€59; dinner €11　**ON SITE:** Hiking
NEARBY: Bathing (12km)　Horse riding (3km)　Forest (15km)　Theme park
(80km)　Fishing (2km)　Swimming pool (12km)　Stretch of water (12km)
Tennis (3km)　Railway station (15km)　Shops (3km)　PRAHECQ (3km)
NOTES: No pets　English spoken

ST-VINCENT-LA-CHATRE

ᵚᵚᵚ Chambre d'hôtes Béatrice BOUTIN
Le Bourg, 79500 ST-VINCENT-LA-CHATRE
☎ 05 49 29 94 25 ᐧ 05 49 29 94 25
e-mail: VIEUXfour.@mellecom.fr

*Tumulus de Bougon 30 km. Marais-Poitevin 50 km. Futuroscope
65 km.* Situated in the heart of this village, 10 km from Melle, a
stunning farm property with a small enclosed garden. One family
bedroom with one double and two twin beds, a private shower
room and wc and two further twin rooms with private shower
room and wc. Ferme-auberge on site. Silver mines 10 km.
Open all year.
PRICES: s €30; d €40; t €52; extra person €11　**ON SITE:** Hiking Tennis
NEARBY: Bathing (15km)　Horse riding (5km)　Forest (10km)　Theme park
(65km)　Fishing (8km)　Swimming pool (8km)　Stretch of water (15km)
Railway station (25km)　Shops (10km)　Restaurant nearby　MELLE (10km)
NOTES: No pets

VALLANS

ᵚᵚᵚ ᶦ◯ᶦ Le Logis d'Antan Françis GUILLOT
140, rue St-Louis, 79270 VALLANS
☎ 05 49 04 86 75 ᐧ 05 49 04 86 75
e-mail: lelogisdantan@wanadoo.fr
http://perso.wanadoo.fr/lelogisdantan/
La Rochelle, Ile de Ré 50 km. Futuroscope 1 h. Only 10 km from
the Marais-Poitevin this establishment offers two bedrooms on the
ground floor with private entrance, each with two doubles and two
twins, a sofa, TV and private shower room and wc. On the first
floor there is one double room, a room with three singles, TV and
private shower room and wc. A romantic double room with TV
and private shower room and wc. Living room and library with TV.
Fridge available for guests. There is also a two-bedroom suite at
the bottom of the park. Food may be ordered and breakfast is
available. Open all year. Reservation required.
PRICES: s €46-€53; d €46-€53; extra person €15; dinner €20　**ON SITE:**
Hiking Tennis　**NEARBY:** Horse riding (1km)　Forest (12km)　Theme park
(70km)　Fishing (2km)　Swimming pool (10km)　Railway station (12km)
FRONTENAY ROHAN ROHAN (3km)　**NOTES:** Pets admitted　English
spoken

VAUSSEROUX

ᵚᵚᵚ ᶦ◯ᶦ La Ferme de la Roseraie Ludivine BETIS
Les Touches, 79420 VAUSSEROUX
☎ 05 49 70 05 54 ᐧ 05 49 70 05 54
Futuroscope & Marais-Poitevin 50 km. Mouton-Village 9 km. A
beautifully restored Gatinaise farm with an 11-hectare park,

continued　　　　　　　　　　　　　　　　　　　　　　*continued*

situated in beautiful wooded countryside. Two bedrooms on the first floor, two double beds and two single, private shower room and wc with each room. One large bedroom on the ground floor has one double, one sofa bed, and a private shower room and wc and TV. One room is in a separate building with one double bed and a sofa bed and private wash facilities. Sitting room, kitchenette table tennis, mountain bikes and boules. Ornithology festival at Menigoute. Golf 10 km. Open all year.
PRICES: s €34; d €40; t €49; extra person €9; dinner €14
NEARBY: Bathing (16km) Horse riding (16km) Forest (5km) Theme park (50km) Fishing (9km) Swimming pool (16km) Stretch of water (15km) Hiking (9km) Tennis (4km) Railway station (19km) MENIGOUTE (10km)
NOTES: No pets English spoken

VERNOUX-EN-GATINE

♦♦♦ 🐓 iOi La Rémondière Jean-Louis MAURY
79240 VERNOUX-EN-GATINE
☎ 05 49 95 85 90 📠 05 49 95 96 07
Futuroscope 70 km. Marais-Poitevin, Puy-du-Fou 50 km. Pescalis 12 km. In the heart of the Gatinaise countryside, this wonderful old bake house is surrounded by apple trees. There are four independent furnished rooms. One family room on the first floor with two double beds, shower room and private wc. There are three double rooms on the same floor, two rooms with two double beds and one room with twin beds, private shower room and wc. It is possible to sleep extra people on a mezzanine. A kitchenette allows for self-catering. Open all year.
PRICES: s €26; d €34-€36; extra person €11; dinner €13
ON SITE: Fishing Hiking **NEARBY:** Bathing (9km) Horse riding (7km) Forest (10km) Theme park (70km) Swimming pool (9km) Stretch of water (9km) Tennis (2km) Railway station (45km) Shops (9km) SECONDIGNY (8km) **NOTES:** Pets admitted

VIENNE

ARCHIGNY

♦♦♦ Logis de la Talbardière Pascale LONHIENNE
La Talbardière, 86210 ARCHIGNY
☎ 05 49 85 32 51 📠 05 49 85 69 72
e-mail: jacques.lonhienne@interpc.fr
http://www.interpc.fr/mapage/lonhienne/indexhtm

La Roche-Posay 15 km. The owners say that tranquillity is guaranteed in this 17th-century residence and its outbuildings. It has three ground-floor and first-floor rooms. There are two double rooms, with beds which can act as doubles or twins, as required. Extra beds and cots if needed. The third room has three single beds. Guests' lounge. Discounts for longer stays. At Roche-Posay, 15 km, there is a spa and bicycle hire. Open all year.
PRICES: s €38; d €46; t €53 **NEARBY:** Bathing (6km) Horse riding (18km) Golf (15km) Theme park (20km) Fishing (6km) Hiking (6km) Tennis (6km) Sailing (20km) Railway station (20km) Shops (6km) VOUNEUIL-SUR-VIENNE (10km) **NOTES:** No pets English spoken

AVAILLES-LIMOUZINE

♦♦♦ Logis de la Mothe André et Marie-Reine MAY
86460 AVAILLES-LIMOUZINE
☎ 05 49 48 51 70
Vigeant Motor Circuit 6 km. A stunning family home right in the heart of the village. The property has three bedrooms, one grade 3 double guest room, one grade 2 double guest room each with private bathroom and one grade 2 guest room with a double bed and two single with a private bathroom on the landing. The sitting room has an open fireplace, books and magazines and the shaded garden has outdoor furniture. Isle Jourdain leisure centre 10 km. Garage parking. Open all year except 1-15 October.
PRICES: s €27-€30; d €35-€38; t €43 **ON SITE:** Fishing Hiking Tennis **NEARBY:** Bathing (12km) Theme park (82km) Sailing (6km) Railway station (35km) AVAILLES-LIMOUZINE **NOTES:** Pets admitted

AVANTON

♦♦♦ Ferme du Château Annie ARRONDEAU
Martigny, 86170 AVANTON
☎ 05 49 51 04 57 & SR : 05 49 49 59 11 📠 05 49 51 04 57
e-mail: annie.arrondeau@libertysurf.fr
http://www.lafermeduchateau.fr
Poitiers 10 km. Futuroscope 2 km. In the grounds of the Château de Martigny, stands a stunningly restored Poitou farmhouse. There are three guest rooms all with their own private bathrooms and wc. One double with a cot and one double with a 130cm bed. There is also a grade 2 family room with a mezzanine which has one double, one 120cm bed and one single. This room also has a TV and shower. Kitchenette, sitting room and library. Delicious breakfasts can be enjoyed on the terrace overlooking the enclosed garden. Swimming pool, table and bicycles. Reduced rates for stays over two nights; tax is included in the price. Open all year.
PRICES: s €34-€39; d €42-€45; t €54-€57 **ON SITE:** Bathing Hiking **NEARBY:** Canoeing (3km) Horse riding (10km) Golf (12km) Theme park (2km) Fishing (3km) Tennis (3km) Sailing (11km) Railway station (11km) Shops (3km) NEUVILLE-DE-POITOU (5km) **NOTES:** No pets English spoken

♦♦♦ Chambre d'hôtes Jocelyne FERRAND-MOREAU
15, route de Preuilly, Martigny, 86170 AVANTON
☎ 05 49 54 02 02
Poitiers 10 km. Futuroscope 2 km. Situated in an large, enclosed garden full of trees this independent house offers two studio rooms, one with two doubles and one with one double and a 130cm bed. In the main house there is a grade 1 room with one double and one single bed. All the rooms have their own private wash facilities, wc and kitchenette. Terraces, garden furniture, a barbecue and parking. Table tennis, table football and other games, a TV and hi-fi are all available for guests. Reduced rates for stays of more than two nights. Tourist tax payable. Open all year.
PRICES: s €30; d €38; t €49 **NEARBY:** Bathing (10km) Canoeing (15km) Horse riding (12km) Golf (10km) Theme park (2km) Fishing (3km) Tennis (5km) Sailing (10km) Railway station (11km) Shops (3km) NEUVILLE-DE-POITOU (5km) **NOTES:** Pets admitted English spoken

BEUXES

♦♦♦ Moulin Pallu Danielle LECOMTE
86120 BEUXES
☎ 05 49 98 70 55
Chinon 12 km. Loudun 12 km. Close to the Châteaux of the Loire, a 19th-century family home with a wonderful rustic feel. The property has three guest rooms. On the ground floor is a double room with an extra single bed and a cot can be provided. On the second floor there is one double room, and one room with a double and a single bed. All the rooms have their own private

continued

shower room and wc. Library. Near Richelieu Fontevraud Abbey.
Restaurant 6 km. Open all year.
PRICES: s €34; d €40; t €49 **NEARBY:** Bathing (12km) Canoeing
(12km) Horse riding (12km) Golf (18km) Theme park (25km) Fishing
(3km) Hiking (1km) Tennis (8km) Sailing (12km) Railway station (12km)
Shops (1km) LOUDUN (12km) **NOTES:** Pets admitted

BONNES

🕪 I◎I Les Barbalières Dannie HERVE
1 rue des Courlis, 86300 BONNES
☎ 05 49 46 53 58 📠 05 49 01 86 54
Chauvigny 2 km. Futuroscope 25 km. Chauvigny, city of art and
history, is situated in the heart of a popular tourist region and has
guided tours and a wonderful summer festival. This large early
19th-century family house is situated very close to the D749, in
beautifully picturesque gardens. Five guest rooms, one double,
one room with two doubles, and a third room with one double
and one single. All the rooms have private shower rooms and wc.
Living room with plenty of books to read, a TV and telephone.
Guest menu available with prior notice. Open all year.
PRICES: s €34; d €42; t €54; dinner €14 **NEARBY:** Bathing (2km) Horse
riding (6km) Golf (12km) Theme park (12km) Fishing (2km) Hiking
(2km) Tennis (12km) Sailing (12km) Railway station (15km) Shops (2km)
SAINT-JULIEN-L'ARS (8km) **NOTES:** No pets

BONNEUIL-MATOURS

🕪 Les Pierres Blanches Nicole GALLAIS-PRADAL
Chemin des Pierres Blanches, 86210 BONNEUIL-MATOURS
☎ 05 49 85 24 75 & SR : 05 49 49 59 11
Poitiers 20 km. Futuroscope 15 km. Situated between forest and
Vienne a large house in a wonderful wooded park which boasts
over 200 rose bushes. One double room with an extra single bed,
one double room and a third, grade 2 double room. There are
private washing facilities and wc as well as extra beds available on
request. A private terrace overlooks the park, there is a sitting
room with an open fireplace and magazines for the guests. The
private swimming pool is unsupervised and has a wonderful
summer dining room for picnics by the pool. Fresh sandwiches can
be ordered. Parking. Open all year.
PRICES: s €34; d €40-€43; t €55 **ON SITE:** Bathing Canoeing Fishing
Hiking Tennis **NEARBY:** Horse riding (10km) Golf (10km) Theme park
(10km) Sailing (10km) Railway station (20km) Shops (1km) VOUNEUIL-
SUR-VIENNE (5km) **NOTES:** Pets admitted by arrangement English
spoken

See advert on this page

BOURNAND

🕪 I◎I La Dorelle Joseph THOMAS
86120 BOURNAND
☎ 05 49 98 72 23 📠 05 49 98 62 88
e-mail: ladorelle@voila.fr http://www.ladorelle.com
Chinon 5 km. Loudun 5 km. In a calm hamlet four guest rooms in
a beautifully restored stone farmhouse, separate from the owners'
home. Very close to Fontevraud Abbey, Roiffé golf course and
Futuroscope. One double room on the ground floor. On the first
floor there are three guest rooms; one twin, and two doubles each
with private bathroom and wc. A sitting room with open fireplace,
magazines and books as well as a kitchenette for self-catering. A
terrace overlooks the garden, with barbecue and garden furniture.
Extra beds are available on request. Open all year.
PRICES: s €38; d €46; dinner €17 **NEARBY:** Bathing (10km) Golf
(10km) Theme park (20km) Fishing (3km) Tennis (2km) Sailing (10km)
Railway station (30km) Shops (5km) LES-TROIS-MOUTIERS (5km)
NOTES: No pets English spoken

Les Pierres Blanches

A large house of charm, which is situated in a park
of trees and flowers including several varieties of
roses, has three en-suite bedrooms. Two of the
bedrooms have a private terrace with garden
furniture, all en-suite. Private swimming pool with
deckchairs and take-away sandwiches, ideal for
summer eating and sun bathing.
Futuroscope 15kms. Poitiers, town of art and
history, 20kms.

**Chemin des Pierres Blanches
86210 Bonneuil-Matours
Tel: 05 49 85 24 75**

BRUX

🕪 🐦 I◎I Chez Saboureau Danielle TOULAT
86510 BRUX
☎ 05 49 59 23 04 📠 05 49 53 41 87
Vallée des Singes 10 mn. Three large farmhouse-style guest rooms
on the first floor of this lovely old house with independent
entrance for guests. The first room has one double and two
singles, the second has one double and an extra bed if required,
the third has two 120cm beds. Each room has its own private
bathroom and wc. There is a lounge exclusively for the guests, a
veranda, and games for children as well as table tennis. Picnics can
be arranged and a guest menu is available with prior notice. The
well-tended garden offers shade. Leisure park 15 km away with a
miniature port, ULM Aerodrome 10 km and many Roman churches
close by. Inn 1 km Open all year.
PRICES: s €31; d €36-€38; t €45; dinner €10-€13 **ON SITE:** Children's
play area Hiking **NEARBY:** Bathing (12km) Horse riding (9km) Theme
park (15km) Fishing (15km) Tennis (5km) Railway station (15km) Shops
(5km) COUHE (11km) **NOTES:** No pets

CELLE-L'EVESCAULT

🕪 🐦 I◎I Château de la Livraie Eva MORIN
La Livraie, 86600 CELLE-L'EVESCAULT
☎ 05 49 43 52 59
Poitiers 22 km. Marais-Poitevin 50 km. Futuroscope 25 mn. In this
fabulous undulating countryside a renovated château surrounded
by a densely wooded park. A peaceful and beautiful setting with a
small river and farm animals. The comfortable rooms have antique
furniture. One double room, one double with an extra single bed,
one double room with a 120cm bed and a single bed, all with
private bathroom facilities and wc. One family suite consisting of
two rooms, one double and one twin with shower room and wc.

continued

Lounge with TV, table tennis and other games. A guest menu is available on request. Open from 15 January to 1 December.

Château de La livraie, Celle-l'Evescault

PRICES: s €37; d €43-€46; t €53-€58; dinner €14 **ON SITE:** Fishing **NEARBY:** Bathing (3km) Horse riding (8km) Theme park (35km) Hiking (1km) Tennis (3km) Railway station (6km) Shops (3km) LUSIGNAN (5km) **NOTES:** No pets

CHAMPNIERS

⊪ Chambre d'hôtes Jean-Louis et G FAZILLEAU
Le Bourg, 86400 CHAMPNIERS
☎ 05 49 87 19 04 ▤ 05 49 87 96 94
e-mail: jeanlouis.fazilleau@free.fr
Vallée des Singes 4 km. In a quiet market town this traditional stone house is situated only 9 km from St Nicolas de Civray, famous for its Roman churches. Three rooms on the first floor, one grade 3 guest room with one double and two singles and a private bathroom. One grade 2 room with two 110cm beds and a private shower room and one grade 2 double room with a shower room on the landing and wc. Extra beds can be arranged on request. There is a guests' sitting room with books, table tennis and a piano. The veranda overlooks a very pretty garden and parking is available. Open all year.
PRICES: s €31-€34; d €34-€38; t €53 **ON SITE:** Hiking **NEARBY:** Bathing (9km) Canoeing (9km) Horse riding (14km) Theme park (60km) Fishing (9km) Tennis (3km) Sailing (30km) Railway station (14km) Shops (9km) CIVRAY (7km) **NOTES:** Pets admitted English spoken

CHARRAIS

⊪ Charrajou Jean-Yves et Martine MARTINET
16 rue des Ormeaux, 86170 CHARRAIS
☎ 05 49 51 14 62 ▤ 05 49 51 14 62

Poitiers 18 km. Futuroscope 12 km. Jean-Yves and Martine welcome guests to their traditional stone Poitevin house situated in the heart of the Haut Poiteau wine region. The house has four first floor guest bedrooms with independent access for guests. There are two rooms with one double and one single, one room with three singles and one double. All the guest rooms have private

shower room and wc. The lounge and kitchenette are exclusively for the guests. There is a large enclosed courtyard that also has parking. Open all year.
PRICES: s €32; d €37; t €49 **NEARBY:** Bathing (3km) Canoeing (20km) Horse riding (15km) Golf (25km) Theme park (12km) Fishing (12km) Hiking (10km) Tennis (3km) Sailing (12km) Railway station (18km) Shops (3km) NEUVILLE-DE-POITOU (2km) **NOTES:** No pets English spoken
See advert on opposite page

CHAUVIGNY

⊪ Chambre d'hôtes Bernadette BRACHET
8, Plan St-Pierre, Le Montléon, 86300 CHAUVIGNY
☎ 05 49 46 88 96
Futuroscope 20 mn. On the doorstep of Futuroscope, in the heart of a charming medieval town, this house dating back to the 12th and 15th centuries has five guest rooms. On the first floor there are four double rooms and one room with one double and one single, all with private shower room and wc. Extra beds can be arranged. Parking 50m. Chauvigny, city of art and history that has a renowned summer festival and spectacular falcon displays. Open all year.
PRICES: s €26; d €37; t €49 **ON SITE:** Hiking **NEARBY:** Bathing (1km) Canoeing (14km) Horse riding (15km) Golf (25km) Theme park (25km) Fishing (1km) Tennis (1km) Railway station (25km) CHAUVIGNY **NOTES:** No pets

⊪ La Veaudepierre Jacques et Claude DE GIAFFERRI
8, rue du Berry, 86300 CHAUVIGNY
☎ 05 49 46 30 81 & 05 49 41 41 76 ▤ 05 49 47 64 12
e-mail: laveaudepierre@club-internet.fr
http://www.perso.laveaudepierre.club-internet.fr

Futuroscope 20 mn. A stunning 18th-century residence with exceptional views of the châteaux, close to Chauvigny, this is a great place to stay. The accommodation offers one single, two doubles, one of which has an adjoining single room and one grade 2 double room with private bathroom and wc. Extra beds are available on request. Sitting room. Parking on site and the garden offers shade and excellent views. Open from Easter to 1 November school holidays reservations only.
PRICES: s €32-€40; d €40-€47; t €56 **ON SITE:** Bathing Fishing Tennis **NEARBY:** Canoeing (14km) Horse riding (21km) Golf (18km) Theme park (25km) Hiking (1km) Sailing (25km) Railway station (23km) CHAUVIGNY **NOTES:** No pets English spoken

CHENECHE

⊪ Château de Labarom Eric LE GALLAIS
86380 CHENECHE
☎ 05 49 51 24 22 & SR : 05 49 49 59 11 ▤ 05 49 51 47 38
e-mail: chateau.de.labarom@wanadoo.fr
A 16th and 18th-century château nestled in a stunning park with a swimming pool. One room with two single beds, private shower room and wc, two family suites, the first comprising one room with double bed, one room with two single beds, private bathroom and wc. The second suite has one room with two 110cm beds, one

continued

continued

room with two single beds and a private shower room and wc. There is a sitting room full of books for guests. Proprietor's mobile phone: 06.83.57.68.14. Open from Easter to 1 November.

PRICES: s €53-€61; d €61-€69; t €76-€84 **ON SITE:** Bathing Hiking **NEARBY:** Horse riding (16km) Golf (18km) Theme park (15km) Fishing (5km) Tennis (2km) Sailing (18km) Railway station (22km) Shops (4km) POITIERS (22km) **NOTES:** No pets English spoken

DANGE-SAINT-ROMAIN

ＴＴＴ ＩＯＩ **La Grenouillière** Annie et Noël BRAGUIER
17 rue de la Grenouillère,
86220 DANGE-ST-ROMAIN
☎ 05 49 86 48 68　🖷 05 49 86 46 56

Futuroscope 25 mn. A stunning 19th-century farmhouse in a glorious wooded park with a river running through it. On the ground floor are two rooms, one with three single beds has access for the less mobile, and the other is a double room with private washing facilities and wc. On the first floor are three guest rooms, each with private washing facilities and wc. One double room is in the proprietors' part of the house; the other two rooms are in an annexe and consist of one double and one grade 2 room with three single beds. The sitting room boasts an open fireplace. There is an enclosed courtyard, a conservatory, table tennis and other outdoor games available. The owners are happy to suggest interesting excursions, the Châteaux of the Loire is one of the most popular. Guest menu is available, except 24 December to 2 January, if notice is given by midday. Open all year.
PRICES: s €28-€34; d €42-€45; t €45-€55; dinner €18
ON SITE: Children's play area Fishing Hiking **NEARBY:** Bathing (15km) Canoeing (15km) Horse riding (3km) Golf (25km) Theme park (25km) Tennis (2km) Sailing (15km) Railway station (1km) DANGE-SAINT-ROMAIN **NOTES:** No pets English spoken

JOURNET

ＴＴＴ ＹＹ ＩＯＩ **Le Haut Peu** Jacques et Chantal COCHIN
86290 JOURNET
☎ 05 49 91 62 02　🖷 05 49 91 59 71
St-Savin 15 km. A farm offering three guest rooms in a family mansion. One double with private shower room and wc, one room

Chambres d'hôte
chez Martine Martinet

On arrival, there is a warm welcome by your hosts with a glass of cider and information about the region and places to visit. The four spacious bedrooms each with its own entrance have been modernised with much care; all include en-suite facilities. Some overlook the courtyard or the fields. Peace and quiet is assured. You will enjoy a hearty breakfast with homemade preserves and milk from the farm. Ideal for exploring the numerous wine routes of the area or visiting Futuroscope 13 kms.

**16 rue des Ormeaux au hameau de Charrajou
86170 Charrais
Tel: 05 49 51 14 62**

with double cm bed, private shower room and wc. In a separate building there is a family suite with mezzanine which has one double, two singles and one double bed, private bathroom and wc. There is a kitchen as well. This beautiful, shady park has its own lake. A guest menu is available except on Sundays. 10% reduction for stays of one week or more and for couples under 28 years. The frescoes in St-Savin are classified by UNESCO as a world heritage site. Open from 1 February to 30 November.
PRICES: s €41; d €44; t €58; dinner €17 **ON SITE:** Fishing Hiking **NEARBY:** Bathing (10km) Canoeing (20km) Horse riding (10km) Tennis (10km) Railway station (10km) Shops (10km) LA TRIMOUILLE (5km) **NOTES:** No pets English spoken

LA TRIMOUILLE

ＴＴＴ ＩＯＩ **Toel** Gérard VOUHE
86290 LA TRIMOUILLE
☎ 05 49 91 67 59　🖷 05 49 91 55 66
Montmorillon 15 km. L'Ile aux Serpents 3 km. With the collegiate of St Savin, famous for its frescoes, nearby this beautifully renovated house is only two km off the Paris-Limoges road. There are three rooms in all, one grade 3 room with a double and a single bed, as well as its own private bathroom and wc. Two, grade 2, double rooms also have the potential for extra beds if required. Each room has its own shower room and wc. Centrally heated, sitting room, library, garden room and games. There is also a park with ponies. Open all year, reservation required.
PRICES: s €30; d €34-€41; t €50; dinner €14 **NEARBY:** Canoeing (15km) Horse riding (15km) Golf (7km) Theme park (76km) Fishing (2km) Hiking (15km) Tennis (2km) Sailing (15km) Railway station (15km) Shops (2km) MONTMORILLON (12km) **NOTES:** No pets

continued

POITOU-CHARENTES

LATILLE

♦♦♦ ⑩ Chambre d'hôtes Yvonne FLAMBEAU
1 place Robert Gerbier, 86190 LATILLE
☎ 05 49 51 54 74 🖷 05 49 51 56 32
e-mail: latille@chez.com http://www.chez.com/latille

An old post office dating back to 1785, 20 minutes from Futuroscope and Poitiers. There are three double rooms, one room with a 160cm bed and a family suite consisting of one double, one twin and private shower room and wc for each. Extra beds are available if required. Table tennis, boules and other outdoor games. Library and TV. Open February to mid-November.
PRICES: s €39; d €40; t €54; extra person €11; dinner €11-€21
ON SITE: Children's play area Fishing Hiking Tennis **NEARBY:** Bathing (4km) Canoeing (25km) Horse riding (15km) Golf (7km) Theme park (4km) Sailing (4km) Railway station (25km) VOUILLE (8km)
NOTES: Pets admitted by arrangement English spoken

LUCHAPT

♦♦♦ ⑩ Chez Mairine Annemée et Patrick VAN AUBEL
86430 LUCHAPT
☎ 05 49 48 89 65
e-mail: PatrickVanaubel@wanadoo.fr
Nestled in a wonderful undulating region, only 5 km from the Isle Jourdain leisure centre, is a pleasant Poitevine farmhouse. Donkeys, horses, sheep and poultry. A grade 2 double, one double with an extra single and a twin room. Each room has its own private shower room and wc. There is a cosy sitting room with books, magazines and music, and a kitchenette. The owners breed deer on site and a visit to the deer farm is free.
Open 1 March to 31 December.
PRICES: s €30; d €37; t €46; dinner €18 **ON SITE:** Hiking **NEARBY:** Bathing (5km) Canoeing (7km) Horse riding (5km) Theme park (5km) Fishing (2km) Tennis (5km) Sailing (8km) Railway station (23km) Shops (5km) L'ISLE JOURDAIN (5km) **NOTES:** Pets admitted English spoken

NEUVILLE-DE-POITOU

♦♦♦ 🐓 ⑩ La Galerne Yvette PAVY
Chemin de Couture, 86170 NEUVILLE-DE-POITOU
☎ 05 49 51 14 07 & SR : 05 49 49 59 11 🖷 05 49 54 47 82
Poitiers 15 mn. Futuroscope 10 mn. In the heart of a stunning park full of trees and flowers stands this contemporary house with five guest rooms, each with independent access. This is a really friendly place to stay. There is one double with an extra two single beds, a room with one double and one single bed and three double rooms. Each has private shower room and wc. Extra beds on request. There is a terrace looking out onto the park, garden furniture and an unsupervised swimming pool. Open all year.
PRICES: s €30; d €38; t €46; dinner €14 **ON SITE:** Bathing
NEARBY: Canoeing (16km) Golf (16km) Theme park (8km) Fishing (16km) Tennis (1km) Sailing (16km) Railway station (10km) Shops (1km) NEUVILLE-DE-POITOU **NOTES:** No pets

♦♦♦ ⑩ La Roseraie Christian PRAY
78 rue Armand Caillard, 86170 NEUVILLE-DE-POITOU
☎ 05 49 54 16 72 & SR : 05 49 49 59 11 🖷 05 49 51 69 04
e-mail: evelynepray@aol.com

Poitiers 15 km. A stunning family home in the heart of a park. The property has four guest rooms, one double on the ground floor, two doubles on the first floor each with its own bathroom and wc. On the second floor there is a family suite with one double and one twin, private shower room and wc. Another family room houses five single beds. Extra beds can be arranged. The sitting room has an open fireplace and there is a large terrace and garden furniture, outdoor games and table tennis. Heated swimming pool (unsupervised). Table d'hôte meals (€9 for children under 15). A reduction of 10%, outside of school holidays for stays of three nights or more when booked in advance. Open 4 January to 22 December.
PRICES: s €35; d €42; dinner €14 **ON SITE:** Children's play area Bathing **NEARBY:** Theme park (11km) Fishing (9km) Hiking (9km) Tennis (1km) Sailing (16km) Railway station (15km) NEUVILLE-DE-POITOU **NOTES:** No pets English spoken

PAYROUX

♦♦♦ La Touche Jean-Marie DUVIVIER
86350 PAYROUX
☎ 05 49 87 82 78 🖷 05 49 87 02 72
Abbaye de Charroux 12 km. Civray (église St-Nicolas) 17 km. Known for its beautiful winter garden this lovely house offers two doubles and one double with an extra single bed. The rooms share a grade 1 bathroom on the ground floor. There is a grade 3 room with one double and one single bed with its own private bathroom and wc on the first floor. Living room with magazines, a TV and music. Unsupervised swimming pool. Open all year.
PRICES: s €30; d €38; t €46 **ON SITE:** Bathing Fishing
NEARBY: Canoeing (40km) Golf (45km) Theme park (30km) Hiking (2km) Tennis (2km) Sailing (25km) Railway station (25km) Shops (7km) CHARROUX (14km) **NOTES:** No pets

POITIERS

♦♦♦ Château de Vaumoret Daniel et Agnès VAUCAMP
Rue du Breuil Mingot, 86000 POITIERS
☎ 05 49 61 32 11 & SR : 05 49 49 59 11 🖷 05 49 01 04 54
Futuroscope 10 mn. Tucked away in the attic of a small 17th-century château, situated in a peaceful location, are three charming guest rooms. One double with an additional two 80cm beds, and two further twins. Each room has its own private shower room and wc. Kitchen, sitting room with TV, stereo, books and magazines. Bicycles available. The château is a perfect departure point to explore the Haut Poiteau and the valleys of the Vienne region. Open all year.
PRICES: s €46-€56; d €54-€68; t €78 **ON SITE:** Hiking
NEARBY: Bathing (6km) Horse riding (5km) Golf (9km) Theme park (10km) Fishing (16km) Tennis (3km) Sailing (16km) Railway station (8km) Shops (3km) POITIERS **NOTES:** Pets admitted English spoken
See advert on opposite page

SAVIGNY-L'EVESCAULT

♦♦♦ Château de la Touche Michel et Monique TABAU
86800 SAVIGNY-L'EVESCAULT
☎ 05 49 01 10 38 & SR : 05 49 49 59 11 📠 05 49 56 47 82
e-mail: infos@chateaudelatouche.com
http://www.chateaudelatouche.com

In the heart of a 12-hectare park a warm welcome awaits at this
17th-century château, 15 km from both Poitiers and Chauvigny.
There are large air-conditioned rooms, one double with a sitting
room, another double and one twin. All rooms have private
bathrooms and wc. There are restaurants close by. Open from 1
April to 31 October and during school holidays.

PRICES: s €60-€90; d €90-€120 **ON SITE:** Hiking
NEARBY: Bathing (15km) Horse riding (20km) Golf (5km) Theme park
(22km) Fishing (1km) Tennis (2km) Railway station (15km) Shops (5km)
SAINT-JULIEN-L'ARS (2km) **NOTES:** Pets admitted English spoken

ST-GENEST-D'AMBIERE

♦♦♦ ℺ La Garenne Anne MICHEAU
86140 ST-GENEST-D'AMBIERE
☎ 05 49 90 71 98 & 06 11 04 17 95 📠 05 49 90 71 98
e-mail: amicheau@lagarenne.com
http://www.lagarenne.com

Futuroscope 21 km. Situated between the Futuroscope and the
Château of the Loire, is this beautiful house full of character,
surrounded by stunning woodland. Anne offers five pretty guest
rooms. There are two family suites of two rooms with one double
and two children's beds and two doubles. Each room has its own
private bathroom and wc. One of the rooms is situated on the
ground floor with independent access. There is a guests' sitting
room with open fireplace, TV, books and magazines. Health and
beauty centre on site. Open from 5 January to 30 December.

PRICES: s €45; d €48-€55; t €61; dinner €25 **ON SITE:** Hiking
NEARBY: Bathing (15km) Horse riding (10km) Golf (15km)
Theme park (21km) Fishing (15km) Tennis (2km) Sailing (15km) Railway
station (17km) Shops (1km) LENCLOITRE (2km)
NOTES: Pets admitted

Château de Vaumoret
Rue du Breuil Mingot
86000 Poitiers

Situated in a 15-hectare park the 17th century château is
ideal for exploring the historic places of interest of the
surrounding region. Only 10 minutes from Futuroscope
(Theme Park). The nearest town, Poitiers is just six miles
away, has many picturesque squares and pavement cafés
along with the palace, cathedral and several beautiful
churches. The château is very peaceful, perfect for either
relaxing or for the more energetic, bikes can be hired and
there are stables and tennis courts nearby.
The three guest rooms have en-suite facilities, central
heating, television and are charmingly furnished.
One room is suitable for families.

Tel: 00 33 05 49 61 32 11
Fax: 00 33 05 49 01 04 54

ST-SAVIN

♦♦♦ ℺ Siouvres Jacky et Charline BARBARIN
86310 ST-SAVIN ☎ 05 49 48 10 19 📠 05 49 48 46 89
e-mail: Charline.Barbarin@wanadoo.fr
http://www.lafermeapicole.fr.st

Charline and Jacky welcome you to their late 18th-century Poitevine
farmhouse. Tranquillity is guaranteed in this lovely spot not to
mention an insight into bee keeping. Futuroscope is only 40 minutes
away. There are three rooms in total of which two are in an
independent house. There are two doubles on the ground floor, one
room with a double and a fold-out bed, one room on the first floor
with two double beds and a kitchenette. Private wash facilities for
each room. Extra beds on request. There is a barbecue, children's
toys and table tennis. 10% discount for stays of five nights or longer.
Tourist tax payable. Open 1 March until 1 November

PRICES: s €32; d €40; t €47 **ON SITE:** Children's play area Hiking
NEARBY: Bathing (2km) Canoeing (6km) Horse riding (4km) Golf
(35km) Theme park (45km) Fishing (2km) Tennis (2km) Sailing (35km)
Railway station (20km) Shops (2km) SAINT-SAVIN **NOTES:** Pets
admitted

USSEAU

♦♦♦ ⧫ La Motte Jean-Marie et M BARDIN
Château de la Motte, 86230 USSEAU
☎ 05 49 85 88 25 ▤ 05 49 85 89 85
e-mail: j-marie.bardin@wanadoo.fr
This 15th-century château, surrounded by ancient lime trees, offers
a variety of guest rooms including a large suite with its own open
fireplace. Two rooms with one 160cm bed and a 120cm bed and
one room with one 160cm bed. Each room has its own washing
facilities and wc. The grounds have a swimming pool and
badminton court. Guests can enjoy local produce served as part of
the guest menu in the dining room. Music, parlour games and
books are provided in the elegant sitting room, there is also a
library. Open 1 February to 1 December.
PRICES: s €47-€78; d €53-€84; t €84-€99; dinner €11-€23
ON SITE: Bathing **NEARBY:** Canoeing (7km) Horse riding (4km) Golf
(20km) Theme park (20km) Fishing (5km) Hiking (1km) Tennis (7km)
Sailing (20km) Railway station (8km) Shops (8km) SAINT-GERVAIS-LES-3-
CLOCHERS (13km) **NOTES:** No pets English spoken

VARENNES

♦♦♦ Manoir de Vilaines Philippe SIMONNET
Vilaines, 86110 VARENNES
☎ 05 49 60 73 93 & SR : 05 49 49 59 11
Leisure park at St-Cyr 20 km. Dominating the wine region of Haut-
Poitou this is a house with real character. On the ground floor one
family suite that has a sitting room with one single and one 120cm
bed and another room with one double and a single. On the first
floor another family suite with one double, a sitting room which
can be used as a bedroom and another double room. All the
rooms have private bathrooms and wc. Extra beds can be
arranged. Large guests' living room, a garden room and stunning
landscaped grounds. The property is close to the regions' wine
circuit. Open all year.
PRICES: s €32-€37; d €40-€43; t €55 **ON SITE:** Hiking
NEARBY: Bathing (20km) Horse riding (16km) Golf (20km) Theme park
(20km) Fishing (1km) Tennis (4km) Sailing (20km) Railway station
(25km) Shops (4km) MIREBEAU (4km) **NOTES:** No pets

VELLECHES

♦♦♦ 🐓 ⧫ La Blonnerie Marie-France MASSONNET
86230 VELLECHES
☎ 05 49 86 41 72 ▤ 05 49 86 41 72
Futuroscope 30 km. In beautifully wooded surroundings, this farm
has three rooms on offer. One suite comprises one double room,
and a sitting room with two pull-out beds and a TV. One double
room with two extra pull-out beds, TV and a double sofa bed.
Finally there is one room with a single bed and a 160cm bed,
sitting area and TV. Each room has private washing facilities and
wc. Guests' lounge with games and a furnished terrace with
wonderful views. There is a lake in the grounds where guests can
fish and a botanical park. Hunting in season. Inn on site. The
house is very close to the Châteaux of the Loire. Open all year.
PRICES: s €33; d €39; t €48; dinner €14 **ON SITE:** Children's play area
Fishing Hiking **NEARBY:** Bathing (13km) Canoeing (13km) Horse riding
(15km) Golf (35km) Theme park (27km) Tennis (7km) Sailing (27km)
Railway station (13km) Shops (7km) Restaurant nearby SAINT-GERVAIS-
LES-3-CLOCHERS (7km) **NOTES:** No pets

VENDEUVRE

♦♦♦ ⧫ Domaine de la Fuie Micheline CHAUZAMY
Bataille, 86380 VENDEUVRE-DU-POITOU
☎ 05 49 51 34 95 & SR : 05 49 49 59 11 ▤ 05 49 54 08 81
http://lafuie.com
Futuroscope 10 mn. Poitiers 15 mn. This 17th-century stately home

is set in the heart of wonderful wooded grounds with lots of
interesting flowers. M and Mme Chauzamy welcome you to their
peaceful home. The property offers one grade 2 room with one
double and one single. On the first floor there are two rooms with
one double and one single in each, one grade 2 room, with two
double beds and one single bed each. All the rooms have their
own bathroom and wc. There is a further grade 2 double room
with private bathroom and wc. Garden with a covered swimming
pool, (swimming, unsupervised, guaranteed between 15 May-30
September). Boules, table tennis and private parking. Open all year.

PRICES: s €34; d €37; t €49; dinner €14 **ON SITE:** Bathing
NEARBY: Horse riding (1km) Golf (15km) Theme park (9km) Fishing
(3km) Hiking (4km) Tennis (3km) Sailing (15km) Railway station (17km)
Shops (4km) NEUVILLE-DE-POITOU (9km) **NOTES:** No pets

VOULON

♦♦♦ Moulin de Villenon Janick CUVILLIER
86700 VOULON
☎ 05 49 42 07 38 ▤ 05 49 42 88 09
Futuroscope 35 km. A beautifully restored windmill offer peace
and quiet. The property has three double guestrooms, on one
floor, each with a private shower room and wc. There is also a
lovely sitting room. Outside the grounds are wooded and there is a
lake for fishing; five minutes away is a boating centre. Mountain
bikes can be hired on site. Open from 1 July to 31 August.
PRICES: ; d €46 **ON SITE:** Canoeing Horse riding Fishing Hiking
NEARBY: Bathing (12km) Theme park (3km) Railway station (2km)
Shops (10km) COUHE (12km) **NOTES:** No pets English spoken

VOUNEUIL-SOUS-BIARD

♦♦♦ ⧫ Le Grand Mazais Jean-Pierre CARCEL
86580 VOUNEUIL-SOUS-BIARD
☎ 05 49 53 40 31 ▤ 05 49 43 69 94

Poitiers 4 km. Futuroscope 12 km. At the gateway into Poitiers
stands this beautiful late 17th-century master's house. On the first
floor are three large guest rooms each containing a double bed.
All the rooms have private bathrooms or shower rooms and wc.
There is also a family suite consisting of two rooms each with one

continued

continued

double, two singles and private shower room and wc. Sitting room, menu available with 48 hours notice. There is a swimming pool, unsupervised, in the 1.5-hectare grounds. Open all year.
PRICES: s €58-€66; d €69-€76; t €84; dinner €38 **ON SITE:** Bathing
NEARBY: Canoeing (3km) Horse riding (2km) Golf (6km) Theme park (3km) Fishing (1km) Hiking (1km) Tennis (3km) Railway station (4km) Shops (2km) POITIERS (4km) **NOTES:** No pets English spoken

VOUNEUIL-SUR-VIENNE

₩₩₩ **La Pocterie** Martine POUSSARD
86210 VOUNEUIL-SUR-VIENNE
☎ 05 49 85 11 96 & SR : 05 49 49 59 11

Futuroscope 16 km. Close to a nature reserve and only 11 km from a leisure centre is a very pretty house full of charm and quality. On the ground floor is one grade 3 room with one double and one

continued

single, private shower room and wc. Also on the ground floor a grade 2 double room again with private shower room and wc. On the first floor is a large grade 3 guestroom with one double and a sofa bed, also with private washing facilities. A terrace overlooks the large garden which is full of flowers. Open all year.
PRICES: s €34; d €40-€43; t €55 **ON SITE:** Bathing Hiking
NEARBY: Canoeing (3km) Horse riding (4km) Golf (11km) Theme park (11km) Fishing (1km) Tennis (3km) Sailing (11km) Railway station (13km) Shops (2km) VOUNEUIL-SUR-VIENNE **NOTES:** Pets admitted English spoken

₩₩₩ **Les Hauts de Chabonnes** Florence PENOT
86210 VOUNEUIL-SUR-VIENNE
☎ 05 49 85 28 25 & SR : 05 49 49 59 11   ▤ 05 49 85 55 17
In a small hamlet only 6 km from the nearest leisure centre and 500m from a forest and nature reserve with stunning flora and fauna, is this stylishly renovated house. Guest accommodation is separate from the proprietors' own home. On the ground floor are three rooms each with one double and one single as well as private bathroom and wc. On the first floor are two grade 2 double rooms, again each with private bathroom and wc. The sitting room has an open fireplace, TV, books and magazines and there is also a garden. For visits out of season or for three nights or more there is a reduction of 10%. Open all year.
PRICES: s €37; d €43-€46; t €58 **ON SITE:** Hiking **NEARBY:** Bathing (6km) Canoeing (3km) Horse riding (2km) Golf (6km) Theme park (6km) Fishing (6km) Tennis (1km) Sailing (6km) Railway station (15km) Shops (1km) VOUNEUIL-SUR-VIENNE **NOTES:** Pets admitted English spoken

PROVENCE-ALPES-CÔTE-D'AZUR

ALPES-DE-HAUTE-PROVENCE

ALLEMAGNE-EN-PROVENCE

₩₩₩ **Domaine de Bertrandy**
Bert et Gerda VERREPT-DE SMET
04500 ALLEMAGNE-EN-PROVENCE
☎ 04 92 77 83 58   ▤ 04 92 77 83 58
Riez 5 km. Moustiers-Ste-Marie and the Gorges du Verdon 15 km. Two gîtes created from the proprietors' house in the lavender fields of the Valensole Plateau. With ground floor entry on one side of the house, this property consists of three double bedrooms with private bathrooms and wc, one twin room with a shower room and wc, a family room with a double bed and two singles on the mezzanine floor and next to that a double room with shower room and wc. There is also a furnished terrace. Nearby is the castle of Allemagne-en-Provence and the listed town of Riez. Prices: four people 78-88 euros; five people 98-104 euros; six people 108-119 euros.
PRICES: s €32-€37; d €44-€49; t €59-€66 **ON SITE:** Hiking
NEARBY: Bathing (15km) Horse riding (1km) Fishing (3km) Stretch of water (13km) Shops (15km) **NOTES:** No pets

BARCELONNETTE

₩₩₩ **Le Bosquet** Claudine VILLAIN
2, avenue Watton de Ferry, 04400 BARCELONNETTE
☎ 04 92 81 41 28
Jausiers 8 km. Pra-Loup 12 km. This renovated chambres d'hôtes is in the heart of bustling Barcelonnette, with its museum and

Mexican houses. It offers a ground-floor double bedroom, while the first floor is home to two rooms with a double and a single bed each, and another bedroom with a double bed and bunk beds. All bedrooms have private shower room and wc. Large lounge with fireplace. Nearby is a local swimming pool, forest walks, the Mercantour National Park, paragliding at the local aerodrome (2 km), the lake at Jausiers, skiing at Pra-Loup, and water-sports on the Ubaye. Special offer from 29 December to 22 October, stay one week get the seventh night free.
PRICES: d €41-€45; t €50-€53 **NEARBY:** Horse riding (2km) Forest (1km) Fishing (1km) Swimming pool (1km) Stretch of water (8km) Hiking (1km) Downhill skiing (12km) **NOTES:** Pets admitted by prior arrangement

CHATEAUNEUF-VAL-SAINT-DONAT

₩₩₩ ◎ **Mas Saint-Joseph** Hélène et Olivier LENOIR
04200 CHATEAUNEUF-VAL-SAINT-DONAT
☎ 04 92 62 47 54
e-mail: lenoir.st.jo@wanadoo.fr
Sisteron 12 km. Les Mées 10 km. At the foot of the Lure Mountain with its immense forest, this 18th-century former farm is surrounded by four hectares of land. There is one double room, a family room with a double bed and two singles, and two other rooms, one with three single beds and one with four single beds. Each has a shower room and wc. Table d'hôtes meals are served on the terrace with views of the hills, or in the converted wooden barn. Lounge, library, swimming pool (14 x 5m) and table-tennis. Numerous opportunities for rambling and mountain biking - maps

continued

continued

and route information available. Reductions for half-board breaks during the week. Price for four people: 70 euros per night. Open all year.
PRICES: s €35; d €44; t €57; extra person €13; dinner €15
ON SITE: Forest Hiking **NEARBY:** Bathing (12km) Horse riding (6km) Aerial sports (12km) Railway station (12km) Shops (6km) **NOTES:** Pets admitted English spoken

CRUIS

₩₩ ⊚ Mas de Foulara Richard et Odile HARTZ
04230 CRUIS
☎ 04 92 77 07 96
Montagne de Lure. Forcalquier 20 km. Surrounded by hills and lavender fields, this 17th-century farmhouse is situated on an Arab stud farm at the foot of the Lure Mountain, close to hiking trail GR6. There are five bedrooms with private bathrooms, and a lounge with fireplace. Outdoor attractions include covered terraces, shaded park and a pond. Central heating. Open 1 March to 30 November.
PRICES: s €38; d €45; t €53; dinner €15 **ON SITE:** Hiking
NEARBY: Horse riding (3km) Forest (2km) Swimming pool (5km) Stretch of water (20km) Railway station (20km) Shops (2km)
NOTES: No pets English spoken

DAUPHIN

₩₩ Le Moulin des Encontres
Marie-Claude ROCHON-BOUFFIER
04300 DAUPHIN
☎ 04 92 79 53 84
Manosque 18 km. Forcalquier 6 km. You are promised a pleasant stay at this restored mill in the heart of Luberon with its calm, green and shady surroundings. Elzéard is a first-floor room for two to four people, while Agathe is a double room on the ground floor. Marthe et Anthonin is suitable for four people. All have bathroom and wc, a kitchen area, terrace and a private entrance. There are numerous activities and excursions nearby including a cycle track, lavender tours, the Lure Mountain, the Gorges of Verdon and Luberon's Regional Nature Park. Tariff: 4 people 70 euros per night. Child prices can be discussed with the proprietor. Open all year.
PRICES: d €38-€43; t €60 **NEARBY:** Horse riding (4km) Forest (2km) Golf (20km) Shops (4km) **NOTES:** No pets

DIGNE-LES-BAINS

₩₩ ❦ Gaubert Jean-Pierre FRISON
Route des Fonts - Gaubert, Les Oliviers,
04000 DIGNE-LES-BAINS
☎ 04 92 31 36 04
Digne-les-Bains 6 km. Situated in the geological reserve of Haute-Provence, this farmhouse provides a very peaceful and rural environment. Accommodation consists of two double rooms on the ground floor and two doubles on the first floor. Each room is provided with either a bath or a shower and a wc. There is also a large lounge and terrace available for guest to use. Rural gîtes and camping available on this site. Open 1 April to 30 October.
PRICES: s €36; d €39 **NEARBY:** Horse riding (10km) Golf (1km) Fishing (1km) Swimming pool (6km) Stretch of water (2km) Aerial sports (6km) Shops (6km) **NOTES:** No pets

ENCHASTRAYES

₩₩ ⊚ Le Villard Marc et Lyliane VAN ZURK
04400 ENCHASTRAYES
☎ 04 92 81 33 75 ▤ 04 92 81 13 47
e-mail: champ-rond@ifrance.com www.ifrance.com/champ-rond
Barcelonnette 4 km. Le Sauze 6 km. In the heart of the Ubaye

Valley, this mountain wood chalet offers two double rooms with balconies and one family room (double bed and one single), all with private shower room and wc. Lounge with library and open fire available for guest use. Evening meals can be ordered in advance. Local attractions include walks, alpine skiing, cross-country skiing, water-sports, fishing, bike tours and hang-gliding. Open all year.
PRICES: d €37-€43; extra person €12; dinner €14 **ON SITE:** Hiking
NEARBY: Fishing (4km) Swimming pool (4km) Stretch of water (5km) Downhill skiing (6km) Aerial sports (7km) Railway station (70km) Shops (4km) **NOTES:** No pets

ESPARRON-DE-VERDON

₩₩₩ Le Château B Cte et Ctesse de CASTELLANE
Château d'Esparron, 04800 ESPARRON-DE-VERDON
☎ 04 92 77 12 05

Riez 19 km. Gréoux-les-Bains 20 km. This château has been owned by the same family since the 17th century. The property reflects the juxtaposition of three major architectural époques, the Middle Ages, the Renaissance and the 18th century. Benefiting from the shade offered by the plane trees, the château overlooks the meadow and dominates the lake. There are five suites furnished in period style, complete with antechambers and private bathrooms. Outdoor facilities include a courtyard and garden. Check with proprietor with regards to pets. Close to the Verdon lakes, and the Verdon Regional Nature Park. Open Easter until 1 November.
PRICES: d €107-€198; extra person €23 **ON SITE:** Horse riding Hiking **NEARBY:** Bathing (1km) Fishing (1km) Railway station (20km) **NOTES:** No pets CC English spoken

FORCALQUIER

₩₩₩ Beaudine Marie-Louise PAGLIANO
Bergerie la Beaudine, 04300 FORCALQUIER
☎ 04 92 75 01 52
Parc du Lubéron 5 km. Colorado Provençal 20 km. In a large, shaded park this former sheepfold offers superb views in tranquil surroundings. There are three double rooms with private entrances, and two family rooms (one with a double bed and one single, the other with one double bed and two singles). A beautiful dining room and lounge are available, as is a TV on request. Private swimming pool, furnished garden and bowls. Situated at the heart of the Haute-Provence, where author Giono once made his home. Close to Forcalquier with its concerts and Provençal market, and the Verdon Regional Nature Park. Price for four people per night: 79.25 euros. Additional bed: 15.25 euros. Open all year.
PRICES: s €41; d €49; t €65 **NEARBY:** Horse riding (3km) Fishing (5km) Stretch of water (6km) Hiking (1km) Aerial sports (2km) Shops (1km) **NOTES:** No pets

continued

♦♦♦ Campagne le Paradis Gilbert POURCIN
Quartier Paradis, 04300 FORCALQUIER
☎ 04 92 75 37 33 & 06 87 69 87 07
Forcalquier 700 m. Manosque 23 km. Situated at the heart of the Haute-Provence region, with views of the Luberon, this chambre d'hôtes adjoins the proprietor's property. Accommodation includes two double rooms and two family rooms (one double bed and two singles), all with private facilities. Furnished terrace, barbecue and closed parking. Breakfast is served in a vaulted room, which was once the barn. Refrigerator, microwave, high-chair and TV available on request. In nearby Forcalquier attractions include festivals, concerts and the local Provençal market. Price for four people: 80 euros per night. Open all year.
PRICES: s €40; d €50; t €65 **ON SITE:** Hiking **NEARBY:** Horse riding (3km) Fishing (5km) Swimming pool (2km) Stretch of water (6km) Aerial sports (25km) Railway station (15km) Shops (1km) **NOTES:** No pets

GREOUX-LES-BAINS

♦♦♦ Chambre d'hôtes Hubert WANTZEN
Bastide Saint-Donat, Route de Vinon,
04800 GREOUX-LES-BAINS
☎ 04 92 78 01 77 ▯ 04 92 78 12 97
e-mail: wantzen@wanadoo.fr
Gréoux-les-bains 4 km. Lac d'Esperron-de-Verdon and Manosque 15 km. Close to the Gréoux-les-Bains thermal baths, this renovated country house, situated in a large park, offers four rooms, one of which is a double. All rooms have private shower and wc. Generous breakfasts are served by the swimming pool in high season, and the kitchen is available for guest use during this period. Nearby attractions include gliding at Vinon-sur-Verdon, and museums, the Carzou Foundation, a theatre, swimming and fishing in Manosque. Open 1 April to 31 October.
PRICES: s €35-€43; d €50-€59; extra person €12 **NEARBY:** Bathing (4km) Horse riding (8km) Golf (4km) Fishing (4km) Aerial sports (8km) Railway station (20km) Shops (4km) **NOTES:** No pets

JAUSIERS

♦♦♦ La Mexicaine Marie-Hélène ORRU
Les Clos de Guéniers, 04850 JAUSIERS
☎ 04 92 84 69 63
Barcelonnette 8 km. Saint-Paul-sur-Ubaye 14 km. With communal enclosed grounds, a private furnished garden and a barbecue, this house is built in the typical Mexican style of the region. On the first floor, there is a dining room and lounge with open fire, TV, hi-fi and library, while the bedrooms are on the second floor. La Méditerranéenne is a double room which can be transformed into a twin room on request. La Romantique is a double and la Montagnarde a double room with an additional single bed. There is also a family room with one double bed and two singles. All rooms have their own shower room and wc. Close to the Resteford Pass (the highest road in Europe), Jausier Lake, and the Mercantour National Park. There are two self-catering gîtes on site.
PRICES: s €34; d €40-€46 **ON SITE:** Hiking **NEARBY:** Horse riding (1km) Stretch of water (1km) Downhill skiing (12km) Aerial sports (8km) Shops (1km) **NOTES:** No pets English spoken

LA PALUD-SUR-VERDON

♦♦♦ ♥ ⊙ L'Enchastre Jocelyne COLOMBERO
Chateauneuf les Moustiers, 04120 LA PALUD-SUR-VERDON
☎ 04 92 83 76 12
La Palud du Verdon 11 km. A house full of character situated on an agricultural property, which is home to sheep, goats and chicken. Guest facilities include a large dining room, a lounge with fireplace, billiards, TV, library, board games and a private swimming pool. At the heart of the Verdon Gorges, this isolated

house surrounded by pastures, is at an altitude of 1100m and is ideally located for walking in the Verdon Regional Nature Park. There are two double rooms and three family rooms, which sleep three people. All rooms have private bathroom and wc. Open April to November.
PRICES: d €46; t €61; HB €38; dinner €15 **ON SITE:** Children's play area Forest Hiking Swimming pool **NEARBY:** Horse riding (11km) Shops (11km) **NOTES:** No pets

LE CASTELLET

♦♦♦ Chambre d'hôtes Jean et Catherine CIRAVEGNA
Quartier Combe-Croix, 04700 LE CASTELLET
☎ 04 92 78 74 97
Oraison 5 km. Buissonnades water 10 km. An independent chambre d'hôtes at the foot of the Valensole Plateau. Double bedrooms with an extra single bed, with shower room and wc. Private access. Terrace, solarium, swimming pool. Small room with stove, refrigerator, barbecue, crockery and washing machine. Garden furniture is also available. Bowls are available for guest use. Situated in a green valley, Le Castellet is a quiet village with a restaurant and a fishing lake. Open all year.
PRICES: s €34; d €43; t €53; extra person €14 **ON SITE:** Hiking **NEARBY:** Bathing (10km) Horse riding (8km) Fishing (1km) Stretch of water (10km) Railway station (10km) Shops (5km) **NOTES:** No pets

LES MEES

♦♦♦ ⊙ Campagne du Barri Olga MANCIN
Quartier de la Croix, 04190 LES MEES
☎ 04 92 34 36 93 & 04 92 74 20 89 ▯ 04 92 34 39 06
Set in the Val de Durance, close to Digne-les-Bains, this rural gîte, situated in two hectares of plush green fields, forms part of an 18th-century house which has maintained the discreet charm of the time with its use of period furnishings. There is one family room, two double rooms, one split-level apartment for four people and one family room for three people with an adjoining single room, all equipped with private facilities. There is also a double room in a separate chalet which is equipped with shower room, wc, grounds and garden furniture. Meals feature homegrown vegetables. Open all year. Book in advance for November to March.
PRICES: s €42; d €50; t €60; HB €80-€135; dinner €15 **ON SITE:** Hiking **NEARBY:** Horse riding (2km) Golf (25km) Fishing (2km) Swimming pool (1km) Stretch of water (16km) Aerial sports (5km) Railway station (8km) Shops (1km) **NOTES:** Pets admitted English spoken

♦♦♦ ⊙ Le Mas des Oliviers Daniel et Danielle VERGER
Les Bourelles, 04190 LES MEES
☎ 04 92 34 36 99 & 06 09 52 67 11
e-mail: d-verger@wanadoo.fr
Les Mées 2 km. Danielle and Daniel welcome you to their independent chambre d'hôtes offering two double rooms, one with a terrace and one with a solarium, one twin room and one room with three singles. All rooms have private facilities. Lounge with fireplace. Bowls pitch. Food is served between September and the end of June, while in July and August a barbecue is available underneath a covered patio. Children's menu available for those aged 4 to 12 years (6.90 euros). Olive trees grow within the wooded grounds, and from here there are panoramic views of the Préalpes, the Lure Mountain and the Ganagobie Priory. Open all year except Christmas and New Year. Bookings must be made in advance December to February.
PRICES: s €34-€37; d €40-€46; t €53; dinner €14 **ON SITE:** Children's play area Hiking **NEARBY:** Horse riding (2km) Golf (20km) Fishing (1km) Swimming pool (2km) Aerial sports (6km) Railway station (9km) Shops (2km) **NOTES:** Pets admitted

continued

LES OMERGUES

⌘ ⫴ Le Moulin de la Viorne
Danielle COLONNA-BOUTTERIN
04200 LES OMERGUES
☎ 04 92 62 01 65 ▤ 04 92 62 06 03

Sederon 8 km. Set in the countryside of the Jabron Valley, close to the River Drôme, this restored 17th-century mill offers one double room, a family room (with one double bed and a single), and a twin room. All have private bathrooms. Central heating, billiard room, lounge with library, swimming pool, grounds, a covered, furnished terrace, private parking and meals upon request. Display of paintings open to guests. Open Easter until end October.
PRICES: s €49; d €53; t €72; extra person €14; dinner €21
ON SITE: Swimming pool Fishing Hiking **NEARBY:** Horse riding (2km) Aerial sports (8km) Shops (8km) **NOTES:** No pets English spoken

MEOLANS-REVEL

⌘ ⫴ Les Méans Frédéric & Elisabeth MILLET
Méolans, 04340 MEOLANS-REVEL
☎ 04 92 81 03 91 ▤ 04 92 81 03 91
e-mail: lesmeans@chez.com www.chez.com/lesmeans
Barcelonnette 12 km. A restored 16th-century farm set in a mountain hamlet offering four double rooms, two with balconies, and all with private facilities. There is also a suite with private bathroom, wc and balcony. Lounge with TV, library and open fire. Refrigerator and washing machine on request. Meals are served Tuesday, Thursday and Saturday in the vaulted former sheepfold. Open garden with a working baker's oven. Rafting, fishing and climbing nearby. Mountain tours are given by M. Millet. Book in advance for 10 May to 10 October.
PRICES: s €46; d €54-€58; extra person €16; dinner €20
ON SITE: Hiking **NEARBY:** Bathing (10km) Aerial sports (10km) Shops (10km) **NOTES:** Pets admitted English spoken

MONTLAUX

⌘ ⫴ ⫴ Grand-Champ Philippe et Fabienne PATRIER
04230 MONTLAUX
☎ 04 92 77 01 10 ▤ 04 92 77 09 54
e-mail: ppatrier@aol.com www.multimania.com/grangcham
Sisteron 25 km. Forcalquier 20 km. Flanked by the Lure Mountain, this large building is in the heart of the countryside set in four hectares and surrounded by the fragrances of thyme and lavender. The three first-floor bedrooms all lead out onto a covered terrace, and there are two bedrooms on the ground floor. All have a private bathroom. A lounge, dining room with fireplace and library are available. Outdoor facilities include a swimming pool, a toboggan run, table-tennis and a bowls pitch. Mountain bikes available for hire. Camping area. Open all year.
PRICES: s €30; d €40; t €50; extra person €10; HB €34; dinner €14
ON SITE: Swimming pool Children's play area **NEARBY:** Horse riding (2km) Stretch of water (20km) Hiking (20km) Downhill skiing (14km) Aerial sports (16km) Shops (2km) **NOTES:** No pets English spoken

⌘ ⫴ Le Moulin d'Anaïs Pierre DESCUBE
04230 MONTLAUX
☎ 04 92 77 07 28 ▤ 04 92 77 07 28
Forcalquier 20 km. This renovated former mill is on the banks of the Lauzon, at the foot of the Lure Mountain near the old village of Montlaux. Accommodation consists of two double rooms, two family rooms for three people and one family room which sleeps four. All rooms have private bathroom and wc. Prices start from 74.70 euros for two people staying half-board. Open all year.
PRICES: s €37; d €47; t €62; HB €53; dinner €15 **ON SITE:** Hiking **NEARBY:** Golf (30km) Fishing (6km) Swimming pool (5km) Stretch of water (25km) Aerial sports (25km) Shops (5km) **NOTES:** No pets

MOUSTIERS-SAINTE-MARIE

⌘ ⫴ Monastère de Ségries
Christian & Florence ALLEGRE
04360 MOUSTIERS-SAINTE-MARIE
☎ 04 92 74 64 32 ▤ 04 92 74 64 22
Lac de Sainte-Croix 10 km. Moustiers-Sainte-Marie 6 km. This renovated former monastery enjoys a calm and privileged setting, chosen by monks in the 19th-century, close to the Valensole plateau. There are five spacious bedrooms all with private facilities. Meals, which are in the local style and can be booked in advance, are eaten with the patrons. Nearby attractions include the Verdon Regional Nature Park and Moustiers, a listed town famous for its earthenware. Special offer: 10% reduction on your stay from the third night. Open Easter to end October.
PRICES: s €37; d €45; extra person €8; HB €36; dinner €14
ON SITE: Hiking **NEARBY:** Bathing (10km) Aerial sports (10km) Shops (6km) **NOTES:** No pets English spoken

NIOZELLES

⌘ Le Relais d'Elle Jacques et Catherine PENSA
Route de la Brillanne, 04300 NIOZELLES
☎ 04 92 75 06 87 ▤ 04 92 75 06 87
www.multimania.com/relaisdelle
Niozelles 1 km. Forcalquier 4 km. Manosque 20 km. Between Luberon and the Lure Mountain this restored former farmhouse offers five spacious bedrooms decorated in the Provençal style of the époque: one double room, one large room with three double beds and another room with five singles. All have private facilities. The farmhouse has everything required for a peaceful stay. Central heating, lounge, library and meals on request. The farmhouse is close to the Roman pathway, Via Domitia, numerous walks, mountain biking and horse riding. Price for four people: 76 euros. Open all year. Swimming pool planned for 2002.
PRICES: s €31; d €45; t €58-€64 **ON SITE:** Hiking **NEARBY:** Horse riding (2km) Fishing (1km) Swimming pool (1km) Shops (4km) **NOTES:** Pets admitted

NOYERS-SUR-JABRON

⌘ ⫴ Le Jas de la Caroline Henri et Monique MOREL
04200 NOYERS-SUR-JABRON
☎ 04 92 62 03 48 ▤ 04 92 62 03 46
Sisteron 12 km. Set in the Jabron Valley, this renovated former 16th-century sheepfold offers two double rooms with private facilities and one suite with three single beds, shower, wc, and a lounge/kitchen transformed from a former baker's oven. All rooms have a furnished terrace. Lounge with fireplace and library. Meals served on reservation. Pets 3 euros per night. Attractions include walks, mountain biking, theme breaks, walks following the steps of the famous writers of the region: Paul Arène, Jean Giono and Pierre Magnan. Nearby Sisteron is host to the Nights of the Citadel. There is also a lake here. Open all year, advanced reservations are required during the low season.

continued

PRICES: s €42-€49; d €49-€69; t €87; extra person €16; dinner €19
ON SITE: Hiking **NEARBY:** Forest (3km) Stretch of water (12km) Aerial sports (16km) Railway station (12km) Shops (1km) **NOTES:** Pets admitted English spoken

PIERRERUE

♦♦♦ Le Jas de Nevières Philippe et Joëlle DUERMAEL
Route de Saint-Pierre, 04300 PIERRERUE
☎ 04 92 75 24 99 ▤ 04 92 75 03 75
e-mail: Duermael@wanadoo.fr
Forcalquier 6 km. A stay full of charm and relaxation is offered in this tastefully restored 17th-century farmhouse. Located in the heart of Haute-Provence and Giono Country, between Luberon and the Lure Mountain, there are four bedrooms decorated in the old regional style. All are equipped with either private bath or shower and wc. Other facilities include a restored former sheepfold, a large family swimming pool, terraces and grounds. Nearby attractions include walks, mountain biking and a Provençal market at Forcalquier. Group bookings welcome. Open 1 April to 31 October, advance prior booking for other periods.
PRICES: d €62; extra person €14 **ON SITE:** Hiking Swimming pool
NEARBY: Horse riding (15km) Fishing (10km) Stretch of water (13km) Aerial sports (11km) Railway station (15km) Shops (11km) **NOTES:** Pets admitted

REILLANNE

♦♦♦ Le Mas des Collines Rose SELLAM
04110 REILLANNE
☎ 04 92 76 43 53 ▤ 04 92 76 50 14

Manosque, Apt & Forcalquier 20 km. Situated in the Luberon Regional Nature Park, between Céreste and Reillanne, this remote farmhouse is surrounded by oak trees in a countryside setting. Offering four family rooms (one double bed and a single bed on the mezzanine floor), with private shower rooms and wc and television, and two other bedrooms with shower room and use of communal wc. Arched lounge/dining room with fireplace, music, a TV area, library and a kitchen area. Fountain, swimming pool, football pitch and bowls pitch. A generous organic brunch is served daily. Large paved picnic area shaded by 200-year old trees. Swimming pool open 1 May to 15 September. Open all year.
PRICES: s €52-€74; d €65-€84; extra person €15-€33 **ON SITE:** Hiking Swimming pool **NEARBY:** Horse riding (4km) Aerial sports (20km) Railway station (20km) Shops (4km) **NOTES:** Pets admitted

REVEST-DU-BION

♦♦♦ ⊖ Le Petit Labouret J-C et M MOUCHENIK
04150 REVEST-DU-BION
☎ 04 92 77 20 43 & 06 80 58 16 14 ▤ 04 92 77 20 44
e-mail: labouret@petit-labouret.com www.petitlabouret.com
Revest-du-Bion 2,5 km. Sault 12 km. Manosque 40 km. At the boundary of Vaucluse and the Alpes-de-Haute-Provence, between Mont Ventoux and the Lure Mountain, this renovated farmhouse lies in the middle of protected countryside. Four bedrooms with private entrances, three of which have mezzanine floors. There are two double rooms, one large room with two double beds and a room which sleeps seven people in single beds. All have private shower rooms and wc. Lounge with fireplace, laundry with fridge-freezer, washing machine and tumble-dryer. Children's menu for the under 12s (11 euros). Open grounds with woodland and lavender fields, and garden furniture. Nearby: country walks, horse riding (also on site) and mountain biking. Open all year.
PRICES: s €42; d €60; t €60; dinner €19 **ON SITE:** Horse riding Hiking
NEARBY: Shops (3km) **NOTES:** Pets admitted

SIMIANE-LA-ROTONDE

♦♦♦ Les Granges de Saint-Pierre
Jean et Josiane TAMBURINI
04150 SIMIANE-LA-ROTONDE
☎ 04 92 75 93 81 ▤ 04 92 75 93 81
Pays d'Apt 20 km. Colorado Provençal 10 km. Set in the Luberon Regional Nature Park, these renovated 14th-century barns offer three bedrooms with private bathrooms. Kitchen, lounge, garage, laundry, TV, central heating, covered terrace, swimming pool and a shaded park. In nearby Simiane-la-Rotonde, there are exhibitions, a music festival and local handicrafts. Close to several hiking trails. For stays of five nights or more, the price for one person is 41 euros, and for two this rises to 47 euros. Open all year. During winter, reservations should be made in advance.
PRICES: s €44; d €54; extra person €13 **ON SITE:** Hiking
NEARBY: Forest (5km) Aerial sports (10km) Railway station (30km)
NOTES: Pets admitted English spoken

ST-ETIENNE-LES-ORGUES

♦♦♦ ⊖ Le Château Eric et Aurélia BOUILLOT
Place Pasteur, 04230 ST-ETIENNE-LES-ORGUES
☎ 04 92 73 00 03
e-mail: tollioub@aol.com http://perso.club-Internet.fr/orgues
Forcalquier 15 km. Former 15th-century château in a village setting offers spacious rooms all equipped with private bathroom. Facilities include lounge, billiard room, reading room, video room, table-tennis, a plush green garden filled with multiple scents, a fountain and a shaded terrace. The 100-metre village swimming pool can be used free of charge by guests. Situated between the Lure Mountain and Luberon this accommodation is ideally located for mountain hikes. Open all year.
PRICES: s €41; d €45; extra person €8; HB €37; dinner €15
ON SITE: Swimming pool Hiking **NEARBY:** Horse riding (6km) Forest (1km) Golf (30km) **NOTES:** Pets admitted

ST-GENIEZ

♦♦♦ ⊖ Domaine des Rayes Bruno et Micheline MASURE
04200 ST-GENIEZ
☎ 04 92 61 22 76 ▤ 04 92 61 06 44
Saint-Geniez 3.5 km. Sisteron 18 km. Deep in the countryside this renovated former sheepfold offers four double rooms and one family room which sleeps four, all with private bathrooms and wc. Facilities include private terraces equipped with garden furniture. At the heart of the Geological Reserve of Haute-Provence this chambre d'hôtes has an unrestricted view over the Durance Valley and towards the Chapel of Dromon, which also houses a crypt. In nearby Sisteron there is a lake, a citadel, the River Durance, the Rock of Beaume and numerous other sites of interest. Rate reduction after two nights. Open all year.
PRICES: d €49-€58; dinner €15 **ON SITE:** Hiking Aerial sports Swimming pool **NEARBY:** Horse riding (4km) Railway station (18km) Shops (18km) **NOTES:** No pets English spoken

continued

ST-MARTIN-LES-EAUX

▦ ◯ Domaine d'Aurouze
J et V NOEL-SCHREIBER
04300 ST-MARTIN-LES-EAUX
☎ 04 92 87 66 51 & 04 92 87 56 35
e-mail: aurouze@karatel.fr

Manosque 10 km. Avignon 75 km. A haven of peace in the middle of the countryside, in the heart of the Luberon, this 17th-century country house offers three luxury rooms, with private bathroom, wc and TV. Other facilities include dining room, swimming pool, volley-ball, pétanque, fitness equipment and mountain bikes. Terrace with panoramic views over Forcalquier and the Alps. Tasty regional specialities and gourmand buffet-style breakfasts are served daily. Numerous activities and excursions to places such as medieval villages, archaeological sites, Roman abbeys and châteaux. Marseille-Provence airport 70 km. All-inclusive price for breaks from Saturday to Saturday. Open 15 May to 15 September. Advance booking necessary.
PRICES: s €65; d €80; HB €55; dinner €15 **ON SITE:** Swimming pool **NEARBY:** Horse riding (8km) Forest (5km) Golf (15km) Stretch of water (12km) Railway station (10km) Shops (8km)
NOTES: No pets English spoken

ST-MICHEL-L'OBSERVATOIRE

▦ ◯ Le Farnet Pascal et Cathy DEPOISSON
04870 ST-MICHEL-L'OBSERVATOIRE
☎ 04 92 76 65 52
www.guideweb.com/provence/bb/farnet/

Saint-Michel-l'Observatoire 3 km. The large Farnet Estate extends a warm welcome to guests in this calm and relaxing environment surrounded by two hectares of woodland. A renovated stone country house offers four bedrooms, all with private bathroom, wc and entrance. Central heating and baby equipment on request. Family swimming pool, furnished terrace, table-tennis, table football and pétanque. Mountain bikes available for hire. Meals served every evening except Sunday. Close to the Luberon Regional Nature Park and the Provençal Colorado. Prices: two people staying half-board, high season: 460 euros, low season: 430 euros. Four people: 73 euros. Open 15 April to 15 October.
PRICES: s €39; d €45; t €59; extra person €11; dinner €14
ON SITE: Forest Hiking **NEARBY:** Bathing (22km) Horse riding (7km) Stretch of water (15km) Shops (3km)
NOTES: Pets admitted

ST-VINCENT-SUR-JABRON

▦ ◯ La Maison de ma Cousine
Andrée ARNAUD
Le Village, 04200 ST-VINCENT-SUR-JABRON
☎ 04 92 62 06 94

Sisteron 18 km. Noyers-sur-Jabron 7 km. In the green, protected Valley of Jabron, on the outskirts of the village, lies this chambre d'hôtes complete with lawn, garden and swimming pool. Four double rooms (two with double beds sized 160cm) and one room to sleep three people. All rooms have private bathrooms and wc. Large lounge with TV and library available. Meals upon request. Nearby attractions include various mountain walks, and beautiful Roman churches which can be found at the foot of the Lure Mountain. In nearby Sisteron there is a lake, museums, a citadel and the Baume Rock. Open all year except July and August.
PRICES: s €49; d €53; extra person €14; HB €64; dinner €15
ON SITE: Hiking **NEARBY:** Bathing (19km) Horse riding (8km) Fishing (2km) Swimming pool (19km) Stretch of water (10km) Railway station (18km) Shops (15km) **NOTES:** No pets

VALAVOIRE

▦ ◯ Le Serre Alain PICHON
04250 VALAVOIRE
☎ 04 92 68 32 75

Sisteron (citadel) 25 km. La Motte du Caire 10 km. With an exceptional view over the Monges Massif, this large 18th-century house has been lovingly restored to create three double bedrooms, each with private shower rooms and wc. There is also a lounge, library and a shaded terrace. Outdoors you can play table-tennis or practise your golf. Traditional cuisine served daily. Well off the beaten track, the property is ideal for newcomers to the area who wish to experience the pleasures of the Haute-Provence region, including tranquillity and mountain walks. Price for four people: 82 euros. Open all year
PRICES: s €40; d €46; t €76; dinner €15 **NEARBY:** Horse riding (5km) Fishing (4km) Swimming pool (10km) Stretch of water (25km) Aerial sports (8km) Railway station (25km) Shops (8km) **NOTES:** Pets admitted

VAUMEILH

▦ ◯ La Ferme de Valauris Claude LE CLEACH
04200 VAUMEILH
☎ 04 92 62 13 99 & 06 15 22 55 72
e-mail: vaumeilh@club-internet.fr www.ferme-de-valauris.com

Sisteron 12 km. Vaumeilh 3 km. Located in 12 hectares of moors and woodland, this renovated former farm, facing the Gache and Lure Mountains, is full of character. There are one double room and three twin rooms. All rooms are decorated in the Provençal style and come equipped with private shower rooms and wc. Central heating, video library and beautiful interior courtyard. Meals are served in the vaulted former sheepfold. Art courses, workshops and professional meeting are held on site. Nearby attractions include the airfield with gliders (3 km), and the lake, the citadel and the Baume Rock in Sisteron. Open 15 February to 15 December.
PRICES: s €35; d €46; t €61; dinner €15 **ON SITE:** Hiking
NEARBY: Horse riding (7km) Swimming pool (12km) Stretch of water (12km) Aerial sports (3km) Railway station (12km) Shops (12km)
NOTES: Pets admitted English spoken

VENTEROL

♦♦♦ ΪΟΪ Le Blanchet Sonia BOYER

La Méridienne, 05130 VENTEROL
☎ 04 92 54 18 51 📠 04 92 54 18 51
Lac de Serre-Ponçon 20 km. Tallard 8 km. Gap 15 km. This
renovated 18th-cenury farmhouse looks over the Durance Valley.
Five bedrooms all with private bathroom and wc, three with a
mezzanine floor. Lounge and library. The farm produces red fruits
and poultry, and is surrounded by two hectares of shaded
parkland. Outdoor attractions include sign-posted pedestrian
walkways and 200 kilometres of forest tracks exclusive to
pedestrians, where you can experience the abundance of greenery
and flora. Price for two people for one week: 480.20 euros (10%
reduction). Children: 22.85 euros. Open all year.
PRICES: s €35; d €46; extra person €23; HB €38; FB €53; dinner €15
ON SITE: Children's play area Hiking Swimming pool **NEARBY:** Forest
(1km) Fishing (5km) Stretch of water (10km) Aerial sports (8km) Railway
station (20km) Shops (8km) Restaurant nearby **NOTES:** No pets

VILLENEUVE

♦♦♦ ΪΟΪ La Maurissime Nicole MOUCHOT

Chemin des Oliviers, 04180 VILLENEUVE
☎ 04 92 78 47 61
Manosque 15 km. Gourmand cuisine and a refined interior are
promised at this beautiful, new residence located outside the
village, surrounded by pine forest. Accommodation includes two
double rooms, one family room to sleep three and another to
sleep four. All have private bathroom, wc and terrace. Other
facilities include a lounge with fireplace and TV, a meeting room
where you can join up with other guests and a large communal
terrace with a magical view over Oraison. Nearby attractions
include Manosque, the town of the author Giono, where you can
visit the Carzou foundation, the Jean le Bleu theatre and the
Vannades Lake, the Luberon Regional National Park, the Valensole
Plateau, the Salagon and Ganagobie priories. Price for four people:
85.35 euros. Open all year.
PRICES: s €43; d €50; t €58; HB €84-€108; dinner €17 **NEARBY:** Horse
riding (8km) Golf (22km) Fishing (5km) Swimming pool (12km) Stretch
of water (8km) Aerial sports (20km) Railway station (15km) Shops (1km)
NOTES: Pets admitted English spoken

VOLONNE

♦♦♦ Chambre d'hôtes Monique REVELLI

Quartier Saint-Jean, Villa el Cantara, 04290 VOLONNE
☎ 04 92 64 30 38 & 06 85 22 54 83 📠 04 92 64 30 38
e-mail: monique.revelli@infonie.fr
http://perso.infonie/monique.revelli
Volonne 2 km. Sisteron 10 km. Digne 30 km. Manosque 40 km.
Country house situated in the Durance Valley offers a calm
environment surrounded by olive trees and fields. Two ground-
floor rooms sleep three people, have private entrances and
terraces. The third room also sleeps three but is accessed through
the proprietor's property and has its own private staircase. Each
room has a private shower, wash-hand basin, wc, TV and electric
heating. Nearby places of interest include Volonne, an old
picturesque village high up in the mountains with a beautiful view
of the Durance Valley. Sisteron is also close-by. Open all year. Book
in advance for October to November.
PRICES: s €35; d €41; extra person €17 **ON SITE:** Hiking
NEARBY: Horse riding (7km) Fishing (2km) Swimming pool (3km)
Stretch of water (10km) Aerial sports (7km) Railway station (5km) Shops
(2km) **NOTES:** Pets admitted

> Use the atlas at the back of the guide to
> locate your chambre d'hôtes

ANTIBES

♦♦♦ La Bastide du Bosquet Christian AUSSEL

14 chemin des Sables, le Bosquet, 06160 ANTIBES
☎ 04 93 67 32 29 & 04 93 34 06 04 📠 04 93 67 32 29
e-mail: sylvie.aussel@wanadoo.fr
Le Bosquet, a charming 18th-century country house once
frequented by Guy de Maupassant, is situated at the start of the
Antibes headland between the two beaches of Antibes and Juan-
les-Pins. The first floor hosts the Blue Bedroom, a double room
which also includes a single bed. The second floor is home to the
Yellow Bedroom, which is a family room with one double bed and
two singles, and the Green Bedroom, a double room with a cot.
Each room has a private bath or shower and wc. Lounge and TV
available to guests. Terrace and grounds with green oak trees. On
site parking. Tourist tax included in the rates. Open all year except
15 November to 20 December. Reduced rates in low season.
PRICES: d €84; extra person €19 **ON SITE:** Fishing
NEARBY: Horse riding (8km) Swimming pool (3km) Hiking (10km)
Cross-country skiing (60km) Downhill skiing (60km) Tennis (3km)
Railway station (3km) Shops (1km) ANTIBES **NOTES:** No pets English
spoken

ASCROS

♦♦♦ ΪΟΪ 4 Chambres d'hôtes Huguette JUGLARIS

Balmont-Est, 06260 ASCROS
☎ 04 93 05 82 86 & 06 85 27 48 49 📠 04 93 05 82 86
This ground-floor farmhouse consisting of four bedrooms is
annexed to the owner's property. There are two family rooms
containing a double bed and a set of bunk beds, and another two
double rooms. Shower room, wc and television in each room.
Grounds and on-site parking. Sliding scale of charges for groups of
eight, or half-board. Fixed rate charge for full-board plus use of a
horse: 457.34 Euros. Horse rides around the local tracks can also
be booked. Open all year. Discounts for children under 10.
PRICES: s €35; d €42; HB €39; dinner €16 **ON SITE:** Horse riding
Hiking **NEARBY:** Sea (62km) Fishing (17km) Swimming pool (17km)
Cross-country skiing (50km) Downhill skiing (50km) Tennis (17km)
Railway station (17km) PUGET-THENIERS (16km) **NOTES:** Pets admitted
English spoken

BERRE-LES-ALPES

♦♦♦ Les Lys François NOBILE

288 chemin de Meingarde, 06390 BERRE-LES-ALPES
☎ 04 93 91 81 09 & 06 03 22 39 34 📠 04 92 12 13 41

A peaceful chambre d'hôtes annexed from the owner's home, this
three double bedroom property is situated between the sea and
the mountains, and is an ideal base for nature, walking and
mountain-biking. Each bedroom has its own private facilities and
an extra bed available upon request. Lounge with open fire, colour
TV and hi-fi available. There is also a terrace with table, chaise
longue and a barbecue which leads out onto the 3500 metres-

continued

PROVENCE-ALPES-CÔTE-D'AZUR

enclosed grounds. On-site parking. Medieval villages in close proximity and numerous restaurants nearby. Open all year.
PRICES: s €33; d €45; extra person €13 **ON SITE:** Hiking
NEARBY: Horse riding (9km) Sea (20km) Fishing (5km) Swimming pool (8km) Cross-country skiing (30km) Downhill skiing (30km) Tennis (2km) Railway station (4km) Shops (2km) CONTES (8km) **NOTES:** Pets admitted English spoken

♦♦♦ ⍾◯⍾ **Villa Saint-Benoit** Alain LEGRAS
61 chemin de la roche d'Argent, 06390 BERRE-LES-ALPES
☎ 04 93 91 81 07 & 04 93 91 84 30 🖹 04 93 91 85 47
e-mail: villastbenoit@wanadoo.fr

This large three-bedroom villa, formerly a recording studio, stands two kilometres from Berre-les-Alpes. Lavande is a double room with a single bed, Rose is a double room but also has two single beds, while Chataîgne compromises one double bed, one single and a small sofa bed. Each bedroom has its own bathroom, wc and telephone. Large lounge with open fire, library and art collection. Furnished garden, children's play area and swimming pool on site. Mountain bikes, ping-pong, bowls and table football. Peace and quiet guaranteed. Nice 25 km. Open all year.
PRICES: s €37; d €54; extra person €15; dinner €18
ON SITE: Children's play area Swimming pool Hiking **NEARBY:** Horse riding (11km) Sea (25km) Fishing (7km) Cross-country skiing (35km) Downhill skiing (35km) Tennis (2km) Railway station (25km) Shops (2km) CONTES (11km) **NOTES:** Pets admitted English spoken

CABRIS

♦♦♦ **Chambre d'hôtes** Jocelyne FARAUT
297 route des Trois Ponts, 06530 CABRIS
☎ 04 93 60 52 36 🖹 04 93 60 52 36
Situated in the heart of Cabris, this chambre d'hôtes can be found amongst the picturesque houses that surround the ruins of the 10th-century feudal castle in this old Provençal village. On the ground floor there is a double room with shower room and wc, while the first floor compromises another double room and two twin rooms (one with balcony), all with shower room and wc. On the second floor there is a further double with bathroom and wc. The dining room has panoramic views of Lake Saint-Cassien. Golf 2 km. Closed 15 October to 31 March.
PRICES: d €46-€52; extra person €16 **ON SITE:** Hiking Tennis
NEARBY: Horse riding (6km) Sea (22km) Fishing (12km) Swimming pool (5km) Cross-country skiing (37km) Downhill skiing (35km) Railway station (22km) SAINT-VALLIER-DE-THIEY (7km) **NOTES:** Pets admitted English spoken

COURMES

♦♦♦ ⍾◯⍾ **La Cascade** Patrice BARACCO
06620 COURMES
☎ 04 93 09 65 85 🖹 04 93 09 67 07
e-mail: LacascadeB@wanadoo.fr
In a countryside location, La Cascade is built on a projecting ledge of the Courmes mountain. There are three family rooms, each

containing one double bed and two singles, two double rooms and one twin room. All bedrooms have a private bathroom and wc. Facilities include lounge, grounds, parking and children's games, which are free for the under twos. Horse riding 3 km, paragliding 10 km. A wildlife and flora slideshow is organised twice a month by Mr Baracco between 15 April and 15 September at a cost of €5.34 per person. During the week there is also a weaving class, which must be reserved in advance. Open all year.
PRICES: d €46; dinner €13 Child & off-season reductions
ON SITE: Children's play area Hiking **NEARBY:** Horse riding (3km) Sea (27km) Fishing (4km) Swimming pool (25km) Cross-country skiing (29km) Downhill skiing (29km) Tennis (12km) Railway station (27km) Shops (10km) BAR-SUR-LOUP (9km) **NOTES:** Pets admitted

GOLFE-JUAN VALLAURIS

♦♦♦ **Le Mas Samarcande** Mireille DIOT
138 grand bld de Super Cannes,
06220 GOLFE-JUAN VALLAURIS
☎ 04 93 63 97 73 🖹 04 93 63 97 73
http://www.stpaulweb.com/samarcande
Situated in Vallauris, a town famous for its art and pottery, this chambre d'hôtes with a view over the Baie des Anges offers high levels of comfort in the peace of the hills. There are five guest rooms, two of which are adjoining, Manosque 1 and 2. The first of these is a double room and the second is a twin room. Lérins and Samarcande are also double rooms. Finally Porquerolles contains one double bed and one small child's bed. All rooms have a bathroom, wc, TV and air conditioning. The lounge opens up onto a large panoramic terrace, a garden and parking. Nearby: the Côte d'Azur, golf (3 km). Open all year.
PRICES: d €100-€115; extra person €16 **NEARBY:** Horse riding (5km) Sea (3km) Fishing (3km) Swimming pool (3km) Hiking (5km) Cross-country skiing (65km) Downhill skiing (65km) Tennis (3km) Railway station (3km) Shops (1km) GOLFE-JUAN VALLAURIS (2km) **NOTES:** No pets English spoken

LA BRIGUE

♦♦♦ **Le Pra Reound** Jean-Louis MOLINARO
chemin St Jean, 06430 LA BRIGUE
☎ 04 93 04 65 67
A chambre d'hôtes joined onto the owner's farm, situated on the outskirts of the Mercantour Park, in the Menton hinterland close to Italy. The accommodation consists of five double rooms and one twin room, all of which have their own private bathroom and wc. An additional bed is available upon request. Facilities include grounds, a 50-metre children's garden, terrace, river and parking on site. Games of bowls and ping-pong are available to guests, while televisions can be hired. Electric heating. Closed 1 December to 1 March.
PRICES: s €31; d €43; extra person €11 **ON SITE:** Children's play area Fishing Hiking **NEARBY:** Horse riding (5km) Sea (40km) Swimming pool (4km) Cross-country skiing (17km) Downhill skiing (16km) Tennis (1km) Railway station (1km) Shops (1km) TENDE (6km) **NOTES:** Pets admitted English spoken

LA COLLE-SUR-LOUP

♦♦♦ **Bastide Saint-Donat** Alphonse ROSSO
parc St-Donat, D 6, 06480 LA COLLE-SUR-LOUP
☎ 04 93 32 93 41 🖹 04 93 32 80 61
This renovated riverside country house boasts three suites and two twin rooms. The first suite is situated on the ground floor and contains one double bed and one single, a lounge, shower room and wc. The second and third suites also contain one double bed and one single bed each and have their own bathroom, lounge and wc. The second suite also has a private terrace. Both bedrooms are double rooms, and one has a balcony. Communal

continued   continued

lounge with open fire and television. Additional separate television room. Telephone, terrace and parking. Close to the Gorges du Loup. A stay here affords you all the peace of Provence within close proximity of the Côte d'Azur. Open all year.
PRICES: d €61-€92; extra person €16　**ON SITE:** Fishing
NEARBY: Horse riding (20km) Sea (12km) Swimming pool (2km) Hiking (20km) Cross-country skiing (40km) Downhill skiing (40km) Tennis (2km) Railway station (10km) Shops (2km) CAGNES-SUR-MER (10km)　**NOTES:** Pets admitted　English spoken

NICE

♦♦♦♦ |◯| Chambre d'hôtes Michele GOLLE
69 vieux chemin de Cremat, Raccourci No 3, 06200 NICE
☎ 04 93 37 94 31 & 04 92 15 11 25　🖷 04 92 15 11 25
e-mail: michele.golle@wanadoo.fr
http://perso.wanadoo.fr/michele.golle
Beautiful Mediterranean chambre d'hôtes with sea views. Pistou and Capelina, both double rooms with bathroom and wc; Cigalou, a single room with bathroom and separate wc and Bella Vista, a double room with bathroom and separate wc. Each room has a TV and air conditioning. Cots and highchairs available. Games room with billiards and table football, weights room, lounge with TV and fireplace. Large park with swimming pool. Tourist tax payable. Open all year. Reduced prices for children.
PRICES: s €77; d €100-€130; dinner €31　**ON SITE:** Swimming pool
NEARBY: Horse riding (5km) Sea (10km) Fishing (6km) Hiking (20km) Cross-country skiing (63km) Downhill skiing (63km) Tennis (1km) Railway station (7km) Shops (5km) NICE (7km)　**NOTES:** No pets　English spoken

♦♦♦♦ Le Castel Enchanté Jacqueline OLIVIER
61 route St Pierre de Feric, 06000 NICE
☎ 04 93 97 02 08 & 06 20 59 66 53　🖷 04 93 97 13 70
e-mail: castel.enchante@wanadoo.fr
A beautiful Italian-style property dating back to the beginning of the last century. Close to the French Riviera's capital, this pretty chambre d'hôtes offers spacious, bright and comfortable accommodation. There is one family room on the first floor, comprising a double and twin room, a bathroom, wc and a furnished terrace. On the second floor there are two double rooms both with bathrooms and wc. All rooms have a TV. Communal lounge with TV and video. Large park decked with flowers and shaded terraces. A buffet breakfast is served inside or on the outside terraces. Open all year.
PRICES: s €100; d €100; Family room €180　**NEARBY:** Horse riding (6km) Sea (2km) Fishing (3km) Swimming pool (1km) Hiking (30km) Cross-country skiing (66km) Downhill skiing (66km) Tennis (1km) Railway station (2km) Shops (1km) NICE (3km)
NOTES: No pets　English spoken

SAINT-MARTIN-VESUBIE

♦♦♦♦ Chalet Paule Paule ROSSI
1 bis rue Cluviar, 06000 NICE　☎ 04 93 86 57 88
Clean air and a change of scenery are guaranteed at this three-storey chalet whose location promises rest and relaxation. The ground floor is home to the entrance hall and a double bedroom. The lounge with TV and fireplace, the dining room and another double room can all be found on the first floor. The second floor contains the final double bedroom; each bedroom has private bathroom facilities. An additional twin bedroom can be made available upon request. The enclosed grounds contain a lawn, terrace and barbecue. Tourist tax payable, contact proprietor for further information. Open 13 May to 18 September.
PRICES: d €61-€92　**ON SITE:** Horse riding Fishing Hiking Cross-country skiing　**NEARBY:** Sea (73km) Swimming pool (8km) Downhill skiing (15km) Tennis (8km) Railway station (42km) Shops (8km) SAINT-MARTIN-VESUBIE (8km)　**NOTES:** No pets

SAINT-PAUL-DE-VENCE

♦♦♦♦ Le Mas des Serres Jacques MAUBE
2000 route des Serres, 06570 ST-PAUL-DE-VENCE
☎ 04 93 32 81 10　🖷 04 93 32 85 43
http://www.stpaulweb.com/mds/
In the heart of the Provençal countryside, this detached farmhouse has been tastefully furnished. The five personalised and comfortable guestrooms are all equipped with bathroom, TV, telephone and individual gardens; the property also includes a dining room and lounge with TV. Cots available upon request. Terrace, lawn, swimming pool, 4500 m_ garden, on site parking. French-style breakfast served daily. Nearby in the streets of the fortified village you will find the Maeght Foundation, art collections and local handicrafts. Golf 5 km. Open April to October inclusive. Child bed €10.
PRICES: s €77; d €92; extra person €23　**ON SITE:** Swimming pool
NEARBY: Horse riding (5km) Sea (8km) Fishing (8km) Hiking (20km) Cross-country skiing (45km) Downhill skiing (45km) Tennis (1km) Railway station (3km) Shops (3km) CAGNES-SUR-MER (3km)
NOTES: No pets　English spoken

TOURRETTES-SUR-LOUP

♦♦♦♦ |◯| La Demeure de Jeanne
Yolande COHEN-DICHTEL
907 route de Vence, 06140 TOURRETTES-SUR-LOUP
☎ 04 93 59 37 24 & 06 66 76 53 32　🖷 04 93 59 37 24
e-mail: yolande6@libertysurf.fr
http://mageos.ifrance.com/la-jeanne
A beautiful Provençal chambre d'hôtes with a sea view, close to the Esterel mountains. The ground floor is home to a double bedroom (160cm bed) with lounge area, bathroom and wc. The first floor contains a double bedroom (180cm bed), a large bathroom with wc, lounge area, dressing room and a private terrace. The second room on this floor is a twin room with a shower room and wc. There is also a suite on this floor, with a 160cm bed, private lounge and shower room and wc. All rooms have a TV and video, and guests can borrow films from a video library. Garden and swimming pool. Open all year.
PRICES: s €75-€125; d €75-€125; extra person €20; dinner €35-€45
ON SITE: Swimming pool Hiking Tennis　**NEARBY:** Horse riding (8km) Sea (17km) Fishing (3km) Cross-country skiing (40km) Downhill skiing (40km) Railway station (15km) Shops (4km) BAR-SUR-LOUP (11km)
NOTES: No pets　English spoken

♦♦♦♦ Le Mas des Cigales Mareka MONTEGNIES
1673 route des Quenières, 06140 TOURRETTES-SUR-LOUP
☎ 04 93 59 25 73　🖷 04 93 59 25 78
e-mail: macigale@aol.com　http://mascigale.online.fr
Tourrettes-sur-Loup is a medieval village full of character and famous for its violet cultivation, it is also known as a place of artistic meeting. Here, you can stay in one of the five independent, well-maintained and decorated rooms on a Provençal farm with sea views. Pivoine and Violette are twin rooms, while Capucine, Olive (both with 160 x 200cm beds) and Papillon are all double rooms. All rooms have private bathrooms. Hearty breakfasts are served on the patio or on the swimming pool terrace. Outdoor facilities include a tennis court, bowls and parking. Open 1 March to 30 October.
PRICES: s €69; d €77; extra person €23　**ON SITE:** Swimming pool Hiking Tennis　**NEARBY:** Horse riding (8km) Sea (17km) Fishing (3km) Cross-country skiing (40km) Downhill skiing (40km) Railway station (15km) Shops (2km) BAR-SUR-LOUP (11km)　**NOTES:** No pets　English spoken

VENCE

♦♦♦ ⫯○⫯ La Bastide aux Oliviers Claude OLLIVIER
1260, chemin de la Sine, 06140 VENCE
☎ 04 93 24 20 33 & 06 16 09 85 73 📠 04 93 58 55 78
e-mail: frenchclaude@aol.com http://bastidoliv.virtualave.net
Two kilometres from St-Paul-de-Vence, La Bastide aux Oliviers is an
extremely beautiful stone building situated in a one-hectare park
with a magnificent view of the Plaine du Loup. Comprising four
superior double bedrooms, one of which is a suite with a private
lounge, the accommodation is harmoniously decorated in the
Provençal style and all rooms have a bathroom, colour TV and
either a terrace or a solarium. Swimming pool, tennis, private
parking, table d'hôtes meals. Generous breakfasts served under
the covered terrace in front of the swimming pool. Mountain bikes,
table tennis, table football, darts and pétanque available. Open all
year.
PRICES: t €92-€168; HB €28; dinner €16-€23 **ON SITE:** Swimming pool
Hiking Tennis **NEARBY:** Horse riding (8km) Sea (14km) Fishing (5km)
Cross-country skiing (40km) Downhill skiing (40km) Railway station
(13km) Shops (3km) VENCE (3km) **NOTES:** Pets admitted English
spoken

See advert on opposite page

♦♦♦ La Colline de Vence Frederic et Kristin BRONCHARD
808 chemin des Salles, 06140 VENCE
☎ 04 93 24 03 66 & 06 15 35 53 20 📠 04 93 24 03 66
e-mail: collinevence@libertysurf.fr
http://collinevence.online.fr
Three kilometres from St-Paul-de-Vence, La Colline de Vence is an
authentic 200-year-old farm in the style of the area. The
accommodation consists of three individually decorated rooms,
Amandiers, Orangers and Mimosas, all with panoramic views of
the countryside and sea. All of the rooms have a king-size bed,
shower room and wc, satellite TV and mini-bar. An extra bed can
be installed if required. Orangers has an open fireplace. Central
heating, terrace, private gardens and parking. The farm is situated
at the start of many country pathways and is close to numerous
leisure facilities and attractions. Open all year. Low season
discounts.
PRICES: d €89; extra person €15 **ON SITE:** Hiking **NEARBY:** Horse
riding (8km) Sea (12km) Fishing (4km) Swimming pool (3km) Cross-
country skiing (40km) Downhill skiing (40km) Tennis (3km) Railway
station (12km) Shops (2km) VENCE (1km) **NOTES:** No pets English
spoken

BOUCHES-DU-RHÔNE

AIX-EN-PROVENCE

♦♦♦ ⫯○⫯ Chambre d'hôtes Martine ALEXANDRIAN
670, chemin des loups, Campagne Jeanne-Les Milles,
13290 AIX-EN-PROVENCE
☎ 04 42 60 83 10 📠 04 42 20 16 35
e-mail: martine@campagne-jeanne.com
http://www.campagne-jeanne.com
Set in the countryside around Aix, this house offers four pretty
bedrooms decorated in the traditional colours of Provence. Three
ground floor double rooms, one twin room and bathroom. Cot
available. Private terrace with furniture. In the winter, guests are
invited to share the lounge's open fire with their hosts. 4 km from
the town centre. Car park. Open all year.
PRICES: s €50; d €55; dinner €20 **NEARBY:** Horse riding (1km) Golf
(2km) Sea (30km) Swimming pool (2km) Tennis (3km) Railway station
(4km) Shops (2km) AIX EN PROVENCE (4km) **NOTES:** No pets English
spoken

AURONS

♦♦♦ ✿ ⫯ Chambre d'hôtes Dominique BRULAT
Château du petit Sonnailler, 13121 AURONS
☎ 04 90 59 34 47 📠 04 90 59 32 30
e-mail: dbrulat@petit-sonnailler.com
http://www.petit-sonnailler.com
Situated on a site of archaeological interest, with a château dating
from the 12th century and a vineyard. This pretty house, in 80
hectares, offers one ground floor room with double bed, single
bed, (additional child's bed available), shower-room with
wheelchair access. Also one double room with private bathroom
and separate lounge, and one large double room with bathroom
and extra bed available. Private terrace and garden with furniture.
Mini bar. Microwave. Covered car park. Open all year.
PRICES: s €46-€53; d €53-€61; extra person €15 **NEARBY:** Horse riding
(5km) Golf (10km) Sea (30km) Swimming pool (1km) Tennis (1km)
Railway station (9km) Shops (7km) SALON DE PROVENCE (9km)
NOTES: Pets admitted Minimum 2 night stay

♦♦♦ Chambre d'hôtes Monique BRAUGE
Le Castelas, Vallon des Eoures, 13121 AURONS
☎ 04 90 55 60 12 & 06 08 53 61 29 📠 04 90 55 60 12
e-mail: mbrauloy@aol.com http://www.lecastelas.com
The pretty house is situated in a village that dates from the 10th
century. One twin room, one double room and one triple room, all
with bathroom and furnished with antiques. Situated in closed
grounds with car park, a private terrace with furniture and a large
veranda with panoramic views where breakfast can be served.
Separate guest entrance. Open all year.
PRICES: s €61; d €64-€74; extra person €23 **NEARBY:** Horse riding
(5km) Golf (9km) Sea (35km) Swimming pool (8km) Tennis (5km)
Railway station (9km) Shops (5km) SALON DE PROVENCE (7km)
NOTES: No pets English spoken

CABRIES

♦♦♦ ⫯○⫯ Chambre d'hôtes J M VINCENT ET PERRIER
route de la cesarde, La Bastide de la cluée, 13480 CABRIES
☎ 04 42 22 59 00 & 06 13 90 26 50 📠 04 42 22 59 00
This peaceful 19th-century house set in shady grounds offers three
attractive guest rooms, comprising of two double rooms with
bathroom and one room with double bed and single bed on a
mezzanine; and one suite with private entrance. The suite has a
bathroom and small lounge, one double bed and two bunk beds.
A lounge with fireplace, a living room with TV and a dining room
are available for guest use. Also outdoor kitchen, pool house, and
open-air swimming pool. Open all year.
PRICES: s €46-€59; d €61-€72; t €85; extra person €12; dinner €20
ON SITE: Swimming pool **NEARBY:** Horse riding (2km) Golf (5km)
Sea (15km) Tennis (2km) Railway station (10km) Shops (2km) AIX EN
PROVENCE (10km) **NOTES:** No pets English spoken

CHATEAURENARD

♦♦♦ Mas des Cactus Françoise et Patrick BASNEL
3501 Chemin Roumieux, 13160 CHATEAURENARD
☎ 04 90 90 14 65 📠 04 90 90 14 65
e-mail: patrick.basnel@worldonline.fr
Two charming guest rooms in a house set in two hectares of
grounds and surrounded by farmland. One twin room and one
double room are available, both with shower room and wc.
Lounge with library and TV, covered swimming pool and car park.
Pleasant, shady garden. Reduced rate from October to March:
43 euros for one person; 46 euros per couple. Open all year.
PRICES: s €50; d €53; extra person €15 **ON SITE:** Swimming pool
NEARBY: Horse riding (2km) Golf (6km) Sea (60km) Fishing (999km)
Tennis (2km) Railway station (10km) Shops (2km) SAINT REMY DE
PROVENCE (6km) **NOTES:** No pets English spoken

Chambre d'hôtes Jacqueline SARRAZIN
1001 chemin du mas de Raton, 13160 CHATEAURENARD
☎ 04 90 94 00 33 ▤ 04 90 94 00 33
This large house close to Avignon, offers three guest rooms with a separate entrance. One double room with private bathroom facilities opposite, and a further two rooms with bathroom. Private terrace with furniture, well-kept garden, swimming pool, table tennis table and car park. Open 1 January to 12 December.
PRICES: s €43-€46; d €53-€58 **NEARBY:** Horse riding (1km) Golf (5km) Sea (70km) Swimming pool (5km) Tennis (5km) Railway station (8km) Shops (5km) AVIGNON (8km) **NOTES:** No pets

EYGALIERES

Chambre d'hôtes Danielle et Maurice PERNIX
Quartier du Contras, 13810 EYGALIERES
☎ 04 90 95 04 89 & 06 19 01 28 77 ▤ 04 90 95 04 89
Five guest rooms are offered in this renovated house set on a peaceful smallholding with a beautiful view of the Alpilles. Three first- floor double rooms with independent exterior stairs and private shower room, and two twin rooms on the ground floor with shower room and en suite wc. First-floor lounge and a living area on the ground floor. Fridge, freezer and microwave reserved for guests and an extra bed and cot are available on request. Open, shady garden with furniture. Parking. Many walks nearby. Picnic baskets available. Open 15 February to 15 October.
PRICES: s €35-€38; d €42-€46; t €54-€61 **NEARBY:** Horse riding (3km) Golf (15km) Sea (40km) Swimming pool (10km) Tennis (4km) Railway station (9km) Shops (1km) SAINT REMY DE PROVENCE (10km) **NOTES:** No pets Minimum 2 night stay

FUVEAU

Chambre d'hôtes Francette et Daniel DUBOIS
min chemin des Pradels, Quartier des Longs Cols, 13710 FUVEAU
☎ 04 42 68 15 88 & 06 76 03 68 12 ▤ 04 42 68 15 88
Set on nine hectares of land, this house offers four attractive rooms with great views, each with lounge corner. Two double rooms, one twin room and one suite consisting of one double room and one single room, with bath/shower, are available. Two rooms have king-size beds. A cot available. Library. Communal terrace with furniture, covered swimming pool and car park. Walks and bike riding. Open all year.
PRICES: s €44-€49; d €49-€53; t €64 **ON SITE:** Swimming pool **NEARBY:** Horse riding (1km) Golf (2km) Sea (40km) Tennis (2km) Railway station (10km) Shops (2km) AIX EN PROVENCE (12km) **NOTES:** No pets English spoken

GRANS

Château de Couloubriers
Evelyne/Jean-Pierre GONIN
13450 GRANS ☎ 04 90 42 27 29 ▤ 04 90 42 27 29
e-mail: couloubriers@libertysurf.fr
http://www.guideweb.com/provence/chateau/couloubriers
The Château de Couloubriers is an elegant 18th-century Provençal building, painstakingly preserved, set in 40-hectare grounds with pine woods and olive groves. There is independent access to the three spacious, comfortable and traditionally styled rooms. One triple room, one twin and one suite with double room, twin room and lounge. All have shower rooms and mini bars. Indulgent breakfasts are served. Library, billiard table, croquet, two swimming pools and mountain bikes are available. Open 1 May to 30 September.
PRICES: s €84; d €105; t €130-€175 **ON SITE:** Swimming pools Tennis **NEARBY:** Horse riding (3km) Golf (3km) Sea (20km) Railway station (7km) Shops (3km) SALON DE PROVENCE (7km) **NOTES:** No pets

La Bastide aux Oliviers

1260 Chemin de la Sine
06140 Vence
Tel: 00 33 4 93 24 20 33   Fax: 00 33 4 93 58 55 78
Web: http://bastidoliv.virtualave.net/
Situated 3 kms from the famous old artists' village of Saint-Paul de Vence between the sea and the mountains. A large Provençal house built of local stone in 10,000 square metres of pine and old olive trees. Laurence and Claude extend a warm welcome to their guests. The guest rooms consist of 3 en-suite bedrooms some with terrace or solarium and 1 luxurious suite with full facilities and a large terrace. Within the grounds you can enjoy free of charge; swimming, tennis, ping pong, bicycle riding and pétanque. The ideal location for rest and relaxation.
Prices from 120 to 175€ per 2 people bed & breakfast.

Chambre d'hôtes Marie-Jehanne MARTINI
12 rue des moulins, 13450 GRANS
☎ 04 90 55 86 46 ▤ 04 90 55 86 46
This 17th-century former mill, set in the heart of a historic village, offers one triple room with private shower and bathroom, a further triple room and one double room, both with independent shower facilities. All rooms look out on the garden. Rooms have direct access to the swimming pool and solarium. Shady garden and communal patio. Large room with TV, library, fridge and microwave. Open 1 April to 31 October.
PRICES: s €45; d €55; t €70; extra person €15 **ON SITE:** Swimming pool **NEARBY:** Horse riding (1km) Golf (10km) Sea (25km) Tennis (1km) Railway station (4km) SALON DE PROVENCE (4km) **NOTES:** No pets

Chambre d'hôtes Véronique/J.Pierre RICHARD
Domaine Du Bois Vert, Quartier Montauban, 13450 GRANS
☎ 04 90 55 82 98 ▤ 04 90 55 82 98
e-mail: leboisvert@hotmail.com
http://www.multimania.com/leboisvert
Two triple rooms with shower room and wc, and one double room with bathroom are available in this pretty Provençal farmhouse situated in grounds on the river's edge. Private terrace, garden furniture and independent guest entrance. Lounge with fireplace, TV and library. Shared fridge for the three rooms. Table tennis, tennis and other games. Sculpture and literature courses offered in the village. Open 15 March to 5 January.
PRICES: s €54; d €58-€64; t €83 **ON SITE:** Swimming pool **NEARBY:** Horse riding (2km) Golf (9km) Sea (25km) Tennis (1km) Railway station (6km) Shops (2km) SALON DE PROVENCE (6km) **NOTES:** No pets Minimum 2 night stay English spoken

PROVENCE-ALPES-CÔTE-D'AZUR

JOUQUES

⚘ ⊙I Chambre d'hôtes Magalie et Philippe MARY
Campagne Le Catelan, 13490 JOUQUES
☎ 04 42 67 69 43 📠 04 42 67 69 43
e-mail: philippe.mary@libertysurf.fr
Peace and quiet guaranteed in this renovated stone house, in 40 hectares which offers guest rooms decorated in traditional local colours. Ground floor double room and triple room, both with shower facilities. Also offers a family room with double bed and twin beds, and, in an separate building, one double room with shower. Communal terrace with furniture, boules, volleyball and car park. Set in 40 hectares of land. Open all year.
PRICES: s €42; d €55; t €70; extra person €15; dinner €15
ON SITE: Swimming pool **NEARBY:** Horse riding (5km) Golf (30km) Sea (50km) Tennis (3km) Railway station (10km) Shops (3km) AIX EN PROVENCE (30km) **NOTES:** No pets English spoken

LE PARADOU

⚘ L'Espelido Mireille JOLY
route des tours de Castillon, 13520 LE PARADOU
☎ 04 90 54 38 55 📠 04 90 54 38 55
e-mail: lespelido@wanadoo.fr
In the Baux de Provence Valley, this attractive old-fashioned house benefits from a large, shady garden. Two double rooms with private bathrooms, one family room with private terrace and bathroom and one double room with private shower room are offered. Telephone available if guests purchase a phone card. Reservations necessary in the winter. Close to Les Baux, St Rémy, Avignon, Arles, the Camargue, and Lubéron. Open all year.
PRICES: s €50-€54; d €50-€54; extra person €17 **NEARBY:** Horse riding (2km) Golf (2km) Sea (40km) Swimming pool (2km) Tennis (1km) Railway station (15km) Shops (1km) SAINT REMY DE PROVENCE (15km)
NOTES: No pets Minimum 2 night stay English spoken

LES PALUDS DE NOVES

⚘ Chambre d'hôtes S et N LASCOMBES ET ROUSSEAU
Mas de Jauffret, 13550 LES PALUDS DE NOVES
☎ 04 32 61 09 76 📠 04 32 61 09 76
One double room (king size bed) with shower facilities, one twin room with bathroom and one family room with shower facilities, are available in this renovated 18th-century farmhouse set in two hectares surrounded by orchards. Lounge with TV and fireplace, communal terrace with garden furniture and car park. In a peaceful setting between the Alpilles and Lubéron. Open all year.
PRICES: d €69-€91; extra person €15 **ON SITE:** Swimming pool
NEARBY: Horse riding (2km) Golf (15km) Sea (60km) Tennis (1km) Railway station (19km) Shops (1km) SAINT REMY DE PROVENCE (7km)
NOTES: No pets English spoken

LES SAINTES-MARIES-DE-LA-MER

⚘ Chambre d'hôtes Babeth ANDRE
Route du Bac-D85, Mazet du Maréchal Ferrand,
13460 LES SAINTES-MARIES-DE-LA-MER
☎ 04-90-97-84-60 📠 04 90 97 84 60
e-mail: babeth@showlorenzo.com http://www.showlorenzo.com
Three rooms are available in this cosy, rustic house set in the heart of the Carmargue with its marshes, reeds and horses. The rooms all have private bathrooms and the house has a shady garden with car park and terrace. One double room, one twin room and one family room for four people are offered. Open all year.
PRICES: d €50; t €59 **NEARBY:** Horse riding (1km) Sea (4km) Tennis (4km) Railway station (35km) Shops (4km) ARLES (35km) **NOTES:** No pets Minimum 2 night stay

PLAN D'ORGON

⚘ Mas de la Miougrano Magali RODET
447, route des Ecoles, 13750 PLAN-D'ORGON
☎ 04 90 73 20 01 & 06 81 04 12 93 📠 04 90 73 20 01
e-mail: lamiougrano@net-up.com
http://perso.net-up.com/lamiougrano
The attractive, flowery garden of this traditionally decorated Provençal house is laid out around a 100-year-old plane tree. The ground floor double room with shower looks directly onto the garden. First floor accommodation consists of one suite of two rooms, a double and a twin, and has a communal shower room, independent wc, and a private lounge with TV point. Open all year.
PRICES: s €49-€53; d €58-€61; t €76-€84; extra person €15
ON SITE: Swimming pool **NEARBY:** Horse riding (5km) Golf (15km) Sea (60km) Tennis (1km) Railway station (5km) Shops (1km) CAVAILLON (5km) **NOTES:** Pets admitted English spoken

PUYLOUBIER

⚘ Domaine Genty Gwenaelle et Laurent COULON
Routre de St Antonin, 13114 PUYLOUBIER
☎ 04 42 66 32 44 📠 04 42 66 32 44
e-mail: domaine-genty@wanadoo.fr
http://www.guideweb.com/provence/bb/domaine-genty
On a peaceful 30-hectare estate in the Sainte Victoire mountains, this guest house offers five distinctive, comfortable guest rooms decorated with a southern feel. One double room, one twin room and one triple room all have private shower rooms and wc, and the rest of the accommodation consists of a two-room suite (one twin room and one single room) with bathroom and private terrace. Cot available. Communal lounge, garden with furniture, open-air swimming pool and car park. Open 1 March to 3 November.
PRICES: s €53; d €69-€91; t €84-€105 **ON SITE:** Swimming pool
NEARBY: Horse riding (10km) Golf (12km) Sea (50km) Tennis (4km) Railway station (17km) Shops (3km) AIX EN PROVENCE (17km)
NOTES: No pets English spoken

ROGNES

⚘ La Cheneraie Annie et Michel MABILEAU
Bastide du Plan, 13840 ROGNES
☎ 04 42 50 19 01 📠 04 42 50 19 01
Three attractive double rooms, each one with en suite shower or bathroom, and one family suite with bathroom, are available in this 18th-century house set in a shady 1.5 hectare park. Lounge with TV, open-air swimming pool and car park. There is also a holiday home on the property. Open all year.
PRICES: s €76; d €84; t €135; extra person €6 **ON SITE:** Swimming pool **NEARBY:** Horse riding (4km) Golf (15km) Sea (50km) Tennis (4km) Railway station (23km) Shops (4km) AIX EN PROVENCE (23km)
NOTES: No pets

SAINT-ETIENNE-DU-GRES

⚘ Mas la Saladelle C et G DESORT/LAFUENTE
Chemin d'Altaves, 13103 ST-ETIENNE-DU-GRES
☎ 04 90 49 13 04 & 06 09 51 29 82 📠 04 90 49 13 05
e-mail: maslasaladelle@wanadoo.fr
Attractive, elegantly decorated guest rooms are available in this peaceful house set in a two-hectare estate situated between orchards and woods. Two double rooms with bath/shower, one twin room with shower room, one triple room with bathroom and one suite with two double beds and bathroom. Guest lounge with large fireplace. Communal terrace with furniture, boules equipment and car park. Open-air swimming pool. Open all year.
PRICES: s €52-€76; d €59-€91; extra person €15 **ON SITE:** Swimming pool **NEARBY:** Horse riding (2km) Golf (15km) Sea (55km) Tennis (2km) Railway station (7km) Shops (2km) SAINT REMY DE PROVENCE (15km) **NOTES:** No pets English spoken

♦♦♦♦ Aux Deux Soeurs Carolyn WOOD
Vieux Chemin d'Arles, 13103 SAINT-ETIENNE-DU-GRES
☎ 04 90 49 10 18   🖷 04 90 49 10 30
e-mail: ads.wood.gites@infonie.fr
Eleven-hectare property in the Alpilles with three guest rooms
and two separate holiday cottages available. This 18th-century
house has access to recognised hiking routes and a covered
swimming pool. One room with double four-poster bed and
bathroom. One twin room with bathroom. A suite with one
double room, one twin room, bathroom, kitchen corner and
lounge is also available. The three rooms all have telephone,
TV and video recorder. Cot available. Terraces with garden
furniture. Car park. Open all year.
PRICES: s €84; d €99-€135; t €145 **ON SITE:** Swimming pool
Tennis **NEARBY:** Horse riding (5km) Golf (4km) Sea (30km)
Railway station (8km) Shops (2km) SAINT REMY (4km)
NOTES: No pets Minimum 2 night stay English spoken

SAINT-MARC-JAUMEGARDE

♦♦♦♦ Chambre d'hôtes Geneviève MELIN
La ferme, chemin de l'Ermitage St-Marc-Jaumegarde,
13100 AIX-EN-PROVENCE
☎ 04 42 24 92 97   🖷 04 42 24 92 79
e-mail: infos@la-ferme-en-provence.com
www.la-ferme-en-provence.com
This very pretty house close to Aix, with views of Mount Sainte
Victoire, offers a suite consisting of one double room (with
king size bed and desk), bathroom, a connecting twin room
with TV, independent access. One double room with desk, TV,
private bathroom and wc and a further double room with a
private bathroom. The garden and pinewood are part of the
one-hectare estate. Garden furniture, table-tennis. Open all
year.
PRICES: d €69-€91; t €105 **NEARBY:** Horse riding (2km) Golf
(20km) Sea (35km) Swimming pool (5km) Tennis (2km) Railway
station (5km) Shops (5km) AIX EN PROVENCE (5km)
NOTES: No pets Minimum 2 night stay English spoken

SAINT-MARTIN-DE-CRAU

♦♦♦♦ 🌺 🍴 Chambre d'hôtes
Marie-Andrée et Jean PINCEDE
Domaine de Vergières, 13310 ST-MARTIN-DE-CRAU
☎ 04-90-47-05-25 & 04 90 47 17 16
🖷 04 90 47 38 30
e-mail: vergieres@vergieres.com www.vergieres.com
Elegant and stylish 18th-century house, in a wonderful isolated
setting in the heart of the immense Crau plains. The château is
bordered by 100-year-old trees and acres of meadows. Five
comfortable double rooms each with private bathroom.
Communal billiards and TV room, phone point, garden with
furniture, open-air swimming pool, table tennis ,and bicycles.
Close to the Crau Nature Reserve, a site of special
ornithological interest. Open 1 January to 31 October.
PRICES: s €140; d €150; extra person €46; dinner €53
ON SITE: Swimming pool **NEARBY:** Horse riding (50km) Golf
(15km) Sea (15km) Tennis (8km) Railway station (20km) Shops
(8km) ARLES (20km) **NOTES:** No pets Minimum 2 night stay
English spoken

Prices are given in Euros €1 = £0.62
at the time of going to press

SAINT-REMY-DE-PROVENCE

♦♦♦ Le Mas de Manon
M DE DIEULEVEULT ET XIBERRAS
Chemin des Lônes, 13210 SAINT-REMY-DE-PROVENCE
☎ 04 32 60 09 86 & 06 09 44 92 22
e-mail: masdemanon@libertysurf.fr
http://www.alpilles.com/mas_manon.htm
This fully restored Provençal house offers one double room, one
twin room and two triple rooms, all with shower and wc. Lounge
with fireplace and satellite TV, which receives foreign channels. Cot
available. Barbecue, car park and covered terrace with furniture.
The four guest rooms are warmly decorated and the house
benefits from the calm of its rural setting. Open all year.
PRICES: s €50; d €58; t €73 **NEARBY:** Horse riding (4km) Golf (12km)
Sea (70km) Swimming pool (3km) Tennis (4km) Railway station (18km)
Shops (3km) CENTRE (3km) **NOTES:** No pets English spoken

♦♦♦ Chambre d'hôtes Myriam FEIGE
Mas Clair de Lune, Plateau de la Crau,
13210 SAINT REMY DE PROVENCE
☎ 04 90 92 02 63 & 06 89 43 65 43
One twin room, one triple room and one single room, all with
shower and wc facilities, are available in this detached house set in
wooded grounds with panoramic views of the Alpilles. Each room
has a private terrace and separate entrance. Lounge with TV and
fireplace. Table tennis, swimming pool, boules and car park. Peace
and quiet guaranteed. Open all year.
PRICES: s €47; d €58; t €73 **ON SITE:** Swimming pool
NEARBY: Horse riding (2km) Golf (10km) Sea (50km) Tennis (2km)
Railway station (19km) Shops (2km) AVIGNON (19km) **NOTES:** Pets
admitted Minimum 2 night stay English spoken

VAUVENARGUES

♦♦♦ Chambre d'hôtes Madeleine BOSC
La Dame D'Oc, Claps, 13126 VAUVENARGUES
☎ 04 42 66 02 36
Housed in an separate building, three guest rooms are offered in
this wonderful property in surroundings of Mount Sainte Victoire.
Three double rooms are available, one with separate bathroom,
one with shower and one with shower. Private terrace
with furniture, tennis court and garden with pond. Open all year.
PRICES: s €55; d €61 **ON SITE:** Tennis **NEARBY:** Horse riding (18km)
Golf (18km) Sea (50km) Swimming pool (18km) Railway station (18km)
Shops (3km) AIX EN PROVENCE (18km) **NOTES:** Pets admitted
Minimum 2 night stay English spoken

VERQUIERES

♦♦♦ Chambre d'hôtes Evelyne et Philippe SAVOURNIN
Bergerie de Castellan, 13670 VERQUIERES
☎ 04 90 95 02 07   🖷 04 90 59 02 07
e-mail: gitesdefrance@visitprovence.com www.visitprovence.com
This former farm building is pleasantly situated in a large shady
park with a small wood and offers three rooms for guest use. The
accommodation available includes one family room with double
bed and a mezzanine housing twin beds. Also offered are two
double rooms. All rooms have private shower and wc facilities.
Dining room and lounge with library and fireplace at guests'
disposition. Covered swimming pool and car park. Open 1
February to 31 December.
PRICES: s €53-€61; d €61-€69; t €76 **ON SITE:** Swimming pool
NEARBY: Horse riding (2km) Golf (10km) Sea (60km) Tennis (4km)
Railway station (14km) Shops (2km) SAINT REMY DE PROVENCE (8km)
NOTES: No pets English spoken

continued

♯♯♯ Mas de Castellan René PINET
13670 VERQUIERES
☎ 04 90 95 08 22 📠 04 90 95 44 23
http://www.mas-de-castellan.net

Three double rooms and one twin room, all with en suite shower rooms, are offered in this ivy-covered house, part of which dates from the 18th century. Lounge, winter garden, swimming pool and large shady terrace. Set amongst orchards between the Alpilles and Lubéron. Open 5 March to 31 December.
PRICES: d €77 **ON SITE:** Swimming pool **NEARBY:** Horse riding (5km) Golf (14km) Sea (80km) Tennis (3km) Railway station (20km) Shops (2km) SAINT REMY DE PROVENCE (8km) **NOTES:** No pets Minimum 2 night stay

HAUTES-ALPES

ANCELLE

♯♯♯ ⭘ Edelweiss Jacky et Josiane MEIZEL
les Auches, 05260 ANCELLE
☎ 04 92 50 82 39 & 06 86 18 91 52
e-mail: j-meizel@club-internet.fr
http://www.chambresdhote-ancelle.com
At the entrance to the National Park des Ecrins, rooms with their own access, in our new house. On the first floor: one room for three (bath and wc); one double (bath and wc); one double with balcony (shower and wc); one double (grade 2) (shower and wc on landing) with balcony. Lounge, sitting room, television, electric heating, lawn, leisure area. Parking, bowls area, regional cooking with bread baked on a wood fire. Meals if booked. Lac de Serre-Ponçon 20km. Hiking and skiing close at hand. Open all year.
PRICES: s €34-€35; d €41.5-€45; t €57.5-€59; meal €13; HB €33-€35 **ON SITE:** Forest **NEARBY:** Bathing (7km) Rock climbing (8km) Stretch of water (20km) Cross-country skiing (1km) Downhill skiing (1km) Tennis (1km) Railway station (17km) Shops (1km) SAINT BONNET (16km) **NOTES:** No pets

ARVIEUX

♯♯♯ ❤ La Girondole Noel MOREL
horticulteur la Girandole, Brunissard, 05350 ARVIEUX
☎ 04 92 46 84 12 📠 04 92 46 86 59
e-mail: lagirandole@aol.com
The owner and his family welcome you to their guest house which comprises their accommodation, two gîtes, and on the first floor four double rooms and a suite for four with bathrooms and wc, plus a television lounge. On the second floor, living room with open fireplace, kitchen, library, music area, children's games room and sauna. Outside, terrace, garden, enclosed grounds, summer swimming pool, balneotherapy bath.

continued

PRICES: s €46; d €55; t €77; extra person €22 **ON SITE:** Children's play area Rock climbing **NEARBY:** Bathing (1km) Forest (1km) Stretch of water (30km) Cross-country skiing (1km) Downhill skiing (1km) Tennis (1km) Railway station (25km) Shops (1km) AIGUILLES (15km) **NOTES:** No pets English spoken

BENEVENT ET CHARBILLAC

♯♯♯ ⭘ Le Cairn Brigitte GOURDOU
Charbillac, 05500 BENEVENT ET CHARBILLAC
☎ 04 92 50 54 87
e-mail: GITE.LE.CAIRN@wanadoo.Fr http://le.cairn.free.fr
This village house has a vaulted ground floor, containing dining room, sitting area with fire. On the mansard second floor are four guest rooms each with shower room and wc. Cooking over a wood fire. Electric heating. Enclosed grounds with garden furniture. Several mountain bike routes on the doorstep. Open all year.
PRICES: s €35; d €39; extra person €19.50; HB €29-€31; dinner €11.50 **NEARBY:** Bathing (7km) Rock climbing (10km) Forest (1km) Stretch of water (7km) Cross-country skiing (11km) Downhill skiing (11km) Tennis (5km) Railway station (20km) Shops (5km) SAINT BONNET (5km) **NOTES:** Pets admitted English spoken

BUISSARD

♯♯♯ ⭘ Les Chemins Verts Nathalie DUBOIS
05500 BUISSARD ☎ 04 92 50 57 57 📠 04 92 50 75 25
On this 18th-century renovated farm, as well as the owners' apartment, there are a country gîte, and four rooms for guests, each with shower room and wc. On the ground floor: large (90m2) dining room/lounge with open fire, television, wc. First floor: two rooms (two and four people). Upper mansard floor: two rooms for two and three people. Central heating. Grounds and garden furniture. Parking. Open all year.
PRICES: s €35; d €43-€49; t €52; extra person €9; dinner €12.50 **NEARBY:** Bathing (3km) Rock climbing (5km) Forest (1km) Stretch of water (3km) Cross-country skiing (6km) Downhill skiing (6km) Tennis (3km) Railway station (20km) Shops (3km) SAINT BONNET (8km) **NOTES:** Pets admitted English spoken

CHABOTTES

♯♯♯ ❤ ⭘ La Chabottine Catherine & Alain DUSSERRE
les Fangeas, 05260 CHABOTTES ☎ 04 92 50 72 29
Near the Park des Ecrins, on their working farm, Catherine and Alain offer you five guest rooms in a converted farm building. The ground floor contains dining room, sitting area with fireplace and television. The first floor has two three-bedded rooms opening on to a terrace. The mansard second floor has three double rooms. Each room has shower room and wc. Grounds, garden furniture, parking. Meals out of season if booked. Open all year
PRICES: s €32; d €40; t €48; dinner €12 **ON SITE:** Forest **NEARBY:** Bathing (10km) Rock climbing (3km) Stretch of water (4km) Cross-country skiing (3km) Downhill skiing (5km) Tennis (2km) Railway station (20km) Shops (2km) SAINT BONNET (10km) **NOTES:** No pets English spoken

GAP

♦♦♦♦ La Lauluna Nathalie TOMASI
domaine des Eterlous, chemin du Haut Varsie, 05000 GAP
☎ 04 92 56 06 00 📠 04 92 56 06 00
Six kilometres from an 18-hole golf course, in a new house at the foot of the Charance mountain. Three rustic-style bedrooms (each with en suite facilities) for two or three people, two of which have entrances from a private terrace, while the third is upstairs. Large lounge with fireplace, and library of mountain books. Sports information. Refrigerator for guests' use. Open all year.
PRICES: s €50; d €50; t €63; extra person €13 **NEARBY:** Bathing (5km) Rock climbing (10km) Forest (1km) Stretch of water (15km) Cross-country skiing (6km) Downhill skiing (8km) Tennis (5km) Railway station (2km) Shops (2km) GAP (3km) **NOTES:** No pets English spoken

♦♦♦♦ Le Parlement Bruno & Anne DROUILLARD
route du Lac, quartier de Charance, 05000 GAP
☎ 04 92 53 94 20
e-mail: bruno.drouillard@wanadoo.fr

An 18th-century residence, near the château de Charance and its lake. Ground floor dining room/salon with open fire. Five first floor rooms with separate access, for two to four people. Most have shower and wc. One room has a bathroom and a balcony. Central heating, sauna, billiards. Terraced park with garden furniture, children's play area, swimming pool. Summer kitchen at disposal. Garage parking possible. 15km to 18-hole golf course. Open all year.
PRICES: s €55-€77; d €55-€77; extra person €8-€16 **ON SITE:** Children's play area Forest **NEARBY:** Bathing (14km) Rock climbing (20km) Stretch of water (25km) Cross-country skiing (14km) Downhill skiing (17km) Tennis (5km) Railway station (5km) Shops (5km) GAP (1km) **NOTES:** No pets English spoken

♦♦♦♦ Les Eyssagnieres Orietta MANENT
Esparceu, 27 route des Eyssagnieres, 05000 GAP
☎ 04 92 52 04 81
e-mail: d.gauthier@worldonline.fr
In a large meadow stands the owner's house, with two gîtes. Dining room on the ground floor. First floor: one guest room with shower and wc. Second floor: reading area and four bedrooms each with bath or shower room and wc. TV in each room. Public phone. Central heating. Grounds open to guests; garden furniture. Parking. Open all year; booking required outside holiday periods.
PRICES: s €30-€44; d €34-€48; extra person €11 **NEARBY:** Bathing (2km) Rock climbing (10km) Forest (2km) Stretch of water (6km) Cross-country skiing (9km) Downhill skiing (13km) Tennis (2km) Railway station (4km) Shops (2km) GAP (3km) **NOTES:** Pets admitted

GUILLESTRE

♦♦♦♦ ⛧🍴 Le Clos de Phasy Marie-Jane et Roger JARNIAC
plan de Phasy, 05600 GUILLESTRE
☎ 04 92 45 37 53 & 06 03 54 49 38 📠 04 92 45 37 53
Risoul Vars ski resort nearby. Near the hot spring at Plan du Phasy, this large house (originally a postal relay station) offers five rooms,

each individually designed. Each room accommodates two to four guests, and has shower and wc. Separate entrances to guest rooms. Reading room; television; large vaulted living room with open fireplace. One hectare of grounds with orchard and garden. Garden furniture and shelter. Open all year.
PRICES: s €40; d €53; t €61; extra person €12; HB €40; dinner €15 **NEARBY:** Bathing (1km) Rock climbing (3km) Forest (1km) Stretch of water (18km) Cross-country skiing (15km) Downhill skiing (14km) Tennis (2km) Railway station (5km) GUILLESTRE (2km) **NOTES:** Pets admitted CC English spoken

LA CHAPELLE EN VALGAUDEMAR

♦♦♦♦ La Fontaine Fleurie
J. Claude & Sylvette CATELAN
05800 LA CHAPELLE EN VALGAUDEMAR
☎ 04 92 55 27 66
In a new building, over a grocery, and below a gîte. On the first floor, four rooms each with shower and wc, one of which is a single room (grade 1), plus a communal kitchen. The dining room is on the ground floor. Central heating. Small charming garden with fountain and garden furniture. Parking. Opposite - tennis and communal games area. Open all year.
PRICES: s €31; d €39; t €47; extra person €8 **ON SITE:** Forest Cross-country skiing Tennis **NEARBY:** Bathing (25km) Rock climbing (1km) Stretch of water (25km) Downhill skiing (40km) Railway station (50km) SAINT FIRMIN (16km) **NOTES:** No pets English spoken

LA PIARRE

♦♦♦♦ 🍴 ♿ Le Chanelou Dominique et Bernard GIRAUD
la Calade, 05700 LA PIARRE
☎ 04 92 67 08 35
http://www.buech-serrois.com
Overlooking the village of La Piarre stands this renovated farmhouse. Dominique and Bernard offer four guest rooms (in the style of the region) for two to four people, with en suite shower and wc. Swimming pool and terrace for guests' use. Meals feature regional cuisine and are served in a large vaulted dining room. Relaxing area exclusively for guests. Garage for bicycles and motor bikes. Open all year.
PRICES: s €29; d €38-€43; t €53-€58; HB €33; dinner €14 **ON SITE:** Bathing **NEARBY:** Rock climbing (4km) Forest (1km) Stretch of water (10km) Cross-country skiing (40km) Downhill skiing (40km) Tennis (10km) Railway station (10km) Shops (10km) SERRES (10km) **NOTES:** Pets admitted

LES ORRES

♦♦♦♦ 🍴 La Jarbelle Michel & Claude HURAULT
les Ribes, 05200 LES ORRES
☎ 04 92 44 11 33 📠 04 92 44 11 23
e-mail: lajarbelle@wanadoo.fr

In a hamlet, this renovated farmhouse from 1836 includes the owners' accommodation plus guest rooms. On the first floor are

continued   continued

five rooms for two to four people, each with shower room, wc and balcony. The attic has one double with shower room and wc, and games/reading room with television area. Central heating. The ground floor has the dining room, lounge area with open fireplace; underfloor heating. Grounds, garden furniture, table tennis, parking. Storage for skis and mountain bikes. Snowshoes available. Open all year; booking required.
PRICES: s €20-€23; d €40-€46; t €60-€69; extra person €20-€23; HB €34-€37; dinner €16 **ON SITE:** Forest **NEARBY:** Bathing (3km) Rock climbing (4km) Stretch of water (12km) Cross-country skiing (3km) Downhill skiing (3km) Tennis (3km) Railway station (14km) Shops (3km) EMBRUN (14km) **NOTES:** Pets admitted English spoken

PRUNIERES

♦♦♦ ৬ Les Carlines Louis VELAY
les Vignes Larignier, 05230 PRUNIERES
☎ 04 92 50 63 27
http://www.gites.net/car6327/index.htm

In a park with its own lake, the house looks out on the Lac de Serre-Ponçon and the Alps. Veranda, lounge, sitting room with fire, kitchen for use of guests. At the garden level, with its flower-bedecked terraces: three bedrooms with shower rooms and wc. On the second floor: two rooms again with shower and wc. All rooms have TV, fridge and air conditioning. Skiing and fishing. Picnic area, garden furniture, table tennis, barbecue, boules. Washing machine available. Parking. Open end December to beginning November.
PRICES: s €40; d €44-€47; extra person €6-€12 **NEARBY:** Bathing (1km) Rock climbing (8km) Forest (5km) Stretch of water (2km) Cross-country skiing (12km) Downhill skiing (12km) Tennis (5km) Railway station (5km) Shops (5km) CHORGES (5km) **NOTES:** Pets admitted

RISOUL

♦♦♦ IOI La Maison de Josephine Philippe MAUREL
L'Eglise, 05600 RISOUL
☎ 04 92 45 28 01
Opposite Pelvoux, in Risoul village, a traditional house with five guest rooms, each with shower room or bathroom and wc. Vaulted dining room, sitting area, library, games room and sauna for guests. Nearby swimming pool and children's area. Large terrace and managed grounds. Organic vegetarian meals.
PRICES: s €45; d €66; HB €50; dinner €20 **ON SITE:** Bathing **NEARBY:** Rock climbing (5km) Forest (3km) Stretch of water (25km) Cross-country skiing (10km) Downhill skiing (10km) Tennis (3km) Railway station (5km) Shops (3km) GUILLESTRE (5km) **NOTES:** Pets admitted English spoken

♦♦♦ IOI La Source Chantal GADRAT
Chauvet, 05600 RISOUL
☎ 04 92 45 37 48 & 06 87 34 68 43 ▯ 04 92 45 23 58
Chantal will welcome you into this old farmhouse with its view over the valley of the Durrance and the citadel of Mont-Dauphin. Five bedrooms (of which one is a family room for four), decorated

with old furniture and ornaments. Each room has shower room or bathroom. Two rooms have a terrace. Dining room, living room in old cowshed with an open fireplace, library. Tended outside areas.
PRICES: s €35-€43; d €70-€85; extra person €20-€27; HB €46-€53 **ON SITE:** Forest **NEARBY:** Bathing (5km) Rock climbing (13km) Stretch of water (30km) Cross-country skiing (15km) Downhill skiing (15km) Tennis (5km) Railway station (5km) Shops (5km) GUILLESTRE (5km) **NOTES:** No pets CC English spoken

ROSANS

♦♦♦ ▶ IOI La Conviviance
Thomas DE SAINT-JEAN
Le Beal Noir, 05150 ROSANS
☎ 04 92 66 65 42
e-mail: conviviance@libertysurf.fr
The Saint-Jean family (market gardeners, cattle breeders and farm producers) invite you into their completely restored traditional farmhouse. One family room for four, and two doubles (with extra bed if required). Each room has private shower and wc. Living room and sitting room for guests (open fire, television, books). Communal dining room. The cooking is based on the produce of the farm. Terrace, grounds, parking. Open all year.
PRICES: s €31-€37; d €38-€43; t €53-€58; dinner €14 **ON SITE:** Forest **NEARBY:** Bathing (2km) Rock climbing (40km) Stretch of water (25km) Tennis (2km) Railway station (23km) Shops (2km) ROSANS (2km) **NOTES:** Pets admitted English spoken

♦♦♦ IOI L'Ensoleillée Bernadette & Didier PACAUD
le Beal Noir, 05150 ROSANS
☎ 04 92 66 62 72 ▯ 04 92 66 62 87
e-mail: l.ensoleillee@infonie.fr
At the heart of the baronies, at the entrance to Drôme Provençale, guest rooms in annexes to the owners' residence. Ground floor entry to each of six rooms is by a terrace. Each room has television and bathroom or shower room and wc. Two rooms have sitting room and mezzanine. Dining room opens onto terrace. Open fireplace, telephone, reading corner, solarium, swimming pool, shady parking. Garage for motor bikes. Meals on the terrace with a view over the valleys to the mountains, or in the dining room. Open all year.
PRICES: s €37; d €42; t €55; extra person €13; dinner €14 **ON SITE:** Bathing Forest **NEARBY:** Stretch of water (23km) Cross-country skiing (55km) Downhill skiing (55km) Tennis (2km) Railway station (23km) Shops (2km) ROSANS (1km) **NOTES:** Pets admitted English spoken

SAINT JACQUES EN VALGAUDEMAR

♦♦♦ ▶ ৬ Les Clarines Pierre, J.& enfants BARBAN
Entrepierres, 05800 ST JACQUES EN VALGAUDEMAR
☎ 04 92 55 20 31
http://www.valgaudemar.com

Skiing nearby 1400 to 1880 m. A farmhouse inn, with four double rooms and country gîte. One ground floor room with shower/wc.

continued   continued

Dining room on first floor. On the upper mansard level: two rooms with shower and wc (one room has an extra single bed). The fourth room is in a separate annexe, with shower and wc. Television lounge. Central heating. Shady grounds with fountain. Golf 20km. Many walking routes in the National Park des Ecrins. Open all year.
PRICES: s €34-€36; d €40-€43; t €53-€56; HB €31-€36; dinner €14
ON SITE: Forest **NEARBY:** Bathing (3km) Rock climbing (3km) Stretch of water (12km) Cross-country skiing (5km) Downhill skiing (15km) Tennis (3km) Railway station (25km) Shops (3km) Restaurant nearby SAINT FIRMIN (3km) **NOTES:** No pets

SAINT JEAN SAINT NICOLAS

♥♥♥ ❦ Ⱶⵧ ㋡ ♿ Les Haies Sauvages
Andre & Claudine DAVIN
Chabottonnes, 05260 ST JEAN ST NICOLAS
☎ 04 92 50 41 40

Guest rooms in a former farm, on two levels. Ground floor: dining room with kitchen area; wc; one double room (16m²) with private shower/wc. Upstairs: three similar rooms (two doubles and one twin), each with shower and wc; small bunk room for two, with washbasin. Grounds with garden furniture. Parking. Boules pitch and children's games. Covered storage for cycles, motorbikes, skis, etc. Open all year.
PRICES: s €32; d €41; extra person €10; dinner €11 **ON SITE:** Children's play area **NEARBY:** Bathing (5km) Rock climbing (6km) Forest (3km) Stretch of water (10km) Cross-country skiing (3km) Downhill skiing (5km) Tennis (3km) Railway station (22km) Shops (3km) ORCIERES (10km)
NOTES: No pets English spoken

SAINT LEGER LES MELEZES

♥♥♥ ㋡ Les Coustilles Veronique TOLLA
05260 ST LEGER LES MELEZES
☎ 04 92 50 76 74
e-mail: veronique.t@oreka.com
In the heart of the Vallée du Champsaur, Véronique and Pascal offer five completely renovated guest rooms. The rooms sleep two or three, and have television, shower room and wc. Four of the rooms have direct access to the garden. Communal dining room and sitting room. Complementary facilities include Turkish bath and whirlpool. Garden, garden furniture, children's games, parking. In high season a session in the whirlpool bath is offered. Golf 15km. Open all year.
PRICES: s €21-€24; d €42-€48; t €62-€71; extra person €83-€95; HB €29-€32; dinner €11 **ON SITE:** Children's play area Cross-country skiing **NEARBY:** Bathing (3km) Rock climbing (6km) Forest (1km) Stretch of water (10km) Downhill skiing (1km) Tennis (1km) Railway station (25km) Shops (1km) SAINT BONNET (10km) **NOTES:** Pets admitted English spoken

SAINTE COLOMBE

♥♥♥ Le Mas de Rome Roger GUTIERREZ
chevalet le haut le Mas Rome, Orpierre, 05700 SERRES
☎ 04 92 66 31 19 🖹 04 92 66 31 19
In the Buëch valley, facing the Alps, the Mas de Rome has been hidden in its grounds since the 18th century, and is reached by a forest track. Separate entry by a terrace to the four guest rooms, each with its shower room and wc. Electric heating. Communal living room. Access to grounds. A hectare of lavender is planted around the house. Open 15 May to 15 October.
PRICES: s €65; d €65; extra person €23 **ON SITE:** Forest **NEARBY:** Bathing (20km) Rock climbing (7km) Stretch of water (23km) Cross-country skiing (70km) Downhill skiing (70km) Tennis (5km) Railway station (14km) Shops (5km) ORPIERRE (5km) **NOTES:** No pets English spoken

SAVINES LE LAC

♥♥♥ Le Relais Alain BELLET
les Chaumettes, 05160 SAVINES LE LAC
☎ 04 92 44 27 31 & 06 87 87 44 15
e-mail: information@hautes-alpes.org
http://www.hautes-alpes.org
Rooms on three floors of the owner's house. Four rooms with shower/wc; two mansard rooms with bathroom; two rooms (one grade 2) sharing a wc. The dining room opens onto a balcony and terrace with a view over the lake. Kitchen area, television, hi-fi. Grounds, chaises longues. Local shops. Marina 200m. Open all year.
PRICES: d €38-€59 **ON SITE:** Bathing Forest Stretch of water **NEARBY:** Rock climbing (3km) Cross-country skiing (7km) Downhill skiing (7km) Tennis (1km) Railway station (1km) SAVINES LE LAC **NOTES:** Pets admitted English spoken

SIGOTTIER

♥♥♥ Le Moulin du Paroy Pierrette AULONNE
05700 SIGOTTIER
☎ 04 92 67 13 95
http://www.buech-serrois.com
An old mill of considerable character, entirely renovated, on a 9ha estate. The guest rooms are in an annexe with its own access. Two double rooms with private shower and wc. One large room with a double bed and two singles, terrace and private shower/wc. Large living room, with kitchen area for guests. Summer kitchen, terrace, trout river. Open June to September.
PRICES: s €45; d €52; t €60; extra person €8 **ON SITE:** Bathing Forest **NEARBY:** Rock climbing (2km) Stretch of water (3km) Cross-country skiing (35km) Downhill skiing (35km) Tennis (2km) Railway station (2km) Shops (1km) SERRES (1km) **NOTES:** No pets

BAGNOLES-EN-FORET

♥♥♥ ㋡ Pont Couverte Stéphane et Valérie BEAUMESNIL
D 47, Pont Couverte l'Ensoleillée, 83600 BAGNOLS-EN-FORET
☎ 04 98 11 30 44 & SR : 04 94 50 93 93 🖹 04 98 11 30 44
e-mail: valeriebeaumesnile@libertysurf.com
Fréjus, St-Raphaël 20 km. Grasse 30 km. A 19th-century Provençal village house offering five guest rooms. 2500m² garden, terrace with panoramic view. First floor: two-roomed suite with shower and wc; bedroom with shower and wc. Second floor: bedroom with shower and wc. Third floor: two rooms with separate shower rooms. Facilities for babies. Open all year.
PRICES: s €42; d €46; t €61; extra person €16; dinner €14 **NEARBY:** Horse riding (2km) Swimming pool (20km) Stretch of water (20km) Tennis (2km) Railway station (22km) FREJUS **NOTES:** No pets Minimum 2 night stay English spoken

CC - credit cards accepted

continued

BARGEME

ᵀᵀᵀ ⭐ Les Roses Trémmières Annie NOEL
Le Village, 83840 BARGEME
☎ 04 94 84 20 86 & SR : 04 94 50 93 93
A medieval site - the highest in the Var - is where Annie's house clings to a rock overlooking such pretty countryside, in the waft of a thousand perfumes. Near the Gorges of Verdon and precipitous villages. Five individually styled rooms with private shower and wc, in Provençal décor. Open mid-March to mid-November.
PRICES: s €43; d €54; dinner €17 **NEARBY:** Horse riding (4km) Swimming pool (4km) Stretch of water (4km) Tennis (4km) Railway station (40km) Shops (4km) COMPS/ARTUBY **NOTES:** No pets Minimum 2 night stay English spoken

BARJOLS

ᵀᵀᵀ ⭐ St-Jaume Michel PASSEBOIS
83670 BARJOLS
☎ 04 94 77 07 88 ▯ 04 94 77 18 01
e-mail: s.d.n.saint-jaume@wanadoo.fr
http://perso.wanadoo.fr/sdn.saint-jaume/
Bedrooms of about 20m², in an 18th-century priory. The owner promotes organic agriculture (wheat, lavender, vines). Organised discovery holidays, Sunday to Saturday 'Wild Provence On Foot'. Swimming pool open May to September. Four upstairs guest rooms - three twins and one triple, each with shower and wc. Downstairs common room for reading and table tennis. Open April to October.
PRICES: s €50; d €67; t €84; dinner €21 **ON SITE:** Swimming pool **NEARBY:** Horse riding (4km) Stretch of water (25km) Tennis (4km) Shops (4km) BARJOLS **NOTES:** No pets Minimum 2 night stay English spoken

BAUDUEN

ᵀᵀᵀ ⭐ Domaine de Majastre Philippe DE SANTIS
83630 BAUDUEN
☎ 04 94 70 05 12 & SR : 04 94 50 93 93 ▯ 04 94 84 01 88
Gorges du Verdon and Lake Ste-Croix 5 km. Le Domaine de Majastre is a 400ha truffle-growing estate. The house belonged to the last king of France. Five guest rooms. On the first floor a double room and a triple; on the second floor a room for four and three double rooms. All have bath or shower and wc. Swimming pool. Open all year.
PRICES: ; d €61; t €76; extra person €15; dinner €18 **NEARBY:** Horse riding (2km) Stretch of water (5km) Tennis (5km) Railway station (30km) Shops (5km) AUPS **NOTES:** Pets admitted Minimum 2 night stay

BESSE-SUR-ISSOLE

ᵀᵀᵀ ⭐ Maison Saint Louis Henri et Ursula THONI
38 rue Jean Aicard, 83890 BESSE-SUR-ISSOLE
☎ 04 94 69 82 23 ▯ 04 94 69 82 06
www.maison-st-louis.ch
Architects Henri and Ursula open their house to you, offering real quality holidays. Their beautiful house is tucked away in the centre of a pretty village. The old penitents' chapel, completely restored now, has kept all its charm. Only 200m away is a 4ha lake. Four individual rooms with shower and wc; two twin rooms, one with three single beds, and one with a double and two singles. Large sitting room with open fire, library, piano, flowery courtyard with terrace, garden furniture, relaxing area. Open April to October.
PRICES: s €43; d €62; t €81; dinner €25 **ON SITE:** Stretch of water **NEARBY:** Horse riding (1km) Swimming pool (5km) Tennis (1km) Railway station (40km) BESSE SUR ISSOLE **NOTES:** No pets Minimum 2 night stay English spoken

BRAS

ᵀᵀᵀ ⭐ Domaine le Peyrourier Claude & Martina FUSSLER
SARL Une Campagne en Provence, Le Peyrourier, 83149 BRAS
☎ 04 98 05 10 20 & SR : 04 94 50 93 93 ▯ 04 98 05 10 21
e-mail: provence4u@hotmail.com www.provence4u.com
In open country at the heart of a 170ha estate. Six restored guest rooms of great comfort, in a number of buildings on an old farm. Access to a shady patio. Reading room with video. Large kitchen/living room. Enjoy strolling in the vines and hills. All double rooms with shower or bath and wc. Telephone and television. Tariff for one person: 105 euros (Three Little Pigs or The Oaks); 100 euros (Honeymoon or The Vines); 90 euros (The Time or The Angels).
PRICES: s €105; extra person €8; dinner €25 **ON SITE:** Swimming pool **NEARBY:** Horse riding (20km) Stretch of water (20km) Tennis (10km) Railway station (45km) Shops (7km) BRAS **NOTES:** No pets Minimum 2 night stay English spoken

ᵀᵀᵀ ⭐ Les Restanques Christine IMBERT
Ancien chemin de Barjols, 83149 BRAS
☎ 04 94 69 96 13 & 06 85 02 86 77 ▯ 04 94 69 96 13
e-mail: chistine.imbert@freesbee.fr
www.provenceweb.fr/83/lesrestanques
St-Maximin 9 km. Iles d'Or, Porquerolles & Port Cros 65 km. In green countryside among olives and oaks, on the Ste Baume. On ground floor suite with double bed, sitting room, shower room and wc, with separate access (tariff 69 euros per person). Upstairs; twin room with bath and wc, and one double room with shower and wc (tariff 53 euros for two people). Swimming pool and barbecue. Meals available (regional dishes and family specialities). 20km golf. 50km Verdon. Open all year.
PRICES: d €69; extra person €8; dinner €18 **ON SITE:** Swimming pool **NEARBY:** Horse riding (15km) Stretch of water (22km) Tennis (3km) Railway station (60km) Shops (1km) BARJOLS **NOTES:** No pets Minimum 2 night stay

CALLAS

ᵀᵀᵀ Chambre d'hôtes Dominique FOEX
Pays Cavier Occidental, Route de Grasse, 83830 CALLAS
☎ 04 94 47 86 71 ▯ 04 94 47 86 71

Draguignan 10 km. Large Provençal house, quiet amidst pines, with its shady garden, terrace, enclosed grounds, swimming pool, summer kitchen, barbecue, chaises longues. Four upstairs suites each of two rooms (studios of 36 to 44m²), individually decorated, with their own access. Luxury beds (160 x 200cm). Each with shower room, wc, refrigerator. Between the sea and the Gorges of Verdon, 10 km from the 'perched villages'. Open all year.
PRICES: s €46; d €50; t €59; extra person €9 **NEARBY:** Horse riding (5km) Tennis (4km) Railway station (25km) Shops (4km) CALLAS (4km) **NOTES:** No pets Minimum 2 night stay English spoken

COLLOBRIERES

ⅢⅢ ◯⧧ La Bastide de la Cabrière Loïc DE SALENEUVE
83610 COLLOBRIERES
☎ 04 94 48 04 31 & SR : 04 94 50 93 93 ▤ 04 94 48 09 90
e-mail: loic.de.saleneuve@libertysurf.fr
www.provenceweb.fr/83/cabriere
A down-to-earth, country couple offer you peace and quiet in the heart of the Maures in their renovated house, 600m from the road in an oasis of greenery. Enclosed swimming pool, garden furniture, sitting room, reading room. Four double rooms and one triple, all with separate entrance, shower or bath and wc. Open all year.
PRICES: d €105; dinner €34 **ON SITE:** Horse riding Swimming pool
NEARBY: Tennis (6km) Railway station (50km) Shops (6km)
COLLOBRIERES **NOTES:** No pets Minimum 2 night stay English spoken

COTIGNAC

ⅢⅢ ◯⧧ Domaine de Nestuby Nathalie ROUBAUD
83570 COTIGNAC
☎ 04 94 04 60 02 & 04 94 04 79 22 ▤ 04 94 04 79 22
e-mail: nestuby@wanadoo.fr
Nathalie and Jean-François run this beautiful, completely restored 19th-century house in the middle of a 45ha wine-growing estate. You will love the warm atmosphere of this typical Provençal establishment. Beautiful local furniture and sunny fabrics. Four rooms, one of them enormous, with private facilities; one double room, one twin, one sleeping three and the other sleeping four. Reading room with television and hi-fi system, garden, outdoors furniture, swimming pool, children's games. Open 1 March to 30 October.
PRICES: s €54, d €54, t €67; extra person €13; dinner €18
ON SITE: Children's play area **NEARBY:** Horse riding (10km) Swimming pool (10km) Stretch of water (11km) Tennis (5km) Railway station (30km) Shops (5km) COTIGNAC (5km) **NOTES:** Pets admitted Minimum 2 night stay English spoken

EVENOS

ⅢⅢ ◯⧧ Le Mas du Cimai Frédéric CERDAN
2473 Route D'Evenos, 83330 EVENOS
☎ 04 94 25 28 41 & 04 94 74 49 56 ▤ 04 94 90 34 74
e-mail: cerdan-frderic@hotmail.com
http://multimania.com/lemas ducimai
Sanary 12 km. Bandol 14 km. Old restored wine-growing farm, in an undisturbed location. Two ground floor rooms opening onto a shady terrace with outdoors furniture. View over the Falaises and the Restanques. Scrambling routes only 800m away. Open all year.
PRICES: s €43; d €47; t €60; dinner €17 **NEARBY:** Horse riding (4km) Swimming pool (12km) Tennis (5km) Railway station (12km) Shops (3km) OLLIOULES **NOTES:** No pets Minimum 2 night stay

FAYENCE

ⅢⅢ Les Suanes Hautes Eric HEREMANS
83440 FAYENCE
☎ 04 94 76 11 28 & SR : 04 94 50 93 93
Provençal stone house in 2ha grounds, renovated in 1995. Gardens, terrace, garden furniture, billiards, parking. On the ground floor: one room with double bed and two singles on a mezzanine; cooking area, shower and wc. On the first floor: two twin rooms with shower and wc. Second floor: two rooms with double bed and four singles, shower, wc, television and separate kitchenette. Open all year.
PRICES: s €37; d €45; t €52; extra person €8 **NEARBY:** Horse riding (7km) Swimming pool (7km) Stretch of water (17km) Tennis (7km) Railway station (27km) Shops (7km) FAYENCE **NOTES:** No pets Minimum 2 night stay

ⅢⅢ ◯⧧ Villa Tonton Nini Pierre GUYOT
83440 FAYANCE
☎ 04 94 76 10 77 & 06 81 79 82 99
Nicole and Pierre happily welcome you to their villa in the heart of the country with access to waymarked tracks for rambling or mountain biking. Swimming pool, parking, terrace, garden furniture, table tennis, pétanque pitch. A fully equipped kitchen is available as well as a leisure room. Three double rooms. Open all year.
PRICES: s €41; d €50; dinner €14 **NEARBY:** Horse riding (10km) Swimming pool (4km) Stretch of water (12km) Tennis (4km) Railway station (30km) Shops (4km) FAYENCE **NOTES:** Pets admitted Minimum 2 night stay

FREJUS

ⅢⅢ 🐾 ◯⧧ Chambre d'hôtes Jean ARTAUD
Les Vergers de Montourey, 83600 FREJUS
☎ 04 94 40 85 76 & SR : 04 94 50 93 93 ▤ 04 94 40 85 76
e-mail: arttotof@wanadoo.fr
An 18th-century building on a fruit farm, offering four guest rooms and two suites. Sitting room with open fireplace, terrace, barbecue and children's games. One suite with three single beds; one suite with four singles, and four double rooms. All with shower and wc, and television. Baby equipment. Open from Easter to end October.
PRICES: s €41; d €49; t €64; extra person €15; dinner €18
ON SITE: Children's play area **NEARBY:** Horse riding (6km) Swimming pool (6km) Stretch of water (6km) Tennis (6km) Railway station (6km) Shops (6km) FREJUS (6km) **NOTES:** Pets admitted Minimum 2 night stay English spoken

GINASSERVIS

ⅢⅢ ◯⧧ Domaine d'Espagne Paule GRECH
83560 GINASSERVIS
☎ 04 94 80 11 03 ▤ 04 94 80 12 07
St-Maximin and Manosque 25 km. Aix-en-Provence 40 km. On an agricultural estate, enjoy local farm produce, hiking, and for thrill-seekers, rafting in the Gorges de Verdon. Three guest rooms on the ground floor, each with a double and single bed, shower and wc. Terrace with outdoor furniture. Open 15 February to 31 December.
PRICES: s €42; d €50; t €65; extra person €17; dinner €19
NEARBY: Horse riding (13km) Swimming pool (5km) Stretch of water (13km) Tennis (5km) Railway station (25km) Shops (5km) RIANS
NOTES: Pets admitted Minimum 2 night stay English spoken

ⅢⅢ ◯⧧ La Rougonne Jean-Marie PERRIER
83560 GINASSERVIS
☎ 04 94 80 11 31
A 14th-century house, clinging to the hillside and dominating the plain. Antique furniture - every piece with a story to tell. Your hosts are idealists and enthusiasts, and will exchange with you their talk, their ideas, their laughter, good cheer and enthusiasm for the country of the writer Giono. Three suites with private facilities and television; two rooms sleeping three, and one double room. Billiards, library, open fires, sitting rooms. Open 1 March to 30 December.
PRICES: s €50; d €53; t €62; extra person €15; dinner €20
NEARBY: Horse riding (10km) Swimming pool (3km) Stretch of water (10km) Tennis (4km) Railway station (30km) Shops (3km) RIANS **NOTES:** Pets admitted Minimum 2 night stay English spoken

GRIMAUD

ⅢⅢ Domaine du Prignon Paul BERTOLOTTO
83310 GRIMAUD
☎ 04 94 43 34 84
St-Tropez 15 km. Only ten minutes from the sea, Christine and Paul invite you into their 12ha vineyard. Three guest rooms of great

continued

character at garden level, each with separate entrance and private terrace. Outdoor furniture and deckchairs in the shade of the oak trees, refrigerator, lounge, library. One double room and two twin rooms, each with shower and wc. Baby equipment.
PRICES: ON SITE: Stretch of water **NEARBY:** Horse riding (3km) Swimming pool (10km) Tennis (7km) Railway station (35km) Shops (4km) GRIMAUD **NOTES:** Pets admitted Minimum 2 night stay English spoken

♦♦♦ La Paressanne Catherine BARTH
Route du Plan de la Tour, 83310 GRIMAUD
☎ 04 94 56 83 33 & 06 80 67 16 36 🗎 04 94 56 01 94
Port-Grimaud 2 km. St-Tropez 9 km. A very beautiful and quiet dwelling in an outstanding location on the Gulf of St Tropez, surrounded by pines and vines, bordered by a stream, cascading pool (nicknamed Little Heaven by guests). Three rooms for two or three visitors, with private terraces and separate entrances, bathrooms, wc and television. Boules, parking. Reduced tariff in low season: 55 euros. Open all year.
PRICES: s €75; d €75; t €90; extra person €15 **ON SITE:** Swimming pool **NEARBY:** Horse riding (1km) Tennis (2km) Railway station (30km) Shops (2km) GRIMAUD **NOTES:** Pets admitted Minimum 2 night stay English spoken

♦♦♦ Bastide de l'Avelan Patricia HERMANGE
Quartier Robert, 83310 GRIMAUD
☎ 04 94 43 25 79
www.flv.fr
St-Tropez 10 km. Nestled in the shade of the parasol pines, just two minutes from the sea, la Bastide de l'Avelan offers rest, quiet and leisure. Vineyard, garden furniture, deckchairs, swimming pool. Rocky inlets, bays and capes. Four rooms, three doubles and one twin. All have shower and wc. Private terrace. Open all year. Child supplement 15 euros.
PRICES: d €65 **ON SITE:** Swimming pool **NEARBY:** Horse riding (2km) Tennis (2km) Railway station (35km) Shops (2km) GRIMAUD **NOTES:** No pets Minimum 2 night stay English spoken

LA SEYNE-SUR-MER

♦♦♦♦ La Lézardière Norma JOUAN
Allée des Tamaris, 83500 LA SEYNE-SUR-MER
☎ 04 94 30 08 89
A welcome from Norma at her very fine colonial style home. Enclosed garden with outdoor furniture. Two ground floor rooms (double bed, bath, wc) with separate entry. On the second floor another double room with 160cm bed, bath and wc. Television lounge. First floor living room. Classic or English breakfast. Open all year.
PRICES: s €61; d €69 **ON SITE:** Stretch of water **NEARBY:** Railway station (3km) Shops (1km) LA SEYNE SUR MER **NOTES:** Pets admitted Minimum 2 night stay English spoken

LE BEAUSSET

♦♦♦ Le Vallon E et F GUIBERT DE BRUET
1253, chemin de la Baro Nuecho,
83330 LE BEAUSSET
☎ 04 94 98 62 97
e-mail: le-vallon@club-internet.fr
Hyères & Iles d'Or 35 km. Bandol 10 km. Welcome to Le Vallon, a haven of peace in the hills, with its swimming pool, flower garden and trees. Three charming ground floor guest rooms with shower rooms and wc. One room with private terrace. Laundry. Summer kitchen. Open all year.

continued

PRICES: s €53; d €61; dinner €15 **ON SITE:** Swimming pool **NEARBY:** Horse riding (2km) Stretch of water (9km) Tennis (2km) Railway station (11km) Shops (2km) LE BEAUSSET **NOTES:** Pets admitted Minimum 2 night stay English spoken

♦♦♦ Les Cancades Charlotte & Marceau ZERBIB
Ch. Fontaine 5 Sous No 1195,
83330 LE BEAUSSET
☎ 04 94 98 76 93 & SR : 04 94 50 93 93 🗎 04 94 90 24 63
e-mail: charlotte.zerbib@wanadoo.fr
Toulon 17 km. Four guest rooms in the owners' house, in enclosed green grounds of 5000m², and remarkable quiet. Thoroughly equipped outside kitchen, garden furniture in the park. One ground floor twin room with shower and wc and separate garden. Upstairs two twin rooms and one double room with shower or bath and wc. Circuit du Castellet. Open all year.
PRICES: d €68; extra person €15 **ON SITE:** Swimming pool **NEARBY:** Horse riding (1km) Stretch of water (10km) Tennis (4km) Railway station (17km) Shops (1km) LE BEAUSSET **NOTES:** No pets Minimum 2 night stay

LE CANNET-DES-MAURES

♦♦♦ La Githomière Monique FAUVET
Route de St-Tropez, 83340 LE CANNET-DES-MAURES
☎ 04 94 60 81 50 🗎 04 94 60 81 50
www.provenceweb.com
Monique welcomes you to her stone country house, located in a 3ha park, looking over a vast plain of parasol pines and the Massif des Maures. Shady terrace with garden furniture, open air pool, boules, billiards, library, large sitting room with open fire, television and music. Two double rooms and two rooms for three, all with bath or shower and wc. Closed January.
PRICES: s €53; d €61; t €73 **ON SITE:** Swimming pool **NEARBY:** Horse riding (7km) Stretch of water (2km) Tennis (5km) Railway station (15km) Shops (5km) LE LUC EN PROVENCE **NOTES:** Pets admitted Minimum 2 night stay English spoken

LES ARCS-SUR-ARGENS

♦♦♦ ⊠ Lou Nie, Les Plaines Valter TOGNELLI
Quartier les Plaines, Route des Nouradons,
83460 LES ARCS-SUR-ARGENS
☎ 04 94 85 28 15 & SR : 04 94 50 93 93 🗎 04 94 85 28 15
e-mail: martine.Tognelli@wanadoo.fr
A warm greeting from Martine and Valter in their beautiful house in the quiet of the country. Enclosed 5000m² grounds, terraces, swimming pool, garden furniture, deckchairs, reading room, boules. At the garden level, three rooms each with their own entrance. 'Tournesol' and 'Papaye' are double rooms; 'Almande' sleeps three. Each has shower, wc, television. Meals available.
PRICES: s €43; d €54; t €65; dinner €16 **ON SITE:** Swimming pool **NEARBY:** Horse riding (2km) Stretch of water (6km) Tennis (5km) Railway station (4km) Shops (4km) LORGUES **NOTES:** No pets Minimum 2 night stay English spoken

LES MAYONS

♦♦♦ |O| Domaine de la Fouquette

Michèle et Yves AQUADRO
83340 LES MAYONS
☎ 04 94 60 00 69 📠 04 94 60 02 91
St-Tropez 25 km. A welcome awaits from Michèle and Yves on their vineyard and farm with its panoramic view over the plain of Maures. Three upstairs guest rooms, two twins and one sleeping three, each with shower and wc. Meals available. Television in the sitting room. Baby equipment available.
PRICES: s €43; d €48; t €62; extra person €15; dinner €16
NEARBY: Horse riding (10km) Swimming pool (10km) Stretch of water (5km) Tennis (2km) Railway station (25km) Shops (5km) LE LUC EN PROVENCE **NOTES:** Pets admitted Minimum 2 night stay

LORGUES

♦♦♦ |O| La Matabone Dino DISCACCIATI

1614, route de Vidauban, 83510 LORGUES
☎ 04 94 67 62 06 & SR : 04 94 50 93 93 📠 04 94 67 62 06
Teresa and Dino are your hosts. Their house is 30 minutes from the sea, in a 2ha wooded park (pines, huge diversity of trees, flowers and fruits, shrubs). Landscaped swimming pool with waterfall and diving board. Terrace, garden and pool furniture, children's games. Very large sitting room with bar. Meals available. Five rooms each with shower and wc and television. Open all year.
PRICES: ; d €61; t €75; extra person €14; dinner €27
ON SITE: Children's play area **NEARBY:** Horse riding (3km) Swimming pool (5km) Stretch of water (5km) Tennis (5km) Railway station (8km) Shops (5km) LORGUES (5km) **NOTES:** No pets Minimum 2 night stay

MOISSAC-BELLEVUE

♦♦♦ |O| La Commanderie des Templiers Patrice LEVY

Chemin la Gineste, 83630 MOISSAC-BELLEVUE
☎ 04 94 70 51 65 & SR : 04 94 50 93 93 📠 04 94 70 51 65
e-mail: commanderie.aups@wanadoo.fr
In an old building in a hectare of landscaped grounds, guest rooms in restored outbuildings. In the heart of the Varoise country, near the lake and Gorges of Verdon. Ideal for all outdoor pursuits. Absolute tranquillity, rest assured. Three double rooms with bathroom and wc. Television if wanted. Baby equipment. Open Easter to mid-October.
PRICES: s €77; d €92; dinner €23 **NEARBY:** Horse riding (5km) Swimming pool (5km) Stretch of water (10km) Tennis (5km) Railway station (40km) Shops (5km) TAVERNES **NOTES:** Pets admitted Minimum 2 night stay English spoken

MONTMEYAN

♦♦♦ Au Jardin de Mon Père Louis et Dany FONTICELLI

La Ferrage, Route de Riez, 83670 MONTMEYAN
☎ 04 94 80 72 84 & SR : 04 94 50 93 93 📠 04 94 80 72 84
Gorges & Lac du Verdon (Gréoux, Quinson & Ste-Croix) 7 km. Dany and Louis' beautiful house is at the foot of the village. Terrace and small garden with a magnificent view over the Préalpes. Closed parking. Musée de la Préhistoire at Quinson. Five rooms, two on the ground floor. All have shower and wc. Open all year.
PRICES: s €40; d €45; extra person €15 **ON SITE:** Tennis
NEARBY: Horse riding (20km) Swimming pool (7km) Stretch of water (7km) Railway station (70km) TAVERNES **NOTES:** No pets Minimum 2 night stay

---

♦♦♦ Chambre d'hôtes Dany et Vincent GONFOND
Campagne St-Maurinet, Route de Quinson,
83670 MONTMEYAN
☎ 04 94 80 78 03 & SR : 04 94 50 93 93 📠 04 94 80 78 03
Gorges du Verdon 5 km. Lake Ste-Croix 15 km. Farmers Danièle and Vincent welcome you to their old house perched upon the hillside among wheatfields and meadows, looking over the Préalpes. Relax in the shade of the hundred year old pine or in the pool. Three guest rooms. On the ground floor, one double and one twin room (with private terrace). Upstairs a room for three with summer kitchen. All have shower and wc. Baby equipment. Musée de la Préhistoire at Quinson, Moustiers-Ste-Marie 25 km. Open all year.
PRICES: s €46; d €49; t €64; extra person €15 **ON SITE:** Swimming pool **NEARBY:** Horse riding (15km) Stretch of water (5km) Tennis (1km) Railway station (40km) Shops (1km) TAVERNES **NOTES:** Pets admitted Minimum 2 night stay English spoken

NEOULES

♦♦♦ |O| Domaine de la Vidalière

Yves et Edith SET-MARIE
Chemin des Grès 470, 83136 NEOULES
☎ 04 94 72 71 26 📠 04 94 72 71 26
e-mail: ysetmarie@net-up.com
Lovely Provence-style house in a green setting, with 10 x 5m swimming pool, pétanque, tennis, mountain bikes, table tennis. Each room has private terrace. 15ha grounds, parking. Lounge with open fire, outside kitchen, barbecue. Five ground floor rooms: one two-roomed suite with two double beds, bathroom and wc; four double rooms with shower and wc. Open all year.
PRICES: s €48; d €52; t €64; extra person €12; dinner €17
ON SITE: Swimming pool **NEARBY:** Horse riding (5km) Stretch of water (8km) Tennis (2km) Railway station (30km) Shops (2km) LA ROQUEBRUSSANNE **NOTES:** Pets admitted Minimum 2 night stay

PIERREFEU

♦♦♦ Le Clos de Lette Alain CASAL

SARL Dom Casal du Gré, 52 Ch. de la Luquette,
83390 PIERREFEU
☎ 04 94 48 21 71 📠 04 94 48 21 71
In open country between the Massif des Maures and the vineyards of the Provence coast. Simone and Alain, winegrowers from the oldest families in the region, welcome you into their haven of peace. Two twin-bedded rooms and two double rooms, with private bath and wc. Separate entrances at ground level. Wonderful view. Cooking area for guests. Open all year.
PRICES: s €46; d €58; t €75; extra person €17 **NEARBY:** Horse riding (6km) Swimming pool (15km) Stretch of water (6km) Tennis (1km) Railway station (6km) Shops (1km) CUERS **NOTES:** Pets admitted Minimum 2 night stay English spoken

PLAN-DE-LA-TOUR

♦♦♦ |O| La Bergerie Gilles CARANTA

Le Clos de San Peire, 83120 PLAN-DE-LA-TOUR
☎ 04 94 43 74 74 📠 04 94 43 11 22
e-mail: labergeriecaranta@wanadoo.fr
An old restored sheep farm is the home of Françoise and Gilles. Three guest rooms and two gîtes. Communal gardens, private terrace, garden furniture, leisure area, swimming pool. Meals if required. Upstairs, two double rooms and a twin, each with shower or bath and wc. Open all year.
PRICES: d €61; extra person €13; dinner €22 **ON SITE:** Swimming pool **NEARBY:** Horse riding (2km) Stretch of water (3km) Tennis (1km) Railway station (35km) Shops (2km) GRIMAUD **NOTES:** No pets Minimum 2 night stay English spoken

PROVENCE-ALPES-CÔTE-D'AZUR

PONTEVES

♥ Domaine de St Ferréol
A et G DE JERPHANION
83670 PONTEVES
☎ 04 94 77 10 42 📠 04 94 77 19 04
e-mail: saint-ferreol@wanadoo.fr
Armelle and Guillaume welcome you to the heart of their 100ha farm and vineyard which clings to the hillside. The rooms are located in a restored wing of the 18th-century farm and are filled with antique country furniture and lovely Provençal fabrics. One double room, one sleeping three, and a suite four. Each has private facilities. Communal kitchenette. Swimming pool. 1.6km and 3km to restaurants. Open March to end October.
PRICES: d €58; extra person €13 **ON SITE:** Swimming pool
NEARBY: Horse riding (6km) Stretch of water (40km) Tennis (3km) Railway station (60km) Shops (3km) Restaurant nearby BARJOLS
NOTES: No pets Minimum 2 night stay English spoken

RAMATUELLE

Ferme de l'Audrac Sylvie BONNAURE GHENO
CD 93, 83350 RAMATUELLE
☎ 04 98 12 91 00 📠 04 98 12 91 01
St-Tropez 9 km. Calm and rest reign in the restored farmhouse on this 30ha wine and forest estate. Two double rooms and one triple, each with private terrace, shower and wc. Swimming pool. Walking tracks. Open 1st April to October.
PRICES: d €56; extra person €8 **ON SITE:** Swimming pool
NEARBY: Horse riding (2km) Tennis (3km) Railway station (35km) Shops (3km) ST TROPEZ **NOTES:** Pets admitted Minimum 2 night stay English spoken

Lei Souco Gustave GIRAUD
83350 RAMATUELLE
☎ 04 94 79 80 22 📠 04 94 79 88 27
Four kilometres from Ramatuelle, near the beaches, Leï Souco is a beautiful Provençal house in 10ha of vines, planted with olives, mimosas, eucalyptus and blackberries. The spacious rooms have Provençal furnishings; each has a different colour running through the décor. M and Mme Giraud will encourage you to try the local rosé and the fruits of the garden. Four rooms and one suite, all with private terrace and private facilities. Safe deposit box, refrigerator, private tennis, pétanque ground. Nearby restaurants. Open Easter to mid-October.
PRICES: d €95; t €112; extra person €16 **ON SITE:** Tennis
NEARBY: Horse riding (2km) Swimming pool (7km) Stretch of water (2km) Railway station (40km) Shops (1km) ST TROPEZ **NOTES:** Pets admitted Minimum 2 night stay English spoken

ROQUEBRUNE-SUR-ARGENS

Verte Campagne - le Blavet Pierre FILIPPI
83520 ROQUEBRUNE
☎ 04 94 45 42 50 & SR : 04 94 50 93 93 📠 04 94 45 42 20
e-mail: pierrefilippi@hotmail.com
Near the best beaches of St-Raphaël at St-Tropez, the warm welcome extends to aviation and nautical yarns with Pierre, and singing and karaoke with Monique. 8000m² shady park. A very beautiful house with three ground floor double rooms, each with their own access and private terrace. Bathroom, wc, television and refrigerator in each room. Communal laundry. Low season tariff: 54 euros. Open all year.
PRICES: d €59 **ON SITE:** Swimming pool **NEARBY:** Horse riding (1km) Stretch of water (1km) Tennis (1km) Railway station (12km) Shops (2km) LE MUY **NOTES:** Pets admitted Minimum 2 night stay

SALERNES

🍴 La Bastide Rose Karel et Caroline HENNY
Haut Gaudran BP 24, 83690 SALERNES
☎ 04 94 70 63 30 & SR : 04 94 50 93 93 📠 04 94 70 77 34
e-mail: labastiderose@wanadoo.fr www.bastide-rose.com
Amidst vines and fruit trees, a pretty pink farmhouse where Dutchwoman Caroline greets you. Three very comfortable guest rooms, plus a holiday gîte. Three ground floor suites; one with double bed and two singles on a half-floor with a balcony; two suites with lounge/kitchenette; one suite with four single beds, two on a mezzanine. All have bath or shower and wc. Baby equipment. Terrace, garden, outdoor furniture, swimming pool. Open Easter to mid-October.
PRICES: d €62; t €76; extra person €15; dinner €20 **NEARBY:** Horse riding (3km) Swimming pool (3km) Stretch of water (3km) Tennis (3km) Railway station (35km) Shops (3km) SALERNES **NOTES:** No pets Minimum 2 night stay English spoken

🍴 Le Mas des Oliviers Marie-Claire BOISARD
Route de Sillans la Cascade, 83690 SALERNES
☎ 04 94 70 75 20 & SR : 04 94 50 93 93 📠 04 94 70 75 20
e-mail: masdesoliviers@libertysurf.fr
Marie-Claire and Yvon are your hosts. One ground floor room for three people with separate entrance, shower and wc. Two double rooms upstairs (bath and wc), with separate access from street level, and one room for three with shower and wc. Refrigerators in rooms. Satellite television room, reading room, billiard room. Meals if booked. Shady terrace, table tennis, 8 x 4m swimming pool. Open all year.
PRICES: s €46; d €53; t €69; extra person €15; dinner €20
NEARBY: Horse riding (2km) Swimming pool (5km) Stretch of water (30km) Tennis (1km) Railway station (35km) Shops (1km) SALERNES **NOTES:** No pets Minimum 2 night stay English spoken

SANARY-SUR-MER

🍴 Chambre d'hôtes Bruno CASTELLANO
646 routede Bandol, 83110 SANARY-SUR-MER
☎ 04 94 88 05 73 & 06 10 24 13 57 📠 04 94 88 24 13

Between Sanary and Bandol, 400m from the beach, a vast 19th-century town house in a luxuriant garden surrounded by palms and hundred-year-old cypresses. Four rooms beautifully decorated with bright curtains. Annie and Bruno want you to have the holiday of your dreams. Swimming pool, tennis. Three twin rooms with shower and wc, and one double with bath and wc. Air-conditioning. Library. Flower-bedecked garden. Open all year.
PRICES: s €61; d €69; t €100; extra person €31; dinner €28
ON SITE: Swimming pool Tennis **NEARBY:** Horse riding (4km) Railway station (3km) OLLIOULES **NOTES:** No pets Minimum 2 night stay English spoken

SILLANS-LA-CASCADE

⌘ Le Haut Ricoui Bernard BOUCHET

83690 SILLANS-LA-CASCADE

☎ 04 94 04 75 35 & SR : 04 94 50 93 93   🖹 04 94 04 75 35

e-mail: chezbernard@net-up.com

www.provenceweb.fr/83/bernard

In the quiet of the open country in 3ha of grounds, with terrace, 12x3m swimming pool, and underfloor central heating. Four guest rooms with shower and wc (160 x 200cm bed on mezzanine). Television available in winter only. Open April to October.

PRICES: d €61; extra person €15 **ON SITE:** Swimming pool
NEARBY: Railway station (35km) TAVERNES **NOTES:** No pets
Minimum 2 night stay English spoken

ST-CYR-SUR-MER

⌘ Chambre d'hôtes Margueritte GRANIER

1011 chemin du Péras, 83270 ST-CYR-SUR-MER

☎ 04 94 26 38 77

Three guest rooms in a country house which stands alone. Private access to each room. Individual terraces. One two room suite with three single beds; one twin room; one double room. Each has shower or bath and wc. Refrigerator. Reduced rates for extended stays. Baby equipment. Open 15 May to 15 September.

PRICES: s €49-€52; d €49-€52; t €71 **NEARBY:** Swimming pool (3km) Stretch of water (3km) Tennis (2km) Railway station (3km) Shops (2km) LE BEAUSSET **NOTES:** No pets

STE-MAXIME

⌘ Chambre d'hôtes Fausto PIMENTEL

67 route du Plan de la Tour, 83120 STE-MAXIME

☎ 04 94 49 21 38   🖹 04 94 49 21 39

Alice and Fausto are your hosts in their pretty roadside house, just 800m from the beach and the town centre. Garden, terrace and swimming pool. One ground floor double room with shower and wc. Two suites upstairs, each sleeping four, with shower or bath and wc. Open all year.

ON SITE: Swimming pool **NEARBY:** Horse riding (2km) Tennis (1km) Railway station (28km) Shops (1km) GRIMAUD
NOTES: Pets admitted Minimum 2 night stay

ST-MAXIMIN

⌘ ⦵ Domaine de Garrade Alain VAN'T HOFF

Route de Bras, 83470 ST-MAXIMIN-LA-STE-BAUME

☎ 04 94 59 84 32   🖹 04 94 59 83 47

e-mail: garrade@aol.com www.provenceweb.fr/83/garrade
Aix-en-Provence and Calanques de Cassis 35 km. Gorges du Verdon 45 km. The Garrade estate is far from the madding crowd, with a view over the Ste-Baume Massif. The old house, surrounded by forest, has been restored to its original state; the farm now grows organic aromatic herbs. Swimming pool. Five guest rooms: two double rooms and two triples, each with shower and wc. Baby facilities. Coin-operated laundry. Open all year except November.

PRICES: s €61; d €69; t €84; dinner €23 **ON SITE:** Swimming pool
NEARBY: Horse riding (2km) Stretch of water (25km) Tennis (5km) Railway station (35km) Shops (5km) SAINT MAXIMIN **NOTES:** Pets admitted Minimum 2 night stay English spoken

---

For further information on these and
other chambres d'hôtes, consult
the Gîtes de France website
www.gites-de-france.fr

TOURTOUR

⌘ Le Mas de l'Acacia Claude BOUILLARD

Route d'Aups, 83690 TOURTOUR

☎ 04 94 70 53 84   🖹 04 94 70 53 84

http://www.verdon-tourtour.com

Peaceful 6000m² property. Just 300m from a village classed as 'one of the most beautiful in France' with a stunning view, Janine and Claude open the doors of the Mas de l'Acacia to you. Three rooms with separate entrances, two doubles and a triple, with bath or shower and wc. Communal lounge. Swimming pool, terrace, barbecue, outdoor furniture. Near the Regional Park of Verdon, walking and cycling routes, the Lac and Gorges of Verdon. Open all year.

PRICES: d €54; extra person €16 **ON SITE:** Swimming pool Tennis
NEARBY: Horse riding (8km) Stretch of water (10km) Railway station (25km) SALERNES **NOTES:** No pets Minimum 2 night stay English spoken

TRANS-EN-PROVENCE

⌘ Chambre d'hôtes Marie-Camille WAHL

986, route de La Motte, Saint-Amour,

83720 TRANS-EN-PROVENCE

☎ 04 94 70 88 92   🖹 04 94 70 88 92

A splendid 18th-century private house in the peaceful solitude of a 2ha park. Ornamental lake, river, waterfall, swans, summer kitchen, barbecue, terrace, car shelter, swimming pool. Three rooms with terrace and separate entrance. Two 20m² double rooms, each with double bed, sitting area, shower, wc and television. One 'boat' for two people, with bathroom, wc, television and well-equipped kitchenette. Baby facilities.

PRICES: d €64; extra person €18 **ON SITE:** Swimming pool Stretch of water **NEARBY:** Horse riding (2km) Tennis (2km) Railway station (8km) Shops (1km) DRAGUIGNAN **NOTES:** No pets Minimum 2 night stay

VINS-SUR-CARAMY

⌘ Château de Vins Jean BONNET

83170 VINS-SUR-CARAMY

☎ 04 94 72 50 40 & SR : 04 94 50 93 93   🖹 04 94 72 50 88

e-mail: chateau.de.vins@free.fr

Brignoles 7 km. Welcome to the 16th-century Château de Vins - admire the courtyard, the loggias, the terraces and the medieval bridge. Five guest rooms. Ground floor suite 'Campra' (two rooms, double and single bed, bathroom, wc, kitchen area). Three first floor double rooms 'Faure,' 'Debussy' and 'Berlioz' (with shower and wc). Second floor suite for three 'Couperin' with shower and wc. Open April to October.

PRICES: s €46; d €66 **ON SITE:** Tennis **NEARBY:** Horse riding (10km) Swimming pool (7km) Stretch of water (1km) Railway station (60km) BRIGNOLES **NOTES:** Pets admitted English spoken

VAUCLUSE

ALTHEN-DES-PALUDS

▒▒ ⏺ Le Clos de la Cousin Alain BONTON
426 chemin de Toutblanc, 84210 ALTHEN-DES-PALUDS
☎ 04 90 62 13 88 🖹 04 90 62 13 88
Set in verdant countryside, this old *mas* (farmhouse) is typical of the Comtadine region. There is independent access to the bedrooms, one on the ground floor with private shower room and wc, and one on the first floor with the same facilities. There is also a suite of two bedrooms with private shower and wc, plus a lounge and TV in the library. Fridge, electric central heating with fireplace. Terraces with garden furniture, a rest and leisure area and car park. Meals if booked in advance. Open all year.
PRICES: s €43; d €47; t €61–€69; extra person €12; dinner €17
NEARBY: Bathing (8km) Horse riding (4km) Golf (8km) Fishing (2km) Swimming pool (8km) Hiking (15km) Downhill skiing (45km) Tennis (3km) Railway station (17km) Shops (3km) AVIGNON (15km)
NOTES: Pets admitted English spoken

ANSOUIS

▒▒ ⏺ Mas du Grand Lubéron Jacqueline CORDIER
La Parine, 84240 ANSOUIS
☎ 04 90 09 97 92 🖹 04 90 09 93 69
e-mail: jacqueline.cordier@wanadoo.fr
http://perso.wanadoo.fr/lemas
An old *mas*, surrounded by vines, just outside a village with a beautiful panoramic view of the Lubéron and swimming pool, has five bedrooms. Two of these are on the ground floor with en suite facilities, and three are on the first floor with TV, private showers and wc. Terrace, enclosed grounds, car park. Open 5 March to 5 January.
PRICES: s €55; d €60; t €81; dinner €21 **ON SITE:** Swimming pool Hiking **NEARBY:** Bathing (4km) Horse riding (5km) Golf (25km) Fishing (8km) Tennis (8km) Railway station (70km) Shops (1km) PERTUIS (8km)
NOTES: Small pets admitted English spoken

APT

▒▒ Les Mylanettes Brigitte HEUZARD LA COUTURE
Par la rue des Bassins, 84400 APT
☎ 04 90 74 67 15 🖹 04 90 74 47 20
Four spacious bedrooms in this fine house in a quiet area on the edge of the town, with a panoramic view. Each of the bedrooms has a private bathroom and wc, with possibility of an extra bed. There is also a large living room with fireplace, TV, loggia and terrace. The town centre is within walking distance. Open all year.
PRICES: s €39; d €51; t €58; extra person €13 **NEARBY:** Horse riding (5km) Fishing (4km) Swimming pool (4km) Tennis (4km) Shops (1km)
NOTES: Pets admitted English spoken

AUBIGNAN

▒▒ ⏺ La Rodde Christine et Jean JAUME
84810 AUBIGNAN
☎ 04 90 60 63 16 & 06 87 10 87 58
http://www.larodde.com
An annexe in the west section of a farm has been converted to four first-floor bedrooms with private shower rooms and wc. The property features an enclosed swimming pool (11 x 5m). There is electric central heating, a shared living room and a summer dining room. Terrace, open garden and car park. Open all year.
PRICES: d €53–€64; extra person €15; dinner €17 **NEARBY:** Horse riding (3km) Golf (20km) Fishing (2km) Swimming pool (3km) Hiking (6km) Tennis (2km) Railway station (25km) Shops (3km) CARPENTRAS (3km)
NOTES: No pets English spoken

AVIGNON/ILE-DE-LA-BARTHELASSE

▒▒ ⏺ La Bastide des Papes
Laurence ROUBY et Alain RHODES
352 ch., des poiriers, Ile Barthelasse, 84000 AVIGNON
☎ 04 90 86 09 42 🖹 04 90 82 38 30
Discover this renovated country house, formerly home to the family of Pope Innocent VI, in the orchards of the Ile de Barthelasse. There is a private swimming pool on the four-hectare estate, and five bedrooms. Two bedrooms have TV, private bathroom and wc, and three have private shower, TV and wc. Central heating and shared living room with working fireplace. Library, TV and kitchen at the guests' disposal. Meals provided certain evenings Open all year.
PRICES: s €89; d €99; t €119; extra person €20; dinner €25
ON SITE: Swimming pool Hiking **NEARBY:** Horse riding (1km) Golf (15km) Fishing (1km) Tennis (1km) Railway station (6km) Shops (6km) AVIGNON (6km) **NOTES:** No pets English spoken

AVIGNON-MONTFAVET

▒▒ Chambre d'hôtes Jean-Michel MOUZAC
1044 chemin de Sourdaine, 84140 MONTFVAVET
☎ 04 90 89 77 81 🖹 04 90 89 77 81
e-mail: clos.st.pierre@libertysurf.fr
The green belt just south of Avignon is the location of this *mas* with swimming pool and enclosed grounds. Bedrooms are on the first floor and are accessible by a communal lounge reserved for guests. There are two bedrooms with TV, private shower and wc, and one with TV, kitchen and private facilities. Central heating and open fire in working order. Terrace, gardens and car park. Open all year.
PRICES: s €50–€70; d €60–€80; t €90 **ON SITE:** Swimming pool
NEARBY: Horse riding (8km) Golf (6km) Fishing (1km) Hiking (20km) Tennis (2km) Railway station (6km) Shops (3km) AVIGNON (6km)
NOTES: No pets English spoken

BEDOIN

▒▒ Les Tournillayres Marie-Claire RENAUDON
84410 BEDOIN
☎ 04 90 12 80 94 🖹 04 90 12 80 94
A very fine group of small, charming independent houses at the foot of Mont-Verdun have been renovated to provide accommodation in the countryside. Four rooms with en suite showers and wc, TV, fireplace, kitchen area, and private garden, and one suite of two bedrooms with private facilities. This has a living room, TV, kitchen area, private garden, dining room, shared lounge, central heating and reading material. Cot available. Open 1 March to 1 November.
PRICES: d €77–€99; extra person €16 **ON SITE:** Hiking
NEARBY: Bathing (7km) Horse riding (2km) Golf (30km) Fishing (7km) Swimming pool (1km) Downhill skiing (15km) Tennis (1km) Railway station (45km) Shops (2km) CARPENTRAS (15km) **NOTES:** No pets English spoken

BONNIEUX

▒▒ ⏺ Le Clos du Buis MAURIN
Rue Victor Hugo, 84480 BONNIEUX
☎ 04 90 75 88 48 & 06 08 63 64 76 🖹 04 90 75 88 57
e-mail: le-clos-du-buis@wanadoo.fr http://www.luberon-news.fr
A beautiful village house restoration with swimming pool and enclosed garden of 1500m² with trees. Wonderful panoramic view of Mont-Ventoux and the Lubéron countryside. One ground-floor bedroom, with access for the handicapped, with bathroom and wc. A further five bedrooms, one of which is a family suite on the first floor with en suite facilities. Gas central heating, shared living room with library and TV. Real open fire, veranda, and enclosed parking. Meals if required. Open 1 February to 30 November and Christmas/New Year.

continued

PRICES: d €60-€92; extra person €15; dinner €20 **ON SITE:** Swimming pool Hiking Tennis **NEARBY:** Bathing (15km) Horse riding (3km) Golf (18km) Fishing (15km) Railway station (50km) APT (12km) **NOTES:** No pets English spoken

▥▥▥ Les Terrasses du Lubéron Serge et M.Paule AGNEL
Quartier les Bruyères, 84480 BONNIEUX
☎ 04 90 75 87 40 ▤ 04 90 75 87 40
This accommodation features a private terrace for each bedroom, with a magnificent view of Mont-Ventoux, and a shared terrace overlooking the Calavon plain. There are three bedrooms on the ground floor of an annexe to the owners' villa, with private bathroom and wc, and one with private shower and wc. There is a lounge in an adjoining building and the use of a kitchen and barbecue. Central heating. Shared swimming pool. Enclosed parking. Open 1 April to 30 November.
PRICES: s €53; d €61-€69; extra person €15 **ON SITE:** Swimming pool Hiking **NEARBY:** Horse riding (4km) Golf (30km) Fishing (10km) Tennis (1km) Railway station (45km) Shops (1km) APT (10km) **NOTES:** No pets

BUISSON

▥▥▥ L'Ecole Buissonnière Monique et John ALEX-PARSONS
Les Pres - D 75, 84110 BUISSON
☎ 04 90 28 95 19 ▤ 04 90 28 95 19
e-mail: ecole.buissonniere@wanadoo.fr
An attractive house, pleasantly restored on the edge of a quiet country lane with an enclosed courtyard and open garden offers three bedrooms. Upstairs there is one room with shower and private wc, one with bathroom and wc, and a third with mezzanine, shower, wc, and private balcony. Central and underfloor heating. Shared living room with real open fireplace. Library, TV, telephone, and car park. Open from Easter to 1 November.
PRICES: d €43-€49; t €56; extra person €11 **ON SITE:** Hiking **NEARBY:** Bathing (4km) Horse riding (4km) Golf (25km) Fishing (1km) Swimming pool (7km) Downhill skiing (45km) Tennis (2km) Railway station (45km) Shops (7km) VAISON LA ROMAINE (7km) **NOTES:** Pets admitted English spoken

▥▥▥ ◉ Mas Grateloup Gérard PORON
84110 BUISSON
☎ 04 90 28 97 34 ▤ 04 90 28 98 75
e-mail: masgrateloup@aol.com http://www.mas-grateloup.com
Three separate suites, each with its own access, in an authentic 18th-century Provençal farm. The U-shaped property has a swimming pool, terraces and a park of pine trees and other ancient trees. A charming, restful location with fine views. On the first floor there is one suite of two bedrooms with entrance, bathroom and wc. On the ground floor there are a further two suites with private facilities. Electric central heating, lounge with TV and working fireplace. Reading area, dining room, boules, mountain bike rental. Car park. Open all year. Please book in advance.
PRICES: s €53; d €61; t €84; extra person €15; HB €11; dinner €23 **ON SITE:** Swimming pool Hiking **NEARBY:** Horse riding (2km) Golf (20km) Fishing (2km) Downhill skiing (40km) Tennis (2km) Railway station (50km) Shops (2km) VAISON LA ROMAINE (8km) **NOTES:** No pets English spoken

CABRIERES-D'AVIGNON

▥▥▥ Chambre d'hôtes Jacquy TRUC
84220 CABRIERES-D'AVIGNON
☎ 04 90 76 97 03 ▤ 04 90 76 74 67
An independent house just outside a village with enclosed courtyard and swimming pool, five bedrooms with showers and private wc. Central heating, shared living room, balcony, and terrace. Restaurant in the village, cedar forest 500 m away. Open all year except July and August.

PRICES: s €49; d €53-€58; extra person €15 **ON SITE:** Swimming pool **NEARBY:** Horse riding (1km) Golf (5km) Fishing (10km) Hiking (1km) Tennis (1km) Railway station (10km) ISLE SUR LA SORGUE (10km) **NOTES:** No pets

▥▥▥ La Magnanerie Magali FRANTZ
84220 CABRIERES-D'AVIGNON
☎ 04 90 76 89 65 ▤ 04 90 76 82 35
Beautiful 18th-century *mas*, with swimming pool, patio and enclosed courtyard surrounded by vines. One ground floor bedroom with shower and private wc, one upstairs bedroom with the same facilities, and a third room with bathroom, wc and private terrace. Central heating, shared living room, lounge, dining room and working open fireplace. TV, telephone, terrace, and car park. Open from Easter to 31 October.
PRICES: d €65-€105; t €105 **ON SITE:** Swimming pool **NEARBY:** Horse riding (10km) Golf (10km) Fishing (10km) Hiking (2km) Tennis (12km) Railway station (12km) Shops (1km) CAVAILLON (12km) **NOTES:** No pets English spoken

CADENET

▥▥▥ La Madeleine Martine et J.Charles GARNAUD
ch. de Lourmarin, Quartier les Roques, 84160 CADENET
☎ 04 90 68 12 95 ▤ 04 90 68 35 65
e-mail: MGarnaud@aol.com
An attractive house and swimming pool, just outside a village, offering three ground floor bedrooms. Two rooms have TV, shower, refrigerator, hot plate, garden furniture and private terrace. The third is a double room with bathroom, wc, refrigerator, hotplate, and garden furniture. Central heating, library, enclosed, shady garden, terrace, barbecue and summer kitchen. Open all year.
PRICES: s €44-€46; d €49-€58; t €69-€76 **ON SITE:** Swimming pool **NEARBY:** Bathing (2km) Horse riding (2km) Fishing (2km) Hiking (3km) Tennis (1km) Shops (1km) PERTUIS (12km) **NOTES:** Pets admitted English spoken

▥▥▥ ◉ La Tuilière Clotilde et Didier BORGARINO
84160 CADENET
☎ 04 90 68 24 45 ▤ 04 90 68 24 45
e-mail: clo@latuiliere.com http://www.latuiliere.com
Large 18th-century farmhouse with gardens and swimming pool, on a private estate of 12 hectares of vines and woods, just 700 metres from the village. Here, there is one ground floor bedroom with shower and private wc, three bedrooms upstairs with shower and private wc, and a further bedroom with bathroom and wc. Each with central heating and independent exterior access. Terraces and car park. Meals if required. Low season from 48.78 euros for two people. Open all year.
PRICES: s €49; d €61-€76; t €75-€90; dinner €20 **ON SITE:** Swimming pool Hiking **NEARBY:** Bathing (2km) Horse riding (2km) Golf (20km) Fishing (2km) Tennis (1km) Railway station (58km) Shops (1km) PERTUIS (12km) **NOTES:** No pets English spoken

▥▥▥ Les Ramades Marie-Pierre MAGDINIER
84160 CADENET
☎ 04 90 68 34 51 ▤ 04 90 68 01 38
e-mail: lesramades@free.fr http://aux.ramades.free.fr
This restored farm amidst fields with a swimming pool has two bedrooms with shower and private wc. There is also a suite of two bedrooms with the same facilities. These enjoy electric heating, the use of a kitchen, and a terrace. The grounds of 12 hectares are not fenced. There is a car park and two loose boxes for horses. Open from 1 April to 15 November.
PRICES: d €58-€61; t €88; extra person €15 **ON SITE:** Swimming pool Hiking **NEARBY:** Bathing (1km) Horse riding (2km) Golf (20km) Fishing (1km) Tennis (3km) Railway station (50km) Shops (4km) PERTUIS (10km) **NOTES:** No pets English spoken

continued

CAIRANNE

♯♯♯ iOi Domaine Bois de la Cour Elisabeth PARA
84290 CAIRANNE
☎ 04 90 30 84 68   📠 04 90 30 84 68

An 18th-century mas was restored in Provençal tradition, on a 19-hectare wine producing estate with swimming pool. One large room on the ground floor with private bathroom and wc, two large rooms on the first floor with the same facilities, and a further large bedroom on the second floor, again with the same en suite arrangements. Electric heating, lounge with working fireplace, library and TV. Terrace, and car park. Animals accepted with a supplement of 7.62 euros. Open from January 1 to 30 November.
PRICES: s €69; d €84; extra person €15; dinner €21   **ON SITE:** Swimming pool **NEARBY:** Horse riding (3km) Golf (9km) Fishing (3km) Hiking (5km) Tennis (6km) Railway station (40km) Shops (2km) VAISON LA ROMAINE (15km) **NOTES:** Pets admitted English spoken

♯♯♯ iOi Le Moulin Agape Denise MOLLA
84290 CAIRANNE
☎ 04 90 30 77 04   📠 04 90 30 77 04

Old mill surrounded by vines in the middle of the countryside, on a hectare of unfenced land, with swimming pool. Two ground-floor bedrooms with shower and wc, and one bedroom with bathroom and wc upstairs. Two first-floor suites, each with shower and wc. Electric heating, shared living room, lounge, dining room, terrace and car park. Meals for residents (2-3 times a week) if booked in advance. Apéritif, wine and coffee included in the meal price. Child's bed for children under ten: 10.67 euros. Open all year but advisable to book 1 November to 31 March.
PRICES: s €38; d €44-€50; t €59-€66; extra person €15; dinner €17 **ON SITE:** Horse riding Fishing Swimming pool **NEARBY:** Golf (15km) Hiking (1km) Downhill skiing (40km) Tennis (2km) Railway station (15km) Shops (2km) VAISON LA ROMAINE (15km) **NOTES:** No pets English spoken

♯♯♯ L'Oliveraie Marie-Paule CHARAVIN
Route de St-Roman, 84290 CAIRANNE
☎ 04 90 30 72 85 & SR : 04 90 85 45 00   📠 04 90 30 72 85

Olive trees around an enclosed swimming pool, open from June to September. Five bedrooms on the ground floor with shower, wc and private terrace. Electric heating, shared living room with open fireplace and the use of a kitchen. Telephone, open garden of 2000m², car park. Open all year.
PRICES: s €37; d €45; t €58; extra person €13 **ON SITE:** Swimming pool Hiking **NEARBY:** Horse riding (2km) Golf (15km) Fishing (2km) Downhill skiing (45km) Railway station (15km) Shops (2km) VAISON LA ROMAINE - ORANGE (15km) **NOTES:** Pets admitted

CARPENTRAS

♯♯♯ Bastide Ste-Agnès Maryse et Michel PINBOUEN
Chemin de la Fourtrouse, 84200 CARPENTRAS
☎ 04 90 60 03 01   📠 04 90 60 02 53
e-mail: Pinbouenmichel@aol.com
http://www.avignon-et-provence.com/sainte-agnes

Numerous restaurants are within easy reach of this old, pleasantly restored *mas* with swimming pool. There is a suite of two bedrooms (one downstairs and one upstairs) with living room, equipped kitchen, TV, telephone, bathroom, wc, terrace, garden and private barbecue. There are also five further bedrooms, one of which looks onto the park, each with private facilities. Lounge with TV, library, living room, dining room, working fireplace and terrace. Very beautiful enclosed garden, boules area and car park. Telephone and fax (with a meter). Excellent breakfasts for those with a sweet tooth. Picnics and barbecues possible. Open all year.
PRICES: s €62-€73; d €70-€108; t €92-€124; extra person €20
ON SITE: Swimming pool **NEARBY:** Bathing (6km) Horse riding (9km)

Golf (15km) Fishing (6km) Hiking (6km) Downhill skiing (25km) Tennis (2km) Railway station (28km) Shops (3km) CARPENTRAS (3km)
NOTES: No pets

CAVAILLON

♯♯♯ iOi Mas du Souleou Nadine LEPAUL
5 ch. St-Pierre des Essieux, 84300 CAVAILLON
☎ 04 90 71 43 22 & 06 62 39 43 22   📠 04 90 71 43 22
http://www.souleou.com

A large lounge with billiard table, TV, library and open fireplace can be found in this 19th-century *mas*, which has been sympathetically restored. In the calm of the countryside, the property also benefits from a swimming pool and a large terrace with a shady bower. On the first floor there is one bedroom with bathroom, wc, private terrace and its own entrance, and another bedroom with shower, wc and independent entrance. There are two further bedrooms with showers and wc. Fuel-fired central heating. Wine included in the meal price. Closed February.
PRICES: s €57-€69; d €70-€73; t €88; extra person €15; dinner €20
ON SITE: Swimming pool **NEARBY:** Horse riding (3km) Golf (11km) Fishing (1km) Hiking (8km) Tennis (3km) Railway station (25km) Shops (3km) CAVAILLON (3km) **NOTES:** No pets English spoken

♯♯♯ iOi Le Mas du Platane Noël et Danièle MAUREL
22 quartier des Trente Mouttes, 84300 CAVAILLON
☎ 04 90 78 29 99   📠 04 90 78 35 17
e-mail: noel.maurel@wanadoo.fr   http://lemasdu platane.free.fr

Two private first floor suites and one ground floor bedroom are found in this restored mas, set among fields in the countryside. The ground floor bedroom and one of the suites has shower, bathroom and private wc, and the other suite has a shower and wc. The property also benefits from electric heating, a shared living room with fireplace, library, TV and telephone. Terrace and car park. Meals need to be booked in advance. Open all year.
PRICES: s €61; d €69; t €90; dinner €18 **ON SITE:** Swimming pool
NEARBY: Bathing (4km) Horse riding (3km) Golf (8km) Fishing (4km) Hiking (2km) Tennis (2km) Railway station (4km) Shops (1km) CAVAILLON (4km) **NOTES:** No pets English spoken

continued

CHEVAL-BLANC

♦♦♦ ᴵᴼᴵ La Malleposte Colette et Thierry HAMEL
Font Vive, 84460 CHEVAL-BLANC
☎ 04 90 72 89 26 📠 04 90 72 88 38
e-mail: info@malle-poste.com http://www.malle-poste.com

Old 18th-century coaching house on the banks of the Carpentras canal in the small Lubéron park with swimming pool and extensive wooded grounds proposes five bedrooms. These all have TV, shower and private wc. Fuel-fired central heating, dining room, lounge with library and lounge with a fireplace. There is also a billiard room, terrace, boules area, and table tennis. Open all year (booking necessary between November and March).
PRICES: s €70; d €86; t €102; extra person €16; dinner €26
ON SITE: Swimming pool Hiking **NEARBY:** Horse riding (1km) Golf (10km) Fishing (1km) Downhill skiing (70km) Tennis (6km) Railway station (35km) Shops (6km) CAVAILLON (9km) **NOTES:** No pets English spoken

CRILLON-LE-BRAVE

♦♦♦ ᴵᴼᴵ Domaine la Condamine Marie-Josée EYDOUX
84410 CRILLON-LE-BRAVE
☎ 04 90 62 47 28 📠 04 90 62 47 28
e-mail: christellemasclaux@yahoo.com
http://domainelacondamine.here.de
The hills at the foot of the Mont-Ventoux, on a wine producing estate, is the location of this large independent *mas* with swimming pool. Two bedrooms on the first floor with private shower and wc, and two bedrooms with the same facilities are situated on the second floor. One suite of two bedrooms with kitchenette, living room, two showers and two private wcs. Electric heating, lounge with reading material and TV. There is also a summer kitchen, barbecue and arbour for residents. Terrace, car park and unfenced gardens. Open all year.
PRICES: s €43-€44; d €50-€53; t €66-€69; extra person €15; dinner €23
ON SITE: Swimming pool Hiking **NEARBY:** Bathing (5km) Horse riding (4km) Golf (30km) Fishing (5km) Downhill skiing (15km) Tennis (1km) Railway station (30km) Shops (4km) CARPENTRAS (10km) **NOTES:** No pets English spoken

♦♦♦ ᴵᴼᴵ Moulin d'Antelon M. Luce et Valérie RICQUART
Route de Bedoin, 84410 CRILLON-LE-BRAVE
☎ 04 90 62 44 89 📠 04 90 62 44 90
e-mail: Moulin-dantelon@wanadoo.fr
http://www.art-vin-table.com
A large 1820 farmhouse (old wheat mill), overlooking a park, with large swimming pool and stream, provides five bedrooms. Three of these are on the courtyard level in the annexe with private shower and wc and two bedrooms are on the first floor with private bathroom and wc. Central heating and parking facilities. Animals refused in July and August. Lake and stream. Meals if reserved. Open all year.

PRICES: s €52; d €56-€59; t €82; extra person €23; dinner €21
ON SITE: Swimming pool **NEARBY:** Bathing (5km) Horse riding (4km) Hiking (4km) Tennis (4km) Shops (2km) CARPENTRAS (10km)
NOTES: No pets July and August English spoken

ENTRAIGUES-SUR-LA-SORGUE

♦♦♦ ᴵᴼᴵ Le Moulin de Souchières
Anca et Philippe BOURDON, 279 route de St-Albergaty,
84320 ENTRAIGUES-SUR-LA-SORGUE
☎ 04 90 48 00 20 📠 04 90 48 00 20
e-mail: souchieres@infonie.fr

Old 19th-century mill with five bedrooms and a swimming pool, set in wooded grounds bordered by two streams with a view of Mont-Ventoux. On the first floor there is one room with its own bathroom, and another two bedrooms with showers. On the second floor there are two bedrooms, one with private shower, and one with private bathroom. All have private wcs. Electric heating, shared lounge with fireplace and TV. Library, telephone, terrace, covered shelter and car park. Open all year
PRICES: s €55-€60; d €70-€75; t €90; dinner €22 **ON SITE:** Fishing Swimming pool **NEARBY:** Horse riding (3km) Golf (7km) Hiking (15km) Downhill skiing (37km) Tennis (3km) Railway station (15km) Shops (2km) AVIGNON (10km) **NOTES:** No pets English spoken

♦♦♦ Mas des Platanes Jean-Christian COPPIETERS
19 chemin des Tempines,
84320 ENTRAIGUES-SUR-LA-SORGUE
☎ 04 90 62 14 39 📠 04 90 62 14 39
e-mail: jcoppiet@club-internet.fr
Come and relax in a comfortable seat on this shaded enclosed property, belonging to a 19th-century farm. Two bedrooms upstairs, one with bathroom and private wc on the landing, the other with en suite shower and wc. Second-floor suite with private shower and wc. Central heating and electric heating, communal lounge with working fireplace, and TV complete the facilities. Car park. Open Easter to 1 November and winter holidays.
PRICES: s €43-€46; d €46-€50; t €66-€70; extra person €20 **NEARBY:** Horse riding (2km) Golf (4km) Fishing (1km) Swimming pool (2km) Hiking (10km) Downhill skiing (30km) Tennis (3km) Railway station (4km) Shops (2km) AVIGNON (13km) **NOTES:** No pets English spoken

continued

ENTRECHAUX

♦♦♦ L'Escleriade Natacha SUBIAT

Route de St-Marcellin, 84340 ENTRECHAUX
☎ 04 90 46 01 32 ▤ 04 90 46 03 71
e-mail: lescleriade@wanadoo.fr
This rural property is in an exceptional setting with a swimming pool, shaded park and picnic area on the banks of the river. Downstairs there are two bedrooms with telephone, TV, bathroom, wc and private terrace. Upstairs there is a further bedroom with telephone, TV, and private bathroom and wc. In addition, there is a suite with telephone, TV, shower room, wc and private terrace. Electric heating, shared living room, library and refrigerator. Outside boules ground, enclosed garden and a secure car park with access by code. Open 1 April to 31 October.
PRICES: d €63-€70; t €85; dinner €23 **ON SITE:** Bathing Fishing Swimming pool **NEARBY:** Horse riding (2km) Hiking (2km) Downhill skiing (25km) Tennis (2km) Railway station (30km) Shops (1km) VAISON LA ROMAINE (4km) **NOTES:** No pets English spoken

GORDES

♦♦♦ La Badelle Michèle CORTASSE

84220 GORDES
☎ 04 90 72 33 19 ▤ 04 90 72 48 74
e-mail: badelle@club-internet.fr
A pleasant new construction with terrace and awning, next to an old farm with a swimming pool, offers five bedrooms. All the bedrooms are on the ground floor, two with private bathrooms, and two with showers. Each has its own wc. Electric heating, summer dining room and open kitchen with well designed verandah at the guests' disposal. Car park. Open grounds of one hectare. Open from 1 February to 31 December.
PRICES: s €69; d €74; t €89; extra person €15 **ON SITE:** Swimming pool Hiking **NEARBY:** Horse riding (7km) Golf (15km) Fishing (15km) Tennis (7km) Railway station (17km) Shops (4km) ISLE SUR LA SORGUE (17km) **NOTES:** No pets English spoken

♦♦♦ Mas des Oliviers Isabelle DONAT

Près de St-Pantaléon, Les Coucourdons, 84220 GORDES
☎ 04 90 72 43 90 ▤ 04 90 72 43 90
e-mail: mas-des-oliviers@club-internet.fr
http://www.masdesoliviers.fr.st
A new stone-built farmhouse and swimming pool in olive groves with a panoramic view of the Lubéron, Bonnieux and the Ochres de Roussillon, provides five bedrooms. Each has its own private shower, wc and terrace. Oil-fired central heating, dining room and verandah. There is also a barbecue and summer kitchen at the guests' disposal in the pool house. Open grounds and terrace. Car park, boules area and table tennis. Reduction of 10-20% for stays of a minimum of seven nights, according to the season. Open all year but advisable to book between November and March.
PRICES: s €60; d €68-€77; t €85; extra person €12 **ON SITE:** Swimming pool Hiking **NEARBY:** Horse riding (6km) Golf (16km) Fishing (15km) Tennis (7km) Railway station (36km) Shops (5km) CAVAILLON (15km) **NOTES:** No pets English spoken

♦♦♦ Les Martins Claude PEYRON

84220 GORDES
☎ 04 90 72 24 15
Among the vines, just outside a hamlet, is this charming farm with four bedrooms, each with private shower and wc. Electric heating, shared living room and terraces, some of which capture the sun, and some the shade. Enclosed garden. Reduction of 10% for more than ten nights. Open 15 March to 15 November.
PRICES: s €40; d €46; t €54 **NEARBY:** Bathing (5km) Horse riding (3km) Fishing (10km) Swimming pool (5km) Tennis (5km) Shops (2km) ISLE SUR LA SORGUE (10km) **NOTES:** No pets

♦♦♦ Mas de la Beaume Nadine CAMUS

84220 GORDES
☎ 04 90 72 02 96 ▤ 04 90 72 06 89
e-mail: la.beaume@wanadoo.fr
This old mas at the entrance of a village enjoys a very fine view of a chateau, church and Lubéron countryside. Here there are three bedrooms with shower, wc and private terrace, and two suites with shower, wc and private terrace. Central heating, shared living room, terrace and enclosed garden of 2500m². Enclosed car park. Open all year.
PRICES: d €95-€150; extra person €18 **ON SITE:** Swimming pool Hiking **NEARBY:** Horse riding (10km) Golf (20km) Tennis (2km) Railway station (35km) Shops (1km) APT (20km) **NOTES:** No pets English spoken

GOULT

♦♦♦ ⏲ La Borie Dominique et Alfred PAUWELS

Chemin de la Verrière, 84220 GOULT
☎ 04 90 72 35 84 ▤ 04 90 72 35 84
e-mail: alfred.pauwels@wanadoo.fr http://www.la-borie.com
A very fine 17th-century bastide with beautiful landscaped gardens has been very pleasantly restored to provide four bedrooms. The ground floor of an annexe is the location for two of these, with refrigerator, TV, shower and private wc, plus a third bedroom with a bathroom. Upstairs in the annexe there is the fourth bedroom with bathroom, refrigerator, TV and private wc. Fuel-fired central heating, shared living room with fireplace and library. There is also a swimming pool and tennis court. A well-placed awning for meals. Meals for residents on Mondays, Wednesdays and Fridays. Large grounds. Member of the SPA (RSPCA). Open all year.
PRICES: d €61-€91; t €105; dinner €21 **ON SITE:** Swimming pool Hiking Tennis **NEARBY:** Horse riding (8km) Golf (25km) Fishing (20km) Railway station (40km) Shops (1km) APT (12km) **NOTES:** No pets

♦♦♦ ⏲ Mas Marican Maryline et Claude CHABAUD

84220 GOULT
☎ 04 90 72 28 09 ▤ 04 90 72 28 09
Come and discover this quiet, 18th-century country mas, which has been very well restored, and is situated on a working farm. It benefits from a very fine view. One bedroom on the ground floor with private bathroom and wc, plus two bedrooms on the first floor with bathroom and private wc. Two further bedrooms on the first floor with showers and private wc. Central heating, shared living room, terrace, interior courtyard and car park. Half-board rates from the third night (no meals provided on Sundays and on bank holidays). Open from 10 February to 31 December.
PRICES: s €37; d €45; t €57; dinner €14 **ON SITE:** Hiking **NEARBY:** Bathing (15km) Horse riding (2km) Fishing (15km) Swimming pool (12km) Tennis (2km) Railway station (40km) Shops (2km) APT (12km) **NOTES:** No pets

GRAMBOIS

♦♦♦ Le Jas de Monsieur Monique MAZEL

84240 GRAMBOIS
☎ 04 90 77 92 08
Large country residence dating from the 18th century in a charming spot in the heart of the South Lubéron national park on a property of 130 hectares. Here, you can stay in three upstairs bedrooms with bathroom and private wc. There is central heating, a terrace, and the park, with private footpaths at the guests' disposal. Open all year, except 15 July to 15 August.
PRICES: s €50; d €53; extra person €12 **ON SITE:** Bathing Hiking **NEARBY:** Golf (10km) Tennis (1km) Railway station (10km) Shops (1km) PERTUIS (7km) **NOTES:** No pets English spoken

GRILLON

♥ 🍽 Au Vieux Chêne Yvette HILAIRE
Ancienne route de Valreas, 84600 GRILLON
☎ 04 90 35 24 47 📠 04 90 35 24 47
Lavender fields are the setting for this property, which offers four bedrooms with private bath or shower room and wc. Electric heating, kitchen for the use of guests or meals if booked in advance. Access to the bedrooms and the lounge-living room is from a covered terrace, at the west of the house. Breakfasts are served in the living room reserved for guests or on the terrace area. Open from 5 January to 30 November.
PRICES: s €38; d €42; t €56; extra person €14; dinner €16
ON SITE: Hiking **NEARBY:** Bathing (15km) Horse riding (4km) Golf (10km) Fishing (3km) Swimming pool (4km) Tennis (1km) Railway station (35km) Shops (1km) VALREAS (5km) **NOTES:** Pets admitted

🍽 Les Buis d'Augusta Geneviève SPIERS
Avenue du Comtat, 84600 GRILLON
☎ 04 90 35 29 18 & 06 09 89 86 78 📠 04 90 37 41 86
e-mail: gdspiers@club-internet.fr
http://www.buisdaugusta.com
A discreet and refined reception will be found on arriving at this beautiful village house with authentic charm, in a shady, enclosed park of 2000m². There is a saltwater swimming pool and very spacious rooms decorated with attention to detail. Two suites of two bedrooms each, and four other bedrooms, one of which is a mezzanine. All have TV, private wc and shower rooms with hairdryer and bathrobes. Central heating, lounge with fireplace and magazines. Up-to-date tourist information. Large summer lounge under a 100m² barn. Courtyard, terraces, sauna, table-tennis, bicycles, and phone. Meals available four times a week. Truffles served in season. Light food (*cuisine légère*). Open all year but advisable to book in November and December.
PRICES: s €61-€76; d €61-€91; t €84-€105; extra person €15; dinner €15-€23 **ON SITE:** Swimming pool **NEARBY:** Bathing (4km) Horse riding (4km) Golf (10km) Fishing (1km) Hiking (10km) Tennis (1km) Railway station (35km) VALREAS (4km) **NOTES:** Pets admitted English spoken

ISLE-SUR-LA-SORGUE

Mas St-Damien Hans et Anne-Christine NETZLER
144 chemin des Madeleines, 84800 ISLE-SUR-LA-SORGUE
☎ 04 90 38 38 42 📠 04 90 38 15 17
e-mail: netzler@mas-saintdamien.com
http://www.mas-saintdamien.com
Almond trees, olive trees, and cypresses in a park of three hectares is the setting for this 17th-century farmhouse with swimming pool. Four ground floor bedrooms with individual showers and wc. There is also central heating, a lounge, a terrace, a large garden with trees, and a car park. Open 15 March to 15 November.
PRICES: d €73-€110; extra person €17 **ON SITE:** Swimming pool Hiking **NEARBY:** Horse riding (2km) Golf (4km) Fishing (2km) Tennis (3km) Railway station (25km) Shops (3km) ISLE SUR LA SORGUE (3km) **NOTES:** No pets English spoken

🍽 Domaine de la Fontaine
Irmy et Dominique SUNDHEIMER
920 chemin du Bosquet, 84800 ISLE-SUR-LA-SORGUE
☎ 04 90 38 01 44 📠 04 90 38 53 42
e-mail: domainedelafontaine@wanadoo.fr
http://www.domainedelafontaine.com
A restored individual mas dating from the nineteenth century, with swimming pool, set in large unfenced grounds, offers the following bedrooms: one ground floor room with shower, wc and private

Mas de la Coudoulière

Situated in the heart of Provence between the river and the mountains this 17thC farm has all the flavours of the Mediterranean. The restaurant is decorated in traditional style of the area, breakfast can be taken either in the dining room in front of the imposing fireplace or in the summer months on the terrace under the ancient chestnut tree. There is a choice of bedrooms on two levels varying from two spacious, one suite with two rooms or two lovely large airy rooms.
You will enjoy peace and calm whilst strolling along the hill paths. Just five minutes away is the town of L'Isle sur la Sorgue an antique hunter's paradise.
1854 route de Carpentras
84800 L'Isle-sur-la-Sorgue
Tel: 04 90 38 16 35 Fax: 04 90 38 16 89
Web site: www.isle-sur-sorgue.en-provence.com/mas-coudou/

terrace, and one upstairs room with small lounge and shower and private wc. Two suites upstairs with private facilities and a small adjoining room. On the second floor there is a further bedroom with en suite facilities. Fuel-fired central heating, lounge, dining room, telephone and TV on demand. Terrace with shade and car park. Meals provided three times a week. Tourist tax: 0.38 euros per person per day. Open all year.
PRICES: s €73-€87; d €79-€93; t €110-€131; extra person €17; dinner €23 **ON SITE:** Swimming pool **NEARBY:** Bathing (2km) Horse riding (2km) Golf (3km) Fishing (2km) Hiking (1km) Tennis (2km) Railway station (2km) Shops (2km) ISLE SUR LA SORGUE (2km) **NOTES:** No pets English spoken

La Coudoulière Régis SOUBRAT
Mas la Coudoulière, 1854 route de Carpentras, 84800 ISLE-SUR-LA-SORGUE
☎ 04 90 38 16 35 📠 04 90 38 16 89
http://www.isle-sur-sorgue.en-provence.com
Come and discover this independent monastic farm in the country with swimming pool, which accepts small pets. Bedrooms are on the first and second floors, and all have private facilities. In addition there is electric heating, mini-refrigerators, a shared living room, lounge with TV, terrace with trees and car park. 10% reduction between October and May. Open all year except November.
PRICES: s €61-€71; d €69-€79; t €85-€95 **ON SITE:** Swimming pool **NEARBY:** Bathing (2km) Horse riding (2km) Golf (2km) Fishing (1km) Hiking (4km) Downhill skiing (60km) Tennis (2km) Railway station (2km) Shops (1km) ISLE SUR LA SORGUE (2km) **NOTES:** Pets admitted CC
See advert on this page

continued

⁂ La Meridienne Jérôme TARAYRE
Chemin de la Lone, 84800 ISLE-SUR-LA-SORGUE
☎ 04 90 38 40 26 📠 04 90 38 58 46
Part of the owner's character house has been renovated to provide five ground floor bedrooms, with showers, wc and private terrace. On the rural property there is also a swimming pool, electric heating, a shared room with kitchen area for guests and dining room. Car park. Open all year.
PRICES: s €44; d €53-€61; t €72; extra person €11 **ON SITE:** Swimming pool **NEARBY:** Bathing (2km) Horse riding (2km) Fishing (2km) Hiking (2km) Tennis (3km) Railway station (3km) Shops (3km) CAVAILLON (10km) **NOTES:** Pets admitted English spoken

⁂ Le Clos St-Antoine Jacqueline TAUB
338 chemin des Florides, 84800 ISLE-SUR-LA-SORGUE
☎ 04 90 38 90 94 📠 04 90 38 92 46
e-mail: jw.taub@wanadoo.fr
http://www.clos-saint-antoine.com

Breakfast is served in the bower by the swimming pool at this residence of Gordes stone, set in an oak grove. Discover four spacious ground floor bedrooms with bathrooms, wc and private terraces. Electric heating. Large garden with trees. Car park. Open 16 March to 14 November.
PRICES: d €84-€115 **ON SITE:** Swimming pool Hiking **NEARBY:** Horse riding (2km) Golf (8km) Fishing (2km) Tennis (2km) Railway station (30km) Shops (1km) ISLE SUR LA SORGUE (2km) **NOTES:** No pets English spoken

LA MOTTE-D'AIGUES

⁂ ▯◎▯ La Clef des Champs
Géraldine et Laurent DROMENQ
Rte de la tour, ch. du claux, 84240 LA MOTTE-D'AIGUES
☎ 04 90 77 69 80 📠 04 90 77 69 80
e-mail: maslaclefdeschamps@net-up.com
This stone *mas* with swimming pool is situated 800 metres from the Bonde lake. Set in vineyards, there are two bedrooms on the first floor with TV, bathroom, wc and private terrace. There is also a family room (two bedrooms and kitchen) on the first floor, with TV, bathroom, wc and private terrace. Electric heating, shared room with working fireplace and library. Open grounds. Individual access to all bedrooms. Open all year.
PRICES: s €61; d €75; t €98; extra person €23; dinner €20 **ON SITE:** Swimming pool Hiking **NEARBY:** Bathing (1km) Horse riding (3km) Golf (30km) Fishing (1km) Tennis (3km) Railway station (80km) Shops (3km) PERTUIS (10km) **NOTES:** No pets English spoken

🐓Places with this symbol are farmhouses

Ask the proprietor for directions
when booking

LACOSTE

⁂ Bonne Terre Roland LAMY
84710 LACOSTE
☎ 04 90 75 85 53 & 04 90 75 85 53 📠 04 90 75 85 53
e-mail: bonneterre@fr.st http://www.bonneterre.fr.st

Personalised double rooms in a character house, near a village with a panoramic view, in a site of exceptional natural beauty. Very tranquil, shaded park, and swimming pool. Four comfortable bedrooms with shower and private wc and one room with bathroom and wc. Electric heating, terraces, telephone and closed car park. Dogs accepted: 6 euros. Open 1 February to 30 November.
PRICES: s €82-€94; d €87-€99; extra person €20 **ON SITE:** Swimming pool **NEARBY:** Golf (25km) Tennis (4km) APT (15km) **NOTES:** Pets admitted English spoken

⁂ ▯◎▯ Domaine Layaude Basse Olivier et Lydia MAZEL
Chemin de St-Jean, 84710 LACOSTE
☎ 04 90 75 90 06 📠 04 90 75 99 03
www.luberon news-domaine de layaude
A 17th century family *mas*, situated at the foot of the Lubéron, just 800 m from a country village, provides six bedrooms. All of these have private showers and wc, and local ochre decoration. Large dining room furnished in a very pure Provençal tradition, with a lounge area and an open fire in winter. Outside there is a terrace, table tennis, and a swimming pool with a very attractive view of the village and Mont-Verdun. Picnic area and a boules court. Shaded car park. Meals three nights a week with Provençal cooking. Wine and honey from the property. Generous breakfasts. Small dogs accepted (5 euros a night). Open 1 March to 30 November. Possibility of opening for groups in winter.
PRICES: d €64-€88; dinner €27 **ON SITE:** Swimming pool **NEARBY:** Bathing (20km) Horse riding (10km) Golf (20km) Fishing (10km) Hiking (4km) Tennis (4km) Railway station (40km) Shops (1km) APT (8km) **NOTES:** Pets admitted English spoken

⁂ Relais du Procureur COURT DE GEBELIN
Rue Basse, 84710 LACOSTE
☎ 04 90 75 82 28 📠 04 90 75 86 94
e-mail: relaisprocureur@luberon.org http://www.luberon.org

RELAIS DU PROCUREUR

continued

Six bedrooms have been built in this very fine 17th-century village property with a swimming pool. The six bedrooms, three of which have air-conditioning, all have bathrooms, private wc, TV, mini-bar and telephone. There is also a shared lounge, living room, and terrace. Horse-riding and car rental on the premises. Forest 5 km. Walking, bicycle touring and hunting. Restaurant in the village. Further details by telephone only. Open all year but advisable to book during January, February and March.

PRICES: s €76-€105; d €76-€105; t €99-€115; HB €56-€78; dinner €18-€24 **ON SITE:** Horse riding Swimming pool Hiking **NEARBY:** Golf (20km) Fishing (15km) Tennis (8km) APT (12km) **NOTES:** No pets CC English spoken

LAGARDE-PAREOL

￦￦￦ ⁄⃝ Domaine les Serres
Loeke et Ton KRIJGER-BEAUMONT
84290 LAGARDE-PAREOL
☎ 04 90 30 76 10 ▤ 04 90 30 74 31
e-mail: domaine-les-serres@wanadoo.fr
Five spacious bedrooms are located in this large stone mas, in a wooded park of one hectare with swimming pool and numerous terraces and gardens. Four of these are family rooms, sleeping four, and all have their own bathrooms and wc. Gas central heating, shared living room with working fireplace, library, TV, video and telephone. Car park. Meals for residents three times a week. Open all year.

PRICES: s €75-€135; d €105-€135; t €105-€135; extra person €17; dinner €23 **ON SITE:** Swimming pool Hiking **NEARBY:** Bathing (10km) Horse riding (6km) Golf (8km) Fishing (10km) Downhill skiing (30km) Tennis (2km) Railway station (15km) Shops (3km) ORANGE (10km) **NOTES:** No pets English spoken

LAGNES

￦￦￦ La Pastorale Elisabeth et Robert NEGREL
Rte de Fontaine de Vaucluse, 84800 LAGNES
☎ 04 90 20 25 18 ▤ 04 90 20 21 86
Isle-sur-la-Sorgue 5 mn. A very fine stone farmhouse in the country has been restored to provide two single and two double rooms on the first floor. One single and one double room have private showers and wc, and the other single and double rooms have private bathrooms and wc. In addition there is electric heating, shared living room, dining room, and summer kitchen reserved for guests. Locked garage, terrace and open grounds providing shade. Open all year.

PRICES: s €60; d €60; t €75; extra person €15 **ON SITE:** Horse riding **NEARBY:** Bathing (1km) Golf (2km) Fishing (1km) Swimming pool (1km) Hiking (1km) Downhill skiing (35km) Tennis (1km) Railway station (5km) Shops (1km) ISLE SUR LA SORGUE (5km) **NOTES:** Pets admitted English spoken

￦￦￦ ⁄⃝ Le Mas du Grand Jonquier
François et Monique GRECK
84800 LAGNES
☎ 04 90 20 90 13 ▤ 04 90 20 91 18
e-mail: masgrandjonquier@wanadoo.fr
http://www.grandjonquier.com
Two hectares of lawns, cherry and plum trees is the setting for this very fine 18th-century restored *mas* in the country with private swimming pool. Two double bedrooms on the ground floor with TV, telephone, mini-bar, shower and wc, and three double bedrooms with the same facilities on the first floor. A further double room on the first floor with TV etc. has a shower and wc on the landing. Central heating, lounge with fireplace, living room, dining room with fireplace, terrace and car park. Individual meals if booked (refined gourmet cooking). Generous breakfasts (cheese, yoghurts …). Open all year.

PRICES: s €78; d €78; t €96; dinner €23 **ON SITE:** Swimming pool Hiking **NEARBY:** Bathing (13km) Horse riding (3km) Golf (5km) Fishing (5km) Tennis (4km) Railway station (13km) Shops (3km) ISLE SUR SORGUE (5km) **NOTES:** No pets CC English spoken

LAMOTTE-DU-RHONE

￦￦￦ ⁄⃝ Mas Zazezou Monique et Pierre CARDINAEL
Quartier Malatras, 84840 LAMOTTE-DU-RHONE
☎ 04 90 40 45 16 ▤ 04 90 40 45 16
Many activities, including swimming pool, boules area, billiard table and a weights room can be found in this 19th-century restored *mas*, which is isolated amidst fields. Three bedrooms are available with showers, private wc and their own entrance. There is also a 3000m² garden, and a shady terrace for meals. Private car park. Picnics are not allowed. Open 1 April to 31 October.

PRICES: s €38; d €46; t €61; extra person €15; dinner €21 **ON SITE:** Swimming pool **NEARBY:** Bathing (12km) Horse riding (5km) Fishing (1km) Hiking (8km) Tennis (2km) Railway station (6km) Shops (2km) ORANGE (25km) **NOTES:** Pets admitted English spoken

LAURIS

￦￦￦ Bastide du Piecaud
Famille SCHLUMBERGER-CHAZELLE
Chemin de l'Escudier, 84360 LAURIS
☎ 04 90 08 32 27 & 06 82 86 10 30 ▤ 04 90 08 32 27

This large farmhouse with swimming pool, dating from the 17th century, boasts an inner and outer courtyard overlooking the surrounding hills. There are two first floor bedrooms with private shower and wc, and two bedrooms with private bathroom and wc. In addition, on the first floor, there is a suite with private bathroom and wc. Central heating, library, TV and terrace. Open grounds of seven hectares. Car park. Open 15 March to 15 November and other periods if requested.

PRICES: s €61-€76; d €61-€76; t €89-€99; extra person €20-€23 **ON SITE:** Swimming pool Hiking **NEARBY:** Bathing (3km) Horse riding (3km) Golf (14km) Fishing (3km) Tennis (2km) Railway station (45km) Shops (2km) CAVAILLON (27km) **NOTES:** No pets English spoken

continued

♦♦♦♦ ⅝◯⅜ La Maison des Sources
Martine COLLART-STICHELBAUT
Chemin des Fraysses, 84360 LAURIS
☎ 04 90 08 22 19 & 06 08 33 06 40   📠 04 90 08 22 19
e-mail: contact@maison.des.sources.com
http://www.maison-des-sources.com
This pleasantly restored *mas* in the country, with a beautiful view of the Durance valley, has terraces and a private garden of three hectares. Inside, there are three bedrooms on the first floor with private bath or shower room and wc. In addition on the first floor, there is an ideal room for four people, with private shower, bathroom and wc. Central heating, shared living room, lounge, dining room, TV, library and fireplace. Telephone, table tennis and car park. Animals accepted if asked in advance. Meals available occasionally. Open all year.
PRICES: s €58-€61; d €71-€73; t €87-€93; extra person €18; dinner €23
ON SITE: Hiking **NEARBY:** Bathing (5km) Horse riding (2km) Golf (15km) Fishing (2km) Swimming pool (4km) Tennis (1km) Railway station (20km) Shops (1km) CAVAILLON (20km) **NOTES:** Pets admitted

♦♦♦♦ ⅝◯⅜ Les Jardins du Soleil
Francine NOWAK et Bruno KEYEUX
Le Rocher de Malan, 84360 LAURIS
☎ 04 90 08 37 27   📠 04 90 08 37 27
e-mail: bruno.keyeux@wanadoo.fr
A pine forest is the setting for four small houses with swimming pool, on a property of 1.3 hectares. The houses provide four downstairs bedrooms with TV, and private shower and wc. There is also electric heating, dining room/living room with TV and library. Terraces. The car park/village square has a vine arbour, fountain, and boule area. Open all year.
PRICES: s €45; d €52; t €66; dinner €23 **ON SITE:** Swimming pool Hiking **NEARBY:** Horse riding (3km) Golf (25km) Fishing (10km) Tennis (2km) Railway station (40km) Shops (3km) CADENET (15km) **NOTES:** No pets English spoken

LE BARROUX

♦♦♦ Ferme les Belugues Nadine et Bernard ROUX
Rte du Paty - Chaudeirolles, 84330 LE BARROUX
☎ 04 90 65 15 16   📠 04 90 65 15 16
e-mail: ferme.des.belugues@libertysurf.fr
An 18th-century farm, typical of this area, located in the wooded foothills of Mont Verdoux, with swimming pool. The three guest rooms are on the ground floor of an annexe; all have private facilities. Large room with piano and equipped kitchen area, plus shared living room with library TV and telephone. Terrace and large non-enclosed grounds. One animal per guest accepted. 5% reduction from three nights, and 10% from six nights. No charge for children under three (in a cot). Open 1 April to 11 November. For other periods consult the owner.
PRICES: s €53; d €61; t €76; extra person €18 **ON SITE:** Swimming pool Hiking **NEARBY:** Bathing (2km) Horse riding (12km) Golf (40km) Fishing (2km) Downhill skiing (20km) Tennis (3km) Railway station (40km) Shops (3km) CARPENTRAS (15km) **NOTES:** Pets admitted English spoken

LE THOR

♦♦♦ ⅝◯⅜ Le Domaine des Coudelières
N et A MARCHAL - BUSTILLO
560 chemin des Coudelières, 84250 LE THOR
☎ 04 90 02 12 72 & 06 62 53 54 62   📠 04 90 02 12 72
e-mail: domcoudelieres@free.fr
http://www.guideweb.com/provence/bb
Charming, attractively restored 19th-century *mas* amidst three hectares of cypress trees, laurels, lavender, and surrounded by apple orchards. There is an infinity pool and beach shared with a self-catering gîte. Four bedrooms, of which one is a family room, and a suite with a Provençal theme, all with bathroom or shower and private wc. Shaded terrace with hundred-year-old plane trees. Central heating, lounge with fireplace and TV, reading material, floodlit car park, boules area, table tennis. Near village. Meals if reserved (twice a week in July/August and long weekends, with wine and coffee included, or as requested). Open all year.

PRICES: s €64; d €75-€102; t €87-€138; extra person €15; HB €17; dinner €22 **ON SITE:** Swimming pool **NEARBY:** Horse riding (5km) Golf (10km) Fishing (1km) Hiking (2km) Downhill skiing (40km) Tennis (1km) Railway station (2km) Shops (2km) ISLE SUR LA SORGUE (5km) **NOTES:** No pets English spoken

♦♦♦ Mas des Prés Véronique GAUDIN
946 chemin de la Treille, 84250 LE THOR
☎ 04 90 02 14 22   📠 04 90 02 15 44
This delightful old Provençal *mas* has a view of the Château de Thouzon, and is situated in the peace and quiet of 2¹/₂ hectares. There are three bedrooms, two of which have independent entrances, with large shower rooms and private wc. Fuel-fired central heating, lounge with working fireplace, library, and TV. Terrace, car park. Out of season rates on demand. Open all year.
PRICES: d €85-€90 **ON SITE:** Swimming pool **NEARBY:** Horse riding (10km) Golf (8km) Fishing (1km) Hiking (10km) Downhill skiing (50km) Tennis (3km) Railway station (18km) Shops (3km) ISLE SUR LA SORGUE (7km) **NOTES:** No pets English spoken

LES TAILLADES

♦♦♦ ⅝◯⅜ Mas Chante Ruisseau Viviane VOUSURE
1207 route de Mourre-Poussin, 84300 LES TAILLADES
☎ 04 90 76 06 78   📠 04 90 76 06 78
A stream, a small wood and a large shady garden plus swimming pool are the attractions of this old farmhouse at the foot of the Lubéron. There is one bedroom on the first floor with bathroom and private wc, and two with showers and private wc. Central heating, two shared reception rooms with working fireplace, terrace, and garden dining room. Enclosed parking. Meals available. Small dogs accepted. Open all year
PRICES: s €56; d €64; extra person €9-€15; HB €105-€130; dinner €21 **ON SITE:** Swimming pool **NEARBY:** Horse riding (2km) Golf (20km) Fishing (1km) Hiking (2km) Tennis (4km) Railway station (30km) Shops (4km) CAVAILLON (4km) **NOTES:** Pets admitted English spoken

LORIOL-DU-COMTAT

♦♦♦ Le Deves Josette et Claude GUILLERMIN
84870 LORIOL-DU-COMTAT
☎ 04 90 65 70 62 & 06 11 16 18 38   📠 04 90 65 70 62
A completely renovated farm in the heart of an agricultural enterprise of six hectares (melons, strawberries, courgettes), in the country with shaded park and swimming pool. Two bedrooms have private bathrooms and wc, and three have private showers and wc. Central heating, equipped kitchen with cooker, microwave,

continued   continued

refrigerator, crockery, barbecue and dining room. Telephone, terrace with picnic table, car park and independent entrance. Restaurant 900 m. A calm spot with plenty of trees. Open all year.
PRICES: s €40-€43; d €43-€47; t €58　**ON SITE:** Swimming pool Tennis
NEARBY: Bathing (1km) Horse riding (1km) Fishing (2km) Hiking (5km) Downhill skiing (40km) Railway station (15km) Shops (3km) CARPENTRAS (3km) **NOTES:** No pets

LOURMARIN

♦♦♦ La Lombarde Eva LEBRE
La Lombarde - BP 32, Puyvert, 84160 LOURMARIN
☎ 04 90 08 40 60　📠 04 90 08 40 64
e-mail: la.lombarde@wanadoo.fr
http://perso.wanadoo.fr/lalombarde
Four bedrooms with exterior access have been incorporated into this 17th-century *mas*, situated in six hectares of wooded park with swimming pool, in the country. The bedrooms have a hall, refrigerator, TV, shower, wc and private terrace. Central heating, shared courtyard, dining room, reception room/lounge, with the possibility of a kitchen. Bicycles, mountain-bikes, table tennis, pétanque, volley-ball. Barbecue area. Open 1 March to 10 November.
PRICES: d €60-€64; extra person €18　**ON SITE:** Swimming pool Hiking
NEARBY: Bathing (1km) Horse riding (2km) Golf (15km) Fishing (1km) Tennis (2km) Shops (1km) LOURMARIN (2km) **NOTES:** No pets English spoken

♦♦♦ Villa St-Louis Bernadette LASSALETTE
35 rue Henri de Savournin, 84160 LOURMARIN
☎ 04 90 68 39 18　📠 04 90 68 10 07
An 18th-century coaching house at the entrance of a village with a large shaded garden has one bedroom on the second floor with TV, telephone, bathroom and private wc, and a further four bedrooms. These have private showers, TV, telephone and wc. Central heating, lounge, library, and mountain-bikes on the premises. Extra child: 7.62 euros. Open all year.
PRICES: s €53-€69; d €53-€69; extra person €7　**ON SITE:** Hiking Tennis
NEARBY: Bathing (1km) Horse riding (1km) Golf (20km) Fishing (4km) Swimming pool (1km) Railway station (30km) Shops (30km) APT (15km)
NOTES: Pets admitted English spoken

MALAUCENE

♦♦♦ Le Château Cremessiere
M et E DALLAPORTA-BONNEL
84340 MALAUCENE
☎ 04 90 65 11 13
In the village of Malaucène, this very attractive property is set in meadows and wooded grounds of two hectares. On the ground floor, there are two bedrooms and one suite of two bedrooms with terrace, kitchen and TV. A further suite on the ground floor with terrace, kitchen, living room, TV and private fireplace. All have private bath or shower rooms. Use of refrigerator. Central heating. Shady terrace. Car park. Garden chairs on the lawn. Garage for bikes/motorbikes. Picnics possible. Breakfasts served on the terrace in fine weather. Numerous restaurants close by. Open 1 June to 30 September and during the Ascension and Pentecost holidays if requested.
PRICES: s €69-€72; d €67-€84; extra person €20　**ON SITE:** Hiking
NEARBY: Bathing (3km) Horse riding (3km) Golf (35km) Fishing (3km) Swimming pool (9km) Downhill skiing (10km) Tennis (1km) Railway station (40km) VAISON LA ROMAINE (9km) **NOTES:** Pets admitted Minimum 2 night stay English spoken

MENERBES

♦♦♦ Les Peirelles Didier et Muriel ANDREIS
84560 MENERBES
☎ 04 90 72 23 42　📠 04 90 72 23 56
e-mail: les-peirelles@worldonline.fr
A large unenclosed park of one hectare is the location for this building on terraces with swimming pool, on the same land as the owners' house. There are three double bedrooms on the ground floor with terrace, private shower and wc, plus two rooms for four people, with terrace, bathroom and private wc. Electric heating, use of shared room with kitchen, refrigerator, and microwave. Library, card telephone, communal terrace, very large park, car park, locked garage for bicycles. Open 1 March to 31 December.
PRICES: s €69-€76; d €72-€79; t €88-€109; extra person €16-€20
ON SITE: Horse riding Swimming pool Hiking **NEARBY:** Golf (15km) Tennis (2km) Railway station (40km) Shops (2km) APT (20km)
NOTES: No pets English spoken

MONIEUX

♦♦♦ ◯◯ Chambre d'hôtes GIARDINI
Gaec le Viguier, 84390 MONIEUX-SAULT
☎ 04 90 64 15 52 & 06 12 43 78 50　📠 04 90 64 15 52
e-mail: MATHY010173@.fr
Gordes and summit of Mont-Ventoux 20 km. Agricultural farm, situated between Mont-Ventoux and the Luberon, in the heart of the lavender country. Here you will find five bedrooms, in an independent building, with shower and private wc on the ground floor. All benefit from central heating, shared room with fireplace and TV, terrace and car park. Mountain bikes available. Close to fishing lake. Theme holidays: truffles, nature trips in Provence and a tour to discover local products. Open all year.
PRICES: s €50; d €50; t €65; extra person €15; HB €44; dinner €19
ON SITE: Fishing Hiking **NEARBY:** Bathing (15km) Golf (25km) Swimming pool (7km) Downhill skiing (25km) Tennis (7km) Railway station (60km) Shops (7km) CARPENTRAS (35km) **NOTES:** No pets English spoken

MORMOIRON

♦♦♦ Lou Mas de Carboussan Jean-Pierre ESCOFFIER
84570 MORMOIRON
☎ 04 90 61 93 02 & SR : 04 90 85 45 00　📠 04 90 61 93 03

A new detached villa on the side of a hill, in an orchard of cherry and olive trees, provides one ground floor bedroom with terrace, bathroom, and private wc, and two bedrooms with showers, terrace and private wc. In addition, on the first floor, there are two bedrooms also with shower and private wc. Gas central heating, shared room with working fireplace and kitchen available. Communal terrace, grounds with trees, car park. Open all year.
PRICES: s €38-€43; d €46-€51; t €61-€66; extra person €15
ON SITE: Hiking **NEARBY:** Bathing (2km) Horse riding (5km) Golf (25km) Fishing (2km) Swimming pool (5km) Downhill skiing (20km) Tennis (1km) Railway station (40km) Shops (1km) CARPENTRAS (12km)
NOTES: Pets admitted

OPPEDE-LE-VIEUX

▓▓▓ Chambre d'hôtes Dominique BAL
Le vieux village, 84580 OPPEDE-LE-VIEUX
☎ 04 90 76 93 52 & 06 63 43 75 68 📠 04 90 76 93 52
Come and discover this period village house at the foot of the old Chateau of Oppède, perched on the side of a mountain, and situated in the very heart of the National Lubéron Park. Three first-floor bedrooms with shower and private wc. Electric heating, shared living room, terrace and dining room. The old village of Oppède forms the crossroads of several walking routes and bike trails. Forest 100 metres away. Open all year.
PRICES: s €40; d €51; t €61; extra person €6 **ON SITE:** Hiking
NEARBY: Horse riding (1km) Golf (15km) Fishing (10km) Swimming pool (10km) Tennis (2km) Shops (1km) CAVAILLON (10km) **NOTES:** No pets English spoken

---

PERNES-LES-FONTAINES

▓▓▓ iOi Domaine de Nesquière
Isabelle DE MAINTENANT
5419 route d'Althen, 84210 PERNES-LES-FONTAINES
☎ 04 90 62 00 16 📠 04 90 62 02 10
e-mail: demaintemant.provence@mnet.fr
http://www.guideweb.com/provence/bb/la-nesquiere
This fine 18th-century family house on a large agricultural property offers four pleasantly decorated bedrooms. Situated in a calm, relaxing, spacious environment, there are two second-floor suites (for 2-4 people) and one double room, all with shower, wc, small refrigerator, tea making facilities and TV. There is a further double room with bathroom, wc, kitchen area and TV. Lounge, library and piano available. Covered car park and laundry room. Meals available if booked except for Wednesdays. There is a holiday gîte and a riverside footpath in the grounds. Open all year.
PRICES: s €46-€54; d €51-€61; t €76; extra person €9-€14; dinner €22
NEARBY: Horse riding (5km) Golf (15km) Fishing (1km) Swimming pool (6km) Hiking (8km) Downhill skiing (35km) Tennis (6km) Railway station (15km) Shops (4km) AVIGNON (15km) **NOTES:** Pets admitted English spoken

▓▓▓ Hauterive Mireille COIZY
473 chemin des Coudoulets,
84210 PERNES-LES-FONTAINES
☎ 04 90 61 57 94
e-mail: pierre.coisy@wanadoo.fr
http://perso.wanadoo.fr/hauterive
Four bedrooms can be found in this town house with enclosed garden and swimming pool. Three bedrooms with shower and private wc and one bedroom in an annexe with kitchen area, lounge, TV, shower and private wc. All rooms enjoy central heating, a shared living room, TV and terrace. Open all year.
PRICES: s €61-€76; d €69-€84; t €99-€105 **ON SITE:** Swimming pool
NEARBY: Horse riding (8km) Golf (10km) Fishing (10km) Hiking (5km) Downhill skiing (40km) Tennis (1km) Railway station (25km) Shops (1km) CARPENTRAS (6km) **NOTES:** No pets

▓▓▓ iOi Le Mas Pichony Françoise & J-P FAURE-BRAC
1454 rte de St-Didier (RD28),
84210 PERNES-LES-FONTAINES
☎ 04 90 61 56 11 & 06 20 83 72 35 📠 04 90 61 56 33
e-mail: mas-pichony@wanadoo.fr
http://www.eurobandb.com/gites/pichony_f.htm
An independent 17th-century *mas* of character in vineyards with swimming pool, shaded terrace and open grounds in a beautiful setting. Four bedrooms are on the first floor with shower and private wc, and one bedroom is on the second floor with bathroom and private wc. All rooms benefit from central heating, shared living room with working fireplace, library, TV and

telephone. Cot available at no extra charge. Car park, local produce, evening meals if booked in advance. Open all year.

PRICES: s €69; d €73-€84; t €99; extra person €18; dinner €24
ON SITE: Swimming pool Hiking **NEARBY:** Bathing (8km) Horse riding (4km) Golf (15km) Fishing (6km) Downhill skiing (25km) Tennis (3km) Railway station (28km) Shops (2km) CARPENTRAS (6km) **NOTES:** No pets

▓▓▓ Moulin de la Baume Eddy LECOMPTE
182 route d'Avignon, 84210 PERNES-LES-FONTAINES
☎ 04 90 66 58 36 📠 04 90 61 69 42

A pleasantly restored mill just outside a village, on 5000 m² of open ground with swimming pool. Four bedrooms on the first floor with TV, bath or shower room and wc. On the ground floor, there is one room with TV, bathroom, living room and wc. Central heating, shared living room, terrace and car park. Open 1 March to 15 November.
PRICES: s €91-€110; d €91-€110; t €130; extra person €19
ON SITE: Swimming pool **NEARBY:** Horse riding (2km) Golf (10km) Fishing (4km) Hiking (2km) Downhill skiing (25km) Tennis (1km) Railway station (15km) Shops (1km) CARPENTRAS (10km) **NOTES:** No pets English spoken

▓▓▓ Chambre d'hôtes Jacqueline MANGEARD
Route de Mazan D1, St-Barthélémy,
84210 PERNES-LES-FONTAINES
☎ 04 90 66 47 79 & 04 90 66 47 79 📠 04 90 66 47 79
e-mail: mangeard.jacqueline@wanadoo.fr
http://www.itea.fr/84/1089
Fully restored 18th-century Provençal farmhouse in the country with swimming pool and tennis court. One bedroom with bathroom and private wc and four bedrooms with showers and private wc. Central heating, shared lounge, dining room, refrigerator and terrace. Next to a shaded, enclosed park. Closed car park. Phone booth, free bicycle, table tennis and badminton. Open all year.
PRICES: s €40; d €52; t €71; extra person €19 **ON SITE:** Swimming pool Hiking Tennis **NEARBY:** Bathing (1km) Horse riding (5km) Golf (10km) Fishing (1km) Railway station (20km) Shops (2km) (2km) **NOTES:** No pets English spoken

continued

PROVENCE-ALPES-CÔTE-D'AZUR

PUYMERAS

♦♦♦ ◎ Domaine le Puy du Maupas
Christian SAUVAYRE
Route de Nyons, 84110 PUYMERAS
☎ 04 90 46 47 43 🖷 04 90 46 48 51
www.guideweb.com/provence/chambres_hotes/maupas
No smoking please in this large new house adjoining a wine-tasting cellar, situated in the country with swimming pool. On the first floor, there are five bedrooms with private bath or shower room and wc. Central heating, shared living room, lounge, dining room, fireplace, TV, terrace and car park. Phone available (metered). Sink for washing picnic items, refrigerator for cold drinks. Meals available from 15 June to 15 September if booked and/or if offered by your hostess. Sample the local produce wines from the estate. Open 15 March to 31 October.
PRICES: s €43; d €48; t €61; dinner €20 **ON SITE:** Wine tasting Swimming pool Hiking **NEARBY:** Bathing (4km) Horse riding (8km) Fishing (5km) Tennis (2km) Railway station (35km) Shops (2km) VAISON LA ROMAINE **NOTES:** No pets CC

♦♦♦ ◎ L'Oustau des Oliviers Marie-Françoise ROUSTAN
Quartier des Eyssarettes, 84110 PUYMERAS
☎ 04 90 46 45 89 🖷 04 90 46 40 93
e-mail: Marie-Francoise.2@wanadoo.fr
www.guideweb.com/provence/bb/oustau-des-oliviers
Situated amidst hills in the middle of a wine-producing enterprise, this recent house provides four bedrooms on the ground floor with showers and private wc. The swimming pool is located well away from the bedrooms to preserve the peace and quiet. Shared living room, refrigerator, microwave, lounge, dining-room, and library. Terrace, garden furniture, barbecue, ornamental pond, boules area and table tennis. Well-marked hiking trails starting from the house, mountain bike rental 6 km. Sale of our own olive oil and Côtes du Rhone wine. Meals available if booked, except on Tuesday and Saturday evenings. Apéritif, wine and coffee included. Theme weeks. Open 1 April to 15 October (end March and end October if booked in advance).
PRICES: s €46; d €52; t €69; dinner €20 **ON SITE:** Swimming pool Hiking **NEARBY:** Bathing (15km) Horse riding (7km) Golf (25km) Fishing (15km) Downhill skiing (35km) Tennis (2km) Railway station (30km) Shops (5km) VAISON LA ROMAINE (7km) **NOTES:** Pets admitted

PUYVERT

♦♦♦ Le mas de Foncaudette Anny et Loïc JEANPIERRE
La Lombarde, 84160 PUYVERT
☎ 04 90 08 42 51 & 06 15 20 41 54 🖷 04 90 08 42 51
e-mail: foncaudette@yahoo.fr
http://www.guideweb.com/provence
A 16th-century mas, with a Templar knights' command post and pigeon house, classed as an historic monument, provides two suites. These enjoy a swimming pool set in vines and olive trees, and consist of a ground-floor lounge, private shower or bathroom and wc, and access to the first floor by a wooden step ladder to a bedroom with two single beds. In the house there is one bedroom with shower, wc, and private terrace. Central heating, lounge, library, TV, interior courtyard and closed car park. Animals accepted if requested. Open all year.
PRICES: s €88-€104; d €88-€104; t €124 **ON SITE:** Swimming pool Hiking **NEARBY:** Bathing (3km) Horse riding (2km) Golf (18km) Fishing (3km) Tennis (2km) Railway station (50km) Shops (1km) LAURIS (2km) **NOTES:** Pets admitted English spoken

Prices are given in Euros €1 = £0.62
at the time of going to press

RICHERENCHES

♦♦♦ ◎ Ferme de la Commanderie
J.Marie & Françoise GULIELMO
Domaine Hugues de Bourbouton, 84600 RICHERENCHES
☎ 04 90 28 02 29 & 06 80 94 85 86 🖷 04 90 28 04 45
http://www.guideprovence.com/bb/commanderie
A fine Templar knights' farm, dating from the 16th century with shaded interior courtyard and gardens and park of eight hectares, has an ornamental lake. Situated in the country, at the foot of a hill, the residence offers one bedroom with kitchen area and lounge on the ground floor, and two bedrooms on the first floor; all have private bathrooms and wcs. Fuel-fired central heating, shared living room, lounge, fireplace, and library. Telephone, car park. Extremely well decorated. Peaceful atmosphere. Refined food with delicate flavours. Wine and coffee included in the meal price. Open all year.
PRICES: d €69-€91; t €91-€115; extra person €23; dinner €27 **ON SITE:** Horse riding Hiking **NEARBY:** Golf (7km) Fishing (1km) Swimming pool (7km) Tennis (3km) Railway station (35km) Shops (3km) VALREAS (7km) **NOTES:** No pets English spoken

ROAIX

♦♦♦ ◎ Les Auzières Alain CUER
84110 ROAIX
☎ 04 90 46 15 54 🖷 04 90 46 12 75
Owners' farm with swimming pool, patios, terraces, courtyards and large, unenclosed grounds has five guest rooms. These are all on the ground floor with TV, showers and private wc. There is also electric heating, a lounge with piano and reading material, dining room, working fireplace, and telephone. Outside there is table tennis table, billiard table and possible mountain bike rental. Reduction for long stays. Meals only if booked in advance. Open from 1 April to 15 November.
PRICES: s €60; d €69; extra person €15; dinner €23 **ON SITE:** Swimming pool Hiking **NEARBY:** Bathing (5km) Horse riding (8km) Golf (18km) Fishing (5km) Downhill skiing (40km) Tennis (8km) Railway station (18km) Shops (3km) VAISON LA ROMAINE (8km) **NOTES:** Pets admitted

ROBION

♦♦♦ ◎ Domaine Canfier Michel et Catherine CHARVET
84440 ROBION
☎ 04 90 76 51 54 🖷 04 90 76 67 99
e-mail: canfier@aol.com
This countryside farm has plenty of character and a swimming pool. There are two bedrooms on the first floor and two on the second floor. All have private shower or bathrooms and wcs, and all benefit from central heating, a communal room, lounge, dining room, working fireplace, library, piano and TV. There is also a telephone, terrace, enclosed garden, and car park. Meals for residents three or four times a week. Open all year.
PRICES: s €57; d €65-€75; HB €52; dinner €20 **ON SITE:** Fishing Swimming pool Hiking **NEARBY:** Bathing (7km) Horse riding (5km) Golf (15km) Downhill skiing (35km) Tennis (1km) Railway station (5km) Shops (1km) CAVAILLON (5km) **NOTES:** No pets English spoken

ROUSSILLON

♦♦♦ La Bastide Basse P & J-P FRANCIN
84220 ROUSSILLON
☎ 04 90 05 77 76 & 06 07 96 21 38 🖷 04 90 05 77 76
e-mail: jean-philippe.francin@wanadoo.fr
Set in the hills, on six hectares of beautiful landscaped grounds, this fine, pleasantly restored mas offers a suite on the first floor, with a small lounge, one bedroom, and private bathroom and wc. Also, on the first floor there are a further two bedrooms, one with

continued

PROVENCE-ALPES-CÔTE-D'AZUR

private shower and wc, and one with private bathroom and wc. Electric heating. Open from 15 March to 15 October.

La Bastide Basse, Roussillon

PRICES: s €69-€105; d €72-€115; t €130; extra person €15 **ON SITE:** Swimming pool Hiking **NEARBY:** Horse riding (1km) Golf (25km) Fishing (10km) Tennis (3km) Railway station (35km) Shops (2km) APT (10km) **NOTES:** No pets English spoken

▓▓▓ La Bastide des Grand Cyprés Mary-José LAVAL
Hameau les Yves, 84220 ROUSSILLON
☎ 04 90 05 62 10 & 06 08 91 01 62 📠 04 90 05 70 41
e-mail: grands.cypres@wanadoo.fr
http://www.guideweb.com/provence/bb/grands-cypres
Come and stay in this large 18th-century farmhouse close to a hot-air ballooning centre. The property, with swimming pool and enclosed wooded garden, is in a very quiet hamlet with cherry trees. On the first floor, there are two bedrooms with shower and wc, and three on the second floor with similar facilities. There is central heating, a lounge with fireplace, library, TV, terrace and car park. Mountain bikes, table tennis, and boules. Open 1 March to 30 November, other periods if booked in advance.
PRICES: d €84-€105; extra person €23 **ON SITE:** Swimming pool Hiking **NEARBY:** Horse riding (3km) Golf (20km) Fishing (8km) Downhill skiing (40km) Tennis (3km) Railway station (37km) Shops (2km) APT (9km) **NOTES:** No pets English spoken

RUSTREL
▓▓▓ ⏹ La Forge Dominique BERGER-CECCALDI
Notre Dame des Anges, 84400 RUSTREL
☎ 04 90 04 92 22 📠 04 90 04 95 22
This large 19th-century building is a listed monument because of its blast furnace, and is situated on the edge of the Colorado Provençal forest. Accommodation consists of three bedrooms in an annexe with terraced lawn, bathrooms and private wcs. There is also a suite with bathroom and private wc. Gas central heating, shared living room, working fireplace, TV, telephone and barbecue. Garage and car park. Meals if reserved. Open from 1 March to 20 November and from 26 December to 10 January.
PRICES: s €74-€124; d €79-€129; t €120-€134; extra person €21; dinner €28 **ON SITE:** Swimming pool Hiking **NEARBY:** Bathing (7km) Horse riding (10km) Golf (35km) Fishing (7km) Tennis (7km) Railway station (30km) Shops (3km) APT (7km) **NOTES:** No pets English spoken

SABLET
▓▓▓ ⏹ Les Catalans Murièle CASAS
84110 SABLET
☎ 04 90 46 92 42
Interior and exterior access for these five bedrooms in the owners' country home with swimming pool, each with en suite facilities. There is also a dining room/verandah, electric heating, communal room, lounge, and a refrigerator at guests' disposal. Unfenced grounds. Open all year.

PRICES: d €41; dinner €18 **ON SITE:** Swimming pool **NEARBY:** Golf (10km) Fishing (2km) Hiking (1km) Tennis (1km) Shops (2km) VAISON LA ROMAINE (9km) **NOTES:** Pets admitted

SAIGNON
▓▓▓ La Pyramide
Rue du Jas, 84400 SAIGNON
☎ 04 90 04 70 00 📠 04 90 04 78 87
An attractive house with shared swimming pool, patio, and enclosed landscaped garden on the outskirts of a village offers the following accommodation: one bedroom on the garden level with bathroom and private wc, and two bedrooms on the ground floor with bathroom and private wc. On the first floor there is a further room with bathroom and private wc. Central heating. Shared living room, car park. Open all year.
PRICES: s €55-€59; d €59-€64; t €88; extra person €15 **ON SITE:** Swimming pool Hiking **NEARBY:** Bathing (4km) Horse riding (1km) Tennis (2km) Railway station (55km) APT (4km) **NOTES:** No pets English spoken

SARRIANS/VACQUEYRAS
▓▓▓ ⏹ Le Mas des Grandes Roques Sébastien LEJEUNE
Route de Vacqueyras, 84260 SARRIANS
☎ 04 90 12 39 42 📠 04 90 12 39 56

This typical restored *mas* at the foot of the Dentelles de Montmirail, on the Route du Vin, is in a calm setting of three hectares of trees, with ornamental garden, and private swimming pool. Here there are four bedrooms and a suite, each with private showers or bathrooms and wc. Central heating, dining room, bar area, reading room, TV and phone. Outside there is a shaded terrace and car park. Evening meals if booked in advance. Open all year.
PRICES: s €78; d €70-€82; t €91; extra person €17; dinner €20 **ON SITE:** Swimming pool Hiking **NEARBY:** Bathing (7km) Horse riding (5km) Golf (15km) Fishing (7km) Downhill skiing (30km) Tennis (7km) Railway station (30km) Shops (2km) CARPENTRAS (10km) **NOTES:** No pets English spoken

SAULT
▓▓▓ ⏹ Piedmoure M-Jeanne et J-Pierre BONNARD
Route de St-Christol, 84390 SAULT
☎ 04 90 64 09 22 📠 04 90 64 09 22
e-mail: piedmoure@caramail.com
A large independent 17th-century *mas*, set in woods and lavender fields overlooking the Croc valley, offers three bedrooms on the first floor with bathroom, shower, and private wc. There is a further room with shower and private wc. Floor and fuel heating, shared living room, TV, terrace and enclosed garden. Open all year.
PRICES: d €58-€64; extra person €18; dinner €20 **ON SITE:** Hiking **NEARBY:** Horse riding (10km) Swimming pool (3km) Downhill skiing (25km) Tennis (3km) Railway station (70km) Shops (3km) SAULT (3km) **NOTES:** Pets admitted with conditions

continued

SEGURET

₩₩ Domaine St-Just Jacqueline MONTJEAN
Route de Vaison, 84110 SEGURET
☎ 04 90 46 11 55
A beautiful *mas*, on a hill with a fine view, and interior courtyard,
proposes five bedrooms on the second floor with private showers
and wc. There is also electric heating, a shared living room and
dining room. Open from 1 April to 15 October.
PRICES: s €30; d €43; t €49-€53; extra person €7 **NEARBY:** Horse riding
(10km) Golf (20km) Fishing (3km) Swimming pool (5km) Hiking (10km)
Tennis (5km) Shops (2km) VAISON LA ROMAINE (5km) **NOTES:** Pets
admitted

₩₩₩ St-Jean Gisèle AUGIER
84110 SEGURET
☎ 04 90 46 91 76   📠 04 90 46 83 88

This fine, Italian inspired residence set in a very attractive park
with swimming pool, has a wonderful view. On the ground
floor there are two suites with refrigerator, TV, shower and
wc, one of which also has a telephone and a terrace with
private verandah. On the first floor there is a bedroom with
refrigerator, TV, telephone, shower and wc. Central heating,
shared living room, dining room/lounge, library, terrace,
unfenced grounds and car park. Refined, varied and generous
breakfasts. Mountain bike rental 6 km. Climbing club 10 km.
Small animals accepted: 7.62 euros per day. Open all year.
PRICES: s €63-€76; d €76-€90; t €100-€110; extra person €18
ON SITE: Swimming pool **NEARBY:** Bathing (4km) Horse riding
(14km) Fishing (4km) Tennis (1km) Railway station (20km) Shops
(2km) VAISON LA ROMAINE (6km) **NOTES:** Pets admitted English
spoken

ST-DIDIER

₩₩ ⌇◯⌇ Le Mas des Abricotiers Christine DUBUC
193 chemin des Terres Mortes, 84210 ST-DIDIER
☎ 04 90 66 19 16   📠 04 90 66 19 22
e-mail: abricotier@bleu-provence.com
http://www.bleu-provence.com
Very attractive surroundings for this independent *mas* on the
outskirts of a village, with swimming pool, enclosed courtyard and
large grounds planted with apricot trees. View of Mont-Ventoux
and Dentelles de Montmirail. Three bedrooms, one of which has a
mezzanine, with private showers and wc. Two bedrooms with
bathroom and wc. Central heating, dining room with TV, summer
kitchen. Enclosed car park. Meals twice a week. Open all year.
PRICES: s €73-€92; d €59-€84; extra person €20; dinner €25
ON SITE: Swimming pool Hiking **NEARBY:** Horse riding (2km) Golf
(10km) Downhill skiing (30km) Tennis (1km) Railway station (23km)
Shops (1km) CARPENTRAS (9km) **NOTES:** No pets English spoken
                                        See advert on this page

Le Mas des Abricotiers
193 Chemin des Terres Mortes
84210 St Didier

Christine and Jean-Michel Dubuc welcome you to their
Provence home, near Luberon. Situated 800 metres from the
centre of the village it commands wonderful views of Mont
Ventoux and the "Laces of Montmirail". You will find calm and
relaxation in the shade of apricot trees, around the swimming
pool or under the almond tree in courtyard. All the beautiful
large bedrooms are non-smoking and en-suite. The five
rooms, each named after a tree, is individually and tastefully
decorated. A delightful breakfast includes homemade jams
and pastries along with local regional products. A warm
welcome and a family atmosphere await you.
Tel: 00 33 4 90 66 19 16   Fax: 00 33 4 90 66 19 22
Web: www.bleu-provence.com

ST-PIERRE-DE-VASSOLS

₩₩₩ La Barjaquière
Ghislaine ANDRE et D PONCET
84330 ST-PIERRE-DE-VASSOLS
☎ 04 90 62 48 00 & 06 16 33 21 05   📠 04 90 62 48 06
e-mail: dponcet@club-internet.fr www.barjaquiere.com

Prepare to be seduced by the charm and refined décor of this
very fine 17th-century house, in a privileged setting at the foot
of Mount Ventoux. There are three bedrooms with private
bathroom facilities, one of which has a power shower. The
two suites also have private facilities, and one benefits from a
balcony. Lounges, terraces, Provençal bistro, patio,
conservatory, indoor and outdoor swimming pools, sauna,
gym. Open all year except 15 January to 15 February and 20
November to 10 December.
PRICES: s €110-€170; d €110-€170; t €195; extra person €15
ON SITE: Swimming pool Hiking **NEARBY:** Bathing (5km) Horse
riding (6km) Golf (30km) Fishing (5km) Downhill skiing (20km)
Tennis (6km) Railway station (40km) Shops (3km) CARPENTRAS
(8km) **NOTES:** No pets English spoken

ST-SATURNIN-LES-AVIGNON

♥♥♥ |O| Le Mas de l'Amandier
Nadine et Philippe AUGIER
102 impasse des Centenaires,
84450 ST-SATURNIN-LES-AVIGNON
☎ 04 90 22 02 77
e-mail: le.mas.de.l.amandier@wanadoo.fr
http://www.lemasdelamandier.com
Village house in a large enclosed courtyard with swimming pool
and summer house. The bedrooms are in an annexe. The four
bedrooms have private shower, wc and terrace. Central heating
and air conditioning. Dining room with working fireplace, library
and TV, enclosed garden, car park, evening meals available if
booked. Private hunting possible. Open all year.
PRICES: s €75; d €84; extra person €15; dinner €23; HB €69; FB €76
ON SITE: Swimming pool **NEARBY:** Horse riding (8km) Golf (5km)
Fishing (8km) Hiking (10km) Tennis (1km) Railway station (8km)
AVIGNON (8km) **NOTES:** No pets English spoken

♥♥♥ |O| Les Gendalis Edith BACULARD
Chemin des Gendalis, 84450 ST-SATURNIN-LES-AVIGNON
☎ 04 90 22 07 54 & 06 13 21 26 33 📠 04 90 22 05 78
This accommodation can be found on part of a large property with
enclosed wooded garden of 2000 m² and swimming pool. There
are five bedrooms on the ground floor with independent access,
shower and private wc. Gas central heating and air conditioning.
Shared living room with fireplace and terrace. Open all year.
PRICES: s €64; d €64; t €79; dinner €23 **ON SITE:** Swimming pool
NEARBY: Horse riding (7km) Golf (5km) Fishing (4km) Hiking (20km)
Tennis (1km) Railway station (10km) Shops (2km) AVIGNON (10km)
NOTES: No pets English spoken

UCHAUX

♥♥♥ |O| La Cabanole Leen et Patrick DEBLAERE
Beauchamp, 84100 UCHAUX
☎ 04 90 30 07 28 📠 04 90 30 08 75
e-mail: deblaere.cabanole@wanadoo.fr
Castle farmhouse with swimming pool, set in vineyards and olive
groves in an area of cultural and tourist interest. There are five
bedrooms, two of which are for four people, with private
bathroom facilities. Floor and electric heating, shared reception
room with working fireplace. Dining room, library, TV and
telephone if requested. Enclosed grounds, terrace, car park. Open
from 15 March to 15 November.
PRICES: s €69-€84; d €79-€96; t €105; extra person €15; dinner €14-€21
ON SITE: Swimming pool Hiking **NEARBY:** Horse riding (1km) Golf
(12km) Tennis (4km) Railway station (40km) Shops (7km) ORANGE
(12km) **NOTES:** No pets CC English spoken

VACQUEYRAS

♥♥♥ Domaine l'Ousteau des Lecques Claude CHABRAN
84190 VACQUEYRAS
☎ 04 90 65 84 51 📠 04 90 65 81 19
Close to a hamlet, this residence is set amidst vineyards and has a
covered swimming pool (open from April to October). Six
bedrooms with private showers and wc. Electric and central
heating, shared sitting room, living room and air-conditioned
lounge and dining room. TV, washing machine, refrigerator and
kitchen. Car park, open grounds, garden furniture and barbecue
on the terrace. Lake and forest 10 km. Discover Provençal flora at
the botanical garden 50 m away. Restaurant 600 m. Child's cot
available at 7.62 euros. Open 1 March to 31 October.
PRICES: d €43-€46; t €55-€59 **ON SITE:** Bathing Swimming pool
Hiking **NEARBY:** Horse riding (4km) Golf (20km) Fishing (4km)
Downhill skiing (30km) Tennis (1km) Railway station (15km) Shops (1km)
BEAUMES DE VENISE (4km) **NOTES:** No pets

VAISON-LA-ROMAINE

♥♥♥ Chambre d'hôtes Aude VERDIER
Rue de l'évêché, Haute Ville, 84110 VAISON-LA-ROMAINE
☎ 04 90 36 13 46 📠 04 90 36 32 43
e-mail: eveche@aol.com http://eveche.free.fr
The medieval town of Vaison-la-Romaine is the location of this
18th-century restored house of character. There are three first-floor
bedrooms with private bath or shower rooms, wc and telephone,
and one on the second floor offering the same facilities. Heating,
shared living room and lounge with working fireplace. Terrace with
superb view of the new town. Swimming pool and tennis court in
the town. Mountain bikes available. Open all year.
PRICES: s €56-€66; d €66-€73; t €98 **NEARBY:** Bathing (5km) Horse
riding (5km) Swimming pool (1km) Hiking (1km) Tennis (1km) Railway
station (20km) **NOTES:** No pets English spoken

♥♥♥ Château de Taulignan Michel DAILLET
St-Marcellin les Vaison, 84110 VAISON-LA-ROMAINE
☎ 04 90 28 71 16 📠 04 90 28 75 04
e-mail: chateau@pacwan.fr http://www.chateaudetaulignan.com
The 15th-century Château de Taulignan is rurally set in 10 hectares
of grounds, which include a swimming pool, terrace, open
parkland with mature trees, fountains and ornamental ponds.
Three of the suites have a small sitting room, private bathroom
and wc. Two further suites have private bathrooms and wc. Central
heating, shared living room, satellite TV, fridge, open fires, library
and card telephone. Car park, animals admitted under certain
conditions, forest 200 m. Reduced rates for long stays and in
winter. Open all year.
PRICES: s €53-€105; d €53-€105; t €69-€120; extra person €15
ON SITE: Swimming pool **NEARBY:** Bathing (10km) Horse riding (5km)
Golf (30km) Fishing (1km) Hiking (1km) Downhill skiing (25km) Tennis
(2km) Railway station (30km) Shops (2km) VAISON LA ROMAINE (2km)
NOTES: Pets admitted English spoken

♥♥♥ La Calade C HAGGAI et R TERRISSE
St-Romain en Viennois, 84110 VAISON-LA-ROMAINE
☎ 04 90 46 51 79 📠 04 90 46 51 82
http://www.avignon-et-provence.com

Town house with enclosed courtyard and roof terrace accessible at
the end of the day. One bedroom on the first floor with shower
and private wc. Two bedrooms on the second floor with shower
and wc. A further bedroom on the second floor with bathroom
and wc. Central heating, shared living room with fireplace and
library. Open from Easter to 15 November.
PRICES: s €60; d €70 **ON SITE:** Hiking **NEARBY:** Bathing (15km)
Horse riding (5km) Golf (30km) Fishing (2km) Swimming pool (3km)
Downhill skiing (25km) Tennis (3km) Railway station (45km) Shops
(3km) VAISON LA ROMAINE (3km) **NOTES:** No pets English spoken

---

CC - credit cards accepted

VALREAS

♥♥♥ ¡O¡ Domaine les Grands Devers
Paul-Henri BOUCHARD
84600 VALREAS
☎ 04 90 35 15 98 📠 04 90 37 49 56
e-mail: phbouchard@grandsdevers.com
http://www.grandsdevers.com
This house is situated in the heart of a 69-hectare private estate (vines, truffles and woodland). There are four bedrooms on the first floor with shower and wc. Underfloor heating, shared living room, dining room, working fireplace, TV and telephone. Terrace, car park and grounds. Meals available every other day. Truffle museum at St-Paul-Trois-Châteaux. University of wine at Suze. Open all year, including the truffle season (your hosts can take you truffle hunting), but advisable to book.
PRICES: s €48; d €53; extra person €10; dinner €17 **NEARBY:** Bathing (6km) Horse riding (10km) Golf (25km) Fishing (6km) Swimming pool (6km) Hiking (1km) Tennis (6km) Shops (6km) VALREAS (6km)
NOTES: Pets admitted English spoken

VAUGINES

♥♥♥ L'Eléphant de Vaugines Thierry CHOME
Les Trailles, 84160 VAUGINES
☎ 04 90 77 15 85 & 02 75 67 37 31 📠 04 90 77 14 13
http://www.ibicenter.com
Quality contemporary villa with swimming pool, situated on a hill with several tree-lined terraces and an attractive view of the Durance valley. Three bedrooms on the ground floor with shower and wc, plus one suite (two bedrooms) with bathroom, kitchen and wc. On the first floor there is a further bedroom with shower and wc. Electric heating, shared living room with working fireplace, TV and library. Open grounds, car park and garage for four cars. Table tennis and pétanque. Open all year.
PRICES: s €76; d €76-€220; HB €61 **ON SITE:** Swimming pool Hiking
NEARBY: Bathing (10km) Horse riding (10km) Golf (35km) Tennis (2km) Railway station (60km) Shops (1km) LOURMARIN (5km)
NOTES: No pets (small dogs accepted) English spoken

♥♥♥ Les Grandes Garrigues Paule et Michel MATTEI
Route de Cadenet, 84160 VAUGINES
☎ 04 90 77 10 71 & 06 10 01 31 96
Old Provençal *mas* in the country with swimming pool, panoramic views of the Lubéron, St-Victoire and the Alpilles. Five ground-floor bedrooms, one of which has a lounge, with independent entrances, TV, shower, wc and private terrace. Animals admitted by prior arrangement. Boules area and start of walking trails. Summer kitchen for fine weather. Open all year.
PRICES: s €61-€84; d €69-€91; t €99-€105; extra person €15
ON SITE: Swimming pool Hiking **NEARBY:** Bathing (5km) Horse riding (3km) Golf (15km) Fishing (5km) Tennis (3km) Railway station (50km) Shops (3km) LOURMARIN (3km) **NOTES:** Pets admitted English spoken

VEDENE

♥♥♥ La Jelotte Fabienne LACKER
62 rue du Pélican, 84270 VEDENE
☎ 04 32 40 93 31 & 06 03 11 14 24 📠 04 32 40 93 31
e-mail: jelotte@hotmail.com http://www.jelotte.com
Eighteenth-century residence in the heart of a village with a courtyard to the south, an enclosed garden with trees and swimming pool. One large suite (two bedrooms) with shower and wc and two large bedrooms with mezzanine bath or shower room and wc. Lounge, library, video. Secure parking. Open all year.
PRICES: s €75; d €75; t €95-€130 **ON SITE:** Swimming pool Tennis
NEARBY: Horse riding (2km) Golf (2km) Fishing (2km) Hiking (30km) Downhill skiing (50km) Railway station (7km) AVIGNON (7km)
NOTES: No pets English spoken

VELLERON

♥♥♥ ¡O¡ Villa Velleron Simone SANDERS et Wim VISSER
84740 VELLERON
☎ 04 90 20 12 31 📠 04 90 20 10 34
e-mail: Villa.Velleron@wanadoo.fr
An old olive oil mill with enclosed courtyard has been converted into a village house with terraced garden and swimming pool. On the first floor there are four bedrooms with bathroom and wc. There are two bedrooms in an annexe, of which one has a mezzanine and open fireplace, with bathroom, wc and private terrace. Electric heating, communal room, lounge, dining room, working fireplace, library, TV and telephone. Car park. Open Easter to 1 November.
PRICES: d €85-€105; dinner €26 **ON SITE:** Swimming pool
NEARBY: Horse riding (1km) Golf (8km) Fishing (1km) Hiking (2km) Downhill skiing (30km) Tennis (1km) Railway station (6km) ISLE SUR SORGUE (6km) **NOTES:** No pets English spoken

VENASQUE

♥♥♥ Chambre d'hôtes Régis BOREL
Quartier du Camp-Long, 84210 VENASQUE
☎ 04 90 66 03 56 & 06 03 16 44 36 📠 04 90 66 60 34
e-mail: camplong84@aol.com
http://members.aol.com/camplong84
Restored farm in the hills near woods, with swimming pool. Four bedrooms with shower and wc and one with bathroom and wc. Central heating, lounge with video, hi-fi, TV, shared living room, refrigerator, microwave and grill. Open shaded garden with barbecue and car park. Hiking trails from the premises (GR 91), footpaths marked for shorter walks. Restaurant 3 km. Open all year.
PRICES: s €42-€46; d €46-€50; t €55; extra person €10; HB €38
ON SITE: Swimming pool Hiking **NEARBY:** Bathing (12km) Horse riding (4km) Golf (10km) Fishing (12km) Tennis (3km) Railway station (30km) Shops (3km) PERNES LES FONTAINES (12km) **NOTES:** No pets

♥♥♥ ¡O¡ La Maison aux Volets Bleus Martine MARET
Le Village, 84210 VENASQUE
☎ 04 90 66 03 04 📠 04 90 66 16 14
e-mail: voletbleu@AOL.COM

A Provençal house of character in a village with an exceptional panoramic view. Four bedrooms with bathroom and wc. Central heating, shared reception room, living room, lounge and working fireplace. Floral garden, terrace and tennis court. Hiking and hunting from the premises. Evening meals for residents on Mondays, Wednesdays and Saturdays. Drinks extra. Open 15 March to 3 November.
PRICES: ; d €72-€88; t €100-€108; extra person €20; dinner €23
ON SITE: Hiking Tennis **NEARBY:** Bathing (10km) Horse riding (2km) Golf (10km) Fishing (10km) Swimming pool (3km) Railway station (30km) CARPENTRAS (12km) **NOTES:** Pets admitted English spoken

🍴 La Tour du Pinet Eve et Jean-Claude CHIROUSE
84210 VENASQUE
☎ 04 90 66 60 80 📠 04 90 66 64 21
http://www.venasquebb.com
This independent villa in the hills with swimming pool offers one suite on the ground floor with bathroom and wc, plus a further two bedrooms with bathroom and wc. Central heating, shared living room, dining room and working fireplace. Bedrooms accessible from both exterior and interior. Terrace, car park, open grounds of three hectares. Meals available in season when offered by your hostess. Open all year.
PRICES: s €56-€75; d €56-€75; t €75-€105; dinner €18
ON SITE: Swimming pool Hiking **NEARBY:** Horse riding (4km) Golf (12km) Fishing (18km) Downhill skiing (40km) Tennis (4km) Railway station (40km) Shops (2km) CARPENTRAS (12km) **NOTES:** Pets admitted English spoken

Maison Provençale Gérard et Jany RUEL
Le Village, 84210 VENASQUE
☎ 04 90 66 02 84 📠 04 90 66 61 32
e-mail: maisonprovencale@freesurf.fr

You will find this Provençal house opposite the village post office. Four bedrooms with shower and wc and one bedroom with kitchenette, shower and wc. Fuel central heating, living room, TV and kitchen; cooking possible. Terrace with flowers and panoramic view, enclosed garden and car park. Restaurant within 200 m. Forest and hunting on the premises. Open February to 31 December.
PRICES: s €35-€38; d €41-€55; t €53-€58 **ON SITE:** Hiking Tennis
NEARBY: Bathing (7km) Horse riding (5km) Golf (7km) Fishing (10km) Swimming pool (5km) Railway station (10km) SAINT DIDIER (5km)
NOTES: Pets admitted English spoken

VIOLES

La Farigoule Augustine CORNAZ
Le Plan de Dieu, 84150 VIOLES
☎ 04 90 70 91 78 📠 04 90 70 91 78
Beautiful 18th-century restored farm amidst vineyards with an interior courtyard. One bedroom on the first floor with shower and wc. On the second floor there is a bedroom with shower, wc, kitchen and lounge. Three further bedrooms with shower and wc. Electric heating, lounge with radio, TV, library with local maps and guidebooks. Generous breakfasts served in a beautiful vaulted hall. Summer kitchen, telephone, car park, terrace, barbecue and bicycles. The owners are booksellers. Open 1 April to 31 October.
PRICES: s €34-€50; d €41-€50; t €56-€63; extra person €12
NEARBY: Bathing (2km) Horse riding (5km) Golf (8km) Fishing (2km) Swimming pool (5km) Hiking (5km) Tennis (5km) Railway station (10km) Shops (2km) ORANGE (10km) **NOTES:** No pets

---

VISAN

Château Vert Christian et Josiane TORTEL
84820 VISAN
☎ 04 90 41 91 21 📠 04 90 41 94 63
This Templar knights' farm has been converted into guest rooms overlooking a terrace, olive groves and swimming pool. There is also an 18th-century château in the wooded park. Two ground-floor bedrooms with shower and wc. Three first-floor bedrooms with shower and wc. Shared living room with working fireplace, library and TV at guests' disposal. Terrace. Open all year.
PRICES: d €61-€69 **ON SITE:** Swimming pool Hiking
NEARBY: Horse riding (9km) Fishing (6km) Tennis (6km) Railway station (35km) Shops (6km) VALREAS (6km) **NOTES:** No pets

---

VITROLLES-EN-LUBERON

🍴 Le Tombareau Pierre BRUZZO
84240 VITROLLES-EN-LUBERON
☎ 04 90 77 84 26
http://perso.wanadoo.fr/tombareau

An old renovated sheepfold with stacks of charm, in grounds of three hectares with swimming pool, shady terraces, a verdant, rural setting with horses. Two quiet bedrooms and one spacious suite, each with its own bathroom and wc. Shared living room with piano, games, TV, library, fridge and solarium. Central heating and open fire. Car park. Open mid February to mid November.
PRICES: d €60; extra person €15; dinner €20 **ON SITE:** Swimming pool Hiking **NEARBY:** Bathing (15km) Horse riding (12km) Golf (18km) Fishing (10km) Tennis (7km) Railway station (75km) Shops (7km) PERTUIS (18km) **NOTES:** Pets admitted English spoken

RHÔNE-ALPES

AIN

ARBIGNY

♦♦♦♦ Les Ormes Jacques BARDAY
Sci les Fins Palais, 01190 ARBIGNY
☎ 03 85 30 69 00 & 03 85 30 34 72　🖷 03 85 30 69 00
e-mail: jabarday@aol.com
A detached stone-built house on the edge of a village which is on the Route de la Bresse and 5km from a river port. There are five rooms in two self-catering cottages, one twin with bathroom and wc, three doubles with shower and wc and one en suite room at garden level. Guests have use of a lounge, library and games room with table tennis and billiards. There is a reduced rate for bookings of more than five days. There is a restaurant 2.5 km away. Open all year.
PRICES: s €27; d €40; t €55　**ON SITE:** Hiking Tennis
NEARBY: Bathing (4km) Golf (15km) Fishing (4km) Swimming pool (1km) Railway station (22km) Shops (5km) PONT DE VAUX (5km)
NOTES: Pets admitted CC

BRENS

♦♦♦♦ ♥ ○ Le Petit Brens Noel et Monique VEYRON
01300 BRENS
☎ 04 79 81 90 95　🖷 04 79 81 90 95
Four rooms in the owners' farmhouse on the first floor and in the attic, with views over the Alps, Monts du Bugey and the Rhone. 3km from Belley and near Aix-les-Bains, on the Bugey wine and ovens trail. The rooms have independent access from a large terrace. Two double and two twin rooms, each with a shower and wc. The two attic rooms have air-conditioning. The guest living room with kitchenette is in the attic. The table d'hote meals are served in the country-style dining room using home-grown produce. There is a large, well maintained garden, with furniture, and pets are welcome (a supplement is payable). Open 20 December to 15 November.
PRICES: s €31; d €37; t €47; extra person €11; HB €42; dinner €12
NEARBY: Bathing (10km) Horse riding (6km) Golf (30km) Fishing (2km) Swimming pool (3km) Hiking (3km) Cross-country skiing (20km) Downhill skiing (35km) Tennis (3km) Railway station (15km) Shops (3km) BELLEY (3km)　**NOTES:** Pets admitted English spoken

CHATILLON SUR CHALARONNE

♦♦♦♦ Chambre d'hôtes Alain et Solange SALMON
150, place du Champ de Foire,
01400 CHATILLON SUR CHALARONNE
☎ 04 74 55 06 86　🖷 04 74 55 42 56
e-mail: alsalmon@club-internet.fr

This character house is in the centre of the historic, flower-filled town on the tourist lakes route. First-floor double, twin and bunk-bed rooms, grades 2 and 3, with television and telephone. Additional beds and cot available. There is a fully equipped kitchen and lounge for guests. Enclosed garden, parking, games. Beautifully presented breakfasts with galettes and a huge selection of local jams. There is a restaurant 150m away. Closed between Christmas and New Year.
PRICES: s €36; d €45; t €61; extra person €16　**ON SITE:** Fishing Swimming pool Hiking Tennis　**NEARBY:** Horse riding (4km) Golf (15km) Railway station (25km) BOURG EN BRESSE (25km)　**NOTES:** No pets English spoken

CHAZEY SUR AIN

♦♦♦♦ ♥ L'Hopital P et M DEBENEY-TRUCHON
01150 CHAZEY SUR AIN
☎ 04 74 61 95 87　🖷 04 74 61 95 87
Six independent rooms in two buildings on a flower-filled country small holding in a hamlet. One double, one twin and one family room each with a shower room and wc. Two grade 2 rooms (one double, one twin) with a private shower room each and a shared wc. Additional bed and cot are available. There is a large lounge, a kitchenette and a reading corner for guests with a log fire, a barbecue, children's games and pétanque. There is a garden and enclosed courtyard and pets are welcome, supplement payable. And there is a restaurant 1km away. Open all year.
PRICES: s €28; d €37; t €46; extra person €8　**ON SITE:** Hiking
NEARBY: Bathing (10km) Horse riding (9km) Golf (12km) Fishing (2km) Swimming pool (10km) Tennis (1km) Railway station (8km) Shops (1km) AMBERIEU EN BUGEY (9km)　**NOTES:** Pets admitted

GERMAGNAT

♦♦♦♦ ○ Le Tillerey Mike et Hiroko MOORE
01250 GERMAGNAT
☎ 04 74 51 73 70　🖷 04 74 51 73 70
Three rooms on the first floor of the owners' house on the edge of this pretty Revermont village. A lush and peaceful place near the Jura and the Bresse tourist route with waterfalls, forests and lakes. There are two twin rooms and one single, each with a bathroom and wc. Guest lounge, terrace and a garden with outdoor furniture; also a field and stream. Beautifully presented breakfasts are offered and table d'hôte meals can be reserved, with Asian food a speciality. Zen themed weekends. Open March to November.
PRICES: s €45; d €45-€70; extra person €15; dinner €15
ON SITE: Fishing Hiking　**NEARBY:** Bathing (15km) Horse riding (3km) Golf (25km) Swimming pool (24km) Tennis (7km) Railway station (25km) Shops (5km) CHAVANNES SUR SURAN　**NOTES:** No pets English spoken

GIRON

♦♦♦♦ ○ Le Bellevue Martine et Pierre BOUVARD
01130 GIRON
☎ 04 50 59 89 42
A large house in the heart of a village in the Parc Naturel Régional du Haut Jura. Three beautifully decorated rooms on the first floor with independent access. One double and one twin room with private bathrooms with spa baths and wc. One double room with massage shower and private wc. All the rooms are non-smoking. There is a large library, lounge/diner with TV and large terrace with a beautiful open aspect overlooking the sheltered flower

continued　　　　　　　continued

RHÔNE-ALPES

garden, where in summer meals can be enjoyed. Table d'hôte evening meals can be reserved. Open all year.
PRICES: s €40; d €46; extra person €14; dinner €16 **ON SITE:** Hiking Cross-country skiing Tennis **NEARBY:** Bathing (12km) Horse riding (6km) Golf (25km) Fishing (5km) Swimming pool (20km) Downhill skiing (17km) Shops (9km) BELLEGARDE (20km) **NOTES:** No pets English spoken

GRAND ABERGEMENT

🗤 🐓 🍽 La Ferme des Routes
Claude et Maryse BALLET
Les Routes, 01260 LE GRAND ABERGEMENT
☎ 04 79 87 65 76 📠 04 79 87 65 76
Home of the world biathlon championships, in a traditional, secluded farm that has a cross-country ski instructor in season. Four rooms on the first and second floors, one with three single beds, one with a double and a single, one with four single beds, one suite with a double and three single beds. Each room has a shower room and wc. There is a shared lounge with a huge fireplace and bread oven. Facilities on offer including ski and skate hire, a cross-country ski course for beginners, orienteering, trekking and biathlon. Open all year.
PRICES: s €17-€19; d €34-€36; t €50-€52; HB €27-€30; dinner €11-€12
ON SITE: Hiking Cross-country skiing **NEARBY:** Bathing (20km) Horse riding (10km) Fishing (10km) Swimming pool (20km) Downhill skiing (4km) Tennis (4km) Railway station (25km) Shops (8km) CULOZ (25km)
NOTES: No pets English spoken

MIJOUX

🗤 🍽 Le Boulu Bernard et Claire GROSFILLEY
01410 MIJOUX
☎ 04 50 41 31 47
A historic farmhouse renovated by the owner on the edge of the Valserine at the foot of the Jura's snowy peaks, between the ski resorts of Mijoux-La Faucille and Lélex-Crozet. The rooms are on the first and second floors of this house each with a private bathroom and wc. Two rooms with either double or twin beds and two rooms with a double and twin beds, one room with a double and a single bed. There is a lounge with a fireplace and ample breakfasts on offer. Long stays are bookable with holiday tax supplement. Open Christmas to Easter and July to August.
PRICES: d €50; t €65; extra person €8; HB €40; dinner €17
ON SITE: Fishing Hiking Cross-country skiing **NEARBY:** Bathing (20km) Horse riding (4km) Golf (6km) Swimming pool (12km) Downhill skiing (4km) Tennis (4km) Railway station (30km) Shops (4km) GEX (24km)
NOTES: No pets English spoken

MONTCET

🗤 🍽 Les Vignes J.Louis et Eliane GAYET
01310 MONTCET
☎ 04 74 24 23 13 📠 04 74 24 23 13
e-mail: jean-louis.gayet2@libertysurf.fr
An old, restored Bressan farm in peaceful parkland with a fishing lake, private swimming pool and games field and the chance to see some Roman art. The accommodation is next to the owners' house with independent access. Four comfortable first floor, non-smoking rooms, with either double or twin beds, shower room and wc. There is a lounge, television room, video and library available, a courtyard, parking, table tennis and volleyball. Reservations can be made for table d'hôte meals with free meals for children under four. Healthy menus. Open all year.
PRICES: s €40; d €50; t €58; dinner €18 **ON SITE:** Fishing Swimming pool Hiking **NEARBY:** Horse riding (12km) Golf (12km) Tennis (12km) Railway station (12km) Shops (2km) BOURG EN BRESSE (12km)
NOTES: No pets English spoken

NEUVILLE SUR AIN

🗤 Bosseron Annie RIVOIRE
325, rte de Geneve, 01160 NEUVILLE SUR AIN
☎ 04 74 37 77 06 📠 04 74 37 77 06
e-mail: arivoire@free.fr

A house of character on the banks of the Ain River set in two hectares. Four well decorated, second floor rooms each with a bathroom or shower room and a wc. There are two twin rooms, two doubles, two large lounges with fireplaces, piano, television, and library. Generous breakfasts are served looking out over the river. Fishing, swimming, table tennis, billiards, and weights are all available on site. Direct access to municipal tennis courts. Nearby are the GR59, the Tour du Revermont, local crafts and a restaurant 300m. Open all year.
PRICES: s €42; d €50 **ON SITE:** Bathing Fishing Hiking Tennis **NEARBY:** Horse riding (2km) Golf (15km) Swimming pool (12km) Cross-country skiing (20km) Downhill skiing (23km) Railway station (6km) Shops (1km) PONT D'AIN (6km) **NOTES:** No pets English spoken

ORDONNAZ

🗤 Chambre d'hôtes Bernard GRINAND
la ville d'en Bas, 01510 ORDONNAZ
☎ 04 74 40 90 79
A peaceful location near a mountain village. Three rooms on the first and second floors of a renovated building that includes two self-catering cottages, next to the owner's country hotel. One twin and two doubles, each with a shower room and wc. A cot is available. There is a guest lounge and large open area outside with garden furniture. Full or half-board bookings and take-away snacks provided. Enjoy the summer activities and local festivals and visit the dairy in the village. Open all year.
PRICES: s €29-€32; d €35-€40; extra person €11; dinner €11
ON SITE: Hiking Cross-country skiing Tennis **NEARBY:** Bathing (15km) Horse riding (20km) Fishing (12km) Swimming pool (20km) Downhill skiing (50km) Railway station (12km) Shops (12km) Restaurant nearby BELLEY (20km) **NOTES:** Pets admitted CC

🗤 🐓 Le Charveyron Rene et Michele LARACINE
01510 ORDONNAZ ☎ 04 74 40 90 20

Three rooms on the level in a detached house on the edge of the

continued

village - also with a self-catering cottage. Two double rooms and one twin with a shower and wc in each room. Television corner and books for guest use. There is parking, a terrace, a field and stabling may be available. The GR59 is nearby and a lake 11km away. Open February to November.
PRICES: s €31; d €36; extra person €8 **ON SITE:** Hiking Cross-country skiing **NEARBY:** Bathing (11km) Horse riding (20km) Fishing (11km) Swimming pool (20km) Downhill skiing (50km) Tennis (1km) Railway station (10km) Shops (12km) Restaurant nearby BELLEY (20km)
NOTES: No pets

SAINT ANDRE D'HUIRIAT

♥♥♥ ⏃ Château de Bourdonnel
Paule BRAC DE LA PERRIERE
01290 ST ANDRE D'HUIRIAT
☎ 04 74 50 03 40　🖷 04 74 50 22 29
Five rooms on the first floor of this château in wooded parkland. There are two grade 3 rooms for two or three people and one grade 2 twin room, each with a shower room and private wc. There is also one children's room. In the summer there are two grade 1 rooms, one with four single beds, one with two single beds. A cot is available. Facilities include a communal lounge and dining room, a private swimming pool, parking, a courtyard and enclosed grounds. Open all year.
PRICES: s €30-€36; d €40-€46; extra person €16; dinner €17
ON SITE: Swimming pool Hiking **NEARBY:** Bathing (12km) Horse riding (12km) Golf (15km) Tennis (6km) Railway station (17km) Shops (6km) MACON (17km) **NOTES:** Pets admitted English spoken

SAINT ETIENNE SUR REYSSOUZE

♥♥♥ ⏃ Le Vert Bocage Georges et Arlette CHERVET
01190 ST ETIENNE SUR REYSSOUZE
☎ 03 85 30 97 27　🖷 03 85 30 97 27
e-mail: levertbocage@oreka.com
Five non-smoking rooms on the first floor of this typical Bressan house, set in peaceful, secluded woodland. There are two grade 3 rooms for three people each with shower room and wc. Three grade 2 rooms for two to three people with private shower rooms and two shared wcs. All with independent access from an outside staircase. Reservations must be made for evening gourmet and wholefood table d'hôte meals. The non-smoking dining room is available for use by guests throughout the day. There is garden furniture and a pond. Discounts for stays of 3 nights or more. Open all year by reservation.
PRICES: s €32-€38; d €38-€44; t €50-€58; extra person €5; HB €58; dinner €12-€18 **ON SITE:** Hiking **NEARBY:** Bathing (6km) Horse riding (17km) Golf (15km) Fishing (2km) Swimming pool (5km) Tennis (4km) Railway station (20km) Shops (5km) MACON (20km) **NOTES:** Pets admitted

SAINT MARTIN DE BAVEL

♥♥♥ ♥ ⏃ Les Charmettes Juliette VINCENT
la Vellaz, 01510 ST MARTIN DE BAVEL
☎ 04 79 87 32 18　🖷 04 79 87 34 51
Three rooms on the ground floor of a renovated farm building. One double room, room with one double and one single bed and one room with three single beds, each with a private shower room and wc. One room with disabled access. Lounge and dining room for guests. Kitchen with four microwaves and washing machine for guest use. Large courtyard, parking, orchard and lawn. Situated at the gateway to Savoie and in the heart of Bugey and the Marais de Lavours. Discounts offered for long-stay and groups. Open all year.
PRICES: s €30; d €37; t €47; extra person €11 **ON SITE:** Hiking **NEARBY:** Bathing (5km) Horse riding (3km) Fishing (3km) Swimming pool (4km) Cross-country skiing (20km) Downhill skiing (20km) Tennis (3km) Shops (3km) BELLEY (12km) **NOTES:** Pets admitted English spoken

SAINT TRIVIER SUR MOIGNANS

♥♥♥ ⏃ Domaine de Paspierre
Paskale JUILLAC-BERNAND
Pampra, 01990 ST TRIVIER SUR MOIGNANS
☎ 04 74 55 90 29　🖷 04 74 55 90 29
e-mail: paspierre@free.fr
There are five rooms on the first floor of this charming, restored farm. Two double rooms with a sitting area, one room with double and bunk beds, two rooms for four with a mezzanine. Each room has a shower room, satellite TV and telephone socket. Indoor facilities include a ground-floor dining room, a reading corner, an open fire, a piano, a billiard table and table tennis. Outside is a verandah, a swimming pool and a tennis court. Table d'hôte meals served in the evenings only. Parking available. Open all year.
PRICES: s €46; d €58; t €73; extra person €15; dinner €19
ON SITE: Swimming pool Hiking Tennis **NEARBY:** Bathing (10km) Horse riding (20km) Golf (10km) Fishing (10km) Railway station (15km) Shops (2km) SAINT TRIVIER SUR MOIGNANS (2km) **NOTES:** Pets admitted English spoken

SERGY

♥♥♥ ♥ Le Verger/La Forge Liliane MOINE
Chemin de la Charriere, 01630 SERGY
☎ 04 50 42 18 03　🖷 04 50 42 11 34
These two newly-built buildings are in the heart of a peaceful village in the foothills of the Jura Gessien, overlooking the Alps: Le Verger with two rooms on the first floor and La Forge with four rooms, each with a telephone. Each room has twin beds, a shower room and wc and tea-making facilities. There are extra beds available. There is a guests' lounge, terrace and the grounds have parking spaces. There are woodland footpaths nearby. Open all year.
PRICES: s €32; d €38; t €42 **ON SITE:** Hiking **NEARBY:** Bathing (22km) Horse riding (7km) Golf (10km) Fishing (3km) Swimming pool (8km) Cross-country skiing (20km) Downhill skiing (3km) Tennis (2km) Railway station (25km) Shops (3km) GEX (14km) **NOTES:** Pets admitted English spoken

SERVAS

♥♥♥ ⏃ Le Nid à Bibi Elsie BIBUS
Lalleyriat, 01960 SERVAS
☎ 04 74 21 11 47　🖷 04 74 21 02 83
Welcome to the peaceful and restful Nid à Bibi, a beautifully restored farmhouse, with five rooms on the first floor. There are rooms for two to three people with bathroom and wc, one room has a spa bath. On site facilities include a library and dining room (where brunch breakfasts are served), the landscaped garden, private parking, two synthetic tennis courts, indoor heated swimming pool with wave machine, sauna, weights, table tennis, bicycles. Nearby are a river, golf and water-skiing. Discounts offered for stays of two nights or more. Open all year by reservation.
PRICES: s €76-€92; d €90-€120; t €145; dinner €25-€28
ON SITE: Swimming pool Hiking Tennis **NEARBY:** Bathing (7km) Horse riding (3km) Golf (10km) Fishing (3km) Railway station (7km) Shops (4km) BOURG EN BRESSE (7km) **NOTES:** Pets admitted CC English spoken

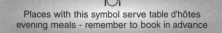
⏃
Places with this symbol serve table d'hôtes evening meals - remember to book in advance

RHÔNE-ALPES

VILLARS LES DOMBES

♦♦♦ Etang de Chafaud Daniel et Zdenka BACK
735 route du Chatelard, 01330 VILLARS LES DOMBES
☎ 04 74 98 17 74 📠 04 74 98 17 74
Three grade 2 double rooms in the owners' house. They have independent access and each has a washbasin and shower with a shared wc. There is also a grade 3 double room with bathroom (large shower cubicle, bath and wc). Facilities include a lounge with kitchenette, fireplace and a terrace with garden furniture. The enclosed, wooded grounds ensure guests' privacy. Visit the bird sanctuary, 2 km or the Route des Etangs de la Dombes. Bicycles for hire, €9.15 per day. Open all year.
PRICES: s €34-€40; d €37-€43 **ON SITE:** Fishing Hiking
NEARBY: Bathing (15km) Horse riding (15km) Golf (3km) Swimming pool (1km) Tennis (1km) Railway station (1km) Shops (1km) VILLARS LES DOMBES (1km) **NOTES:** Pets admitted

VILLEMOTIER

♦♦♦ La Recouvrance Jacheet B. et TUFFIN P.
la recouvrance Montfollet, 01270 VILLEMOTIER
☎ 04 74 42 01 18
Three rooms on the first floor of the owners' house - a typical old, restored, farmhouse surrounded by a botanical garden containing more than 300 varieties of maple and magnolia. The grounds also contain a swimming pool, verandah and koi carp pond. The accommodation consists of two double rooms (one is grade 2) and one room with three single beds. They each have a private shower room and wc. A cot is also available. There is an independent entrance, a large lounge with satellite TV and a fireplace. Generous breakfasts on offer. Discounts for long-stays out of season. The house is near the A39-A40 tourist routes with a farmhouse hotel and restaurant nearby. Open all year.
PRICES: s €24; d €37; t €48; extra person €11 **ON SITE:** Swimming pool Hiking **NEARBY:** Bathing (12km) Horse riding (15km) Golf (17km) Fishing (1km) Tennis (4km) Railway station (20km) Shops (3km) BOURG EN BRESSE (20km) **NOTES:** Pets admitted English spoken

VILLEREVERSURE

♦♦♦ 🐓 🍴 L'Agnoblens Annie et Eric GUILLERMIN
Noblens, 01250 VILLEREVERSURE
☎ 04 74 30 60 50
A working farm in the heart of Revermont, built of stone in 1812. The six rooms each have a private shower room and wc. There are four double rooms, one room with one double and one single bed and one room with one double and two single beds. Also on offer is a large lounge with a television and library, a peaceful, shaded flower garden for meals, private parking, petanque, and table tennis. The table d'hôte meals are only available in the evenings by reservation. Freshly cooked bread and galettes are available to taste and buy. Open all year.
PRICES: s €29; d €34; t €43; extra person €9; dinner €12
ON SITE: Fishing Hiking **NEARBY:** Bathing (3km) Horse riding (3km) Golf (15km) Swimming pool (15km) Cross-country skiing (30km) Tennis (1km) Railway station (2km) Shops (1km) BOURG EN BRESSE (15km) **NOTES:** Pets admitted

VILLES

♦♦♦ Chambre d'hôtes Myriam et Daniel HENRIOUX
6, rue de la Promenade, 01200 VILLES
☎ 04 50 59 97 29 📠 04 50 59 97 29
e-mail: mhenrioux@free.fr
Three rooms on the first floor of the owners' large house in the beautiful setting of the Retord. There are two rooms with two double beds (one grade 2) and one twin room all with private facilities. One room has a TV and a cot is available. The guest

lounge has a satellite TV and library. Also available are a telephone, boules and table tennis with 'Carnotzet' during the evenings. Set in a large park with beautiful views and a field with horses. Open all year.
PRICES: s €45; d €48; extra person €15 **ON SITE:** Hiking
NEARBY: Bathing (7km) Horse riding (6km) Golf (28km) Fishing (8km) Swimming pool (7km) Cross-country skiing (15km) Downhill skiing (20km) Tennis (6km) Railway station (4km) Shops (4km) Restaurant nearby BELLEGARDE (4km) **NOTES:** No pets

VIRIAT

♦♦♦ 🍴 Moulin de Champagne Anne-Marie FAMY
01440 VIRIAT
☎ 04 74 25 16 04
On the site of an historic, renovated mill, there are four rooms in an outbuilding with independent, level access. Two rooms with one double and one single bed, one room with three single beds - each room has a bathroom and wc. Also one room with a double bed and a single bed on a mezzanine with a shower room and wc. There is also a day room and seating areas with a fireplace for guest use, as are the grounds and terrace with garden furniture. Table d'hôte meals are available. Open all year.
PRICES: s €37; d €46; t €53; dinner €16 **ON SITE:** Hiking
NEARBY: Bathing (5km) Golf (5km) Fishing (2km) Swimming pool (1km) Tennis (1km) Railway station (3km) Shops (2km) BOURG-EN-BRESSE (3km) **NOTES:** Pets admitted English spoken

ALBA LA ROMAINE

♦♦♦ Le Jeu du Mail Maurice & M-Françoise ARLAUD
07400 ALBA
☎ 04 75 52 41 59 📠 04 75 52 41 59
e-mail: lejeudumail@free.fr http://lejeudumail.free.fr
This 19th-century former silkworm house, on the edge of a medieval village has retained the simplicity of the local architecture. There are three first-floor guest rooms with private bathroom and wc, and two suites (each sleeping four) with private shower room and wc. Lounge with fireplace, second-floor salon, tree-lined garden, private pool. Etchings exhibition. Local wines, walks or relaxation, your hosts Marie-Françoise and Maurice hope you will enjoy their home. Open all year.
PRICES: s €36-€43; d €51-€93; t €85-€91; extra person €15
ON SITE: Swimming pool Tennis **NEARBY:** Bathing (10km) Canoeing (20km) Horse riding (10km) Fishing (10km) Railway station (16km) LE TEIL (10km) **NOTES:** No pets Minimum 2 night stay English spoken

ARDOIX

♦♦♦ 🍴 ♿ Beauvoir Helene et J.Marc SEITIER
07290 ARDOIX
☎ 04 75 34 48 82 & 06 83 11 05 39

Take time to unwind in the peace of green Ardèche, at this

continued

continued

restored barn in the heart of the St Joseph vineyard. This detached house is an idyllic place for holidays with families and friends. Three spacious ground-floor rooms with their own entrance, one of which is accessible to the less mobile.
PRICES: s €35; d €40; t €55; extra person €15; dinner €15
NEARBY: Bathing (2km) Canoeing (15km) Horse riding (5km) Rock climbing (15km) Fishing (2km) Swimming pool (2km) Tennis (3km) Shops (3km) ANNONAY (20km) **NOTES:** No pets English spoken

AUBENAS

♥♥♥ 🍽 Combe Chaude Jacques LOPEZ
qtier de Ville, 07200 AUBENAS
☎ 04 75 35 74 77 & 06 81 91 73 16 📠 04 75 37 49 49
Two guest rooms, one with exterior access, double bed, shower room and wc, and one attic room with a large double bed, shower room and wc (not partitioned). Two further rooms in an annexe building each have a double bed, shower room and wc. Dining room, lounge, garden furniture, sunbeds, swimming pool (shared with gîtes). Swimming and fishing in the Ardèche 600m. Shops etc. in Aubenas. Open all year.
PRICES: s €38; d €46-€52; extra person €12; dinner €14
ON SITE: Swimming pool **NEARBY:** Bathing (1km) Canoeing (10km) Horse riding (5km) Rock climbing (10km) Fishing (1km) Tennis (3km) Shops (2km) AUBENAS (3km) **NOTES:** Pets admitted

BANNE

♥♥♥ 🍽 La Bastide des Chenes
Alain THOLL DE L'ENCLOS
le Gibet, 40 chemins des Romains, 06740 ETALLE
☎ 04 75 39 89 01 & 02 63 45 64 30 📠 02 63 45 64 30
On a five-hectare terraced estate, three very lovely guest rooms with private bathrooms are available in a country house. Exposed stonework and Provençale decor. Dining room and small lounge open onto a pretty, part-shaded terrace, where copious breakfasts and table d'hôte meals (ask the proprietors) are served. Swimming pool. Nearby: Grottes de la Cocalière, Bois de Paiolive, Aven Orgnac, Gorges de la Ardèche and the Cèze, Banne (listed character village with castle). Open 1 July to 31 August.
PRICES: d €59-€66; t €76; extra person €15; dinner €20
ON SITE: Bathing Fishing Swimming pool **NEARBY:** Canoeing (3km) Horse riding (3km) Rock climbing (3km) Tennis (3km) Railway station (25km) Shops (2km) LES VANS (8km) **NOTES:** No pets English spoken

BEAUMONT

♥♥♥ 🍽 La Petite Cour Verte Henri ROUVIERE
la Roche, 07110 BEAUMONT
☎ 04 75 39 58 88 📠 04 75 39 43 00
e-mail: henri.rouviere@wanadoo.fr
http://www.lapetitecourverte.com
Recharge your batteries at this superb 16th-century country house, peacefully set overlooking a valley of chestnut trees. The charming and comfortable bedrooms each have a private shower room and wc. Large lounge with fireplace opening onto a terrace and garden. Mini swimming pool (heated and covered), sauna (charged). Generous table d'hôte meals feature regional dishes and local produce. Warm welcome assured. Open 1 April to 31 December.
PRICES: d €59; extra person €23; dinner €20 **ON SITE:** Swimming pool
NEARBY: Bathing (3km) Canoeing (30km) Horse riding (8km) Rock climbing (15km) Fishing (3km) Cross-country skiing (30km) Tennis (15km) Shops (15km) JOYEUSE (15km) **NOTES:** No pets

BESSAS

♥♥♥ Le Château de Bessas
Brigitte BONNEFIN et M. Claude THOULOUZE
le Chateau, 07150 BESSAS
☎ 04 75 38 64 34 & 06 70 82 16 17 📠 04 75 38 60 90
e-mail: bandb.au.chateau.de.bessas@wanadoo.fr

In a renovated part of the Château de Bessas, in Basse Ardèche and close to the Pont d'Arc and the Cèze Valley, four beautiful guest rooms each have a different character. Each sleeps two or four people and has a private bathroom. Lounge, large sunny terrace, table tennis, mountain bikes on demand, swimming pool with hydromassage jets. Numerous activities nearby. Under fives: €8. 7 night stay: €280 for one, €322 for two, €434 for three. Open 1 March to 15 November.
PRICES: s €40; d €46; t €62; extra person €16 **ON SITE:** Swimming pool
NEARBY: Bathing (6km) Canoeing (15km) Horse riding (4km) Rock climbing (10km) Fishing (3km) Tennis (4km) Railway station (15km) Shops (5km) VALLON PONT D'ARC (12km) **NOTES:** No pets

BOFFRES

♥♥♥ 🍽 Domaine de Maisonneuve
Elisabeth DE BOISSIEU
07440 BOFFRES
☎ 04 75 58 35 97
e-mail: elie-maisonneuve@wanadoo.fr
The Domaine de Maisonneuve is situated 3 km from the village of Boffres and 10 km from Vernoux, and benefits from both a fishing lake and an 18-metre swimming pool. The 18th-century former farm has been completely restored to provide three guest rooms, each with a private bathroom and its own entrance. Vaulted salon, pretty dining room. Table d'hôte meals (family or gourmet) feature local produce. Numerous walking/cycling paths lead from the house. Shops, doctor, lake and pool in nearby Vernoux. Open 1 April to 15 October.
PRICES: s €30; d €52; t €73; extra person €18; dinner €14
ON SITE: Fishing Swimming pool **NEARBY:** Bathing (10km) Horse riding (2km) Tennis (10km) Shops (10km) VERNOUX (10km)
NOTES: Pets admitted English spoken

BURZET

♥♥♥ 🍽 Lamades Viviane et Pierre LIEVENS
07450 BURZET
☎ 04 75 94 59 50 📠 04 75 94 59 50
e-mail: pierre.lievens@free.fr
http://www.guideweb.com/ardeche/ch-hote/lamades/
Viviane and Pierre welcome you to their 19th-century former mill, isolated in a magnificent setting in the Bourges valley, and accessed by a stone bridge overhanging a 17-metre waterfall. Three spacious bedrooms sleep two people each and each has a lounge area, wc and bathroom. Large dining room, pretty, separate lounge for rest or reading. Table d'hôte meals are taken

continued

on the terrace and feature local produce. The property is situated in a protected area, alongside a river with 3 km of private fishing. Open Easter to October.
PRICES: d €60-€69; t €79-€87; extra person €18-€23; dinner €23
ON SITE: Bathing Fishing **NEARBY:** Canoeing (10km) Horse riding (10km) Rock climbing (10km) Cross-country skiing (20km) Tennis (2km) Shops (2km) BURZET (2km) **NOTES:** No pets English spoken

♥♥ 🍴 Pratmiral André FICHOT
07450 BURZET
☎ 04 75 94 47 58
Amid the Cévenoles mountains, three guest rooms in a restored hamlet of some character can sleep between two and six people. Each has a private shower room and wc. Cot and high chair on demand. Table d'hôte meals are taken in a pretty, typically Ardéchois room or on the terrace, and feature regional cuisine based on local produce. Ray Pic Falls nearby. The hamlet overlooks the pretty Bourge valley, well known for its trout fishing. Halfway between Aubenas and the Ardèchois plateau. Open all year on reservation.
PRICES: s €35; d €43; t €56; extra person €14; dinner €15
NEARBY: Bathing (2km) Canoeing (3km) Horse riding (10km) Rock climbing (10km) Fishing (2km) Swimming pool (20km) Cross-country skiing (30km) Tennis (3km) Shops (3km) BURZET (3km) **NOTES:** Pets admitted Minimum 2 night stay English spoken

CASTELJAU

♥♥ 🐓 L'Ensolleiade Jean NEGRE
07460 CASTELJAU
☎ 04 75 39 01 14 📠 04 75 39 01 14
http://www.les-vans.com/ensolleiade
On an agricultural holding beside the Gorges du Chassezac and the Bois de Paiolive, between the Gorges of the Ardèche and Cévennes. Five spacious guest rooms in a charming building adjacent to the owner's house. Semi-shaded enclosed garden. The rooms sleep two to four; all have terrace, shower, wc. Communal television lounge. Kitchen available for guests to use. Swimming pool. Barbecue, boules, children's games, table tennis, parking. High season tariff from 8 July to 25 August. Open 1 April to 11 November.
PRICES: d €38-€46; t €46-€53; extra person €7 **ON SITE:** Children's play area Swimming pool **NEARBY:** Bathing (1km) Canoeing (1km) Horse riding (3km) Rock climbing (1km) Fishing (1km) Tennis (1km) Shops (3km) LES VANS (10km) **NOTES:** No pets

CHALENCON

♥♥ 🍴 Le Village Philippe et Sylvie CHOLAT
porte de Besse, 07240 CHALENCON
☎ 04 75 58 15 18
e-mail: ph.cholat@free.fr www.portedebesse.free.fr
This house is part of the original ancient fortified village of Chalencon (13th-century). Philippe and Sylvie give you the choice of a grade 2 room sleeping two (with separate washing facilities), and two grade 3 rooms sleeping two to four. Lovely salon for guests' use. Breakfast and dinner served in restored medieval dining room. Local produce plus home-grown and home-made. Dinner only available by booking. This type of dwelling was in olden times called 'remparts habités' (occupied walls); the Gate of the Austrians still marks the entry to the village. Open Easter to 1 November.
PRICES: s €34-€40; d €38-€44; t €56; extra person €12; dinner €15
NEARBY: Bathing (7km) Canoeing (14km) Horse riding (4km) Fishing (4km) Swimming pool (9km) Tennis (1km) VERNOUX (9km) **NOTES:** No pets

CHASSIERS

♥♥ 🐓 🍴 Chalabreges Jean Remy VALETTE
07110 CHASSIERS
☎ 04 75 88 37 79 📠 04 75 88 37 79
Rémy and Chantal welcome you to this renovated 18th-century working farm. The five guest rooms (with shower and wc) can accommodate two to four guests each. Breakfast is served on the terrace with a view over the Tanargue. Dinner by reservation, or summer kitchen at your disposal. Pirate the pony is waiting to play with your children; the grown-ups may prefer a game of billiards. Lots of nearby attractions. For stays over three nights: €43/two persons. Reduced rates for groups. Open all year on reservation.
PRICES: d €43-€48; t €58-€63; extra person €15; dinner €14
NEARBY: Bathing (1km) Canoeing (15km) Horse riding (10km) Rock climbing (10km) Fishing (1km) Swimming pool (20km) Cross-country skiing (35km) Tennis (5km) Shops (5km) LARGENTIERE (5km) **NOTES:** No pets English spoken

CHAUZON

♥♥ 🐓 ♿ Les Clapas Chantal MARCEL
le Village, 07120 CHAUZON
☎ 04 75 39 79 67 & 04 75 39 72 31 📠 04 75 39 79 67
e-mail: les.clapas@free.fr http://les.clapas.free.fr
In a small village full of character, Chantal, a young winegrower, welcomes you to her five guest rooms, each with private shower and wc in an 18th-century farmhouse. One two-roomed suite sleeping four has disabled access; one suite on two floors accommodates four; two double rooms; and one room sleeping three. Open all year.
PRICES: s €32; d €40; t €51; extra person €11 **NEARBY:** Bathing (1km) Canoeing (2km) Horse riding (9km) Rock climbing (1km) Fishing (1km) Swimming pool (22km) Tennis (4km) Railway station (40km) VALLON PONT D'ARC (11km) **NOTES:** Pets admitted Minimum 2 night stay English spoken

GLUIRAS

♥♥ 🍴 Château de Mours Pieter DE GROOT
07190 GLUIRAS
☎ 04 75 66 62 32

Eighteenth-century bourgeois house in a 3,000m² botanic garden, 15 minutes from the valley of l'Eyrieux. The house is artistically decorated with traditional furniture in a soothing atmosphere. Library, television, separate sitting rooms. In the park there are plenty of spots to relax in. Three rooms for two or three guests, all with private facilities. Dinner available if booked. Open 1 April to 31 October.
PRICES: s €46; d €46; t €61; dinner €19 **NEARBY:** Bathing (12km) Canoeing (12km) Horse riding (15km) Rock climbing (7km) Fishing (3km) Swimming pool (17km) Cross-country skiing (25km) Tennis (5km) Shops (12km) ST SAUVEUR DE MONTAGUT (10km) **NOTES:** Pets admitted English spoken

GRAS

♨ ♥ ᛃᠬᠯ Mas de Marquet

Mathilde GRANIER-CHAUTARD
07700 GRAS
☎ 04 75 04 39 56

Seven kilometres from St Remèze and St Montan, Mathilde and Olivier, young Ardèchois farmers, offer a choice of three double rooms, one suite for five people, and one similar sized room for four people. All have private facilities. Communal room with piano, library. Central heating. Covered terrace. Evening meal must be booked; otherwise cooking facilities are available. Gorges de l'Ardèche at 12km. Farm animals (chickens, rabbits, sheep and cows). Open 1 February to 1 December.

PRICES: s €30; d €40-€45; t €55; extra person €15; dinner €12
NEARBY: Bathing (13km) Canoeing (17km) Horse riding (2km) Rock climbing (7km) Fishing (13km) Swimming pool (2km) Tennis (2km) Railway station (28km) Shops (7km) BOURG ST ANDEOL (16km)
NOTES: No pets Minimum 2 night stay English spoken

GROSPIERRES

♨ ♥ Les Monteils Pierre TEYSSIER

07120 GROSPIERRES
☎ 04 75 39 67 44 & 04 75 93 94 67

Seven kilometres from the Gorges de the Ardèche and Vallon Pont d'Arc, four vaulted guest rooms on the ground floor of an 18th-century farmhouse. Separate access for each room, with private shower and wc. Pleasant open grounds with garden furniture, deckchairs and barbecue. Small kitchen for guests to make use of. Television lounge. Washing machine. Lavish breakfasts with home-made preserves. Restaurant 500m. Give Henriette and Pierre the opportunity to show you the real Ardèche. Open all year.

PRICES: s €35; d €40; t €52; extra person €12 **NEARBY:** Bathing (1km) Canoeing (7km) Horse riding (2km) Rock climbing (6km) Fishing (1km) Swimming pool (20km) Cross-country skiing (30km) Tennis (1km) Shops (1km) RUOMS (7km) **NOTES:** No pets

♨ ᛃᠬᠯ Lou Couradou

Ariane TRAPAND et Laurent GONTARD
les Vezias, 07120 GROSPIERRES
☎ 04 75 39 79 97 & 06 21 16 24 02
http://www.loucouradou.fr.st

In the heart of the Ardèche garrigue, guests are welcomed to this 18th-century silk house, which has five rooms sleeping two to four people, all with private shower and wc. One vaulted room has a double bed, private lounge area, shower and wc. The sitting room and dining room are vaulted with open fires. Reading room. Games. Flowery Provençal courtyard. Terrace. Solarium. Near the GR4. Vallon Pont d'Arc 10 km.

PRICES: s €30; d €43-€47; t €53-€58; extra person €12; dinner €14
NEARBY: Bathing (4km) Canoeing (4km) Horse riding (5km) Rock climbing (10km) Fishing (4km) Swimming pool (4km) Tennis (2km) Shops (2km) RUOMS (8km) **NOTES:** No pets English spoken

ISSANLAS

♨ ᛃᠬᠯ Ferme Souche Marie Josee LEONIS

la Garde, 07660 ISSANLAS
☎ 04 66 46 10 69 ᛃ 04 66 46 12 26

Three kilometres from Coucouron, this superb traditional farmhouse on the plateau has been restored to its original condition, with beautiful old furniture. Superb dining room with pretty sitting area in front of the open Ardèchois style fireplace. Five tastefully arranged guest rooms with private facilities. Dinner (must be reserved) using local produce. Extensive grounds with garden furniture. 2km from the road connecting Aubenas to Puy en Velay. In winter you can go skiing and dog-sleighing.

continued

PRICES: s €55; d €55; extra person €14; dinner €16
NEARBY: Bathing (3km) Horse riding (4km) Fishing (3km) Cross-country skiing (3km) Tennis (3km) Railway station (17km) Shops (3km) COUCOURON (3km) **NOTES:** No pets CC

JAUJAC

♨ ♥ ᛃᠬᠯ Le Monteil C et A BRUN-MARECHAL

07380 JAUJAC
☎ 04 75 93 28 56 ᛃ 04 75 93 28 56

Within the Regional Natural Park of the Monts d'Ardèche, Catherine and Alain welcome you to their restored stone farmhouse in a hamlet looking south over Jaujac and the valley of the Lignon with its basalt columns. Salon, terrace, flower meadow, games room. Four rooms (two of them suitable for families) sleeping two to four, all with private shower and wc. Central heating. At dinner, enjoy produce from the garden farm and local area, lush old-fashioned vegetables, wild plants and aromatic herbs. No smoking. Tariff, half board: €31/person based on a stay of five nights for two people. Open April to 15 October.

PRICES: s €34; d €41; t €55; extra person €14; dinner €17
NEARBY: Bathing (3km) Horse riding (10km) Fishing (4km) Swimming pool (15km) Cross-country skiing (27km) Tennis (4km) Shops (4km) THUEYTS (11km) **NOTES:** No pets English spoken

♨ ♥ ᛃᠬᠯ Le Rucher des Roudils

Marie et Gil FLORENCE
les Roudils, 07380 JAUJAC
☎ 04 75 93 21 11 ᛃ 04 75 93 21 11

This haven of peace overlooks a large valley of the Hautes Cévennes, in the middle of a preserved landscape. The restored farmhouse accommodates three guest rooms, all with shower and wc. One room sleeps three; one suite sleeps five; and one sleeps two. Private terrace facing south with a superb view. Dinner is served on the terrace or in the communal living room. Natural cuisine with organic produce. The owners are beekeepers. Open February to November.

PRICES: ; d €45; extra person €16; dinner €17 **NEARBY:** Bathing (4km) Canoeing (10km) Horse riding (10km) Fishing (2km) Swimming pool (15km) Cross-country skiing (26km) Tennis (4km) Shops (4km) THUEYTS (11km) **NOTES:** No pets

LA SOUCHE

♨ ᛃᠬᠯ Quartier de l'Eglise

Annie et Dominique SCANDOLERA
07380 LA SOUCHE
☎ 04 75 37 92 53

In the Hautes Cévennes Ardèchoises, at the foot of the Tanargue, Annie and Dominique welcome you into their old church school standing on the heights of the village. Five rooms for two to four people, each with shower and wc. Dining room, sitting area, television, board games. Leisure facilities (Croix de Beauzon)13km - mountain bikes, climbing, hiking, downhill and cross-country skiing. In the village, swimming, fishing, small shops. Spa resort of Neyrac-les-Bains 15 mins. Open all year.

PRICES: s €30; d €43; t €55; extra person €12; dinner €13
NEARBY: Bathing (1km) Horse riding (13km) Rock climbing (13km) Fishing (1km) Swimming pool (16km) Cross-country skiing (13km) Tennis (1km) Shops (1km) JAUJAC (6km) **NOTES:** No pets Minimum 2 night stay English spoken

For further information on these and other chambres d'hôtes, consult the Gîtes de France website
www.gites-de-france.fr

LABASTIDE DE VIRAC

♦♦♦ ○ Le Mas Rîvé
Guido et Marie Rose GOOSSENS
07150 LABASTIDE DE VIRAC
☎ 04 75 38 69 13
e-mail: masreve@ifrance.com   http://masreve.ifrance.com
Marie-Rose and Guido invite guests to this 17th-century *mas provençale*, which owes its charm in part to its location in the Nature Reserve of the Gorges de l'Ardèche. The cliffs over the gorges are only 350m away. Four rooms of great comfort, with private facilities. Each room has separate access and sitting area. Terrace with garden furniture. Vaulted salon; library on regional topics. Meals are enhanced by use of local produce.
PRICES: s €52-€59; d €61-€76; extra person €18; dinner €21
NEARBY: Bathing (2km) Canoeing (12km) Horse riding (12km) Rock climbing (1km) Fishing (2km) Swimming pool (9km) Tennis (6km) Shops (10km) VALLON PONT D'ARC (12km) **NOTES:** No pets English spoken

LEMPS

♦♦♦♦ Château Chavagnac Christian REALE
07610 LEMPS
☎ 04 75 08 33 08   📠 04 75 08 33 08

On the route around the great vintages, you will find this Directoire château on an agricultural holding of 15ha. Two suites for guests, with bathroom and wc; one room with shower and wc. Very comfortable rooms, furnished in 19th-century style. Large dining room and similarly large salon with library opening out over the terrace and park. Booking required for winter. Several restaurants in Tournon 8 km. L'Hermitage 15km. Cot and spare beds available. Open 1 March to 15 November, and by reservation in winter.
PRICES: s €46-€61; d €53-€69; extra person €15 **ON SITE:** Wine tasting **NEARBY:** Bathing (4km) Canoeing (8km) Horse riding (5km) Fishing (4km) Swimming pool (8km) Tennis (8km) Railway station (10km) Shops (8km) TOURNON (8km) **NOTES:** No pets Minimum 2 night stay English spoken

♦♦♦ ○ Château de Lemps Nicole DU TREMOLET
07610 LEMPS
☎ 04 74 35 88 52 & 06 82 99 18 60
e-mail: nicole.dutremolet@free.fr
At the heart of Lemps village near the valley of the Rhône and the Wine Route, this old building offers two family rooms for two to four people, with shower and wc; one room for two or three, again with shower and wc. 2ha park. A quiet and relaxing spot. Dinner (family fare) must be booked. Meals are served in the dining room in medieval style with the proprietor's family. Open 1 April to 30 September.
PRICES: s €30-€32; d €37-€42; t €52-€69; extra person €12; dinner €13 **ON SITE:** Wine tasting **NEARBY:** Bathing (10km) Horse riding (10km) Fishing (10km) Swimming pool (7km) Tennis (7km) Shops (7km) TOURNON (15km) **NOTES:** No pets Minimum 2 night stay English spoken

LES VANS

♦♦♦ ○ Chambre d'hôtes
Marie-Antoinette THEBAULT
chemin de la Transhumance, 07140 LES VANS
☎ 04 75 88 52 02 & 06 21 64 09 39   📠 04 75 88 52 02
Near the Bois de Païolive come and recharge your batteries in the peace of the garrigue countryside on the byways of the south. In an old silk house on 8,000m² of olive trees, mulberries and fruit trees, five lovely rooms, each in a different style. All sleep two (one with extra child's bed in a corner) and have private shower and wc. Central heating. Television lounge reserved for guests. You have the use of the owner's private swimming pool. On reservation, you may dine in the evening under the lime tree or in cooler seasons by the fireside. Cooking is based on local ingredients. Four person gîte also available. Open 15 February to 11 November.
PRICES: d €54-€65; dinner €20 **ON SITE:** Swimming pool
NEARBY: Bathing (4km) Canoeing (4km) Horse riding (10km) Rock climbing (4km) Fishing (4km) Tennis (3km) Shops (3km) LES VANS (3km) **NOTES:** No pets English spoken

MARCOLS LES EAUX

♦♦♦ ○ Salomony Hans et Carla VAN DER MEER
07190 MARCOLS LES EAUX
☎ 04 75 65 61 65   📠 04 75 65 61 58
An 18th-century stone building situated in the wilds of the Parc Naturel des Monts d'Ardèche, at the foot of the Gluyère valley on the bank of the river. Two rooms sleeping two or three, with private facilities. One grade 2 double room, with separate facilities. Possibility of room for two children. Living room, salon, television, interior courtyard, terrace, games, sun loungers, boules. Cot available. Dinner prepared with vegetables and aromatic herbs from the organic kitchen garden, and home-made preserves. Wander on foot or bike; great torrents from the mountains for fishing fans; heritage trails; etc. Open all year.
PRICES: s €37; d €40-€43; t €58; extra person €15; dinner €15
ON SITE: Fishing **NEARBY:** Bathing (2km) Canoeing (20km) Cross-country skiing (20km) Tennis (1km) Shops (1km) ST PIERREVILLE (10km) **NOTES:** No pets English spoken

MARS

♦♦♦ ○ La Souche Susanne et Rudolf BUHLER
Gourgouras, 07320 MARS
☎ 04 75 30 70 81
e-mail: rudolf.buhler@wanadoo.fr http://www.souche.ch
A superb traditional farmhouse, completely restored to its original condition, with four guest rooms, all with shower and wc. Large games room, salon with open fire and television corner, dining room where we serve dinner prepared with local produce. 9km from St Agrève and 15km from Cheylard.
PRICES: s €43-€49; d €50-€56; extra person €15; dinner €17
ON SITE: Tennis **NEARBY:** Bathing (9km) Horse riding (10km) Rock climbing (20km) Fishing (9km) Swimming pool (9km) Cross-country skiing (20km) Shops (9km) Golf (5km) ST AGREVE (9km) **NOTES:** No pets English spoken

MERCUER

♦♦♦ ○ La Gibaudelle Pierre-Max GADIN
le Juge, 07200 MERCUER
☎ 04 75 93 77 75   📠 04 75 93 77 75
e-mail: pierre-max.gadin@wanadoo.fr
http://perso.wanadoo.fr/gibaudelle
In the middle of a pine forest, 5km from Aubenas, La Gibaudelle offers a warm welcome. Select from one room with mezzanine sleeping two to four, with shower and wc; one double room with

continued

RHÔNE-ALPES

shower and wc; and one room for two people, with separate ground floor access, balneotherapy bath and wc. Private swimming pool. Meals must be booked.
PRICES: s €30-€38; d €43-€53; t €58; extra person €15; dinner €15
ON SITE: Swimming pool **NEARBY:** Bathing (7km) Canoeing (7km) Horse riding (1km) Rock climbing (20km) Fishing (10km) Cross-country skiing (30km) Tennis (5km) Shops (5km) AUBENAS (5km) **NOTES:** No pets

♦♦♦ ❧ Mas de Mazan Alain et Michele CROZE
07200 MERCUER
☎ 04 75 35 41 88 🖷 04 75 35 41 88
http://perso.wanadoo.fr/masdemazan/
Between the plateau and south Ardèche, five minutes from Aubenas and Vals les Bains, Alain and Michèle offer five guest rooms sleeping two to four, each with private shower and wc. Communal dining room and small kitchen for guests' use. Perfect for ramblers - pathways on the estate. Swimming and fishing 5km. Swimming pool in grounds. Breakfast served at the grand table or in the grounds in the shade of the mulberries, if weather permits. Home-made jams and pastries.
PRICES: s €34; d €40; t €49; extra person €12 **ON SITE:** Swimming pool **NEARBY:** Bathing (5km) Canoeing (15km) Horse riding (5km) Rock climbing (10km) Fishing (5km) Cross-country skiing (35km) Tennis (3km) Shops (3km) AUBENAS (5km) **NOTES:** No pets

MONTSELGUES
♦♦♦ ❧ ⑩ Le Chastagnier Françis CHAZALON
07140 MONTSELGUES
☎ 04 75 36 97 00
Four guest rooms in a very beautiful 17th-century house, the home of a sheep farmer. A magnificent spot, and isolated in 50ha of private ground. Two double rooms; one sleeping three and a room with two double beds. All have private bathroom and wc. Salon and lounge are communal. Regional specialities at dinner. Fishing lake. Booking essential. Open all year.
PRICES: s €32; d €43; extra person €15; dinner €14 **ON SITE:** Fishing **NEARBY:** Bathing (6km) Horse riding (6km) Rock climbing (6km) Swimming pool (6km) Cross-country skiing (6km) Tennis (6km) Shops (10km) LES VANS (23km) **NOTES:** No pets Minimum 2 night stay English spoken

PAILHARES
♦♦♦ ❧ ⑩ Le Petit Marchand Jacques ANDRY
col du Marchand, 07410 PAILHARES
☎ 04 75 06 06 80 🖷 04 75 06 13 46
e-mail: jacques.andry@wanadoo.fr
http://perso.wanadoo.fr/petit.marchand
Between the Safari-Parc de Peaugres and Tournon, four beautiful rooms (one of them grade 2) in an old restored farmhouse. Incomparable view. Each room has a sitting area, shower, wc, refrigerator. Dinner is based on local produce, regional recipes and specialities of Alsace. Plenty of activities on the spot or nearby. Special prices for half board and children. Open all year.
PRICES: s €32; d €39; t €50-€53; extra person €12; dinner €15
NEARBY: Bathing (7km) Horse riding (8km) Fishing (2km) Swimming pool (8km) Cross-country skiing (5km) Tennis (5km) Shops (5km) ST FELICIEN (8km) **NOTES:** Pets admitted Minimum 2 night stay English spoken

POURCHERES
♦♦♦ ⑩ Chambre d'hôtes Marcelle GOETZ
07000 POURCHERES
☎ 04 75 66 81 99 🖷 04 75 66 81 99
Four guest rooms with separate access, opening on to the garden, in an old Ardéchois house surrounded by greenery. Dinner

(communal or separate) employs produce from the garden. Vegetarian meals on request. The village is situated on the slopes of an old volcano, with lovely walks. Get involved in psychotherapy, astrology, tarot, botany or complementary medicine. Open all year.
PRICES: s €35-€45; d €45-€55; extra person €12; dinner €18
NEARBY: Bathing (8km) Swimming pool (10km) Tennis (10km) Shops (10km) PRIVAS (10km) **NOTES:** Pets admitted Minimum 2 night stay English spoken

PRADONS
♦♦♦ ❧ Les Ranchins Françis RANCHIN
quartier les Ranchins, 07120 PRADONS
☎ 04 75 93 98 33 & 06 07 10 07 79 🖷 04 75 93 98 33
e-mail: ranchins@aol.com http://members.aol.com/ranchins/
Five guest rooms in an entirely restored farmhouse, on a vineyard 5km from Ruoms. Living room for guests' use only. Three double rooms and two rooms sleeping three, all with shower and wc. Breakfast served on the veranda or on the terrace. Central heating. Communal swimming pool due to open on 1st July 2002. Groups welcome with a seven person gîte nearby. Garage for motor bikes and cycles. Wine sold. Open all year.
PRICES: s €32; d €41; t €52; extra person €11 **NEARBY:** Bathing (1km) Canoeing (2km) Horse riding (7km) Rock climbing (2km) Fishing (1km) Cross-country skiing (50km) Railway station (50km) Shops (2km) RUOMS (5km) **NOTES:** Pets admitted

ROCHEMAURE
♦♦♦ ⑩ Le Chenavari Henriette COLENSON
quartier les Videaux, 07400 ROCHEMAURE
☎ 04 75 49 10 16 & 06 87 39 32 49 🖷 04 75 49 10 16
e-mail: henriette.colenson@wanadoo.fr
Henriette welcomes you to a quiet and sunkissed spot. You will overlook the magnificent Château de Rochemaure (12th-century). Five minutes from the RN86. One downstairs room and three upstairs, all sleeping two, with private shower and wc. Farm and garden produce. Traditional cooking. Honey for sale, and home-made preserves. Half board available. Private parking. Open all year.
PRICES: s €35-€38; d €41-€44; extra person €11; dinner €14
NEARBY: Bathing (10km) Canoeing (25km) Horse riding (10km) Rock climbing (25km) Fishing (5km) Swimming pool (10km) Tennis (3km) Railway station (15km) Shops (3km) LE TEIL (8km) **NOTES:** No pets

ST ALBAN AURIOLLES
♦♦♦ ⑩ Mas de Chantressac
Chantal et Patrick ALTARE
07120 ST ALBAN AURIOLLES
☎ 04 75 39 79 05 & 06 07 30 95 67 🖷 04 75 39 79 05
In open countryside at the heart of southern Ardèche, stay for a night or the whole holiday in a traditional country house, completely restored, in an oak wood. Three carefully arranged rooms for two to four people, each with private facilities. Rate for 4 people €170. Swimming pool. Our breakfasts will be served to you in our salon or outside on the stone terraces, if weather permits. Dinner (except July and August) - booking required.
PRICES: s €44-€49; d €49-€64; t €64-€79; extra person €11-€15; dinner €17 **ON SITE:** Swimming pool **NEARBY:** Bathing (2km) Canoeing (3km) Horse riding (1km) Rock climbing (6km) Fishing (2km) Tennis (3km) Shops (2km) RUOMS (5km) **NOTES:** No pets

---

⑩
Places with this symbol serve table d'hôtes evening meals - remember to book in advance

continued

⚜ Villa St Patrice
Michael TOURRE GUILLEMETTE ET
07120 ST ALBAN AURIOLLES
☎ 04 75 39 37 78 & 06 73 50 50 92
e-mail: contact@villastpatrice.com http://villastpatrice.com
In the middle of a Provençal village a Florentine-style house set in quiet parkland. Three double rooms, each with shower and bath, and one suite for two to four people, with salon, bathroom and wc. Breakfast on the terrace opposite the vineyard and Samson's Rock. Living room is shared with the owner. Parking on the property, shady grounds, garden furniture, sunbeds. Open all year.
PRICES: d €69-€105; extra person €15 **NEARBY:** Bathing (2km) Canoeing (4km) Horse riding (1km) Rock climbing (1km) Fishing (2km) Tennis (4km) Shops (1km) RUOMS (5km) **NOTES:** No pets

ST ANDEOL DE FOURCHADES

⚜ 🍴 La Calmeraie Sebastien LIABEUF
Longeagne - La Calmeraie, St Andéol de Fourchades, 07310 ST MARTIAL
☎ 04 75 29 19 38 📠 04 75 29 19 38
Three kilometres from the Lac du St Martial on 100ha of open land, opposite Gerbier de Jonc, Nadine and Sébastien welcome you to La Calmeraie, a traditional 17th-century farmhouse, now restored to its original condition. Five refined guest rooms with private facilities (one has a bathroom - tariff €50). Lounge with television and open fire. Classes can be arranged for painting on wood and metal. Meals (local cuisine) are served under the lime tree. Mountain biking and rambling on marked tracks, cross country skiing, mushroom hunting. Open all year.
PRICES: d €43-€50; extra person €15; dinner €14 **ON SITE:** Fishing **NEARBY:** Bathing (3km) Horse riding (15km) Rock climbing (15km) Cross-country skiing (15km) Tennis (3km) Shops (3km) ST MARTIAL (3km) **NOTES:** No pets

ST ANDRE DE CRUZIERES

⚜ 🐦 La Manaudiere Jean Luc MAISTRE
07460 ST ANDRE DE CRUZIERES
☎ 04 75 39 34 58 📠 04 75 39 34 58
e-mail: auberge.la.manaudiere@wanadoo.fr
Four guest rooms on the second floor of a family house of traditional southern character, surrounded by pine woods, olive trees and garrigue countryside, 2km from the village. Rooms have shower and wc. Communal salon. A quiet spot, shady, with a sundrenched terrace. Private parking, and great space for children to play. At the auberge discover meals prepared using farm produce. Ask us about prices for board and half board. Open all year.
PRICES: s €37; d €42; extra person €12; dinner €14
ON SITE: Children's play area **NEARBY:** Bathing (10km) Canoeing (20km) Horse riding (10km) Rock climbing (10km) Fishing (10km) Swimming pool (4km) Tennis (3km) Railway station (30km) Restaurant nearby LES VANS (20km) **NOTES:** Pets admitted Minimum 2 night stay English spoken

⚜ 🐦 Les Muriers Christian DUMAS
Pierregras, 07460 ST ANDRE DE CRUZIERES
☎ 04 75 39 02 02 📠 04 75 39 02 02
www.sud-ardeche.com/tourism/lesmuriers
Elisabeth and Christian invite you into The Mulberries, their Provençal house between the Ardèche and the Gard. Four guest rooms with every comfort for two or three, all with shower and wc. Communal living room and television with corner kitchen for guests' use. Electric heating. Breakfast may be taken on the shady terrace; spare beds available. Barbecue. Several restaurants, from 800m.

PRICES: s €36; d €40; t €50; extra person €11 **NEARBY:** Bathing (14km) Canoeing (15km) Horse riding (12km) Rock climbing (10km) Fishing (20km) Swimming pool (10km) Tennis (10km) Railway station (30km) Shops (1km) LES VANS (20km) **NOTES:** Pets admitted

ST CHRISTOL

⚜ 🍴 Le Moulinage
Bernard et Danye JOUANNIGOT
les Echarlives, 07160 ST CHRISTOL
☎ 04 75 29 00 34 📠 04 75 29 96 39
e-mail: lemoulinage@free.fr http://www.lemoulinage.fr.st
Danye and Bernard invite you into their old mill, now entirely restored, and offer you the choice of four rooms each sleeping two, all with shower and wc. You have the use of the lounge or music room. Meals are served either outside in the courtyard if weather permits or in our dining room. Also available a rural gîte sleeping five. Mountain bikes available. We are 12km from Cheylard (medical services, large shops, public swimming pool), among the mountains and woods.
PRICES: s €30; d €40; extra person €15; dinner €13 **ON SITE:** Fishing **NEARBY:** Bathing (12km) Rock climbing (10km) Swimming pool (12km) Cross-country skiing (15km) Tennis (12km) Shops (12km) LE CHEYLARD (12km) **NOTES:** No pets

ST DESIRAT

⚜ 🍴 La Désirade Philippe MEUNIER
07340 ST DESIRAT
☎ 04 75 34 21 88
e-mail: contact@desirade-fr.com http://www.desirade-fr.com
On the Wine Route, 45 minutes south of Lyon in a small Ardéchois village, La Désirade is perfect for rest and relaxation. Six guest rooms: three double rooms and two rooms sleeping three, all have shower and wc; a two-roomed suite has two double beds and a single, bathroom and wc. Salon. Shady park. Locked parking. Five minutes from RN86. Sample our regional cuisine at dinner (booking required). Open all year.
PRICES: s €30; d €43; t €58; extra person €15; dinner €16
ON SITE: Wine tasting **NEARBY:** Bathing (3km) Canoeing (7km) Horse riding (10km) Rock climbing (2km) Fishing (3km) Swimming pool (3km) Tennis (3km) Railway station (15km) Shops (2km) SERRIERES (10km) **NOTES:** Pets admitted English spoken

See advert on opposite page

ST JEURE D'AY

⚜ 🐦 🍴 La Crinière Jocelyne CASTAN
07290 ST JEURE D'AY
☎ 04 75 34 58 96 📠 04 75 34 58 96
e-mail: dagrain@club-internet.fr
http://www.rent-a-holiday.com/info/lacriniere

In the open countryside, this restored farmhouse is full of charm, on the river bank. Four double rooms have exposed beams, warm

continued

continued·

colours and beautiful bathrooms. Dinner with local cuisine - by torchlight on the terrace in summer, or in front of the hearth in winter. Salon with lounge area; music; television; board games. Terrace and solarium. Lyon 80 km. Annonay/Sarras 12 km. Hiking and riding; hot air ballooning (bookings can be made on the spot). Stabling available and equestrian facilities. Packed lunches on request. Open all year.
PRICES: s €38; d €46; t €58; extra person €12; dinner €14
ON SITE: Bathing Fishing **NEARBY:** Canoeing (20km) Horse riding (2km) Swimming pool (7km) Tennis (2km) Railway station (12km) Shops (2km) ANNONAY (12km) **NOTES:** No pets English spoken

ST JULIEN DU SERRE

♥♥♥ 🍽 Mas de Bourlenc
Thierry et Dorothée VENTALON
07200 ST JULIEN DU SERRE
☎ 04 75 37 69 95 📠 04 75 37 69 95
www.guideweb.com/ardeche/ch-hote/mas-de-bourlenc
Five guest rooms are waiting for you, all with independent access, every comfort, and a superb view; you will also love the lounge with its beautiful fireplace. Organic garden and farm produce. Tasty cuisine using savoury herbs and freshly harvested produce; must be booked. Sit on the terrace or in the shade of the vine. Buy honey and home-made preserves from Thierry, the beekeeper. Open all year.
PRICES: d €44-€49; t €61-€64; extra person €15; dinner €23
NEARBY: Bathing (1km) Canoeing (25km) Horse riding (6km) Rock climbing (18km) Fishing (1km) Swimming pool (8km) Cross-country skiing (30km) Tennis (3km) Shops (2km) AUBENAS (12km)
NOTES: No pets Minimum 2 night stay English spoken

ST JUST D'ARDECHE

♥♥♥ 🍽 La Melinass
M VANDENBERGHE-DE-PERMENTIER
07700 ST JUST D'ARDECHE
☎ 04 75 04 61 36 📠 04 75 04 61 36
e-mail: la-melinas@wanadoo.fr http://www.la-melinas.com
Isabelle and Marc welcome you into their cosy house. Vaulting, old stones and hearths recall the age of the Knights Templar. Three guest rooms. Two suites for two to four people, with bathroom and wc; and one family room for four with shower and wc. Interior courtyard with swimming pool; terrace with outdoor furniture; garden; children's play area. Large vaulted salon with traditional fireplace. Meals taken on the terrace or in the vaulted kitchen. Meals must be booked.
PRICES: s €53-€59; d €59-€63; t €75-€78; extra person €15; dinner €18
ON SITE: Swimming pool Tennis **NEARBY:** Bathing (4km) Canoeing (4km) Horse riding (2km) Fishing (1km) Railway station (10km) Shops (2km) BOURG ST ANDEOL (4km) **NOTES:** Pets admitted

La Désirade
07 340 Saint-Desirat
Tel: 04 75 34 21 88
Email: contact@desirade-fr.com
Site: www.desirade-fr.com

Approximately sixty kilometres south of Lyon, situated in a small village in the Ardèche region, "La Désirade" is a large XIX century residence, which has been entirely renovated to offer six pretty and very comfortable bedrooms. In the middle of Saint-Joseph vineyard, "La Désirade" provides an exceptional situation for rest and relaxation. Take advantage of the pleasant weather in the park and also enjoy the cuisine and wine of the area. A warm and friendly welcome can be assured for your stay. The ideal location to unwind.

ST LAGER BRESSAC

♥♥♥♥ Château de Fontblachère
Bernard LIAUDOIS
07210 ST LAGER BRESSAC
☎ 04 75 65 15 02 & 06 07 62 74 23 📠 04 75 65 15 02
e-mail: bernard.liaudois@wanadoo.fr
http://www.chateaudefontblachere.com
Ten kilometres off the A7 in a protected environment by the forest, the 18th-century Château de Fontblachère stands on the hills overlooking the valley of the Rhône. Choose from three rooms sleeping two/three and a suite for four, all with private shower and wc. You have the use of the private swimming pool and tennis court in the large shaded park. Vaulted dining room; terrace with garden furniture. Nearby horse riding centre. A little further, golf, marina, flying club. Small dogs welcome. Cot available. Open 1 April to 31 October.
PRICES: d €90-€120; t €135; extra person €16
ON SITE: Swimming pool Tennis **NEARBY:** Bathing (15km) Horse riding (3km) Fishing (15km) Shops (6km) CHOMERAC (6km)
NOTES: No pets Minimum 2 night stay English spoken

ST MONTAN

♥♥♥ 🍽 La Pacha Sylvie et Geoffroy CHARLIER
route de Viviers, 07220 ST MONTAN
☎ 04 75 52 57 41 📠 04 75 52 57 41
e-mail: lapacha.lemoure@wanadoo.fr
Restored 18th-century farmhouse, typically Ardéchois, near a medieval village with panoramic outlook. 15km from the autoroute and the Gorges de l'Ardèche. Four pretty rooms. Private terrace and garden furniture for each room. Private swimming pool. Breakfast served under the arbour during summer. Communal living room with open fire; small salon; games; pétanque; restaurant 5km. Closed Christmas and New Year.

continued

PRICES: ; d €55; extra person €14; dinner €19 **ON SITE:** Swimming pool **NEARBY:** Bathing (6km) Canoeing (15km) Horse riding (10km) Rock climbing (3km) Fishing (6km) Tennis (3km) Railway station (17km) Shops (3km) BOURG ST ANDEOL (10km) **NOTES:** No pets English spoken

ST PAUL LE JEUNE

♦♦♦ La Passiflore Godeliva LUYPAERTS
Sauvas, 07460 ST PAUL LE JEUNE
☎ 04 75 39 80 74 📠 04 75 39 80 74
In a renovated building of some character, three rooms for two to four guests, all with private facilities and independent access. Salon, television, refrigerator, small kitchen, spare beds. Big breakfasts served on the terrace or in the flower garden. Cycle garage. RD 104 is just down from the house. Must visit: Grotte de la Cocalière, Barjac, les Vans, the Bois Païolive, Vallon Pont d'Arc, Gorges de l'Ardèche. Dogs accepted with prior booking. Booking advised.
PRICES: s €27-€32; d €37-€41; t €55; extra person €10
NEARBY: Bathing (5km) Canoeing (5km) Horse riding (1km) Rock climbing (5km) Fishing (5km) Swimming pool (5km) Tennis (1km) Shops (1km) ST PAUL LE JEUNE (2km) **NOTES:** No pets English spoken

ST PIERREVILLE

♦♦♦ Moulinage Chabriol Edouard DE LANG
Chabriol Bas, 07190 St PIERREVILLE
☎ 04 75 66 62 08 📠 04 75 66 65 99
e-mail: chabriol@infonie.fr http://www.chabriol.com
The 18th-century Moulinage Chabriol has been remarkably well restored, and was once a silk-spinning mill. The industrial character has been preserved with care. Six rooms of quality (all with bathrooms and wcs) with exposed stones, vaulted ceilings, antique furniture and modern materials. Large lounge with open fire. On the river bank. Swimming and fishing on site. Chestnut trees. Thirty or so walking trails. Displays of silk-making. Good restaurants nearby. Holiday tax included in price. Open all year on reservation.
PRICES: d €57 **ON SITE:** Bathing Fishing **NEARBY:** Canoeing (15km) Horse riding (25km) Rock climbing (15km) Swimming pool (35km) Cross-country skiing (20km) Tennis (4km) Shops (4km) ST PIERREVILLE (4km) **NOTES:** No pets English spoken

♦♦♦ ❛○❜ Pont d'Aleyrac
Annie et Bernard MIRABEL
07190 ST PIERREVILLE
☎ 04 75 66 65 25 📠 04 75 66 65 25
Guest rooms in an old mill in the heart of the Regional Natural Park, 5km from the village by the ancient Route des Dragonnades, beside the river. Top grade rooms: three rooms for two or three guests and a suite for four, all with bathroom and wc. Common room with open fire; terraces; flowery courtyard; country garden. Meals available except Thursday (must be booked). Trails for walking and mountain bikes. Half way between the Vallée du Rhône and Mont Gerbier des Joncs. In the countryside, yet near to a very pretty village. Gallery with changing exhibitions. Open 29 March to 12 November.
PRICES: s €37; d €49; t €64; extra person €15; dinner €18
ON SITE: Fishing **NEARBY:** Bathing (1km) Canoeing (15km) Horse riding (15km) Rock climbing (15km) Swimming pool (30km) Cross-country skiing (20km) Tennis (2km) Shops (1km) ST PIERREVILLE (1km) **NOTES:** Pets admitted English spoken

ST REMEZE

♦♦♦ ❛○❜ La Martinade Sylvette MIALON
07700 St REMEZE
☎ 04 75 98 89 42 📠 04 75 04 36 30
e-mail: sylvetlm@aol.com
http://www.angelfire.com/la/lamartinade/
Sylvette and Gérard, both of them Ardéchois, welcome you to their old farmhouse which has been in their family for over a century, and offer you a choice of four rooms for two people (with spare beds available), all with private shower and wc. Dinner is served, providing bookings are made for four or more. Ardéchois and regional cuisine. No animals allowed in rooms. Open all year.
PRICES: s €37; d €43; t €52; extra person €15; dinner €14
ON SITE: Swimming pool Tennis **NEARBY:** Bathing (9km) Canoeing (10km) Horse riding (12km) Rock climbing (16km) Fishing (9km) Railway station (20km) Shops (2km) BOURG ST ANDEOL (16km) **NOTES:** No pets Minimum 2 night stay English spoken

ST SAUVEUR DE CRUZIERES

♦♦♦♦ ❛○❜ Le Bourdet
Rocco et Martine D'ADDETTA
07460 ST SAUVEUR DE CRUZIERES
☎ 04 75 36 00 21 📠 04 75 36 01 99
http://www.guideweb.com/ardeche/ch-hote/bourdet/

On the way to Provence, stop amongst the olives and vines to enjoy the charms and tastes of this superb house of character, very southern in its colours and atmosphere. Martine and Rocco offer a choice of five rooms in their home. Large salon/dining room with open fire, television. Pétanque; parking; garden. Relax by the side of the pool, or on one of the sunkissed terraces. Generous breakfasts with home-made preserves. Ardéchois and southern specialities. Well-behaved cats and dogs are welcome. Open all year on reservation.
PRICES: s €65; d €110; extra person €38; dinner €38
ON SITE: Bathing Rock climbing Fishing Swimming pool **NEARBY:** Canoeing (7km) Horse riding (4km) Tennis (2km) Railway station (30km) Shops (6km) ST PAUL LE JEUNE (6km) **NOTES:** No pets Minimum 2 night stay

♦♦♦ ❛○❜ Mas des Molieres
Richard REUTHER
les Molieres, 07460 ST SAUVEUR DE CRUZIERES
☎ 04 75 39 08 75 & 06 84 25 29 95 📠 04 75 39 08 75
In the land of the Cruzières, among vines and olive trees, a typical *mas* of the 16th century, with indoor swimming pool in the courtyard, and terraces enjoying a superb view. Four guest rooms finished in pastel colours. Vaulted dining room; lounge with television, billiard table, sofas, shaded boules pitch. Richard will prepare a meal of seasonal produce for you to enjoy either under the vaults or in the shade of the lime tree. 10% reduction for stays of three nights or more (except July and August). Open all year.

continued

PRICES: s €51; d €55; extra person €16; dinner €19 **ON SITE:** Swimming pool **NEARBY:** Bathing (8km) Canoeing (8km) Horse riding (4km) Rock climbing (2km) Fishing (3km) Tennis (2km) Railway station (30km) Shops (2km) ST PAUL LE JEUNE (12km) **NOTES:** No pets Minimum 2 night stay English spoken

VAGNAS

Le Mas d'Alzon Michele DEVILLE
07150 VAGNAS
☎ 04 75 38 67 33 & 06 86 20 37 54 🖷 04 75 38 67 33
Choose from three rooms in this former 17th-century priory - one room for two or three with salon, television, mini-bar, large bathroom and wc; one room for two or three guests with separate access from outside, shower and wc, sofa, television, beautiful terrace, private solarium; one room for two or three with salon, television, shower and bath. Everything is arranged with lots of charm and antique furniture (18th and 19th-century). There are lots of restaurants nearby and plenty of cultural and leisure activities.
PRICES: s €61-€91; d €61-€91; t €76-€105; extra person €15
ON SITE: Swimming pool **NEARBY:** Bathing (7km) Canoeing (7km) Horse riding (4km) Rock climbing (7km) Fishing (7km) Tennis (1km) Shops (4km) VALLON PONT D'ARC (7km) **NOTES:** No pets Minimum 2 night stay

Mas de Lassagne Stephane DOLYMPE
07150 VAGNAS
☎ 04 75 38 65 36
In Lower Ardèche, a stone's throw from the Gard, five guest rooms in our traditional *mas* dating from the 18th century in a quiet and very sunny spot. Our rooms, for two to four people, all have private shower and wc. Living room and vaulted sitting room reserved for our guests. Take the nearby GR4 for the Gorges de l'Ardèche and la Cèze. Private swimming pool.
PRICES: s €30; d €41; t €58; extra person €23 **ON SITE:** Swimming pool **NEARBY:** Bathing (5km) Canoeing (5km) Horse riding (6km) Rock climbing (5km) Fishing (5km) Tennis (1km) Shops (1km) VALLON PONT D'ARC (5km) **NOTES:** No pets Minimum 2 night stay

VERNON

Mas de la Cigale Catherine GOHIER
EURL les Cigales, La Croix, 07260 VERNON
☎ 04 75 39 68 69 & 06 80 05 89 75 🖷 04 75 39 68 69
e-mail: la.cigale@wanadoo.fr
http://www.guideweb.com/ardeche/ch-hote/la-cigale
Sandstone house on the vine terraces of the Ardèche Cévenne. Five spacious and refined guest rooms, all with private facilities. Dining room and vaulted sitting room. Swimming room shared with two rural gîtes.
PRICES: s €63; d €69; extra person €22; dinner €23
ON SITE: Swimming pool **NEARBY:** Bathing (3km) Canoeing (15km) Horse riding (10km) Rock climbing (20km) Fishing (3km) Tennis (7km) Shops (5km) JOYEUSE (5km) **NOTES:** No pets

VERNOUX

Roiseland Roland ESPOSITO-MASCHIO
10 rue Boissy d'Anglas, 07240 VERNOUX
☎ 04 75 58 19 32
Very beautiful family mansion from 1870 with private park in the village, offering five guest rooms. Private sitting room for guests, with open fire and television. Garnier suite has one double bed and two singles, shower and wc. One upper room has double bed, bathroom and wc. One double room; one sleeping three and one twin room; all with shower and wc. Private swimming pool. Rooms accessible by stairlift for guests with mobility problems. Possibility of letting complete house. Permanent exhibition of modern, risqué engravings. In July there is an exhibition by Ardéchois painters. Rooms are emphatically no smoking. Open Easter to 1 November.
PRICES: s €43; d €50; t €67; extra person €14 **ON SITE:** Swimming pool **NEARBY:** Bathing (1km) Canoeing (70km) Horse riding (3km) Rock climbing (10km) Fishing (1km) Tennis (1km) Railway station (30km) VERNOUX **NOTES:** No pets Minimum 2 night stay

VILLENEUVE DE BERG

Laudun Nicole LOYRION
07170 VILLENEUVE DE BERG
☎ 04 75 94 83 03 & 04 75 94 75 63 🖷 04 75 94 75 63
e-mail: loyrion@club-internet.fr http://auberge-laudun.com
In a hamlet 1km from the village between the Plateau of Coiron and the Vallée d'Ardèche, Laudun waits to welcome you to this old agricultural holding which accommodates six comfortable guest rooms. Shady park with children's playground and relaxing area. The local auberge is only 100m away, facing the valley of the Ibie - it offers generous and respectable fare using local ingredients. Themed holidays available. Open all year.
PRICES: s €35; d €41; t €53; extra person €12; FB €14 **NEARBY:** Bathing (15km) Canoeing (20km) Horse riding (2km) Rock climbing (12km) Fishing (8km) Swimming pool (3km) Cross-country skiing (30km) Tennis (1km) Railway station (25km) Shops (1km) Restaurant nearby VILLENEUVE DE BERG (1km) **NOTES:** Pets admitted Minimum 2 night stay CC

Le Mas de Fournery
Benoit HENNICO & Sophie RATY
route de St Andeol de Berg,
07170 VILLENEUVE DE BERG
☎ 04 75 94 83 73 & 06 80 75 78 14
e-mail: ben.hennico@worldonline.fr
http://www.sud-ardeche.com/tourism/fournery
Come and relax at the Mas de Fournery where you can enjoy a quiet holiday in a remote spot on the heights with a panoramic view over the hills. Sophie and Benoit are happy to share their 16th-century stone home. Four spacious rooms all with private bath and wc, television and mini-bar. Local wines; garden; covered terrace; solarium; private swimming pool; pétanque; walking trail; and mountain bike hire. Access by 3km of unpaved road. Open 1 April to 15 October.
PRICES: s €40-€46; d €46-€60; t €69-€81; extra person €10
ON SITE: Swimming pool **NEARBY:** Bathing (15km) Canoeing (15km) Horse riding (3km) Rock climbing (15km) Fishing (15km) Tennis (3km) Railway station (30km) Shops (3km) VILLENEUVE DE BERG (3km) **NOTES:** Pets admitted Minimum 2 night stay CC English spoken

Use the atlas at the back of the guide to locate your chambre d'hôtes

RHÔNE-ALPES

♦♦♦ Le Petit Tournon Beatrice et Antoine CHAMPIER
07170 VILLENEUVE DE BERG
☎ 04 75 94 74 39

In an early 19th-century silkworm house now restored, just 1km from the village, your hosts offer five beautiful and comfortable rooms, each with wc and shower. An enormous vaulted room of 150m² is there for breakfast or relaxation in bad weather. Outdoor facilities include terrace; park; sunbath; and 78m² swimming pool which is free until midday. Parking. We are situated on the tourist route through the valley of the Ibie, 22km from Vallon Pont d'Arc and from the Grotte Chauvet. Closed November to March.
PRICES: s €38; d €44; t €53; extra person €7 **ON SITE:** Swimming pool **NEARBY:** Bathing (15km) Canoeing (25km) Horse riding (3km) Rock climbing (15km) Fishing (8km) Tennis (2km) Railway station (30km) Shops (2km) VILLENEUVE DE BERG (2km) **NOTES:** No pets Minimum 2 night stay

VION

♦♦♦ ⏹ La Cayra Lucienne et Michel BESSET
rue de la Vierge, 07610 VION
☎ 04 75 07 20 70 📠 04 75 07 20 70
e-mail: la.cayra@wanadoo.fr

Old restored stone house with private enclosed flower-bedecked courtyard in a little village 7km north of Tournon. Two double rooms and one double room with two spare beds, all with private shower and wc. Salon with open fire; garden furniture. Family cuisine based on local produce. Home-made preserves. Nearby Wine Trail. Tourist steam railway at Vivarais. Open 15 January to 15 December.
PRICES: s €35; d €40; t €53; extra person €14; dinner €14
ON SITE: Wine tasting **NEARBY:** Bathing (6km) Canoeing (7km) Horse riding (10km) Rock climbing (20km) Fishing (2km) Swimming pool (7km) Tennis (2km) Railway station (10km) TOURNON (7km) **NOTES:** No pets Minimum 2 night stay

DRÔME

ALBON

♦♦♦ ⏹ Le Pré aux Anes Jacques et Nadine TONDUT
Les Barris, 26140 ALBON
☎ 04 75 03 11 73
e-mail: pre.aux.anes@wanadoo.fr www.lepreauxanes.com

On the edge of the Drôme hills, a verdant and tranquil region. Evening meals with regional specialities are served by Nadine and there are two donkeys (Princess and Picotin) for children's delight. Two bedrooms for two, bathroom and wc. Two bedrooms for three with a mezzanine level, bathroom and wc. Private parking. Golf 1km. Meals for under-10s €6.10. Available all year.
PRICES: s €34; d €37; t €46; extra person €9; dinner €13
ON SITE: Swimming pool **NEARBY:** Bathing (2km) Horse riding (15km) Stretch of water (2km) Hiking (1km) Tennis (3km) Bicycle hire (6km) Shops (1km) ST RAMBERT D'ALBON (6km) **NOTES:** Pets admitted English spoken

AURIPLES

♦♦♦ ⏹ La Berte Bleue Yves DUROUX
26400 AURIPLES
☎ 04 75 25 04 25 📠 04 75 25 04 25

In the heart of the hillsides and forests of the Saou region, this large, comfortable restored house is in a quiet setting in a small hamlet. Three bedrooms sleep two; one bedroom sleeps four, with two linked rooms and private bathroom, dining room and communal sitting room. Parking area. Numerous activities on site or nearby. Rate for four people: €77. Evening meals on reservation. Open 1st March to 1st December.

PRICES: s €34; d €46; t €61; dinner €15 **ON SITE:** Swimming pool Hiking Bicycle hire **NEARBY:** Horse riding (2km) Rock climbing (8km) Stretch of water (6km) Tennis (3km) Railway station (10km) Shops (3km) CREST (10km) **NOTES:** Pets admitted

BOURDEAUX

♦♦♦ ♥ ⏹ Les Junchas Joëlle et Claudio SAMMARCO
26460 BOURDEAUX
☎ 04 75 53 38 11 & 06 68 45 42 43 📠 04 75 53 38 11
e-mail: lesjunchas@wanadoo.fr www.lesjunchas.com

Between Provence and Vecors, with a magnificent view over the Roubion valley, Joëlle and Claudio offer five double bedrooms with private bathrooms (one on the ground floor). Evening meals in a large, light dining room or on the terrace. Sitting room for cooler evenings. Camping spot nearby. Available all year.
PRICES: s €35; d €46; extra person €12; dinner €15 **ON SITE:** Hiking **NEARBY:** Horse riding (5km) Rock climbing (12km) Swimming pool (2km) Stretch of water (2km) Tennis (2km) Bicycle hire (2km) Railway station (25km) Shops (2km) CREST (25km) **NOTES:** Pets admitted English spoken

CHABRILLAN

♦♦♦ ⏹ Le Domaine de la Vaumane
Josette et Jacques ROLLAND
26400 CHABRILLAN
☎ 04 75 76 89 46 📠 04 75 76 89 46
e-mail: JACQUES.ROLLAND@wanadoo.fr
http://perso.wanadoo.fr/jjrolland

Between Vercors and Provence, in the heart of the countryside and opposite lovely scenery, is this old, restored, stone farmhouse. Four bedrooms with private bathrooms. Meals are served in the flower garden, or under the eaves of the dining room. Evening meals are available on reservation. Swimming pool. Kitchen area and parking space. Open 1st February to 30th November.
PRICES: s €36; d €48; extra person €15; dinner €16 **ON SITE:** Swimming pool Hiking **NEARBY:** Bathing (6km) Horse riding (6km) Rock climbing (15km) Stretch of water (3km) Aerial sports (15km) Tennis (6km) Bicycle hire (6km) Railway station (6km) CREST (6km) **NOTES:** Pets admitted English spoken

CHALANCON

♦♦♦ ♥ Les Bayles Yves RAYE
26470 CHALANCON
☎ 04 75 27 24 38

At the top of the Oule valley, nestled under the Eyriot mountains, this is a typical farmhouse, situated in a small hamlet. Anya and Yves offer three bedrooms on the ground floor with private bathrooms. A triple bedroom with a mezzanine, a double bedroom, a bedroom for three and a bedroom for two with twin beds, in an independent wing of the farm. Meals are served in a room of the small ferme-auberge, using the farm meat and organic vegetables. 'Truffle' weekends November-January. Open all year.
PRICES: s €38-€41; d €43-€46; t €56; dinner €17 **ON SITE:** Hiking **NEARBY:** Bathing (5km) Horse riding (6km) Rock climbing (5km) Swimming pool (5km) Stretch of water (2km) Aerial sports (20km) Tennis (5km) Railway station (30km) Shops (5km) Restaurant nearby NYONS (37km) **NOTES:** No pets English spoken

> ⏹
> Places with this symbol serve table d'hôtes evening meals - remember to book in advance

continued

CHANOS-CURSON

▦ ♥ Ferme des Denis Jacqueline et Jean-P SAUVAJON
26600 CHANOS-CURSON
☎ 04 75 07 34 11 & SR : 04 75 83 09 23 📠 04 75 07 34 46
e-mail: ferme.des.denis@wanadoo.fr www.fermedesdenis.fr.st
In the vineyards of Crozes Hermitage, you will receive a warm
welcome at this renovated 15th century farmhouse, with an
enclosed courtyard. Ground floor: one bedroom with disabled
access. First floor: three bedrooms for two or three people with
private bathrooms. Large independent lounge with kitchen area,
leading to a swimming pool. Games room. Jams and home-made
bread. Open all year.
PRICES: s €35; d €45; t €61-€66; extra person €11 **ON SITE:** Swimming
pool Hiking Bicycle hire **NEARBY:** Bathing (10km) Horse riding (2km)
Rock climbing (15km) Stretch of water (6km) Aerial sports (12km) Tennis
(2km) Railway station (5km) Shops (5km) TAIN L'HERMITAGE (5km)
NOTES: No pets English spoken

▦ ⭐○⭐ La Farella Rose-Marie ROIGE
Les Champs Ratiers, 26600 CHANOS-CURSON
☎ 04 75 07 35 44 📠 04 75 07 39 90
e-mail: accueil@lafarella.com www.lafarella.com
Three kilometres from the A7 autoroute, in the heart of the
orchards and vineyards, this old house has lots of character. Two
separate courtyards and a swimming pool. One of the bedrooms is
furnished and decorated in an antique style. Private bathrooms.
Evening meals on reservation. Children under ten: €8.5. Open all
year.
PRICES: s €35-€40; d €46-€50; extra person €15; dinner €16
ON SITE: Swimming pool **NEARBY:** Bathing (15km) Horse riding (3km)
Stretch of water (8km) Tennis (3km) Railway station (8km) Shops (8km)
TAIN L'HERMITAGE (8km) **NOTES:** Pets admitted

CHANTEMERLE-LES-GRIGNAN

▦ ⭐○⭐ Le Parfum Bleu
G et L LAMBERTS et RINGOET
26230 CHANTEMERLE-LES-GRIGNAN
☎ 04 75 98 54 21 📠 04 75 98 54 21
In the heart of provençale Drôme, between plains and hills,
vineyards and Tricastin lavender, this house offers five comfortable
two/three people bedrooms with shower rooms and private wcs,
dining room and private sitting room, open fireplace and private
parking. Golf course 2km. Evening meals are available on
reservation, except Sundays and Mondays. Open all year.
PRICES: s €72-€81; d €79-€88; t €100-€110; dinner €25
ON SITE: Swimming pool **NEARBY:** Horse riding (10km) Stretch of
water (3km) Hiking (1km) Aerial sports (15km) Tennis (3km) GRIGNAN
(7km) **NOTES:** No pets English spoken

CHARPEY

▦ ♥ ⭐○⭐ Les Marais Christiane & J-Pierre IMBERT
St-Didier de Charpey, 26300 CHARPEY
☎ 04 75 47 03 50 & 06 68 92 74 16
e-mail: imbert.jean-pierre@wanadoo.fr
www.guideweb.com/drome/bb/marais/
This shady farm lies in the middle of the countryside between
Valence and Romans, at the foot of the Vercors mountain, and just
a few paces from beautiful walking and driving routes. Three
bedrooms for two people, on the ground floor. First floor: private
bathroom, lounge and sitting room area, library, TV, parking area
and play area. Children under ten: €7/meal. Open all year.
PRICES: s €29; d €40; t €50; extra person €10; dinner €13
NEARBY: Bathing (10km) Horse riding (3km) Swimming pool (10km)
Hiking (6km) Tennis (10km) Bicycle hire (7km) Railway station (10km)
Shops (3km) BOURG DE PEAGE (6km) **NOTES:** No pets

CHATEAUDOUBLE

▦ ⭐○⭐ Les Peris Madeleine CABANES
Rte de Combovin, 26120 CHATEAUDOUBLE
☎ 04 75 59 80 51 📠 04 75 59 48 78

A large, traditional house in the countryside, set in a small hamlet
at the foot of the Massif du Vercors, not far from the farm. Three
triple bedrooms on the ground floor and the first floor. Private
bathrooms, dining room, communal sitting rooms, open fireplace,
TV, play area. Farm produce and evening meals available. Open
throughout the year.
PRICES: s €26; d €36; t €49; extra person €13; dinner €14
ON SITE: Bathing Stretch of water **NEARBY:** Horse riding (3km)
Swimming pool (5km) Hiking (3km) Tennis (5km) Railway station (16km)
VALENCE (16km) **NOTES:** Pets admitted

CHATEAUNEUF-SUR-ISERE

▦ Les Communaux Sylvie et Gérard COMBET
26300 CHATEAUNEUF-SUR-ISERE
☎ 04 75 84 58 88 📠 04 75 84 58 88
e-mail: info@naturedeaux.com www.naturedeaux.com
Five bedrooms with private bathrooms. One bedroom on the
ground floor, with disabled access (twin beds). Four bedrooms on
the first floor, one with a four-poster bed. Three bedrooms with
mezzanines for three/four people (one double bed and twin beds).
Kitchen available for longer stays. Jacuzzi €15 per person.
Available all year.
PRICES: s €37; d €46; t €61; extra person €15 **ON SITE:** Hiking
NEARBY: Bathing (1km) Horse riding (7km) Swimming pool (6km)
Railway station (6km) Shops (3km) ROMANS (20km) **NOTES:** No pets
English spoken

COLONZELLE

▦ ⭐○⭐ La Maison de Soize Nicole CONVERCY
26230 COLONZELLE
☎ 04 75 46 58 58 📠 04 75 46 58 58
In the heart of the village, in a building protected by large walls,
your hosts offer five colourful bedrooms, with a bathroom and
private wc: Violette, Capucine, Pâquerette, Iris and Eglantine.
Large sitting room with fireplace. Generous meals are served in
the dining room or on the charming west terrace. The tree-lined
garden includes a vegetable garden. Golf 18km. Open 1st March
to 31st October.
PRICES: s €60; d €70; dinner €23 **ON SITE:** Bathing Stretch of water
Hiking Bicycle hire **NEARBY:** Horse riding (3km) Swimming pool (3km)
Tennis (1km) Railway station (22km) Shops (2km) GRIGNAN (22km)
NOTES: No pets CC

Prices are given in Euros €1 = £0.62
at the time of going to press

††† ¡Ⓞ¡ Le Moulin de l'Aulière Marie BERAUD
26230 COLONZELLE
☎ 04 75 91 10 49   📠 04 75 91 10 49
In a park, on the banks of the Aulière, Marie and Guy welcome
you to their 19th century building, where you will find five
bedrooms. First floor: two bedrooms for two and three people.
Second floor: two double bedrooms, one with a terrace, one triple
bedroom. Private bathrooms, kitchen area, lounge, fireplace and
TV. Parking space. No evening meals are served on Friday and
Sunday evenings and in August and November. Open throughout
the year.
PRICES: s €40; d €50; t €75; extra person €20; dinner €20–€30
ON SITE: Stretch of water Hiking Bicycle hire **NEARBY:** Bathing (10km)
Horse riding (4km) Rock climbing (30km) Swimming pool (4km) Cross-
country skiing (40km) Aerial sports (18km) Tennis (1km) Shops (2km)
GRIGNAN (4km) **NOTES:** Pets admitted Minimum 2 night stay English
spoken

COMPS

††† ❦ Le Château Marilou TERROT
26220 COMPS
☎ 04 75 46 30 00   📠 04 75 46 30 00
Rooms are available in the majestic setting of this 12th century
chateau and in a connected wing, semi-detached from the farm.
Marilou and son offer four comfortable single and double
bedrooms, with shower room or bathroom, private wc. Breakfast
room, private sitting room and parking space. Reduction after third
night (out of season). Winter on reservation only. Open all year.
PRICES: s €38; d €46–€49; t €53 **ON SITE:** Tennis **NEARBY:** Bathing
(4km) Horse riding (5km) Swimming pool (6km) Stretch of water (4km)
Hiking (1km) Shops (6km) DIEULEFIT (6km) **NOTES:** No pets

DIVAJEU

††† Le Clos de Lambres Jeannette GORCE
26400 DIVAJEU
☎ 04 75 76 75 91
e-mail: closlambre@aol.com
http://members.aol.com/closlambre/index.html
In this calm, green setting near to the Drôme valley, Jeanette and
Jacques welcome guests. Two bedrooms for two and three people,
one family room for four. Ground floor and first floor private
bathrooms, dining room, sitting room, communal lounge (shared
with the owners). TV in each room. Private parking. Open 15th
February to 1st November.
PRICES: s €34; d €46; t €61; extra person €16 **NEARBY:** Bathing (3km)
Horse riding (3km) Rock climbing (15km) Swimming pool (3km) Stretch
of water (3km) Hiking (1km) Aerial sports (15km) Tennis (3km) Bicycle
hire (3km) Railway station (3km) Shops (3km) CREST (3km)
NOTES: No pets

ETOILE-SUR-RHONE

††† ❦ ¡Ⓞ¡ La Mare S.A.R.L. ACCUEIL Famille CHAIX
Rte de Montmeyran, Quartier La Mare, 26800 ETOILE
☎ 04 75 59 33 79 & SR : 04 75 83 09 23   📠 04 75 59 33 79
In a lovely rural setting, near to the Rhône valley, the Chaix family
will help you to discover the region. Four (grade 3) bedrooms on
the ground floor, with independent access, private bathrooms, two
(grade 2) bedrooms on the first floor, with private shower rooms.
Communal wc, shared between two bedrooms, dining room, sitting
room with TV, fireplace. Playground, large grounds around the farm.
Shady parkland. Evening meals (children: €6.3). Open all year.
PRICES: s €27; d €40; extra person €11; dinner €14 **NEARBY:** Bathing
(4km) Horse riding (6km) Swimming pool (5km) Stretch of water (4km)
Hiking (1km) Tennis (3km) Bicycle hire (1km) Railway station (15km)
Shops (4km) VALENCE (15km) **NOTES:** Pets admitted

EYGALAYES

††† ¡Ⓞ¡ La Forge Sainte-Marie
Jacques et Gaby LAURENT
26560 EYGALAYES
☎ 04 75 28 42 77   📠 04 75 28 42 77
e-mail: gaby.laurent@libertysurf.fr
www.guideprovence.com/chambres_hotes/forge-ste-marie
Jacques and Gaby welcome you to their house which is full of
character. Four comfortable bedrooms on two levels of the
building. The 'Lavande' relaxation room offers relaxation and well
being (spa bath and jacuzzi). Open all year.
PRICES: s €38; d €46; t €55; dinner €17 **ON SITE:** Hiking Bicycle hire
NEARBY: Horse riding (2km) Swimming pool (8km) Stretch of water
(2km) Aerial sports (10km) Tennis (3km) Shops (8km) SEDERON (8km)
NOTES: Pets admitted English spoken

FERRASSIERES

††† ❦ ¡Ⓞ¡ Château la Gabelle Marguerite BLANC
26570 FERRASSIERES
☎ 04 75 28 80 54   📠 04 75 28 85 56
This 12th century building, fortified in the 15th century, is set on
the outskirts of Lubéron and the Haute-Provence alps, in the
middle of the prairies and fields of lavender. The bedrooms are
comfortable with private bathrooms. Lounge and sitting room,
(with a fireplace) in the tower, are the ideal setting for meals
prepared with farm produce. Available all year.
PRICES: s €61–€84; d €69–€90; extra person €27; dinner €21
ON SITE: Hiking **NEARBY:** Bathing (8km) Horse riding (8km) Rock
climbing (30km) Swimming pool (8km) Stretch of water (8km) Aerial
sports (15km) Bicycle hire (9km) Shops (9km) SEDERON (15km)
NOTES: No pets English spoken

GRIGNAN

††† ❦ Ferme le Grand Cordy
Béatrice et Dario DUARTE
26230 GRIGNAN
☎ 04 75 46 91 81   📠 04 75 46 51 88
Vines, lavender and oak forests all surround the Grand Cordy
Farm. Five guest rooms with private bathrooms. Walks, river,
tranquillity in a comfortable, rustic setting. Golf: 5km. Open all
year.
PRICES: s €43; d €43–€46; extra person €11 **ON SITE:** Hiking
NEARBY: Horse riding (3km) Swimming pool (3km) Tennis (3km)
Shops (3km) GRIGNAN (3km) **NOTES:** No pets English spoken

††† ¡Ⓞ¡ L'Autre Maison Christophe MONGE
Rue du Grand Faubourg, 26230 GRIGNAN
☎ 04 75 46 58 65
e-mail: infos@lautremaison.com   www.lautremaison.com

In the heart of provençale Drôme, 'L'autre maison' is a large 18th
century provençaie house. Just a short distance from the
renaissance chateau, there are four very large charming

continued

bedrooms. Terrace, garden with water lily pond, provençale dinners. Bike hire: €9 for half a day, €15 for a whole day. Guided trips and bike trips (minimum of six people) for half a day. Local produce available. Open 1st March-31st October and 14th December to end of winter holiday.

PRICES: s €53-€76; d €53-€76; extra person €15; HB €81-€110; dinner €14-€17 **ON SITE:** Swimming pool Tennis **NEARBY:** Horse riding (1km) Rock climbing (15km) Stretch of water (1km) Hiking (1km) Aerial sports (15km) Railway station (25km) GRIGNAN (25km) **NOTES:** No pets English spoken CC

HOSTUN

♦♦♦ ¡◯¡ Les Bruyères Annie et Serge NATTIER
26730 HOSTUN
☎ 04 75 48 81 94 📠 04 75 48 93 50
e-mail: infosbruyeres@net-up.com
http://lesbruyeres.multimania.com

This large house is surrounded by a shady park, in two hectares of grounds. Annie and Serge will be happy to welcome you to their home and to their table. Two bedrooms for two, one bedroom for three and one family suite for four, with private bathrooms. Dining room and communal sitting room. Children's meals (under seven). Private parking, golf 20km. Available all year.

PRICES: s €43; d €49; t €66; extra person €15; dinner €15
ON SITE: Swimming pool Hiking **NEARBY:** Bathing (4km) Horse riding (1km) Rock climbing (20km) Stretch of water (4km) Cross-country skiing (30km) Aerial sports (20km) Tennis (1km) Bicycle hire (5km) Railway station (10km) Shops (1km) ROMANS (10km) **NOTES:** No pets Minimum 2 night stay English spoken

LA BATIE-ROLLAND

♦♦♦ ¡◯¡ La Joie Françis et Jackie MONEL
26160 LA BATIE-ROLLAND
☎ 04 75 53 81 51 📠 04 75 53 81 51
e-mail: f.monel@infonie.fr www.lajoie.fr

A comfortable restored farmhouse in a verdant setting. One of the bedrooms on the garden level has disabled access. Breakfast and dinner are served in a vaulted room, or in the shady courtyard in the summer. Children under 12: €13. Private entrance to bedrooms. Golf 5km. Friendly welcome. Available all year.

PRICES: s €40; d €52-€60; t €70-€88; extra person €18; dinner €19
ON SITE: Stretch of water Hiking **NEARBY:** Horse riding (2km) Swimming pool (5km) Tennis (2km) Bicycle hire (5km) Shops (5km) MONTELIMAR (10km) **NOTES:** Pets admitted English spoken

> Use the atlas at the back of the guide to locate your chambre d'hôtes

LA BEGUDE-DE-MAZENC

♦♦♦ ¡◯¡ La Faventine André SORDET
Quartier Blache Bouteille, 26160 LA BEGUDE-DE-MAZENC
☎ 04 75 90 15 02 📠 04 75 90 17 26
e-mail: la.faventine@wanadoo.fr
www.guideweb.com/provence/bb/faventine

In the Drôme countryside, at the heart of the Valdaine plains, Brigitte and André welcome you to their restored farmhouse. La Faventine offers: four double bedrooms (two of which are on the ground floor) and one triple bedroom. Evening meals on reservation. Dining room and private sitting room with fireplace,. Boules and swimming pool. Kids' meals (under 12): €10. Holiday tax. Private parking. Golf 10km. Available all year.

PRICES: s €52; d €57; t €73; extra person €17; dinner €20
ON SITE: Swimming pool Hiking **NEARBY:** Horse riding (4km) Rock climbing (15km) Stretch of water (10km) Aerial sports (30km) Tennis (4km) Bicycle hire (15km) Railway station (15km) Shops (4km) MONTELIMAR (15km) **NOTES:** No pets English spoken

LA GARDE-ADHEMAR

♦♦♦ 🐾 ¡◯¡ Gîte du Val des Nymphes
Christian & Isabelle ANDRUEJOL
26700 LA GARDE-ADHEMAR
☎ 04 75 04 44 54

This 17th century house lies in thirty hectares of land, amongst the scents of truffles and apricots, amid orchards and woods. Traditional regional cooking. Three bedrooms for two people, on the ground floor, with private bathrooms, Dining room, lounge, TV. Parking spaces. Three rural gîtes. Open all year.

PRICES: s €34; d €43; extra person €12; dinner €16 **ON SITE:** Swimming pool Hiking **NEARBY:** Horse riding (6km) Aerial sports (8km) Tennis (1km) Railway station (8km) Shops (2km) ST PAUL TROIS CHATEAUX (6km) **NOTES:** Pets admitted Minimum 2 night stay English spoken

LA PENNE-SUR-OUVEZE

♦♦♦ ¡◯¡ Mourre Genus René et Joan BOMPARD
26170 LA PENNE-SUR-OUVEZE
☎ 04 75 28 73 96 📠 04 75 28 73 96

Three large en suite family rooms, with a mezzanine and shady terrace area and a view over the Bluye mountain. Kitchen area. Evening meals, where you can taste farm produce (lamb, olives, apricots, cherries) are served either in the communal dining room or outside, depending on the weather and the season. Swimming pool. Children between 5 and 12 €7.5. Available all year.

PRICES: s €30; d €42; extra person €11; dinner €13 **ON SITE:** Swimming pool Hiking Bicycle hire **NEARBY:** Horse riding (7km) Rock climbing (4km) Aerial sports (8km) Tennis (4km) Railway station (40km) Shops (4km) BUIS LES BARONNIES (4km) **NOTES:** No pets

LA ROCHE-SUR-GRANE

♦♦♦ ▯◎▯ La Magerie Roger et Pierrette BOHLER
26400 LA ROCHE-SUR-GRANE
☎ 04 75 62 71 77 🖷 04 75 62 71 77
e-mail: LA.MAGERIE@wanadoo.fr
http://perso.wanadoo.fr/la.magerie/
This restored farmhouse is in the middle of the countryside, with a beautiful view over the old village, the wooded hills and the Vercors mountains. Communal evening meals are served. Five bedrooms with private bathrooms and wc. Communal dining room and lounge. Private parking, play area, garden. Mediterranean TGV route nearby. Discounts for long stays and for children. Half board for two people: €72. Available all year.
PRICES: s €32; d €43; extra person €15; dinner €14
ON SITE: Swimming pool Stretch of water Hiking Bicycle hire
NEARBY: Horse riding (12km) Rock climbing (12km) Tennis (6km) Railway station (12km) CREST (12km) **NOTES:** Pets admitted

LA ROCHETTE-DU-BUIS

♦♦♦ ▯◎▯ La Honas Cathy et Pascal DUCROS
26170 LA ROCHETTE-DU-BUIS
☎ 04 75 28 55 11 🖷 04 75 28 55 11
lahonas@club-internet.fr
Cathy and Pascal Ducros welcome you to their lovingly restored, 17th century farmhouse, situated in an isolated spot in the heart of thirty hectares of lavender, thyme, oak and lime trees. Situated at the crossroads of the gorges of Toulourenc and l'Ouvèze, La Honas is a calm site of exceptional beauty. Four bedrooms (one is a suite for four) with bathrooms. Dining room, sitting room. Evening meals every evening, except Sunday. Meals for under-twelves: €9. Swimming pool and very large garden. Open 15 March to 15 November.
PRICES: s €40; d €50-€58; t €65; extra person €15; dinner €17
ON SITE: Swimming pool Hiking **NEARBY:** Bathing (5km) Horse riding (11km) Rock climbing (5km) Stretch of water (5km) Aerial sports (5km) Tennis (11km) Shops (10km) BUIS LES BARONNIES (20km)
NOTES: Pets admitted Minimum 2 night stay English spoken

MARIGNAC-EN-DIOIS

♦♦♦ ▯🐓▯ ▯◎▯ La Rollandière Jacky et Renée SEGOND
L'Hermite, 26150 MARIGNAC-EN-DIOIS
☎ 04 75 22 08 51 🖷 04 75 22 08 51
In this calm, country location, at the foot of the massif of Vercors, Renée and Jacky welcome you to their lovely farmhouse and will help you appreciate their region, their food and their homemade produce. One triple bedroom with private bathroom, two double bedrooms on the ground floor. Private bathrooms, private lounge. Open Easter to 1 November.
PRICES: s €26; d €39; t €50; dinner €12 **ON SITE:** Hiking
NEARBY: Bathing (7km) Horse riding (10km) Swimming pool (7km) Stretch of water (7km) Cross-country skiing (20km) Tennis (7km) Railway station (7km) Shops (7km) DIE (8km) **NOTES:** Pets admitted

MIRABEL-AUX-BARONNIES

♦♦♦ L'Ormeraie Véronique DUROUGE
Les Blaches, 26110 MIRABEL-AUX-BARONNIES
☎ 04 75 27 19 49 & 06 74 64 63 45 🖷 04 75 27 19 49
In the heart of the Baronnies countryside, between Mirabel and Nyons, Véronique welcomes you to her home, surrounded by vines and olives. Two double bedrooms with private bathrooms, one triple bedroom with private bathroom. One bedroom suite for four people, (€99) with private bathroom. Kitchen area, lounge, dining room, parking area, barbecue, garden furniture, swimming pool. Closed January.
PRICES: s €38-€58; d €53-€69; t €61-€84; extra person €11-€15

ON SITE: Swimming pool Hiking **NEARBY:** Bathing (4km) Horse riding (5km) Rock climbing (27km) Stretch of water (10km) Cross-country skiing (27km) Aerial sports (27km) Tennis (3km) Bicycle hire (5km) Shops (5km) NYONS (5km) **NOTES:** Pets admitted Minimum 2 night stay

MIRIBEL

♦♦♦ 🐓 La Charière Jean-Louis et Livia VASSY
26350 MIRIBEL
☎ 04 75 71 75 13 🖷 04 75 71 71 71
In the heart of the hills of the Drôme, Livia and Jean-Louis welcome you to their farm. They offer two double bedrooms with a terrace, private bathrooms, dining room and communal sitting room. One three-person bedroom with a terrace, kitchen area and private bathroom. Playground and parking area. Available all year.
PRICES: s €32; d €40; extra person €10 **NEARBY:** Bathing (10km) Horse riding (3km) Swimming pool (13km) Stretch of water (1km) Hiking (1km) Tennis (4km) Shops (4km) ROMANS (22km) **NOTES:** Pets admitted

MIRMANDE

♦♦♦ Chambre d'hôtes Marinette et Tieno GORIOU
26270 MIRMANDE
☎ 04 75 63 01 15 🖷 04 75 63 14 06
This house has a balcony overlooking the Rhône valley, with panoramic views over the Vivarais Mountains, near to a medieval village (classed as one of the most beautiful villages in France). Marinette and Tieno welcome you to their large, comfortable house, near to a sculpture workshop: three bedrooms for two people with bathrooms and private terraces. Communal sitting room, kitchen and parking area. Closed January.
PRICES: s €44; d €55; extra person €22 **ON SITE:** Swimming pool Hiking Bicycle hire **NEARBY:** Stretch of water (1km) Tennis (4km) Railway station (15km) Shops (1km) MONTELIMAR (15km) **NOTES:** No pets English spoken

♦♦♦ Le Petit Logis Maryse BRUN
La Colline, 26270 MIRMANDE
☎ 04 75 63 02 92 🖷 04 75 63 02 92
www.lepetitlogis.com02.com
In a house, near to that of the owner, in the middle of a green and calm park, with a view over the medieval village, Maryse and René offer you three bedrooms, accessible from the ground floor, with private bathrooms and the possibility of an extra small bedroom. Small kitchen, swimming pool, parking area, play area. Dining room and lounge to be shared with the owners. Open March to November, winter on reservation.
PRICES: s €34; d €44; t €55; extra person €11 **ON SITE:** Swimming pool Hiking **NEARBY:** Stretch of water (12km) Tennis (4km) MONTELIMAR (20km) **NOTES:** Pets admitted Minimum 2 night stay

MOLLANS-SUR-OUVEZE

♦♦♦ Les Fouzarailles Valérie et Marc GRENON
Route de Veaux, 26170 MOLLANS-SUR-OUVEZE
☎ 04 75 28 79 05 🖷 04 75 28 79 05
At the foot of Mount Ventoux, with an impressive view, Valérie and Marc welcome you to their provençale farm, nestled between woods and vineyards in the Toulourenc valley. Numerous activities nearby: sports and bathing in the Toulourenc, 300m away. Three bedrooms for two, one bedroom for three, with private bathrooms. Play area. Table tennis, boules pitch. Terrace, private parking, barbecue and fridge. Mollans is situated on the outskirts of the Baronnies. Open Easter to 1 November.
PRICES: s €32; d €39; extra person €11 **ON SITE:** Stretch of water Hiking Bicycle hire **NEARBY:** Horse riding (4km) Rock climbing (10km) Swimming pool (1km) Aerial sports (10km) Tennis (1km) Railway station (50km) Shops (3km) VAISON (12km) **NOTES:** Pets admitted Minimum 2 night stay English spoken

continued

MONTBRISON-SUR-LEZ

††† 🐓 Roussoullie Rémi et Marie-Nöelle BARJAVEL
26770 MONTBRISON-SUR-LEZ
☎ 04 75 53 54 04 📠 04 75 53 54 04
e-mail: barjavel@club-internet.fr www.domainebarjavel.com
Marie-Nöelle and Rémy, winegrowers, welcome you to their
provençale house, in the middle of the vineyards of Côtes du Rhône.
There are two rural, semi-detached gîtes and three guest bedrooms
with private entrances. One double bedroom on the ground floor,
with private bathroom, two bedrooms for two/three people, with
bathroom, wc. Kitchen area, lounge. Available all year.
PRICES: s €34-€36; d €36-€40; t €47; extra person €7
ON SITE: Swimming pool Hiking Bicycle hire **NEARBY:** Bathing (2km)
Stretch of water (2km) Tennis (6km) Railway station (7km) Shops (7km)
NYONS (15km) **NOTES:** Pets admitted

MONTBRUN-LES-BAINS

††† Chambre d'hôtes René AIME
Montée du Château, 26570 MONTBRUN-LES-BAINS
☎ 04 75 28 84 92
At the top of Montbrun-Les-Bains, in a charming village, with a
view over the Ventoux mountains. René offers you two double
bedrooms, and a large bedroom for two with a bed, kitchen area,
private bathroom and communal dining room. Garden furniture
and private parking. Near to the centre of the village. Open April to
November.
PRICES: s €34-€38; d €38-€46; extra person €12 **NEARBY:** Bathing
(10km) Horse riding (2km) Rock climbing (10km) Swimming pool (1km)
Stretch of water (10km) Hiking (10km) Aerial sports (15km) Tennis (1km)
NYONS (40km) **NOTES:** Pets admitted Minimum 2 night stay

MONTFROC

††† ⦿| Le Château Claire et Paul THIELEMANS
26560 MONTFROC
☎ 04 92 62 06 64 📠 04 92 62 06 64
The Château de Montfroc was built in 1638 and lies within the
confines of the Drôme and the Alpes de Haute-Provence. This
château has been restored and offers a sunny and relaxing setting.
Four bedrooms, two of which are family bedrooms, and one suite,
all with private bathrooms. Golf 70km. Available all year.
PRICES: d €55-€75; extra person €15; dinner €18 **ON SITE:** Stretch of
water Hiking **NEARBY:** Bathing (28km) Horse riding (1km) Rock
climbing (10km) Swimming pool (10km) Aerial sports (15km) Tennis
(10km) Bicycle hire (15km) Railway station (28km) Shops (10km)
SEDERON (10km) **NOTES:** Pets admitted English spoken

MONTSEGUR-SUR-LAUZON

†††† ⦿| Le Moulin de Montségur
Sabine BARRUCAND
26130 MONTSEGUR-SUR-LAUZON
☎ 04 75 98 19 67 📠 04 75 98 87 71
e-mail: sbarrucand@aol.com
This large building, in the middle of the woods, on the banks
of the Lez, offers four spacious bedrooms and a suite, all with
private bathrooms. Large sitting room and lounge. Walks,
boules, fishing. Private parking. Beach on the banks of the
river. Golf 7km. Suite: €99. Available throughout the year.
PRICES: s €67-€82; d €75-€90; extra person €23; dinner €30
ON SITE: Bathing Stretch of water Hiking **NEARBY:** Horse riding
(10km) Swimming pool (8km) Aerial sports (6km) Tennis (2km)
GRIGNAN (6km) **NOTES:** Pets admitted English spoken

RECOUBEAU-JANSAC

††† 🐓 ⦿| Chambre d'hôtes
M et P CHAFFOIS-BOURGEAT
26310 RECOUBEAU-JANSAC
☎ 04 75 21 30 46 📠 04 75 21 30 46
In the hamlet of Jansac, opposite the Diois mountains and
amongst the fields of lavender, Mireille and her son Philippe offer
a warm welcome to their stone house. Two double bedrooms
(grade 3), one triple bedroom (grade 2), two double bedrooms
(grade 1), with both private and communal bathrooms. 11th-
century dining room. Meals available. Farm produce. Open all
year.
PRICES: s €24-€32; d €32-€41; t €46; dinner €13 **ON SITE:** Hiking
NEARBY: Bathing (4km) Horse riding (4km) Swimming pool (4km)
Stretch of water (4km) Cross-country skiing (27km) Tennis (7km) Shops
(4km) LUC EN DIOIS (8km) **NOTES:** No pets

ROCHEGUDE

††† ⦿| Le Mas des Vignes
Georges et Babette LURAULT
26790 ROCHEGUDE
☎ 04 75 98 26 60
In the heart of the vineyards, opposite the chateau and the forest
of Rochegude and with the backdrop of the Mont Ventoux,
Georges and Babette's home has a comfortable and relaxed
atmosphere. Five bedrooms for two/three people, with private
bathrooms, dining room, sitting room with TV, books, fireplace.
Private parking. Golf 15, 25 and 45km away. Available throughout
the year.
PRICES: s €35; d €43; t €56; extra person €11; dinner €17
ON SITE: Swimming pool Hiking Bicycle hire **NEARBY:** Horse riding
(6km) Stretch of water (4km) Tennis (2km) Railway station (15km) Shops
(2km) BOLLENE (12km) **NOTES:** Pets admitted

SAUZET

††† 🐓 ⦿| Le Sagnac Jean et Françoise FAUGIER
26740 SAUZET
☎ 04 75 46 71 78
A beautiful, traditional farmhouse, in the countryside on the edges
of provençale Drôme. Françoise and Jean offer three bedrooms
for two/three people with private bathrooms and private access.
11km from the A7 on the D105. Available all year.
PRICES: s €34; d €43; t €56; extra person €14; dinner €13
ON SITE: Hiking **NEARBY:** Horse riding (10km) Swimming pool (2km)
Stretch of water (3km) Tennis (2km) Railway station (10km) Shops (2km)
Rock climbing (20km) MONTELIMAR (10km) **NOTES:** Pets admitted

ST-AUBAN-SUR-OUVEZE

††† 🐓 ⦿| La Galane
J-Y et B ROCHAS-DENUZIERE
26170 ST-AUBAN-SUR-OUVEZE
☎ 04 75 28 62 37 & 06 22 65 70 44 📠 04 75 28 63 88
e-mail: galane@free.fr
In this stone farmhouse, with a view over the village and the
valley, in the middle of fields of lavender, Jean-Yves and Bruna will
help you to appreciate provençale Drôme and their farm produce.
Three bedrooms for two people with private bathrooms, one
bedroom suite for four people, dining room, TV, sitting room on a
mezzanine, laundry. No meals on Wednesday and Sunday
evenings. Open 1st March to 15th November.
PRICES: s €30; d €37-€40; t €52; extra person €12; dinner €13
ON SITE: Swimming pool **NEARBY:** Bathing (1km) Rock climbing
(17km) Stretch of water (1km) Hiking (1km) Aerial sports (10km) Tennis
(17km) BUIS LES BARONNIES (17km) **NOTES:** Pets admitted English
spoken

ST-JEAN-EN-ROYANS

⍭ ❦ ⚏ Ferme de Fontepaisse

Michèle CHABERT
26190 ST-JEAN-EN-ROYANS
☎ 04 75 48 60 65
e-mail: michele.chabert@wanadoo.fr
http://fontepaisse.multimania.com

Michèle and Fernand welcome you to an 18th-century farmhouse, in a tree-lined setting. First floor: two triple bedrooms. Second floor: two double bedrooms with private bathrooms. Dining room, sitting room, central heating. Evening meals on reservation. Cot on request. Open all year.

PRICES: s €32; d €41; t €56; extra person €14; HB €34; dinner €14 **ON SITE:** Swimming pool Stretch of water Hiking **NEARBY:** Horse riding (3km) Rock climbing (5km) Cross-country skiing (18km) Aerial sports (3km) Tennis (3km) Bicycle hire (2km) Shops (1km) ROMANS (15km) **NOTES:** Pets admitted Minimum 2 night stay

⍭ ⚏ Les Tourelons Monique NUBLAT

37 avenue de la Forêt de Lente,
26190 SAINT-JEAN-EN-ROYANS
☎ 04 75 48 63 96

In this restored 18th century farmhouse, in the heart of Royans country and at the foot of the Massif du Vercors, on the Route des Cols, Monique offers three bedrooms for two/three people, with shower room or private bathroom. Large dining room, private sitting room. Private parking. Available throughout the year.

PRICES: s €32; d €41; extra person €14; HB €34; dinner €14 **NEARBY:** Horse riding (1km) Rock climbing (6km) Swimming pool (1km) Hiking (1km) Cross-country skiing (12km) Tennis (1km) Bicycle hire (2km) ROMANS (25km) **NOTES:** Pets admitted

ST-JULIEN-EN-QUINT

⍭ ⚏ Le Moulin du Rivet Wim et Leni SEMPELS

26150 ST-JULIEN-EN-QUINT
☎ 04 75 21 20 43 📄 04 75 21 20 43
e-mail: le.moulin.du.rivet@wanadoo.fr

Charming old restored mill in the south of the Parc Naturel Régional du Vercors. On the banks of the river with a superb view of the Ambel mountains and the Quint circle. Evening meals feature original and inspired recipes using local produce. Wim and Léni welcome you to their very comfortable rooms with private shower rooms. Children under two go free. Children's meals (under ten): €7. Available all year.

PRICES: s €32; d €42; t €52; extra person €10; dinner €13 **ON SITE:** Bathing Stretch of water Hiking Bicycle hire **NEARBY:** Horse riding (10km) Rock climbing (13km) Swimming pool (14km) Cross-country skiing (30km) Aerial sports (15km) Tennis (14km) Railway station (14km) Shops (14km) DIE (14km) **NOTES:** No pets English spoken

SUZE-LA-ROUSSE

⍭ ⚏ La Poupaille Pierre FOSSOYEUX

26790 SUZE-LA-ROUSSE
☎ 04 75 04 83 99 📄 04 75 04 83 99

A large provençale house, surrounded by vineyards and the woods of Tricastin. Five double bedrooms on the ground floor and first floor, with private bathrooms. Dining room, sitting room with open fireplace. Private parking, garden. Available all year.

PRICES: s €35; d €44; extra person €14; dinner €18 **ON SITE:** Swimming pool Hiking Bicycle hire **NEARBY:** Horse riding (13km) Stretch of water (2km) Tennis (6km) Shops (3km) ST PAUL 3 CHATEAUX (6km) **NOTES:** Pets admitted English spoken

TAULIGNAN

⍭ La Rialhe Aline MARQUIS

Place de la République, 26770 TAULIGNAN
☎ 04 75 53 51 79 & 06 89 63 64 80

In the heart of Taulignan village, this old mill has been entirely restored. On the ground floor, you will find a small gîte for four people. Five spacious, relaxing bedrooms, each have private bathrooms. Available all year.

PRICES: s €34; d €41; t €49; extra person €12 **NEARBY:** Bathing (1km) Horse riding (7km) Swimming pool (7km) Stretch of water (1km) Hiking (2km) Tennis (1km) Bicycle hire (2km) Railway station (30km) GRIGNAN (7km) **NOTES:** No pets English spoken

TRUINAS

⍭ ⚏ Les Volets Bleus Pilar et Carlo FORTUNATO

26460 TRUINAS
☎ 04 75 53 38 48 📄 04 75 53 49 02
e-mail: lesvolets@aol.com.
www.guideweb.com/provence/chambres_hotes/volets-bleus

This old farm is wonderfully situated between woods and plains, between Vercors and Provence. Panoramic views over the Préalpes. Mediterranean cooking and farm produce (partially organic). Five comfortable bedrooms for two to three people, with bathrooms. Separate dining room and sitting room. Play area under the oak trees, private parking. No smoking house. Tourist tax €0.15 per adult per day. Available all year.

PRICES: s €44; d €50; t €63; extra person €12; dinner €19 **ON SITE:** Hiking Bicycle hire **NEARBY:** Bathing (5km) Horse riding (6km) Rock climbing (15km) Swimming pool (5km) Stretch of water (5km) Tennis (5km) Shops (5km) BOURDEAUX (5km) **NOTES:** Pets admitted English spoken

TULETTE

⍭ La Ramade Arnaud MARTINET-DUMARQUEZ

Chemin de Visan Nord, 26790 TULETTE
☎ 04 75 98 31 12 📄 04 75 98 31 12

'La Ramade' is a provençale house huddled in the middle of vineyards, in a calm spot. Three large bedrooms for two or three people with private bathrooms. Dining room, sitting room. Electric heating, private parking, shady terrace. Swimming pool. Open all year.

PRICES: s €46; d €52; t €64 **ON SITE:** Swimming pool Hiking **NEARBY:** Horse riding (2km) Rock climbing (15km) Stretch of water (4km) Tennis (2km) Railway station (23km) Shops (2km) SAINT PAUL TROIS CHATEAUX **NOTES:** No pets Minimum 2 night stay

⍭ ⚏ Le Mas des Santolines

Claude et Roselyne DUMARQUEZ
Chemin de Visan Nord, 26790 TULETTE
☎ 04 75 98 30 00 📄 04 75 98 30 00
www.guideweb.com/provence/bb/santolines

Le Mas des Santolines is a restored provençale home, situated in the middle of the vineyards in a lovely calm spot. Roselyne and Claude will be happy to welcome you and to offer you their provençale cooking, with aperitifs, wines, coffee all included. Two double bedrooms on the first floor, two triple bedrooms on the ground floor. Private bathrooms, dining room, sitting room with TV. Terrace. Electric heating. Private parking, garden, swimming pool. Available all year.

PRICES: s €46; d €52; t €64; dinner €20 **ON SITE:** Swimming pool Hiking **NEARBY:** Horse riding (2km) Rock climbing (15km) Stretch of water (4km) Tennis (2km) Railway station (23km) Shops (2km) SAINT PAUL TROIS CHATEAUX (35km) **NOTES:** No pets

UPIE

♨ 🍴 La Bergerie V et G LOUVET-DELAUNAY
Les Cornerets, 26120 UPIE
☎ 04 75 84 38 95 📠 04 75 84 38 95
e-mail: gdelaunay@wanadoo.fr
In this old 18th century wooden house, Miéry, Viviane and Gérard offer you three bedrooms on the first floor, one has a solarium, with private bathrooms. Lounge, dining room. Salt water swimming pool in a country park. Mediterranean TGV route is nearby. Open all year.
PRICES: s €46; d €49-€53; t €66; extra person €12; dinner €18
ON SITE: Swimming pool Hiking **NEARBY:** Bathing (6km) Horse riding (3km) Rock climbing (4km) Stretch of water (6km) Aerial sports (15km) Tennis (4km) Bicycle hire (4km) Railway station (20km) Shops (8km) CREST (8km) **NOTES:** No pets Minimum 2 night stay CC

VALAURIE

♨ 🐓 🍴 Le Val Leron Mick et François PROTHON
26230 VALAURIE
☎ 04 75 98 52 52 📠 04 75 98 52 52
Mick and François welcome you to their provençale Drôme home; an old, renovated boarding house in the middle of the countryside, on a sheep farm, where organic cheese and truffles are produced. One bedroom for two with wc and bathroom, two bedrooms for four with wc, bathroom and kitchen area. Private entrances, sitting room, TV, reading room, piano. Swimming pool, garden furniture. Golf 500m away. Meals for children under six: €8. Open 1st February to 1st December.
PRICES: s €31; d €46; t €58; extra person €12; dinner €16-€20
ON SITE: Swimming pool Stretch of water Hiking **NEARBY:** Bathing (7km) Horse riding (7km) Tennis (3km) Railway station (20km) Shops (2km) GRIGNAN (10km) **NOTES:** Pets admitted English spoken

HAUTE-SAVOIE

ABONDANCE

♨ 🍴 Champfleury Nadine AVOCAT-MAULAZ
Richebourg, 74360 ABONDANCE
☎ 04 50 73 03 00 & SR: 04 50 10 10 11 📠 04 50 73 03 00
Abbaye d'Abondance 2 km. Chatel 12 km. At an altitude of 1000 metres, in the heart of the Abondance valley, this old chalet has been renovated in the traditional Savoie style. Champfleury has four en suite guest rooms, all furnished with double beds, some with extra singles. Use of sitting room with TV. Owner Nadine offers home-cooked local specialities. Downhill skiing in the valley and other Ports du Solely resorts. Luge runs, skating, and swimming and water sports also nearby. Reduced rate for children. Single supplement.
PRICES: s €23; d €38; t €50; HB €30 **ON SITE:** Fishing Cross-country skiing **NEARBY:** Horse riding (7km) Swimming pool (8km) Stretch of water (30km) Place of interest (3km) Downhill skiing (3km) Aerial sports (8km) Tennis (3km) Spa (30km) Railway station (30km) Shops (3km) ABONDANCE (3km) **NOTES:** No pets

BELLEVAUX

♨ 🐓 🍴 La Clusaz
Geneviève & Francis PASQUIER
74470 BELLEVAUX
☎ 04 50 73 71 92 📠 04 50 73 71 92
Lac Léman & Thonon-les-Bains 20 km. This large farmhouse, covered with flowers, stands in a leafy spot in a hamlet. Geneviève and Francis offer six en suite guest rooms: five doubles and one twin room. Central heating. Use of dining room, guests' sitting room with fireplace, TV, washing area, courtyard, garden and games. Reduction for children. Downhill skiing at nearby Chevrerie and Hirmentaz resorts. Open 20 December to 1 October.

PRICES: HB €32; FB €38 **ON SITE:** Fishing Cross-country skiing **NEARBY:** Horse riding (4km) Swimming pool (10km) Stretch of water (25km) Place of interest (25km) Downhill skiing (4km) Aerial sports (5km) Tennis (4km) Spa (25km) Railway station (25km) Shops (4km) THONON-LES-BAINS (25km) **NOTES:** Pets admitted

BLUFFY

♨ Chalet Adagio Marie-José et Roland TILLIER
Le Bosson, 74290 BLUFFY
☎ 04 50 02 89 85 & SR: 04 50 10 10 11 📠 04 50 02 89 85
e-mail: chadagio@wanadoo.fr
Lac d'Annecy 2.5 km. Château de Menthon-St-Bernard 1 km. Standing at the foot of the Dents de Lanfon and overlooking the Lake of Annecy and the Menton-St-Bernard chateau, these three en suite guest rooms, grouped around the garden, all have superb views. Owners Marie-José and Roland offer a warm welcome. Use of large living room with kitchen area and shady terrace where guests can relax and enjoy the panorama. Restaurants, beaches, golf, skiing nearby. Open all year.
PRICES: s €37; d €46; t €61 **NEARBY:** Horse riding (3km) Fishing (3km) Swimming pool (10km) Stretch of water (3km) Place of interest (1km) Cross-country skiing (10km) Downhill skiing (10km) Aerial sports (3km) Tennis (3km) Spa (40km) Railway station (11km) Shops (2km) ANNECY-LE-VIEUX (7km) **NOTES:** No pets English spoken

CHAMONIX-ARGENTIERE-LE-TOUR

♨ 🍴 Le Gratapia Caroline et Denis PILLOT
24, chemin des Demi-Jours,
74400 LE TOUR-ARGENTIÈRE
☎ 04 50 54 22 49 & 06 09 43 93 21 📠 04 50 54 22 49
e-mail: denis.pillot@libertysurf.fr
http://www.imedserv.com/gratapia
This traditional chalet stands at the foot of the Tour Glacier, facing Mont Blanc. Owners offer a warm welcome and five guest rooms: four double and two attached doubles, ideal for families. All have south-facing balconies. Private parking. Ski runs outside chalet. Dinner for more than four, on reservation (except Sundays). Reduced rate after three nights. Children's rate. Open all year, except May and in autumn.
PRICES: d €63-€70; dinner €17 **ON SITE:** Place of interest Cross-country skiing Downhill skiing **NEARBY:** Horse riding (4km) Fishing (3km) Swimming pool (10km) Stretch of water (25km) Aerial sports (10km) Tennis (5km) Spa (25km) Railway station (1km) Shops (3km) CHAMONIX MONT-BLANC (10km) **NOTES:** No pets English spoken

CHAMONIX-MONT-BLANC

♨ La Girandole Pierre et Georgette GAZAGNES
46 chemin de la Persévérance,
74400 CHAMONIX-MONT-BLANC
☎ 04 50 53 37 58 📠 04 50 55 81 77
Cable car at l'Aiguille du Midi 1.5 km. Mer de Glace 1.5 km. Standing on a sunny slope at the edge of a forest and facing the Mont Blanc range, this beautiful chalet has three comfortable guest rooms: two double and one with twin beds, all of which have bath or shower room and wc. Use of peaceful garden. Breakfast in large dining room with panoramic view and fireplace. Parking. Open all year.
PRICES: s €48; d €58 **NEARBY:** Horse riding (2km) Fishing (2km) Swimming pool (2km) Stretch of water (20km) Place of interest (2km) Cross-country skiing (2km) Downhill skiing (1km) Aerial sports (1km) Tennis (2km) Spa (20km) Railway station (2km) Shops (1km) CHAMONIX MONT-BLANC (2km) **NOTES:** No pets English spoken

🐓 Places with this symbol are farmhouses

continued

RHÔNE-ALPES

CHATILLON-SUR-CLUSES

▓▓▓ ﾔ◯ﾔ La Ferme de Beatrix Brigitte DECAUDIN

Chef-lieu, 74300 CHATILLON-SUR-CLUSES
☎ 04 50 89 43 97 & 06 74 93 53 40 SR: 04 50 10 10 11
🖹 04 50 89 44 04
Cluses 8 km. Chartreuse-de-Melan 3 km. At the crossroads between the great Haute-Savoie, Grand-Massif, Portes du Soleil and Praz de Lys-Sommand ski ranges, this former farm offers three guest rooms, decorated like forest cabins, all doubles with extra beds available, and en suite bathrooms and wc. Large living room with fireplace and pool table, walled orchard, spacious grounds with beautiful panorama over the Aravis. Dinner by reservation. Open all year.
PRICES: s €38; d €46; t €61; dinner €14 **NEARBY:** Horse riding (5km) Fishing (3km) Swimming pool (10km) Stretch of water (25km) Place of interest (3km) Cross-country skiing (8km) Downhill skiing (9km) Aerial sports (6km) Tennis (3km) Spa (32km) Railway station (8km) CLUSES (8km) **NOTES:** No pets English spoken

CHAVANOD

▓▓▓ ﾔ◯ﾔ Le Savoisien Bernard BOUVIER

98, Route de Corbier, 74650 CHAVANOD
☎ 04 50 69 02 95 & SR: 04 50 10 10 11 🖹 04 50 69 02 95
e-mail: gite_savoisien@compuserve.com
http://ourworld.compuserve.com/homepages/gite_savoisien
Annecy 6 km. Château de Montrottier, Gorges du Fier 2 km. Situated in the centre of the village of Corbier, this former farm has been fully renovated in the local style. The four guest rooms - two doubles, one double with extra single and one twin - all have private bath or shower room and wc. Folding bed available. Dining room, grounds with outdoor seating, games. Evening meals, except Saturdays and Sundays. Open all year.
PRICES: s €37; d €43; extra person €20; dinner €16 **ON SITE:** Children's play area **NEARBY:** Horse riding (4km) Fishing (4km) Swimming pool (3km) Stretch of water (6km) Place of interest (3km) Cross-country skiing (20km) Downhill skiing (20km) Aerial sports (20km) Tennis (3km) Spa (40km) Railway station (6km) Shops (1km) SEYNOD (3km) **NOTES:** No pets English spoken

COPPONEX

▓▓▓ 🐓 La Bécassière André et Suzanne GAL

Chatillon, 74350 COPPONEX
☎ 04 50 44 08 94 🖹 04 50 44 08 94
Geneva 18 km. Annecy 20 km. In the heart of the Avant-pays, between Geneva and Annecy stands this beautiful restored farm, full of character, which has central heating and is very comfortable. It has three guest rooms: one double and two twin, all with private shower room and wc. Guests' sitting room, games, grounds, garden. Good restaurants nearby. Open 1 February to 15 November.
PRICES: s €46-€49; d €52-€55 **ON SITE:** Children's play area **NEARBY:** Horse riding (2km) Fishing (8km) Swimming pool (8km) Stretch of water (8km) Place of interest (10km) Cross-country skiing (15km) Downhill skiing (35km) Aerial sports (15km) Tennis (8km) Spa (50km) Railway station (15km) Shops (8km) CRUSEILLES (7km) **NOTES:** No pets

ESERY

▓▓▓ ﾔ◯ﾔ Chambre d'hôtes Monique MABBOUX

291, Chemin de la Thébaïde, Esery, 74930 REIGNIER
☎ 04 50 36 57 32 & 06 70 40 29 52 SR: 04 50 10 10 11
Geneva 10 km. La Roche-sur-Foron 12 km. This beautiful villa, situated near Geneva, lies between forest and mountain. Monique and René offer four very pleasant guest rooms: one grade 3 en suite double room, one grade 2 room with double, extra single,

private shower and shared wc, and two grade 1 rooms with double and extra single. Guests' sitting room, large walled garden, terrace, games. Central heating. Dinner by reservation. Restaurants nearby. Free for children under three, reduction for under tens.
PRICES: s €26-€29; d €34-€40; t €43-€46; dinner €13
ON SITE: Children's play area **NEARBY:** Horse riding (12km) Fishing (1km) Swimming pool (6km) Stretch of water (10km) Place of interest (10km) Cross-country skiing (20km) Downhill skiing (20km) Aerial sports (10km) Tennis (5km) Spa (50km) Railway station (6km) Shops (3km) REIGNIER (6km) **NOTES:** No pets

LES GETS

▓▓▓ ﾔ◯ﾔ Chalet L'Envala Thérèse GOSSET

Route des Platons, 74260 LES GETS
☎ 04 50 75 89 15 🖹 04 50 75 89 15
e-mail: chalet.lenvala@libertysurf.fr www.lenvala.com
Morzine 8 km. Samoens 20 km. On a sunny slope above the village, between Leman and Mont-Blanc, stands this charming wooden chalet. It boasts spectacular panoramic alpine views of the peaks right across to Switzerland. The rooms are warmly decorated and furnished completely in wood. Sitting room with open fire, flower-filled terrace. Homemade dinner includes numerous local specialities. Open all year.
PRICES: d €55-€90; t €83-€135; HB €43-€70 **NEARBY:** Horse riding (2km) Fishing (2km) Swimming pool (2km) Stretch of water (2km) Place of interest (2km) Cross-country skiing (2km) Downhill skiing (2km) Aerial sports (2km) Tennis (2km) Spa (35km) Railway station (25km) Shops (2km) TANINGES (7km) **NOTES:** No pets English spoken
See advert on opposite page

LES HOUCHES

▓▓▓ ﾔ◯ﾔ La Ferme d'en Haut Marie-Joëlle TURC

152, Route des Aillouds, 74310 LES HOUCHES
☎ 04 50 54 74 87 🖹 04 50 54 74 87
http://tvmountain.com/service/index.htm
Chamonix 6 km. Aiguille du Midi 5 km. A peaceful haven for Mont Blanc hill-walkers and mountaineers, this is a charming 19th-century wooden chalet with a snug living room with fireplace and gourmet dining next to a purring stove. Sunny terrace, ski runs and paths on the doorstep. Four guest rooms: two double and two with two doubles, all with en suite bath or shower rooms and wc. Close to Chamonix. Open all year.
PRICES: d €55; dinner €15; HB €42 **ON SITE:** Downhill skiing **NEARBY:** Fishing (2km) Swimming pool (6km) Stretch of water (18km) Place of interest (6km) Cross-country skiing (2km) Aerial sports (6km) Tennis (2km) Spa (15km) Railway station (3km) Shops (2km) CHAMONIX MONT-BLANC (6km) **NOTES:** No pets English spoken

LULLY

▓▓▓ ﾔ◯ﾔ Le Pré d'Emma Agnès CHARMOT

Les Parrets, 74890 LULLY
☎ 04 50 31 75 18 & 04 50 36 34 41 SR: 04 50 10 10 11
Thonon-les-Bains 11 km. Col de Cou 13 km. Sciez 8 km. Between Lake Lemoin and the Col de Cou - Vallee Verte Mountains, in the middle of a village, stands this old chalet, owned by Agnès and Michèle. They offer four en suite guest rooms, all double, with entrances off their own private terraces. Use of large pleasant wooden living room with TV, library and games, kitchen area, and flowery garden. Dinner on reservation. Open all year.
PRICES: s €38; d €46; extra person €15; dinner €15 **ON SITE:** Fishing **NEARBY:** Horse riding (6km) Swimming pool (11km) Stretch of water (8km) Place of interest (1km) Cross-country skiing (13km) Downhill skiing (13km) Aerial sports (13km) Tennis (2km) Spa (11km) Railway station (11km) DOUVAINE (5km) **NOTES:** No pets Minimum 2 night stay English spoken

continued

SALES

⚑⚑⚑ C'est la Lune
E et C BASSO-BONDINI-RAMOS
Chef-lieu, 74150 SALES
☎ 04 50 01 47 31 ▤ 04 50 01 47 31
e-mail: selalune@yahoo.fr

Rumilly 1.5 km. Annecy 15 km. This fully restored farmhouse has three spacious, charming and comfortable guest rooms. One is a double, one has a double with extra single and the other is a family room for four. All have private bath or shower room and wc. Cot available. Shared sitting room with TV and kitchen area, pleasant garden. Fishing, cycling, riding, skiing, rambling, water sports nearby. Open all year.
PRICES: s €38; d €46; t €61; extra person €15 **ON SITE:** Horse riding
NEARBY: Fishing (1km) Swimming pool (2km) Stretch of water (2km) Place of interest (3km) Cross-country skiing (25km) Downhill skiing (25km) Aerial sports (20km) Tennis (2km) Spa (20km) Railway station (2km) Shops (1km) RUMILLY (3km) **NOTES:** No pets English spoken

SAMOENS

⚑⚑⚑⚑ La Maison de Fifine Liliane BELLENGER
Les Moulins, 74340 SAMOENS
☎ 04 50 34 10 29 & 06 13 27 61 77

Sixt-Fer-à-Cheval 10 km. Morzine 20 km. This ancient Savoie building stands at the foot of the Criou and has a cosy alpine atmosphere. Owner Liliane offers four en suite guest rooms: one double, two with double and single on mezzanine, and one family room for four. Use of friendly guests' sitting room with open fire, TV and kitchen area, sauna, walled garden, and new heated pool. Reduced rate after three nights. Animals accepted after consultation. Open all year.
PRICES: s €61; d €75; t €93 **ON SITE:** Fishing Place of interest Cross-country skiing **NEARBY:** Horse riding (1km) Swimming pool (1km) Stretch of water (2km) Downhill skiing (4km) Aerial sports (4km) Tennis (2km) Spa (50km) Railway station (18km)
NOTES: No pets

SCIEZ

⚑⚑⚑⚑ ⎇⎇ La Cyprière Dominique FERRAGLIA-SEIZ
Route du Moulin de la Glacière, 74140 SCIEZ
☎ 04 50 72 16 80 & 06 87 03 29 29 SR: 04 50 10 10 11
▤ 04 50 72 16 81
e-mail: la.cypriere.ferraglia@wanadoo.fr

Yvoire 7 km. Thonon-les-Bains 10 km. Geneva & Evian 20 km. At the entrance to the Coudree Chateau estate, by the banks of Lake Leman, this house offers four elegant double guest rooms, all with en suite bathroom and wc. Use of dining room, sitting room with fireplace, library and TV. Weather permitting, breakfast served in sunny country garden. Dinner by reservation. In estate: walks, adventure park. Skiing and many tourist sites nearby. Open all year.

Chalet L'Envala
Route des Platons
74260 Les Gets
Tel: 00 33 4 50 75 89 15

The chalet is situated in the ski resort of Les Gets in the Portes du Soleil region. This old alpine village is full of charm and has retained much of the old village style. Built in traditional wooden style the chalet is ideal for holidays in either summer or winter, as it is open all year with varying rates according to the season. Golfing can be enjoyed at the local course with special green fees available to guests. Stunning views of the surrounding area can be enjoyed from the terrace or relax in front of a roaring fire.

PRICES: s €61; d €69; t €84; dinner €27 **NEARBY:** Horse riding (3km) Fishing (1km) Swimming pool (10km) Stretch of water (1km) Place of interest (1km) Cross-country skiing (30km) Downhill skiing (30km) Aerial sports (25km) Tennis (1km) Spa (10km) Railway station (10km) Shops (1km) THONON-LES-BAINS (10km)
NOTES: No pets English spoken

SERVOZ

⚑⚑⚑ L'Alpe Josiane et Hervé ANSELME
Chemin du Rucher, 74310 SERVOZ
☎ 04 50 47 22 66 & SR: 04 50 10 10 11 ▤ 04 50 91 40 66
This guest house, in a friendly, untouched village with traditional wooden buildings, is set among tranquil mountains. It has six grade 3 guest rooms, two of which are family rooms, sleeping up to five people. Use of kitchen, sitting room and large garden. The owner, a ski instructor and mountain guide, offers advice and can arrange activities. Free for children under two. Reduced rate after third night. Open all year.
PRICES: d €45-€50; t €59-€64 **ON SITE:** Fishing Tennis
NEARBY: Horse riding (8km) Swimming pool (10km) Stretch of water (8km) Place of interest (10km) Cross-country skiing (5km) Downhill skiing (5km) Aerial sports (10km) Spa (6km) Railway station (1km) CHAMONIX MONT-BLANC (10km) **NOTES:** No pets English spoken

SEYNOD-SUR-VIEUGY

⚑⚑⚑ ♥ La Ferme de Vergloz
Nicole et Philippe MARTEL
46 Route de Vergloz, 74600 SEYNOD-SUR-VIEUGY
☎ 04 50 46 71 98 & SR: 04 50 10 10 11 ▤ 04 50 46 71 98
Annecy 5 km. Skiing at Semnoz 17 km. Overlooking the town of Annecy and facing the Semnoz massif, the Ferme de Vergloz is a collection of buildings typical of the Avant-Pays. Nicole and

continued　　　　　　　　　　　　　　　　　continued

Philippe welcome guests. Their four charming guest rooms have mezzanine floors and private bathrooms, and sleep two to four people each Breakfast, which is served beside the fireplace in the dining room, features produce from the farm. The relaxing lounge has panoramic views. Restaurants 2 km. Reduced rates for children. Open all year.
PRICES: s €35; d €46; t €69; extra person €15 **NEARBY:** Horse riding (3km) Fishing (4km) Swimming pool (4km) Stretch of water (6km) Place of interest (5km) Cross-country skiing (17km) Downhill skiing (17km) Aerial sports (17km) Tennis (4km) Spa (35km) Railway station (7km) Shops (2km) SEYNOD (4km) **NOTES:** No pets

ST-FELIX

♦♦♦♦ ◎ Les Bruyères Bernard et Denyse BETTS
Mercy, 74540 ST-FELIX
☎ 04 50 60 96 53 📠 04 50 60 94 65

Annecy 23 km. Aix-les-Bains 20 km. Standing at the foot of the Alps, between Annecy and Aix-Les-Bains, this ancient Savoie farmhouse is peaceful and charming. Denyse and Bernard offer three luxurious guest rooms, each with double bed, fireplace, cable TV, en suite bathroom, wc and winter garden. No smoking. Folding bed available. Dinner on reservation. Country park and tennis court on site. Open all year.
PRICES: d €115; t €130; dinner €40 **ON SITE:** Tennis **NEARBY:** Horse riding (15km) Fishing (1km) Swimming pool (5km) Stretch of water (5km) Place of interest (17km) Cross-country skiing (20km) Downhill skiing (20km) Aerial sports (10km) Spa (17km) Railway station (5km) Shops (1km) ALBY-SUR-CHERAN (4km) **NOTES:** No pets CC English spoken

ST-JEAN-DE-SIXT

♦♦♦ ♥ La Passerelle Marie-Claude MISSILLIER
Chef Lieu, 74450 ST-JEAN-DE-SIXT
☎ 04 50 02 24 33 & SR : 04 50 10 10 10 📠 04 50 63 21 36
e-mail: info@gites-chaletlapasserelle.com
http://www.gites-chaletlapasserelle.com
Annecy 30 km. La Clusaz 5 km. Le Grand Bornand 5 km. In the centre of a village between La Clusaz and Grand-Bornand, this pretty chalet stands next to the owners' farmhouse. It houses four cosy guest rooms, each with double bed and extra single, TV, en suite bathroom and wc, and private terrace. Folding bed and cot available. Upstairs is a large guests' living room. In summer, breakfast is served on a large terrace with view of the Aravis Mountains. Open all year.
PRICES: s €34-€37; d €43-€49; t €58-€64 **ON SITE:** Fishing Tennis **NEARBY:** Horse riding (3km) Swimming pool (2km) Stretch of water (30km) Place of interest (15km) Cross-country skiing (2km) Downhill skiing (2km) Aerial sports (3km) Spa (50km) Railway station (30km) THONES (8km) **NOTES:** Pets admitted

TANINGES

♦♦♦♦ La Grange Nicole et M-Jeanne BASTARD
Avonnex, 74440 TANINGES
☎ 04 50 34 31 36
Les Gets 7 km, Praz-de-Lys 10 km, Chartreuse-de-Melan 3 km. This former farmhouse is in a pretty hamlet facing the Aravis, Buet and Marcelly Mountains, it enjoys spectacular views. The three guest rooms, housed in a converted barn, are split-level and spacious but cosy. Each has two doubles, with private bath or shower room and wc. Breakfast served in large dining room, with sitting/reading area. Situated between the Grand Massif and Portes du Soleil, excellent location for skiing. Many tourist sites nearby. Open all year.
PRICES: s €38; d €46; t €61 **NEARBY:** Horse riding (7km) Fishing (2km) Swimming pool (10km) Stretch of water (10km) Place of interest (2km) Cross-country skiing (7km) Downhill skiing (7km) Aerial sports (15km) Tennis (2km) Spa (40km) Railway station (13km) Shops (2km) TANINGES (2km) **NOTES:** No pets

THONES

♦♦♦ ◎ Chalet les Lupins Patricia et Rémi TALEB
Glapigny, La Closette, 74230 THONES
☎ 04 50 63 19 96 & SR: 04 50 10 10 11 📠 04 50 69 19 19
Resorts of Grand-Bornand & La Clusaz 15 km, Lac d'Annecy 20 km." This chalet stands at an altitude of 1200m in the heart of the Aravis range, facing La Tournette. It offers three guest rooms, all with double and extra single and en suite bath or shower room and wc. Use of sitting room, TV, washing facilities, terrace with panoramic views. Friendly dinners around large farmhouse table, regional specialities. No smoking. Reduced rates for children. Open all year.
PRICES: s €28; d €41; t €60; dinner €13 **NEARBY:** Horse riding (6km) Fishing (5km) Swimming pool (15km) Stretch of water (20km) Place of interest (5km) Cross-country skiing (15km) Downhill skiing (15km) Aerial sports (15km) Tennis (5km) Spa (45km) Railway station (30km) Shops (5km) THONES (5km) **NOTES:** No pets English spoken

♦♦♦ Pré Varens la Cour
Gilbert & Bernadette JOSSERAND
Route de la Clusaz, Pré Varens, 74230 THONES
☎ 04 50 02 12 22 & 06 74 39 30 46 SR: 04 50 10 10 11
Annecy 20 km. La Clusaz & Le Grand Bornand 10 km. Standing on the riverbank, surrounded by a pretty garden, this guest house has five rooms, two of which are grade 3 suites with double bed, sofa, kitchen area, en suite bathroom, wc, and private terrace. Upstairs are three grade 2 rooms: two doubles and a family room with double and twin beds. All have en suite shower rooms. Shared wc. Communal room with TV, games. Barbecue, table tennis. Reduced rate for children under eight. Open all year.
PRICES: s €24; d €30-€40; t €40-€51 **NEARBY:** Horse riding (2km) Fishing (1km) Swimming pool (2km) Stretch of water (18km) Place of interest (2km) Cross-country skiing (10km) Downhill skiing (10km) Aerial sports (5km) Tennis (2km) Spa (50km) Railway station (20km) Shops (2km) THONES (2km) **NOTES:** Pets admitted

VALLORCINE

♦♦♦ ◎ L'Anatase C et G DEPUYDT-KRAVTCHENKO
Les Plans, 74660 VALLORCINE
☎ 04 50 54 64 06 & SR : 04 50 10 10 10 📠 04 50 54 69 41
e-mail: c.kravtchenko@wanadoo.fr
Chamonix 16 km. Le Tour & Grands Montets 8 km. In protected alpine surroundings, between Chamonix and Switzerland, stands this old stone house, in the local style. It houses five charming guest rooms, all with double bed, extra single(s) and en suite bath or shower room and wc. Cot available. Use of large living room, furnished with Savoie antiques, cosy sitting room with TV, hi-fi,

continued

RHÔNE-ALPES

telescope. Open May to October.
PRICES: s €53-€64; d €64-€79; t €96-€110; extra person €15; dinner €19
NEARBY: Horse riding (15km) Fishing (1km) Swimming pool (19km)
Stretch of water (35km) Place of interest (7km) Aerial sports (15km)
Tennis (2km) Spa (30km) Railway station (1km) CHAMONIX MONT-
BLANC (15km) **NOTES:** No pets English spoken

VAULX

♛ ♥ ◎ La Ferme sur les Bois
Marie-Christine SKINAZY
Le Biolley, 74150 VAULX
☎ 04 50 60 54 50
e-mail: annecy.attelage@wanadoo.fr
http://www.annecy-attelage.fr
Annecy 14 km. Semnoz 32 km. This authentic 19th-century Savoie
farmhouse stands deep in untouched beautiful countryside. It has
four cosy guest rooms; three with double and extra single on the
mezzanine level, and a family room with double and twin beds on
the ground floor with its own entrance. All rooms have private
bath or shower rooms and wc. Cot available. Use of library,
grounds and terrace. Parking. Dinner available. Reduced rates for
children. Open all year.
PRICES: s €40; d €46; t €65; dinner €16 **NEARBY:** Horse riding (2km)
Fishing (5km) Swimming pool (14km) Stretch of water (14km) Place of
interest (3km) Cross-country skiing (32km) Downhill skiing (32km) Aerial
sports (32km) Tennis (3km) Spa (40km) Railway station (14km) Shops
(3km) RUMILLY (14km) **NOTES:** No pets English spoken

ISÈRE

ANNOISIN-CHATELANS

♛ ◎ La Maison de la Noisette
Marie N. & Thierry JANIN
la Prairie, 38460 ANNOISIN CHATELANS
☎ 04 74 83 86 09 ▤ 04 74 83 11 53

Lovely enclosed wooded garden with private swimming pool in a
quiet rural location. Large veranda with exposed beams and an
open fire. Four delightful bedrooms, each with shower and wc.
Lavish family dinners. A lovely area for tourists, near the medieval
city of Crémieu, the caves at la Balme, the Larina archaeological
site. Hiking, mountain biking, horseriding, ornamental lakes. Open
all year.
PRICES: s €35; d €46; extra person €14; dinner €14 **ON SITE:** Swimming
pool Hiking **NEARBY:** Bathing (10km) Horse riding (10km) Rock
climbing (5km) Fishing (5km) Railway station (30km) Shops (5km)
Golf (20km) CREMIEU (6km) **NOTES:** Pets admitted English spoken

AUTRANS

♛ ◎ Belle Combe Laurence & Roland CAILLET
GITES DE FRANCE-SERVICE RESERVATION, 5 allée Sully,
29322 QUIMPER Cedex
☎ 04 76 40 79 40 & PROP: 04 76 94 79 84 ▤ 04 76 40 79 99
e-mail: sirt38@wanadoo.fr www.gites-de-france-isère.com
In this old restored farmhouse Laurence and Roland offer you the
choice of five guest rooms, all individually decorated, and all with
shower and wc. Dining/sitting room with open fire in the old
stable. Home-made preserves at breakfast. Friendly atmosphere at
dinner, when regional and farm produce are served. Lovely
garden. Meals under the arbour in summer. Roland, a cook by
profession, can offer you lessons in regional cuisine. Open from
1st December to 30th October.
PRICES: s €35; d €45; t €66; extra person €21; dinner €15
ON SITE: Fishing Hiking **NEARBY:** Bathing (40km) Horse riding (2km)
Rock climbing (10km) Swimming pool (2km) Cross-country skiing (1km)
Downhill skiing (1km) Potholing (5km) Aerial sports (12km) Railway
station (40km) Shops (1km) VILLARD DE LANS (12km) **NOTES:** No pets
English spoken

♛ ◎ Entre Chiens et Loups
Florence & Bernard DUMOULIN
GITES DE FRANCE-SERVICE RESERVATION, 5 allée Sully,
29322 QUIMPER Cedex
☎ 04 76 40 79 40 & PROP: 04 76 95 36 64 ▤ 04 76 40 79 99
e-mail: sirt38@wanadoo.fr www.gites-de-france-isère.com
On the edge of the forest, Bernard and Florence invite you into the
wooden house where they live (along with their 40 sledge dogs).
Four cosy and comfortable guest rooms, each with shower and wc.
After a dog-sleigh ride, a ski-run or a ramble though the forest,
Florence serves good food at the family table. Bernard - the
'musher' and a keen advocate of fishing - will teach you dog-
driving in winter, and in summer the joys of fishing in mountain
streams. Open all year.
PRICES: s €38; d €47; t €68; extra person €16; dinner €15
ON SITE: Fishing Hiking Cross-country skiing **NEARBY:** Horse riding
(2km) Rock climbing (15km) Swimming pool (5km) Downhill skiing
(2km) Potholing (4km) Aerial sports (17km) Railway station (35km)
Shops (1km) VILLARD DE LANS (17km) **NOTES:** No pets CC English
spoken

AVIGNONET

♛ ◎ Château des Marceaux Didier DE MARCHI
GITES DE FRANCE-SERVICE RESERVATION, 5 allée Sully,
29322 QUIMPER Cedex
☎ 04 76 40 79 40 & PROP: 04 76 34 18 94 ▤ 04 76 40 79 99
e-mail: sirt38@wanadoo.fr www.gites-de-france-isère.com
Lac de Moneynard 5km. 25km from Grenoble, near the Lake of
Monteynard, stands this 18th-century castle with its French-style
garden. In the pigeon loft and the entrance tower, Nathalie and
Didier have tastefully arranged two rooms with mezzanine, each
sleeps four. Shower room or bathroom and wc. In a separate
building is a two-roomed suite for four people, with kitchenette,
shower and wc. Dine in the castle, in an enormous dining room.
Large shady park (1ha) with swimming pool. Plenty of walking
routes around. Open all year.
PRICES: s €45; d €53-€56; t €69-€72; extra person €16; dinner €21
ON SITE: Swimming pool Hiking **NEARBY:** Bathing (5km) Horse riding
(10km) Fishing (5km) Cross-country skiing (20km) Downhill skiing
(20km) Aerial sports (20km) Railway station (6km) Shops (6km)
MONESTIER DE CLERMONT (5km) **NOTES:** No pets Minimum 2 night
stay CC English spoken

BESSINS

✦✦✦ Le Maroubra Jocelyne & Jean M. TOUCHER
GITES DE FRANCE-SERVICE RESERVATION, 5 allée Sully,
29322 QUIMPER Cedex
☎ 04 76 40 79 40 & PROP: 04 76 64 11 62 🖅 04 76 40 79 99
e-mail: sirt38@wanadoo.fr www.gites-de-france-isere.com
Old pebble-fronted farmhouse in the traditional architectural style
of the Antonin countryside. In an annexe to the main house are
four ground level guest rooms for two, three or four people, each
with shower and wc. Dining room and sitting room with open fire.
Beautiful estate with swimming pool and large shady garden, sun
loungers and garden furniture. Near to tourist sites. Open all year.
PRICES: s €32; d €39; t €51; extra person €12 **ON SITE:** Swimming pool
Hiking **NEARBY:** Bathing (10km) Horse riding (13km) Fishing (10km)
Cross-country skiing (30km) Railway station (11km) Shops (7km) ST
MARCELLIN (10km) **NOTES:** No pets CC English spoken

BOSSIEU

✦✦✦ |Ô| Le Cellier Pascale & Jean Luc CHABOUD
GITES DE FRANCE-SERVICE RESERVATION, 5 allée Sully,
29322 QUIMPER Cedex
☎ 04 76 40 79 40 & PROP: 04 74 54 32 85 🖅 04 76 40 79 99
e-mail: sirt38@wanadoo.fr www.gites-de-france-isere.com
The ancient winestore of the Abbaye de Bonnevaux, with its 12th-
century tower, now stylishly restored. Huge bright living room with
open fire, opening out onto the Plain of la Bièvre and 3ha of
meadow where horses graze. Three beautiful rooms with all
facilities. Reading room; hi-fi; concert grand piano. Horseriders
welcome; stables and adjacent park; 20x30m paddock. Walks in
the nearby forest; foot and riding trails; mountain biking. Parking.
Garden. Open all year except Christmas.
PRICES: s €36; d €47; t €61; extra person €14; dinner €16
ON SITE: Horse riding Hiking **NEARBY:** Bathing (8km) Fishing (2km)
Swimming pool (12km) Cross-country skiing (40km) Downhill skiing
(40km) Railway station (25km) Shops (3km) COTE ST ANDRE (LA) (8km)
NOTES: Pets admitted CC English spoken

BOUVESSE-QUIRIEU

✦✦✦ |Ô| Domaine de la Source de Diane
Marie Dominique TERROT
GITES DE FRANCE-SERVICE RESERVATION, 5 allée Sully,
29322 QUIMPER Cedex
☎ 04 76 40 79 40 & PROP: 04 74 83 40 73 🖅 04 76 40 79 99
e-mail: sirt38@wanadoo.fr www.gites-de-france-isere.com
A 19th-century bourgeois house with charming flower garden. On
the first and second floors are four rooms for two or three people
and a two-roomed suite for five. All have shower or bathroom and
wc. Opposite the cliffs of Bugey. Salon with open fire, library, video
recorder, television. Large cosy dining room. Near the Blue Valley,
Morestel, Crémieu, Walibi theme park. Open all year.
PRICES: s €39; d €46-€61; t €61-€77; extra person €16; dinner €24
NEARBY: Bathing (4km) Horse riding (6km) Fishing (4km) Swimming
pool (4km) Cross-country skiing (20km) Railway station (35km) Shops
(2km) MORESTEL (15km) **NOTES:** No pets CC English spoken

CHARNECLES

✦✦✦ ❤ Ferme du Bois Vert Jean Louis & Eugénie ROSSET
GITES DE FRANCE-SERVICE RESERVATION, 5 allée Sully,
29322 QUIMPER Cedex
☎ 04 76 40 79 40 & PROP: 04 76 65 26 46 🖅 04 76 40 79 99
e-mail: sirt38@wanadoo.fr www.gites-de-france-isere.com
Old farm buildings entirely renovated, near the home of the
proprietors. On the ground floor: dining room, sitting room with
open fire. Upstairs: three lovely bedrooms sleeping two, each with
shower and wc. Breakfast is taken either in the dining room or on

the terrace under the shade of the lime tree. Enjoy the farm
produce - fruits, fruit juices and home-made preserves. Open all
year.
PRICES: s €35; d €46; extra person €14 **ON SITE:** Hiking
NEARBY: Bathing (14km) Horse riding (4km) Rock climbing (13km)
Fishing (3km) Swimming pool (3km) Railway station (3km) Shops (1km)
RIVES (3km) **NOTES:** No pets English spoken

CHASSE-SUR-RHONE

✦✦✦ |Ô| Domaine de Gorneton
Jacqueline & Jean FLEITOU
712 Chemin de Violans, 38670 CHASSE SUR RHONE
☎ 04 72 24 19 15 🖅 04 78 07 93 62
e-mail: gorneton@wanadoo.fr
Fifteen minutes from Lyon and five from Vienne, the Gallo-
Roman town, at the foot of the Parc Régional du Pilat and
near the Côtes Rôties vineyard, Gorneton is a 17th-century
fortified house with gardens, lake, fountains and enclosed
courtyard. One duplex apartment sleeping four; two double
rooms and a suite for two people. Bathrooms and wcs and
independent access. Generous family fare served at the dinner
table. Swimming pool and tennis. Open all year.
PRICES: s €77; d €89-€115; extra person €16; dinner €31
ON SITE: Swimming pool Hiking **NEARBY:** Bathing (10km) Horse
riding (4km) Fishing (2km) Railway station (4km) Shops (2km)
VIENNE (3km) **NOTES:** No pets English spoken
See advert on opposite page

CHICHILIANNE

✦✦✦ ❤ |Ô| Ruthieres Jean Luc SAUZE
38930 CHICHILIANNE
☎ 04 76 34 45 98 & 04 76 34 42 20 🖅 04 76 34 45 98
Traditional farmer's house in a little hamlet. Four guest rooms and
two gîtes in an adjoining building. The rooms are large, with
English country furniture, and accommodate two to four people.
Each has a lounge area and private shower and wc. Breakfast and
dinner are served in the old vaulted sheep building, where local
painters exhibit their watercolours. Large fireplace; board games;
bookshelves. Small terrace. Cattle rearing. Open all year.
PRICES: s €32; d €40; t €52; extra person €12; dinner €13
ON SITE: Rock climbing Fishing Hiking Cross-country skiing
NEARBY: Bathing (25km) Horse riding (1km) Swimming pool (5km)
Downhill skiing (25km) Railway station (4km) Shops (3km) CLELLES
(5km) **NOTES:** Pets admitted English spoken

FAVERGES-DE-LA-TOUR

✦✦✦ |Ô| Le Traversoud
J.Margaret & Albert GARNIER
GITES DE FRANCE-SERVICE RESERVATION, 5 allée Sully,
29322 QUIMPER Cedex
☎ 04 76 40 79 40 & PROP: 04 74 83 90 40 🖅 04 76 40 79 99
e-mail: sirt38@wanadoo.fr www.gites-de-france-isere.com
Walibi 6 km. Four km off the RN75, and 6km from the Tour du Pin,
a Dauphinois house of character, with three bedrooms sleeping
two or three, each with shower and wc. The bedrooms are
decorated with the theme of painters and have separate access.
Relax in the large shady park, and sample the produce of the
kitchen garden and the farmyard. Children's play equipment;
boules; table tennis; badminton. Marked walking trails. Many
tourist attractions. Open all year.
PRICES: s €35; d €42-€44; t €57; extra person €10; dinner €14
ON SITE: Hiking **NEARBY:** Bathing (14km) Horse riding (3km) Fishing
(14km) Swimming pool (3km) Cross-country skiing (35km) Downhill
skiing (35km) Railway station (6km) Shops (3km) Golf (3km)
TOUR DU PIN (LA) (6km) **NOTES:** No pets CC English spoken

continued

GRESSE-EN-VERCORS

♦♦♦ La Chicoliere Janick et Gerard MOUTTET

GITES DE FRANCE-SERVICE RESERVATION, 5 allée Sully, 29322 QUIMPER Cedex

☎ 04 76 40 79 40 & PROP: 04 76 34 33 70 🖷 04 76 40 79 99

e-mail: sirt38@wanadoo.fr www.gites-de-france-isere.com

Lac de Monteynard 18 km. In the heart of the old village, a restored farmhouse with a small mountain shelter. Dining room with open fire for visitors, reading corner, view of the Little Dolomites. Upstairs: five rooms for two, three or four guests, with shower and wc. Sample home-made bread and preserves and the vegetables from the garden. Open all school holidays and out of season with prior booking.

PRICES: s €35; d €43; t €56; extra person €13; dinner €15

ON SITE: Fishing Hiking Cross-country skiing **NEARBY:** Horse riding (1km) Rock climbing (3km) Swimming pool (1km) Downhill skiing (1km) Aerial sports (1km) Railway station (13km) Restaurant nearby MONESTIER DE CLERMONT (13km) **NOTES:** No pets CC English spoken

♦♦♦ ⏱ La Fruitière Fernand MOURIER

38650 GRESSE EN VERCORS

☎ 04 76 34 32 80 🖷 04 76 34 32 80

Lac de Monteynard 17 km. Tastefully renovated former fruit farm in a mountain setting, containing one ground level room with double bed and single bed, shower, wc, kitchenette, terrace. Upstairs: one double room and three triple rooms, with showers and wcs. Vast living room with kitchen area, and wide windows opening onto the countryside. Terrace, grounds. Breakfast served in a lovely spot, with home-made preserves. An adjacent annexe houses two gîtes. Play area and paddling pool. Sauna. Paragliding school. Open 1st June to 15th September.

PRICES: s €32; d €37; t €47; dinner €13 **ON SITE:** Children's play area Fishing Hiking **NEARBY:** Horse riding (3km) Rock climbing (3km) Swimming pool (3km) Cross-country skiing (1km) Downhill skiing (3km) Aerial sports (1km) Railway station (13km) Shops (1km) MONESTIER DE CLERMONT (13km) **NOTES:** No pets CC

♦♦♦ ⏱ La Grange aux Loups Annie MANCHE

GITES DE FRANCE-SERVICE RESERVATION, 5 allée Sully, 29322 QUIMPER Cedex

☎ 04 76 40 79 40 & PROP: 04 76 34 11 08 🖷 04 76 40 79 99

e-mail: sirt38@wanadoo.fr www.gites-de-france-isere.com

Completely renovated 18th-century farmhouse at the foot of Mont Aiguille, containing pretty guest rooms in an annexe on the house. Upstairs: three rooms for two or three people, with shower and wc. On the ground floor, a huge living room with an old restored bread oven. Annie will share her passion for the craft of weaving, and tempt you into her little tea room. Browse through the library on the flora and fauna of Vercors. Open 20th December to 30th October.

PRICES: s €34; d €43; t €54; extra person €11; dinner €14

ON SITE: Hiking **NEARBY:** Bathing (27km) Horse riding (7km) Rock climbing (4km) Fishing (1km) Swimming pool (7km) Cross-country skiing (6km) Downhill skiing (8km) Aerial sports (8km) Railway station (14km) Shops (7km) MONESTIER DE CLERMONT (15km) **NOTES:** No pets CC English spoken

---

Prices are given in Euros €1 = £0.62
at the time of going to press

⏱

Places with this symbol serve table d'hôtes
evening meals - remember to book in advance

Domaine de Gorneton

Prop: J et J Fleitou

712 Chemin de Violans
38670 Chasse sur Rhone
Tel: 04 72 24 19 15 Fax: 04 78 07 93 62

at the intersection of A7/A46/A47 towards St Etienne exit Chasse to 'Centre Commercial' under railway bridge, then left and right towards Trembas, 2 km on right. Forest area.

3 en-suite (bth/shr) (1 fmly), full central heating, open and covered parking available. Outdoor swimming pool, tennis, fishing, boule, table tennis all in a 5 hectares park. English & Spanish spoken. Travellers cheques accepted.

LE BOURG-D'OISANS

♦♦♦ ⏱ Les Petites Sources Pauline DURDAN

le Vert, 38520 LE BOURG D'OISANS

☎ 04 76 80 13 92 🖷 04 76 80 13 92

e-mail: durdan@club-internet.fr

A warm and comfortable restored barn in a mountain location. First floor with balcony: two double rooms; one triple room; one two-roomed suite for four. Each has shower and wc. Second floor: two triple rooms with private facilities. Breakfast and dinner are served in the vaulted dining room. Eric, a mountain guide, can organise ski holidays, snowshoe outings and walks in the Parc National des Ecrins. Garden with children's games. Activities room with climbing wall. Evening activities. Open 15th December to 15th April and from 1st June to 8th October.

PRICES: s €30-€33; d €45-€52; t €61-€69; extra person €16; dinner €15

ON SITE: Fishing Hiking **NEARBY:** Horse riding (5km) Rock climbing (5km) Swimming pool (2km) Cross-country skiing (1km) Downhill skiing (15km) Aerial sports (15km) Railway station (50km) Shops (2km) BOURG D OISANS (LE) (2km) **NOTES:** Pets admitted English spoken

LE PERCY

♦♦♦ ⏱ Les Volets Bleus

Nicole & Jacques REMILLAT

hameau des Blancs, 38930 LE PERCY

☎ 04 76 34 43 07

On the tracks of Giono, still in the Alps, but with a hint of Provence in the air, you will find Les Volets Bleus, a farmhouse from 1753, now restored. Three bedrooms with very individual décor, separate access, bathrooms and wcs. In the evening, try regional dishes from Trieves, the Midi or further afield, but always prepared with local produce. Jacques will welcome you to dinner in the large vaulted dining room which opens on to the garden. Reduced rates after the second day. Open Easter to October.

continued

RHÔNE-ALPES

PRICES: s €36; d €45; t €58; extra person €13; dinner €15
ON SITE: Hiking **NEARBY:** Bathing (25km) Horse riding (3km) Rock climbing (10km) Swimming pool (12km) Cross-country skiing (10km) Downhill skiing (20km) Potholing (25km) Aerial sports (10km) Railway station (5km) Shops (5km) CLELLES (20km) **NOTES:** No pets

LE PIN

¶¶¶ ΙΟΙ Les Brimbelles Monique JOLY
GITES DE FRANCE-SERVICE RESERVATION, 5 allée Sully, 29322 QUIMPER Cedex
☎ 04 76 40 79 40 & PROP: 04 76 06 60 86 📠 04 76 40 79 99
e-mail: sirt38@wanadoo.fr www.gites-de-france-isère.com
Dauphinois house tucked away in greenery 800m from the Lac de Paladru, in the heart of the village. You can choose from three bedrooms for two or three people, with showers and wcs. Breakfast is served on the veranda which looks out over a pretty garden. Dining room and sitting room with open fire. Evening meal must be booked. Monique serves salads, fish dishes, garden vegetables, tarts. Parking on the premises. Open from February to November.
PRICES: s €32; d €39; t €47; extra person €11; dinner €14
ON SITE: Horse riding Fishing Hiking **NEARBY:** Bathing (1km) Railway station (14km) VIRIEU SUR BOURBRE (5km) **NOTES:** Pets admitted CC English spoken

LE SAPPEY-EN-CHARTREUSE

¶¶¶ ΙΟΙ Gîte du Chant de l'Eau
Colette & Bruno CHARLES
GITES DE FRANCE-SERVICE RESERVATION, 5 allée Sully, 29322 QUIMPER Cedex
☎ 04 76 40 79 40 & PROP: 04 76 88 83 16 📠 04 76 40 79 99
e-mail: sirt38@wanadoo.fr www.gites-de-france-isère.com
An old barn of character on the edge of the village, facing the forest, adjoining the house of the owners. On the first and second floors, large cosy living room with open fire; five rooms for two, three or four guests with shower or bathroom and wc. The owners are local and will happily help you discover the landscape, flora and fauna here in the Parc Naturel Régional de Chartreuse. Open all year.
PRICES: s €33; d €42-€47; t €53; extra person €11; dinner €15
ON SITE: Fishing Hiking Cross-country skiing Downhill skiing
NEARBY: Bathing (30km) Horse riding (15km) Rock climbing (15km) Swimming pool (8km) Potholing (20km) Aerial sports (15km) Railway station (12km) Shops (1km) MEYLAN (12km) **NOTES:** No pets CC English spoken

LE TOUVET

¶¶¶ Le Pré Carre Jacqueline FONTRIER
81 rue de la Charrière, le Pré Carre, 38660 LE TOUVET
☎ 04 76 08 42 30 📠 04 76 08 56 43
In an 18th-century farmhouse in the middle of the village, one very large room divided to sleep two or four, with bathroom and wc and covered terrace. One large room for two, and one sleeping three, again with bathroom and wc. Pretty shaded flower garden. Breakfast served in the garden house. Sitting room with enormous fireplace. Private locked parking; garage. Open all year.
PRICES: s €47; d €56; t €72; extra person €16 **ON SITE:** Fishing Hiking
NEARBY: Bathing (5km) Horse riding (4km) Swimming pool (2km) Cross-country skiing (10km) Downhill skiing (10km) Aerial sports (10km) Railway station (4km) TOUVET (LE) **NOTES:** No pets English spoken

> Ask the proprietor for directions
> when booking

LES ABRETS

¶¶¶¶ La Bruyère Claude CHAVALLE REVENU
38490 LES ABRETS
☎ 04 76 32 01 66 📠 04 76 32 06 66
e-mail: carbone38@aol.com
A renovated Dauphinois farmhouse surrounded by wooded parkland. Come and stay in a friendly atmosphere. Six very comfortable double rooms (two of them suites), each with bathroom and shower. Separate access. Swimming pool. Open all year apart from three weeks in November.
PRICES: s €54-€77; d €69-€92 **ON SITE:** Swimming pool Hiking **NEARBY:** Bathing (10km) Horse riding (3km) Fishing (10km) Cross-country skiing (38km) Downhill skiing (38km) Railway station (5km) Shops (2km) PONT DE BEAUVOISIN (LE) (7km) **NOTES:** No pets CC English spoken

LES DEUX-ALPES

¶¶¶ Le Chalet Raymond GIRAUD
3 rue de l'Oisans, le Chalet, 38860 LES DEUX ALPES
☎ 04 76 80 51 85 📠 04 76 80 51 85
The Girauds welcome you to their chalet by the ski slopes. Downstairs a rural gîte sleeps six. Upstairs six guest rooms for two to four people with shower or bath and wc. Central heating; television lounge with fireplace. In summer relax in the large garden. Lots of sports and leisure activities. Private parking. Open from 1st December to 2nd May and 20th June to 5th September.
PRICES: s €29; d €53; t €59 **ON SITE:** Hiking **NEARBY:** Bathing (7km) Horse riding (1km) Rock climbing (1km) Fishing (3km) Swimming pool (1km) Cross-country skiing (1km) Downhill skiing (1km) Aerial sports (1km) Railway station (75km) BOURG D'OISANS (LE) **NOTES:** No pets

MAUBEC

¶¶¶ Château de Césarges Angèle & Jean POPINEAU
GITES DE FRANCE-SERVICE RESERVATION, 5 allée Sully, 29322 QUIMPER Cedex
☎ 04 76 40 79 40 & PROP: 04 74 93 20 42 📠 04 76 40 79 99
e-mail: sirt38@wanadoo.fr www.gites-de-france-isère.com
Tennis 3km, golf 10km, St-Exupéry airport 35km. In the middle of parkland studded with stately trees, the Château de Césarges, offers a charming stay. Upstairs are three lovely bedrooms for two or three people whose windows open over the park. Private showers and wcs. Breakfast is served in the dining room by the open fire, or outside in the shade of the 400-year-old lime tree. Drawing room with piano. Dine in one of the many restaurants and inns. Open 1st April to 15th November.
PRICES: s €44; d €53; t €69; extra person €16 **ON SITE:** Hiking
NEARBY: Bathing (8km) Horse riding (12km) Fishing (8km) Swimming pool (6km) Railway station (6km) Shops (6km) BOURGOIN JALLIEU (6km) **NOTES:** No pets CC

MENS

¶¶¶ L'Engrangeou Janic GRINBERG
place de la Halle, 38710 MENS
☎ 04 76 34 85 63 & 04 76 34 94 48
In the middle of the old village, opposite the covered market, stands this tastefully restored house, with an art gallery on the ground floor. Upstairs is a choice of three lovely bedrooms sleeping two, with shower and wc. A warm and cultivated atmosphere. Janic will share his enthusiasm for painting and old cars, and could offer you a trip in his 1960s cabriolet. Fast food available in the village. Open all year.
PRICES: s €38; d €44; dinner €13 **NEARBY:** Bathing (1km) Horse riding (1km) Fishing (1km) Swimming pool (1km) Hiking (1km) Cross-country skiing (30km) Downhill skiing (30km) Aerial sports (5km) Railway station (12km) MENS **NOTES:** Pets admitted English spoken

MONESTIER-DU-PERCY

♦♦♦ ﾈ◯ﾈ Le Chauchari Catherine JUGE

le Serre, Chaucharri, 38930 MONESTIER DU PERCY
☎ 04 76 34 42 72

Welcome to this old restored farmhouse in the heart of Trièves, on a protected rural site between Vercors and Devoluy. Two rooms with bathroom and wc; two with shower and wc; and two (grade 2) rooms sharing a shower and wc. TV lounge/library. Open all year.

PRICES: s €25-€30; d €30-€39; t €38-€50; extra person €12; dinner €14
ON SITE: Children's play area Fishing Swimming pool Hiking
NEARBY: Bathing (30km) Horse riding (10km) Rock climbing (12km) Cross-country skiing (12km) Downhill skiing (35km) Potholing (50km) Aerial sports (10km) Railway station (10km) Shops (10km) CLELLES (8km) **NOTES:** Pets admitted

MORESTEL

♦♦♦ ﾈ◯ﾈ La Roche Rolande CLARET

GITES DE FRANCE-SERVICE RESERVATION, 5 allée Sully, 29322 QUIMPER Cedex
☎ 04 76 40 79 40 & PROP: 04 74 92 81 34 ▤ 04 76 40 79 99
e-mail: sirt38@wanadoo.fr www.gites-de-france-isère.com

This house basks in flowers and sunshine amid 4ha of parkland. Upstairs: three large rooms for two/three people, with antique furniture, shower and wc. Television corner, library, fireplace. Breakfast and dinner are served in the shade of the arbour in the garden. Garden furniture, including sun loungers. Nearby attractions: Walibi, Vallée Bleue, Crémieu and Morestel. Booking essential for evening meal. Kitchenette for guests to use. Open 1st March to 1st November.

PRICES: s €35; d €44; t €58; extra person €15; dinner €14
ON SITE: Children's play area **NEARBY:** Bathing (2km) Horse riding (2km) Rock climbing (3km) Fishing (1km) Swimming pool (3km) Hiking (1km) Aerial sports (20km) Railway station (15km) Shops (3km) MORESTEL (12km) **NOTES:** No pets

NANTES-EN-RATIER

♦♦♦ ﾈ◯ﾈ La Voute de Seraphin

Fabienne & Marcel BARD
GITES DE FRANCE-SERVICE RESERVATION, 5 allée Sully, 29322 QUIMPER Cedex
☎ 04 76 40 79 40 & PROP: 04 76 81 21 46 ▤ 04 76 40 79 99
e-mail: sirt38@wanadoo.fr www.gites-de-france-isère.com
Bungee jumping 5 km. A restored family farmhouse, set back from the roads and the noise, near a working farm. Second floor: three sunny rooms for two/three, with shower and wc. Small sitting area. In an enormous vaulted room, you can try the dishes of the region - *murçon*, squash pie, prune tart. Fabienne, a passionate reader and gardener, and Marcel, just as passionate about animals and nature, will advise you on ways to explore their countryside. Near the Route Napoléon, the Lacs de Laffrey and Notre Dame de la Salette. Open all year.

PRICES: s €33; d €41; t €54; extra person €13; dinner €14
ON SITE: Hiking **NEARBY:** Bathing (8km) Fishing (8km) Swimming pool (3km) Cross-country skiing (9km) Downhill skiing (22km) Aerial sports (3km) Railway station (36km) Shops (3km) MURE (LA) (3km)
NOTES: No pets CC English spoken

PRESLES

♦♦♦ ﾈ◯ﾈ Les Fauries Carmen WINTZENRIETH

GITES DE FRANCE-SERVICE RESERVATION, 5 allée Sully, 29322 QUIMPER Cedex
☎ 04 76 40 79 40 & PROP: 04 76 36 10 50 ▤ 04 76 40 79 99
e-mail: sirt38@wanadoo.fr www.gites-de-france-isère.com

Old farmhouse with exposed stonework. Quiet and restful, with panoramic views over the plateau of Vercors. On the first floor: four bright and comfortable rooms for two/three people, with shower or bathroom and wc. The windows open onto the countryside. Enjoy breakfast in the shade of the lime tree. Family dinner, with natural and varied ingredients. On the edge of the Forest of the Coulmes. Downhill skiing heaven (70km of pistes). Parc Régional Naturel du Vercors. Closed 2 November to 25 December and 5-13 April.

PRICES: s €27; d €36; t €49; extra person €11; dinner €14
ON SITE: Hiking Potholing **NEARBY:** Bathing (12km) Horse riding (12km) Rock climbing (4km) Fishing (10km) Swimming pool (18km) Cross-country skiing (4km) Downhill skiing (35km) Railway station (18km) Shops (12km) PONT EN ROYANS (13km) **NOTES:** No pets CC

SECHILIENNE

♦♦♦ ﾈ◯ﾈ Cotte Fournier Michèle & Jean Louis CHEMIN

au Bout du Chemin,
38220 SECHILIENNE
☎ 04 76 72 15 06 ▤ 04 76 72 15 06
Grenoble 25km, Vizille 10km. In the peace of the forest Michèle and J.Louis offer three cheery guest rooms with independent access. Two rooms for two/three people; one room with mezzanine sleeping four. Each has shower and wc. Guests have the use of a well-equipped kitchen, sitting room, large dining room, barbecue, hi-fi system. Perfect for small groups. Relax on the terrace or in the salon with a view which plunges down into the valley. Grade 3 rural gîte sleeping six adjacent to guest house. Open all year.

PRICES: s €33; d €41; t €54; extra person €13 **ON SITE:** Fishing Hiking **NEARBY:** Bathing (11km) Horse riding (10km) Swimming pool (10km) Cross-country skiing (15km) Downhill skiing (15km) Aerial sports (15km) Shops (3km) VIZILLE (10km) **NOTES:** Pets admitted English spoken

---

ﾈ◯ﾈ
Places with this symbol serve table d'hôtes
evening meals - remember to book in advance

---

continued

ST-ANTOINE-L'ABBAYE

♦♦♦ Chambre d'hôtes Eliane & Alain BISCARAS
GITES DE FRANCE-SERVICE RESERVATION, 5 allée Sully,
29322 QUIMPER Cedex
☎ 04 76 40 79 40 & PROP: 04 76 36 41 53 ▯ 04 76 40 79 99
e-mail: sirt38@wanadoo.fr www.gites-de-france-isère.com
Beautiful house in the middle of the medieval village of St Antoine.
Large living room with bread oven and fireplace. On the first floor:
one room for three; one enormous room sleeping four; and three
doubles, all with shower and wc. Central heating. Small enclosed
garden. At the gateway to the Drôme, within Vercors. Local crafts.
Railway garden. Cheese museum at St Marcellin. Abbey church,
with treasures and music concerts. Open all year.
PRICES: s €32; d €38; t €53; extra person €15 **ON SITE:** Fishing Hiking
NEARBY: Bathing (12km) Horse riding (5km) Swimming pool (10km)
Cross-country skiing (20km) Railway station (10km) ST MARCELLIN
(12km) **NOTES:** Pets admitted CC

♦♦♦ ❦ ◉ Les Voureys M.Thérèse & Henri PHILIBERT
38160 ST ANTOINE L ABBAYE
☎ 04 76 36 41 65
St-Antoine village with 12th-century abbey 2.5km. In their small
farmhouse, typical of the Pays Antonin, Marie Thérèse and Henri
present three lovely country-style bedrooms, each with shower
and wc and every modern comfort. Lavish and varied breakfasts
are served in the enormous cosy kitchen. Lounge for guests; shady
grounds with garden furniture. Visit the railway garden at Chatte
and the cheese museum at St Marcelin. Open all year.
PRICES: s €30; d €36; t €47; extra person €11; dinner €14
ON SITE: Fishing Hiking **NEARBY:** Bathing (15km) Horse riding (10km)
Swimming pool (10km) Cross-country skiing (20km) Downhill skiing
(30km) Railway station (10km) Shops (3km) ST MARCELLIN (10km)
NOTES: Pets admitted English spoken

ST-APPOLINARD

♦♦♦ ❦ ◉ La Combe de Mouze Monique & Henri PAIN
38160 ST APPOLINARD
☎ 04 76 64 10 52
Monique and Henri welcome you to their farmhouse. Four
cheerful double rooms with views over the slopes of the Pays
Antonin and the mountains of Vercors. Each has shower and wc.
South-east facing balcony and terrace. In an annexe is a four-
person duplex, with lounge, open fire, kitchenette, shower and wc.
Perfect for a family holiday. Shady flower garden. Dine outside or
in the huge country-style dining room in front of the fire. Farm
produce. Warm family atmosphere. Open all year.
PRICES: s €32; d €38-€44; t €59; extra person €16; dinner €13
ON SITE: Hiking **NEARBY:** Bathing (8km) Fishing (8km) Swimming
pool (10km) Cross-country skiing (20km) Downhill skiing (20km) Railway
station (10km) Shops (7km) ST MARCELLIN (7km) **NOTES:** Pets
admitted

ST-BAUDILLE-DE-LA-TOUR

♦♦♦ ◉ Les Basses Portes
M et V GIROUD DUCAROY
GITES DE FRANCE-SERVICE RESERVATION, 5 allée Sully,
29322 QUIMPER Cedex
☎ 04 76 40 79 40 & PROP: 04 74 95 18 23 ▯ 04 76 40 79 99
e-mail: sirt38@wanadoo.fr www.gites-de-france-isère.com
A house of character, with exposed stonework, restored with care,
in a rural and relaxing spot. Three cheerful rooms with individual
décor. On the ground floor: one twin room. Upstairs: one room
sleeping three; and a double room. All have shower and wc. Sitting
room with open fire; enormous living room/kitchen with exposed
beams. Flowery and shaded grounds. Close by: Crémieu,

archaeological sites, caves at La Balme, mountain biking, caravan
routes, climbing. Open from February to 15th November.
PRICES: s €35; d €45; t €64; extra person €16-€19; dinner €16
ON SITE: Hiking **NEARBY:** Bathing (12km) Horse riding (3km) Rock
climbing (4km) Fishing (10km) Swimming pool (12km) Shops (10km)
CREMIEU (15km) **NOTES:** No pets English spoken

ST-CHRISTOPHE-EN-OISANS

♦♦♦ Le Champ de Pin Christiane AMEVET
la Berarde, 38520 ST CHRISTOPHE EN OISANS
☎ 04 76 79 54 09 ▯ 04 76 79 54 09
e-mail: champdepin@free.fr
In this high spot of Alpine climbing, home of the great mountain
guide families of Oisans, Christiane carries on the tradition,
welcoming you to a huge chalet where you can enjoy this
remarkable location. Four lovely rooms, each with shower and wc.
Independent access. Terrace. Meals served in the Auberge, a room
reserved for guests. Holiday gîte adjacent (accommodates 16). Parc
des Ecrins; walks accessible to all. Open from 1st April to 1st
October.
PRICES: s €50; d €62; dinner €15 **ON SITE:** Rock climbing Fishing
Hiking **NEARBY:** Bathing (20km) Swimming pool (15km) Railway station
(25km) Restaurant nearby BOURG D OISANS (LE) (31km) **NOTES:** Pets
admitted CC English spoken

ST-CLAIR-DU-RHONE

♦♦♦ ◉ Chambre d'hôtes
Raymond & Andrée PASQUARELLI
6 chemin de Prailles, 38370 ST CLAIR DU RHONE
☎ 04 74 87 29 15
Pretty mountain house with swimming pool and large shady
flower garden. One very large room for three people, with shower,
wc and terrace. On the ground floor another room for three, with
shower and wc. Television lounge and kitchen for guests. In an
adjoining building, three rooms for two/three people, with shower
and wc. Dine on the terrace or in the dining room in front of a
roaring fire. Visit the wine cellars of St Joseph, Côtes Roties and
Condrieu. Meals must be booked. Open all year.
PRICES: s €34-€37; d €39-€46; t €54-€61; extra person €16; dinner €19
ON SITE: Swimming pool **NEARBY:** Bathing (4km) Horse riding (15km)
Fishing (1km) Hiking (5km) Railway station (5km) Shops (3km)
ROUSSILLON **NOTES:** Pets admitted

ST-HILAIRE-DE-BRENS

♦♦♦ ◉ Le Saint Hilaire
Andrée & Maurice COUPARD
GITES DE FRANCE-SERVICE RESERVATION, 5 allée Sully,
29322 QUIMPER Cedex
☎ 04 76 40 79 40 & PROP: 04 74 92 81 75 ▯ 04 76 40 79 99
e-mail: sirt38@wanadoo.fr www.gites-de-france-isère.com
Crémieu 7km. Tennis 0.1km. Charming house in the middle of the
village, embracing a small country grocery/café. A warm and
attentive welcome is assured from your hosts. Have breakfast in
the sun in the enclosed garden, with swimming pool. On the first
floor: five lovely rooms with separate access for two/three, with
shower and wc. Plenty of local tourist sites. Table tennis. Open
from 1st October to 31st August.
PRICES: s €35; d €45; t €58; extra person €13; dinner €14
ON SITE: Swimming pool Hiking **NEARBY:** Bathing (4km) Horse riding
(5km) Fishing (4km) Railway station (15km) Shops (5km) CREMIEU
(7km) **NOTES:** No pets CC

continued

ST-LATTIER

♈ 🐓 🍽 ♿ Montena des Collines
Geneviève & Patrick EFFANTIN
GITES DE FRANCE-SERVICE RESERVATION, 5 allée Sully,
29322 QUIMPER Cedex
☎ 04 76 40 79 40 & PROP: 04 76 64 52 59 📠 04 76 40 79 99
e-mail: sirt38@wanadoo.fr www.gites-de-france-isère.com
A beautiful house in the depths of the countryside between Vercors
and Drôme, with large gardens, leisure area and swimming pool. At
ground level: three bright, comfortable rooms with shower and wc -
two rooms for two/three, and one two-roomed suite sleeping five.
Sitting room; friendly dining room; sheltered terrace for summer
evening parties. Families and small groups welcome. The farm
produces cereals, asparagus and nuts. Mini-farm with animals.
Garden produce. Open all year except school holidays.
PRICES: s €32; d €41; t €53; extra person €12; dinner €14
ON SITE: Swimming pool Hiking **NEARBY:** Bathing (15km) Horse
riding (4km) Cross-country skiing (25km) Downhill skiing (35km) Railway
station (7km) Shops (3km) ST MARCELLIN (15km) **NOTES:** Pets
admitted CC English spoken

ST-MARTIN-DE-LA-CLUZE

♈ 🍽 Château de Paquier
Hélène & Jacques ROSSI
GITES DE FRANCE-SERVICE RESERVATION, 5 allée Sully,
29322 QUIMPER Cedex
☎ 04 76 40 79 40 & PROP: 04 76 72 77 33 📠 04 76 40 79 99
e-mail: sirt38@wanadoo.fr www.gites-de-france-isère.com

Jacques and Hélène welcome you to their charming 16th-century
castle. Five beautiful guest bedrooms each with private bathroom.
Dine with your hosts in the huge dining room. Home produced
bread, with vegetables and fruit from the garden. Relax in the
shady park. Ponies and games for children. Closed parking. Lac de
Monteynard, small tourist train, hiking. Open all year.
PRICES: s €45; d €52; extra person €15; dinner €17 **ON SITE:** Hiking
NEARBY: Bathing (8km) Horse riding (12km) Fishing (8km) Swimming
pool (10km) Cross-country skiing (20km) Downhill skiing (20km) Aerial
sports (20km) Railway station (10km) MONESTIER DE CLERMONT (10km)
NOTES: Pets admitted CC English spoken

ST-MICHEL-LES-PORTES

♈ Le Goutarou Virginie & Denis GOUTOR
les Granges de Thoranne,
38650 ST MICHEL LES PORTES
☎ 04 76 34 08 28 📠 04 76 34 17 75
e-mail: auberge.du.goutarou@mageos.com
Virginie and Denis are your hosts in this country auberge - an
18th-century restored farm between Trièves and Vercors. On the
first floor: six rooms sleeping three or four, with mezzanine,
exposed beams, shower and wc. Breakfast and dinner are taken at
the large table in an old vaulted room, where Denis prepares the
classic dishes. Sitting room with open fire. Flower-bedecked

garden and terrace. Shaded parking. Babies welcome. Laundry
available. Reduced rates for stays over two nights. Packed lunches
prepared for ramblers. Open all year.
PRICES: s €41; d €49; t €68; extra person €20; dinner €14
ON SITE: Wine tasting Children's play area Hiking **NEARBY:** Bathing
(17km) Horse riding (9km) Rock climbing (9km) Swimming pool (10km)
Cross-country skiing (9km) Downhill skiing (12km) Aerial sports (12km)
Railway station (9km) Shops (9km) Restaurant nearby CLELLES (9km)
NOTES: Pets admitted English spoken

ST-ONDRAS

♈ 🍽 Le Pas de l'Ane Josiane & Philippe ROBERGE
GITES DE FRANCE-SERVICE RESERVATION, 5 allée
Sully, 29322 QUIMPER Cedex
☎ 04 76 40 79 40 & PROP: 04 76 32 01 78
📠 04 76 40 79 99
e-mail: sirt38@wanadoo.fr www.gites-de-france-isère.com
A beautiful Dauphinois house with shell-tiled roof, near the
Château de Virieu. Four guest rooms, all beautiful and large,
very comfortable, with individual décor, opening onto a pretty
balcony. Each room has a sitting area with sofa bed, bathroom
and wc. Calm and relaxation under the silver birches. Soirées
by the fireside; piano; library; telescope. Many museums and
castles, near to Lac de Paladru. Parking and garage. Open all
year.
PRICES: s €58; d €69; t €92; extra person €16; dinner €19
ON SITE: Hiking **NEARBY:** Bathing (9km) Horse riding (4km)
Fishing (7km) Swimming pool (4km) Cross-country skiing (40km)
Downhill skiing (40km) Railway station (5km) Shops (3km) LA TOUR
DU PIN (9km) **NOTES:** No pets CC English spoken

ST-PRIM

♈ 🍽 Le Pré Margot Maurice & Martine BRIOT
chemin de Pré Margot, 38370 ST PRIM
☎ 04 74 56 44 27 📠 04 74 56 30 93
e-mail: lamargotine@wanadoo.fr
An enormous modern house in the green countryside above the
waters of the Roches de Condrieu and its marina. Six rooms for
two/three, with shower and wc. Television and individual air-
conditioning. Large veranda with open fire where breakfast is
served. Dinner must be booked. Closed parking. View over Mont
Pilat and the vineyard of Côtes Rôties. Billiards, board games. Two
(grade 3) rural gîtes. Swimming pool. Open all year.
PRICES: s €37; d €42; t €57; dinner €14 **ON SITE:** Fishing Swimming
pool **NEARBY:** Bathing (1km) Horse riding (10km) Hiking (1km) Cross-
country skiing (27km) Downhill skiing (27km) Railway station (1km)
Shops (1km) VIENNE **NOTES:** Pets admitted

THEYS

♈ 🍽 Chez ma Cousine Anne LETOURNEAU
GITES DE FRANCE-SERVICE RESERVATION, 5 allée Sully,
29322 QUIMPER Cedex
☎ 04 76 40 79 40 & PROP: 04 76 71 17 01 📠 04 76 40 79 99
e-mail: sirt38@wanadoo.fr www.gites-de-france-isère.com
A little corner of Québec in the Alps. In an enormous modern
house, Anne gives you a choice of three rooms on the ground
floor, and two upstairs with balconies, all sleeping two guests. All
have shower and wc. Dining room with panorama over the
surrounding Massifs. Some delicious dishes from Québec are
served. For mountain hikes, packed lunches are available. 30km
from Grenoble and Chambéry. Open 15th December to 15th April
and 15th June to 15th October.
PRICES: s €39; d €49-€61; t €75; dinner €23 **ON SITE:** Horse riding
Hiking **NEARBY:** Bathing (8km) Cross-country skiing (12km) Downhill
skiing (12km) Aerial sports (10km) Railway station (8km) Shops (3km)
GONCELIN (12km) **NOTES:** No pets CC English spoken

continued

VAUJANY

♦♦♦ ⲓΟⲓ **Solneige** Jan & Mirjam DEKKER
Pourchery, 38114 VAUJANY
☎ 04 76 79 88 18
e-mail: solneige@planet.nl

An old farmhouse, restored with taste, near the charming village of Vaujany, an ideal base for ski holidays, or summer holidays in the Alps. Five charming rooms for two or three guests, with shower and wc. Each room has a balcony with an outstanding view over the Vallée d'Eau d'Olle. Dinner and breakfasts are taken in the comfortable vaulted living room, or in the garden in summer. Two six person gîtes are on the second floor. Two of the guest rooms are in a separate maisonette. Open all year.

PRICES: s €40; d €50; t €69; extra person €18; dinner €20
ON SITE: Hiking **NEARBY:** Horse riding (8km) Rock climbing (2km) Fishing (4km) Swimming pool (2km) Cross-country skiing (2km) Downhill skiing (2km) Aerial sports (2km) Railway station (50km) Shops (3km) BOURG D OISANS (LE) (16km) **NOTES:** Pets admitted English spoken

VERNIOZ

♦♦♦ ⲓΟⲓ **Bois Marquis** Chantal FRECHET
38150 VERNIOZ
☎ 04 74 84 49 40

Condrieu 10km, Vienne 12km. Guest rooms in a house adjoining that of the owners. On the ground floor: living room with kitchenette; one double room with shower and wc. Upstairs: one room for two and a large room sleeping three, each with shower and wc. The windows open onto countryside. Shaded grounds with garden furniture. Open all year.

PRICES: s €30; d €38; t €49; extra person €11; dinner €13
ON SITE: Hiking **NEARBY:** Bathing (10km) Fishing (3km) Swimming pool (15km) Railway station (15km) Shops (3km) ROUSSILLON (12km) **NOTES:** No pets

VILLARD-BONNOT

♦♦♦♦ ⲓΟⲓ **Domaine du Berlioz**
Martine & Robert ESSA
rue du Berlioz, 38190 VILLARD BONNOT
☎ 04 76 71 40 00 & SR : 04 76 40 79 40
📠 04 76 13 05 98
e-mail: domaineduberlioz@wanadoo.fr

A 12th-century manor, just a quarter of an hour from Grenoble, at the foot of the Belledonne chain. Choose from two beautiful double rooms or one suite sleeping four. All have shower and wc. Dining room with vast fireplace, television lounge, video, library. Generous dinners, with specialities cooked in the bread oven. 1.5ha park in country surroundings. Open 1st April to 31st October.

PRICES: s €65; d €80; t €105; extra person €25; dinner €30
NEARBY: Bathing (10km) Horse riding (5km) Fishing (2km) Swimming pool (5km) Cross-country skiing (10km) Downhill skiing (10km) Aerial sports (15km) Railway station (2km) Shops (2km) GRENOBLE (15km) **NOTES:** Pets admitted English spoken

For further information on these and other chambres d'hôtes, consult the Gîtes de France website
www.gites-de-france.fr

VILLARD-DE-LANS

♦♦♦ ⲓΟⲓ **La Croix du Liorin** Nicole BERTRAND
Bois Barbu, 38250 VILLARD DE LANS
☎ 04 76 95 82 67   📠 04 76 95 85 75

At an altitude of 1235m, the view of the mountains to the east and Vercors is exceptional. Look down onto the village of Corrençon. Cosy inside, there are three bedrooms to choose from. All are small and delightful, and have French windows opening at ground level. All have shower and wc. Share meals with the owners in a friendly atmosphere and relax in front of the big wood fire. Golf at Corrençon. Open all year.

PRICES: s €32; d €39; t €49; dinner €14 **ON SITE:** Hiking Cross-country skiing **NEARBY:** Horse riding (5km) Rock climbing (5km) Fishing (3km) Swimming pool (5km) Downhill skiing (3km) Potholing (5km) Aerial sports (5km) Railway station (35km) Shops (3km) VILLARD DE LANS (5km) **NOTES:** No pets

♦♦♦ ⲓΟⲓ **La Jasse** Michel IMBAUD
222 rue du Lycée Polonais, 38250 VILLARD DE LANS
☎ 04 76 95 91 63
e-mail: imbaud.lajasse@wanadoo.fr
http://www.imbaud-lajasse.com

A modern house in the Parc du Vercors in the middle of a lively resort. Cosy rustic interior. Odile and Michel offer three comfortable rooms: one duplex for three people; and two double rooms. The menu changes regularly. At your disposal: terrace, garden, parking. Open all year.

PRICES: s €37; d €44; t €59; dinner €15 **ON SITE:** Swimming pool **NEARBY:** Horse riding (4km) Rock climbing (3km) Fishing (1km) Hiking (1km) Cross-country skiing (3km) Downhill skiing (3km) Potholing (10km) Aerial sports (5km) Railway station (30km) VILLARD DE LANS **NOTES:** No pets English spoken

♦♦♦ ⲓΟⲓ **Le Val Sainte Marie**
Dominique & Agnès BON
Bois Barbu, 38250 VILLARD DE LANS
☎ 04 76 95 92 80   📠 04 76 95 92 80

In a green bowl in the heart of the Vercors, Agnès and Dominique offer you in their traditional farmhouse three intimate and comfortable bedrooms (with shower and wc), a friendly table with regional fare in a warm atmosphere. With garden, terrace, stove room, library. Open all year.

PRICES: s €40; d €46; t €60; extra person €14; dinner €14
ON SITE: Hiking Cross-country skiing Potholing **NEARBY:** Horse riding (5km) Rock climbing (4km) Fishing (2km) Swimming pool (3km) Downhill skiing (7km) Aerial sports (7km) Railway station (35km) Shops (4km) VILLARD DE LANS (3km) **NOTES:** No pets English spoken

♦♦♦ ⲓΟⲓ **Les 4 Vents** Jean-Paul & Sylvie UZEL
Bois Barbu, 38250 VILLARD DE LANS
☎ 04 76 95 10 68

A Vercors farmhouse, in a peaceful location, offering five bedrooms with shower, basin and wc; dining room; open fire; sitting room. Tuck into real family food, prepared using produce from the garden and local area. Breakfast features home-made preserves and Vercors honey. The nearby village provides plenty to do. Ski guide Jean-Paul will advise you on leisure activities. Garage. Reduced rates according to season. Open all year.

PRICES: d €42; extra person €13; dinner €14 **ON SITE:** Hiking Cross-country skiing **NEARBY:** Horse riding (6km) Rock climbing (4km) Fishing (3km) Swimming pool (4km) Downhill skiing (7km) Potholing (4km) Aerial sports (4km) Railway station (30km) Shops (4km) VILLARD DE LANS (3km) **NOTES:** No pets English spoken

RHÔNE-ALPES

VOREPPE

▥▥▥▥ 🍴 Château Saint Vincent

Sylvia & Bruno LAFFOND
GITES DE FRANCE-SERVICE RESERVATION, 5 allée
Sully, 29322 QUIMPER Cedex
☎ 04 76 40 79 40 & PROP: 04 76 50 67 87 📠 04 76 40 79 99
e-mail: sirt38@wanadoo.fr www.gites-de-france-isère.com
On the way to Grenoble, capital of the Alps, this 16th-century
castle harmoniously combines charm and modernity. The five
bedrooms have period windows which open onto the park
with its stately trees. Convivial atmosphere, tasty meals and
breakfast served either on the terrace or beside the
monumental fireplace at the family dining room. Perfect for
exploring the town of Grenoble, with its blend of high-tech, art
and history, among the soaring mountains. Open all year.
PRICES: s €75; d €91-€130; extra person €30; dinner €24
ON SITE: Swimming pool Hiking **NEARBY:** Horse riding (4km)
Rock climbing (3km) Fishing (4km) Cross-country skiing (29km)
Downhill skiing (29km) Railway station (4km) Shops (2km) VOIRON
(14km) **NOTES:** No pets CC

LOIRE

CIVENS

▥▥▥ 🐓 🍴 Les Rivières Bernard & Simone PALAIS

42110 CIVENS
☎ 04 77 26 11 93
Feurs 2.5 km. Three upstairs guest rooms in a farmhouse, each
with private facilities. One double room; one with double bed and
bunks; one twin room. Salon with TV and open fireplace. Terrace
with outdoor furniture. At dinner you may sample the produce
from the garden and farm, and the home-made preserves
(dandelion/wild rose). Open all year.
PRICES: s €25; d €33; dinner €11 **NEARBY:** Horse riding (8km) Fishing
(3km) Swimming pool (2km) Hiking (4km) Tennis (2km) Bicycle hire
(3km) Railway station (2km) Shops (2km) ST-ETIENNE (40km)
NOTES: No pets

COLOMBIER-SOUS-PILAT

▥▥▥ Vernollon Odile GRANGE

42220 COLOMBIER-SOUS-PILAT
☎ 04 77 51 56 58
Three guest rooms in the Parc du Pilat, with wonderful view over
the Alps. One double room with wc and washbasin; one twin room
with shower and wc; one two-roomed suite with a double and
single in one room plus two singles and bunks in the other,
shower and wc. Extra beds available. Large communal room with
sitting area and library. Grounds, terrace, garden furniture. Table
tennis room. Circular walking trails. Information folder to help you
discover local flora and fauna. Open all year.
PRICES: s €19-€28; d €26-€34; t €34-€49; HB €31-€40; dinner €13
ON SITE: Hiking Cross-country skiing **NEARBY:** Horse riding (3km)
Golf (20km) Fishing (9km) Swimming pool (17km) Stretch of water
(13km) Downhill skiing (4km) Tennis (8km) Bicycle hire (8km) Railway
station (25km) Shops (9km) Restaurant nearby ST-ETIENNE (25km)
NOTES: Pets admitted English spoken

COMMELLE-VERNAY

▥▥▥▥ 🍴 Château de Bachelard

Daniéla & Hervé NOIRARD
Bachelard, 42120 COMMELLE-VERNAY
☎ 04 77 71 93 67 & SR : 04 77 79 18 49 📠 04 77 72 10 20
e-mail: bachelard@worldonline.fr
http://accueil.com/bachelard
Roanne 4 km. In wide green parkland enclosing a 6ha lake
stands the 17th-century Château de Bachelard. Three double

rooms and one suite with a double bed and four singles, each
with private facilities and lounge area. Huge reception rooms;
salon with open fire; dining room looking over the swimming
pool. At the dining table, family cuisine is based on the
produce of the kitchen garden. Ideal for lovers of hunting and
fishing. Mallard shooting at the outlet or on the banks of the
lake. Open all year.
PRICES: s €81; d €89; dinner €20 **ON SITE:** Fishing Swimming
pool Stretch of water Hiking **NEARBY:** Horse riding (3km) Golf
(3km) Tennis (3km) Railway station (4km) Shops (2km) ROANNE
(4km) **NOTES:** No pets English spoken

EPERCIEUX-ST-PAUL

▥▥▥ 🍴 Les Barges Pascale & Hervé GARDON

42110 EPERCIEUX-ST-PAUL
☎ 04 77 26 54 40 & SR : 04 77 79 18 49
Hervé and family welcome guests to their old restored farmhouse -
four guest rooms all with private facilities. One double room, two
twin rooms and a room sleeping three. Private lounge and kitchen
available for guest use, as well as a TV room. Grounds with lawn,
boules, garden furniture under the shade of the lime tree. Stroll
down to the banks of the Loire (1km). At the dinner table enjoy
family cuisine using home grown vegetables and preserves in
regional recipes. Open all year.
PRICES: s €29; d €37; t €49; dinner €12 **ON SITE:** Hiking
NEARBY: Horse riding (12km) Fishing (1km) Swimming pool (7km)
Tennis (7km) Railway station (7km) Shops (7km) MONTBRISON (27km)
NOTES: No pets

FEURS

▥▥▥ 🍴 La Bussinière Eliane & Daniel PERRIN

GITES DE FRANCE-SERVICE RESERVATION, 5 allée Sully,
29322 QUIMPER Cedex
☎ 04 77 79 18 49 & PROP: 04 77 27 06 36 📠 04 77 93 93 66
e-mail: gites.de.france.42@wanadoo.fr
www.gites-de-france-loire.com
Eliane and Daniel greet guests at their old restored farmhouse.
Three guest rooms in an adjacent building, all doubles, with
private facilities. On the ground floor are a living room with sitting
area with open fire; here breakfast and dinner are served. Ask for
directions. Open all year.
PRICES: s €31; d €39; extra person €13; dinner €13 **ON SITE:** Hiking
NEARBY: Fishing (4km) Swimming pool (4km) Tennis (4km) Railway
station (3km) Shops (3km) ST-ETIENNE (35km) **NOTES:** Pets admitted

FOURNEAUX

▥▥▥▥ Château de l'Aubépin

Laure DE CHOISEUL
42470 FOURNEAUX
☎ 06 19 74 20 19 & 01 46 93 08 08 📠 04 77 62 48 40
e-mail: aubepin42@yahoo.fr
http://www.aubepin.bizland.com
A 17th-century castle overlooking a French-style garden
designed by Le Nôtre. Three rooms, each with private
facilities. Guard Room with monumental fireplace. Impressive
Italianate décor. The swimming pool is for guest use; there is
also a private lake for fishing.
PRICES: s €61-€77; d €92-€122 **ON SITE:** Fishing Swimming pool
Hiking Tennis **NEARBY:** Horse riding (11km) Golf (25km) Stretch
of water (11km) Railway station (11km) Shops (3km) ROANNE
(25km) **NOTES:** No pets English spoken

> 🐓Places with this symbol are farmhouses

continued

RHÔNE-ALPES

GREZIEUX-LE-FROMENTAL

♥ ♥ ◐ Le Thevenon Françoise & J.Marc FARJON
Grézieux le Fromental, 42600 MONTBRISON
☎ 04 77 76 12 93   📠 04 77 76 13 51
Montrond-les-Bains & Montbrison 7 km. Four guest rooms in a
building adjacent to the proprietors' home in a hamlet. Two twin
rooms and two doubles; folding bed also available. All have en
suite shower and wc. Sitting area; dining room (with TV)
exclusively for guests. Fully equipped kitchen with microwave and
washing machine. Large grounds with outdoor furniture; tennis
court; table tennis, volleyball; pétanque. Dinner (must be booked).
Open all year.
PRICES: s €31; d €39; extra person €13; dinner €13   **ON SITE:** Hiking
Tennis   **NEARBY:** Horse riding (14km) Golf (6km) Fishing (5km)
Swimming pool (7km) Stretch of water (30km) Cross-country skiing
(30km) Downhill skiing (30km) Bicycle hire (7km) Railway station (7km)
Shops (7km) ST-ETIENNE (44km)   **NOTES:** Pets admitted English spoken

LA GRESLE

♥ ◐ Le Chalet J.Bernard CHAPON
Les 4 Croix, 42460 LA GRESLE
☎ 04 74 64 47 27 & 06 08 56 60 88 SR: 04 77 79 18 49
📠 04 74 64 33 74
e-mail: chaponjb@aol.com
Lyon 70 km, Autun 75 km, Roanne 22 km. In 2.5ha grounds, a
building with four guest rooms. Two double and two twin rooms,
all with private washing facilities and wc. The rooms are on the
second floor and all have good views over the surrounding
countryside. Gentle strolls in the parklands, perfect after meals
lovingly prepared by J Bernard and served on the terrace in the
shade of century old cedars. For food-lovers, gastronomic meals
can be prepared. Close to Beaujolais, Burgundy and the Auvergne.
Open all year.
PRICES: ; d €58; dinner €16   **ON SITE:** Hiking Tennis   **NEARBY:** Horse
riding (10km) Golf (25km) Fishing (2km) Swimming pool (5km) Stretch
of water (15km) Bicycle hire (5km) Railway station (12km) Shops (5km)
ROANNE (20km)   **NOTES:** No pets CC English spoken

LA TERRASSE-SUR-DORLAY

♥ ◐ Le Moulin Payre Myriam & Pierre MARQUET
42740 LA-TERRASSE-SUR-DORLAY
☎ 04 77 20 91 46
In the Parc Naturel du Pilat, Myriam and Pierre open the doors of
their old family mansion to you: five guest rooms; shady park with
swimming pool; private lake; river bank. All rooms have private
facilities, and a sitting room is for your use (reading, TV, etc).
Meals by arrangement. Conveniently located between Lyon and St-
Etienne, in the open countryside. Open all year.
PRICES: s €39; d €48-€63; extra person €13; dinner €16
ON SITE: Fishing Swimming pool Hiking   **NEARBY:** Horse riding (3km)
Golf (20km) Stretch of water (3km) Cross-country skiing (15km) Downhill
skiing (30km) Tennis (1km) Bicycle hire (8km) Railway station (8km)
Shops (2km) ST-ETIENNE (23km)   **NOTES:** No pets

LA-VALLA-EN-GIER

♥ Le Moulin-du-Bost Annie & Jacques FAURE
42131 LA VALLA-EN-GIER
☎ 04 77 20 06 62
Annie and Jacques live in the middle of the Parc Naturel Régional
du Pilat, near the Saut de Gier. One double room; one twin room;
and one mini studio (refrigerator, washing machine and
dishwasher) with double bed, single and cot in one room plus twin
beds in the lounge. All have shower, wc, and TV; the studio also
has a large bath. Open fireplace; barbecue; veranda. Flower
garden with outdoor furniture. In the evening, the dinner table is

laid with fresh produce using local recipes. Open from Easter to
1st November.
PRICES: s €36; d €45; t €59; extra person €14; dinner €15
ON SITE: Fishing Hiking   **NEARBY:** Swimming pool (10km) Cross-
country skiing (15km) Tennis (15km) Railway station (15km) Shops
(15km) Restaurant nearby ST-ETIENNE (21km)   **NOTES:** Pets admitted

MAROLS

♥ ◐ l'Ecusson Josiane FRACHEY
Le Bourg, 42560 MAROLS
☎ 04 77 76 70 38 & 04 77 32 64 40
St-Bonnet-les-Bains 9 km. A building of character in the village
centre, offering four individually styled bedrooms on two levels:
twin room; room sleeping four; twin with double beds; room
sleeping three. All have en suite shower and wc. Kitchen area;
salon; TV. Closed grounds with interior courtyard; garden
furniture; parking 10m. Close to Forez, Auvergne and Velay (on the
Circuit des Babets). Evening meal (booking essential). Open end
May to end September, and at other times by booking. Book at
weekends.
PRICES: s €37; d €49; t €65; dinner €12-€18   **ON SITE:** Fishing Hiking
NEARBY: Horse riding (5km) Golf (40km) Swimming pool (19km)
Stretch of water (9km) Cross-country skiing (20km) Downhill skiing
(20km) Tennis (4km) Bicycle hire (9km) Railway station (19km) ST-
ETIENNE (40km)   **NOTES:** Pets admitted

ST-BONNET-LE-COURREAU

♥ ♥ ◐ Chambre d'hôtes
J. François & Lucienne FOURNIER
42940 ST-BONNET-LE-COURREAU
☎ 04 77 76 80 20
In the middle of a little village overlooking the Plaine du Forez,
with a view to the Alps, Lucienne and J. François invite you into
their four guest rooms: two large grade 3 rooms (a twin and a
double with a child's bed), each with en suite facilities. Two grade
1 twin rooms with shower and wc on landing. Extra bed available.
1,000m² of grounds; terrace with garden furniture. Visit the farm.
Family cuisine and local produce. Open all year.
PRICES: s €22-€26; d €29-€34; HB €46-€49; dinner €11-€13
ON SITE: Hiking Cross-country skiing   **NEARBY:** Horse riding (8km)
Golf (18km) Fishing (2km) Swimming pool (15km) Downhill skiing
(15km) Tennis (9km) Railway station (15km) ST-ETIENNE (55km)
NOTES: Pets admitted

ST-DIDIER-SUR-ROCHEFORT

♥ ◐ La Closerie Dany TRAPEAU
42111 ST-DIDIER-SUR-ROCHEFORT
☎ 04 77 97 91 26 & 04 70 97 87 07   📠 04 77 97 91 26
Three upstairs guest rooms in this stone village house with private
garden. One double room; one twin; and one sleeping three. All
have en suite facilities. Enormous living room and lounge with
antique furniture and open fireplace. Charming and tasty
breakfasts or lavish dinners served under the shade of the lime.
Haut-Forez is at the hub of several walking trails. Music lovers will
appreciate the concerts given in the nearby priory. Open 1st June
to 30th September.
PRICES: s €33-€40; d €39-€46; extra person €13; dinner €16
ON SITE: Hiking Tennis   **NEARBY:** Horse riding (5km) Golf (35km)
Fishing (1km) Swimming pool (25km) Stretch of water (10km) Cross-
country skiing (15km) Downhill skiing (27km) Railway station (10km)
MONTBRISON (34km)   **NOTES:** Pets admitted English spoken

CC - credit cards accepted

---

continued

STE-FOY-ST-SULPICE

♦♦♦ 💚 🍴 Chambre d'hôtes Lucette & René CLAIR
St-Sulpice, 42110 STE-FOY-ST-SULPICE
☎ 04 77 27 81 08
Three guest rooms upstairs in a wing of the family house with
independent access. One double room and two singles with
private facilities. Spare bed if required. Living room with kitchen
available to guests. At dinner enjoy real family cooking based on
farm and regional produce. Terrace, shady parkland. Central in the
Plaine du Forez, within 5km of two major sites - the Bastie d'Urfé
and Pommiers en Forez. Open all year.
PRICES: s €31; d €36; extra person €11; dinner €12 **ON SITE:** Hiking
NEARBY: Horse riding (8km) Golf (20km) Fishing (9km) Swimming
pool (12km) Tennis (4km) Railway station (9km) Shops (4km)
MONTBRISON (20km) **NOTES:** No pets

ST-GEORGES-EN-COUZAN

♦♦♦ 💚 Le Mazet Camille DECOMBE
GITES DE FRANCE-SERVICE RESERVATION, 5 allée Sully,
29322 QUIMPER Cedex
☎ 04 77 79 18 49 & PROP: 04 77 24 80 95 📄 04 77 93 93 66
e-mail: gites.de.france.42@wanadoo.fr
www.gites-de-france-loire.com
Set in the Monts du Forez, Valérie and Camille are your hosts. Six
large guest rooms (one for parents with children) upstairs in their
home, each with private facilities. TV lounge and day room for
guests. Meals available at adjacent farm-auberge. Exceptional
location, with superb view over the Monts du Forez. Booking
recommended. Closed Sunday evening and Monday outside
school holidays. Open all year.
PRICES: s €29; d €39; extra person €14; HB €29; FB €37; dinner €10
ON SITE: Hiking **NEARBY:** Horse riding (15km) Fishing (8km) Cross-
country skiing (15km) Downhill skiing (15km) Tennis (3km) Railway
station (12km) Shops (3km) Restaurant nearby ST ETIENNE (70km)
NOTES: Pets admitted

ST-HAON-LE-VIEUX

♦♦♦ Magnerot J.François & Claude PRAS
42370 ST-HAON-LE-VIEUX
☎ 04 77 64 45 56 📄 04 77 62 12 52
e-mail: jfpras@iname.com http://www.la-cote-roannaise.com
Three guest rooms in the home of a winegrower on several
walking routes: one twin (grade 3) has shower and wc; two double
rooms (grade 1) have shower and washbasin, sharing the wc.
Lounge. Grounds with outdoor furniture. Small animals permitted.
Reduced rates for stays over three nights. Kitchenette for use by
guests. Grocers in the village (400m) with bread shop; other shops
6km. Sailing 12km. Open 15th March to 15th November except
during harvest.
PRICES: s €24-€30; d €30-€35 **ON SITE:** Hiking Tennis
NEARBY: Horse riding (10km) Golf (15km) Fishing (12km) Swimming
pool (15km) Cross-country skiing (10km) Railway station (16km) Shops
(2km) ROANNE (16km) **NOTES:** Pets admitted

ST-JEAN-ST-MAURICE

♦♦♦ 🍴 l'Echauguette Michèle ALEX
Rue Guy de la Mure, 42155 ST-JEAN-ST-MAURICE
☎ 04 77 63 15 89
Four guest rooms of character: one double and one twin on the
ground floor; one with three single beds on the first floor; and a
double at ground level in a separate maisonette. Each has
bathroom and wc. Salon. Terrace with outdoor furniture. One
room looks over the Lake of Villarest, the second over the village

of St-Jean-St-Maurice, the third over the castle in the village, and
the last overlooks the Loire. Open all year.
PRICES: s €42; d €49; t €57; dinner €19 **ON SITE:** Hiking
NEARBY: Horse riding (5km) Golf (5km) Fishing (2km) Swimming pool
(14km) Stretch of water (6km) Tennis (1km) Railway station (14km)
ROANNE (14km) **NOTES:** Pets admitted English spoken

ST-JULIEN-MOLIN-MOLETTE

♦♦♦♦ 🍴 Castel - Gueret Daniel COULAUD
Drevard, 42220 ST-JULIEN-MOLIN-MOLETTE
☎ 04 77 51 56 04 & 04 77 51 59 13 SR: 04 77 79 18 49
📄 04 77 51 59 13
http://castel.gueret.free.fr
Lyon 65 km. Five rooms (two of them suites) in a fine 19th-
century castle in the heart of the Parc Naturel du Pilat,
between the Loire, the Ardèche and the Isère. Two double
rooms; one twin room; two suites each with a double and two
single beds. All are very comfortable and have private
facilities. Sitting areas; billiard room; kitchen exclusively for
guests. Also a gîte for four to six people. Park of 1.8ha with
hundred year old trees and private swimming pool. St-Joseph
and Côtes-Rôties vineyards are close. Open all year.
PRICES: s €43-€54; d €49-€77; t €80-€107; dinner €19; HB €43-€56
ON SITE: Fishing Swimming pool Hiking Tennis **NEARBY:** Horse
riding (1km) Golf (10km) Stretch of water (4km) Cross-country skiing
(12km) Downhill skiing (13km) Railway station (30km) ST-ETIENNE
(31km) **NOTES:** Pets admitted English spoken

♦♦♦ 🍴 La Rivoire Denise THIOLLIERE
42220 ST-JULIEN-MOLIN-MOLETTE
☎ 04 77 39 65 44 📄 04 77 39 67 86
e-mail: larivoire@chez.com http://www.chez.com/larivoire
*Animal park at Peaugres 15km, Annonay 10km, Bourg-Argental
5km.* In the Parc Naturel du Pilat, Denise and Robert invite you
into their comfortable 18th-century home with its wonderful views
over the landscape. Five rooms, all with private facilities. Two
double rooms, one twin and one room sleeping four, ideal for a
family. Beautiful living rooms, and two rooms for guests' use only.
At breakfast or dinner (served on the terrace in season), you can
enjoy family cooking based on fruit and vegetables from the
garden and other regional produce. Open all year except January.
PRICES: s €37; d €46; t €57; HB €37-€51; dinner €14 **ON SITE:** Hiking
NEARBY: Horse riding (1km) Golf (10km) Fishing (1km) Swimming
pool (5km) Cross-country skiing (15km) Tennis (5km) Railway station
(35km) Shops (4km) ST-ETIENNE (35km) **NOTES:** No pets English
spoken

ST-MARCEL-D'URFE

♦♦♦ 🍴 Il Fut un Temps...
Anne-Marie HAUCK
Les Gouttes, 42430 ST-MARCEL-D'URFE
☎ 04 77 62 52 19 & 06 86 96 59 67 📄 04 77 62 52 19
e-mail: anne-marie.hauck@wanadoo.fr
www.eazyweb.co.uk/ilfut
St-Just-en-Chevalet 10 km. Five guest rooms in an old stone
farmhouse in the depths of the country. One double room; two
single rooms; and two large rooms each with double bed and sofa
bed. All have shower and wc. Dining room and sitting room with
open fire. Story-telling evenings round the fire on occasion. Open
all year.
PRICES: s €34-€49; d €42-€57; t €65; dinner €17 **ON SITE:** Wine tasting
Hiking Cross-country skiing **NEARBY:** Horse riding (3km) Fishing (3km)
Swimming pool (10km) Tennis (3km) Bicycle hire (10km) Railway station
(25km) Shops (3km) ROANNE (36km) **NOTES:** No pets English spoken

continued

RHÔNE-ALPES

ST-MARCELLIN-EN-FOREZ

♦♦♦♦ Chambre d'hôtes Roland & Christine MALCLES
40 Rte de St-Bonnet-le-Château
42680 ST-MARCELLIN-EN-FOREZ
☎ 04 77 52 89 63 & 06 03 00 23 67 SR: 04 77 79 18 49
e-mail: gites.de.france.42@wanadoo.fr
www.gites-de-france-loire.com
This chambre d'hôtes offers five guest rooms: one two-roomed
suite with double and three single beds; two rooms sleeping
three; and two double rooms, each with private facilities. Dining
room, fully equipped kitchen for guests, salon (with two folding
beds available), video and hi-fi system if required for family or
business gatherings. Enclosed parkland, parking, garden furniture,
games. Friendly weekend breaks (booking required). Open all
year.
PRICES: s €31; d €42; t €52; extra person €13 **ON SITE:** Horse riding
Swimming pool Hiking Tennis **NEARBY:** Golf (25km) Fishing (4km)
Stretch of water (10km) Railway station (4km) ST-ETIENNE (25km)
NOTES: No pets CC English spoken

ST-MEDARD-EN-FOREZ

♦♦♦ ❍¶ Chambre d'hôtes Jean & Michèle GOUILLON
Place de l'Eglise, 42330 ST-MEDARD-EN-FOREZ
☎ 04 77 94 04 44 & SR: 04 77 79 18 49 📠 04 77 94 13 49
e-mail: info@chambresdhotesloire.com
www.chambresdhotesloire.com
Michèle and Jean welcome you to five guest rooms in a restored
18th-century home in the middle of a charming village. Four
double rooms (two with spare bed if required) plus one twin
room, each with private facilities. Large living room with table
seating ten. Sitting room with TV. Booking required for dinner.
Open all year.
PRICES: s €31; d €40; extra person €14; dinner €13 **ON SITE:** Hiking
NEARBY: Horse riding (6km) Golf (12km) Fishing (1km) Swimming
pool (8km) Stretch of water (8km) Tennis (6km) Railway station (6km)
ST-ETIENNE (20km) **NOTES:** Pets admitted CC

ST-MICHEL-SUR-RHONE

♦♦♦ ❍¶ L'Ollagnière Georges et Claudette BONNET
42410 ST-MICHEL-SUR-RHONE
☎ 04 74 59 51 01 & 04 74 56 80 74
Condrieu 3 km. In the Parc du Pilat, 3km from the RN86 between
Lyon and Valence, three guest rooms in an old house. Two rooms
are grade 2 - a double and one with three single beds; each have
shower and basin, with wc on the same landing. One grade 3
room with two single beds and child's bed if required. The
proprietors live 500m away. Kitchen, dining room and TV lounge.
Breakfast and dinner available. Terrace and summer kitchen -
perfect for a barbecue. Green surroundings, garden furniture.
Wine-tasting nearby. Open all year.
PRICES: s €29; d €37; t €46; extra person €11; dinner €13-€14
ON SITE: Hiking **NEARBY:** Fishing (2km) Swimming pool (4km)
Stretch of water (4km) Tennis (7km) Railway station (4km) Shops (3km)
ST-ETIENNE (49km) **NOTES:** Pets admitted

ST-NIZIER-DE-FORNAS

♦♦♦ ❍¶ Chambre d'hôtes
J.Louis & M.Paule CHAMBLAS
L'Etrat-Route d'Estivarelles, 42380 ST NIZIER DE FORNAS
☎ 04 77 50 71 19 & 06 88 00 22 05 SR: 04 77 79 18 49
St-Bonnet 2km. In the Monts du Forez, en route to the Auvergne,
J. Louis and M. Paule invite you into their home, an old stone
farmhouse now restored, at 980m altitude. All the rooms have
private facilities and there is a living room/lounge for you to relax
in. At the dinner table you will enjoy family cooking based on

regional recipes and produce, served in front of the open fire. The
area offers many activities. Open all year.
PRICES: s €30; d €37; extra person €11; HB €40; FB €46; dinner €13
ON SITE: Hiking **NEARBY:** Horse riding (3km) Fishing (2km) Stretch of
water (2km) Cross-country skiing (16km) Tennis (2km) Bicycle hire (2km)
Shops (2km) MONTBRISON (31km) **NOTES:** Pets admitted English
spoken

ST-PIERRE-LA-NOAILLE

♦♦♦♦ ❍¶ Domaine Château de Marchangy
M.Colette RUFENER
42190 ST-PIERRE-LA-NOAILLE
☎ 04 77 69 96 76 📠 04 77 60 70 37
e-mail: marchangy@net-up.com
Three guest rooms in an 18th-century house; one double
room and two suites. One suite has two double beds, the
second has a double and two single beds. All have bathrooms,
wc, TV and direct line telephones. Lounge with open fire and
mini-bar. 2.5ha park with garden furniture, swimming pool,
bikes. Generous breakfast. Brunch (extra charge). Candlelit
dinner served outside in season. A quiet spot, superb location,
panoramic view. Many walking trails. Children €13.
PRICES: s €66-€81; d €74-€89; extra person €13-€28; dinner €13-
€23 **ON SITE:** Swimming pool Hiking Bicycle hire
NEARBY: Horse riding (14km) Golf (16km) Fishing (4km) Stretch
of water (20km) Tennis (5km) Railway station (15km) Shops (4km)
ROANNE (15km) **NOTES:** Pets admitted English spoken

ST-PRIEST-LA-ROCHE

♦♦♦ 🐓 ❍¶ Prévieux
André & Odile ROCHE-MERCIER
42590 ST-PRIEST-LA-ROCHE
☎ 04 77 64 92 12
St-Symphorien-de-Lay 11 km. In this old house in a pleasant and
quiet location are three guest rooms each with shower and wc.
The Rose Room is a double; the Forget-me-not Room sleeps four;
the Lily Room accommodates three. On the ground floor are the
dining room, reading room with TV for guests and open fire.
Outside is the terrace with garden furniture, play area, barbecue,
garage. Camping in the grounds. Near the Gorges of the Loire and
the Château de la Roche.
PRICES: s €23; d €29; t €40, dinner €11 **ON SITE:** Fishing Hiking
NEARBY: Horse riding (7km) Golf (10km) Swimming pool (8km)
Stretch of water (10km) Tennis (1km) Shops (5km) ROANNE (15km)
NOTES: Pets admitted English spoken

ST-VICTOR-SUR-LOIRE

♦♦♦ Pracoin Colette GRIMAND
42230 ST. VICTOR-SUR-LOIRE
☎ 04 77 90 37 95 & SR: 04 77 79 18 49
Firminy 6 km. At the gateway to the Gorges of the Loire, three
comfortable rooms in an old renovated barn, all with private

continued   *continued*

RHÔNE-ALPES

facilities. You have the use of an enclosed park with swimming pool, sitting room, and lounge. According to the season, Colette will serve you breakfast either in the barn building or by the side of the pool. She does not offer an evening meal, but will happily make recommendations on the nearby restaurants and auberges. Open all year.
PRICES: s €36; d €43; extra person €13 **ON SITE:** Swimming pool Hiking **NEARBY:** Horse riding (3km) Golf (6km) Fishing (5km) Stretch of water (5km) Cross-country skiing (25km) Tennis (5km) Bicycle hire (2km) Railway station (6km) Shops (1km) ST-ETIENNE (6km)
NOTES: No pets CC

VENDRANGES

☗ ☙ ⦿ Ferme de Montissut
Jean & Suzanne DELOIRE
Montissut, 42590 VENDRANGES
☎ 04 77 64 90 96
St-Symphorien-de-Lay 11 km. Suzanne and Jean welcome you to their cattle rearing farm. Three guest rooms upstairs. Two grade 3 rooms with private facilities - one spacious room overlooking the lake with one double and two single beds; one twin room. A grade 2 double room with wc and basin. Reading room. Extra bed available. Salon, TV, library, open fire. Shady terrace, play area, table tennis. Garage for each room. Camping, fishing on the lake. Visits to farm. Near to the Château de la Roche and Gorges of the Loire. Open all year.
PRICES: s €26; d €34; HB €28; dinner €11 **ON SITE:** Fishing Hiking **NEARBY:** Horse riding (6km) Golf (10km) Swimming pool (10km) Stretch of water (10km) Tennis (1km) Railway station (15km) Shops (8km) ROANNE (13km) **NOTES:** Pets admitted English spoken

RHÔNE

AMPUIS

☗ Chambre d'hôtes Gilles & Marie-Alice BARGE
8 Bd des Allées, 69420 AMPUIS
☎ 04 74 56 13 90 ▤ 04 74 56 10 98
e-mail: gilles.barges@terre-net.fr

Lyon 35 km. Winegrowers M and Mme Barge welcome you to the four guest rooms situated upstairs in their home by the RN86, in the centre of Ampuis. Two double rooms and two twin rooms, with separate access. Shower, basin and wc in each room; spare bed available. Outside: a pleasant enclosed garden with view over the terraced vineyard. Locked garage. Ask owners for directions. Gallo-Roman Museum. Open all year.
PRICES: s €38; d €46-€54; extra person €11 **ON SITE:** Wine tasting Children's play area Hiking Place of interest **NEARBY:** Horse riding (5km) Fishing (5km) Swimming pool (5km) Stretch of water (5km) Tennis (2km) Sailing (5km) Bicycle hire (5km) Railway station (5km) LYON (35km) **NOTES:** No pets CC

☙ Places with this symbol are farmhouses

☗ ⦿ Villa Montplaisir Marcel GAGNOR
9 Ch. de la Viallière -Verenay, 69420 AMPUIS
☎ 04 74 56 16 43
Lyon 30 km. M Gagnor is your host in this new house above the Rhône, easily reached from the nearest autoroute exit (1km). Three rooms, all with double bed, shower, basin and wc. Central heating. Television, telephone, evening meals may be available. Independent access. Communal living room for guests; cooking area; use of proprietor's sitting room possible. Huge grounds with terrace. Explore the Parc du Pilat and the Côtes Rôties vineyard. Board and half board by the week only. Open all year.
PRICES: s €39; d €42; extra person €16; dinner €19 **ON SITE:** Hiking Tennis **NEARBY:** Horse riding (3km) Golf (20km) Fishing (3km) Swimming pool (2km) Stretch of water (3km) Place of interest (1km) Sailing (3km) Bicycle hire (20km) Railway station (3km) Shops (1km) LYON (30km) **NOTES:** Pets admitted

ARNAS

☗ ⦿ Château de Longsard
A et O DU MESNIL DU BUISSON
69400 ARNAS
☎ 04 74 65 55 12 ▤ 04 74 65 03 17
e-mail: longsard@wanadoo.fr.

In this 18th-century castle in its huge French-style garden, Alexandra offers you a choice of five upstairs double rooms, all furnished in style. Each has private facilities and three have 180 x 200cm beds. Private salon and enormous lounge. Evening meals must be booked. Stroll in the park. Closed parking. Table tennis; badminton; trampoline; walking trails. Open all year.
PRICES: d €96; t €116; extra person €15; dinner €32 **ON SITE:** Fishing Stretch of water Hiking Place of interest Sailing Bicycle hire **NEARBY:** Horse riding (1km) Golf (20km) Swimming pool (5km) Tennis (1km) Railway station (8km) Shops (2km) LYON (40km) **NOTES:** No pets CC English spoken

AVENAS

☗ ⦿ La Croix du Py Florence et Patrick VACHER
69430 AVENAS
☎ 04 74 04 76 92 & 06 19 28 35 25 ▤ 04 74 04 74 57
e-mail: p.vacher@free.fr http://p.vacher.free.fr
In the heart of the Haut Beaujolais, Florence and Patrick own this old renovated farmhouse in the open countryside. Two rooms upstairs in a separate adjoining building, each with a double bed and single, shower and wc. One triple room in the home of the proprietors with cot, spare bed, bathroom and wc. Living room/small kitchen reserved for use of guests. Bread oven. Evening meals may be booked. Large grounds; garden furniture; children's games; table tennis; pétanque; local produce. Tariff: family room €58. Open all year.
PRICES: s €30; d €40; extra person €12; dinner €15 **ON SITE:** Hiking Bicycle hire **NEARBY:** Horse riding (6km) Fishing (6km) Swimming pool (20km) Stretch of water (15km) Place of interest (10km) Tennis (6km) Railway station (20km) Shops (3km) LYON (65km) **NOTES:** Pets admitted

RHÔNE-ALPES

BAGNOLS

▓▓▓ Saint-Aigues Jean-Paul GRILLET
69620 BAGNOLS
☎ 04 74 71 62 98 & 06 84 79 35 00   📠 04 74 71 62 98
e-mail: jp.grillet@wanadoo.fr
In the heart of Beaujolais, Jean-Paul welcomes guests to his distinctive house. On the ground floor relax in the huge day room with its open fire, sitting room, fully-equipped kitchen. Upstairs: one double room, one twin room and one room with double bed and bunks - all with shower and wc. Central heating. Vista over the vineyard and the Lyonnais mountains. Parking, lawn, garden furniture; visit to wine cellar with wine on sale. Near to the Castle of Bagnols. Open all year.
PRICES: s €37; d €41; extra person €12   **ON SITE:** Wine tasting Hiking Place of interest   **NEARBY:** Horse riding (3km) Fishing (1km) Swimming pool (12km) Stretch of water (15km) Tennis (1km) Sailing (25km) Railway station (8km) Shops (1km) LYON (26km)   **NOTES:** Pets admitted

BELLEVILLE-SUR-SAONE

▓▓▓ La Combe Frédérique et Jacky PIRET
69220 BELLEVILLE-SUR-SAONE
☎ 04 74 66 30 13   📠 04 74 66 08 94
Lyon 45 km. Winegrowers Frédérique and Jacky offer four guest rooms in their old house with independent access. Upstairs: one double room; one room with a double bed and bunks; one twin room. All have shower and wc. Small kitchen for use of guests. Barbecue. Sitting room and lounge. Electric heating. Television. Large enclosed courtyard. Parking. Sampling and sale of the estate wine. 4km from Belleville exit on A6. Open all year.
PRICES: s €30; d €40; t €52; extra person €12   **ON SITE:** Wine tasting Hiking Place of interest   **NEARBY:** Horse riding (1km) Swimming pool (2km) Stretch of water (2km) Tennis (2km) Sailing (2km) Bicycle hire (15km) Railway station (2km) Shops (2km) LYON (45km)   **NOTES:** Pets admitted CC

BLACE

▓▓▓ Au Milieu des Vignes Eric ENCRENAZ
Berne, 69460 BLACE
☎ 04 74 67 59 69   📠 04 74 67 59 69
e-mail: eric.encrenaz@wanadoo.fr
http://perso.wanadoo.fr/aumilieudesvignes
Lyon 40 km. Some kilometres from Villefranche, Eric's house stands in open country. Choose from four en suite rooms in a completely independent wing of the house. On the ground floor you have full use of the day room with cooking area, opening on to the poolside. Ground floor: one double room and one two-roomed suite with double and twin beds. Two rooms upstairs, one sleeping three and one sleeping four. Mountain bike hire. Table tennis. Hiking. Open all year.
PRICES: s €38; d €47; t €61; extra person €14   **ON SITE:** Wine tasting Swimming pool Hiking Place of interest Bicycle hire   **NEARBY:** Horse riding (8km) Stretch of water (10km) Tennis (1km) Railway station (10km) Shops (1km) LYON (40km)   **NOTES:** No pets English spoken

▓▓▓ Charpenay M.Paule et Patrick BOSSAN
Route de Salles, Blaceret, 69460 BLACE
☎ 04 74 67 56 36   📠 04 74 60 55 23
e-mail: patrick.bossan@wanadoo.fr
http://www.gite-prop.com/69/2081
On their estate in mid-Beaujolais, winegrowers Patrick and M. Paule Bossan will welcome you to their old restored house. Three guest rooms of character on the ground floor: two double rooms with cot available, and one family room with two single beds, bunk, possible spare bed or cot. Each has private facilities. Lounge with television, games, reading material. Breakfast served with the family, either in the family dining room or out in the garden. Six camping pitches on

the farm. Tariff: €70/four persons. Open all year.
PRICES: s €32; d €43; t €58; extra person €12   **ON SITE:** Wine tasting Hiking Place of interest   **NEARBY:** Horse riding (4km) Swimming pool (8km) Stretch of water (10km) Tennis (3km) Railway station (10km) Shops (3km) LYON (40km)   **NOTES:** No pets CC English spoken

BRIGNAIS

▓▓▓ ⫯◯⫯ Au Domaine de Cheron
Sylvie et Jean-Paul VEYRARD
33 Route De Soucieu-D25, 69530 BRIGNAIS
☎ 04 72 31 06 62 & 06 11 86 62 80   📠 04 72 31 90 92
e-mail: aducheron@wanadoo.fr
http://www.multimania.com/aducheron/
Jean-Paul and Sylvie's house basks in quiet and greenery. Four guest rooms all with private facilities are in adjacent farm buildings. On the ground floor: day room and salon for guests; one twin room. Upstairs: three double rooms; one single room; one room sleeping three. Two spare child's beds. In summer one extra ground floor room is available sleeping four, with bath and wc. Courtyard with outdoor furniture, wooded parkland, locked parking. Possible rental of furnished rooms - perfect for professionals. Reduced rates for long stays. Open all year.
PRICES: s €38-€43; d €46-€53; extra person €12; dinner €18   **ON SITE:** Swimming pool Hiking   **NEARBY:** Horse riding (5km) Place of interest (1km) Tennis (2km) Railway station (2km) Shops (2km) LYON (13km)   **NOTES:** Pets admitted English spoken

BRULLIOLES

▓▓▓ ⫷ ♿ Le Pitaval Gérard et Pierre GAREL
GAEC du Pitaval, La Grange, 69690 BRULLIOLES
☎ 04 74 70 53 28 & 06 07 48 22 77   📠 04 74 70 53 28
e-mail: gaec.pitaval@wanadoo.fr
In open country in the Monts du Lyonnais, welcome to the farmhouse of Pierre and Gérard Garel, working farmers. The five guest rooms are in a completely separate stone house. On the ground floor: a fully equipped kitchen for guests, enormous day room, sitting area. Two rooms with double bed and bunk; one room with twin beds and bunk; one room with single bed and bunks. One room with disabled access, containing double bed plus spare single. Each has private facilities. Farm-auberge 500m. Open all year.
PRICES: s €32; d €40; t €52; extra person €12   **ON SITE:** Wine tasting Fishing Hiking   **NEARBY:** Horse riding (9km) Swimming pool (9km) Stretch of water (25km) Tennis (3km) Bicycle hire (9km) Railway station (9km) Shops (3km) LYON (45km)   **NOTES:** No pets

BULLY

▓▓▓ ⫷ ⫯◯⫯ Le Chêne Patouillard
Isabelle et Michel BIRON
69210 BULLY
☎ 04 74 26 89 50 & 06 62 05 89 50   📠 04 74 26 84 98
e-mail: chenepatouillard@free.fr http://chenepatouillard.free.fr
In the land of Pierres Dorées, Isabelle and Michel offer five guest rooms which are arranged with individuality and taste. Three rooms with double and single beds; one Renaissance-style double room; one family room with two double beds and one single. All have shower and wc. Extra bed available. Central heating. Large room with open fire for guests' use; lounge area. Outside: terrace, garden furniture, parking. Evening meals must be booked. (Child's meal €7.) Open all year.
PRICES: s €34-€39; d €39-€49; t €56-€60; dinner €13   **ON SITE:** Wine tasting Horse riding Hiking   **NEARBY:** Fishing (1km) Swimming pool (5km) Stretch of water (35km) Place of interest (2km) Tennis (2km) Sailing (35km) Bicycle hire (5km) Railway station (5km) Shops (2km) LYON (28km)   **NOTES:** No pets English spoken

continued

CERCIE-EN-BEAUJOLAIS

Chambre d'hôtes Marie et Christian BEREZIAT
St-Ennemond, 69220 CERCIE-EN-BEAUJOLAIS
☎ 04 74 69 67 17   📠 04 74 69 67 29
e-mail: christian.bereziat@wanadoo.fr

Lyon 50 km. Marie and Christian live in the hamlet of Saint-Ennemond, and offer three comfortable guest rooms on their vineyard property. Independent access. On the ground floor: communal living room with open fire; one twin room. Upstairs: two rooms with double and single bed; one room plus twin beds and bunks with cot available. Each room has shower and wc. Near RN6, and autoroute A6 exit Belleville S/Saone. Open all year.
PRICES: s €39; d €45; extra person €16 **ON SITE:** Wine tasting Fishing Hiking Place of interest **NEARBY:** Swimming pool (4km) Stretch of water (4km) Tennis (2km) Bicycle hire (15km) Railway station (4km) Shops (2km) LYON (50km) **NOTES:** No pets CC English spoken

CHAPONOST

🍴 Le Ronzere Jean-Claude BRUN
32 Rue F.Ferroussat, 69630 CHAPONOST
☎ 04 78 45 42 03

Jean-Claude's old renovated farmhouse is 10km from the centre of Lyon. Two ground floor rooms with 160cm double bed and shower/wc. Electric heating. Independent access. Upstairs is a single room with bath, basin and wc. Central heating. Cot available. Large living room with sitting area and television corner on mezzanine. Library. Telephone (phone cards). Meals to be booked in advance. Extensive open grounds, terrace, garden furniture, barbecue. Locked parking. Open all year.
PRICES: s €40; d €52; dinner €14 **ON SITE:** Hiking **NEARBY:** Horse riding (3km) Golf (2km) Swimming pool (3km) Tennis (2km) Bicycle hire (3km) Railway station (2km) Shops (2km) LYON (10km) **NOTES:** Pets admitted

CHARENTAY

Les Combes Christine et Denis DUTRAIVE
La Tour de la belle-mère, 69220 CHARENTAY
☎ 04 74 66 82 21   📠 04 74 66 82 21

On the wine estate of Christine and Denis Dutraive, you will find five guest rooms in a separate building adjoining their home. Large guest lounge. Upstairs is a huge lounge/library. Three double rooms and two rooms sleeping three, all with shower and wc. Relax in the great open park which is dominated by the Tour de la Belle-Mère; wallow in the new swimming pool; sample wine in one of many Beaujolais cellars. Open all year.
PRICES: s €52; d €58; t €72 **ON SITE:** Wine tasting Swimming pool Hiking Place of interest **NEARBY:** Horse riding (1km) Fishing (2km) Stretch of water (5km) Tennis (2km) Bicycle hire (5km) Railway station (5km) Shops (1km) LYON (35km) **NOTES:** No pets CC

CHENAS

🍴 Château Lambert Marty FRERIKSEN
69840 CHENAS
☎ 04 74 06 77 74
e-mail: contact@chateau-lambert.com
http://www.chateau-lambert.com
Comfortable rooms set among vineyards and herb gardens. On the ground floor is Chapelle Suite with antechamber, library with open fire, double bedroom, shower and wc. The Grand Suite upstairs has an antechamber/sitting room with wood stove, and bedroom with open fire and canopied fourposter, bathroom/wc. The Alcove Room has a double bed, shower and wc. Vineyard, cellar, estate, terrace, garden, parking. Meals if requested. Open all year.
PRICES: d €75-€115; dinner €23 **ON SITE:** Wine tasting Hiking Place of interest **NEARBY:** Horse riding (9km) Golf (18km) Fishing (5km) Swimming pool (15km) Stretch of water (5km) Tennis (5km) Railway station (12km) Shops (4km) LYON (60km) **NOTES:** No pets CC English spoken

CHIROUBLES

Domaine de la Grosse Pierre
Véronique et Alain PASSOT
69115 CHIROUBLES
☎ 04 74 69 12 17   📠 04 74 69 13 52
e-mail: apassot@terre-net.fr
Lyon 60 km. Winegrowers Véronique et Alain are proud of their guest rooms in this Beaujolais house of character. Five upstairs rooms with separate access, two twin rooms and three doubles, each with private facilities. Cot and child's bed available. Large living room with open fire and sitting room for guests' use on ground floor. Central heating. Swimming pool. Terrace. Large shady courtyard. Garage available. Sampling and sale of estate wines. Open all year except December and January.
PRICES: s €40; d €50 **ON SITE:** Swimming pool Hiking Place of interest **NEARBY:** Horse riding (15km) Fishing (12km) Stretch of water (18km) Tennis (3km) Sailing (18km) Bicycle hire (10km) Railway station (10km) Shops (3km) LYON (60km) **NOTES:** No pets CC English spoken

> For further information on these and
> other chambres d'hôtes, consult
> the Gîtes de France website
> *www.gites-de-france.fr*

COURZIEU

♯♯♯ 🐦 ◎ Les Gouttes
Madeleine et Georges BONNEPART
69690 COURZIEU
☎ 04 74-70-80-74 & 06-83-90-49-97 🖹 04.74.70.80.74

Lyon 28 km. M and Mme Bonnepart have five guest rooms in a block of buildings attached to their own house, all on the ground floor with individual access. Three double rooms and three rooms each with three single beds. Spare adult and child's beds are available. Each room has private facilities. Guests have the use of a lounge, cooking area and sitting area with television. Terrace, grounds, garden furniture, barbecue. Open all year.
PRICES: s €30; d €40; t €53; extra person €13; dinner €13
ON SITE: Hiking **NEARBY:** Horse riding (12km) Golf (20km) Swimming pool (2km) Stretch of water (10km) Place of interest (7km) Tennis (3km) Bicycle hire (10km) Railway station (6km) Shops (3km) LYON (28km) **NOTES:** Pets admitted English spoken

GRANDRIS

♯♯♯ ◎ Les Chênes au Gathier Laurence PERRIER
69870 GRANDRIS
☎ 04 74 60 11 72 🖹 04 74 60 11 72
Lyon 55 km. Laurence and Pierre's house is 4km from Grandris on the Col de la Cambuse road, surrounded by pine trees. Three grade 3 rooms with double beds, shower and wc. Two grade 2 rooms each with double bed and two singles, each with shower. Shared wc. Large living room with open fire. Salon area, library, dining area. Outside: terrace with outdoor furniture; open grounds. Parking. Meals available if booked. Reduced rates for stays over two nights. Open all year.
PRICES: s €32; d €37-€43; extra person €16; dinner €15
ON SITE: Hiking **NEARBY:** Horse riding (10km) Fishing (5km) Swimming pool (16km) Stretch of water (10km) Place of interest (10km) Tennis (4km) Sailing (10km) Bicycle hire (10km) Railway station (7km) Shops (4km) LYON (55km) **NOTES:** No pets English spoken

JULLIE

♯♯♯ Domaine la Chapelle de Vatre Dominique CAPART
Le Bourbon, 69840 JULLIE
☎ 04 74 04 43 57 & 06 85 70 22 00 🖹 04 74 04 40 27
e-mail: dominique.capart@libertysurf.fr
http://perso.libertysurf.fr/domainedevatre
On the heights of Jullié, overlooking the vineyards, you can stay in any of three guest rooms of character in a 17th-century home which incorporates a wine business, a gîte, and the owners' accommodation. One twin room on the ground floor with its own entrance and private terrace, shower and wc. Two rooms in another part of the house, each with twin beds and private sitting room, one with en suite facilities, the other with shower and adjacent wc. Heated swimming pool. Sampling and sale of estate wines. Open all year except harvest time.

PRICES: s €45-€60; d €55-€75; t €90; extra person €15
ON SITE: Swimming pool Hiking Place of interest **NEARBY:** Horse riding (5km) Golf (20km) Fishing (2km) Stretch of water (8km) Tennis (10km) Sailing (50km) Bicycle hire (15km) Railway station (10km) Shops (2km) LYON (70km) **NOTES:** No pets CC English spoken

LAMURE-SUR-AZERGUES

♯♯♯ ◎ Château de Pramenoux
Emmanuel BAUDOIN
69870 LAMURE-SUR-AZERGUES
☎ 04 74 03 16 43 🖹 04 74 03 16 28
e-mail: pramenoux@aol.com chateau-de-pramenoux.com
Lyon 50 km. A 12th-century castle in an enormous park. Huge park and terrace with stupendous view. Exceedingly quiet. Four guest rooms upstairs: three doubles with shower and wc, and the 'Royale' with four-poster and bathroom/wc. Enormous day rooms, salon with open fire. Meals may be booked - candlelit dinner with classical music. A timeless romantic holiday. Open all year.
PRICES: d €100-€115; dinner €26 **ON SITE:** Hiking **NEARBY:** Horse riding (15km) Fishing (3km) Stretch of water (25km) Place of interest (15km) Tennis (3km) Sailing (25km) Bicycle hire (25km) Railway station (3km) Shops (3km) LYON (50km) **NOTES:** No pets English spoken

LANCIE

♯♯♯ ◎ Les Pasquiers L et J GANDILHON-ADELE
69220 LANCIE
☎ 04 74 69 86 33 🖹 04 74 69 86 57
e-mail: ganpasq@aol.com
Lyon 50 km. A huge house of the Second Empire, in a park with swimming pool and tennis court in the middle of Beaujolais. On the ground floor: one room with disabled access (double bed, shower and wc). Upstairs: one double and two twin rooms, each with shower and wc. Living room with open fire. Central heating. Swimming pool with poolhouse, tennis, shady park. High quality cuisine with market produce and selected wine. Open all year.
PRICES: d €65; extra person €15; dinner €20 **ON SITE:** Swimming pool Hiking Tennis **NEARBY:** Horse riding (3km) Stretch of water (8km) Place of interest (1km) Sailing (8km) Railway station (8km) Shops (1km) LYON (50km) **NOTES:** Pets admitted English spoken

LANTIGNIE

♯♯♯♯ Château des Alouettes Martine SIMONET
69430 LANTIGNIE
☎ 04 74 69 24 15 🖹 04 74 04 89 87
The Château des Alouettes is set among the vines. Five prestige rooms. One double and two twin rooms on the first floor. Three double rooms on the second floor. The ground floor has lounge, sitting room and library - all exceedingly comfortable. The swimming pool is surrounded by vines. Garden furniture. Parking. Learn wine-tasting and discover the wines of France in the cellar. Open all year.
PRICES: d €84 **ON SITE:** Swimming pool Hiking Place of interest **NEARBY:** Horse riding (8km) Fishing (3km) Stretch of water (30km) Tennis (2km) Sailing (30km) Bicycle hire (8km) Railway station (15km) Shops (4km) LYON (60km) **NOTES:** No pets CC

◎

Places with this symbol serve table d'hôtes evening meals - remember to book in advance

---

continued

▓▓▓ Domaine des Quarante Ecus
Bernard et M.Claude NESME
Les Vergers, 69430 LANTIGNIE
☎ 04 74 04 85 80 ▤ 04 74 69 27 79
Lyon 55 km. Marie-Claude and Bernard are your hosts in this
winegrowing estate right in the heart of Beaujolais. Five guest
rooms in a house of character with an outstanding view. Upstairs
in the proprietors' house: three double rooms; one room with a
double bed and a sofa bed; one twin room. All have shower and
wc. Central heating and electric heating. Vast shaded garden with
private swimming pool. Parking. Wine-tasting and estate wine
sales. Open all year except for harvest time.
PRICES: s €33; d €42; extra person €16 **ON SITE:** Wine tasting
Swimming pool Hiking Place of interest **NEARBY:** Horse riding (8km)
Golf (30km) Fishing (3km) Stretch of water (15km) Tennis (2km) Sailing
(30km) Bicycle hire (8km) Railway station (13km) Shops (3km) LYON
(55km) **NOTES:** No pets English spoken

▓▓▓ ⭐ Le Tracot Jacqueline MOREL
69430 LANTIGNIE
☎ 04 74 69 25 50
Mme Morel invites you not only to her three guest rooms, but also
into the cellars of her wine enterprise to sample her wine, and visit
her wine museum. The rooms - all upstairs - are separate from her
house. Two grade 3 rooms (one double and one twin) have en
suite shower and wc. One grade 2 twin room has a washbasin in
the room; the shower and wc are separate. Electric heating.
Enclosed courtyard. Beautiful view over the vineyards. Dinner must
be booked. Open all year except during harvest.
PRICES: s €24-€30; d €35-€41; extra person €11; dinner €14
ON SITE: Place of interest **NEARBY:** Horse riding (8km) Swimming
pool (15km) Stretch of water (15km) Hiking (3km) Tennis (1km) Bicycle
hire (8km) Railway station (13km) Shops (3km) LYON (55km)
NOTES: No pets

▓▓▓ ⭐ Les Monterniers Chantal PERRIER
69430 LANTIGNIE
☎ 04 74 04 84 60 ▤ 04 74 04 84 60
Lyon 60 km. Chantal will welcome you to her three guest rooms
located in the middle of this Beaujolais vineyard. Each room has
independent access. Two double rooms (with possible child's bed);
one twin room with double sofa bed. Each room has shower and
wc. Electric heating. Salon for guests' use. Dinner must be booked
- not available Monday and Wednesday. Unsurpassable view over
vineyard. Parking. Lawn with garden furniture. Estate wines can be
sampled and purchased. Child's meal €7.62. Open all year.
PRICES: s €30; d €38; extra person €12; dinner €14 **ON SITE:** Hiking
Place of interest **NEARBY:** Horse riding (8km) Fishing (3km) Swimming
pool (15km) Stretch of water (30km) Tennis (2km) Sailing (30km) Bicycle
hire (8km) Railway station (15km) Shops (3km) LYON (60km)
NOTES: Pets admitted

LE PERREON

▓▓▓ ⭐ Les Volets Bleus Fabienne DUGNY
Le Bourg, 69460 LE PERREON
☎ 04 74 03 27 65 ▤ 04 74 03 27 65
e-mail: fabienne.dugny@free.fr
http://www.eriklorre.com/les_volets_bleus
Lyon 45 km. In the heart of Beaujolais, near the famous village of
Clochemerle, Fabienne and Eric welcome you into their 19th-
century town house. Behind the blue shutters are six tastefully
decorated guest rooms, each with spacious bathrooms or shower
rooms. On the ground floor: large salon; lounge for guests. On
three floors, three rooms for two/three people, and three suites for
four or five. No smoking rooms. Telephone, central heating. Meals
(booking required). Small enclosed garden. Locked garage.
Relaxed atmosphere in refined surroundings for a friendly and

warm stay. Tariff: €67/four persons: €80/five persons. Open all
year.
PRICES: s €35; d €45; t €55; dinner €15-€17 **ON SITE:** Children's play
area Fishing Hiking Place of interest Tennis Bicycle hire
NEARBY: Horse riding (10km) Golf (25km) Swimming pool (15km)
Stretch of water (15km) Sailing (15km) Railway station (15km) LYON
(45km) **NOTES:** No pets English spoken

LES ARDILLATS

▓▓▓ ⭐ Chambre d'hôtes M.Thérèse et Alain BONNOT
Le Bourg, 69430 LES ARDILLATS
☎ 04 74 04 80 20 ▤ 04 74 04 80 20
Lyon 60 km. Meet your hosts M-Thérèse and Alain. Five guest
rooms in a house of character which also has two country gîtes.
Ground floor: large day room; television lounge; bathroom
facilities. Upstairs: three double rooms; one twin room; one two-
roomed family suite with one 160cm double bed plus single bed
and twin beds in the second room. All rooms have shower and wc.
Central heating. Library. Evening meals may be booked. The rooms
have independent access. Pleasant courtyard with garden
furniture. Open all year except January.
PRICES: s €34; d €39; extra person €14; dinner €15 **ON SITE:** Hiking
NEARBY: Horse riding (5km) Fishing (3km) Swimming pool (19km)
Stretch of water (19km) Place of interest (5km) Tennis (5km) Bicycle hire
(10km) Railway station (19km) Shops (3km) LYON (60km) **NOTES:** Pets
admitted

LOIRE-SUR-RHONE

▓▓▓ Le Clos Giroud Etienne GIROUD
16 Rue Etienne Flachy, 69700 LOIRE-SUR-RHONE
☎ 04 72 49 90 94 & 06 60 81 09 36 ▤ 04 72 24 09 71
e-mail: Etienne-giroud@wanadoo.fr
Three guest rooms in a modern stone building of character in the
centre of Loire-sur-Rhône, near the RN86. On the ground floor:
three rooms, each with double bed (cot and child's bed available),
bathroom and wc. Shared living room/lounge with open fire and
television. Telephone (phone card). Outside: enclosed grounds,
small pleasant garden with outdoor furniture, closed parking,
garage available. 4km from the autoroute. Meals available if
requested. Open all year.
PRICES: s €42; d €55; extra person €13 **ON SITE:** Children's play area
Swimming pool Hiking Tennis **NEARBY:** Horse riding (1km) Fishing
(1km) Stretch of water (15km) Place of interest (7km) Sailing (15km)
Bicycle hire (8km) Railway station (4km) LYON (29km) **NOTES:** Pets
admitted CC English spoken

MONTROMANT/YZERON

▓▓▓ 💚 Ferme du Thiollet Christine et Marcel RADIX
69610 MONTROMANT
☎ 04 78 81 00 93 & 06 16 49 91 46 ▤ 04 78 81 00 93
e-mail: mc.radix@wanadoo.fr http://ferme.thiollet.free.fr
Amidst the Monts du Lyonnais, Christine, Marcel and their family
offer guest rooms with independent access in their restored
farmhouse. Breakfast is served in the dining room. Kitchen
available for guests' use. Sitting room with open fire. Two rooms
have direct access to the outside - one double and one triple.
Upstairs are two rooms sleeping four; one has a double bed plus
bunks, the other has twin beds plus bunks. All have private
facilities. Restaurants locally. Open all year.
PRICES: s €38; d €43; t €55; extra person €12 **ON SITE:** Wine tasting
Hiking **NEARBY:** Horse riding (7km) Fishing (1km) Swimming pool
(10km) Stretch of water (1km) Place of interest (15km) Tennis (2km)
Bicycle hire (15km) Railway station (8km) Shops (2km) LYON (30km)
NOTES: Pets admitted

continued

QUINCIE-EN-BEAUJOLAIS

♯♯♯ ○ **Domaine de Romarand**
Annie et Jean BERTHELOT
69430 QUINCIE-EN-BEAUJOLAIS
☎ 04 74 04 34 49 📠 04 74 04 35 92
Lyon 50 km. Annie and Jean invite you into their house of
character (with swimming pool) in the midst of Beaujolais vines.
Three guest rooms with independent access, one twin room and
two doubles, all with en suite facilities. Two spare beds if required.
Large communal room for guests, sitting area with open fire.
Meals may be booked. Central heating. Parking in closed
courtyard. Private swimming pool with pleasant garden. Wine
tasting on the premisies. Open all year.
PRICES: s €42; d €47-€51; t €57; dinner €16-€19 **ON SITE:** Wine tasting
Swimming pool Hiking Place of interest **NEARBY:** Tennis (3km) Bicycle
hire (5km) Railway station (12km) Shops (3km) LYON (50km)
NOTES: Pets admitted English spoken

♯♯♯ ○ **Huire** Jeannine et Gerard LAGNEAU
69430 QUINCIE-EN-BEAUJOLAIS
☎ 04-74-69-20-70 📠 04-74-04-89-44
e-mail: gerard.lagneau@mail.com http://lagneau.operaction.org
Lyon 50 km. Winegrowers Jeannine and Gérard Lagneau farm this
peaceful corner of Beaujolais from their stone house set between
pines and vines. Magnificent view. Four guest rooms of character
on the first floor, with separate access, all with private facilities.
One two-roomed suite with four single beds; two twin rooms; one
double room. Central heating. On the ground floor: lounge for
guests, television. Meals available, booking required. Open
grounds with garden furniture. The owners (producers of Régnié
and Beaujolais Villages wine) would love to share with you their
passion for the area. Tariff: €90/four person suite. Open all year.
PRICES: s €42; d €50; extra person €19; dinner €19 **ON SITE:** Hiking
Place of interest **NEARBY:** Horse riding (10km) Swimming pool (10km)
Stretch of water (18km) Tennis (3km) Sailing (18km) Bicycle hire (10km)
Railway station (12km) Shops (3km) LYON (60km) **NOTES:** Pets
admitted

SALLES-ARBUISSONNAS

♯♯♯♯ **Le Breuil** Famille PATRIGEON
69460 SALLES-ARBUISSONNAS
☎ 06 87 35 91 18 & 04 74 60 53 16
In the shadow of the cloisters of Salles, meet the Patrigeon
family in their mid 19th-century house, and try their three
guest rooms. For leisure and relaxation, you have parkland,
swimming pool, tennis and whirlpool bath. One ground floor
double room. Two rooms upstairs, one double and one twin.
Fold-out bed available in salon. Each room has shower and
wc. Open all year.
PRICES: d €70-€92; t €107; extra person €15 **ON SITE:** Swimming
pool Hiking Tennis **NEARBY:** Stretch of water (10km) Place of
interest (1km) Railway station (10km) Shops (3km) LYON (40km)
NOTES: No pets English spoken

SAVIGNY

♯♯♯ **Lanay** Luc et Aimée DEMAREST
69210 SAVIGNY
☎ 04 74 01 13 64 📠 04 74 01 13 64
Lyon 25 km. Luc and Aimée's farm has five guest rooms arranged
in various farm buildings. Three double rooms and two rooms
sleeping three. (Spare beds available.) Private facilities in each
room. Day rooms with open fires for guests' use only. Kitchen may
be available for guests. Farm visits possible. Plenty of animals on
site - goats, donkeys, chickens. Farm produce for sale, including
wine and cheese.
PRICES: s €29; d €41; t €49 **ON SITE:** Wine tasting Hiking Tennis

NEARBY: Horse riding (3km) Golf (15km) Fishing (15km) Swimming
pool (5km) Stretch of water (15km) Railway station (3km) Shops (4km)
LYON (25km) **NOTES:** Pets admitted

ST-JEAN-LA-BUSSIERE

♯♯♯ ○ **La Clef des Champs** Brigitte VILLAVERDE
La Fedollière, 69550 SAINT-JEAN-LA-BUSSIERE
☎ 04 74 89 52 18 & 06 87 53 16 94
Lac des sapins 1 km. Brigitte welcomes guests to specially built
accommodation at the heart of Beaujolais. On the ground floor:
one double room with disabled access. Upstairs: one room with
double bed and bunks; one room with twin bed and bunks; one
double room; and one single room. All have private facilities.
Living room/lounge for guests. Television, terrace, garden
furniture, parking. Meals must be booked. Open all year.
PRICES: s €29; d €37; extra person €11; dinner €12 **ON SITE:** Children's
play area Hiking **NEARBY:** Horse riding (1km) Fishing (1km) Swimming
pool (4km) Stretch of water (3km) Tennis (3km) Sailing (1km) Bicycle
hire (1km) Railway station (4km) Shops (3km) LYON (60km)
NOTES: No pets

ST-LAURENT-D'OINGT

♯♯♯ **Dalbepierre** Roger et Nicole GUILLARD
69620 ST-LAURENT-D'OINGT
☎ 04 74 71 27 95
Lyon 35 km. At the door of their golden stone house, Nicole and
Roger offer a warm welcome. Three rooms on the first floor: one
grade 3 room with double bed plus spare bed, shower and wc;
one grade 2 room with double bed and two singles (unattached
bathroom and wc); one grade 3 room with separate access
sleeping three with shower and wc. Communal room; kitchen
available. Courtyard, lawn with children's games, parking. Cellar
on site, with sampling and wine sales. Tariff: €58/four persons.
Open all year except harvest time.
PRICES: s €29-€30; d €37-€40; t €47-€50 **ON SITE:** Wine tasting
Children's play area Hiking Place of interest **NEARBY:** Horse riding
(5km) Swimming pool (15km) Stretch of water (25km) Tennis (5km)
Sailing (25km) Railway station (5km) Shops (5km) LYON (35km)
NOTES: No pets English spoken

ST-VERAND

♯♯♯ ○ **Fondvieille** Danièle et Mike RAVILY-ANNING
Taponas, 69620 SAINT-VERAND
☎ 04 74 71 62 64
e-mail: Fondvielle@aol.com
http://www.members.aol.com/fondvielle

Lyon 35 km. Danièle and Mike have recently built extensions to
their home to accommodate four guest rooms. One twin room
with shower and wc; one double room with disabled access and
bathroom with wc; one family room with double bed and bunks,
shower and wc, opening onto the terrace. One completely
separate room in a small house in the grounds with open fire,

continued *continued*

sitting area, shower and wc. Electric heating. Large living room reserved for guests, with lounge area, television, video. Extensive enclosed wooded grounds, boules, garden furniture. Meals if required. Child's tariff: €7.5. Open all year.
PRICES: s €30; d €43; t €53; dinner €14 **ON SITE:** Hiking **NEARBY:** Horse riding (7km) Fishing (5km) Swimming pool (12km) Stretch of water (20km) Place of interest (2km) Tennis (2km) Bicycle hire (12km) Railway station (20km) Shops (2km) LYON (35km) **NOTES:** No pets English spoken

♦♦♦♦ ⏿⃝ Maison d'Hôtes d'Aucherand
Joëlle et Joseph DEGOTTEX
69620 SAINT-VERAND
☎ 04 74 71 85 92 & 04 78 30 41 38 📠 04 74 71 85 92
e-mail: degottex@aol.com
In St Vérand, Beaujolais wine country, a very beautiful guest house with five rooms of character. One double room on the ground floor with bathroom and wc. Four rooms upstairs: two doubles, one twin and one room sleeping three, each with shower and wc. Superb communal room with open fire. Terrace. Meals must be booked. Games room with two billiard tables and table tennis. Huge country park, with hundred year old trees, tennis and swimming pool. The warmest of welcomes from Joëlle (interior decorator) and her antique dealer husband. Open all year.
PRICES: s €69; d €84; t €99; extra person €15; dinner €15
ON SITE: Swimming pool Hiking **NEARBY:** Horse riding (7km) Fishing (5km) Stretch of water (20km) Place of interest (2km) Tennis (2km) Bicycle hire (12km) Railway station (20km) Shops (2km) LYON (35km) **NOTES:** No pets English spoken

TAPONAS
♦♦♦ 🐓 Bois Bettu Brigitte CHAMBAUD
69220 TAPONAS
☎ 04 74 66 38 45 📠 04 74 66 22 98
Lyon 50 km. Brigitte Chambaud offers three guest rooms in her peaceful farmhouse in the Val de Saône, surrounded by countryside, near the great Beaujolais vineyards. All rooms have separate access, shower and wc. Two rooms can accommodate families. Central heating. Common room. Courtyard, lawn, garden furniture, children's games. Not open on Sunday nights, apart from long bookings. 1km out of St-Jean d'Ardières village, towards Mâcon. Child's tariff: €11. No smoking rooms. Open all year.
PRICES: s €37; d €43; extra person €11-€16 **ON SITE:** Wine tasting Hiking **NEARBY:** Horse riding (1km) Golf (20km) Fishing (2km) Swimming pool (4km) Stretch of water (4km) Place of interest (4km) Tennis (4km) Bicycle hire (12km) Railway station (4km) Shops (4km) LYON (50km) **NOTES:** No pets English spoken

VAUX-EN-BEAUJOLAIS
♦♦♦ ⏿⃝ Les Picorettes Josette et Francis BLETTNER
Montrichard, 69460 VAUX-EN-BEAUJOLAIS
☎ 04 74 02 14 07 📠 04 74 02 14 21
e-mail: francis.blettner@picorettes.com
http://www.picorettes.com
Josette and Francis welcome you to their guest house, 1.5km from Vaux-en-Beaujolais. A beautiful spot in the heart of wine country. Four rooms of character with independent access. On the ground floor: one room sleeping three with bath and Jacuzzi, and separate wc; one two-roomed family suite with double bed and two singles, bathroom and wc (spare bed available). Upstairs: two double rooms with shower and wc. In summer your meals will be served outside under the arbour. Swimming pool. Parking. Meals must be reserved. Tariff: €76/family suite. Open 1st March to 30th November.

PRICES: s €53-€76; d €58-€84; t €99; dinner €19 **ON SITE:** Fishing Swimming pool Hiking **NEARBY:** Horse riding (10km) Stretch of water (20km) Place of interest (1km) Sailing (20km) Railway station (16km) Shops (2km) LYON (50km) **NOTES:** No pets CC

VILLIE-MORGON
♦♦♦ ⏿⃝ Le Clachet Agnès et Jean FOILLARD
69910 VILLIE-MORGON
☎ 04 74 04 24 97 📠 04 74 69 12 71
Agnès and Jean welcome you to their home. In a wing of the house is an enormous day room with fireplace. Upstairs an airy salon and library for the use of guests. The bedrooms are spacious, with large beds: one double room (180 x 200cm bed), sofa bed and bathroom with shower and wc; three twin rooms (two have an additional sofa bed). Each has shower and wc. Very close to Belleville exit on autoroute (7km). Open all year.
PRICES: d €70-€80; t €86-€96 **ON SITE:** Hiking Place of interest **NEARBY:** Horse riding (10km) Fishing (7km) Swimming pool (7km) Stretch of water (12km) Tennis (1km) Bicycle hire (20km) Railway station (7km) Shops (1km) LYON (45km) **NOTES:** No pets

SAVOIE

AILLON-LE-JEUNE
♦♦♦ ⏿⃝ Gîte du Vieux Four Robert BAULAT
Les Curiaz, 73340 AILLON-LE-JEUNE
☎ 04 79 54 61 47
Chambéry 24 km, Annecy 37 km. A typical Bauges house, now renovated, looking down onto the village. Three double rooms, one with cot, and one single room; all have bath and wc. Living room, central heating, grounds with bread oven and garden furniture. Traditional breakfast is served in the dining room. Specialities include gratin, *diots, crozets, tartiflette*, pizza and organic bread baked on a wood fire. Walks along forest tracks, over passes and high mountain pastures. Skiing at Aillon-le-Jeune. Reduced meal prices for children.
PRICES: d €42; t €55; dinner €14 **ON SITE:** Fishing Hiking Bicycle hire **NEARBY:** Bathing (13km) Horse riding (3km) Swimming pool (4km) Cross-country skiing (3km) Downhill skiing (3km) Tennis (3km) Railway station (24km) Shops (1km) CHAMBERY (24km) **NOTES:** No pets English spoken

♦♦♦ ⏿⃝ La Grangerie Bruno GUNTHER
Les Ginets, 73340 AILLON-LE-JEUNE
☎ 04 79 54 64 71 📠 04 79 54 69 19
e-mail: lagrangerie@fr.st http://www.lagrangerie.fr.st
Chambéry 24 km, Annecy 37 km, Aix-les-Bains 37 km. A traditional farmhouse, typical of the Massif des Bauges, now entirely restored, with superb views over the valley and Aillon-le-Jeune. Four guest rooms in the mansard roof each with a double and single bed, shower and wc, one with a balcony. Central heating. Enjoy home-made preserves with breakfast, and a variety of organic bread. Specialities include *tarte à la tome, fondue savoyarde, civet, pot-au-feu, diots au vin blanc, raclette*. Explore the Parc Naturel Régional des Bauges. Skiing at Aillon-le-Jeune 0.5 km and le Margériaz 12 km. Children's meals at reduced price.
PRICES: d €42; t €55; dinner €14 **ON SITE:** Hiking Bicycle hire **NEARBY:** Bathing (16km) Horse riding (2km) Fishing (2km) Swimming pool (2km) Cross-country skiing (2km) Downhill skiing (1km) Tennis (2km) Railway station (26km) Shops (2km) CHAMBERY (26km) **NOTES:** Pets admitted

🐓
Places with this symbol are farmhouses

continued

RHÔNE-ALPES

AUSSOIS

♦♦♦ ⎰O⎱ La Roche du Croue Claire TANTOLIN
3 rue de l'Eglise, 73500 AUSSOIS
☎ 04 79 20 31 07 & 04 79 20 31 07 ▯ 04 79 20 48 28
e-mail: roche.croue@libertysurf.fr
Forts de l'Esseillon 4 km, Parc National de la Vanoise 6 km. Semi-detached house in the village, near the entrance to the Parc National de la Vanoise, with five guest rooms upstairs. One double room; two with three single beds; one with a double and a twin; and one with a double bed and bunks. All except the last have a balcony, and all have shower and wc en suite. Lounge area with open fire and TV. Washing machine, drier, terrace, central heating. Specialities include vegetable soup, *crozets*, *tartiflette*, *raclette*, garden vegetables, home-made yoghurt and jams, and various desserts. Open all year.
PRICES: s €35; d €43; t €56; extra person €13; dinner €14
ON SITE: Hiking Cross-country skiing Downhill skiing Bicycle hire
NEARBY: Horse riding (1km) Fishing (7km) Swimming pool (7km) Tennis (1km) Railway station (7km) MODANE (7km) **NOTES:** No pets English spoken

JONGIEUX

♦♦♦ Chambre d'hôtes Arlette et Patrice JACQUIN
Jongieux le Haut, 73170 JONGIEUX
☎ 04 79 44 00 29 & 04 79 44 02 35 ▯ 04 79 44 03 05
Lac du Bourget 12 km, Chanaz 13 km. This guest house is at the entrance to the village on a plateau overlooking the Rhône Valley. Views over the Charvaz mountain and vineyards. Ground floor: one double room with a terrace. First floor: one room with a double and single bed, with balcony; a second room sleeping three. Each has en suite facilities. Superb day room, central heating, grounds. Use of kitchen possible. Restaurant 3 km. Climbing 6 km. Canoeing 8 km. Sailing 12 km. Open all year.
PRICES: s €34-€43; d €42-€51; t €58-€67 **ON SITE:** Hiking Bicycle hire
NEARBY: Bathing (7km) Horse riding (7km) Fishing (4km) Swimming pool (25km) Tennis (7km) Spa (24km) Railway station (19km) Shops (1km) CHAMBERY (20km) **NOTES:** No pets

LA BIOLLE

♦♦♦ Sous la Colline Gilbert et Jeanette GOURY
Villette, 73410 LA BIOLLE
☎ 04 79 54 76 79 ▯ 04 79 54 70 70

Aix-les-Bains 7 km, Annecy 26 km. Typical Albanais house, situated in a hamlet by a wood. Four guest rooms upstairs. Room 1 sleeps three; room 2 is a double; rooms 3 and 4 sleep three, and the latter has a sitting area and balcony. All have full facilities. Kitchen area, courtyard, garden furniture, children's games. Breakfast served in the dining room or on the terrace with preserves, yoghurt, honey and cheese. Skiing at le Revard, climbing, hang-gliding 8 km. Restaurant 2 km. Lac du Bourget 10 km. Reduced rates by agreement.

PRICES: s €28-€32; d €40; t €47 **ON SITE:** Children's play area Hiking Bicycle hire **NEARBY:** Bathing (11km) Horse riding (5km) Fishing (5km) Swimming pool (11km) Cross-country skiing (25km) Downhill skiing (25km) Tennis (3km) Spa (11km) Railway station (5km) Shops (3km) AIX LES BAINS (11km) **NOTES:** No pets

LA COTE-D'AIME

♦♦♦ ⎰O⎱ Le Paradou Bernard et Elisabeth HANRARD
Pré Berard, 73210 LA COTE-D'AIME
☎ 04 79 55 67 79
e-mail: hanrard@aol.com
Bourg-St-Maurice 21 km, Courchevel, Pralognan la Vanoise 48 km. Substantial wooden chalet with lovely view over the mountains. Five guest rooms, all with shower and wc en suite. Upstairs: one double room. Downstairs: two double rooms and two twin rooms. Lounge with open fire reserved for guests, games, electric heating, terrace, grounds, garden furniture. Specialities of the house include *gigot*, *raclette* cooked over a wood fire, ham, *diots*, home-made pastries and jams, lemon tart. Your host is a ski instructor and guide. Skiing at Granier 5 km or Montchavin-la Plagne 20 km. Rafting 5 km. Reduced rate children's meals.
PRICES: s €43; d €52; dinner €17 **ON SITE:** Hiking Bicycle hire
NEARBY: Bathing (8km) Horse riding (15km) Fishing (5km) Swimming pool (18km) Cross-country skiing (5km) Downhill skiing (5km) Tennis (7km) Railway station (5km) Shops (5km) AIME (5km) **NOTES:** No pets English spoken

LA PERRIERE-LA-TANIA

♦♦♦ 🐓 Chalet les Pierrets Guy et Joëlle CARLEVATO
73600 LA PERRIERE
☎ 04 79 55 26 95 ▯ 04 79 55 26 95

A modern house near to the great skiing areas of Courchevel, La Plagne and Pralognan. Four guest rooms and three gîtes, 150 m from the proprietors' home. On the ground floor: one double room and one room sleeping three. Upstairs: two rooms, each sleeping four in a double bed and two singles. All have bath and wc. Lounge, TV, kitchen, grounds. Games. Phone point. Breakfast with home-made preserves and yoghurt. Restaurant 2 km. Hang-gliding 8 km. The chalet can be booked by groups (20-25 people) in winter.
PRICES: s €30; d €55; t €70 **ON SITE:** Fishing Hiking Tennis Bicycle hire **NEARBY:** Horse riding (8km) Swimming pool (2km) Cross-country skiing (8km) Downhill skiing (2km) Spa (2km) Railway station (8km) Shops (2km) MOUTIERS (8km) **NOTES:** No pets English spoken

LE VIVIERS-DU-LAC

♦♦♦ Chambre d'hôtes Bernadette MONTAGNOLE
516 chemin de Boissy, 73420 LE VIVIERS-DU-LAC
☎ 04 79 35 31 26 ▯ 04 79 35 31 26
Aix-les-Bains 4 km, Chambéry 15 km. Modern house on a hill with a fine view of the cliffs on the Plateau du Revard. Three guest

continued

continued

rooms. On the ground floor: one twin room and one double room. Upstairs: one room with single bed and double bed. Each has en suite shower and wc. Electric heating; cooking facilities available; grounds with garden furniture. Quiet living room. Restaurants 1 km. Golf 2 km. Skiing at le Revard. Open 15 April to 15 October.
PRICES: s €25-€28; d €34-€42; t €50 **ON SITE:** Hiking Bicycle hire
NEARBY: Bathing (3km) Horse riding (3km) Fishing (3km) Swimming pool (5km) Cross-country skiing (22km) Downhill skiing (22km) Tennis (3km) Spa (3km) Railway station (5km) Shops (2km) AIX LES BAINS (5km) **NOTES:** No pets

MACOT-LA-PLAGNE

♦♦♦♦ Malezan Sylvain et Marie-Hélène MEREL
Route de la Plagne, 73210 MACOT-LA-PLAGNE
☎ 04 79 55 69 90   📠 04 79 09 75 80
http://www.malezan.com
Parc National de la Vanoise, La Plagne 15 km, Moutiers 18 km.
A house of character, on the edge of the village on the Route de la Plagne, offering three first-floor guest rooms and a gîte. One double room with shower, bath, wc and terrace; one room with two double beds and one room with two singles, sharing shower, bath and wc; one twin room with shower and wc. TV in every room. The rooms can be grouped together with the four-person gîte. Central heating. Extensive grounds at the edge of the forest. Breakfast might include pastries, home-made jams, fruit salad, pork and cheeses. Restaurant 500 m. Many activities nearby including skiing at La Plagne.
PRICES: s €26-€34; d €42-€55; t €52-€57 **NEARBY:** Bathing (2km) Horse riding (15km) Fishing (2km) Swimming pool (13km) Hiking (1km) Cross-country skiing (10km) Downhill skiing (15km) Tennis (1km) Bicycle hire (1km) Railway station (3km) Shops (1km) AIME (3km) **NOTES:** Pets admitted Minimum 2 night stay English spoken

MERIBEL-LES-ALLUES

♦♦♦ ⚲ Chalet Raphaël Bridget DALEY
Le Raffort, 73550 MERIBEL
☎ 04 79 00 45 69   📠 04 79 00 45 69
e-mail: lesalpesbd@hotmail.com   http://www.lesalpes.co.uk
Allues 4.5 km, lac de Tueda 10 km. This renovated old house, with views over the mountain and the valley of Doron, offers six cosy en suite guest rooms in the mansard storey. There are two double rooms, three twin rooms (one with balcony) and one room sleeping four. Outside Jacuzzi, electric heating, sitting room with open fire, terrace, small garden. House specialities include quail stuffed with chestnuts and chestnut mousse gateau. Summer tariff: €61/person; €107/two persons. Group prices. Reduced rates for children's meals. Open all year.
PRICES: s €61-€138; d €107-€260; t €145-€337; extra person €38-€76; dinner €23 **ON SITE:** Fishing Hiking Downhill skiing Bicycle hire
NEARBY: Horse riding (3km) Swimming pool (3km) Cross-country skiing (5km) Tennis (3km) Spa (11km) Railway station (14km) Shops (1km) MOUTIERS (14km) **NOTES:** No pets English spoken

QUEIGE

♦♦♦ ⚲ La Grange aux Loups
Paul et Clotilde CHANTEPERDRIX
Le Villaret, 73720 QUEIGE
☎ 04 79 38 08 32 & SR : 04 79 85 01 09   📠 04 79 38 08 41
e-mail: clotilde.chanteperdrix@freesbee.fr
http://www.multimania.com/grangeauxloups
Albertville 7 km. In a clearing in the woods, with views over the forested mountains of Beaufortain, this house offers six guest rooms with private facilities: two double rooms and two twin rooms with balconies, one room sleeping three (with balcony) and one room sleeping four. Electric heating, open fire, terrace,

grounds. Buffet breakfast features home-made patisserie and preserves. Other specialities: Beaufort tart, fondue, *raclette*, bilberry tart. Nearby activities include skiing at Arêches. Plenty of walking trails through the forests and high Alpine meadows. Reduced rates for children's meals. Open all year.
PRICES: s €35; d €43; t €50; extra person €8; dinner €14
ON SITE: Hiking Bicycle hire Children's play area **NEARBY:** Horse riding (15km) Fishing (2km) Swimming pool (12km) Cross-country skiing (8km) Downhill skiing (18km) Tennis (2km) Railway station (7km) Shops (2km) ALBERTVILLE (7km) **NOTES:** No pets CC English spoken

ST-FOY-TARENTAISE

♦♦♦♦ ⚲ Yellow-Stone Chalet
Nancy et Jean-Marc TABARDEL FOUQUET
Bonconseil, 73640 STE-FOY-TARENTAISE
☎ 04 79 06 96 06   📠 04 79 06 96 05
e-mail: yellowstone@wanadoo.fr
http://www.limelab.com/yellowstone
Bourg-St-Maurice 12 km, Parc de la Vanoise 40 km.
Contemporary chalet on the edge of the resort with a magnificent view over the Isère Valley and the mountains. Five guest rooms include one ground floor double and, upstairs, one room with four single beds and a balcony; one twin room, and one double room with a balcony-terrace. Further double room on the second floor. All have private facilities. Lounge with open fire, TV and library. Sauna, jacuzzi, central heating, grounds, garage. House specialities include stuffed chicken legs and *gigot à la broche*, etc. Lots of skiing opportunities nearby. Negotiable reductions possible.
PRICES: s €95-€135; d €110-€150; t €130-€170; dinner €30
ON SITE: Hiking Cross-country skiing Downhill skiing Bicycle hire
NEARBY: Bathing (14km) Horse riding (16km) Fishing (5km) Swimming pool (19km) Tennis (7km) Railway station (19km) Shops (7km) BOURG ST MAURICE (19km) **NOTES:** No pets CC English spoken

VILLARODIN-BOURGET

♦♦♦ ⚲ Che Catrine Catherine et Christian FINAS
88 rue St-Antoine, 73500 VILLARODIN-BOURGET
☎ 04 79 20 49 32 & SR : 04 79 85 01 09   📠 04 79 20 48 67
e-mail: checatri@club-internet.fr
Parc de la Vanoise on site, Avrieux 1 km, Via Ferrata 2 km.
Interesting 17th-century building with Savoyard furnishings. First floor: one double room, one twin room, and one double room with lounge. Each has an en suite shower and wc. Additional two-roomed suite with salon, television, double bed, twin beds, two showers and two wcs. A second similar suite has a bath as well as a shower. The last room has a single bed, shower and wc. Dining room with open fire; sitting room. Video recorder, library, central heating, grounds. Cuisine uses vegetables from the kitchen garden. Your hosts are ski instructors. Skiing at la Norma 2.5 km, Aussois 9 km, Via Ferrata 4 km. Open all year.
PRICES: s €36-€60; d €48-€80; t €82-€107; extra person €20-€30; dinner €16 **ON SITE:** Hiking Bicycle hire **NEARBY:** Horse riding (3km) Fishing (2km) Swimming pool (3km) Cross-country skiing (3km) Downhill skiing (3km) Tennis (3km) Railway station (3km) Shops (3km) MODANE (2km) **NOTES:** Pets admitted English spoken

For further information on these and other chambres d'hôtes, consult the Gîtes de France website
www.gites-de-france.fr

RHÔNE-ALPES

continued

CORSICA

CORSE-DU-SUD

CERVIONE

ꟿꟿ Casa Corsa - Acqua Nera Anne-Marie DOUMENS
Prunete, 20221 CERVIONE
☎ 04 95 38 01 40 & 04 95 57 00 77 🖹 04 95 38 01 40
Three guest rooms of real character, in the owners' house on two
floors. Ground floor: one family room with its own entrance (one
double, one single bed) with little communal terrace and picnic
area, private shower/wc plus separate wc, lounge and dining room
with television and open fire for guests and owners. First floor:
lounge area, two double rooms (one with small terrace) each with
private shower and wc. Folding bed for a child under ten and a cot
available. Outside: two covered terraces, flower garden, parking.
Open all year.
PRICES: d €51; t €75; extra person €13 **NEARBY:** Horse riding (5km)
Forest (30km) Sea (1km) Swimming pool (45km) Hiking (7km) Tennis
(4km) Railway station (40km) Shops (4km) BASTIA (45km) **NOTES:** No
pets

FIGARI

ꟿꟿ Les Bergeries de Piscia Marc FINIDORI
Piscia, 20114 FIGARI
☎ 04 95 71 06 71 🖹 04 95 71 06 71
In the country - in the heart of the Corsican maquis - at a
farmhouse inn, a stone house of some character on a farmholding
of 100ha. Five rooms. Ground floor: two doubles with separate
access. On the first floor: one double and two rooms for three.
Each bedroom has private bathroom and wc. Wood and plaster
décor, farmhouse/inn room, traditional Corsican family cuisine.
Terrace, swimming pool, waterfall, sunbathing. Marvellous view of
the plain and coast on the south of the island. Open all year.
PRICES: s €49; d €58; t €87; HB €61; dinner €30 **ON SITE:** Swimming
pool Hiking **NEARBY:** Horse riding (14km) Sea (15km) Tennis (12km)
Spa (50km) Shops (13km) Restaurant nearby BONIFACIO (20km)
NOTES: Pets admitted

SAN-MARTINO-DI-LOTA

ꟿꟿ Château Cagninacci Bertrand CAGNINACCI
20200 SAN-MARTINO-DI-LOTA
☎ 04 95 31 69 30 🖹 04 95 31 91 15
Guest rooms in a 17th-century Capucin monastery. Three
double rooms and one twin, each with private bathroom and
wc. One room has use of a terrace. Sitting room exclusively for
guests, dining room with open fireplace. Distinctive
furnishings. Extensive park with summer houses. Table tennis.
Three restaurants in village. The Cagninacci family acquired
the monastery at the turn of this century and transformed it
into a lovely castle. Low season tariff: €62/one guest; €66/two
guests; €81/three guests. Open 18th May to 28th September.
PRICES: s €68; d €72; t €87 **ON SITE:** Hiking **NEARBY:** Sea
(8km) Railway station (11km) Shops (4km) BASTIA (10km)
NOTES: No pets Minimum 2 night stay English spoken

SOLLACARO

ꟿꟿ Cigala Anita TARDIF
Filitosa, 20140 SOLLACARO
☎ 06 62 43 13 69 & 04 95 74 29 48
Just three minutes from the prehistoric site at Filitosa is this bed
and breakfast. Three rooms (one double and two twins) on the
ground floor, with separate access. Shower and wc en suite.
Lounge, sitting area with open fire, used by guests and owners.
Breakfast served on the terrace. Enclosed grounds of 1ha. Parking,
television, summer house for each room. Cot and high chair
available. Summer kitchen, barbecue with pergola, dining area for
guests. Crockery supplied. Stunning view over the sea. Open all
year.
PRICES: s €46; d €58 **NEARBY:** Horse riding (7km) Forest (6km) Sea
(5km) Swimming pool (15km) Hiking (15km) Tennis (15km) Spa (15km)
Railway station (60km) Shops (5km) PROPRIANO (15km) **NOTES:** No
pets

SOTTA

ꟿꟿ ⴹⵔ Petralonga Salvini Sébastien MELA
20146 SOTTA
☎ 04 95 71 25 65 & 06 85 71 08 02

Out in the countryside, guests rooms in an annexe of the owners'
house. Three rooms sleeping three, and two double rooms, each
with private shower and wc. Living room/lounge for guests.
Dinner. Breakfast and meals served on a covered terrace. Low
season tariff: €48/two guests; €63/three guests. Open April to
October.
PRICES: d €58; t €76; dinner €18 **NEARBY:** Sea (5km) Shops (7km)
PORTO VECCHIO (14km) **NOTES:** No pets English spoken

> ⴹⵔ Places with this symbol serve table d'hôtes
> evening meals - remember to book in advance

> Ask the proprietor for directions
> when booking

AIN
Rhône-Alpes

01

Chalons-sur-Saône

LONS-LE-SAUNIER

Saône

D 978

Louhans

N 78

A 39

N 83

**71
SAÔNE-ET-LOIRE**

**39
JURA**

Ain

N 78

N 5

Arbigny

St-Étienne-
sur-Reyssouze

Saint-Claude

Mijoux

Gex

D 975

Villemotier

N 83

D 470

Ain

Germagnat

Sergy

MÂCON

A 40

Virlat

N 79

Montcet

Giron

Saône

BOURG-
EN-
BRESSE

A 40

Villereversure

A 404

Nantua

Saint-Julien-
en-Genevois

N 281

St-André-
d'Huiriat

N 75

Rhône

A 40

N 508

Châtillon-
sur-Chalaronne

Servas

N 83

Le Grand-
Abergement

Villes

D 936 St-Trivier-sur-Moignans

A 40

Neuville-sur-Ain

**74
HAUTE-
SAVOIE**

Villars-les-
Dombes

N 84

Ain

N 504

Fier

A 46

A 42

Chazey-sur-Ain

Ordonnaz

D 904 St-Martin-
de-Bavel

N 84

N 75

Rhône

A 432

N 516

Saône

LYON

D 517

A 43

Brens

N 516

N 904

N 6

**69
RHÔNE**

A 46

**38
ISÈRE**

N 75

Rhône

La Tour-du-Pin

A 43

CHAMBÉRY

N 85

A 48

D 518 D

0   15 km

Bony

Péronne

Canal du Nord

Canal

A 1

D 917

N 44 b

D 932

Somme

Saint-Quentin

Oise

Mondrepuis

N 2

N 43

Sorbais

Oise

D 963

Éparcy

N 43

Vervins

A 29

Canal

D 930

A 26

D 966

Bureilles

D 930

N 2

D 977

Noyon

Oise

D I

N 44

○ LAON

D 966

Étouvelles

Chéret

08
ARDENNES

Canal

Aisne

D I

Braye-
en-Laonnois

Ste-Croix

Berrieux

A 26

N 31

N 44

60
OISE

Ambleny

Soissons

Aisne

N 51

N 2

Cuiry-Housse

N 31

Reims

D 380

A 4

Fère-en-Tardenois

D I

Bruyères-sur-Fère

Villers-Agron-
Alguizy

D 380

A 4

D 31

N 51

Le Charmel

Épernay

Marne

N 3

Marne

Château-
Thierry

Connigis

Reuilly-
Savigny

La Chapelle-
Monthodon

77
SEINE-ET-MARNE

D 405

D 1

D 51

51
MARNE

Meaux

A 4

D 407

l'Épine-
aux-Bois

D 33

D 33

N 77

N

0

15

D 994

Loire

Canal

N 7

Roanne

D 982

71
SAÔNE-ET-LOIRE

42
LOIRE

A 72

N 81

D 60

Le Pin

D 994

Saint-Didier-en-Donjon

N 79

Diou

Le Breuil

Le Mayet-de-Montagne

A 72

D 979

Loire

Canal

Paray-le-Frésil

D 973

Lusigny

N 2079

Thiel-sur-Acolin

Gouise

Servilly

St-Gérand-le-Puy

N 7

D 907

Mariol

D 906

Vichy

D 906 b

D 906

58
NIÈVRE

N 7

N 75

N 9

MOULINS

Coulandon

Montilly

Besson

Châtel-de-Neuvre

La Ferté-Hauterive

Vernueil-en-Bourbonnais

Paray-sous-Briailles

N 209

Allier

D 46

Sioule

D 6

6 N

St-Germain-de-Salles

Monteignet-sur-l'Andelot

N 209

Couzon

Agonges

St-Aubin-le-Monjal

Noyant-d'Allier

Tronget

Le Theil

Fleuriel

Chantelle

Charroux

Saint-Bonnet-de-Rochefort

N 9

Rlom

A 71

Lurcy-Lévis

Pouzy-Mésangy

Ygrande

Buxières-les-Mines

Villefranche-d'Allier

St-Priest-en-Murat

Deux-Chaises

D 46

Montmarault

Louroux-de-Beaune

Valignat

Ébreuil

Chouvigny

N 144

St-Plaisir

A 71

63
PUY-DE-DÔME

D 951

St-Bonnet-Tronçais

Meaulne

Verneix

N 371

Montluçon

N 144

Saint-Amand-Montrond

Cher

Audes

Chambérat

Huriel

D 943

N 145

Cher

23
CREUSE

A 71

18
CHER

N
O E
S

15 km

0

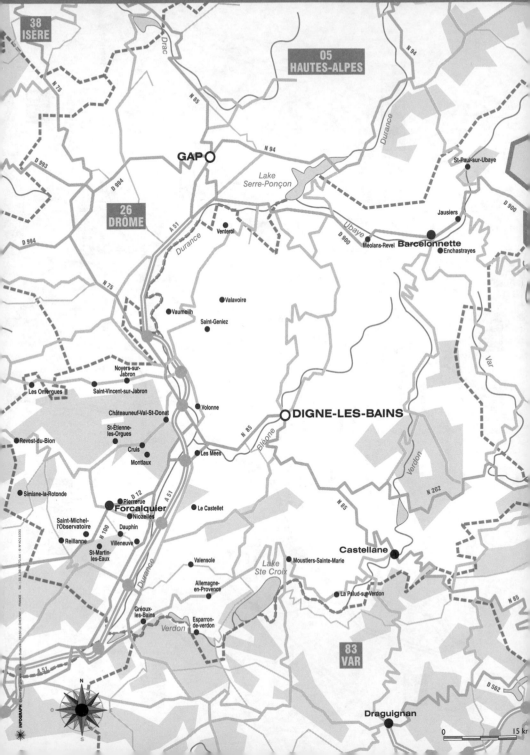

ALPES-HAUTE-PROVENCE
Provence-Alpes-Côte-d'Azur

04

38
ISERE

05
HAUTES-ALPES

N 94

Drac

N 85

26
DRÔME

D 993

D 994

D 994

N 75

GAP

Lake
Serre-Ponçon

N 94

Durance

St-Paul-sur-Ubaye

Jausiers

Ubaye

D 900

Méolans-Revel

Barcelonnette

Enchastrayes

D 900

A 51

Durance

Venterol

N 75

Valavoire

Vaumeilh

Saint-Geniez

Var

Noyers-sur-
Jabron

Les Omergues

Saint-Vincent-sur-Jabron

Châteauneuf-Val-St-Donat

Volonne

N 85

Bléone

DIGNE-LES-BAINS

St-Étienne-
les-Orgues

Revest-du-Bion

Cruis

Montlaux

Les Mées

Verdon

Simiane-la-Rotonde

D 12

Pierrerue

Forcalquier

A 51

Le Castellet

N 85

N 202

Saint-Michel-
l'Observatoire

Niozelles

Dauphin

Reillanne

N 100

Villeneuve

St-Martin-
les-Eaux

Valensole

Moustiers-Sainte-Marie

Castellane

Allemagne-
en-Provence

Lake
Ste Croix

La Palud-sur-Verdon

N 562

Durance

Gréoux-
les-Bains

Esparron-
de-verdon

Verdon

83
VAR

A 51

N
O   E
S

INFOGRAPH

Draguignan

0   15 kr

ITALY

Ubaye

D 900

● Barcelonnette

04
ALPES-DE-HAUTE-
PROVENCE

Var

Tinée

● St-Martin-Vésubie

● La Brigue

Verdon

N 202

N 202

● Ascros

Var

● Berre-des-Alpes

● Castellane

A 8

N 7

● Courmes

NICE

N 85

Tourrettes-sur-Loup ● ● Vence
Saint-Paul-de-Vence
● La Colle-sur-Loup

83
VAR

Cabris ● ● Grasse

N 7

● Antibes
● Golfe-Juan-Vallauris

D 562

A 8

MEDITERRANEAN SEA

Lérins Island

● Draguignan

N 7

N 98

N
O
E
S

INFOGRAPH

0   15 k

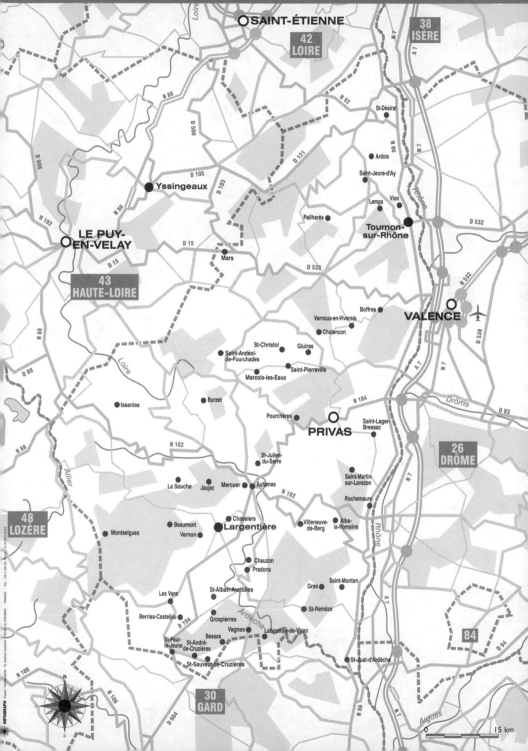

42
LOIRE

38
ISÈRE

SAINT-ÉTIENNE

St-Désirat

Ardoix

Saint-Jeure-d'Ay

Lemps   Vion

Yssingeaux

Pailharès

Tournon-
sur-Rhône

LE PUY-
EN-VELAY

Mars

VALENCE

43
HAUTE-LOIRE

Boffres

Vernoux-en-Vivarais

Chalencon

St-Christol

Gluiras

Saint-Andéol-
de-Fourchades

Saint-Pierreville

Marcols-les-Eaux

Issanlas

Burzet

Pourchères

Saint-Lager-
Bressac

PRIVAS

26
DRÔME

St-Julien-
du-Serre

La Souche   Jaujac   Mercuer   Aubenas

Saint-Martin-
sur-Lavezon

Rochemaure

48
LOZÈRE

Beaumont   Chassiers

Vernon

Montselgues

Largentière

Villeneuve-   Alba-
de-Berg   la-Romaine

Chauzon

Pradons

St-Alban-Auriolles

Gras   Saint-Montan

Les Vans

St-Remèze

Berrias-Casteljau

Grospierres

Vagnas

Bessas

St-Paul-
le-Jeune

St-André-
de-Cruzières   Labastide-de-Virac

St-Sauveur-de-Cruzières

St-Just-d'Ardèche

84

30
GARD

Aigues

0   15 km

Maubeuge

N 2

BELGIUM

Fumay

Oise

D 863

N 43

D 877 Rocroi

Bogny-sur-Meuse

**02
AISNE**

N 43

Bosseval-et-Briancourt

**CHARLEVILLE-
MÉZIÈRES** ○ *Meuse*

Touligny

Doncherie

Sedan

Lalobbe

Viel-Saint-Rémy

Villers-sur-le-Mont

A 34

N 43

D 954

D 985

Rethel

Acy-Romance

Aisne

D 977

D 996

Vieux-les-Asfeld

D 947

Meuse

Brienne-sur-Aisne

N 51

Grivy-Loisy

Vouziers

Champigneulle

D 905

A 26

D 977

D 946

Chatel-Chéhéry

**55
MEUSE**

D 982

D 964

D 980

Reims

D 380

Aisne

A 4

**51
MARNE**

D 31

D 77

D 31

**Sainte-
Menehould**

N 3

A 4

Verdun

N 51

N 44

A 4

N

O   E

S

0   15 km

D 112

Save

N 124

✈ ○ **TOULOUSE**

N 126

A 64

D 622

Muret ●

N 113

A 61

D 624

31
HAUTE-GARONNE

Ariège

N 113

Garonne

N 20

Garonne

Mazères

Le Vernet ● **Montaut** ●

Ste-Croix-
Volvestre

Gaudiès ●

D 119

Ludiès ●

Pamiers ●

D 119

D 625

11
AUDE

D 117

Leran ●

D 117

FOIX ○

Serres-
sur-Arget ● Cos ●

Saint-Girons ●

Le Bosc ● Bénac ●

St-Paul-
de-Jarrat ●

D 117

● Salsein

Tarascon-sur-Ariège ●

Ariège

Aude

N 20

Ax-les-Thermes ●

66
PYRÉNÉES-
ORIENTALES

ANDORRA

N 20

M 116

N

O ✦ E

S

SPAIN

0 _____ 15 km

CHÂLONS-
EN-CHAMPAGNE

D 51

D 33

D 33

D 5

D 51

N 77

A 26

N 44

51
MARNE

N 4

Vitry-
le-François

N 4

D 51

D 373

Aube

D 441

D 951

Seine

N 19

N 77

A 26

Nogent-
sur-Seine

La Motte-Tilly

Pougy

D 400

D 60

Bouy-
Luxembourg

Aube

Brévonnes

D 960

A 5

TROYES

Estissac

Messon

Saint-Germain

Seine

Laubressel

Lusigny-
sur-Barse

Bar-sur-Aube

Vulaines

N 60

Bouilly

A 5

N 19

A 5

Longchamp-
sur-Aujon

Jeugny

N 77

Eaux-Puiseaux

N 71

Fouchères

Virey-sous-Bar

Bourguignons

D 905

Courteron

N 71

D 943

Les Croûtes

Bernon

Seine

Armançon

D 905

89
YONNE

N 77

D 965

21
CÔTE-D'OR

AUXERRE

N

O   E

S

Yonne

A 6

D 965

0   15 km

MEDITERRANEAN SEA

Béziers

N 112

D 909

Orb

Aude

6 V

6 N

Ouveillan

Mirepeisset

Pouzols-Minervois

Azille

D 5

Narbonne

Bizanet

Boutenac

Fabrezan

Moux

Marseillette

Laure-Minervois

Saint-Frichoux

D 610

N 113

A 61

Aude

N 113

34 HÉRAULT

Peyriac-de-Mer

N 9

Leucate

Lake Bages and Lake Sigean

Villeséque-des-Corbières

A 9

Cascastel-des-Corbières

Fontjoncouse

Palairac

Soulatgé

Albières

Fajac-en-Val

Bouisse

Bugarach

PERPIGNAN

D 617

6 N

N 114

N 116

Tét

Lake Leucate

66 PYRÉNÉES-ORIENTALES

D 117

Prades

D 117

Aude

Salsigne

Villardonnel

Aragon

Pennautier

Saint-Martin-le-Vieil

St-Martin-le-Vieil

Saissac

Saint-Martin-Lalande

Labécède-Lauragais

D 118

N 113

CARCASSONNE

Caux-et-Sauzens

N 112

D 621

D 622

D 624

81 TARN

31 HAUTE-GARONNE

Saint-Hilaire

Limoux

Roquetaillade

D 118

Peyrefitte-du-Razès

D 119

D 625

D 117

Aude

Ariège

09 ARIÈGE

Pamiers

FOIX

N 20

D 119

N 20

15 km

0

INFOGRAPH LégendeCartographie - 8, avenue Dutartre - 78150 LE CHESNAY - FRANCE - Tél : 33.1.39.55.70.46 - SIRET1933

N 122

N 120

AURILLAC

Cere

D 920

D 921

N 9

Truyère

46
LOT

N 122

15
CANTAL

Alpuech

Lacroix-Barrez

Truyère

D 987

48
LOZERE

Laguiole

Figeac

D 921

Lot

D 920

N 140

Estaing

Castelnau-de-Mandailles

A 75

N 88

D 922

St-Rémy

Bournazel

D 988

D 988

Aveyron

Villefranche-
de-Rouergue

Rignac

D 984

Onet-le-Château

RODEZ

Aveyron

Lapanouse

Tarn

Aveyron

Colombiès

D 911

N 88

Sanvensa

D 911

Pont-de-Salars

Prades-de-Salars

N 9

Rivière-
sur-Tarn

Peyreleau

Dourbie

D 922

Sauveterre-
de-Rouergue

Viaur

N 88

D 902

D 911

Compeyre

Millau

D 600

N 88

Tarn

Tarn

Lapanouse-de-Cernon

N 88

Tarn

ALBI

Coupiac

D 999

A 75

81
TARN

D 999

Gissac

34
HÉRAULT

Lodève

D 631

Agout

N 112

D 112

D 622

D 622

Agout

A 75

D 908

N

Castres

0   17 km

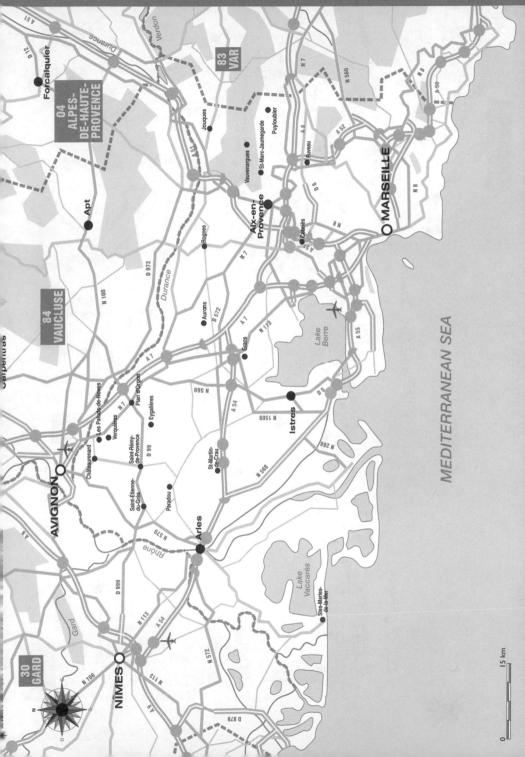

04
ALPES-
DE-HAUTE-
PROVENCE

83
VAR

84
VAUCLUSE

30
GARD

Forcalquier

Apt

Jouques

Vauvenargues
St-Marc-Jaumegarde
Puyloubier
Fuveau

Aix-en-Provence

Cabriès

MARSEILLE

Rognes

Aurons

Grans

Lake Berre

Les Pallud-de-Noves
Plan d'Orgon
Verquières
Eygalières
Châteaurenard
Saint-Rémy-de-Provence
Saint-Etienne-du-Grès
Paradou
St-Martin-de-Crau

Istres

AVIGNON

Arles

Lake Vaccarès

Stes-Maries-de-la-Mer

NÎMES

MEDITERRANEAN SEA

Verdon
Durance
Durance
Rhône
Gard
Serpentras

A 51
A 12
D 973
N 100
N 7
A 7
A 7
D 572
N 113
N 569
A 54
N 570
D 99
D 999
N 113
A 54
N 106
N 113
N 572
D 979
A 9
N 7
A 8
A 52
A 50
N 560
N 8
N 8
D 6
A 51
N 8 N
A 55
D 5
N 1569
N 268
N 568

15 km
0

N

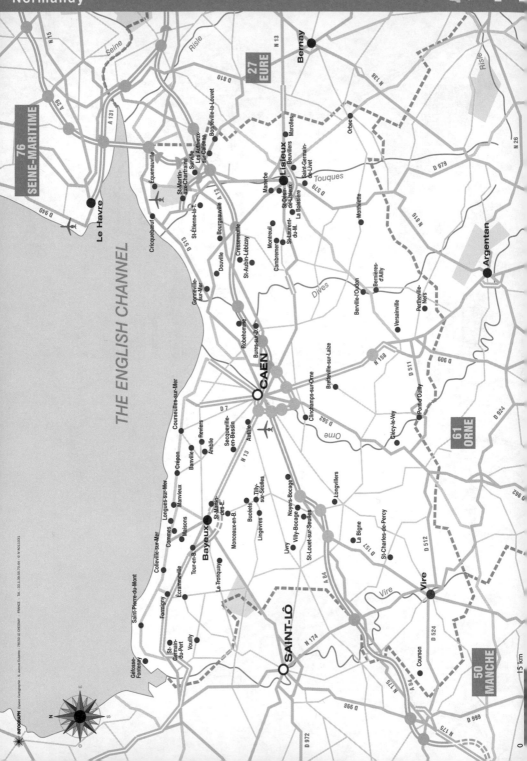

THE ENGLISH CHANNEL

76 SEINE-MARITIME

27 EURE

61 ORNE

50 MANCHE

Bernay

Le Havre

Cricquebœuf
Équemauville

St-Martin-aux-Chartrains
Surville
Les Authieux-sur-Calonne
Bonneville-la-Louvet

Orbec

Marolles
Lisieux
Beuvillers
Saint-Germain-de-Livet
Manerbe
St-Ouen-de-Lisieux
La Boissière
St-Laurent-du-M.
Cambremer

Touques

Montviette

St-Étienne-la-T.
Bourgeauville

Gonneville-sur-Mer

Douville
Cresseveuille
St-Aubin-Lébizay
Montreuil

Berville-l'Oudon

Bernières-d'Ailly

Argentan

Dives

Versainville

Pertheville-Ners

Robehomme

Bures-sur-Dives

CAEN

Breteville-sur-Laize

D 511

D 606

Courseulles-sur-Mer

Clinchamps-sur-Orne

Pont-d'Ouilly

Clécy-le-Vey

Orne

Revière
Secqueville-en-Bessin
Amblie
Crépon
Banville
Manvieux
Longues-sur-Mer
Commes
Maisons
St-Martin-des-E.
Bayeux
Monceaux-en-B.

Bucéels
Tilly-sur-Seulles
Lingèvres
Livry
Villy-Bocage
Noyers-Bocage
St-Louet-sur-Seulles

Longvillers

La Bigne
St-Charles-de-Percy

Vire

Vire

D 524

Colleville-sur-Mer
Tour-en-B.
Le Tronquay

Saint-Pierre-du-Mont
Formigny
Écrammeville

SAINT-LÔ

N 174

St-Germain-du-Pert
Vouilly
Courson

Gefosse-Fontenay

15 km

INFOGRAPH Espace Cartographie - 5, avenue Duclerc - FRESNE LE CRESNAY · FRANCE · Tel.: 33.1.39.59.70.44 · © N°011031

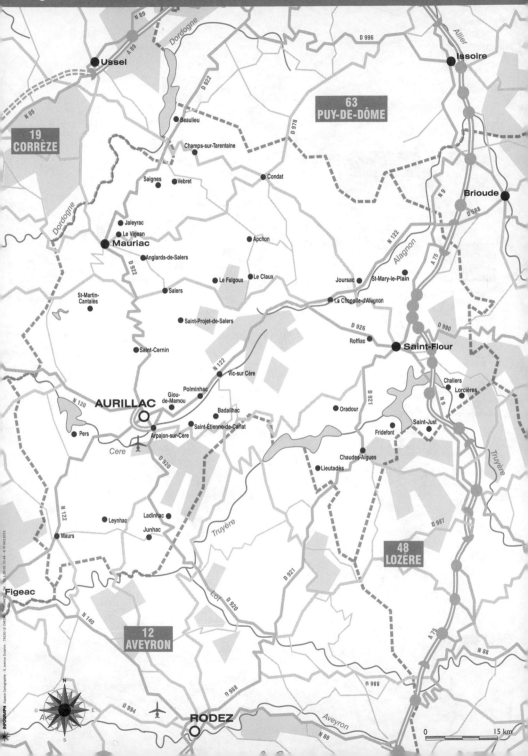

N 89

Dordogne

D 996

Allier

Ussel

A 89

D 922

63
PUY-DE-DÔME

D 978

Issoire

N 89

Beaulieu

Champs-sur-Tarentaine

19
CORRÈZE

Saignes   Vebret

Condat

N 9

Brioude

D 588

Dordogne

Jaleyrac

Le Vigean

Mauriac

Apchon

N 122

Alagnon

A 75

Anglards-de-Salers

D 922

Le Falgoux   Le Claux

Joursac   St-Mary-le-Plain

St-Martin-
Cantalès

Salers

Saint-Projet-de-Salers

La Chapelle-d'Alagnon

D 926

D 990

Saint-Cernin

Roffiac

Saint-Flour

N 122

Vic-sur-Cère

Challers

N 120

Polminhac

Giou-
de-Mamou

AURILLAC

Badailhac

D 921

Oradour

N 9

Lorcières

Saint-Just

Pers

Saint-Étienne-de-Carlat

Arpajon-sur-Cère

Fridefont

Cère

D 920

Chaudes-Aigues

Truyère

N 122

Lieutadès

Leynhac   Ladinhac

Junhac

Truyère

D 987

Maurs

48
LOZÈRE

Figeac

N 140

Lot   D 920

D 921

A 75

12
AVEYRON

N 88

N

O   E

S

D 994

n 988

RODEZ

Aveyron

N 88

0   15 km

○ NIORT

86
VIENNE

79
DEUX-SÈVRES

Charente

Clain

Vienne

D 951

● Confolens

17
CHARENTE-
MARITIME

D 939

● Bioussac

● Villefagnan
● Salles-de-Villefagnan
● Chenon

● Luxé
● Mansle

D 951
D 948

Vienne

● Suaux
● Lésignac-Durand

● Rochechouart

87
HAUTE-
VIENNE

● Mesnac
Louzac-
● St-André ● Réparsac
● Cognac ● Jarnac
● Moulidars
● St-Genis-
d'Hiersac
● Vars
● Vindelle
N 141

● Champniors
Saint-Projet ●
Magnac-sur-Touvre ●

○ ANGOULÊME

● Soyaux

St-Même-
● les-Carrières
● Saint-Preuil
● Lignières-
Sonneville
● Verrières
● Saint-Palais-de-Né

● Roullet

N 10

D 939

● Nontron

24
DORDOGNE

● Chadurie
● Aignes-et-
Puypéroux

N 21

● Condéon
● Berneuil

D 674

● Guizengeard

Dronne

33
GIRONDE

D 939

Isle

Dronne

○ PÉRIGUEUX

N
O — E
S

0 ——— 15 km

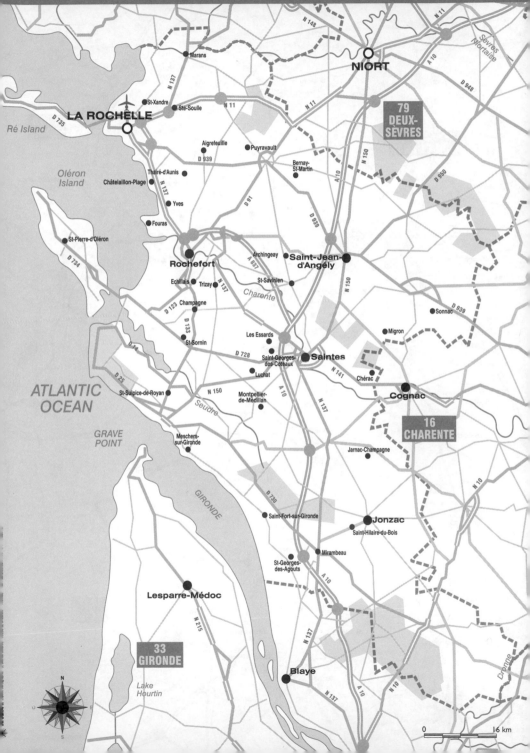

Ré Island

Oléron Island

ATLANTIC OCEAN

GRAVE POINT

Marans

N 148

NIORT

N 11

N 137

St-Xandre

LA ROCHELLE

Ste-Soulle

N 11

N 11

A 10

D 948

79 DEUX-SEVRES

Aigrefeuille

D 939

Puyravault

Bernay-St-Martin

D 950

N 150

Thairé-d'Aunis

Châtelaillon-Plage

N 137

D 91

Yves

D 939

Fouras

St-Pierre-d'Oléron

A 10

D 734

Archingeay

Saint-Jean-d'Angély

Rochefort

A 837

St-Savinien

Echillais

Trizay

N 137

St-Savinien

N 150

Sonnac

D 939

Charente

Champagne

D 123

Migron

D 133

Les Essards

St-Sornin

D 728

Saint-Georges-des-Coteaux

Saintes

Chérac

Cognac

Luchat

N 141

16 CHARENTE

U 14

D 25

St-Sulpice-de-Royan

N 150

Montpellier-de-Médillan

A 10

N 137

Seudre

Meschers-sur-Gironde

Jarnac-Champagne

N 10

GIRONDE

D 730

Saint-Fort-sur-Gironde

Jonzac

Saint-Hilaire-du-Bois

Mirambeau

St-Georges-des-Agouts

A 10

Lesparre-Médoc

N 215

33 GIRONDE

Lake Hourtin

Blaye

N 137

A 10

N 10

0   16 km

Loire

D 940

N 7

D 965

Clémont

Blancafort

Belleville-sur-Loire

58
NIÈVRE

A 71

N 20

41
LOIR-ET-CHER

A 85

Jars

Ivoy-le-Pré

Sens-Beaujeu

Neuvy-sur-
Barangeon

D 944

D 940

Henrichémont

D 955

Sancerre

Crézancy-en-Sancerre

● **Cosne-Cours-**
sur-Loire

Thénioux

N 76

Cher

Vierzon

Saint-Georges-
sur-la-Prée

Vignoux-sur-Barangeon

Foëcy

Mehun-
sur-Yèvre

St-Éloy-
de-Gy

Berry-Bouy

Quincy

Vignoux-sous-les-Aix

Rians

Montigny

Herry

N 151

Gron

A 20

A 71

○ **BOURGES**

Saint-Germain-du-Puy

Farges-en-Septaine

D 976

Loire

NEVERS ○

N 7

Plaimpied-Givaudins

Issoudun ●

Arçay

Annoix

D 976

Lunery

N 151

N 144

Cher

Blet

N 76

D 918

St-Baudel

36
INDRE

D 940

D 951

Allier

N 7

D 943

A 71

Saint-Amand-
Montrond ●

Charenton-
Laugère

Indre

Orval

N 144

Coust

03
ALLIER

Le Châtelet

Ardenais

Beddes

Saulzais-le-Potier

La Châtre ●

Epineuil-le-Fleuriel

Sidiailles

D 943

N

S

0   15 kr

23
CREUSE

Aubusson

LIMOGES

Maulde

Vienne

87
HAUTE-VIENNE

63
PUY-DE-DÔME

Millevaches

Vézère

Chamberet

Aix

Ussel

Corrèze

Benayes

Combressol

Saint-Julien-près-Bort

Sarroux

Arnac-Pompadour

Troche

Neuvic

Bort-les-Orgues

St-Bonnet-l'Enfantier

Naves

Marcillac-la-Croisille

Vars-sur-Roseix

Clergoux

Voutezac

TULLE

Objat

Dordogne

Mansac

Mauriac

Cublac

Palazinges

Brive-la-Gaillarde

St-Cernin-de-Larche

Forgès

15
CANTAL

Saint-Chamant

Nespouls

Noailhac

Argentat

Collonges-la-Rouge

Monceaux-sur-Dordogne

Turenne

Tudeils

Meyssac

Curemonte

Saint-Mathurin-Léobazel

Beaulieu-sur-Dordogne

AURILLAC

Bilhac

Altillac

Dordogne

46
LOT

Cere

N

S

E

O

0   15 km

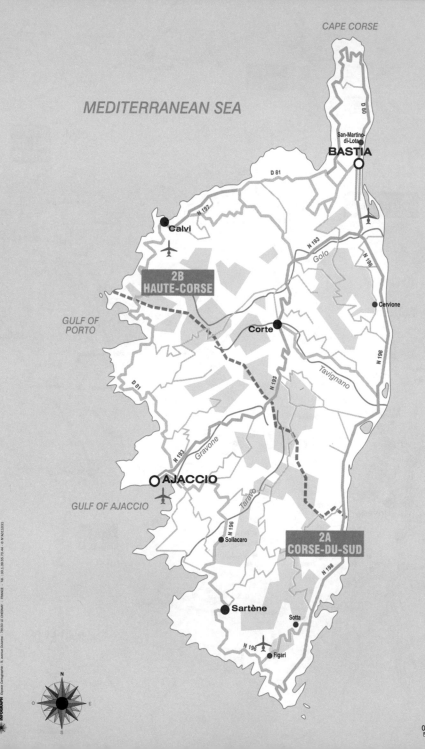

CAPE CORSE

MEDITERRANEAN SEA

San-Martino-
di-Lota

BASTIA

D 80

Calvi

N 197

D 81

N 193

Golo

N 198

**2B
HAUTE-CORSE**

Cervione

GULF OF
PORTO

Corte

D 81

Tavignano

N 198

N 193

N 193

Gravone

O**AJACCIO**

GULF OF AJACCIO

Taravo

N 196

Sollacaro

**2A
CORSE-DU-SUD**

N 198

Sartène

Sotta

N 196

Figari

0   12 k

CHAUMONT

D 417

10
AUBE

52
HAUTE-
MARNE

Marne

Meuse

N 71

Seine

D 65

A 5

N 19

Courban

Aube

Langres

N 4

D 965

89
YONNE

D 980

D 67

Meulson

Aignay-le-Duc

Échalot

Galives

Boussenois

Rougemont

D 996

Montbard

D 905

Bussy-le-Grand

N 71

Seine

Is-sur-Tille

D 980

Corrombles

Villars-
Villenotte

Chanceaux

Noiron-sur-Bèze

A 6

Villeferry

Francheville

Messigny-
et-Vantoux

D 70

Clamerey
(Pont-Royal)

N 71

Aisy-sous-
Thil

Plombières-lès-Dijon

Maxilly-sur-Saône

La Roche-
en-Brenil

N 6

Molphey

Corcelles-les-Monts

Marsannay-la-Côte

DIJON

A 39

Pontailler-sur-Saône

Bellenot-
sous-Pouilly

Chambœuf

Gevrey-
Chambertin

N 74

Lamarche-
sur-Saône

A 36

Thoisy-le-Désert
(Cercey)

N 5

Athée

Vandenesse-en-Auxois

Châteauneuf-en-Auxois

Morey-St-Denis

Langecourt-
en-Plaine

Chaudenay-le-Château

Curtil-Vergy

Gilly-lès-Cîteaux

Colombier

A 6

Messanges

Flagey-Echézeaux

Epernay-sous-Gevrey

Canal

Bouilland

Saint-Bernard

Saône

Dole

Savigny-lès-Beaune

Chorey-
lès-Beaune

A 36

N 73

Ecutigny

Beaune-
la-Montagne

Beaune

D 980

N 6

Montceau-Écharnant

Montagny-
lès-Beaune

Corberon

D 973

Seurre

N 81

Baubigny

Auxey-Duresses

Vauchignon

Santenay-
en-Bourgogne

D 973

Doubs

71
SAÔNE-
ET-LOIRE

N 73

D 978

N
O   E
S

INFOGRAPH

0   15 km

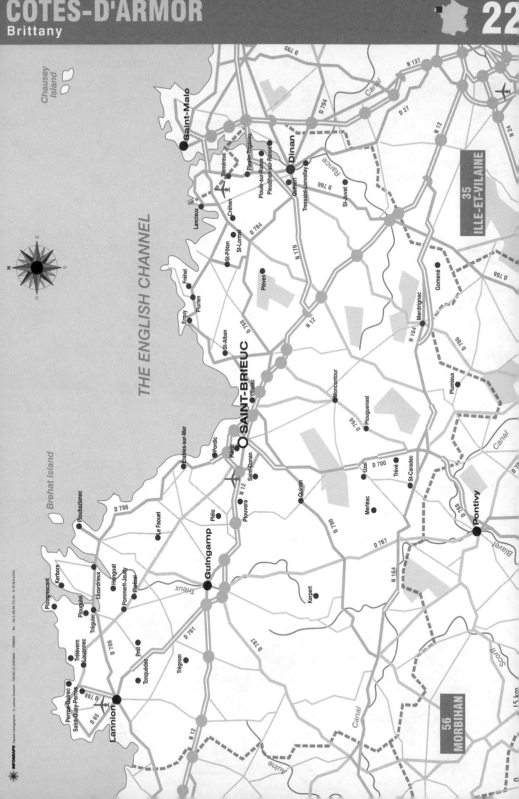

Chausey Island

Saint-Malo

N 795

N 137

Canal

D 794

N 24

D 27

N 12

35 ILLE-ET-VILAINE

Trémereuc
Plaslin-Trigavou
Plouër-sur-Rance
Pleudihen-sur-Rance
Dinan
Quévert
Tressaint-Lanvallay
St-Juvat

D 766

D 766

Lancieux
Créhen
St-Pôtan
St-Lormel

D 794

Frénel
Fréhel
Pléven
Merdrignac
Gomené

N 176

N 164

N 12

D 786

THE ENGLISH CHANNEL

Erquy
Plurien
St-Alban

D 768

D 768

Moncontour
Plumieux

SAINT-BRIEUC
Yffiniac

Plouguenast

Plérin
Éables-sur-Mer
Pordic

D 768

Izel
Trévé
St-Caradec

D 700

Brehat Island

Saint-Donan
Quintin
Merléac
Kerpert

D 760

D 767

Canal

N 12

PONTIVY

Scorff

Blavet

D 768

Ploubazlanec
Le Faouet
Piélo
Plouvara

N 12

Guingamp

Trieux

Ploegrescant
Kerbors
Lézardrieux
Hengoat
Pommerit-Jaudy
Pleizou

D 786

N 164

56 MORBIHAN

Plougiel
Tréguier

Perros-Guirec
Saint-Quay-Perros
Trélévern
Louannec
Prat
Trégrom
Tonquédec
Tréguec

D 786

Lannion

D 65

D 788

D 767

D 761

N 12

Canal

Aulne

15 km

N 151

D 943

Indre

Cher

Saint-Amand-Montrond

N 144

18
CHER

A 71

Creuse

D 927

La Châtre

36
INDRE

D 943

Montluçon

Fresselines

D 951

Chambon-Sainte-Croix

D 940

Bussière-St-Georges

Bétête

Genouillac

Boussac

La Celle-Dunoise

Champsanglard

Roches

Jouillat

N 145

GUÉRET

Le Grand-Bourg

Creuse

N 145

N 145

St-Étienne-de-Fursac

Gartempe

Lussat

Cher

D 942

Saint-Pardoux-les-Cards

St-Martial-le-Mont

Saint-Dizier-Leyrenne

D 940

Pontarion

La Chapelle-St-Martial

St-Hilaire-le-Château

Alleyrat

N 141

Aubusson

St-Pierre-Bellevue

St-Pardoux-le-Neuf

Saint-Bard

Mérinchal

63
PUY-DE-DÔME

LIMOGES

N 141

D 940

Maulde

Saint-Yriex-la-Montagne

Banize

D 941

Vienne

Gentioux-Pigerolles

Creuse

87
HAUTE-VIENNE

N 89

19
CORRÈZE

A 89

Dordogne

Vézère

D 940

Ussel

D 922

N 89

Corrèze

N

0   15 km

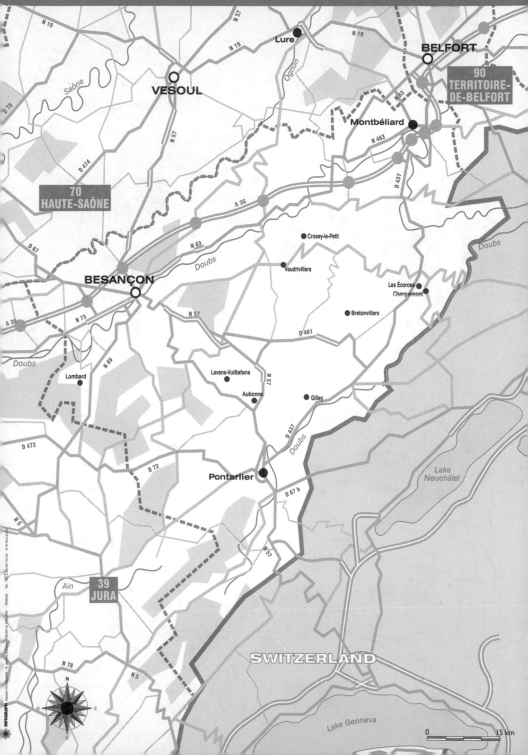

N 19

Lure

N 19

BELFORT

N 19

Ognon

90
TERRITOIRE-
DE-BELFORT

N 83

VESOUL

Saône

N 57

Montbéliard

D 70

N 57

N 463

D 474

70
HAUTE-SAÔNE

A 36

D 437

Doubs

D 67

N 83

Doubs

Crosey-le-Petit

Vaudrivillers

Les Écorces
Charquemont

BESANÇON

N 57

Bretonvillers

A 36

N 73

D 461

N 83

Doubs

Lombard

Lavans-Vuillafans

N 57

D 472

Aubonne

Gilley

D 72

D 437

Doubs

Pontarlier

D 67 b

Lake
Neuchâtel

N 5

Ain

39
JURA

N 57

N 78

N 5

SWITZERLAND

N

O   E

S

Lake Genneva

0   15 km

EURE
Normandy

27

76
SEINE-MARITIME

ROUEN

Conteville
St-Ouen-des-Champs
St-Maclou
Fourmetot
Appeville-Annebault
Bosc-Bénard-Commin
Les Préaux
Campigny
Condé-sur-Risle
Bourgtheroulde-Infreville
Le Bosc-Roger-en-Roumois
St-Georges-du-Vièvre
Le Bec-Hellouin
Brionne
La Neuville-du-Bosc
Épégard
St-Cyr-la-Campagne
St-Didier-des-Bois
Acquigny
La Croix-St-Leufroy
Reuilly
Bernay
St-Germain-la-Campagne
St-Quentin-des-Isles
St-Clair-d'Arcey
Saint-Aubin-le-Guichard
Émanville
Ferrières-St-Hilaire
ÉVREUX
Miserey

Alizier
Barneville-sur-Seine

Bourg-Beaudouin
Pont-St-Pierre
Tournedos-sur-Seine
Les Andelys
Notre-Dame-de-l'Isle
Vernon
Giverny
Fourges

Martagny
Longchamps
Nojeon-en-Vexin
Mainneville
St-Denis-le-Ferment

Mantes-la-Jolie

Jumelles
Manthelon

Dreux

61
ORNE

28
EURE-ET-LOIR

78
YVELINES

0   5 km

EURE-ET-LOIR
Central France

28

N 13

Eure

ÉVREUX N 13

Mantes-la-Jolie

PONTOISE

N 190

Seine

A 13

D 140

D 83

D 140

D 836

Saint-Germain-en-Laye

D 113

A 14

D 307

D 840

D 140

N 154

27 EURE

D 833

D 928

78 YVELINES

D 833

D 983

N 12

N 12

Risle

Iton

N 26

Avre

D 939

Dreux

St-Laurent-la-Gâtine

Eure

Rambouillet

N 10

N 306

N 12

D 928

D 929

Nogent-le-Roi

D 983

Les Châtelets

Villiers-le-Morhier

D 983

Saint-Maixme-Hauterive

D 941

D 939

N 154

D 906

A 11

61 ORNE

Eure

Bailleau-l'Évêque

CHARTRES

N 10

D 920

St-Éliph

Amilly

St-Luperce

Nogent-le-Phaye

N 191

D 923

N 23

Loir

D 920

D 921

Ver-lès-Chartres

N 20

D 955

Nogent-le-Rotrou

A 11

N 10

N 154

A 10

N 23

Bourdinière-Saint-Loup

A 11

Pré-St-Martin

Oinville-Saint-Liphard

Dangeau

D 955

Santilly

72 SARTHE

45 LOIRET

Châteaudun

41 LOIR-ET-CHER

Cloyes-sur-le-Loir

D 955

N 20

D 924

N 60

N 157

ORLÉANS

N 157

Loir

N 10

Loire

D 957

Vendôme

0   15

INFOGRAPH Espace Cartographie - St. avenue Dumoléte - 28500 LE CRESNAY - FRANCE - Tel. 33.1.39.55.70.44 - © N°011031

29

THE ENGLISH CHANNEL

Batz Island

Île-de-Batz

Cléder   Santec

Plougasnou

Plouénan

D 58

Plouider   D 788

Lanhouarneau

Plougar

D 786

St-Martin-
des-Champs

Morlaix

Plouégat-
Moysan

22

Lannilis

Kernilis

Plouvien

Plouigneau

Plourin-lès-Morlaix

N 12

D 788

Lampaul-Guimiliau

St-Thégonnec

Lanildut

Elorn

N 12

Loc-Eguiner-
Saint-Thégonnec

D 785

Scrignac

Saint-Thonan

Guipavas

Brest

Plouzané   D 789

Plougonvelin

Plounéour-Ménez

Saint-Éloy-Hanvec

N 165

Poullaouen

Brasparts

Aulne

Crozon   D 791

Argol

Rosnoën

N 164

Dinéault

Châteaulin

Aulne

D 887

Plomodiern

D 107   Cast

D 785

*he Sein
sland*

Poullan-sur-Mer

Locronan

Quéménéven

Edern

56
MORBIHAN

Plogoff   D 765

Douarnenez

Kerlaz

Le Juch

Odet

RAZ POINT

Mahalon

Plozévet

Elliant

Tourch

Scaër

QUIMPER

D 784

Saint-Yvi

Rosporden

Plogastel-Saint-Germain

D 785

N 165

D 765

Peumérit

D 34

Bannalec

Arzano

D 44

Plomeur

D 783

Pont-Aven

N 165   D 26

Riec-sur-Bélon

PENMARCH
POINT

*Glénan
Island*

Groix Island

ATLANTIC OCEAN

0   15 km

N 21

Gers

Garonne

82
TARN-ET
GARONNE

81
TARN

D 999

Tarn

N 88

N 88

D 631

Cabanac-Séguenville

Castelnau-
d'Estrétefonds

D 630

Tarn

Azas

D 630

D 112

Agout

Bretx

Montpitol

AUCH

N 124

D 923

Save

Garonne

Lavalette

TOULOUSE

32
GERS

N 21

D 929

N 124

N 126

Caraman

A 64

D 932

Muret

N 113

A 61

Varennes

Molas

Vernet

St-Léon

Montesquieu-
Lauragais

Anan

Auterive

Cintegabelle

Ariège

11
AUDE

D 624

Samouillan

Francon

Garonne

Montesquieu-
Volvestre

Latour

N 20

Auzas

Montberaud

Montbrun-
Bocage

Saint-
Gaudens

A 64

N 117

D 8

Pamiers

D 119

D 119

Figarol

09
ARIÈGE

Labroquère

D 117

Saint-Girons

D 117

FOIX

D 625

D 117

St-Paul-
d'Oueil

D 125

N 20

Juzet-de-Luchon

Garonne

Ariège

N 20

SPAIN

ANDORRA

N

0   18 km

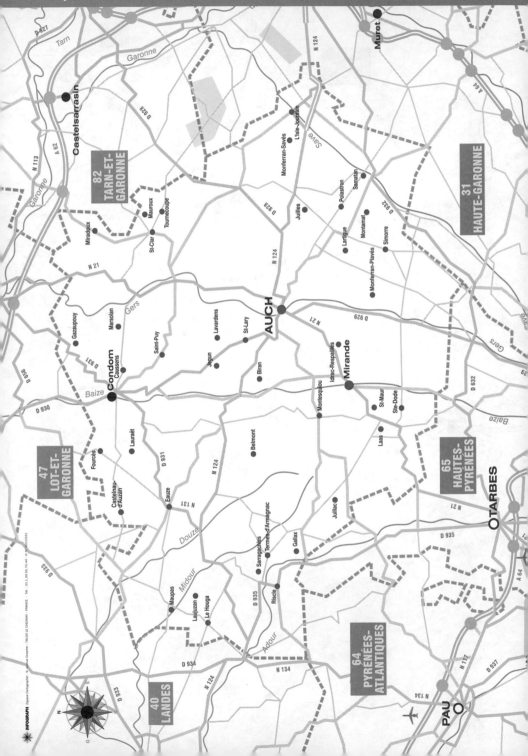

GERS
Midi-Pyrénées

32

Tarn

Garonne

D-927

N 124

Muret

Castelsarrasin

Garonne

D 926

Garonne

A 62

N 113

82
TARN-ET-GARONNE

31
HAUTE-GARONNE

Save

L'Isle-Jourdain
Monferran-Savès

Polastron
Sauvian

Juilles

D 928

Lartigue
Montamat

Simorre

D 932

Montferran-Plavès

Mauroux
Tournecoupe

Miradoux

St-Clar

N 21

Gazaupouy

Marsolan

Gers

N 124

AUCH

D 929

N 21

Gers

Lavardens
St-Lary

Saint-Puy

Caussens

Jegun

Condom

Biran

Idrac-Respaillès

Mirande

Baize

Montesquiou

St-Maur
Ste-Dode

D 632

Baize

D 936

D 931

Lauraët

Laas

47
LOT-ET-GARONNE

Fourcès

D 930

Belmont

N 124

D 931

Eauze

65
HAUTES-PYRÉNÉES

Juillac

Castelnau-d'Auzan

N 131

TARBES

Douze

Termes-d'Armagnac

N 21

D 935

Gaillac

Sarragachies

Maupas

Midour

Riscle

D 935

Laujuzan
Le Houga

Adour

64
PYRÉNÉES-ATLANTIQUES

D 933

D 934

N 124

N 134

40
LANDES

D 933

N

INFOGRAPH

PAU

N 134

A 64

D 937

N 117

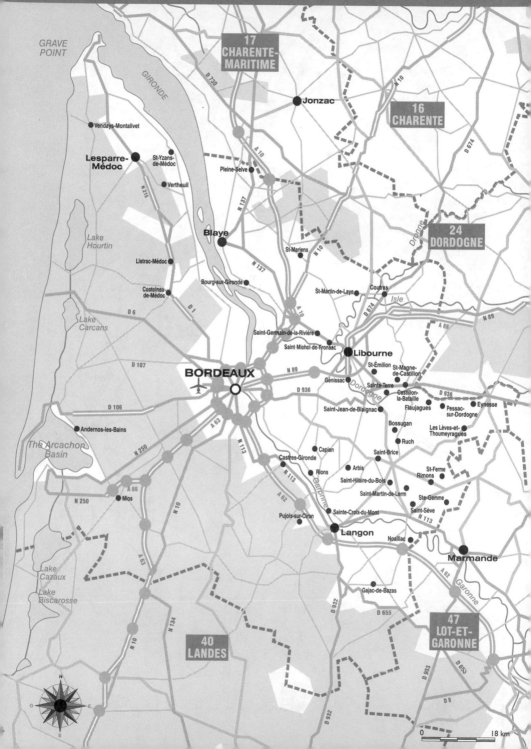

GIRONDE
Aquitaine

33

GRAVE POINT

17 CHARENTE-MARITIME

Jonzac

16 CHARENTE

Vendays-Montalivet

Lesparre-Médoc

St-Yzans-de-Médoc

Pleine-Selve

Vertheuil

24 DORDOGNE

Lake Hourtin

Blaye

St-Mariens

Listrac-Médoc

Castelnau-de-Médoc

Bourg-sur-Gironde

St-Martin-de-Laye

Coutras

Lake Carcans

Saint-Germain-de-la-Rivière

Saint Michel de Fronsac

Libourne

St-Émilion

St-Magne-de-Castillon

BORDEAUX

Génissac

Sainte-Terre

Castillon-la-Bataille

Eynesse

Saint-Jean-de-Blaignac

Flaujagues

Pessac-sur-Dordogne

Andernos-les-Bains

Bossugan

Les Lèves-et-Thoumeyragues

The Arcachon Basin

Ruch

Capian

Saint-Brice

Castres-Gironde

Arbis

St-Ferme

Rions

Rimons

Saint-Hilaire-du-Bois

Mios

Saint-Martin-de-Lerm

Ste-Gemme

Saint-Sève

Pujols-sur-Ciron

Sainte-Croix-du-Mont

Langon

Noaillac

Marmande

Lake Cazaux

Lake Biscarosse

Gajac-de-Bazas

47 LOT-ET-GARONNE

40 LANDES

0   18 km

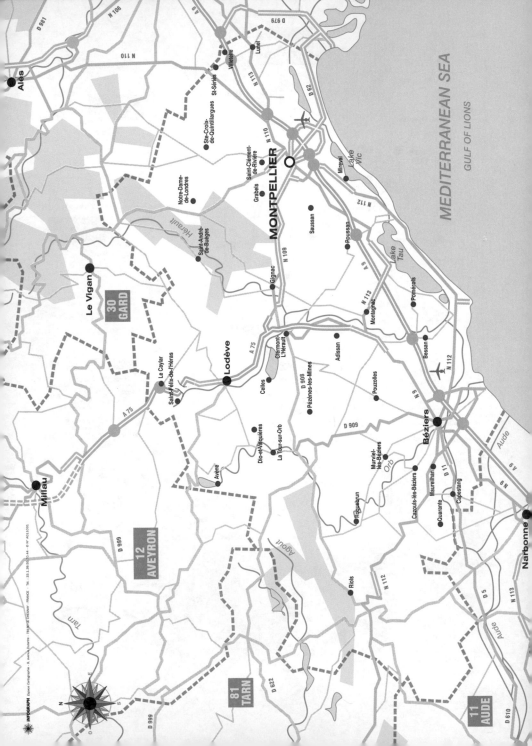

MEDITERRANEAN SEA

GULF OF LIONS

MONTPELLIER

Alès

Lunel

Villetelle

St-Sériès

Ste-Croix-de-Quintillargues

Saint-Clément-de-Rivière

Notre-Dame-de-Londres

Grabels

Saint-André-de-Buèges

Le Vigan

30 GARD

Saussan

Gignac

Mireval

Poussan

Lake Vic

Lake Tau

Pomérols

Montagnac

Bessan

Le Caylar

Saint-Félix-de-l'Héras

Lodève

Celles

Clermont-l'Hérault

Adissan

Pézénas-les-Mines

Pouzolles

Béziers

Millau

Dio-et-Valquières

La Tour-sur-Orb

Avène

Murviel-les-Béziers

Maureilhan

Capestang

Cazouls-lès-Béziers

Quarante

Riols

12 AVEYRON

Faugères

Narbonne

81 TARN

11 AUDE

Chausey
Island

THE ENGLISH CHANNEL

N

50 MANCHE

Saint-Coulomb
Cancale
Saint-Malo
St-Méloir-des-Ondes
St-Briac-sur-Mer
Hirel
Cherrueix
St-Père
Avranches
St-Suliac
Roz-sur-Couesnon
Roz-Landrieux
Dol-de-Bretagne
Pleine-Fougères
Sélune
Mintac-Morvan
Baguer-Morvan
La Boussac
N 176
Le Tronchet
Dinan
Bonnemain
St-Pierre-de-Plesguen
Saint-Ouen-la-Rouërie
La Selle-en-Coglès
Pleuguenuc
La Chapelle-aux-Filtzméens
Fougères
22 CÔTES-D'ARMOR
Marcille-Raoul
D 155
Chauvigné
Billé
Gahard
Montauban-de-Bretagne
Betton
Noyal-sur-Vilaine
Vezin-le-Coquet
RENNES
Vilaine
Monterfil
Paimpont
N 24
Piré-sur-Seiche
Guichen
Essé
53 MAYENNE
Guipry
Vilaine
Bains-sur-Oust
Ste-Marie-de-Redon
44 LOIRE-ATLANTIQUE
Redon
Châteaubriant

0   15 km

41
LOIR-ET-CHER

Loire

D 764

D 765

Romorantin-
Lanthenay

N 76

A 85

Cher

Cher

N 76

Vierzon

37
INDRE-ET-LOIRE

Indre

Loches

18
CHER

Vicq-sur-Nahon

Reboursin

D 956

Gehée

A 20

Fléré-la-Rivière

A 71

N 143

Issoudun

D 975

Chezelles

N 151

Saulnay

Coings

D 918

D 940

CHÂTEAUROUX

Tournon-
St-Martin

Le Poinçonnet

Étrechet

Pruniers

Indre

Mers-sur-Indre

D 943

Le Blanc

N 151

Creuse

Nohant-Vic

Sarzay

N 151

Ingrandes

La Châtre

D 927

Chalais

Pouligny-Notre-Dame

Aigurande-
sur-Bouzanne

86
VIENNE

St-Benoît-
du-Sault

Éguzon-Chantôme

D 951

D 940

A 20

87
HAUTE-VIENNE

23
CREUSE

N

O   E

S

N 145

N 145

0   15 km

Guéret

72 SARTHE

41 LOIR-ET-CHER

49 MAINE-ET-LOIRE

86 VIENNE

36 INDRE

Sarthe

Loir

La Flèche

Vendôme

BLOIS

Épeigné-sur-Dême

Monthodon

Neuvy-le-Roi

Braye-sur-Maulne

Beaumont-la-Ronce

Château-la-Vallière

Souvigné

Neuillé-le-Lierre

St-Ouen-les-Vignes

Hommes

Chançay

Vernou-sur-Brenne

Nazelles-Négron

Limeray

Mosnes

Saint-Étienne-de-Chigny

Berthenay

Vouvray

TOURS

Langeais

Cinq-Mars-la-Pile

Azay-sur-Cher

St-Martin-le-Beau

Civray-de-Touraine

Chisseaux

Ballan-Miré

Monts

Athée-sur-Cher

Bléré

Chenonceaux

Ingrandes-de-Touraine

Bourgueil

Restigné

Azay-le-Rideau

Esvres-sur-Indre

Truyes

Francueil

Épeigné-les-Bois

Saumur

Savigny-en-Véron

Rigny-Ussé

Cheillé

Saché

Candes-Saint-Martin

Beaumont-en-Véron

Huismes

Cormery

Chinon

Cravant-les-Côteaux

St-Branchs

Tauxigny

Azay-sur-Indre

Genillé

Orbigny

Lerné

Neuil

Saint-Épain

Saint-Bauld

Chambourg-sur-Indre

Montrésor

Ligré

Crouzilles

Loches

Loché-sur-Indrois

Chaveignes

Richelieu

Sepmes

St-Hippolyte

Razines

La Celle-St-Avant

Ferrière-Larçon

Charnizay

Châtellerault

Bossay-sur-Claise

N
E
S
O

N 149

0   15 km

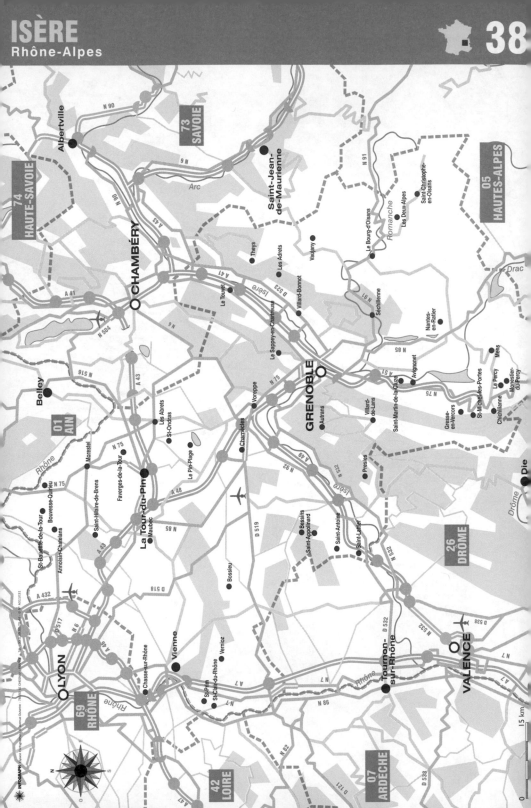

74 HAUTE-SAVOIE

73 SAVOIE

05 HAUTES-ALPES

01 AIN

69 RHÔNE

42 LOIRE

07 ARDÈCHE

26 DRÔME

Albertville

Saint-Jean-de-Maurienne

CHAMBÉRY

Theys

Les Adrets

Vaujany

Le Bourg-d'Oisans

Saint-Christophe-en-Oisans

Les Deux-Alpes

Le Touvet

Villard-Bonnot

Séchilienne

Nantes-en-Ratier

Belley

Les Abrets

St-Ondras

La Sappey-en-Chartreuse

Voreppe

GRENOBLE

Autrans

Avignonet

Mens

Le Percy

Monestier-du-Percy

St-Michel-les-Portes

Chichilianne

Villard-de-Lans

Saint-Martin-de-la-Cluze

Gresse-en-Vercors

Charnècles

Le Pin-Plage

Morestel

Faverges-de-la-Tour

Saint-Hilaire-de-Brens

La Tour-du-Pin

Maubec

Presles

St-Baudille-de-la-Tour

Bouvesse-Quirieu

Ainoisin-Chatelans

Bossieu

Bessins

Saint-Appolinard

Saint-Antoine

Saint-Lattier

Die

Vienne

Chasse-sur-Rhône

St-Prim

St-Clair-du-Rhône

Vernioz

Tournon-sur-Rhône

VALENCE

LYON

N 15 km

21 CÔTE-D'OR

70 HAUTE-SAÔNE

25 DOUBS

BESANÇON

Doubs

Sampans
Châtenois
Dole
Gevry

Doubs

Villers-Robert

Pontarlier

71 SAÔNE-ET-LOIRE

Ain

Arlay
Voiteur
Baume-les-Messieurs
Montigny-sur-l'Ain
Syam
Les Planches-en-Montagnes

LONS-LE-SAUNIER

Charézier
Le Frasnois
Bonlieu

Louhans

Geruge
Bonnaisod
Rotalier
Présilly

SWITZERLAND

St-Amour
Andelot-les-St-Amour
Cernon

Saint-Claude

Gex

Lake Geneva

BOURG-EN-BRESSE

01 AIN

Nantua

Rhône

0   15 km

LANDES
Aquitaine

40

Marmande

D 655

D 8

47
LOT-ET-GARONNE

N 124

N 131

Douze

32
GERS

A 62

D 933

D 655

Midour

D 933

D 932

St-Justin

D 934

Adour

N 134

33
GIRONDE

D 933

D 932

Midouze

D 924

N 124

Buanes

D 933

N 134

MONT-DE-MARSAN

Adour

Maylis

Saugnacq-et-Muret

Sabres

Ousse-Suzan

Campet-et-Lamolère

N 134

N 134

A 63

N 10

Lüe

N 10

Lesperon

Gourbera

Saint-Paul-lès-Dax

D 947

Pouillon

Dax

Mimbaste

N 117

Lake Cazaux

Lake Biscarosse

Mimizan

Adour

Saubusse

St-Jean-de-Marsacq

Magescq

Adour

Tosse

A 63

Seignosse

Blaudos

N 10

Angresse

Tarnos

ATLANTIC OCEAN

1,5 Km

0

N

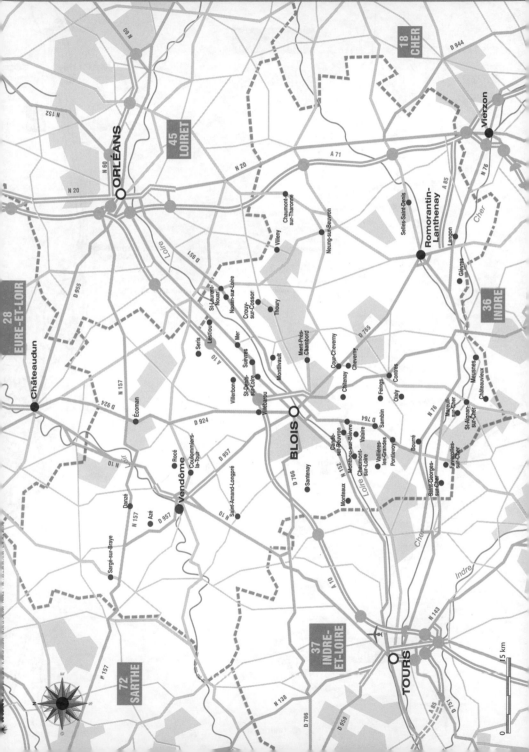

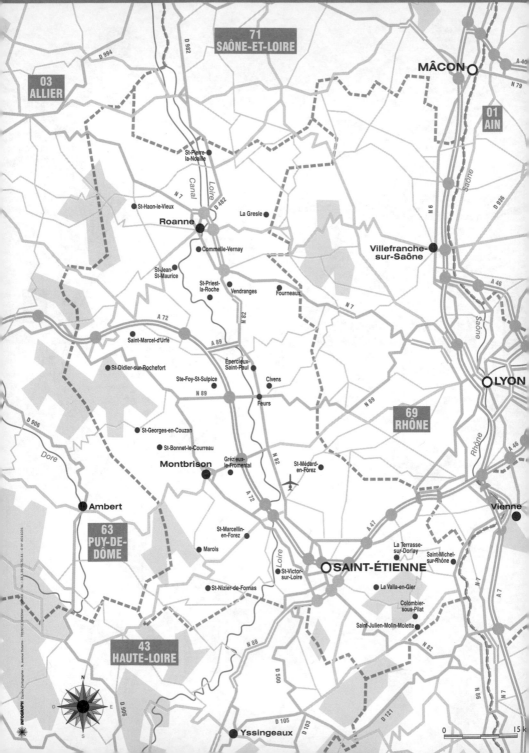

LOIRE
Rhône-Alpes

42

03 ALLIER

71 SAÔNE-ET-LOIRE

D 994

D 982

D 482

01 AIN

MÂCON

N 79

A 40

Canal

Loire

N 7

St-Pierre-la-Noëille

St-Haon-le-Vieux

La Gresle

Roanne

Commelle-Vernay

Villefranche-sur-Saône

Saône

N 6

D 936

A 46

St-Jean-St-Maurice

St-Priest-la-Roche

Vendranges

Fourneaux

N 7

A 72

N 82

Saint-Marcel-d'Urfé

A 89

N 89

St-Didier-sur-Rochefort

Épercieux-Saint-Paul

Ste-Foy-St-Sulpice

Civens

Feurs

N 89

69 RHÔNE

LYON

Saône

Rhône

A 46

N 7

A 47

D 906

Dore

St-Georges-en-Couzan

St-Bonnet-le-Courreau

Montbrison

Grézieux-le-Fromental

St-Médard-en-Forez

N 82

Ambert

63 PUY-DE-DÔME

St-Marcellin-en-Forez

Marols

St-Victor-sur-Loire

St-Nizier-de-Fornas

Loire

A 72

La Terrasse-sur-Dorlay

Saint-Michel-sur-Rhône

SAINT-ÉTIENNE

La Valla-en-Gier

Colombier-sous-Pilat

Saint-Julien-Molin-Molette

Vienne

N 7

A 7

N 88

N 82

43 HAUTE-LOIRE

D 906

D 500

D 105

D 103

D 121

N 88

N 7

N

O E

S

Yssingeaux

0   15 km

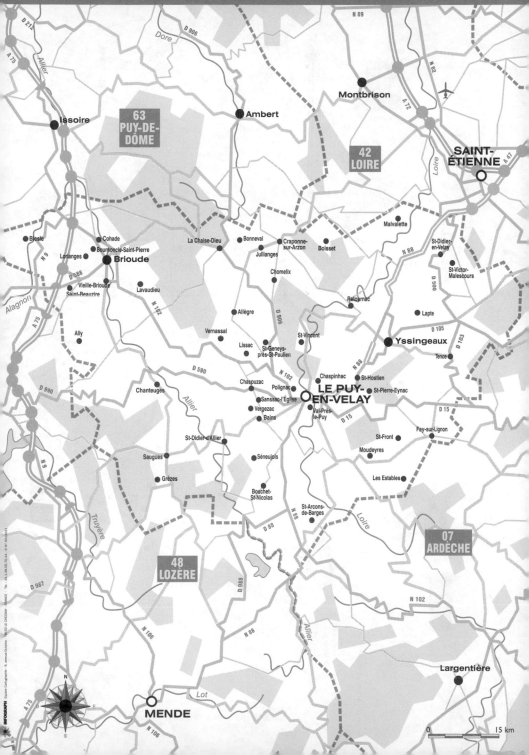

D 212
A 75
Allier
Dore
D 906
N 89

Montbrison

N 82
A 72

Issoire

**63
PUY-DE-
DÔME**

Ambert

**42
LOIRE**

Loire

**SAINT-
ÉTIENNE**

A 47

N 9

Blesle
Cohade
Bournoncle-Saint-Pierre
Lorlanges
Brioude
D 588
Vieille-Brioude
Saint-Beauzire
Alagnon
N 102

La Chaise-Dieu
Bonneval
Craponne-
sur-Arzon
Jullianges
Boisset

Malvalette

St-Didier-
en-Velay
N 88
D 500
St-Victor-
Malescours

Chomelix

Lavaudieu

Allègre
D 906
Retournac
Lapte
D 105
D 103

Ally

Vernassal
Lissac
St-Geneys-
près-St-Paulien
St-Vincent
Yssingeaux
Tence

A 75

D 590
Allier
Chaspuzac
Polignac
D 102
Chaspinhac
St-Hostien
St-Pierre-Eynac
N 88

Chanteuges
D 990
Sanssac-l'Église
Vergezac
Bains
**LE PUY-
EN-VELAY**
Val-Près-
le-Puy
D 15
D 15

St-Didier-d'Allier
St-Front
Fay-sur-Lignon
Moudeyres

Sauges
Séneujols
Les Estables

N 9
Grèzes
Bouchet-
St-Nicolas
St-Arcons-
de-Barges
Loire
**07
ARDÈCHE**

D 987
Truyère
D 88
N 88
**48
LOZÈRE**
D 988
Allier
N 102

N 106

Largentière

N
O — E
S

Lot
MENDE

N 106

0   15 km

INFOGRAPH

49 MAINE-ET-LOIRE

85 VENDÉE

56 MORBIHAN

Segré

Cholet

Ancenis

Varades

Soudan

Châteaubriant

Riaillé

Abbaretz

St-Mars-du-Désert

Le Loroux-Bottereau

Le Landreau

Monnières

Châteauthébaud

La Chapelle-sur-Erdre

Marsac-sur-Don

Nozay

Pont-Saint-Martin

NANTES

La Chevrolière

Fay-de-Bretagne

Port-St-Père

Le Temple de Bretagne

Frossay

Chéméré

Arthon-en-Retz

Chauvé

Redon

Missillac

Ste-Reine-de-Bretagne

Crossac

St-Malo-de-Guersac

St-Nazaire

Pornic

Noirmoutier Island

Herbignac

Assérac

Saint-Molf

Mesquer

ATLANTIC OCEAN

Loire

Sèvres Nantaise

Boulogne

Canal

Vilaine

Canal

N

15 km

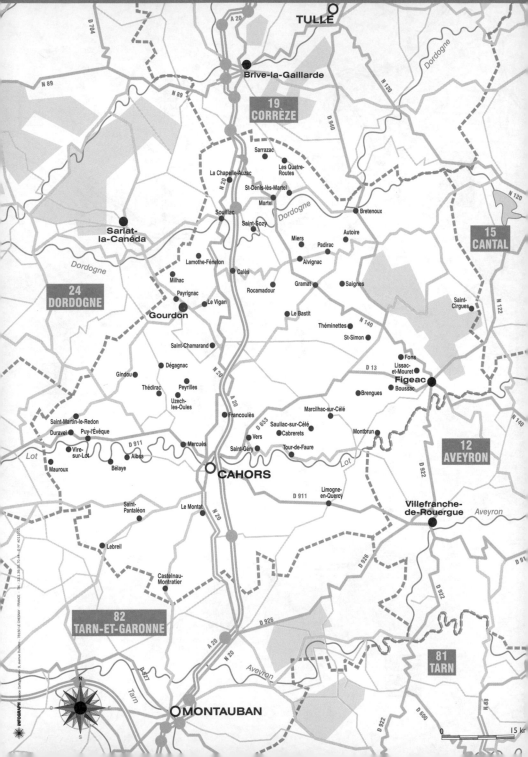

TULLE

Brive-la-Gaillarde

19 CORRÈZE

Sarrazac

La Chapelle-Auzac

Les Quatre-Routes

St-Denis-lès-Martel

Martel

Souillac

Saint-Sozy

Dordogne

Bretenoux

15 CANTAL

Sarlat-la-Canéda

Miers

Autoire

Padirac

Alvignac

Lamothe-Fénelon

Calès

Dordogne

Milhac

Payrignac

Le Vigan

Rocamadour

Gramat

Saignes

Saint-Cirgues

24 DORDOGNE

Gourdon

Le Bastit

Théminettes

St-Simon

Saint-Chamarand

Fons

Lissac-et-Mouret

Dégagnac

D 13

Figeac

Gindou

Thédirac

Peyrilles

Boussac

Uzech-les-Oules

Brengues

Saint-Martin-le-Redon

Francoulès

Marcilhac-sur-Célé

Duravel

Puy-l'Évêque

D 911

Sauliac-sur-Célé

Montbrun

12 AVEYRON

Mercuès

Vers

Cabrerets

Vire-sur-Lot

Albas

Saint-Géry

Tour-de-Faure

Mauroux

Bélaye

Lot

CAHORS

Saint-Pantaléon

Le Montat

D 911

Limogne-en-Quercy

Villefranche-de-Rouergue

Aveyron

Lebreil

Castelnau-Montratier

82 TARN-ET-GARONNE

D 926

81 TARN

N

MONTAUBAN

Tarn

0   15 km

Isle

D 674

N 89

A 89

ibourne

Dordogne

D 936

Bergerac

Dordogne

Dordogne

D 933

N 21

Baleyssagues

Duras

Moustier

Douzains

Villeréal

Saint-Eutrope-de-Born

Laussou

Gavaudun

Salles

N 113

Cancon

Montagnac-sur-Lède

Marmande

A 62

Garonne

N 113

La Sauvetat-
sur-Lède

Lot

Samazan

Grézet-Cavagnan

N 113

Villeneuve-sur-Lot

Courbiac

D 655

Clairac

Lot

D 911

Pujols-le-Haut

D 933

D 655

D 666

Aiguillon

Auradou

Buzet-sur-Baïse

Bazens

N 21

Dondas

D 8

N 113

AGEN

A 62

Vianne

Moncaut

Nérac

Garonne

N 113

D 656

Lisse

D 933

D 930

A 62

Castelsarrasin

Baïze

D 931

N 21

Condom

Gers

D 928

N 131

D 931

0   15 km

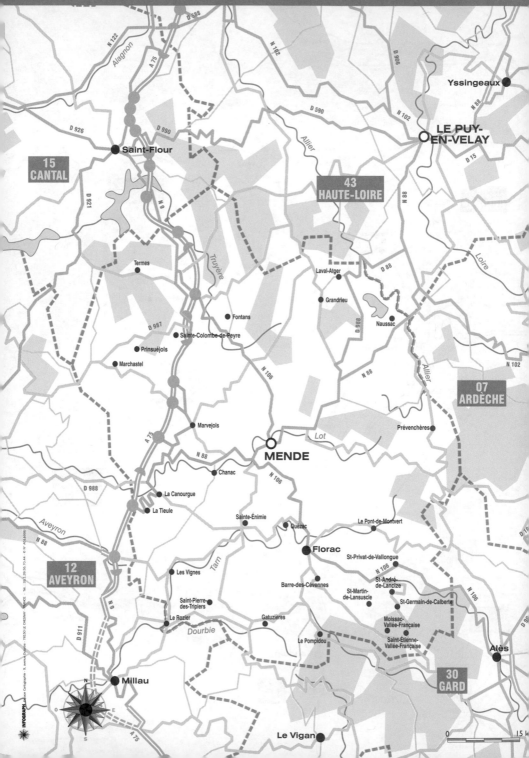

N 122

Alagnon

A 75

D 988

D 906

N 102

Yssingeaux

D 590

LE PUY-
EN-VELAY

Allier

D 926

D 990

Saint-Flour

N 9

N 68

N 102

N 88

D 15

15
CANTAL

D 921

43
HAUTE-LOIRE

Truyère

Laval-Atger

D 88

Loire

Termes

Grandrieu

D 988

Naussac

Fontans

Sainte-Colombe-de-Peyre

Prinsuéjols

Marchastel

N 106

N 88

Allier

N 102

07
ARDÈCHE

A 75

Marvejols

MENDE

Prévenchères

D 988

N 88

Chanac

Lot

N 106

La Canourgue

La Tieule

Sainte-Énimie

Quézac

Le Pont-de-Montvert

Aveyron

Les Vignes

Tarn

Florac

St-Privat-de-Vallongue

N 88

Barre-des-Cévennes

N 106

St-André-
de-Lancize

12
AVEYRON

Saint-Pierre-
des-Tripiers

St-Martin-
de-Lansuscle

St-Germain-de-Calberte

Le Rozier

Gatuzières

Moissac-
Vallée-Française

N 9

D 911

Dourbie

Le Pompidou

Saint-Étienne-
Vallée-Française

N 106

Alès

Millau

30
GARD

N

O   E

S

A 75

Le Vigan

0   15 k

INFOGRAPH

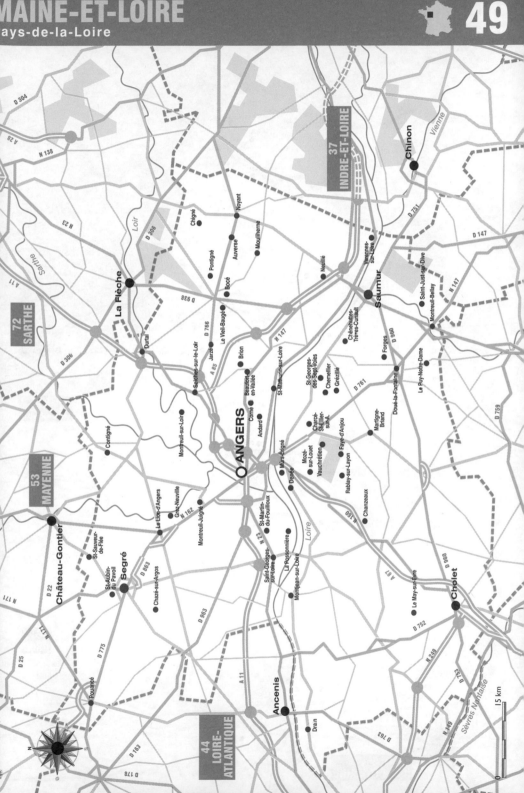

MAINE-ET-LOIRE

Pays-de-la-Loire

37 INDRE-ET-LOIRE

Chinon

Vienne

D 304

92 V

N 138

N 23

Loir

Sarthe

Chigné

Noyant

D 306

Auverse

Moulinherne

Pontigné

Bocé

Neuillé

Varennes-sur-Loire

D 147

Le Vieil-Baugé

Saint-Just-sur-Dive

Montreuil-Bellay

N 147

72 SARTHE

La Flèche

Durtal

D 938

D 766

Seiches-sur-le-Loir

Jarzé

Brion

Beaufort-en-Vallée

Saumur

Chênehutte-Trèves-Cunault

Forges

D 960

ANGERS

Corné

Andard

St-Mathurin-sur-Loire

St-Georges-des-Sept-Voies

Chemellier

Grézillé

D 761

Doué-la-Fontaine

Le Puy-Notre-Dame

D 759

D 306

Montreuil-sur-Loir

Contigné

Charcé-St-Ellier-sur-A.

Mûrs-Érigné

Denée

Mozé-sur-Louet

Vauchrétien

Faye-d'Anjou

Martigné-Briand

53 MAYENNE

Le Lion-d'Angers

Grez-Neuville

N 162

Montreuil-Juigné

St-Martin-du-Fouilloux

Rablay-sur-Layon

Chanzeaux

D 751

D 751

N 23

St-Sauveur-de-Flée

Chazé-sur-Argos

D 863

Ségré

St-Aubin-du-Pavoil

Château-Gontier

D 22

N 171

D 863

Saint-Georges-sur-Loire

La Possonnière

Montjean-sur-Loire

A 87

D 960

Cholet

Le May-sur-Èvre

D 752

N 249

D 775

D 25

Pouancé

D 163

D 178

44 LOIRE-ATLANTIQUE

Ancenis

Drain

A 11

D 763

D 763

N 149

Sèvres Nantaise

15 km

0

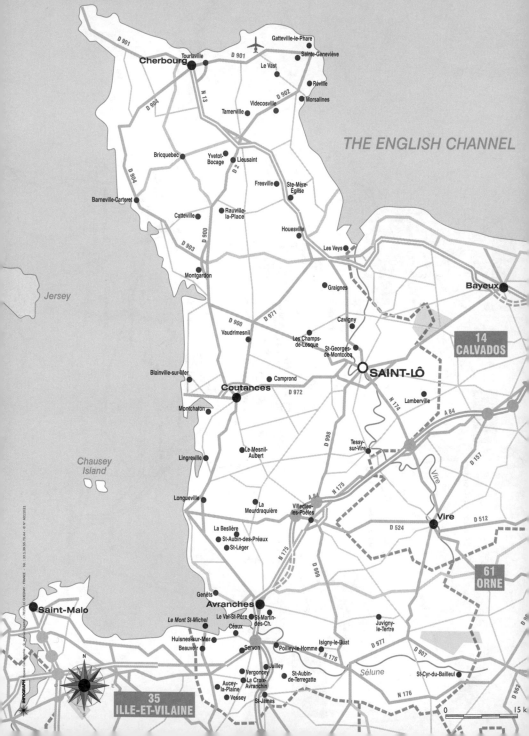

MANCHE
Normandy

50

THE HAGUE PENINSULA

D 901

D 901

Gatteville-le-Phare

Tourlaville
Cherbourg
Sainte-Geneviève

Le Vast

Réville

D 902
Morsalines

Videcosville

D 904

N 13
Tamerville

THE ENGLISH CHANNEL

Bricquebec
Yvetot-Bocage
Lieusaint

D 2

Fresville
Ste-Mère-Église

Barneville-Carteret

D 904
Catteville
Rauville-la-Place

Houesville

D 906

D 903
Les Veys

Montgardon

Jersey
Graignes
Bayeux

Cavigny

D 900
D 971
Vaudrimesnil

14
CALVADOS

Les Champs-de-Losque
St-Georges-de-Montcocq

Blainville-sur-Mer
Camprond
SAINT-LÔ

Coutances
D 972
Lamberville

Montchaton
N 174
A 84

Chausey
Island
Le Mesnil-Aubert
D 998
Tessy-sur-Vire
D 157

Lingreville
Vire

Longueville
N 175
Villedieu-les-Poêles
Vire
D 512

La Meurdraquière
D 524

La Beslière
St-Aubin-des-Préaux
St-Léger
N 175

D 999

61
ORNE

Genêts

Saint-Malo
Avranches

Le Mont St-Michel
Le Val-St-Père
St-Martin-des-Ch.
Juvigny-le-Tertre

Céaux
Huisnes-sur-Mer
Servon
Isigny-le-Buat

Beauvoir
Poilley-le-Homme
D 977
D 907

Juilley
N 176
Sélune
St-Cyr-du-Bailleul

Vergoncey
St-Aubin-de-Terregatte

Aucey-la-Plaine
La Croix-Avranchin

Vessey
N 176

St-James

35
ILLE-ET-VILAINE

0   15 k

N

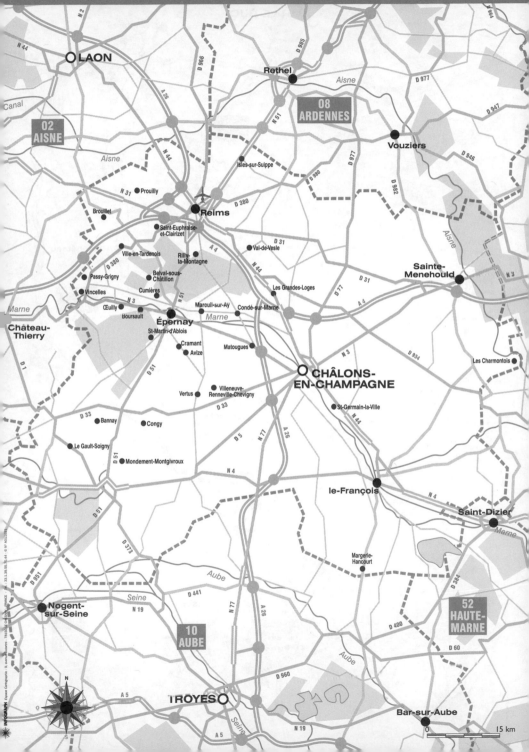

N 2

N 44

Canal

LAON

D 966

A 26

N 44

Aisne

N 31   Prouilly

Brouillet

Saint-Euphraise-
et-Clairizet

D 380

Ville-en-Tardenois

Passy-Grigny

Vincelles

Œuilly

Boursault

Belval-sous-
Châtillon

Cumières

N 3

Rilly-
la-Montagne

Reims

A 4

N 44

Val-de-Vesle

D 31

Les Grandes-Loges

N 51

Épernay

Marne

Mareuil-sur-Aÿ

Condé-sur-Marne

St-Martin-d'Ablois

Cramant

Avize

Matougues

D 51

Vertus

Villeneuve-
Renneville-Chevigny

D 33

CHÂLONS-
EN-CHAMPAGNE

Château-
Thierry

D 1

Marne

D 33   Bannay

Congy

Le Gault-Soigny

D 51

Mondement-Montgivroux

N 4

D 5

N 77

A 26

St-Germain-la-Ville

N 44

D 934

Les Charmontois

D 982

Sainte-
Menehould

N 3

Aisne

D 77

D 31

A 4

N 3

le-François

N 4

Saint-Dizier

Marne

Margerie-
Hancourt

52
HAUTE-
MARNE

D 384

D 400

D 60

02
AISNE

Aisne

D 966

Isles-sur-Suippe

D 380

Rethel

D 995

08
ARDENNES

N 51

D 977

Vouziers

D 977

D 946

D 947

D 964

D 51

D 33

N 44

Seine

Aube

Nogent-
sur-Seine

N 19

D 851

D 441

D 373

N 77

A 26

10
AUBE

D 960

Aube

Seine

N 19

TROYES

Bar-sur-Aube

N 5

A 5

A 5

N

15 km

INFOGRAPH Espace Cartographie / S. www.inforaph / FR : 33.1.39.59.70.44 - © N° AO11091

BAR-LE-DUC

Commercy

Toul

51 MARNE

N 135

Canal de la Marne

N 4

N 411

Saint-Dizier

N 4

N 964

D 974

Chamouilley

55 MEUSE

Marne

D 384

D 60

Thonnance-lès-Joinville

Meuse

A 31

Longeville-sur-la-Laines

D 400

D 60

N 67

D 74

N 74

Neufchâteau

88 VOSGES

10 AUBE

Bar-sur-Aube

N 19

A 31

D 429

Meuse

CHAUMONT

D 417

Mandres-la-Côte

Saône

Louvières

Marne

A 5

N 19

Villiers-sur-Suize

D 65

Aube

Langres

Saône

Bay-sur-Aube

Chalindrey

21 CÔTE-D'OR

Flagey

Pressigny

N 19

Colmier-le-Bas

A 31

N 4

Grandchamp

70 HAUTE-SAÔNE

Prangey

Saint-Broingt-les-Fosses

Prauthoy

Le Val-d'Esnoms

Seine

D 996

Saône

D 67

D 70

N
O E
S

INFOGRAPH

0   15 KM

MAYENNE
Pays-de-la-Loire

53

50 MANCHE

61 ORNE

72 SARTHE

49 MAINE-ET-LOIRE

Argentan

ALENÇON

Fougères

Gorron

Ernée

Mayenne

St-Germain-le-Foullloux

Montsûrs

LAVAL

Changé-les-Laval

Saint-Jean-sur-Erve

Ruillé-Froids-Fonds

Craon

Château-Gontier

St-Denis-d'Anjou

La Flèche

Segré

ANGERS

Sélune

Mayenne

Mayenne

Vilaine

Sarthe

Loir

N 175

D 999

D 977

D 907

D 924

D 962

N 158

D 916

D 908

N 176

D 982

N 176

D 908

D 798

D 177

A 84

N 12

D 23

N 12

D 909

N 138

D 798

N 12

D 31

D 35

N 12

D 178

N 162

D 304

A 81

N 157

D 21

A 11

N 162

D 25

N 171

N 171

D 22

D 775

D 863

N 162

D 306

N 23

D 305

D 938

D 766

D 963

0   15 km

LUXEMBOURG

BELGIUM

GERMANY

Charency-Vezin

N 52

N 43

A 31

N 163

Thionville

N 18

D 156

A 30

D 106

N 43

Forbach

Briey

A 32

Sarregemines

A 4

Boulay-
Moselle

N 3

N 33

N 3

Hatrize

A 4

METZ

N 3

N 56

D 903

D 952

N 43

N 74

D 904

N 57

D 910

55
MEUSE

Moselle

D 955

57
MOSELLE

Éply

Sarre

D 958

Ste-Geneviève

Château-
Salins

D 964

Belleau

A 31

Dommartin-
sous-Amance

D 955

Sarrebourg

N 74

N 4

Commercy

N 411

NANCY

Toul

Canal

Lunéville

Cirey-
sur-Vezouze

N 4

Maizières

Saint-Maurice-
aux-Forges

D 964

N 4

D 974

Moselle

N 4

Lemainville

Meurthe

D 424

Virecourt

D 913

A 31

88
VOSGES

N 74

N 57

Saint-Dié

N 59

N 74

D 166

0   17 k

D 429

INFOGRAPH... Édition Cartographie ... avenue Duquesne 78/55, LE CHESNAY - FRANCE — tél. 33.1.39.55.70.44 - © N° AC11003

LUXEMBOURG

D 964

D 981

D 977

08
ARDENNES

D 947

N 52

A 31

Vouziers

D 946

Meuse

D 905

N 43

N 18

D 156

A 30

N 43

A 31

D 982

D 964

Azannes

D 106

Briey

Aisne

N 3

Verdun

Gussainville

N 3

Sainte-
Menehould

N 3

A 4

Ronvaux

D 903

D 952

N 57

Ancemont

D 964

St-Maurice-
sous-les-Côtes

D 904

Meuse

Moselle

D 934

Thillombois

Meuse

N 35

D 958

51
MARNE

54
MEURTHE-ET-
MOSELLE

D 994

D 964

BAR-LE-DUC

Commercy

N 411

N 135

Toul

N 4

N 4

N 4

Canal de la Marne

D 964

Saint-Dizier

Marne

D 974

52
HAUTE-
MARNE

D 384

D 60

Meuse

A 31

N 74

N
O E
S

0   15 km

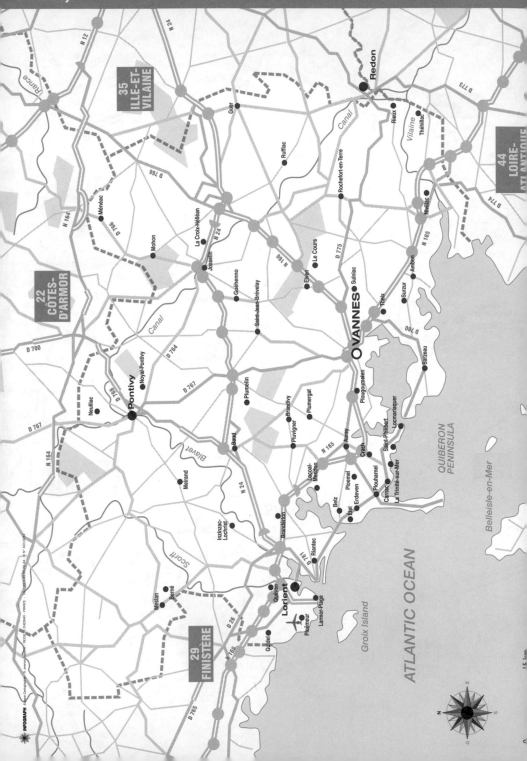

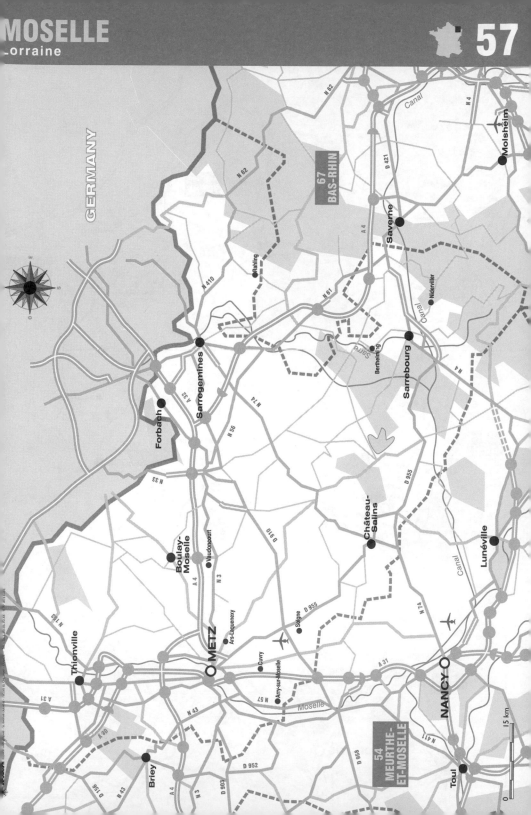

GERMANY

N 62

Canal

N 4

Molsheim

67
BAS-RHIN

D 421

N 62

Saverne

A 4

Rahling

N 410

N 61

Niderviller

Canal

Sarre

Berthelming

Sarrebourg

Sarregemines

A 32

N 74

Forbach

N 56

N 4

N 33

D 955

Château-
Salins

Lunéville

Boulay-
Moselle

Vaudoncourt

A 4

N 3

D 910

Canal

N 74

Thionville

N 153

A 31

METZ

Ars-Laquenexy

D 955

Solgne

Curvy

A 31

NANCY

15 km

A 30

N 43

N 57

Arry-sur-Moselle

Moselle

54
MEURTHE-
ET-MOSELLE

A 4

Briey

N 43

D 156

N 3

D 903

D 952

D 958

N 411

Toul

D 965

Yonne

A 6

N 151

N 6

89 YONNE

A 77

D 965

Loire

St-Amand-en-Puisaye

D 957

Avallon

Clamecy

D 951

21 CÔTE D'O

N 6

Cosne-Cours-sur-Loire

Donzy

Bazoches

Saint-André-en-Morvan

D 958

Yonne

Pouilly-sur-Loire

N 151

Vauclaix

Ouroux-en-Morvan

Raveau

D 977

Chaumard

Yonne

N 7

18 CHER

Mont-et-Marré

St-Hilaire-en-Morvan

Château-Chinon

Guérigny

D 958

Ourouer

Alluy

D 978

NEVERS

Saint-Jean-aux-Amognes

D 978

Tintury

Onlay

Saint-Éloi

La Fermeté

D 976

Loire

N 81

Saint-Gratien-Savigny

Sémelay

Magny-Cours

N 76

Lanty

N 81

Fours

N 81

D 978

Allier

D 951

03 ALLIER

N 7

D 979

D 60

D 994

71 SAÔNE-ET-LOIRE

D 973

Loire

Canal

MOULINS

N 2079

N79

N

E

S

INFOGRAPH

0 15

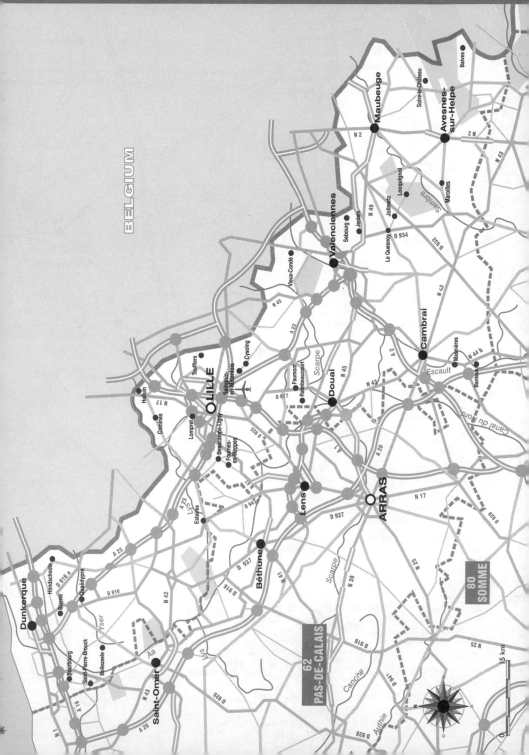

BELGIUM

Bahves
Maubeuge
Solre-le-Château
Avesnes-sur-Helpe
N 2
Locquignol
N 2
Marolles
N 49
Jolimetz
N 43
Le Quesnoy
D 934
Sebourg
Jenlain
D 935
Valenciennes
Vieux-Condé
N 45
A 23
Scarpe
Cambrai
Escaut
Masnières
N 44 b
Banteux
Faumont
Raimbeaucourt
Douai
N 45
D 917
N 43
A 2
Canal du Nord
Touffiers
LILLE
Sainghin-en-Mélantois
Cysoing
Halluin
N 17
Comines
Lompret
Beaucamps-Ligny
Fournes-en-Weppes
D 926
A 1
A 26
ARRAS
N 17
Estaires
A 25
D 945
D 947
Lens
D 937
N 25
Scarpe
D 939
A 25
Dunkerque
Hondschoote
D 916 a
Quaëdypre
Bierne
N 42
D 916
D 947
Béthune
D 937
N 41
D 916
N 39
80 SOMME
Bourbourg
Saint-Pierre-Brouck
Bollezeele
Yser
Aa
Saint-Omer
N 43
D 928
N 1
A 16
A 26
62 PAS-DE-CALAIS
D 916
Scarpe
N 39
Canche
N 25
D 941
Authie
D 928
15 km

80 SOMME

Laverrière · Esquennoy · **Montdidier**

AMIENS

Péronne

Somme

Puits-la-Vallée

Noyon

Cambronne-les-Ribecourt

Oise

Saint-Quentin-des-Prés · Hannaches · Savignies

Montreuil-sur-Brêche

Compiègne · Attichy · Berneuil-sur-Aisne

Aisne

BEAUVAIS

Saint-Léger-en-Bray

Clermont

Saint-Jean-aux-Bois

Flavacourt · Trie-la-Ville

Reilly · St-Crépin-Ibouvillers

Orrouy

Anserville

Oise

02 AISN

Thiers-sur-Thève · Fontaine-Chaalis

Plailly

PONTOISE

95 VAL-D'OISE

Montmorency

Seine

78 YVELINES

Argenteuil

Meaux

NANTERRE

Saint-Germain-en-Laye

BOBIGNY

93

Boulogne-Billancourt

PARIS
75

Le Raincy

Nogent-sur-Marne

Marne

77 SEINE-ET-MARNE

VERSAILLES

92

L'Haÿ-les-Roses

CRÉTEIL

Antony

94

Palaiseau

0   15

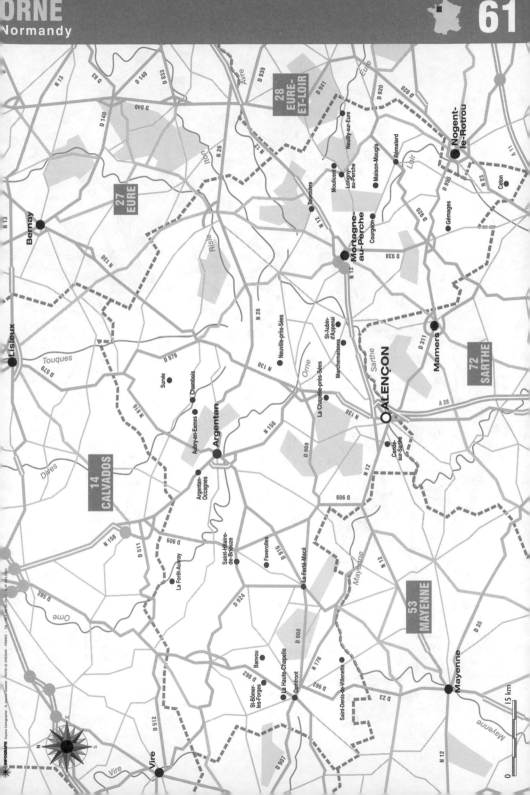

N 13
D 83
D 140
D 833
D 140
D 840
D 939
D 941
Avre
Eure
D 920
D 938 D

N 11
Iton
N 26
Neuilly-sur-Eure
Moulicent
Longny-
au-Perche
Maison-Maugis
Rémalard
Nogent-
le-Rotrou
N 23
Ceton
D 955
D 920
Tourouvre
N 12
Gémages
27
EURE
Risle
Bernay
Loir
D 918
Courgeon
D 920
Mortagne-
au-Perche
N 13
N 12
N 26
N 138
N 138 N
Neuville-près-Sées
St-Aubin-
d'Appenal
Marchemaisons
D 311
Mamers
72
SARTHE
Lisieux
Touques
D 579
D 979
Survie
Chambois
Orne
La Chapelle-près-Sées
Sarthe
ALENÇON
A 28
D 918
Aubry-en-Exmes
Argentan
D 908
N 138
14
CALVADOS
N 158
Condé-
sur-Sarthe
N 12
Argentan-
Occagnes
Dives
Orme
D 587
606 D
N 158
D 511
606 D
Saint-Hilaire-
de-Briouze
Faverolles
D 916
Mayenne
D 908
53
MAYENNE
La Forêt-Auvray
D 924
La Ferté-Macé
N 12
Banvou
N 176
St-Bômer-
les-Forges
D 962
Domfront
La Haute-Chapelle
D 962
Saint-Denis-de-Villenette
D 908
Mayenne
N 35
D 23
D 512
Vire
D 907
Mayenne
N 12
Vire

15 km
0

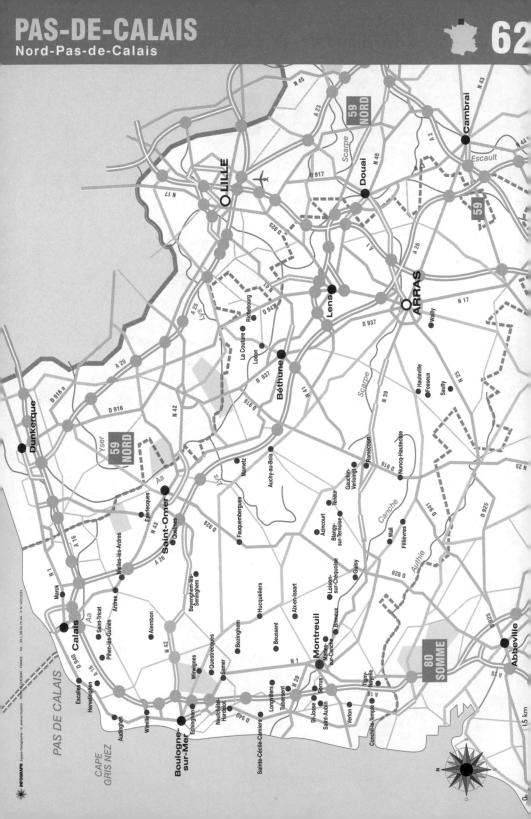

Cambrai

N 45

59 NORD

Escault

A 23

Scarpe

LILLE

N 17

D 917

Douai

N 45

59

A 3

A 2

N 44

D 925

A 1

A 26

Richebourg

D 947

Lens

ARRAS

N 17

Wailly

D 937

N 25

La Couture

Lobon

Béthune

D 937

Scarpe

Hauteville

Fosseux

Saulty

N 39

A 25

LYS

A 25

D 916

Dunkerque

D 916 a

Yser

59 NORD

N 42

D 916

Ramecourt

Nuncq-Hautecôte

D 916

Aa

Saint-Omer

Mametz

Auchy-au-Bois

Gauchin-Verloingt

N 1

Épercques

N 43

Quelmes

D 928

Fauquembergues

Téneur

Azincourt

Blangy-sur-Ternoise

Wail

Fillièvres

D 925

A 16

Marck

D 928

Canche

Bayenghem-lès-Seninghem

Hucqueliers

Loison-sur-Créquoise

Guisy

D 941

Authie

D 928

D 925

Escalles

Hervelinghen

Audinghen

Cape Gris Nez

PAS DE CALAIS

Calais

D 940

Aa

Saint-Tricat

Pihen-lès-Guînes

Ardres

Alembon

Mellles-les-Ardres

N 42

Bezinghem

Questrecques

Samer

Wirwignes

Wimille

Echinghen

Boulogne-sur-Mer

Neuchâtel-Hardelot

D 940

Sainte-Cécile-Camiers

Longvilliers

Tubersent

N 39

Beussent

Alix-en-Issart

Brimeux

Montreuil

Marles-sur-Canche

Sorrus

St-Josse

Saint-Aubin

Verton

Tigny-Noyelle

A 16

Conchil-le-Temple

80 SOMME

A 16

Abbeville

N 1

N 25

15 km

N

INFOGRAPH

Loire
Canal

Roanne

N 7

D 482

A 89

N 89

A 72

42 LOIRE

Montbrison

Ambert

Augerolles
Ollergues
Vollore-Ville
D 906
Tours-sur-Meymont
Cunlhat
Dore

Thiers

03 ALLIER

Saint-Victor-Montvianeix

D 906 D

N 7

Vichy

D 906

N 209

Allier

D 6

6 N

N 209

N 9

St-Éloi

D 1093

Sementizon

N 89

D 997

43 HAUTE-LOIRE

Brioude

Sauxillanges
Varennes-sur-Usson
St-Rémy-de-Chargnat

Les Martres-de-Veyre

Allier
Montpeyroux

Issoire

Mareugheol
Collanges
St-Germazy
Perrier
Clémensat

6 N

Beauregard-Vendon

Riom

Champs

Combronde

Charbonnières-les-Varennes

A 71

N 9

Manzat

N 144

CLERMONT-FERRAND

Orcines

Royat

N 89

Nébouzat

Aulnat

Aydat

Le Vernet-Ste-Marguerite

Montaigut-le-Blanc
Murol
D 996

Saurier

D 978

15 CANTAL

Montaigut-en-Combraille

Saint-Gervais-d'Auvergne

Villossanges

Sioule

Aureilhes

Olby
Sioule

Saint-Pierre-le-Chastel

Prondines

Saint-Bonnet-près-Orcival

Le Mont-Dore

Dordogne

D 941

Cher

23 CREUSE

Glat

Verneughol

D 941

Bourg-Lastic

N 89

A 89

D 922

15 km

0

N

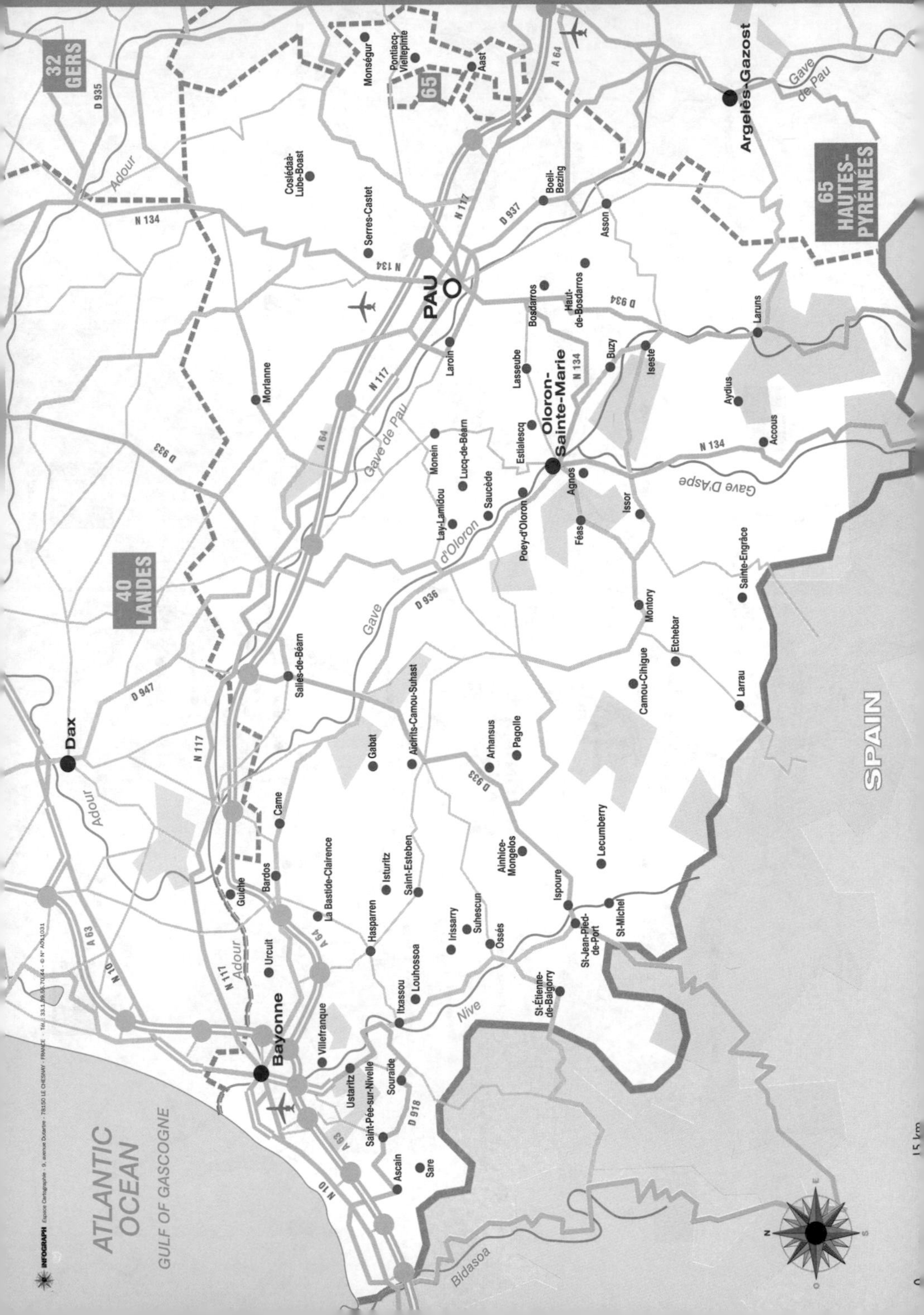

32 GERS

65

65 HAUTES-PYRÉNÉES

40 LANDES

SPAIN

Argelès-Gazost

Gave de Pau

A 64

Pontacq-Vielleplite
Aast
Monségur

D 935

Coslédaà-Lube-Boast

Serres-Castet

Boeil-Bezing

Asson

D 937

N 134

Adour

Morlanne

PAU

N 117

N 134

Laroin

Bosdarros
Haut-de-Bosdarros

D 934

Laruns

Lasseube

Oloron-Sainte-Marie

Buzy

Iseste

Aydius

Accous

Estialesca

Monein

Lucq-de-Béarn

Saucède

Lay-Lamidou

Poey-d'Oloron

Agnos

Féas

Issor

N 134

Gave d'Aspe

Sainte-Engrâce

Gave de Pau

A 64

Gave d'Oloron

D 936

Gave

Montory

Etchebar

Camou-Cihigue

Larrau

Salies-de-Béarn

D 947

D 933

Dax

Adour

N 117

Aïcirits-Camou-Suhast

Gabat

Arhansus

Pagolle

Came

Bardos

Guiche

Urcuit

La Bastide-Clairence

Hasparren

Isturitz

Saint-Esteben

Ainhice-Mongelos

Lecumberry

Ispoure

St-Jean-Pied-de-Port

St-Michel

Irissarry

Suhescun

Ossès

Itxassou

Louhossoa

Bayonne

Villefranque

Ustaritz

Saint-Pée-sur-Nivelle

Souraïde

D 918

Ascain

Sare

Nive

St-Étienne-de-Baïgorry

Bidasoa

A 63

N 10

N 117

Adour

ATLANTIC OCEAN

GULF OF GASCOGNE

15 km

N

INFOGRAPHIE

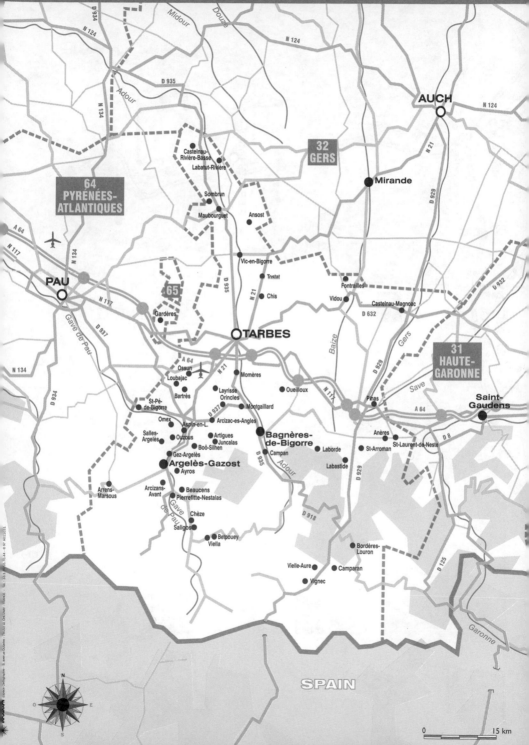

Aude

V 9

6 N

Narbonne

N 113

N 9

A 9

Lake Bages
and Lake Sigean

Lake Leucate

Villelongue-de-la-Salanque

D 617

D 114

Latour-Bas-Elne

Elne

Argelès-sur-Mer

PERPIGNAN

Montesquieu-des-Albères

A 9

6 N

Céret

Cases-de-Pène

Thuir

Camélas

Castelnou

N 116

Têt

Tech

Serralongue

St-Laurent-de-Cerdans

D 115

Montferrer

CARCASSONNE

N 113

A 61

11
AUDE

D 117

Prugnanes

Limoux

Aude

D 118

D 117

Mosset

Prades

Taurinya

SPAIN

Mont-Louis

N 116

Llo

D 119

D 625

09
ARIÈGE

D 117

Aude

N 20

Ariège

N 20

ANDORRA

N 20

Pamiers

FOIX

N 20

15 km

INFOGRAPH

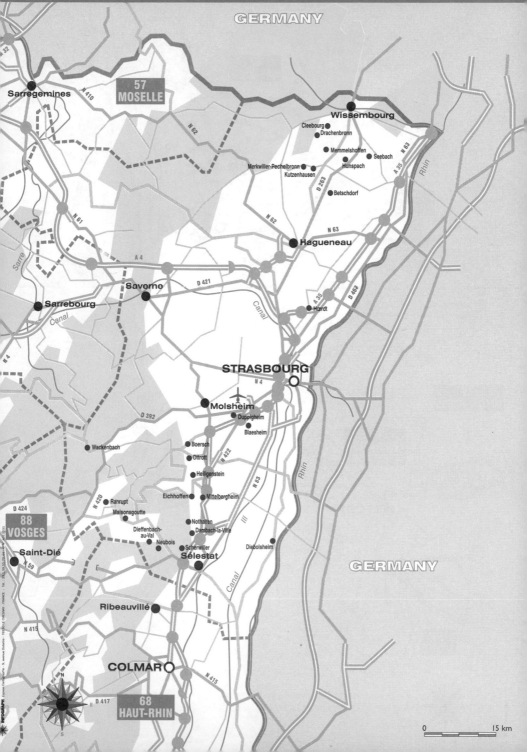

GERMANY

N 32

Sarregemines

57
MOSELLE

N 410

N 62

N 61

Wissembourg

Cleebourg
Drachenbronn

Memmelshoffen
Seebach

Merkwiller-Pechelbronn
Hunspach
Kutzenhausen

N 63

A 35

Rhin

D 263

Betschdorf

N 52

N 63

Hagueneau

A 4

Savorno

D 421

A 35

D 463

Sarrebourg

Canal

Canal

Hœrdt

STRASBOURG

N 4

Rhin

N 4

Molsheim

Duppigheim

Blaesheim

Wackenbach

D 392

Boersch

Ottrott

N 422

Helligenstein

N 83

N 420

Ranrupt

Eichhoffen
Mittelbergheim

D 424

Malsonsgoutte

88
VOSGES

Dieffenbach-
au-Val
Neubois

Nothalten
Dambach-la-Ville

Scherwiller

Diebolsheim

Saint-Dié

N 59

Sélestat

Canal

III

GERMANY

Ribeauvillé

N 415

COLMAR

N 415

N
O   E
S

D 417

68
HAUT-RHIN

0   15 km

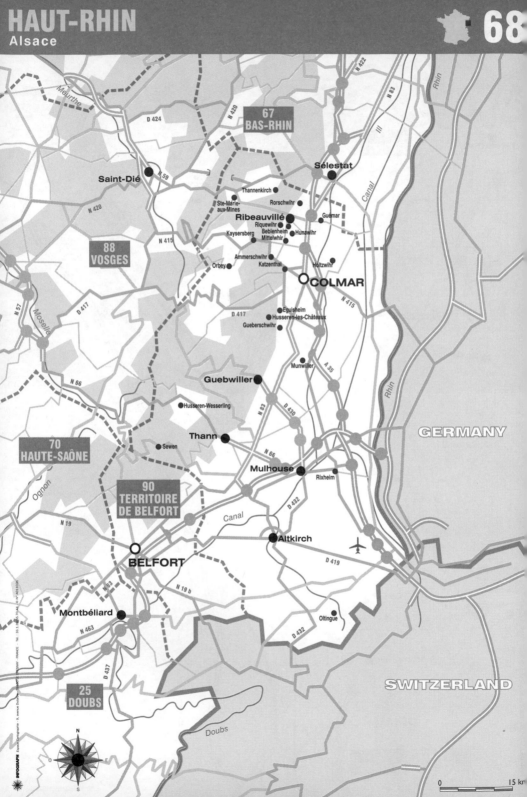

HAUT-RHIN
Alsace

68

67 BAS-RHIN

88 VOSGES

70 HAUTE-SAÔNE

90 TERRITOIRE DE BELFORT

25 DOUBS

Saint-Dié

Sélestat

Thannenkirch

Rorschwihr

Ste-Marie-aux-Mines

Ribeauvillé

Guémar

Riquewihr

Beblenheim

Hunawihr

Kaysersberg

Mittelwihr

Ammerschwihr

Holtzwihr

Orbey

Katzenthal

COLMAR

Eguisheim

Husseren-les-Châteaux

Gueberschwihr

Munwiller

Guebwiller

Husseren-Wesserling

Thann

Sewen

Mulhouse

Rixheim

Altkirch

BELFORT

Montbéliard

Oltingue

GERMANY

SWITZERLAND

Meurthe

Rhin

Canal

N 422

N 83

D 424

N 420

N 59

N 420

N 415

N 57

D 417

Moselle

D 417

N 415

N 66

N 83

D 420

A 35

Rhin

N 66

N 19

Canal

D 432

D 419

Ognon

N 19 b

N 63

N 19 b

D 432

N 463

D 437

Doubs

N

0 15 km

INFOGRAPH

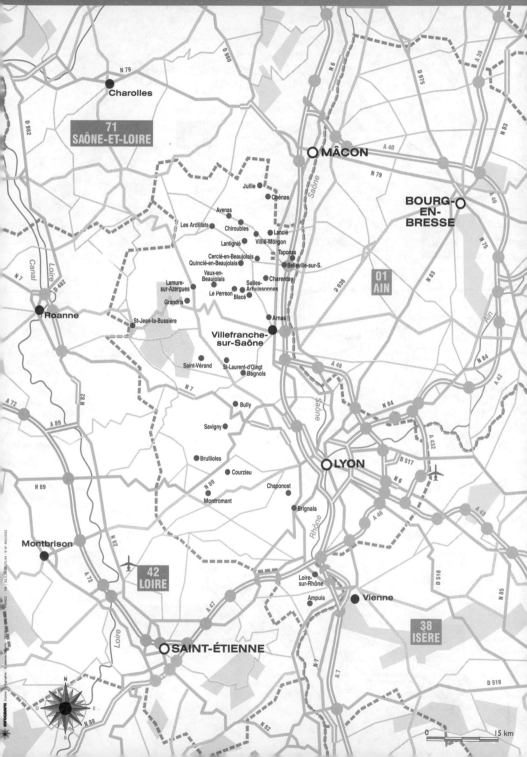

Charolles

N 79

D 980

D 982

71
SAÔNE-ET-LOIRE

D 975

N 83

MÂCON

A 40

N 79

BOURG-O
EN-
BRESSE

N 75

Jullie

Chénas

Avenas

Les Ardillats

Chiroubles

Lancié

Lantignié

Villié-Morgon

Cercié-en-Beaujolais

Taponas

Quincié-en-Beaujolais

Belleville-sur-S.

Vaux-en-
Beaujolais

Charentay

D 936

01
AIN

Lamure-
sur-Azergues

Salles-
Arbuissonnas

Le Perréon

Blacé

N 83

Ain

Grandris

Canal

N 7

Loire

D 482

St-Jean-la-Bussière

Arnas

Roanne

Villefranche-
sur-Saône

A 46

N 84

Saint-Vérand

St-Laurent-d'Oingt

Bagnols

N 7

Bully

A 72

A 89

N 82

Savigny

N 84

D 432

Brullioles

Courzieu

N 89

Montromant

Chaponost

D 517

LYON

N 6

N 89

Brignais

A 43

Saône

A 46

Montbrison

N 82

A 72

42
LOIRE

Loire-
sur-Rhône

D 518

Ampuis

Vienne

N 85

Rhône

A 47

38
ISÈRE

D 519

Loire

N 88

SAINT-ÉTIENNE

N 82

0   15 km

N 74

D 166

D 74

D 429

D 166

ÉPINAL

D 3

A 31

Meuse

D 429

D 164

88
VOSGES

N 420

D 417

Saône

D 26

N 57

Moselle

Canal

52
HAUTE-
MARNE

D 64

N 66

Esmoulières

Ecromagny

Ternuay

Melin

N 19

N 57

N 19

Ognon

Lure

N 19

Frahier

VESOUL

N 83

Saône

D 67

D 70

N 57

Montbéliard

N 463

D 474

A 36

D 437

N 93

25
DOUBS

Sauvigney-
lès-Pesmes

D 67

Hugier

Cult

Doubs

D 70

BESANÇON

39
JURA

A 36

N 73

N 93

N 57

D 461

Doubs

N

O E

S

0   15 km

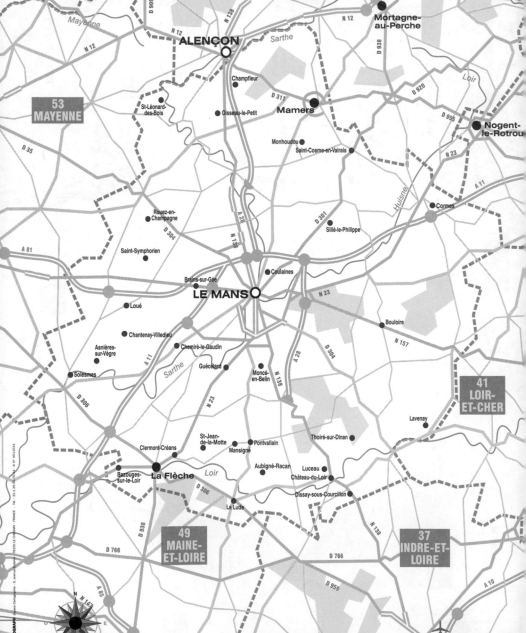

D 916

N 158

N 138

Orne

D 908

D 908

D 908

N 176

D 909

Mayenne

N 12

N 138

N 12

Eure

61
ORNE

N 12

Mortagne-au-Perche

Sarthe

N 12

ALENÇON

D 938

Loir

Champfleur

D 311

D 920

53
MAYENNE

St-Léonard-des-Bois

Oisseau-le-Petit

Mamers

D 955

Nogent-le-Rotrou

D 35

Monhoudou

Saint-Cosme-en-Vairais

N 23

A 11

Huisne

Rouez-en-Champagne

D 301

Cormes

D 304

Sillé-le-Philippe

Saint-Symphorien

N 138

A 81

A 28

Coulaines

Brains-sur-Gée

LE MANS

N 23

Loué

Bouloire

Chantenay-Villedieu

N 157

Asnières-sur-Vègre

Chemiré-le-Gaudin

A 11

D 304

Solesmes

Guécélard

A 28

Moncé-en-Belin

N 138

D 306

Sarthe

N 23

41
LOIR-ET-CHER

Lavenay

Clermont-Créans

St-Jean-de-la-Motte

Pontvallain

Thoiré-sur-Dinan

Mansigné

Bazouges-sur-le-Loir

La Flèche

Aubigné-Racan

Luceau

Loir

Château-du-Loir

D 306

Dissay-sous-Courcillon

Le Lude

D 938

49
MAINE-ET-LOIRE

37
INDRE-ET-LOIRE

D 766

D 766

N 138

D 959

A 10

A 85

N 147

INFOGRAPH

0   15 km

Tunnel du Grand-Saint-Bernard

ITALY

Tunnel du Mont-Blanc

Sainte-Foy-Tarentaise

Isère

La Côte-d'Aime

Arc

N 6

Tunnel de Fréjus

Macôt-la-Plagne

N 515

La Perrière-la Tania

Méribel-les-Allues

Aussois

Villarodin-Bourget

N 90

N 6

Queige

Albertville

N 90

Saint-Jean-de-Maurienne

9 N

N 91

Arc

ANNECY

N 508

74
HAUTE-
SAVOIE

Aillon-le-Jeune

CHAMBÉRY

A 43

N 90

Isère

38
ISÈRE

Romanche

N 91

Fier

A 41

A 41

Isère

D 523

Le Viviers-du-Lac

N 203

La Biolle

N 504

9 N

GRENOBLE

N 75

Rhône

Jongieux

N 516

A 43

Belley

01
AIN

N

S

E

O

15 Km

0

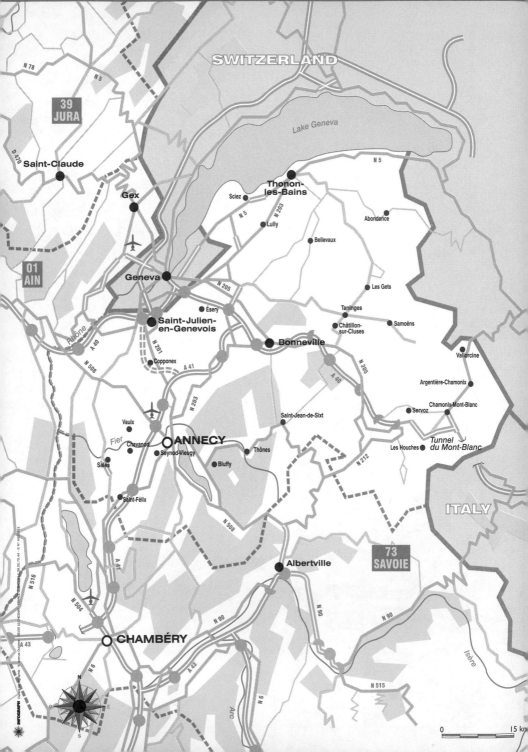

THE ENGLISH CHANNEL

80 SOMME

60 OISE

27 EURE

Somme

Abbeville

D 901

D 925

D 925

A 28

Eu

Ponts-et-Marais

Bresle

D 1015

D 312 Canehan

Melleville

Le Tréport

Nesle-Normandeuse

Les Landes-Vieilles-et-Neuves

Haudricourt

Flamets-Frétils

N 29

Arqueil

N 31

N 31

D 981

D 153

Les Andelys

D 125

N 14

Epte

D 915

D 930

Sommery

Neufchâtel-en-Bray

St-Saëns

Béthune

D 915

D 919

La Vieux-Rue

N 31

A 29

N 29

V 28

St-Aubin-le-Cauf

St-Aubin-sur-Scie

Toutiville-sur-Arques

Dieppe

Omonville

N 27

N 27

D 925

Anceaumeville

Isneauville

St-Jean-du-Cardonnay

ROUEN

Seine

N 15

Quiberville-sur-Mer

St-Aubin-sur-Mer

Sotteville-sur-Mer

Saint-Valery-en-Caux

La Chapelle-sur-Dun

Autigny

Berville-en-Caux

Cliponville

Ectot-l'Auber

Villers-Écalles

Duclair

Birdouville

A 150

A 29

N 15

N 15

Caudebec-en-Caux

La Mailleraye-sur-Seine

Jumièges

A 13

Aubermesnil-la-Manuel

Butot-Vénesville

Sasseto-le-Mauconduit

Carouville

Ouainville

Angerville-la-M.

Bec-de-Mortagne

Angerville-B.

Rouville

Saint-Eustache-la-Forêt

Seine

Risle

D 810

D 810

Sennville-sur-Fécamp

Fécamp

Criquebeuf-en-Caux

Sausseuzemare

Étretat

Turretot

Épouville

Sainneville-sur-Seine

St-Jouin-Bruneval

A 131

Le Havre

A 13

D 513

0

15 km

INFOGRAPH   Espace Cartographie · 9, avenue Duteme · 78150 LE CHESNAY · FRANCE · Tél : 33.1.39.55.70.44 · © N° AGS1031

SEINE-ET-MARNE
Île-de-France

77

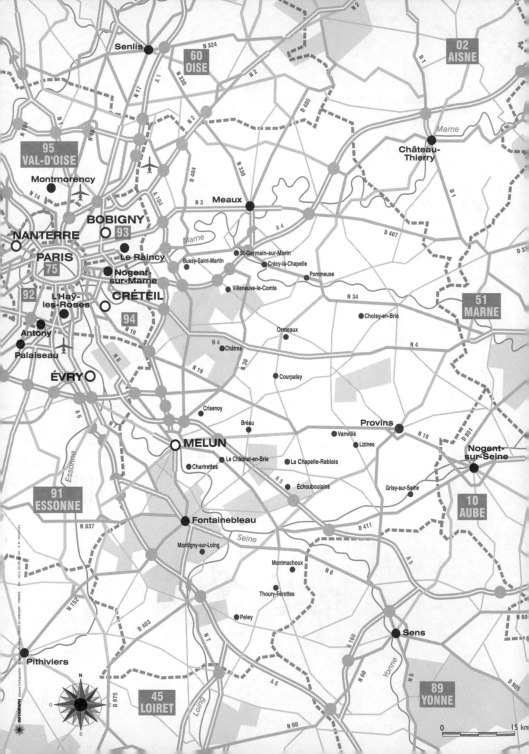

Senlis

60 OISE

N 324

02 AISNE

Marne

Château-Thierry

95 VAL-D'OISE

Montmorency

N 14

Meaux

Marne

N 3

93 BOBIGNY

Le Raincy

NANTERRE

PARIS **75**

Nogent-sur-Marne

St-Germain-sur-Morin

Bussy-Saint-Martin

Crécy-la-Chapelle

Pommeuse

92

L'Haÿ-les-Roses

CRÉTEIL

Villeneuve-le-Comte

51 MARNE

94

N 10

N 34

Choisy-en-Brie

Antony

Ormeaux

N 4

Palaiseau

N 4

Châtres

ÉVRY

N 19

Courpalay

Crisenoy

Bréau

Provins

Vanvillé

Nogent-sur-Seine

MELUN

Lizines

Chartrettes

Le Châtelet-en-Brie

La Chapelle-Rablais

91 ESSONNE

N 837

Échouboulains

Grisy-sur-Seine

10 AUBE

Fontainebleau

D 411

Seine

Montigny-sur-Loing

Montmachoux

N 6

Thoury-Férottes

N 152

Paley

D 403

N 7

Sens

Pithiviers

N

O   E

S

45 LOIRET

D 975

Loing

N 60

89 YONNE

Yonne

0   15 km

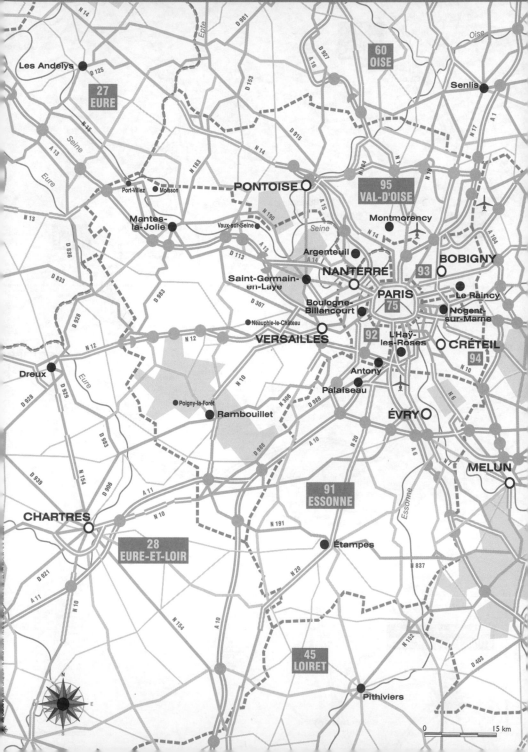

Les Andelys

27
EURE

60
OISE

Senlis

N 14

D 125

Epte

D 981

D 927

A 16

D 153

D 915

N 17

A 1

Seine

Eure

N 15

A 13

N 13

PONTOISE

95
VAL-D'OISE

Montmorency

Port-Villez   Moisson

N 190

Mantes-
la-Jolie

Vaux-sur-Seine

Seine

N 14

Argenteuil

BOBIGNY

N 14

D 113

A 14

NANTERRE

93

Saint-Germain-
en-Laye

D 983

D 307

Boulogne-
Billancourt

PARIS
75

Le Raincy

Nogent-
sur-Marne

Néauphle-le-Château

D 836

D 833

N 12

Dreux

N 12

Eure

VERSAILLES

92

L'Haÿ-
les-Roses

CRÉTEIL
94

Antony

N 10

Palaiseau

D 928

D 929

Poigny-la-Forêt

D 306

D 988

ÉVRY

Rambouillet

D 988

N 10

N 6

A 10

N 20

D 983

A 6

MELUN

N 154

D 905

A 11

A 7

91
ESSONNE

CHARTRES

N 10

Essonne

28
EURE-ET-LOIR

N 191

Étampes

D 921

N 837

A 11

N 20

A 10

N 154

45
LOIRET

N 152

D 403

Pithiviers

N

S

0   15 km

DEUX-SÈVRES
Poitou-Charentes

79

49
MAINE-ET-LOIRE

85
VENDÉE

86
VIENNE

17
CHARENTE-MARITIME

Cholet

Combrand
Cirières
Bressuire
Terves-Bressuire
Moncoutant
Glénay

Verruyes-en-Gâtine
Parthenay
Beaulieu-sous-Parthenay
Vausseroux

Coulonges-sur-l'Autize
Champdeniers
Germond-Rouvre

Fontenay-le-Comte

Niort-Sciecq
La Crèche
Prailles
Chenay

Coulon
Arçais
Le Vanneau
Magné
NIORT

Vallans
Marigny
St-Martin-de-Bernegoue
Saint-Vincent-la-Châtre

Sauzé-Vaussais

Saint-Jean-d'Angély

POITIERS

Chinon

Sèvres Niortaise

Sèvres Nantaise

Thouet

Lay

Charen

D 960
D 751
D 752
N 249
A 87
D 960
N 147
D 147
D 753
D 759
N 149
N 137
N 160
D 938
N 149
D 938 t
D 949 b
N 148
A 83
D 748
D 938
N 149
N 11
A 10
D 938 t
N 148
A 83
N 11
D 743
D 150
N 10
N 11
N 11
D 948
D 939
N 150
A 10
D 950
D 91
D 939

N
O   E
S

0   15 k

Scarpe

Cambrai

59
NORD

Escaut

Saint-Quentin

D 932

N 44 b

N 45

D 930

Douai

N 45

A 26

Péronne

Noyon

Oise

A 26

Canal du Nord

D 917

Canal

Fresnes-
Mazancourt

Omiécourt

D 930

Lens

Glinchy

Frise

Fay

Carrépuis

Curlu

Somme

N 29

A 1

D 935

ARRAS

N 17

Grandcourt

D 929

D 937

Scarpe

62
PAS-DE-CALAIS

N 25

Vecquemont

A 29

D 934

Montdidier

N 39

D 935

60
OISE

Canche

D 916

D 941

AMIENS

Dury

N 1

Authie

N 25

Belloy-sur-Somme

A 16

N 1

A 16

D 925

D 928

L'Étoile

N 1

Bussy-lès-Poix

N 29

D 931

Vauchelles-
lès-Quesnoy

Cocquerel

D 901

N 31

Argoules

Vironchaux

Caours

D 925

Abbeville

Béhen

Citernes

D 925

D 928

Bernay-en-Ponthieu

Noyelles-sur-Mer

Somme

A 28

Rue

Forest-Montiers

Port-le-
Grand

Favières

Quend
(Monchaux)

La Croloy

Ochancourt

D 925

St-Valery-
sur-Somme

Estréboeuf

D 1015

A 28

N 29

Saint-Blimont

Bresle

76
SEINE-MARITIME

D 925

Béthune

D 919

15 km

0

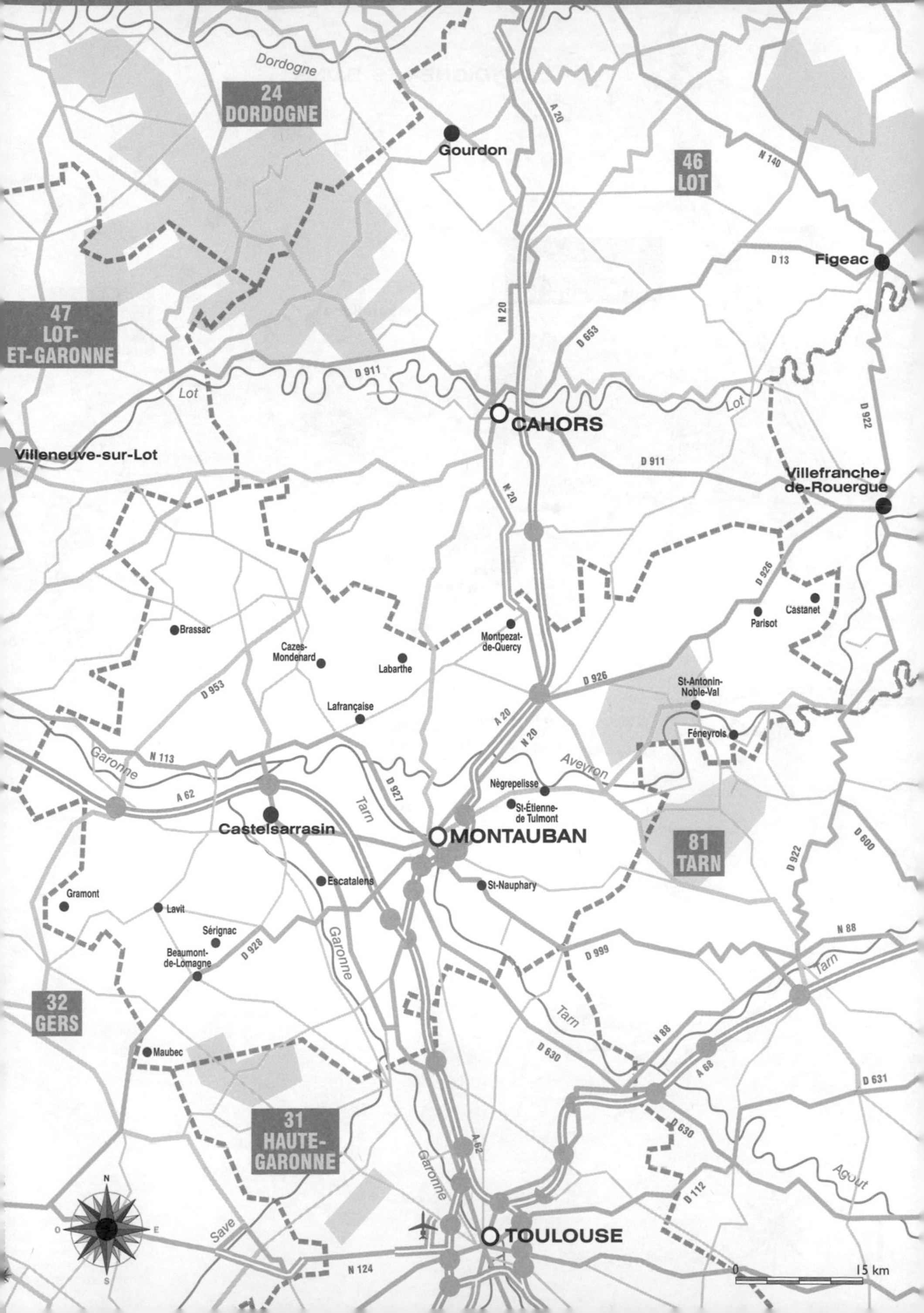

Dordogne
24 DORDOGNE
Gourdon
A 20
46 LOT
N 140
D 13
Figeac
N 20
D 653
47 LOT-ET-GARONNE
D 911
Lot
CAHORS
Villeneuve-sur-Lot
D 911
D 922
Villefranche-de-Rouergue
N 20
D 926
Castanet
Parisot
Brassac
Cazes-Mondenard
Labarthe
Montpezat-de-Quercy
D 926
D 953
Lafrançaise
St-Antonin-Noble-Val
A 20
N 20
Féneyrols
Garonne
N 113
Aveyron
A 62
D 927
Nègrepelisse
Tarn
St-Étienne-de-Tulmont
Castelsarrasin
MONTAUBAN
81 TARN
D 922
D 600
Escatalens
St-Nauphary
Gramont
Lavit
Sérignac
N 88
Beaumont-de-Lomagne
D 928
Garonne
D 999
Tarn
32 GERS
Tarn
N 88
D 630
A 68
Maubec
D 631
D 630
31 HAUTE-GARONNE
A 62
Garonne
D 112
Agout
N
O
E
S
Save
TOULOUSE
N 124
0
15 km

VAR
Provence-Alpes-Côte-d'Azur

83

DIGNE-LES-BAINS

N 85
Bléone
Verdon
N 202

D 12
A 51

Forcalquier

N 85

04
ALPES-DE-HAUTE-PROVENCE

06
ALPES-MARITIMES

Castellane

N 85

Durance

Bargème

Lac de Ste Croix

Grass

Bauduen

Verdon

Ginasservis

Fayence

Moissac-Bellevue

D 562

Montmeyan

Ampus

A 8

Sillans-la-Cascade

Callas

Bagnols-en-Forêt

Tourtour

Les Adrets-de-l'Estérel

Salernes

N 7

Barjols

Pontevès

Draguignan

Cotignac

Trans-en-Provence

A 8

Bras

Lorgues

Argens

Les Arcs-sur-Argens

Fréjus

N 7

Vins-sur-Caramy

Roquebrune-sur-Argens

Saint-Maximin-la-Saint-Baume

A 8

A 8

Brignoles

Le Cannet-des-Maures

N 98

N 7

Plan-de-la-Tour

N 560

Besse-sur-Issole

Sainte-Maxime

N 97

D 554

Les Mayons

A 57

Grimaud

Néoules

Ramatuelle

Collobrières

N 98

Pierrefeu-du-Var

N 8

A 50

Le Beausset

St-Cyr-sur-Mer

Évenos

TOULON

N 98

Sanary-sur-Mer

La Seyne-sur-Mer

Hyères Island

MEDITERRANEAN SEA

N
O   E
S

INFOGRAPH

0   15 k

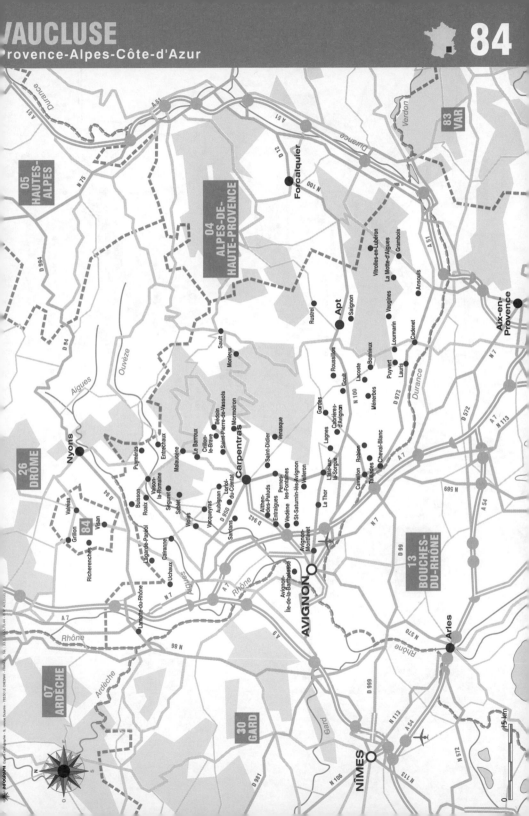

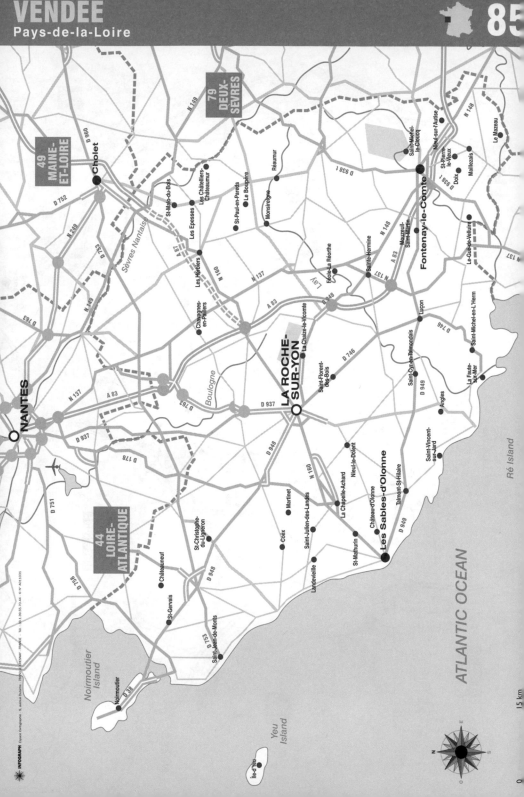

49
MAINE-
ET-LOIRE

79
DEUX-
SEVRES

44
LOIRE-
ATLANTIQUE

NANTES

LA ROCHE-
SUR-YON

Cholet

Fontenay-le-Comte

ATLANTIC OCEAN

Ré island

Noimoutier
Island

Yeu
Island

St-Malo-du-Bois
Les Châtelliers-
Châteaumur
Les Epesses
St-Paul-en-Pareds
Le Boupère
Monsireigne
Réaumur
Saint-Michel-
le-Cloucq
Nieul-sur-l'Autise
St-Pierre-
le-Vieux
Maillezais
Dolx
Le Mazeau
Les Herbiers
L'Oie-La Réorthe
Saint-Hermine
Mouzeuil-
Saint-Martin
Le-Gué-de-Velluire
Chavagnes-
en-Paillers
La Chaize-le-Vicomte
Saint-Florent-
des-Bois
Luçon
Saint-Michel-en-L'Herm
St-Christophe-
du-Ligneron
Saint-Cyr-en-Talmondais
La Faute-
sur-Mer
Châteauneuf
Martinet
Coëx
La Chapelle-Achard
Nieul-le-Dolent
Château-d'Olonne
Saint-Vincent-
sur-Jard
Angles
St-Gervais
Saint-Julien-des-Landes
Talmont-St-Hilaire
Les Sables-d'Olonne
Landevieille
St-Mathurin
Saint-Jean-de-Monts
Noirmoutier
Ile-d'Yeu

D 960
D 752
D 753
D 249
N 149
D 763
N 137
D 937
D 178
D 751
D 758
D 753
D 848
N 160
A 87
A 83
N 137
N 160
N 148
D 938 t
D 936 t
N 148
N 137
D 746
D 949
D 949
D 937
D 746

Sèvres Nantaise
Boulogne
Lay
15 km

INFOGRAPH

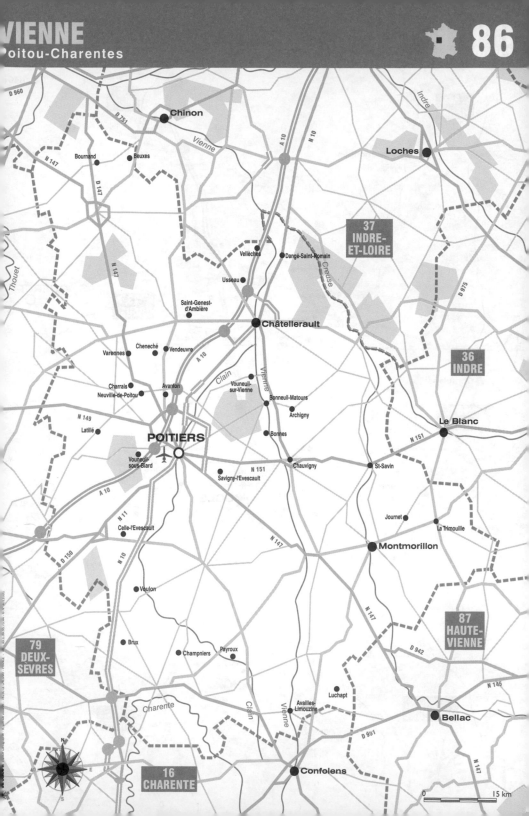

HAUTE-VIENNE
Limousin

87

La Châtre

86 VIENNE

36 INDRE

Montmorillon

N 147

N 147

N 147

Arnac-
la-Poste

Magnac-Laval

D 942

N 145

N 145

GUÉRET

Peyrat-de-Bellac

Fromental

23 CREUSE

Blanzac

Bellac

Gartempe

Bersac-
sur-Rivalier

D 951

Saint-Junien-
les-Combes

Bessines

D 951

St-Pardoux

D 942

Confolens

N 147

Cieux

A 20

Saint-
Sylvestre

D 940

16 CHARENTE

Peyrilhac

Vienne

N 141

Veyrac

St-Martin-Terressus

Saint-Victurnien

Papazol

N 141

D 940

Isle

LIMOGES

St-Léonard-
de-Noblat

Maulde

Rochechouart

Saint-Auvent

Feytiat

Bujaleuf

Peyrat-
le-Château

Boisseuil

Masléon

Vienne

N 21

Cussac

Champagnac-
la-Rivière

Rilhac-
Lastours

Saint-Hilaire-Bonneval

Châteauneuf-la-Forêt

Rempnat

Nexon

La Chapelle-
Montbrandeix

Vézè

Pensol

Dournazac

D 704

Château-
Chervix

Le Chalard

Coussac-
Bonneval

A 20

Nontron

N 21

D 940

Corrèze

A 89

24 DORDOGNE

19 CORRÈZE

N 120

N

O   E

S

INFOGRAPH

0   15 k

67
BAS-RHIN

68
HAUT-RHIN

Guebwiller

Thann

90

N 66

N 83

D 417

D 420

N 420

54
MEURTHE-
ET-MOSELLE

D 424

Saint-Michel-sur-Meurthe

D 59

Saint-Dié

Anould

N 413

Gérardmer

Ventron

N 420

D 417

Meurthe

Moselle

N 57

N 66

Dognon

N 4

Lunéville

N 4

Canal

Moselle

ÉPINAL

La Chapelle-aux-Bois

D 26

D 64

N 57

D 166

70
HAUTE-SAÔNE

NANCY

D 913

Remoncourt

D 429

Norroy-sur-Vair

D 3

Buégneville

Sauxures-
lès-Buégneville

D 164

Saône

Canal

D 429

Toul

D 974

A 31

Soulosse-sous-Saint-Élophe

D 166

Vaudoncourt

N 74

D 74

A 31

55
MEUSE

N 4

D 964

Meuse

Neufchâteau

N 74

Meuse

52
HAUTE-
MARNE

N

O   E

S

15 km

0

Seine

N 19

A 5

A 26

Nogent-
sur-Seine

D 411

10
AUBE

Seine

N 6

A 5

A 5

TROYES

D 960

Seine

Lixy

Foissy-sur-Vanne

N 60

A 160

Sens

N 60

Yonne

N 6

A 6

D 905

N 71

A 5

N 77

N 77

D 943

D 905

45
LOIRET

N 60

Armançon

Dannemoine

Hauterive

Charny

Poilly-sur-Tholon

N 77

Collan

D 965

Lézinnes

Ancy-le-Franc

Égleny

AUXERRE

Lindry

D 965

Chevannes

Escolives-
Ste-Camille

Mélay

Tannerre-en-Puisaye

Gy-l'Évêque

Yonne

A 6

Noyers-
sur-Serein

Fontaines

N 151

Sacy

N 6

Saint-
Fargeau

Lain

Thizy

Brosses

Avallon

Sauvigny-
le-Beuréal

Clamecy

D 957

D 951

St-Germain-
des-Champs

21
CÔTE D'OR

Cosne-Cours-
sur-Loire

N7

58
NIÈVRE

Yonne

D 958

N 6

N
O   E
S

N 151

0   15

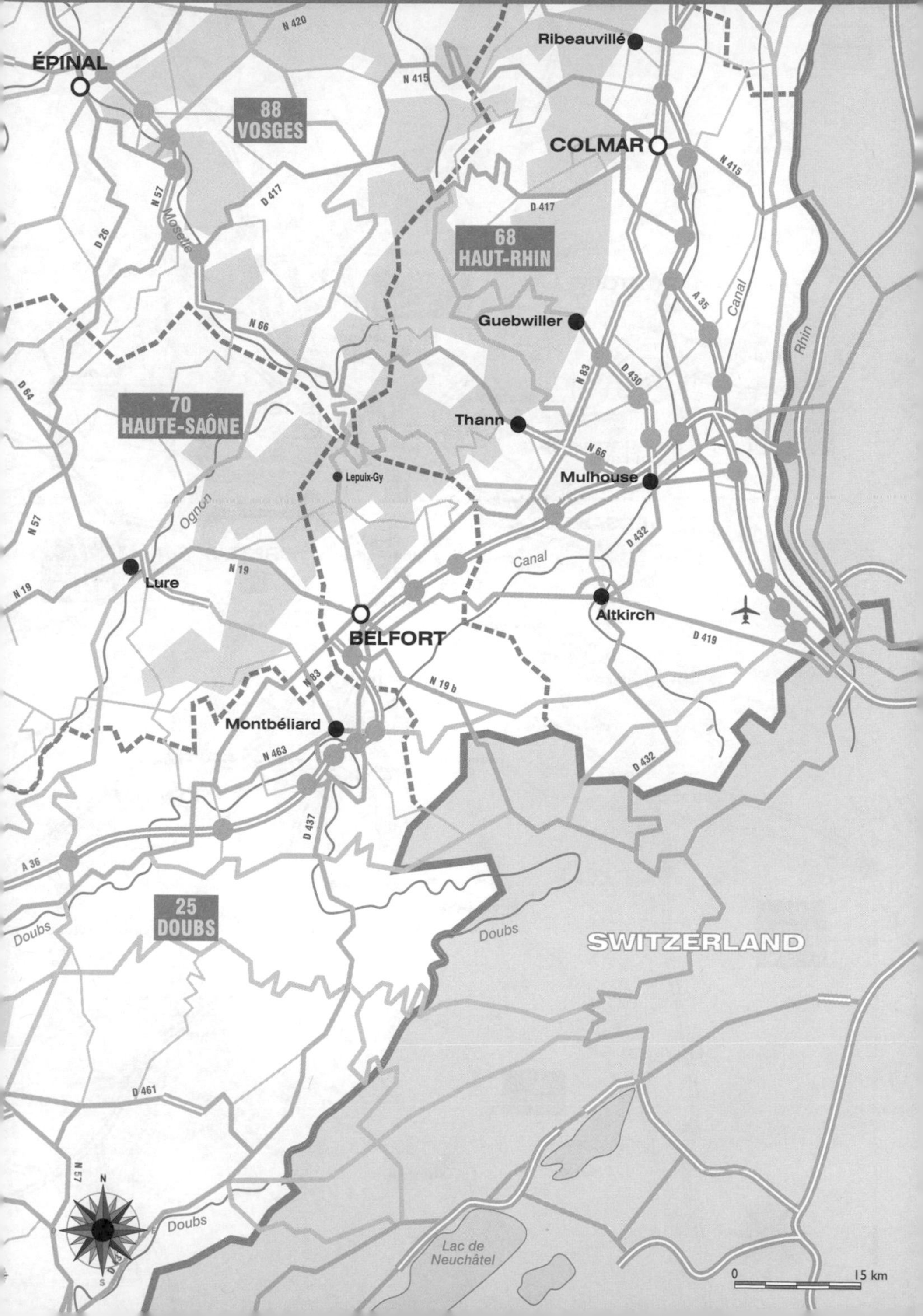

ÉPINAL

N 420

Ribeauvillé

N 415

88 VOSGES

N 57

Moselle

COLMAR

N 415

D 417

D 26

D 417

68 HAUT-RHIN

N 66

Guebwiller

A 35

Canal

Rhin

D 64

70 HAUTE-SAÔNE

N 83

D 430

Thann

N 57

Ognon

Lepuix-Gy

N 66

Mulhouse

N 19

Lure

N 19

Canal

D 432

Altkirch

BELFORT

D 419

N 83

N 19 b

Montbéliard

D 432

N 463

A 36

D 437

Doubs

25 DOUBS

Doubs

SWITZERLAND

D 461

N 57

Doubs

Lac de Neuchâtel

0   15 km

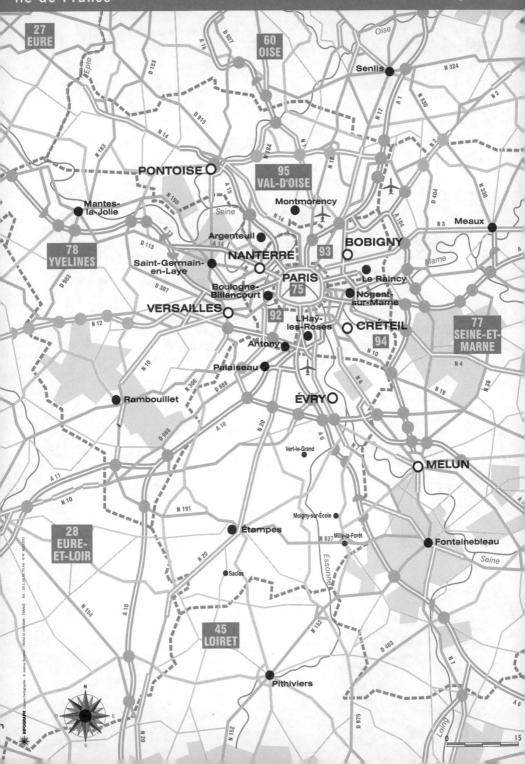

27
EURE

60
OISE

Senlis

N 324

N 2

Oise

D 327

A 16

D 153

D 915

N 14

Epte

D 183

N 330

A 1

N 17

N 2

N 330

D 404

N 184

N 1

N 16

PONTOISE

95
VAL-D'OISE

Montmorency

Meaux

N 3

Mantes-
la-Jolie

A 15

N 190

Seine

N 14

A 13

Argenteuil

BOBIGNY

93

A 104

A 14

78
YVELINES

D 113

NANTERRE

Saint-Germain-
en-Laye

Le Raincy

Marne

A

D 183

D 307

PARIS

75

Nogent-
sur-Marne

Boulogne-
Billancourt

N 12

VERSAILLES

92

L'Haÿ-
les-Roses

CRÉTEIL

77
SEINE-ET-
MARNE

N 10

94

N 4

Antony

N 10

N 6

N 36

Palaiseau

N 19

N 306

D 988

Rambouillet

ÉVRY

A 11

A 10

N 20

A 6

MELUN

N 10

D 968

N 7

Vert-le-Grand

N 191

Moigny-sur-École

Étampes

Milly-la-Forêt

N 837

Fontainebleau

Seine

N 20

28
EURE-
ET-LOIR

Saclas

Essonne

N 154

A 10

N 152

45
LOIRET

D 403

N 7

A 6

Pithiviers

N 152

D 975

Loing

N
O   E
S

INFOGRAPH

Édilarge Cartographie - 9, avenue Dupont - 78150 LE CHESNAY - FRANCE - Tél. : 39.3.13.99 - Fax 39.44 - © N° A681001

N 20

0   15

76
SEINE-
MARITIME

60
OISE

Montdidier

D 930

N 1

A 16

D 935

N 31

BEAUVAIS

N 31

Clermont

Compiègne

N 31

N 1

Oise

D 881

D 915

D 927

D 935

27
EURE

Les Andelys

D 125

A 16

Epte

D 153

Senlis

N 324

N 17

A 1

N 330

N 15

Chérence

D 915

N 14

N 183

La Roche-Guyon

N 190

N 164

PONTOISE

Seine

Parmain

N 14

N 2

D 404

N 330

Mantes-
la-Jolie

Montmorency

Meaux

N 3

N 14

A 15

A 13

A 104

Argenteuil

Marne

D 113

A 14

BOBIGNY

93

D 983

Saint-Germain-
en-Laye

NANTERRE

92

Le Raincy

D 307

Boulogne-
Billancourt

PARIS

75

Nogent-
sur-Marne

VERSAILLES

92

L'Haÿ-
les-Roses

CRÉTEIL

77
SEINE-ET-
MARNE

N 12

N 12

Antony

94

N 10

78
YVELINES

N 10

Palaiseau

N 10

N 4

N 305

D 988

N 6

Rambouillet

ÉVRY

N 19

N 36

D 983

A 10

N 20

A 6

N 7

N 12

Eure

D 906

D 983

MELUN

N 154

91
ESSONNE

N
O   E
S

A 11

N 10

N 191

Essonne

0   15 km

CHARTRES

Étampes

INDEX OF LOCATIONS

Locations are arranged alphabetically in this index. Chambres d'hôtes are listed in the guide under the nearest town or village, which may be several kilometres away. The location name is followed by the département name and number (in brackets). The page number(s) for each location is shown last.

611

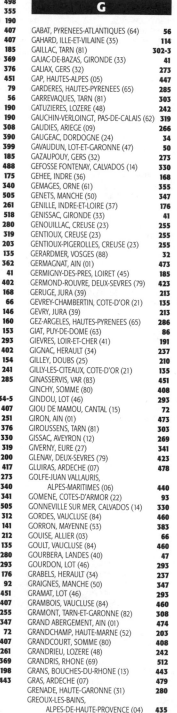

S

Photo Credits

The main pictures in the preliminary pages of this book are held in the Automobile Association's own library (AA PHOTOLIBRARY) and were taken by the following photographers:

AA Photo Library: 1tl (Rick Strange), 1b (Paul Kenward), 3tl (Adrian Baker), 3tr (Rob Moore), 3b (Roger Moss), 4bl (Clive Sawyer), 4tr (Adrian Baker), 5 (Paul Kenward), 10bl (Clive Sawyer), 11b (Rick Strange), 12tl (Roy Victor), 14bl (Tony Oliver), 17t (Rob Moore), 17bl (Paul Kenward), 18tl (Adrian Baker), 18b (Clive Sawyer), 19t (Clive Sawyer), 19tl (Clive Sawyer), 19br (Rick Strange), 20tr (Clive Sawyer), 20b (Tony Oliver), 20bl (Adrian Baker)

Other photographs reproduced with kind permission of Gîtes de France: 1tr, 9b; 10tr, 11br (Jean-Philippe Rainaut)